PHOTONS IN FOCK SPACE AND BEYOND

Volume III
Mathematics for Photon Fields

PHOTONS IN FOCK SPACE AND BEYOND

Volume III
Mathematics for Photon Fields

Reinhard Honegger
Alfred Rieckers

University of Tübingen, Germany

World Scientific

NEW JERSEY · LONDON · SINGAPORE · BEIJING · SHANGHAI · HONG KONG · TAIPEI · CHENNAI

Published by

World Scientific Publishing Co. Pte. Ltd.

5 Toh Tuck Link, Singapore 596224

USA office: 27 Warren Street, Suite 401-402, Hackensack, NJ 07601

UK office: 57 Shelton Street, Covent Garden, London WC2H 9HE

British Library Cataloguing-in-Publication Data
A catalogue record for this book is available from the British Library.

PHOTONS IN FOCK SPACE AND BEYOND
Volume 3: Mathematics for Photon Fields

ISBN 978-981-4618-82-3 (Set)
ISBN 978-981-4618-89-2 (Vol. 3)

In-house Editor: Christopher Teo

Typeset by Stallion Press
Email: enquiries@stallionpress.com

Printed in Singapore

Preface and Overview III

In the present volume III of the three-volume work *Photons in Fock Space and Beyond*, the mathematical tools for algebraic quantum electrodynamics (QED) are arranged in a form adapted to the needs of our physical elaborations in volumes I and II. The treated disciplines of Mathematics could be studied independently, but the mentioned impacts on the physical applications may help to visualize and memorize the mathematical concepts, the terminology of which originating often from physical problems.

Since algebraic QED, in the present approach, is conceived to cover also classical collective variables, especially classical fields of ED in the form of subtheories, it requires a widespread variety of mathematical notions for its concise foundation.

In our treatment of Hilbert space operators, quadratic forms play an important role for demonstrating self-adjointness. The singular parts of quadratic forms are needed for the decomposition theory of quasifree photon states. The differential operators for classical vector fields in spatial domains with boundary conditions are investigated in Sobolev spaces. A very general Helmholtz–Hodge decomposition is derived for vector fields, where the (often poor) type of regularity for the global field sections depends on the (non-) smoothness of the spatial boundaries.

The rather detailed exposition of C*- and von Neumann algebras should relieve the reader from consulting the pertinent text books in Mathematics and Mathematical Physics. Included are only original or simple proofs for illustration of the mathematical concepts.

The chapters on convex state spaces and decomposition measures bring together mathematical techniques which are usually hidden in original papers or specialized monographs. Their relevance for the foundations of quantum theory, and its possible generalizations, is pointed out. It includes an extreme generalization of transition probabilities, of the quantum coherence relation, and of spectral theory (enabling scaled observables). In a mild form, these concepts are used to classify convex sub-sets of material and photonic states in algebraic QED and to describe the coherence breaking arise of classical observables in terms of split faces (state folia).

The Effros theory of orthogonal state decompositions demands a generalization for being applicable to the non-standard measure spaces arising in the convex state space of the non-separable photonic Weyl algebra. The subcentral decompositions of states on the (separable) classically extended CAR algebra are basic for the introduction of so-called "mean field supporting states". The discussed ergodic state decompositions refer mainly to asymptotic Abelian photon systems. The subcentral decompositions of algebraic transition probabilities allow for a clear cut distinction between classical and quantum fluctuations.

The treatment of locally convex (LC) vector spaces aims to construct appropriate test function spaces for the smeared classical and quantized fields. To conform with the needs of the dynamics, the so-called "twofold Gelfand triples" are introduced. The (pre-) measures on duals of LC-spaces contribute to statistical classical field theory, where an original connection to the regular states on the commutative Weyl algebra is established.

The chapters on dynamical perturbation theory cover a large class of mesoscopic radiation models. Detailed convergence estimations supplement the arguments of volume II. Starting from inequalities in photonic Fock space, generalizations to certain non-Fock representations are worked out. A certain kind of cocycle equations is basic for unitary propagators in the weak coupling limit, for which operator-valued spectral integrals are introduced. The perturbation series for the unitary propagators is proved equivalent to a Trotter product.

The section on infinitely dimensional manifolds is intended to supplement the scanty literature on classical field analysis in Theoretical Physics, but is for itself also absolutely fragmentary. Our suggestion to integrate phase space theory for fields into the formulation of commutative Weyl field systems may, however, give some inspiration for further developments.

The gauge bundle theory emphasizes Steenrod's constructive approach in terms of "coordinate bundles". It leads to explicit (non-) triviality criteria. $U(1)$-principal bundles above fixed-time regions are explicitly constructed, taking into account the virtual cuts to make the spatial domain simply connected. Holonomy groups and horizontal liftings deal with phase variables in classical ED. Associated bundles serve for the discussion of quantum phases.

Bundles above force field trajectories provide the connection to the older termi-nology of gauged ED, but include also the gauging of cohomological fields. Cavities with non-smooth boundaries are allowed in many assertions on gauge behavior. A transition between smooth and non-smooth gauge theory is indicated.

The supplementary Section 55.3 treats the special case that the "cavity" Λ for the electrodynamic fields is all of free space $\mathbb{R}^3$. It does not only clarify some aspects of "causality" for gauge potentials and force fields, but provides also helpful hints for the reader how wave solutions of the Maxwell equations are related to our operator solutions, employed throughout volumes I and II.

Information for Use

The exposition of the three-volume work is organized like a single book. It means that the numbering of parts, chapters, sections and pages runs successively from the beginning of the first to the end of the third volume. In the beginning of each volume, there is the detailed table of contents for the entire work, and at the end of each volume one finds the complete bibliography and the index of mathematical symbols preceding that of keywords.

For studying the present volume III, a preliminary knowledge of Hilbert space mathematics, as used in courses on Quantum Mechanics, should be sufficient.

Acknowledgments

It is a pleasure to acknowledge discussions on subjects of the present volume with the following physicists and mathematicians: M. Benner, E. Binz, late H.–J. Borchers, Th. Gerisch, R. Hiptmayr, G. John, G. Raggio, M. P. Wolff, S. Zanzinger, and L. Zsidó.

For technical support we are indebted to Mrs. C. Stiller.

Tübingen, June 2014   *Reinhard Honegger* and *Alfred Rieckers*

Contents

Volume I Photons in Fock Space and Beyond: From Classical to Quantized Radiation Systems

Part A. Preliminaries on Electromagnetism   7

Part C. Classical Electrodynamics in the Smeared Field Formalism   149

Volume II Photons in Fock Space and Beyond: Quantized Mesoscopic Radiation Models

Part H. Squeezing   763

Volume III Photons in Fock Space and Beyond: Mathematics for Photon Fields

Part O. Dynamics and Perturbation Theory 1921

PART M

Observables and Algebras

Hilbert Space Operators

The present chapter gives an introduction to the used notions and results for Hilbert space operators, especially for unbounded operators. The main difficulties, when dealing with unbounded operators, arise from their discontinuity and the fact that their domains of definition in general cannot be the entire Hilbert space (cf. the Hellinger–Töplitz result in Proposition 43.1-2 below). Unfortunately, many important operators used in physics are unbounded, and many problems (and misunderstandings) in theoretical physics struggle, in fact, with this attribute. A rigorous mathematical investigation of the domains may then bring the solution.

Already certain notions and results of this first chapter in our survey on observables and algebras are essential for an understanding of main ideas in this book, especially the formulation of boundary conditions and the derivation of macro-observables by extending the domains of micro-physical operators. (For a more profound introduction to Hilbert space operators the reader may consult e.g., the textbooks [Wei80], [RS73b], [Kre78], [Kat84], [Pru71].)

In the present chapter, we have adopted the convention that the Hilbert spaces and the pertinent operators are always linear over the complex field $\mathbb{C}$ (and not merely over $\mathbb{R}$), if not specified otherwise. The inner product of a Hilbert space $\mathcal{H}$ is denoted by $(\xi|\eta)$, $\xi, \eta \in \mathcal{H}$, and is assumed to be antilinear in the first factor and linear in the second. The associated norm is $\|\xi\| = \sqrt{(\xi|\xi)}$, defining the norm topology of $\mathcal{H}$. $\mathrm{LH}(V)$ denotes the linear hull of the set $V \subseteq \mathcal{H}$. Let us mention, however, that most of the presented results remain valid for linear operators on real Hilbert spaces, as is expounded e.g., in [Wei80].

We must now clarify some comparison relations, which will be especially important for analogous relations for operators, formulated below.

Notational Remark 43.0-1 (Positivity and Set Inclusion). A real number $a \in \mathbb{R}$ is called "positive", if $a \geq 0$, including the case $a = 0$. (In the literature our attribute "positive" is sometimes called "non-negative", a term we avoid.) We write $a > 0$, if a is positive and non-zero, calling a then "strictly positive". Analogously $a \leq 0$ is called "negative", and $a < 0$ is called "strictly negative".

If Λ and Ω are two sets, we write $\Lambda \subseteq \Omega$ if Λ is contained in Ω, including equality, and $\Lambda \subset \Omega$, if equality is excluded.

43.1. Preliminary Notions and Results

An operator B from a Hilbert space $\mathcal{H}_1$ into a Hilbert space $\mathcal{H}_2$ is a linear mapping from a subspace $\mathrm{dom}(B)$ of $\mathcal{H}_1$ with values in $\mathcal{H}_2$. In case of $\mathcal{H}_1 = \mathcal{H}_2 =: \mathcal{H}$ one speaks of an operator "on $\mathcal{H}$" (instead of "in $\mathcal{H}$" used in Physics). The subspace $\mathrm{dom}(B) \subseteq \mathcal{H}_1$ is called the *domain* (of definition) of B. The image or range of B is denoted by $\mathrm{ran}(B)$, a subspace of $\mathcal{H}_2$. B is called to be densely defined, if $\mathrm{dom}(B)$ is dense in $\mathcal{H}_1$ (with respect to the norm arising from the inner product in $\mathcal{H}_1$). The operator B is denoted to be *onto*, if B is surjective, i.e., if its range is all of $\mathcal{H}_2 = \mathrm{ran}(B)$. The kernel of B is defined by $\ker(B) := \{\psi \in \mathrm{dom}(B) \mid B\psi = 0\}$. B is injective, if and only if $\ker(B) = \{0\}$.

For an operator B from the Hilbert space $\mathcal{H}_1$ into the Hilbert space $\mathcal{H}_2$ one has the bi-directional implication

$$B \text{ is continuous} \quad \Longleftrightarrow \quad B \text{ is bounded,}$$

where *boundedness* means that there exists a $c \geq 0$ with $\|B\psi\| \leq c\|\psi\|$ for all $\psi \in \mathrm{dom}(B)$. Clearly, then B has a unique continuous extension to the closure of $\mathrm{dom}(B)$, which is all of $\mathcal{H}_1$ for densely defined bounded B. So when calling an operator B from $\mathcal{H}_1$ into $\mathcal{H}_2$ bounded, we automatically mean that $\mathrm{dom}(B) = \mathcal{H}_1$. Its operator norm is given by

$$
\begin{aligned}
\|B\| &= \inf\{c \geq 0 \mid \|B\psi\| \leq c\|\psi\| \ \forall \psi \in \mathcal{H}_1\} \\
&= \sup\{\|B\psi\| \mid \psi \in \mathcal{H}_1, \ \|\psi\| \leq 1\} \quad\quad\quad (43.1.1) \\
&= \sup\{|(\xi|B\psi)| \mid \xi, \psi \in \mathcal{H}_1, \ \|\xi\| \leq 1, \ \|\psi\| \leq 1\}.
\end{aligned}
$$

Instead of $\|\psi\| \leq 1$ one may equivalently use $\|\psi\| = 1$. By $\mathcal{L}(\mathcal{H}_1, \mathcal{H}_2)$ we denote the Banach space of all bounded operators from $\mathcal{H}_1$ into $\mathcal{H}_2$. In case of $\mathcal{H}_1 = \mathcal{H}_2 = \mathcal{H}$, we obtain the C*-algebra $\mathcal{L}(\mathcal{H}) := \mathcal{L}(\mathcal{H}, \mathcal{H})$ of all bounded operators on $\mathcal{H}$ (cf. Chapter 45 on page 1627). $B \in \mathcal{L}(\mathcal{H})$ is *invertible*, if it is a *bijection*, that is, if it is injective and onto. A special element of $\mathcal{L}(\mathcal{H})$ is the identity mapping $\mathbb{1}$ on $\mathcal{H}$, satisfying $\mathbb{1}\psi = \psi$ for all $\psi \in \mathcal{H}$.

If $\mathcal{H}_1 = \mathcal{H}$ and $\mathcal{H}_2 = \mathbb{C}$, then we often make the identification $\mathcal{H} = \mathcal{L}(\mathcal{H}, \mathbb{C})$ in virtue of the following, well known result.

Theorem 43.1-1 (Riesz). *Let E be a norm-dense subspace of the Hilbert space $\mathcal{H}$. Then for each norm-continuous (i.e., bounded) linear form $L : E \to \mathbb{C}$, $\psi \mapsto L(\psi)$ there exists a unique vector $h \in \mathcal{H}$ such that $L(\psi) = (h|\psi)$ for all $\psi \in E$.*

We say that an operator B on a Hilbert space $\mathcal{H}$ *leaves the subspace D invariant*, if $D \subseteq \mathrm{dom}(B)$ and $B(D) \subseteq D$. Especially, if $U := B$ is a *unitary* on $\mathcal{H}$, that is a norm-preserving bijection, for which both U and U^{-1} leave the subspace D invariant, then we have $U(D) = D$. The latter is especially of relevance, when unitary one-parameter groups are considered, as in the Theorems 43.6-1 on page 1550 and 43.3-3 on page 1536.

For two operators A and B from $\mathcal{H}_1$ into $\mathcal{H}_2$ their sum $A + B$ is defined on the domain

$$\mathrm{dom}(A + B) = \mathrm{dom}(A) \cap \mathrm{dom}(B)$$

and given point-wise, that is by $(A + B)\psi := A\psi + B\psi$ for all $\psi \in \mathrm{dom}(A + B)$. If B acts from $\mathcal{H}_1$ into $\mathcal{H}_2$ and A from $\mathcal{H}_2$ into $\mathcal{H}_3$ then their product AB is defined on the domain

$$\mathrm{dom}(AB) = \{\psi \in \mathrm{dom}(B) \mid B\psi \in \mathrm{dom}(A)\}$$

by the point-wise actions $(AB)\psi = A(B\psi)$ for all $\psi \in \mathrm{dom}(AB)$. Clearly, $\mathrm{dom}(zB) = \mathrm{dom}(B)$ for all $0 \neq z \in \mathbb{C}$. Observe that one may construct pathological cases of unbounded, densely defined A and B, for which $\mathrm{dom}(A) \cap \mathrm{dom}(B) = \{0\}$ respectively $\mathrm{dom}(AB) = \{0\}$, and the sum respectively the product of A and B are meaningless.

An operator A is called an *extension* of B, or equivalently, B is called a *restriction* of A, if we have $\mathrm{dom}(B) \subseteq \mathrm{dom}(A)$, and $B\psi = A\psi$ for all $\psi \in \mathrm{dom}(B)$. In this case, we write

$$A \supseteq B, \quad \text{or} \quad B \subseteq A, \quad \text{respectively} \quad A = B \text{ on } \mathrm{dom}(B),$$

what defines the *operator inclusion*.

If the operators A and B act on the Hilbert space $\mathcal{H}$, then we write $A \geq B$ or $B \leq A$, if $(\psi|A\psi) \geq (\psi|B\psi)$ for all $\psi \in \mathrm{dom}(A) \cap \mathrm{dom}(B)$.

The operator A is called *bounded from below*, with lower bound $a \in \mathbb{R}$, if $A \geq a\mathbb{1}$, i.e., if $(\psi|A\psi) \geq a\|\psi\|^2$ for all $\psi \in \mathrm{dom}(A)$.

The operator A is called *positive*, written as $A \geq 0$, if $(\psi|A\psi) \geq 0$ for all $\psi \in \mathrm{dom}(A)$; in other words, A is positive, if and only if A is bounded from below with lower bound $a = 0$.

The operator A is called *strictly positive*, if $(\psi|A\psi) > 0$ (excluding zero) for all $\psi \in \mathrm{dom}(A)$ with $\psi \neq 0$. This is equivalent to $A \geq 0$ with $\ker(A) = \{0\}$ (by the polarization identity given below).

For a densely defined operator B from the Hilbert space $\mathcal{H}_1$ into the Hilbert space $\mathcal{H}_2$ its *adjoint* operator B^* is an operator from $\mathcal{H}_2$ into $\mathcal{H}_1$, and is defined on the domain

$$\mathrm{dom}(B^*) := \{\xi \in \mathcal{H}_2 \mid \text{the linear functional } \mathrm{dom}(B) \ni \psi \mapsto (\xi|B\psi) \text{ is continuous}\}. \tag{43.1.2}$$

Thus for every $\xi \in \mathrm{dom}(B^*)$ there exists a unique η_ξ with $(\eta_\xi|\psi) = (\xi|B\psi)$ for all $\psi \in \mathrm{dom}(B)$ by the Riesz Theorem 43.1-1. B^* is then defined as $B^*\xi := \eta_\xi$, if $\xi \in \mathrm{dom}(B^*)$. This leads to

$$(B^*\xi|\psi) = (\xi|B\psi), \quad \forall \xi \in \mathrm{dom}(B^*), \quad \forall \psi \in \mathrm{dom}(B).$$

Note that the adjoint B^* exists only for a densely defined operator B.

If $A \in \mathcal{L}(\mathcal{H}_1, \mathcal{H}_2)$, then we have $A^* \in \mathcal{L}(\mathcal{H}_2, \mathcal{H}_1)$, where $\|A\| = \|A^*\|$ and $\|A^*A\| = \|A\|^2$. For a densely defined B from $\mathcal{H}_1$ into $\mathcal{H}_2$ it holds that

$$\ker(B^*) = \mathrm{ran}(B)^{\perp}, \qquad (43.1.3)$$

where $\mathrm{ran}(B)^{\perp}$ means the orthogonal complement of $\mathrm{ran}(B)$ in $\mathcal{H}_2$.

The *direct sum* Hilbert space $\mathcal{H}_1 \oplus \mathcal{H}_2$ consists of pairs (ψ_1, ψ_2), $\psi_i \in \mathcal{H}_i$, with point-wise linear operations and the sum of the single scalar products. A linear subspace G of the direct sum Hilbert space $\mathcal{H}_1 \oplus \mathcal{H}_2$ is called a *graph*, if $(\xi, \psi_1) \in G$ and $(\xi, \psi_2) \in G$ implies $\psi_1 = \psi_2$, making the right entry a function of the left entry. Then one may define the operator B from $\mathcal{H}_1$ into $\mathcal{H}_2$ by setting

$$\mathrm{dom}(B) := \{\xi \in \mathcal{H}_1 \mid (\xi, \psi) \in G \text{ for some } \psi \in \mathcal{H}_2\}, \quad B\xi := \psi \quad \text{for } (\xi, \psi) \in G.$$

Thus $G = G(B) := \{(\xi, B\xi) \mid \xi \in \mathrm{dom}(B)\}$ is the graph of the operator B, the latter being automatically linear. The operator B from $\mathcal{H}_1$ into $\mathcal{H}_2$ is called to be *closed*, if its graph $G(B)$ is a closed subspace of $\mathcal{H}_1 \oplus \mathcal{H}_2$, or equivalently, if $\mathrm{dom}(B)$ is complete with respect to the graph norm $\|.\|_B$ of B,

$$\|\psi\|_B^2 = \|\psi\|^2 + \|B\psi\|^2, \quad \psi \in \mathrm{dom}(B). \qquad (43.1.4)$$

B is denoted *closable*, if the closure of its graph is a graph, too. Then there exists a uniquely defined operator $\overline{B}$ — the closure of B — such that $\overline{G(B)} = G(\overline{B})$, which is the smallest closed extension of B. The domain $\mathrm{dom}(\overline{B})$ is the set of all $\psi \in \mathcal{H}_1$ such that there exists a sequence $\{\psi_n \mid n \in \mathbb{N}\} \subset \mathrm{dom}(B)$ with $\lim_{n\to\infty} \|\psi_n - \psi\| = 0$ and the image sequence $\{B\psi_n \mid n \in \mathbb{N}\}$ is Cauchy in $\mathcal{H}_2$, in which case, we have

$$\overline{B}\psi = \lim_{n\to\infty} B\psi_n.$$

Obviously, for closed B it follows that $B = \overline{B}$, and that $\ker(B)$ is a closed subspace of $\mathcal{H}_1$. The densely defined B is closable, if and only if B^* is densely defined, in which case $B^{**} := (B^*)^* = \overline{B}$. For closable, densely defined B it holds $(\overline{B})^* = B^*$. Note that every bounded $A \in \mathcal{L}(\mathcal{H}_1, \mathcal{H}_2)$ is closed, so that closedness is only remarkable for unbounded operators.

If B is a closed operator, then D is called a *core* for B, if D is a subspace of $\mathrm{dom}(B)$, and if the restriction $B|_D$ is closable and the closure coincides with B itself, that is, $\overline{B|_D} = B$. In applications, it is sometimes difficult to determine the whole domain of an operator B. Thus, when identifying a core, the operator B is essentially known.

The notions of normality, symmetry, and self-adjointness make sense, if $\mathcal{H}_1 = \mathcal{H}_2 = \mathcal{H}$, only. In the following definitions it is pre-supposed that the operator B is densely defined on $\mathcal{H}$ in order that its adjoint B^* exist.

• B is called *symmetric*, if $B \subseteq B^*$, that is, if

$$(\xi|B\psi) = (B\xi|\psi), \quad \forall \xi, \psi \in \mathrm{dom}(B).$$

- B is called *self-adjoint*, if $B = B^*$, that is, if B is symmetric with $\mathrm{dom}(B) = \mathrm{dom}(B^*)$.
- B is called *essentially self-adjoint*, if B is symmetric and if B has a unique self-adjoint extension. This unique self-adjoint extension then is given by the closure of B.
- B is called *normal*, if $\mathrm{dom}(B) = \mathrm{dom}(B^*)$ and $\|B\psi\| = \|B^*\psi\|$ for all $\psi \in \mathrm{dom}(B)$, or equivalently, $B^*B = BB^*$. Especially, every self-adjoint operator is normal.

If B is a closed, densely defined operator from the Hilbert space $\mathcal{H}_1$ into the Hilbert space $\mathcal{H}_2$, then it follows that the operator product B^*B is always a positive, self-adjoint operator on $\mathcal{H}_1$. Moreover, it holds $\ker(B) = \ker(B^*B)$.

Discontinuous, respectively unbounded, symmetric operators cannot be defined on all of $\mathcal{H}$, what is the content of the following proposition.

Proposition 43.1-2 (Hellinger–Töplitz). *Let A be a symmetric operator on the Hilbert space $\mathcal{H}$ with domain $\mathrm{dom}(A) = \mathcal{H}$. Then $A = A^* \in \mathcal{L}(\mathcal{H})$, i.e., A is bounded and self-adjoint.*

If a bounded operator $A \in \mathcal{L}(\mathcal{H})$ is positive, then it follows that A is automatically self-adjoint. This remains, however, not true for unbounded positive operators A.

43.2. The Trace-Class and Hilbert–Schmidt Ideals

Although the present Chapter is devoted mainly to unbounded operators, let us say a word about certain important classes of bounded operators, and their relevance for traditional (= Hilbert space) quantum mechanics.

43.2.1. *Trace-Class, Hilbert–Schmidt, and Compact Operators*

We describe four subspaces of $\mathcal{L}(\mathcal{H})$ of a Hilbert space $\mathcal{H}$ of infinite-dimensions.

Notational Remark 43.2-1. For $\xi, \psi \in \mathcal{H}$ the expression $|\xi)(\psi| \in \mathcal{L}(\mathcal{H})$ means the operator

$$|\xi)(\psi| : \mathcal{H} \ni \phi \longmapsto (\psi|\phi)\xi \, .$$

The image of this "non-orthogonal projection" is the one-dimensional subspace $\mathbb{C}\xi$, whereas its kernel is the closed subspace of $\mathcal{H}$ which consists of the vectors orthogonal to ψ. This notation is taken over from Dirac's formulation of Quantum Mechanics.

If especially $\|\xi\| = 1$, then $|\xi)(\xi|$ denotes the one-dimensional (orthogonal) projection onto $\mathbb{C}\xi$, that is,

$$|\xi)(\xi| : \mathcal{H} \ni \phi \longmapsto (\xi|\phi)\xi \, .$$

An operator $B \in \mathcal{L}(\mathcal{H})$ is said to be of *finite rank*, if its image is of finite dimension. A finite rank operator B is bounded and of the form

$$B = \sum_{j=1}^{n} |\xi_j)(\psi_j|, \quad \xi_j, \psi_j \in \mathcal{H}, \quad n \in \mathbb{N}, \quad (= \text{finite rank operator}),$$

implying its adjoint to be $B^* = \sum_{j=1}^{n} |\psi_j)(\xi_j|$. The set of all finite rank operators on $\mathcal{H}$ is denoted by $\mathcal{FL}(\mathcal{H})$.

D. Hilbert was the first to introduce the following class of operators, most important for our spectral theorems in (Q)ED: A densely defined operator B from a Hilbert space $\mathcal{H}_1$ into a Hilbert pace $\mathcal{H}_2$ is called *compact* or *completely continuous*, if the image $B(M)$ of each bounded set $M \subset \mathrm{dom}(B)$ is pre-compact, that is, if the closure $\overline{B(M)}$ is compact. (Recall that, without further specification, we appeal always to the norm topology for Hilbert space vectors.) Equivalent is: Each sequence in the domain of B contains a subsequence, which is mapped by B on a convergent sequence.

A compact operator is automatically bounded (what follows directly from the second characterization of a compact operator). On that basis there is no loss of generality in assuming that a compact B always belongs to $\mathcal{L}(\mathcal{H}_1, \mathcal{H}_2)$. Let us denote by $\mathcal{C}(\mathcal{H}_1, \mathcal{H}_2)$ the set of all compact operators in $\mathcal{L}(\mathcal{H}_1, \mathcal{H}_2)$, and for $\mathcal{H} = \mathcal{H}_1 = \mathcal{H}_2$ we briefly write $\mathcal{C}(\mathcal{H})$.

The following class has been introduced by J. von Neumann (then a scholar of Hilbert) in his mathematical developments of quantum mechanics: $B \in \mathcal{L}(\mathcal{H})$ is called to be of *trace class*, if

$$\|B\|_{\mathrm{tr}} := \sum_{\alpha \in I} (\xi_\alpha \||B| \, \xi_\alpha) < \infty,$$

for an orthonormal basis $\{\xi_\alpha \mid \alpha \in I\}$ of $\mathcal{H}$ (where I is the index set of the orthonormal basis). Here, we have used $|B| := \sqrt{B^* B}$, where the square-root is defined by means of the spectral calculus below. The set of all trace class operators is denoted by $\mathcal{T}(\mathcal{H})$.

The operator $B \in \mathcal{L}(\mathcal{H})$ is called *Hilbert–Schmidt* (named after Hilbert's scholar E. Schmidt), if

$$\|B\|_{\mathrm{HS}} := \sqrt{\sum_{\alpha \in I} \|B\xi_\alpha\|^2} = \sqrt{\|B^* B\|_{\mathrm{tr}}} < \infty$$

for an orthonormal basis $\{\xi_\alpha \mid \alpha \in I\}$ of $\mathcal{H}$. The set of all Hilbert–Schmidt operators is denoted by $\mathrm{HS}(\mathcal{H})$. The values $\|B\|_{\mathrm{tr}}$ and $\|B\|_{\mathrm{HS}}$ are independent of the chosen orthonormal basis of $\mathcal{H}$ and constitute norms in $\mathcal{T}(\mathcal{H})$ respectively in $\mathrm{HS}(\mathcal{H})$. Clearly $B \in \mathrm{HS}(\mathcal{H})$, if and only if $B^* B \in \mathcal{T}(\mathcal{H})$.

Let us mention the following facts on operator classes. We begin with the inclusions

$$\mathcal{FL}(\mathcal{H}) \subseteq \mathcal{T}(\mathcal{H}) \subseteq \mathrm{HS}(\mathcal{H}) \subseteq \mathcal{C}(\mathcal{H}) \subseteq \mathcal{L}(\mathcal{H}) \,. \tag{43.2.1}$$

The inclusions all are proper, if and only if the dimension of $\mathcal{H}$ is infinite (whereas these operator classes coincide in the finite-dimensional case). We state the invariance properties under algebraic operations, namely that the operator subspaces $\mathcal{FL}(\mathcal{H})$, $\mathcal{T}(\mathcal{H})$, $\mathrm{HS}(\mathcal{H})$, and $\mathcal{C}(\mathcal{H})$ are *-ideals* of $\mathcal{L}(\mathcal{H})$, where a *-ideal $\mathcal{J}$ of $\mathcal{L}(\mathcal{H})$ is a subspace of $\mathcal{L}(\mathcal{H})$ satisfying

$$B \in \mathcal{J} \text{ and } A \in \mathcal{L}(\mathcal{H}) \quad \Longrightarrow \quad B^* \in \mathcal{J}, \, AB \in \mathcal{J}, \text{ and } BA \in \mathcal{J}.$$

We emphasize the completeness relations, namely $\mathcal{T}(\mathcal{H})$ is complete with respect to the trace norm $\|.\|_{\mathrm{tr}}$, $\mathrm{HS}(\mathcal{H})$ is complete with respect to the Hilbert–Schmidt norm $\|.\|_{\mathrm{HS}}$, and $\mathcal{C}(\mathcal{H})$ is complete with respect to the conventional operator norm $\|.\|$ from Eq. (43.1.1). Especially, we deduce that $\mathcal{FL}(\mathcal{H})$ is dense in $\mathcal{T}(\mathcal{H})$ with respect to $\|.\|_{\mathrm{tr}}$, is dense in $\mathrm{HS}(\mathcal{H})$ with respect to $\|.\|_{\mathrm{HS}}$, and is dense in $\mathcal{C}(\mathcal{H})$ with respect to $\|.\|$.

The following lemma makes $\mathrm{HS}(\mathcal{H})$ applicable to the rich analysis of Hilbert space theory.

Lemma 43.2-2 (A Hilbert Algebra). *For $A, B \in \mathrm{HS}(\mathcal{H})$ the formula*

$$(A|B)_{\mathrm{HS}} := \sum_{\alpha \in I} (A\xi_\alpha | B\xi_\alpha) \,,$$

which is independent of the chosen orthonormal basis $\{\xi_\alpha \mid \alpha \in I\}$ of $\mathcal{H}$, defines a scalar product on $\mathrm{HS}(\mathcal{H})$. We have $(A|B)_{\mathrm{HS}} = (B^*|A^*)_{\mathrm{HS}}$, and $\|B\|_{\mathrm{HS}} = \sqrt{(B|B)_{\mathrm{HS}}}$ is disclosed as the norm induced by the scalar product. Since $\mathrm{HS}(\mathcal{H})$ is complete for this norm, it is a "Hilbert space".

*Combined with the *-algebraic structure $\mathrm{HS}(\mathcal{H})$ constitutes the prototype of a so-called "Hilbert algebra".*

Let us compile essential estimations.

Proposition 43.2-3. *The Hilbert-Schmidt-, trace-, and usual operator norms are related as follows.*

(a) *$B \in \mathcal{T}(\mathcal{H})$ implies $\|B\| \leq \|B\|_{\mathrm{HS}} \leq \|B\|_{\mathrm{tr}} < \infty$ and $\|B\|_{\mathrm{tr}} = \|B^*\|_{\mathrm{tr}}$.*

(b) *$B \in \mathrm{HS}(\mathcal{H})$ implies $\|B\| \leq \|B\|_{\mathrm{HS}} < \infty$ and $\|B\|_{\mathrm{HS}} = \|B^*\|_{\mathrm{HS}}$.*

(c) *If $B \in \mathcal{T}(\mathcal{H})$ and $A \in \mathcal{L}(\mathcal{H})$, then $\|AB\|_{\mathrm{tr}} \leq \|A\|\|B\|_{\mathrm{tr}}$ and $\|BA\|_{\mathrm{tr}} \leq \|A\|\|B\|_{\mathrm{tr}}$.*

(d) *If $B \in \mathrm{HS}(\mathcal{H})$ and $A \in \mathcal{L}(\mathcal{H})$, then $\|AB\|_{\mathrm{HS}} \leq \|A\|\|B\|_{\mathrm{HS}}$ and $\|BA\|_{\mathrm{HS}} \leq \|A\|\|B\|_{\mathrm{HS}}$.*

(e) *If $B, C \in \mathrm{HS}(\mathcal{H})$, then $BC, CB \in \mathcal{T}(\mathcal{H})$ and $\|BC\|_{\mathrm{tr}} \leq \|B\|_{\mathrm{HS}}\|C\|_{\mathrm{HS}}$, as well as $\|CB\|_{\mathrm{tr}} \leq \|B\|_{\mathrm{HS}}\|C\|_{\mathrm{HS}}$. Conversely, if $A \in \mathcal{T}(\mathcal{H})$, then there exist some $B, C \in \mathrm{HS}(\mathcal{H})$ with $A = BC$.*

The functional tr : $T(\mathcal{H}) \to \mathbb{C}$ given by

$$\text{tr}(B) := \sum_{\alpha \in I} (\xi_\alpha | B\xi_\alpha), \quad \forall B \in T(\mathcal{H}), \quad (= \text{trace})$$

is called the *trace*. It is independent of the chosen orthonormal basis $\{\xi_\alpha \mid \alpha \in I\}$ of $\mathcal{H}$. The trace functional tr : $T(\mathcal{H}) \to \mathbb{C}$ is linear, satisfies $\text{tr}(B^*) = \overline{\text{tr}(B)}$, and fulfills the commutativity relation, called *trace relation*,

$$\text{tr}(AB) = \text{tr}(BA) \tag{43.2.2}$$

either for $B \in T(\mathcal{H})$ and $A \in \mathcal{L}(\mathcal{H})$, or for $A, B \in \text{HS}(\mathcal{H})$. Furthermore, we have

$$|\text{tr}(B)| \le \text{tr}(|B|) = \|B\|_{\text{tr}}, \quad \forall B \in T(\mathcal{H}). \tag{43.2.3}$$

43.2.2. *Matrix Operators*

The foregoing notions may well be illustrated by the so-called *matrix operators*. For a suitable index set J, let $\{\xi_\alpha \mid \alpha \in J\}$ and $\{\psi_\alpha \mid \alpha \in J\}$ be two orthonormal basis systems for $\mathcal{H}$ and $\{a_{\alpha\beta} \mid \alpha, \beta \in J\}$ a complex matrix. In order to give the formal expression $A = \sum_{\alpha,\beta} a_{\alpha\beta} |\xi_\alpha)(\psi_\beta|$ a precise meaning, one must investigate when its application to vectors $\xi \in \mathcal{H}$,

$$A\xi = \sum_{\alpha,\beta} a_{\alpha\beta} (\psi_\beta|\xi) \, \xi_\alpha \tag{43.2.4}$$

leads again to vectors in $\mathcal{H}$. This is the case, if and only if $\sum_\alpha \left| \sum_\beta a_{\alpha\beta}(\psi_\beta|\xi) \right|^2 < \infty$, and the set of such ξ constitutes the domain of definition $\text{dom}(A)$. If one knows that the condition $\sum_\alpha |a_{\alpha\beta}|^2 < \infty$ is fulfilled for all $\beta \in J$, then any ξ with finitely many components with respect to the basis $\{\psi_\beta \mid \beta \in J\}$ is in $\text{dom}(A)$. Thus A is densely defined and its adjoint A^* exists, where

$$A^*\psi = \sum_{\alpha,\beta} \overline{a_{\beta\alpha}}(\xi_\beta|\psi) \, \psi_\alpha = \left(\sum_{\alpha,\beta} \overline{a_{\beta\alpha}} |\psi_\alpha)(\xi_\beta| \right) \psi, \quad \forall \psi \in \text{dom}(A^*)$$

The characterization of $\text{dom}(A^*)$ parallels that given for $\text{dom}(A)$. If also the second condition $\sum_\beta |a_{\alpha\beta}|^2 < \infty$ is satisfied for each $\alpha \in J$, then $\text{dom}(A^*)$ is dense in $\mathcal{H}$ and A is closable. But A^{**} is the original matrix operator A, and we know, therefore, that A is closed. One can show that in separable Hilbert spaces any closable operator A is a matrix operator, whose matrix satisfies the two conditions of above.

Observe that the validity of the two mentioned conditions is guaranteed by the single condition $\sum_{\alpha,\beta} |a_{\alpha\beta}|^2 < \infty$. The latter is, however, so strong that the corresponding matrix operator is Hilbert–Schmidt. This operator is not only closed but even bounded, even compact.

The boundedness of A may be ensured by $\sum_\alpha |a_{\alpha\beta}| < \infty$ and $\sum_\beta |a_{\alpha\beta}| < \infty$.

If A is a matrix operator with its $\{\xi_\alpha \mid \alpha \in J\}$ equal to its $\{\psi_\alpha \mid \alpha \in J\}$ and with an Hermitian matrix $\overline{a_{\beta\alpha}} = a_{\alpha\beta}$, satisfying the condition $\sum_\alpha |a_{\alpha\beta}|^2 < \infty$, then we conclude: A is densely defined, has an adjoint A^*, for which the given condition guarantees also a dense domain. The domain condition for A^* is now identical to that for A, and on this common domain the two operators coincide. That means that A is a self-adjoint, in general unbounded operator.

Proposition 43.2-4 (Matrix Representation of Compact Operators). *An operator A is compact, i.e., $A \in \mathcal{C}(\mathcal{H})$, if and only if it may be brought into the following form of a special matrix operator*

$$A = \sum_{\alpha \in J} a_\alpha \, |\xi_\alpha)(\psi_\alpha| \,, \quad a_\alpha \geq 0 \,, \qquad \left(\Rightarrow \; A^* = \sum_{\alpha \in J} a_\alpha \, |\psi_\alpha)(\xi_\alpha| \, \right),$$

for two appropriate orthonormal basis systems $\{\xi_\alpha \mid \alpha \in J\}$ and $\{\psi_\alpha \mid \alpha \in J\}$ and with at most countably many positive numbers $a_\alpha \neq 0$ (arranged in decreasing order), satisfying $\lim_\alpha a_\alpha = 0$ in case of an infinite-dimensional $\mathcal{H}$.

$A \in \mathcal{C}(\mathcal{H})$ is Hilbert–Schmidt, that is $A \in \mathrm{HS}(\mathcal{H})$, if and only if $\sum_\alpha |a_\alpha|^2 < \infty$, and $A \in \mathcal{C}(\mathcal{H})$ is of trace class, i.e., $A \in \mathcal{T}(\mathcal{H})$, if and only if $\sum_\alpha |a_\alpha| < \infty$.

Non–positive matrix elements may arise, of course, if the basis systems are altered. The present form is suited for the polar decomposition.

The foregoing result finds its continuation in the spectral theory for normal compact operators outlined in Proposition 43.3-1 below.

43.2.3. *States and Bounded Observables in Traditional Quantum Mechanics*

As an application of some of the introduced operator notions, we discuss first a special set of trace class operators.

Traditional quantum mechanics, in contradistinction to algebraic quantum mechanics or to the convex state space approach, is from the outset connected with a complex Hilbert space $\mathcal{H}$, containing the "wave functions". Schrödinger's wave functions constituted historically the first quantum mechanical state concept, the statistical nature of which having been disclosed by Born. The changeover of a wave function, as a function on position space, to a unit-vector in $\mathcal{H}$ is, in fact, an important abstraction and expresses the unitary invariance of traditional quantum mechanics. More precisely, one has to associate the one-dimensional projection, determined by the unit-vector, with this kind of states. A mixing of these, to increase their statistical fluctuations, leads to the so-called *density operators*. It seems, that von Neumann has not only introduced the notion of a density operator but even the consequent Hilbert space formulation for traditional quantum mechanics (summarized in [vN32]).

Definition 43.2-5 (Density Operators). A density operator T on the (not necessarily separable) Hilbert space $\mathcal{H}$ is a positive, normalized trace class operator, that is an element of the set

$$\mathcal{T}_1^+(\mathcal{H}) := \{T \in \mathcal{T}(\mathcal{H}) \mid T \geq 0,\ \mathrm{tr}(T) = \|T\|_{\mathrm{tr}} = 1\} \qquad (43.2.5)$$

(recall that $T \geq 0$ automatically implies its self-adjointness $T = T^*$, since T is bounded).

As any state space, $\mathcal{T}_1^+(\mathcal{H})$ is convex and the *pure states* are by definition the elements of the extreme boundary $\partial_e \mathcal{T}_1^+(\mathcal{H})$. (Recall that according to Sec. 47.1 on page 1725 T is an extreme element, if and only if $T = \lambda T_1 + (1 - \lambda)T_2$, with a $0 < \lambda < 1$ and with some $T_1, T_2 \in \mathcal{T}_1^+(\mathcal{H})$, implies $T_1 = T_2 = T$.) Thus, a pure state is not a non-trivial mixture of other states, it cannot be further, incoherently decomposed.

Proposition 43.2-6 (Pure States in Traditional Quantum Mechanics).
The pure states $\partial_e \mathcal{T}_1^+(\mathcal{H})$ coincide just with the one-dimensional projections on $\mathcal{H}$, that is,

$$\partial_e \mathcal{T}_1^+(\mathcal{H}) = \{T_\xi := |\xi)(\xi| \mid \xi \in \mathcal{H},\ \|\xi\| = 1\}\,.$$

For a pure state $T_\xi = |\xi)(\xi|$ one obviously has $T_\xi = T_{z\xi}$, for all $z \in \mathbb{C}$ with $|z| = 1$. The corresponding normalized $\xi \in \mathcal{H}$ are called the associated state vectors.

Proof.   Consider first a density operator of the form $T_\xi = |\xi)(\xi|$. Suppose a decomposition $T_\xi = \lambda T_1 + (1 - \lambda)T_2$ with $0 < \lambda < 1$ and some $T_1, T_2 \in \mathcal{T}_1^+(\mathcal{H})$. Denote by $\xi^\perp = (\mathbb{1} - T_\xi)\mathcal{H}$ the sub-Hilbert space of $\mathcal{H}$ orthogonal to ξ. Then

$$\lambda(\psi|T_1\psi) + (1 - \lambda)(\psi|T_2\psi) = (\psi|T_\xi\psi) = 0,\quad \forall \psi \in \xi^\perp.$$

Since $T_j \geq 0$ and $0 < \lambda < 1$, we obtain $0 = (\psi|T_j\psi) = \|(T_j)^{1/2}\psi\|^2$, so that $T_j\psi = (T_j)^{1/2}(T_j)^{1/2}\psi = 0$, for $j = 1, 2$ and for every $\psi \in \xi^\perp$. That means, $\ker(T_j) = \xi^\perp$. The self-adjointness of T_j yields

$$(\psi|T_j\phi) = (T_j\psi|\phi) = 0,\quad \forall \psi \in \xi^\perp,\quad \forall \phi \in \mathcal{H},$$

which implies $\mathrm{ran}(T_j) \subseteq \mathbb{C}\xi$. Consequently, $T_j\xi = z_j\xi$ for some $z_j \in \mathbb{C}$. The normalization implies $1 = \mathrm{tr}(T_j) = z_j$, which leads to $T_j = T_\xi$ for $j = 1, 2$. So, in fact, $T_\xi \in \partial_e \mathcal{T}_1^+(\mathcal{H})$.

Conversely, let $T \in \mathcal{T}_1^+(\mathcal{H})$ be such that the index set I of its spectral decomposition (43.2.8) below has at least two elements. Then we have a $k_0 \in I$ with $0 < \lambda := \lambda_{k_0} < 1$, which enables the decomposition $T = \lambda T_1 + (1 - \lambda)T_2$ with

$$T_1 := |\xi_{k_0})(\xi_{k_0}| \in \mathcal{T}_1^+(\mathcal{H}),\qquad T_2 := \frac{1}{1 - \lambda} \sum_{k_0 \neq k \in I} \lambda_k |\xi_k)(\xi_k| \in \mathcal{T}_1^+(\mathcal{H}),$$

where both density operators differ from T. This makes the decomposition non-trivial. Consequently, $T \notin \partial_e \mathcal{T}_1^+(\mathcal{H})$. $\qquad \square$

The spectral properties of any $T \in \mathcal{T}(\mathcal{H})$ arise as a special case of Proposition 43.3-1 below for compact operators. Such $T \in \mathcal{T}(\mathcal{H})$ is self-adjoint, if and only if it is given by an orthonormalized family $\{\xi_k \mid k \in I\}$ of vectors in $\mathcal{H}$ and by numbers $0 \neq \lambda_k \in \mathbb{R}$, $k \in I$, where the index set I is at most countable (finite or infinite), such that

$$T = \sum_{k \in I} \lambda_k |\xi_k\rangle\langle\xi_k|, \qquad \mathrm{tr}(T) = \sum_{k \in I} |\lambda_k| < \infty. \qquad (43.2.6)$$

The spectral representation may be split into a sum over the positive and a sum over the negative eigenvalues λ_k (the part of T with the eigenvalue 0 is not covered by the index set I), and we obtain

$$\mathcal{T}_{\mathrm{sa}}(\mathcal{H}) \ni T = T^+ - T^-, \qquad T^+, T^- \in \mathcal{T}^+(\mathcal{H}), \qquad T^+ T^- = 0. \qquad (43.2.7)$$

If on the other hand, $T \in \mathcal{T}_{\mathrm{sa}}(\mathcal{H})$ has such a decomposition, then the spectral representations of T^+ and T^- operate on orthogonal subspaces and the uniqueness of the spectral representation of T entails that of the two components.

Especially important is the spectral representation of the density operators

$$T = \sum_{k \in I} \lambda_k |\xi_k\rangle\langle\xi_k|, \qquad \lambda_k > 0, \qquad 1 = \mathrm{tr}(T) = \sum_{k \in I} \lambda_k. \qquad (43.2.8)$$

The spectral representation gives the state T as a special statistical mixture over the pure states $T_k = |\xi_k\rangle\langle\xi_k|$, $k \in I$, where the eigenvalues λ_k express the probabilities for the T_k.

By rescaling of (43.2.7), we obtain

Lemma 43.2-7 (Jordan Decomposition). *For each $T \in \mathcal{T}_{\mathrm{sa}}(\mathcal{H})$ we have the decomposition*

$$\mathcal{T}_{\mathrm{sa}}(\mathcal{H}) \ni T = \lambda_+ T^+ - \lambda_- T^-, \qquad \lambda_+, \lambda_- \geq 0, \qquad T^+, T^- \in \mathcal{T}_1^+(\mathcal{H}), \qquad T^+ T^- = 0, \qquad (43.2.9)$$

where the two numbers λ_+, λ_- and density operators T^+, T^- are unique, if $\lambda_+ T^+$ and $\lambda_- T^-$ do not vanish.

The convex set $\mathcal{T}_1^+(\mathcal{H})$ is, as intersection of the norm-closed positive cone $\mathcal{T}^+(\mathcal{H})$ with the unit-ball $\mathcal{T}_1(\mathcal{H}) = \{T \in \mathcal{T}(\mathcal{H}) \mid \|T\|_{\mathrm{tr}} = 1\}$, for itself closed in the trace norm, but not norm-compact (cf., however, Theorem 26.3-16). Nevertheless, the spectral representation (43.2.8) demonstrates, that each $T \in \mathcal{T}_1^+(\mathcal{H})$ is the $\|.\|_{\mathrm{tr}}$-limit of convex combinations of extremal states (what for compact convex sets is proven by the Krein–Milman Theorem 48.1-8). That such an extremal decomposition is not unique, is already visualized by the qubit space space (cf. Sec. 47.3.2).

If $\mathcal{H}$ is (possibly over-countably) infinite-dimensional, what we assume in the following discussion, then from the set of all projections $\mathcal{P}(\mathcal{H})$ only the finite projections $P \in F\mathcal{P}(\mathcal{H})$ are in $\mathcal{T}^+(\mathcal{H})$. The set $F\mathcal{P}(\mathcal{H})$ is an increasingly directed net, converging weakly to $\mathbb{1}$. (Recall that $P \leq P' \Leftrightarrow PP' = P$.) Because in $\mathcal{L}_1(\mathcal{H}) = \{A \in \mathcal{L}(\mathcal{H}) \mid \|A\| \leq 1\}$ the weak topology and the σ-weak topology coincide (cf. Proposition 46.1-2) this net converges also σ-weakly and we have

$$\lim_{P \in F\mathcal{P}(\mathcal{H})} PT = T, \quad \forall T \in \mathcal{T}(\mathcal{H}), \quad \text{with respect to the trace norm } \|.\|_{\mathrm{tr}}.$$

(43.2.10)

We show in Chapter 47 that, for a rather general convex state space K, the bounded empirical observables are biunivocally associated with the affine bounded functions $\mathrm{Aff}_b(K)$ and so we are interested to determine $\mathrm{Aff}_b(\mathcal{T}_1^+(\mathcal{H}))$.

Proposition 43.2-8. *The set of all real, affine, and bounded functions* $\mathrm{Aff}_b(\mathcal{T}_1^+(\mathcal{H}))$ *is Banach space isomorphic to* $\mathcal{L}_{\mathrm{sa}}(\mathcal{H})$, *the self-adjoint bounded operators. That is, for each* $a \in \mathrm{Aff}_b(\mathcal{T}_1^+(\mathcal{H}))$ *there is exactly one* $A \in \mathcal{L}_{\mathrm{sa}}(\mathcal{H})$, *with* $a(T) = \mathrm{tr}[TA]$ *for all* $T \in \mathcal{T}_1^+(\mathcal{H})$, *and with* $\|a\| \equiv \sup\{|a(T)| \mid T \in \mathcal{T}_1(\mathcal{H})\} = \|A\|$.

$\mathrm{Aff}_b(\mathcal{T}_1^+(\mathcal{H}))$ *is — by extension respectively restriction — also Banach space isomorphic to* $\mathrm{Aff}_{b,0}(\mathcal{T}^+(\mathcal{H}))$, *the set of bounded affine function on* $\mathcal{T}^+(\mathcal{H})$, *vanishing at* $T = 0$, *what coincides with the real dual Banach space* $(\mathcal{T}_{\mathrm{sa}}(\mathcal{H}))^*$.

Proof. If $A \in \mathcal{L}_{\mathrm{sa}}(\mathcal{H})$, then $\mathcal{T}(\mathcal{H}) \ni T \mapsto a(T) := \mathrm{tr}[TA]$ is linear and $\|.\|_{\mathrm{tr}}$-continuous, with $\|a\| = \|A\|$ (because of Proposition 43.2-3 (c)), and its restrictions to $\mathcal{T}^+(\mathcal{H})$, respectively to $\mathcal{T}_1^+(\mathcal{H})$, are real affine, and the former ones vanish at $T = 0$.

Let a be a real, affine, $\|.\|_{\mathrm{tr}}$-continuous functional on $\mathcal{T}_1^+(\mathcal{H})$. Using (43.2.9) we get by dilation and additivity a unique affine bounded extension to $\mathcal{T}_{\mathrm{sa}}(\mathcal{H})$, vanishing at $T = 0$, and a unique linear, bounded extension to $\mathcal{T}(\mathcal{H})$. For each $P \in F\mathcal{P}(\mathcal{H})$, there is an $A_P \in \mathcal{L}(\mathcal{H})$ with $a(PT) = \mathrm{tr}[TA_P]$ for all $T \in \mathcal{T}(\mathcal{H})$ and $\|A_P\| \leq \|a\|$. Because of the weak compactness of the ball $\mathcal{L}_r(\mathcal{H})$, $r = \|a\|$ (cf. Proposition 46.1-2), the weak net limit A of A_P over a subnet of $F\mathcal{P}(\mathcal{H})$ exists and has norm $\|A\| \leq \|a\|$. This realizes the functional a in terms of $\mathrm{tr}[TA]$ not only on $F\mathcal{P}(\mathcal{H})\mathcal{T}_1^+(\mathcal{H})$ but on all of $\mathcal{T}_1^+(\mathcal{H}) \ni T$ because of (43.2.10). From this follows that also $\|a\| \leq \|A\|$. Realness implies $A \in \mathcal{L}_{\mathrm{sa}}(\mathcal{H})$. $\qquad\square$

43.3. Spectral Theory, Projection-Valued Measures

43.3.1. *Basic Notions: Spectrum and Resolvent*

The complex $z \in \mathbb{C}$ is called an *eigenvalue* of the operator B on the Hilbert space $\mathcal{H}$, if there exists a nonzero $\psi \in \mathrm{dom}(B)$ such that $B\psi = z\psi$. The kernel $\ker(z\mathbb{1} - B)$ is the *eigenspace* of z, and its dimension is called the *multiplicity* of the eigenvalue z. We denote by $\sigma_p(B)$ the set of all eigenvalues of B, the so-called *point spectrum* of B.

If $z \in \mathbb{C}$ is not an eigenvalue, then $\ker(z\mathbb{1} - B)$ vanishes and $z\mathbb{1} - B$ is injective, and thus the inverse operator $(z\mathbb{1} - B)^{-1}$ is well defined on $\mathrm{ran}(z\mathbb{1} - B)$. The *resolvent set* $\rho(B)$ of the operator B on $\mathcal{H}$ is defined by those $z \in \mathbb{C}$ for which $z\mathbb{1} - B$ is a bijection from $\mathrm{dom}(B)$ onto the entire $\mathcal{H} = \mathrm{ran}(z\mathbb{1} - B)$ such that $(z\mathbb{1} - B)^{-1}$ is bounded:

$$\rho(B) := \{z \in \mathbb{C} \mid (z\mathbb{1} - B) \text{ is injective onto } \mathcal{H}, \ (z\mathbb{1} - B)^{-1} \in \mathcal{L}(\mathcal{H})\}. \qquad (43.3.1)$$

The inverse $(z\mathbb{1} - B)^{-1}$ is called the *resolvent* of B at $z \in \rho(B)$. The *spectrum* $\sigma(B)$ of B is defined as the set complement of $\rho(B)$ in $\mathbb{C}$:

$$\sigma(B) := \mathbb{C} \backslash \rho(B), \qquad (43.3.2)$$

B an operator on $\mathcal{H}$. Especially, the eigenvalues of B are contained in $\sigma(B)$.

If B is not closed, then $z\mathbb{1} - B$ and $(z\mathbb{1} - B)^{-1}$ are not closed, and consequently $\rho(B) = \emptyset$. Hence spectral theory is only meaningful for closed operators. But for closed B it follows from the closed graph theorem that the condition $\mathrm{ran}(z\mathbb{1} - B) = \mathcal{H}$ implies the operator $(z\mathbb{1} - B)^{-1}$ to be bounded. So it suffices to define the resolvent set by

$$\rho(B) := \{z \in \mathbb{C} \mid z\mathbb{1} - B \text{ is injective with } \mathrm{ran}(z\mathbb{1} - B) = \mathcal{H}\}. \qquad (43.3.3)$$

For closed, densely defined B it follows that $\sigma(B^*) = \overline{\sigma(B)}$.

For $B \in \mathcal{L}(\mathcal{H})$ its spectrum is always non-empty. If e.g., $B = \mathbb{1}$, then $\mathrm{ran}(z\mathbb{1} - B) = \{0\}$ for $z = 1$, and $\mathrm{ran}(z\mathbb{1} - B) = \mathcal{H}$ for $z \neq 1$, with $(z\mathbb{1} - B)^{-1} = (z - 1)^{-1}\mathbb{1}$. Thus $\varrho(\mathbb{1}) = \mathbb{C}\backslash\{1\}$ and $\sigma(\mathbb{1}) = \sigma_p(\mathbb{1}) = \{1\}$. One has already by the definition of the spectrum that $0 \in \sigma(A)$, if and only if A^{-1} does not exist as a bounded operator on the domain $\mathcal{H}$.

The resolvent set $\rho(B)$ of a *closed operator* B is always an *open* subset of $\mathbb{C}$ and thus the spectrum $\sigma(B)$ is always a *closed* subset of $\mathbb{C}$. Therefore, any limit point of spectral values, e.g., of eigenvalues, is still in the spectrum. If the eigenvalues of a closed B accumulate at 0, such as for compact operators, then $0 \in \sigma(B)$ (and B does not possess a bounded inverse), but 0 is not necessarily an eigenvalue of B.

The spectrum $\sigma(B)$ of every self-adjoint, bounded or unbounded operator B is non-empty and a closed subset of the real line $\mathbb{R}$. In case of bounded $B = B^* \in \mathcal{L}(\mathcal{H})$ it holds $\sigma(B) \subseteq [-\|B\|, \|B\|]$, whereas $\sigma(B)$ is an unbounded set for an unbounded self-adjoint operator B.

A symmetric operator B on the Hilbert space $\mathcal{H}$ is self-adjoint, if and only if $\sigma(B) \subseteq \mathbb{R}$ (as well as if and only if the 2 so-called deficiency indices $\dim[\ker(\pm i\mathbb{1} - B^*)]$ vanish, so that $\pm i$ are not eigenvalues of B^*).

Especially important for our discussion of vacua and ground states is the following: The self-adjoint B is positive, i.e., $B = B^* \geq 0$, if and only if $\sigma(B) \subseteq [0, \infty[$; it is *strictly positive*, if and only if in addition 0 is not an eigenvalue of B. (One may be inclined to require $\sigma(B) \subseteq]0, \infty[$, but closedness of the spectrum provides then nevertheless 0 as possible spectral value).

Let us demonstrate some notions by means of compact operators. The following result is remarkable in that it derives spectral properties from the definition of compact operators, given originally in terms of continuity properties.

Proposition 43.3-1 (Spectral Theory of Compact Operators). *Let $C \in \mathcal{C}(\mathcal{H})$. We have $0 \in \sigma(C)$ for infinite-dimensional $\mathcal{H}$; but not necessarily $0 \in \sigma_p(C)$ for separable $\mathcal{H}$, whereas $0 \in \sigma_p(C)$ if $\mathcal{H}$ is non-separable. Every non-zero element of the spectrum $\sigma(C)$ is an eigenvalue of C, that is,*

$$\sigma(C) \backslash \{0\} = \sigma_p(C) \backslash \{0\}, \qquad C \text{ compact}.$$

Furthermore, C has at most countably many eigenvalues, and every non-zero eigenvalue has finite multiplicity. If there are infinitely many non-zero eigenvalues, then these cluster at $0 \in \sigma(C)$, and only there. The complex number $c \neq 0$ is an eigenvalue of C, if and only if its complex conjugate $\bar{c}$ is an eigenvalue of C^*.

Suppose now $C \in \mathcal{C}(\mathcal{H})$ to be normal, i.e., $\|C\psi\| = \|C^*\psi\|$ for all $\psi \in \mathcal{H}$ (by Sec. 43.1). Then there exists an at most countable family $\{\xi_k \mid k \in I\}$ of orthonormalized eigenvectors for C associated with the eigenvalues $c_k \neq 0$, $k \in I$, such that

$$C = \sum_{k \in I} c_k |\xi_k)(\xi_k|, \qquad converging \text{ in operator norm}.$$

Moreover, C is Hilbert–Schmidt, i.e., $C \in \mathrm{HS}(\mathcal{H})$, if and only if $\sum_k |c_k|^2 < \infty$, and C is of trace class, i.e., $C \in \mathcal{T}(\mathcal{H})$, if and only if $\sum_k |c_k| < \infty$. The normal C is self-adjoint if and only if $c_k \in \mathbb{R}$, and $C \geq 0$ if and only if $c_k \geq 0$.

(In Proposition 43.2-4, the $a_\alpha \geq 0$ and the ψ_α are the eigenvalues respectively eigenvectors of $|C| = (C^*C)^{1/2} \in \mathcal{C}(\mathcal{H})$, and a_α, ξ_α those of $|C^*| = (CC^*)^{1/2}$.)

Applied to the resolvent, the foregoing result is a main tool to determine the spectrum of certain unbounded operators in mathematical physics. Some more information is found in (the proof of) Proposition 43.5-11 and in Sec. 46.1.1 on page 1671.

43.3.2. *Spectral Calculus for Self-adjoint Operators*

Before we turn to the spectral calculus for self-adjoint operators let us recall the following measure theoretic notions (cf. also the beginning of Chapter 50): The Borel subsets $\mathrm{B}(\mathbb{R})$ of $\mathbb{R}$ are the elements of the smallest σ-algebra containing all open sets of $\mathbb{R}$. Especially all open, half-open, and closed intervals are in $\mathrm{B}(\mathbb{R})$, where the latter two kinds may be written as countable intersections of open intervals. Also each singleton $\{z\}$, $z \in \mathbb{R}$, is in $\mathrm{B}(\mathbb{R})$, what follows from the Hausdorff property of $\mathbb{R}$, by which $\{z\}$ is separated from any other $z'_n \in \mathbb{R}$ by an open neighborhood so that, if $z'_n \to z$, $\{z\}$ may be represented as a countable intersection of open neighborhoods (and we can apply this consideration for the Borel sets in any Hausdorff topological space).

A function $\mu : B(\mathbb{R}) \rightarrow [0, +\infty]$ is called a (positive) *Borel measure* on the measure space $(\mathbb{R}, B(\mathbb{R}))$, if $\mu(\emptyset) = 0$, and if μ is countably additive (or σ-additive), i.e., if we have

$$\mu(\textstyle\bigcup_n \Lambda_n) = \sum_n \mu(\Lambda_n)$$

for countably many disjoint sets $\Lambda_n \in B(\mathbb{R})$. If the countably additive function μ on $B(\mathbb{R})$, vanishing on $\emptyset$, takes its values in $\mathbb{R}$, we call it a *signed Borel measure*, and if its values are in $\mathbb{C}$, we call it a *complex Borel measure* (where the adjective "Borel" is often omitted). So the set of all real (complex) linear combinations of Borel measures constitutes the real (complex) vector space of all signed (complex) Borel measures.

Again, we denote by $\mathcal{P}(\mathcal{H}) \subset \mathcal{L}(\mathcal{H})$ the set of the orthogonal projections acting on $\mathcal{H}$.

Definition 43.3-2 (Projection-Valued Measure). A mapping $\Lambda \mapsto P(\Lambda)$ from the Borel subsets $B(\mathbb{R})$ of $\mathbb{R}$ into $\mathcal{P}(\mathcal{H})$ is called a projection-valued measure, if

(a) $P(\Lambda)$ is an orthogonal projection on $\mathcal{H}$ for every $\Lambda \in B(\mathbb{R})$.
(b) $P(\emptyset) = 0$, and $P(\mathbb{R}) = \mathbb{1}$.
(c) $P(\Lambda_1)P(\Lambda_2) = P(\Lambda_1 \cap \Lambda_2) = P(\Lambda_2)P(\Lambda_1)$, for all $\Lambda_1, \Lambda_2 \in B(\mathbb{R})$.
(d) If $\Lambda = \bigcup\limits_{n=1}^{\infty} \Lambda_n$, where $\Lambda_n \in B(\mathbb{R})$ with $\Lambda_m \cap \Lambda_n = \emptyset$ for $m \neq n$, then

$$P(\Lambda) = \operatorname*{s-lim}_{N \to \infty} \sum_{n=1}^{N} P(\Lambda_n), \quad \text{(limit in the strong operator topology, cf. below).}$$

If P is a projection-valued measure, then for every $\psi \in \mathcal{H}$ the mapping $\Lambda \mapsto (\psi|P(\Lambda)\psi)$ is a well defined (positive) Borel measure on $\mathbb{R}$, which we denote by $d(\psi|P(\lambda)\psi)$.

For $\xi, \psi \in \mathcal{H}$ the complex measure $d(\xi|P(\lambda)\psi)$ is then obtained by the polarization of $d(\psi|P(\lambda)\psi)$.

Now suppose $f: \mathbb{R} \rightarrow \mathbb{C}$ to be a Borel measurable function on $\mathbb{R}$ (that is $f^{-1}(\Lambda) \in B(\mathbb{R})$ for $\Lambda \in B(\mathbb{R})$). Then we can define a $\mathbb{C}$-linear operator $P[f]$ in $\mathcal{H}$ by setting

$$\operatorname{dom}(P[f]) := \{\psi \in \mathcal{H} \mid \textstyle\int_{\mathbb{R}} |f(\lambda)|^2 d(\psi|P(\lambda)\psi) < \infty\},$$

$$(\xi|P[f]\psi) := \int_{\mathbb{R}} f(\lambda)\, d(\xi|P(\lambda)\psi), \quad \xi \in \mathcal{H}, \quad \psi \in \operatorname{dom}(P[f]).$$

One writes symbolically

$$P[f] = \int_{\mathbb{R}} f(\lambda)\, dP(\lambda). \tag{43.3.4}$$

Approximating the function f by elementary step functions it follows that the integral converges actually with respect to the norm on $\mathcal{H}$ for every $\psi \in \operatorname{dom}(P[f])$.

(For bounded f the integral exists even in the operator norm, as is discussed in Remark 47.5-5 below). Especially, we may define the self-adjoint operator

$$B := \int_{\mathbb{R}} \lambda \, dP(\lambda) \,,$$

and we obtain its functional calculus by setting $f(B) := P[f]$.

Up to now we have defined a self-adjoint operator B and its functional calculus by means of a given projection-valued measure. The converse procedure is also possible.

Theorem 43.3-3 (Spectral Calculus). *Let B be a self-adjoint operator on the Hilbert space $\mathcal{H}$. Then there exists a unique projection-valued measure $\mathsf{B}(\mathbb{R}) \ni \Lambda \mapsto P_B(\Lambda)$ such that*

$$B = \int_{\mathbb{R}} \lambda \, dP_B(\lambda) \,. \tag{43.3.5}$$

We have $P_B(\rho(B)) = 0$ for the resolvent set $\rho(B)$, and the support of the projection-valued measure P_B coincides just with the spectrum $\sigma(B)$. A $z \in \mathbb{R}$ is an eigenvalue of B, if and only if $P_B(\{z\}) > 0$.

For every Borel measurable function $f : \mathbb{R} \to \mathbb{C}$ the operator function $f(B)$ of the self-adjoint operator B is defined by

$$\mathrm{dom}(f(B)) := \{\psi \in \mathcal{H} \mid \|f(B)\psi\|^2 = \int_{\mathbb{R}} |f(\lambda)|^2 d(\psi|P_B(\lambda)\psi) < \infty\}\,, \tag{43.3.6}$$

$$f(B) := \int_{\mathbb{R}} f(\lambda) \, dP_B(\lambda) = \int_{\sigma(B)} f(\lambda) \, dP_B(\lambda) \,. \tag{43.3.7}$$

If f is bounded, then $\mathrm{dom}(f(B))$ of (43.3.6) is all of $\mathcal{H}$ and $f(B)$ is bounded, with $\|f(B)\| \leq \sup\{|f(\lambda)| \mid \lambda \in \sigma(B)\}$, where there is equality if f is continuous on $\sigma(B)$. Especially, we have $\chi_\Lambda(B) = P_B(\Lambda)$, where χ_Λ is the indicator function of the Borel set $\Lambda \in \mathsf{B}(\mathbb{R})$ (i.e. $\chi_\Lambda(\lambda) = 0$ for $\lambda \notin \Lambda$ and $\chi_\Lambda(\lambda) = 1$ for $\lambda \in \Lambda$.)

With these definitions the following relations, involving two Borel measurable functions $f, g : \mathbb{R} \to \mathbb{C}$ are valid.

(a) *The operator $f(B)$ is self-adjoint, if and only if $f(\lambda) \in \mathbb{R}$ for P_B-almost all $\lambda \in \mathbb{R}$. In this case, we have*

  (1) *$\sigma(f(B)) \subseteq \overline{f(\sigma(B))}$, where it holds equality, if f is continuous on $\sigma(B)$. If B is bounded and f is continuous, then $\sigma(f(B)) = f(\sigma(B))$.*
  (2) *$\exp\{itf(B)\}g(B) = g(B)\exp\{itf(B)\}$ for all $t \in \mathbb{R}$, especially the unitaries $\exp\{itf(B)\}$, $t \in \mathbb{R}$, leave $\mathrm{dom}(g(B))$ invariant, more precisely,*

$$\exp\{itf(B)\}(\mathrm{dom}(g(B))) = \mathrm{dom}(g(B)) \,.$$

(b) *Let both f and g be $\mathbb{R}$-valued. Then $f(\lambda) \le g(\lambda)$ for all $\lambda \in \sigma(B)$ yields $f(B) \le g(B)$. Especially it holds for $a \in \mathbb{R}$ that $f(B) \le a\mathbb{1}$ (respectively $f(B) \ge a\mathbb{1}$), if and only if $f(\lambda) \le a$ (respectively $f(\lambda) \ge a$) for all $\lambda \in \sigma(B)$.*

(c) *For all $\xi \in \mathrm{dom}(f(B))$ and all $\psi \in \mathrm{dom}(g(B))$, we have*

$$(f(B)\xi|g(B)\psi) = \int_{\mathbb{R}} \overline{f(\lambda)}g(\lambda)\,d(\xi|P_B(\lambda)\psi)\,.$$

(d) *$(f + zg)(B) \supseteq f(B) + zg(B)$ for all $z \in \mathbb{C}$, $\mathrm{dom}(f(B) + g(B)) = \mathrm{dom}((|f| + |g|)(B))$.*

(e) *$(fg)(B) \supseteq f(B)g(B)$, $\mathrm{dom}(f(B)g(B)) = \mathrm{dom}(g(B)) \cap \mathrm{dom}((fg)(B))$.*

(f) *$f(B)^* = \overline{f}(B)$, $\mathrm{dom}(f(B)^*) = \mathrm{dom}(f(B))$.*

The connection between spectral measures and empirical observables is accurately expounded in Sec. 47.5.

43.3.3.   *Root, Absolute Value, Polar Decomposition*

With the spectral calculus we are e.g., in the position to define the nth root of a positive self-adjoint operator B.

Proposition 43.3-4 (n-th Root).   *Suppose B to be a positive, self-adjoint operator on the Hilbert space $\mathcal{H}$. Then for each $n \in \mathbb{N}$ there exists a unique positive, self-adjoint linear operator A on $\mathcal{H}$ with $A^n = B$. A is called the nth root of B, it is denoted by $A = B^{1/n}$ and given by $B^{1/n} = \int_{\mathbb{R}} \lambda^{1/n} dP_B(\lambda)$.*

The 2th root is needed in the subsequent polar decomposition of an, in general, unbounded closed operator. We already mentioned that B^*B is positive and self-adjoint on $\mathcal{H}_1$ for every closed, densely defined operator B from a Hilbert space $\mathcal{H}_1$ into another Hilbert space $\mathcal{H}_2$. The *absolute value* of B is defined by

$$|B| := (B^*B)^{1/2} = \int_0^\infty \sqrt{\lambda}\,dP_{B^*B}(\lambda)\,,$$

where the square root is constructed with the projection-valued measure of B^*B (acting on $\mathcal{H}_1$, of course). Especially, it holds

$$\|(B^*B)^{1/2}\psi\| \equiv \| \,|B|\psi\| = \|B\psi\|\,, \quad \forall \psi \in \mathrm{dom}(|B|) = \mathrm{dom}(B)\,, \tag{43.3.8}$$

and $\ker(B) = \ker(B^*B) = \ker(|B|)$, thus $\overline{\mathrm{ran}(B^*)} = \overline{\mathrm{ran}(B^*B)} = \overline{\mathrm{ran}(|B|)}$.

Proposition 43.3-5 (Polar Decomposition).   *Suppose B to be a closed, densely defined operator from the Hilbert space $\mathcal{H}_1$ into the Hilbert space $\mathcal{H}_2$. Then B has the unique (polar) decomposition $B = UB'$, where B' is a positive, self-adjoint operator on $\mathcal{H}_1$ and U is a partial isometry with initial space $\overline{\mathrm{ran}(B')} \subseteq \mathcal{H}_1$ and final space $\overline{\mathrm{ran}(B)} \subseteq \mathcal{H}_2$. (Especially, U^*U is the orthogonal projection onto $\overline{\mathrm{ran}(B')}$ and UU^**

is the orthogonal projection onto $\overline{\mathrm{ran}(B)}$.) *Furthermore, it holds* $B' = |B|$, *and*

$$B = U\,|B| = |B^*|\,U = UB^*U\,, \quad B^* = U^*|B^*| = |B|\,U^* = U^*BU^*\,,$$
$$|B| = U^*B = B^*U = U^*|B^*|\,U\,, \quad |B^*| = UB^* = BU^* = U\,|B|\,U^*\,. \tag{43.3.9}$$

If B is normal (i.e., $\|B\psi\| = \|B^*\psi\|$ *for all* $\psi \in \mathrm{dom}(B) = \mathrm{dom}(B^*)$, *cf. Sec. 43.1), then in addition* $\overline{\mathrm{ran}(B^*)} = \overline{\mathrm{ran}(B)} = \overline{\mathrm{ran}(|B|)}$ *and*

$$|B| = |B^*|\,, \quad U\,|B| = |B|\,U\,, \quad U^*\,|B| = |B|\,U^*\,. \tag{43.3.10}$$

The relations $B = U\,|B|$ and $B^* = |B|\,U^*$ imply: If B and thus $|B|$ are injective, then U coincides with the closure of $B|B|^{-1}$, and U^* is the closure of $|B|^{-1}B^*$.

43.4.   Perturbations of Self-adjoint Operators

In order to have a notion which describes the deviation of one operator from another (physically relevant for Hamiltonians) we recall some facts and definitions from the perturbation theory of operators.

Definition 43.4-1 (Relative Boundedness, Relative Compactness).   Let A and B be densely defined operators on a Hilbert space $\mathcal{H}$ with $\mathrm{dom}(B) \supseteq \mathrm{dom}(A)$.

(a) Suppose that there exist $a, b \in [0, \infty[$, such that

$$\|B\psi\| \le a\|A\psi\| + b\|\psi\|\,, \quad \forall\psi \in \mathrm{dom}(A)\,. \tag{43.4.1}$$

Then B is called *relatively bounded* with respect to A, or briefly A-bounded. The infimum of such a is called the relative bound of B with respect to A. (Observe that $\inf\{a\}$ may not be inserted in place of a in (43.4.1). Especially, if $\inf\{a\} = 0$, then there is still needed, in general, a positive a in (43.4.1).)

(b) The operator B is called *relatively compact* with respect to A, or simply A-compact, if B is compact considered as an operator from $(\mathrm{dom}(A), \|.\|_A)$ into $\mathcal{H}$, where here $(\mathrm{dom}(A), \|.\|_A)$ means the space $\mathrm{dom}(A)$ equipped with the graph norm $\|.\|_A$ of A, which is defined in Eq. (43.1.4).

An equivalent characterization of the A-compactness of B is the compactness of the operator $B(\lambda\mathbb{1} - A)^{-1}$ on $\mathcal{H}$ for some $\lambda \notin \sigma(A)$.

In many interesting physical situations A is self-adjoint and B is a symmetric operator with $\mathrm{dom}(B) \supseteq \mathrm{dom}(A)$. If B is relatively bounded with respect to A, it may be considered as a weak *perturbation* of A. Then $A + B$ may be formed as a self-adjoint operator, what is the main content of the subsequent theorem.

In the following formulation of the famous Kato–Rellich Theorem, we incorporate also its implications to relatively compact perturbations, leading to the stability of the essential spectrum, which for compact perturbations had been proved by Weyl. Recall that the essential spectrum $\sigma_{\mathrm{ess}}(A)$ of a self-adjoint operator A consists of those $\lambda \in \mathbb{R}$ for which the spectral projection $P_A(]\lambda - \varepsilon, \lambda + \varepsilon[)$ is infinite-dimensional for all $\varepsilon > 0$.

Theorem 43.4-2 (Kato–Rellich, Weyl). *Let A and B be two operators on a Hilbert space, such that A is self-adjoint and $\mathrm{dom}(A) \subseteq \mathrm{dom}(B)$.*

(a) *Suppose that B is symmetric and A-bounded with relative bound $a < 1$. Then $A + B$ is self-adjoint (with domain $\mathrm{dom}(A + B) = \mathrm{dom}(A)$), and essentially self-adjoint on every core of A.*

Furthermore, if A (equivalently $\sigma(A)$) is bounded from below with lower bound $\alpha \in \mathbb{R}$, then $A+B$ is bounded from below, with lower bound $\alpha - \max\{\frac{b}{1-a}, a\alpha + b\}$, where a and b are taken from (43.4.1).

(b) *Let B be relatively compact with respect to A. Then:*

(1) *B is A-bounded with relative bound 0.*

(2) *$A + B$ is closed, and also self-adjoint if B in addition is symmetric.*

(3) *The perturbation B leaves the essential spectrum invariant, that is,*

$$\sigma_{\mathrm{ess}}(A) = \sigma_{\mathrm{ess}}(A + B).$$

Proof. [Hint] The first statement (a) is know as the Kato–Rellich Theorem; it is proved e.g., in [RS75] Theorem X.12. The group of assertions in part (b), including the Weyl-type result, is derived in [RS78], Theorem XIII.14, Corollary 1 and Corollary 2. □

Further results on perturbation theory of self-adjoint operators may be found in the classic [Kat84] and e.g., in [Wei80], Chapter 9.

43.5. Sesquilinear Forms

A *sesquilinear form* on a Hilbert space $\mathcal{H}$ is a mapping $s : \mathrm{dom}(s) \times \mathrm{dom}(s) \to \mathbb{C}$, $(\xi, \psi) \mapsto s(\xi, \psi)$, which is antilinear in the first factor and linear in the second factor, where its domain $\mathrm{dom}(s)$ is a subspace of $\mathcal{H}$. The associated *quadratic form* $q_s : \mathrm{dom}(s) \to \mathbb{C}$ is defined by

$$q_s(\psi) := s(\psi, \psi), \quad \forall \psi \in \mathrm{dom}(s), \qquad \text{(quadratic form to } s\text{)}.$$

The sesquilinear form s is called *Hermitian*, if

$$s(\xi, \psi) = \overline{s(\psi, \xi)}, \quad \forall \xi, \psi \in \mathrm{dom}(s).$$

The following result is checked by direct computation.

Lemma 43.5-1 (Polarization Identity). *Let s be a sesquilinear form on a Hilbert space $\mathcal{H}$. Then s may be recovered from its quadratic form q_s by*

$$s(\xi, \psi) = \frac{1}{4}[q_s(\xi + \psi) - q_s(\xi - \psi) + iq_s(\xi - i\psi) - iq_s(\xi + i\psi)], \quad \forall \xi, \psi \in \mathrm{dom}(s). \tag{43.5.1}$$

Furthermore, s is Hermitian, if and only if $q_s(\psi) \in \mathbb{R}$ for all $\psi \in \mathrm{dom}(s)$.

For sesquilinear forms there are analogous notions as for operators.

Definition 43.5-2. The sesquilinear form s is called *densely defined*, if its domain $\mathrm{dom}(s)$ is dense in $\mathcal{H}$. We write $s \subseteq t$, if t is a sesquilinear form extending s, i.e., $\mathrm{dom}(s) \subseteq \mathrm{dom}(t)$ and $s(\xi, \psi) = t(\xi, \psi)$ for all $\xi, \psi \in \mathrm{dom}(s)$.

Suppose for a $\psi \in \mathcal{H}$ that there exists a sequence $\{\psi_n \mid n \in \mathbb{N}\} \subset \mathrm{dom}(s)$ satisfying $\lim_{n \to \infty} \|\psi_n - \psi\| = 0$ and $\lim_{n,m \to \infty} q_s(\psi_n - \psi_m) = 0$ is Cauchy. Then we write

$$\psi_n \xrightarrow{s} \psi. \tag{43.5.2}$$

Note that ψ not necessarily is an element of $\mathrm{dom}(s)$.

- s is called *bounded*, if $|s(\xi, \psi)| \leq c\|\xi\|\|\psi\|$ for all $\xi, \psi \in \mathrm{dom}(s)$ for some $c > 0$.
- s is called *bounded from below*, if there is an $a \in \mathbb{R}$, the lower bound, such that $q_s(\psi) \geq a\|\psi\|^2$ (implying s to be Hermitian, since q_s is real-valued). Especially, if $a = 0$, then s is called *positive* (= non-negative). Similarly one defines the boundedness from above and a negative s.
- s is called *closed*, if for every sequence $\psi_n \xrightarrow{s} \psi$ it follows that $\psi \in \mathrm{dom}(s)$ and $\lim_{n \to \infty} q_s(\psi_n - \psi) = 0$.
- s is called *closable*, if s has a closed extension, i.e., if there is a closed sesquilinear form t with $s \subseteq t$.

Note again that semi-boundedness (from above or below) of a sesquilinear form s implies $q_s(\psi) \in \mathbb{R}$ for all $\psi \in \mathrm{dom}(s)$, and thus the polarization identity Lemma 43.5-1 ensures that a *semi-bounded s is Hermitian*.

For a positive sesquilinear form s on $\mathcal{H}$ one has the *Cauchy–Schwarz inequality*

$$|s(\xi, \psi)|^2 \leq s(\xi, \xi) s(\psi, \psi) = q_s(\xi) q_s(\psi), \quad \forall \xi, \psi \in \mathrm{dom}(s). \tag{43.5.3}$$

A positive sesquilinear form s is also called a *semi-inner product* on the vector space $\mathrm{dom}(s)$, and the square root of the associated quadratic form $\|\psi\|_{q_s} := \sqrt{q_s(\psi)}$, $\psi \in \mathrm{dom}(s)$, is said to define a semi-norm on $\mathrm{dom}(s)$.

43.5.1. *Closable Sesquilinear Forms and Associated Operators*

An operator B on $\mathcal{H}$ is closed, if its graph is closed, which amounts to saying that $\mathrm{dom}(B)$ is complete with respect to the norm $\|\psi\|_B := \sqrt{\|B\psi\|^2 + \|\psi\|^2}$. Analogously one has:

Proposition 43.5-3 (Complete Domain). *A lower bounded sesquilinear form s on a Hilbert space $\mathcal{H}$ is closed, if and only if $\mathrm{dom}(s)$ is complete with respect to the norm*

$$\|\psi\|_s := \sqrt{q_s(\psi) + (1 - a)\|\psi\|^2}, \quad \psi \in \mathrm{dom}(s), \tag{43.5.4}$$

where $a \in \mathbb{R}$ *is a lower bound of* s, *in which case* $\mathrm{dom}(s)$, *for itself, is a Hilbert space with respect to the corresponding inner product*

$$(\xi|\psi)_s := s(\xi, \psi) + (1-a)(\xi|\psi), \quad \xi, \psi \in \mathrm{dom}(s). \quad (43.5.5)$$

(The non–degeneration stems from (.|.)*.) For a further lower bound* $a' \in \mathbb{R}$ *of* s *the associated norm* (43.5.4) *is equivalent to the first given norm.*

If the semi-bounded Hermitian sesquilinear form s is closable, then s has a unique smallest closed extension $\bar{s}$, which is called the *closure* of s. One concludes that s and its closure $\bar{s}$ have the same lower and upper bounds. If t is an arbitrary closed extension of s, then $s \subseteq \bar{s} \subseteq t$.

Proposition 43.5-4 (Characterization of Closure). *The domain* $\mathrm{dom}(\bar{s})$ *of the minimal closed extension of the closable sesquilinear form* s *is the set of all* $\psi \in \mathcal{H}$ *such that there exists a sequence* $\{\psi_n \mid n \in \mathbf{N}\} \subset \mathrm{dom}(s)$ *with* $\psi_n \overset{s}{\to} \psi$. *We have then as the characterizing relation for the closed extension*

$$\bar{s}(\xi, \psi) = \lim_{n \to \infty} s(\xi_n, \psi_n), \quad \text{whenever } \xi_n \overset{s}{\to} \xi \text{ and } \psi_n \overset{s}{\to} \psi.$$

For bounded closed forms one employs the Riesz representation theorem in order to express it in terms of a bounded operator.

Proposition 43.5-5 (Riesz Representation of Bounded Forms). *Let* s *be a densely defined, bounded sesquilinear form on the Hilbert space* $\mathcal{H}$. *Then there exists a unique norm-continuous extension* $\bar{s}$ *of* s *with* $\mathrm{dom}(\bar{s}) = \mathcal{H}$ *(i.e.,* s *is closable with the closure* $\bar{s}$*). Furthermore, there is a* unique $B_s \in \mathcal{L}(\mathcal{H})$ *with* $\bar{s}(\xi, \psi) = (\xi|B_s\psi)$ *for all* $\xi, \psi \in \mathcal{H}$.

Proof. Since $\mathrm{dom}(s)$ is dense, each $\xi \in \mathcal{H}$ is the limit of a $(\xi_n) \subset \mathrm{dom}(s)$. $\bar{s}(\xi, \psi) := \lim_n s(\xi_n, \psi)$ exists, since by boundedness $|s(\xi_n - \xi_m, \psi)| \leq c\|\xi_n - \xi_m\|\|\psi\|$, and the Cauchy criterion is satisfied. In the same manner, the right argument of s is extended to $\mathcal{H}$. The definition by limits leads to the same bound c for $\bar{s}$ as for s.

Since for an arbitrarily given $\psi \in \mathcal{H}$, $|\bar{s}(\xi, \psi)| \leq c\|\xi\|\|\psi\|$ for all $\xi \in \mathcal{H}$, there exists in virtue of the Riesz representation theorem 43.1-1 a unique $\eta \in \mathcal{H}$ with $|\bar{s}(\xi, \psi)| = (\xi|\eta)$ and one defines $B_s\psi := \eta$. According to the preceding inequality B_s possesses the bound c. ☐

The domain problems arise for unbounded forms and operators. The following Proposition gives an easy criterion for the closability of a lower bounded form. Its proof is, however, not so easy and not reproduced here (cf. [Kat84], Theorem VI.1.17).

Proposition 43.5-6 (Closability Criterion for a Lower Bounded Form). *The lower bounded sesquilinear form* s *is closable, if and only if* $\xi_n \overset{s}{\to} 0$ *implies* $q_s(\xi_n) \to 0$. *The closure* $\bar{s}$ *is characterized as in Proposition 43.5-4.*

Let us give an application of the preceding criterion.

Proposition 43.5-7 (Semi–Bounded Form Defined by an Operator). *Let B be a densely defined, symmetric, lower bounded (in general unbounded) operator on $\mathcal{H}$ and use it to define the Hermitian sesquilinear form*

$$s(\xi, \psi) := (\xi|B\psi), \quad \forall \xi, \psi \in \text{dom}(B). \tag{43.5.6}$$

Then s is closable (and, what means the same, B is form-closable).

Proof. Let be $B' := B - a\mathbb{1} \geq 0$, $a \in \mathbb{R}$ being a lower bound of B. If $\xi_n \xrightarrow{s} 0$ according to Eq. (43.5.2), then $q_s(\xi_n) \to 0$, if and only if $q_{s'}(\xi_n) = q_s(\xi_n) - a(\xi_n|\xi_n) \to 0$. Thus we may assume B positive, without loss in generality.

According to the definition of $\xi_n \xrightarrow{s} 0$, there exists for each $\varepsilon > 0$ an $n_\varepsilon \in \mathbb{N}$ such that $|q_s(\xi_n - \xi_m)| < \varepsilon$ for all $n, m \geq n_\varepsilon$. Now the Cauchy-Schwarz inequality yields the estimations

$$0 \leq q_s(\xi_n) = s(\xi_n, \xi_n) \leq |s(\xi_n, \xi_n - \xi_m)| + |s(\xi_n, \xi_m)|$$
$$\leq q_s(\xi_n)^{1/2} q_s(\xi_n - \xi_m)^{1/2} + |(\xi_n|B\xi_m)|$$
$$\leq q_s(\xi_n)^{1/2} \varepsilon^{1/2} + \|B\xi_n\| \|\xi_m\| \xrightarrow{m \to \infty} q_s(\xi_n)^{1/2} \varepsilon^{1/2}, \quad \forall n \geq n_\varepsilon.$$

Consequently, $0 \leq q_s(\xi_n)^{1/2} \leq \varepsilon^{1/2}$, thus $0 \leq q_s(\xi_n) \leq \varepsilon$ for all $n \geq n_\varepsilon$. That is the required result $q_s(\xi_n) \to 0$, allowing us to use Proposition 43.5-6. □

In the foregoing proposition, the symmetric B is a special kind of a closable operator. Let us evaluate the following general relationship.

Proposition 43.5-8 (Corresponding Operator Closedness). *Let S be an operator from the Hilbert space $\mathcal{H}$ into the Hilbert space $\mathcal{H}'$ and s the form defined by*

$$s(\xi, \psi) := (S\xi|S\psi)_{\mathcal{H}'}, \quad \forall \xi, \psi \in \text{dom}(s) := \text{dom}(S) \subseteq \mathcal{H}. \tag{43.5.7}$$

Then s is closed, if and only if S is closed (cf. text before Eq. (43.1.4)).

Proof. Note first that (E1): $\xi_n \xrightarrow{s} \xi$ is equivalent to $\xi_n \to \xi$ combined with $q_s(\xi_n - \xi_m) = \|S(\xi_n - \xi_m)\|_{\mathcal{H}'}^2 \to 0$. And second (E2): $q_s(\xi_n - \xi) \to 0$ is equivalent to $S\xi_n - S\xi \to 0$.

Recall that "s is closed" means, that the first relation in (E1) implies that $\xi \in \text{dom}(s)$ and the first relation in (E2) is valid (cf. Definition 43.5-2).

If now the second relation in (E1) is true and s is closed, then the first relation in (E2) follows. From this follows also $\xi \in \text{dom}(S)$, since otherwise $\xi \in \text{dom}(s)$ would not be possible. Together with the limit in the second relation in (E2) one has then that S is closed.

Similarly one concludes from the first relation in (E1) and S being closed, that $\xi \in \text{dom}(s)$ and the limit in the first relation of (E2) is valid. This means that s is then closed, too. □

Example 43.5-9 (Point Evaluation is Not Closable). Let in the foregoing Proposition $\mathcal{H} = L^2(\mathbb{R}^d, \mathbb{C})$ and $\mathcal{H}' = \mathbb{C}$, and define $\text{dom}(S)$ to consist of all classes ψ in $L^2(\mathbb{R}^d, \mathbb{C})$ which contain a continuous representative $\check{\psi}$, which is unique, so that $(S\psi) := \check{\psi}(0)$ is defined for all $\psi \in \text{dom}(S)$. In the sense of (43.5.7), we obtain

$$s(\xi, \psi) := \overline{\check{\xi}(0)}\, \check{\psi}(0), \quad \forall \xi, \psi \in \text{dom}(s) := \text{dom}(S),$$

to be densely defined and positive.

In order to check closability, we apply Proposition 43.5-6. If $\xi_n \xrightarrow{s} 0$, then according to Eq. (43.5.2) $\|\xi_n\| \to 0$ and $q_s(\xi_n - \xi_m) \to 0$. The continuous representatives $\check{\xi}_n$, which tend, outside of an ever shrinking ball around 0, point-wise to zero, may exhibit values $\check{\xi}_n(0)$, which tend not to 0 (being part of ever thinner peaks at $x = 0$). For, the additional requirement $q_s(\xi_n - \xi_m) = |\check{\xi}_n(0) - \check{\xi}_m(0)|^2 \to 0$ implies convergence of $\check{\xi}_n(0)$, but not necessarily to 0. Thus s is not closable, and neither is S.

If B is a lower bounded self-adjoint operator on $\mathcal{H}$, then $s(\xi, \psi) := (\xi|B\psi)$ defines a Hermitian lower bounded sesquilinear form $s(\xi, \psi) := (\xi|B\psi)$ with the domain $\text{dom}(s) := \text{dom}(B)$. The form s is closable in virtue of Proposition 43.5-7, but its closure $\bar{s}$ has in general a larger domain.

More important is the reverse question, in how far a closed lower bounded sesquilinear s form defines a self-adjoint operator. An answer is given, e.g., in [Kat84]. The main idea is, similar to the treatment of closed operators, to convert $\text{dom}(s)$ into a Hilbert space and use the techniques of bounded functionals and operators, as in Proposition 43.5-5.

Theorem 43.5-10 (Operators Defined by Forms). *Suppose s to be a densely defined sesquilinear form on the Hilbert space $\mathcal{H}$.*

(a) *Let s be closed and bounded from below with a lower bound $a \in \mathbb{R}$ (and thus Hermitian). Then there exists a unique self-adjoint operator B_s in $\mathcal{H}$ such that $\text{dom}(B_s) \subseteq \text{dom}(s)$ and*

$$s(\xi, \psi) = (\xi|B_s\psi), \quad \forall \xi \in \text{dom}(s), \quad \forall \psi \in \text{dom}(B_s).$$

We have the lower bound $B_s \geq a\mathbb{1}$ which implies for the spectrum $\sigma(B_s) \subseteq [a, \infty[$. The operator B_s is specified by the defining relations

$$\text{dom}(B_s) = \{\psi \in \text{dom}(s) \mid \exists \psi' \in \mathcal{H} \text{ with } s(\xi, \psi) = (\xi|\psi') \; \forall \xi \in \text{dom}(s)\},$$
$$B_s\psi = \psi', \quad \text{with the unique } \psi' \text{ of the foregoing relation}.$$

The operator domain $\text{dom}(B_s)$ is dense in $\text{dom}(s)$ with respect to the norm $\|.\|_s$ (and thus is a form core for s).

(b) *Let s be closed and positive. Then we obtain the refined domain characterization $\text{dom}(B_s) \subseteq \text{dom}(s) = \text{dom}(B_s^{1/2})$ and*

$$s(\xi, \psi) = (B_s^{1/2}\xi|B_s^{1/2}\psi), \quad \forall \xi, \psi \in \text{dom}(s) = \text{dom}(B_s^{1/2}),$$

for the associated positive, self-adjoint operator B_s from part (a).

Proof.   (a) Because s is closed, its domain dom(s) is converted into a Hilbert space with scalar product $(\xi|\eta)_s = s(\xi,\eta) + (1-a)(\xi|\eta)$ by Proposition 43.5-3. Since for *each* given $\psi \in \mathcal{H}$, $|(\xi|\psi)| \leq \|\xi\| \, \|\psi\| \leq \|\xi\|_s \|\psi\|$ for all $\xi \in$ dom(s), there exists in virtue of the Riesz representation theorem, now applied for the Hilbert space dom(s) to the bounded linear form $\xi \mapsto (\psi|\xi)$, a unique $\eta \in$ dom(s) with $(\xi|\psi) = (\xi|\eta)_s$ for all $\xi \in$ dom(s). Taking in $|(\xi|\psi)| = |(\xi|\eta)_s|$ the supremum over $\|\xi\|_s \leq 1$ leads to $\|\eta\|_s \leq \|\psi\|$. Thus we may define an operator A in $\mathcal{H}$ with dom(A) = $\mathcal{H}$ by

$$A : \mathcal{H} \rightarrow \text{dom}(s) \subseteq \mathcal{H}, \quad A\psi := \eta,$$
$$\text{with } (\xi|\psi) = (\xi|\eta)_s = (\xi|A\psi)_s \text{ for all } \xi \in \text{dom}(s).$$

For the norm in $\mathcal{H}$, we get $\|A\psi\| = \|\eta\| \leq \|\eta\|_s \leq \|\psi\|$ for all $\psi \in \mathcal{H}$, which provides $\|A\| \leq 1$. The operator A is injective, since $A\psi = 0$ implies $0 = (\xi|A\psi)_s = (\xi|\psi)$ for all $\xi \in$ dom(s), giving $\psi = 0$ for dom(s) is dense in $\mathcal{H}$.

On the other side, if $(\xi|A\psi)_s = (\xi|\psi) = 0$ for all $\psi \in \mathcal{H}$, then $\xi = 0$ and thus ran(A) is $\|.\|_s$-dense in dom(s) and $\|.\|$-dense in $\mathcal{H}$. So the inverse A^{-1} is a densely defined operator on $\mathcal{H}$ with domain dom(A^{-1}) = ran(A) and range ran(A^{-1}) = $\mathcal{H}$. We have for all $A\psi = \eta \in$ ran(A),

$$s(\xi,\eta) - a(\xi|\eta) = \underbrace{(\xi|\eta)_s}_{=(\xi|\psi)} - (\xi|\eta) = (\xi|(A^{-1}-\mathbb{1})\eta). \tag{43.5.8}$$

From $0 \leq s(\xi,\xi) - a(\xi|\xi) = (\xi|(A^{-1}-\mathbb{1})\xi)$ it follows $A^{-1} \geq \mathbb{1}$, and hence $A \geq 0$ is symmetric. From ran(A^{-1}) = $\mathcal{H}$ = dom(A) we conclude that A^{-1} is self-adjoint (apply the Hellinger–Töplitz Proposition 43.1-2 to the symmetric A). With

$$B_s := A^{-1} + (a-1)\mathbb{1}, \quad \text{dom}(B_s) := \text{ran}(A) \subseteq \text{dom}(s),$$

we have found our self-adjoint operator with lower bound a demonstrating (a).

(b) If in the preceding considerations the closed s is positive, then $a = 0$. Hence B_s is positive, and $B_s^{1/2}$ exists on the dense domain dom($B_s^{1/2}$) $\supseteq$ dom(B_s). The form $s'(\xi,\psi) := (B_s^{1/2}\xi|B_s^{1/2}\psi)$ is positive and closed on dom($B_s^{1/2}$) (according to Proposition 43.5-8) and has dom(B_s) as a core. There it coincides with the closed $s(\xi,\psi) = (\xi|B_s\psi)$. Thus $s = s'$. $\quad\square$

Proposition 43.5-11 (Compact Embedding and Eigenvalue Estimations).
Let be $\mathcal{H}$ an infinite-dimensional, separable Hilbert space. Assume the densely defined sesquilinear form s to be closed and bounded from below with a lower bound $a \in \mathbb{R}$ (thus Hermitian), and let B_s be the corresponding operator according to Theorem 43.5-10.

(a) *Let in addition the identical embedding $\psi \mapsto \psi$ from the Hilbert space dom(s) with inner product $(.|.)_s$ (from (43.5.5)) into the Hilbert space $\mathcal{H}$ be compact.*

Then B_s has pure point spectrum $\sigma(B_s) = \{\lambda_k^s \in [a, \infty[\mid k \in \mathbb{N}\}$, where each eigenspace is finite-dimensional. The eigenvalues λ_k^s may be ordered increasingly $\lambda_1^s \leq \lambda_2^s \leq \lambda_3^s \leq \ldots$ (repeated according to their multiplicity); they do not accumulate in $\mathbb{R}$, but $\lim_{k \to \infty} \lambda_k^s = \infty$. Moreover, $(z\mathbb{1} - B_s)^{-1} \in \mathcal{C}(\mathcal{H})$ (compact operators) for every z contained in the resolvent set $\rho(B_s)$ of B_s, especially for real $z < a$.

(b) *Let s and t be two closed, densely defined sesquilinear forms on $\mathcal{H}$, bounded from below, such that $\mathrm{dom}(t) \subseteq \mathrm{dom}(s)$, and*

$$s(\xi, \xi) \leq t(\xi, \xi), \quad \forall \xi \in \mathrm{dom}(t),$$

and such that both identical embeddings $\mathrm{dom}(s) \hookrightarrow \mathcal{H}$ respectively $\mathrm{dom}(t) \hookrightarrow \mathcal{H}$ are compact. If for B_s and B_t the associated eigenvalues, λ_k^s respectively λ_k^t, where k runs through $\mathbb{N}$, are increasingly ordered, we have

$$\lambda_k^s \leq \lambda_k^t, \quad \forall k \in \mathbb{N}.$$

Remark that the identical embedding $\mathrm{dom}(s) \hookrightarrow \mathcal{H}$ being compact, is only possible for separable $\mathcal{H}$ *and* unbounded s, or for the case of a finite-dimensional $\mathcal{H}$, but never for a non-separable Hilbert space $\mathcal{H}$.

Proof. (a) We refer to the proof of Theorem 43.5-10. Let us here use a special symbol $\mathcal{H}_s$ for the Hilbert space $\mathrm{dom}(s)$ with scalar product $(.|.)_s$, and denote $\xi \in \mathrm{dom}(s) \subseteq \mathcal{H}$ by $\hat{\xi}$ if considered as element of $\mathcal{H}_s$. Since $\mathrm{dom}(s)$ is already complete in the $\|.\|_s$-norm, all elements in $\mathcal{H}_s$ are of the form $\hat{\xi}$ for some unique $\xi \in \mathrm{dom}(s)$. The identical embedding $V : \mathcal{H}_s \to \mathrm{dom}(s) \subseteq \mathcal{H}$ may then be written $V\hat{\xi} = \xi$. By construction V is injective and a contraction, $\|V\hat{\xi}\| = \|\xi\| \leq \|\hat{\xi}\|_s$. By assumption $V \in \mathcal{C}(\mathcal{H}_s, \mathcal{H})$ (compact operators). We have with the self-adjoint A and Eq. (43.5.8) from the preceding proof,

$$(\xi|A^{-1}\eta) = (\xi|\eta) + (\xi|(A^{-1} - \mathbb{1})\eta) = (\hat{\xi}|\hat{\eta})_s = (V^{-1}\xi|V^{-1}\eta)_s = (\xi|V^{-1*}V^{-1}\eta),$$

for $\xi \in \mathrm{dom}(s)$ and $\eta \in \mathrm{ran}(A) \subseteq \mathrm{dom}(s)$, where in the last identity the adjoint V^{-1*} refers to two different Hilbert spaces with different scalar products (it is $V^{-1}\eta \in \mathrm{dom}(V^{-1*})$ according to Eq. (43.1.2), since the above equation is $\|.\|$-continuous in $\xi \in \mathrm{dom}(s) = \mathrm{dom}(V^{-1})$). Now, $A^{-1} = V^{-1*}V^{-1} = (VV^*)^{-1}$, and thus $A = VV^* \in \mathcal{C}(\mathcal{H})$, since V is compact. By Proposition 43.3-1, our self-adjoint, compact A is given by ($\mathcal{H}$ infinite-dimensional and separable)

$$A = \sum_{k=1}^{\infty} a_k |\xi_k)(\xi_k|, \quad \lim_{k \to \infty} a_k = 0,$$

where the ξ_k constitute an orthonormal basis of $\mathcal{H}$ of eigenvectors associated to the eigenvalues a_k, the latter arranged in decreasing order. It holds $0 < a_k \leq 1$, thus $a_k^{-1} \geq 1$, since $A \geq 0$ and $\|A\| \leq 1$ by the proof of Theorem 43.5-10, and furthermore, since 0 cannot be an eigenvalue because A is injective. Finally, according to $B_s = A^{-1} + (a - 1)\mathbb{1}$ define $\lambda_k^s := a_k^{-1} + a - 1 \geq a$.

Note, we have $((a-1)\mathbb{1} - B_s)^{-1} = -A \in \mathcal{C}(\mathcal{H})$, and hence the resolvent $(z\mathbb{1} - B_s)^{-1}$ is a compact operator for each $z \in \rho(B_s)$, too, by means of the resolvent formula [RS73b] Theorem VI.5,

$$(z\mathbb{1} - B_s)^{-1} = ((a-1)\mathbb{1} - B_s)^{-1} + [(a-1) - z]((a-1)\mathbb{1} - B_s)^{-1}(z\mathbb{1} - B_s)^{-1},$$

and the ideal property of the compact operators $\mathcal{C}(\mathcal{H})$.

(b) follows from the min–max principle (Theorems XIII.1 and XIII.2 in [RS78]).

We show our remark, and omit the condition of a separable, infinite-dimensional $\mathcal{H}$. Since 0 cannot be an eigenvalue of A, and since there are at most countably many non-zero eigenvalues with finite multiplicity for $A \in \mathcal{C}(\mathcal{H})$ (according to Proposition 43.3-1), we conclude that $\mathcal{H}$ has to be separable. If s is bounded, then the norms $\|.\|$ and $\|.\|_s$ are equivalent, and thus $V = \mathbb{1}$ on $\mathrm{dom}(s) = \mathcal{H}_s = \mathcal{H}$ is compact, if and only if $\mathcal{H}$ is of finite dimensions. □

43.5.2. *Singular Sesquilinear Forms*

Whereas the closed lower-bounded sesquilinear forms are an important tool to construct self-adjoint operators, the so-called singular positive sesquilinear forms, which we are going to describe, are definitely not related to Hilbert space operators.

To adapt the present discussion to our applications in field theory, where also real correlation functions occur as sesquilinear forms, we include from now on also real Hilbert spaces. Thus $\mathcal{H}$ designates now a Hilbert space over $\mathbb{K}$, where $\mathbb{K}$ stands for $\mathbb{R}$ or $\mathbb{C}$. A Hermitian sesquilinear form is henceforth named "symmetric", and we have to take care to use the polarization identity (43.5.1) in a modified manner for real forms. As for the most mentioned propositions, the closability criterion Proposition 43.5-6 is still valid for a symmetric sesquilinear form. In contrast to our closability criterion the notion of a singular form is formulated in the following manner.

Definition 43.5-12 (Singular Sesquilinear Form). A sesquilinear forms s is called *singular* (with respect to $(.|.)$ of $\mathcal{H}$), if for each $\xi \in \mathrm{dom}(s)$ there exists a sequence $(\xi_n) \subset \mathrm{dom}(s)$ with $\lim_{n\in\mathbb{N}} \|\xi_n - \xi\| = 0$ but $\lim_{n\in\mathbb{N}} q_s(\xi_n) = 0$.

First let us introduce some notions. We restrict ourselves here to a *positive*, densely defined sesquilinear form s on some Hilbert space $\mathcal{H}$ over $\mathbb{K}$, which is not necessarily closable. We discriminate (again) elements $\xi \in \mathrm{dom}(s) \subseteq \mathcal{H}$ from the uniquely associated elements $\hat{\xi} \in \mathcal{H}_s := \overline{\mathrm{dom}(s)}^{\|.\|_s}$, where the Hilbert space $\mathcal{H}_s$ is endowed with the scalar product of the previous form,

$$(\hat{\xi}|\hat{\psi})_s = (\xi|\psi) + s(\xi, \psi), \quad \forall \xi, \psi \in \mathrm{dom}(s). \tag{43.5.9}$$

The map $V\hat{\xi} := \xi$, $\xi \in \mathrm{dom}(s)$, is norm decreasing, $\|V\hat{\xi}\| = \|\xi\| \le \|\hat{\xi}\|_s$, and thus may be continuously extended to a *contraction* $V : \mathcal{H}_s \to \mathcal{H}$, denoted by the same symbol.

Lemma 43.5-13 (Closability Criterion for Positive Forms). *For a positive, densely defined sesquilinear form s, let $\mathcal{H}_s$ and V be defined as above. Then the following conditions are equivalent:*

(i) *s is closable.*
(ii) *If $(\xi_n) \subset \mathrm{dom}(s)$ tends to zero in norm $\|.\|$ and if $(\hat{\xi}_n) \subset \mathcal{H}_s$ is Cauchy with respect to $\|.\|_s$, then $(\hat{\xi}_n)$ tends to zero in $\|.\|_s$, too.*
(iii) *$\ker(V) = \{0\}$.*

Proof. The equivalence of (i) and (ii) is Proposition 43.5-6 in the new notation.

(ii)$\Rightarrow$(iii): Let $\eta \in \ker(V)$ and $(\xi_n) \subset \mathrm{dom}(s)$ with $\lim_{n \in \mathbb{N}} \|\hat{\xi}_n - \eta\|_s = 0$. From the continuity of V it follows that $0 = V\eta = \lim_{n \in \mathbb{N}} V\hat{\xi}_n = \lim_{n \in \mathbb{N}} \xi_n$, and, by applying (ii), one concludes $\eta = 0$.

(iii)$\Rightarrow$(ii): Let $(\xi_n) \subset \mathrm{dom}(s)$ be a null-sequence, such that $(\hat{\xi}_n) \subset \mathcal{H}_s$ be Cauchy with limit $\eta \in \mathcal{H}_s$. Then we have again by the continuity of V that $V\eta = \lim_{n \in \mathbb{N}} V\hat{\xi}_n = \lim_{n \in \mathbb{N}} \xi_n = 0$. Since $\ker(V) = \{0\}$ $(\hat{\xi}_n)$ tends to $0 = \eta$, and (ii) is satisfied. $\square$

We see that the non-trivial elements of $\ker(V)$ are the obstruction against s being closable. If $\ker(V) \neq \{0\}$, then we have just shown that the form s is not closable and thus unbounded (cf. Proposition 43.5-5). Hence the "peculiar" part of s is that which acts in $\ker(V)$. Nevertheless, by construction V is injective in restriction to $\mathrm{dom}(S)$, implying

$$\ker(V) \cap \mathrm{dom}(S) = \{0\}.$$

Definition 43.5-14 (Closable and Singular Part). We consider a positive, densely defined sesquilinear form s on a Hilbert space $\mathcal{H}$ over $\mathbb{K}$.

(a) Associated to s let us introduce the orthogonal projections

$$P_s : \mathcal{H}_s \xrightarrow{\text{onto}} \ker(V), \quad P_s^* = P_s^2 = P_s, \quad P_c := P_s^\perp = \mathbb{1} \ominus P_s \text{ in } \mathcal{H}_s,$$

where the index "s" of P_s means "singular" and the index c of P_c "closable".
(b) In terms of the projections of (a) we decompose s into $s = s_c + s_s$ via

$$s_c(\xi, \psi) := (\hat{\xi}|P_c\hat{\psi})_s - (\xi|\psi), \quad \text{closable part},$$
$$s_s(\xi, \psi) := (\hat{\xi}|P_s\hat{\psi})_s, \quad \text{singular part},$$

where $\xi, \psi \in \mathrm{dom}(s_c) = \mathrm{dom}(s_s) = \mathrm{dom}(s)$, cf. Eq. (43.5.9).

Our next result confirms our suggestion, arising with the notions of a closable and a singular part.

Theorem 43.5-15 (Maximal Closable and Minimal Singular Parts). *For a positive, densely defined sesquilinear form s on the Hilbert space $\mathcal{H}$ over $\mathbb{K}$ adopt*

the notations of the foregoing Definition 43.5-14, so that we have the decomposition
$s = s_c + s_s$.

(a) s_c *is closable, and* s_s *is singular.*

(b) s_c *is the largest closable form dominated by* s. *More exactly: If there is a closable form* t *with* $\mathcal{H} \supseteq \mathrm{dom}(t) \supseteq \mathrm{dom}(s)$ *and* $q_s(\xi) \geq q_t(\xi)$, $\forall \xi \in \mathrm{dom}(s)$, *then it follows* $q_{s_c}(\xi) \geq q_t(\xi)$, $\forall \xi \in \mathrm{dom}(s) = \mathrm{dom}(s_c)$.

That means in other words: s_s *is the smallest singular form among all decompositions of* s *into a sum of a closable and a singular form.*

Proof.   [Sketch] (a) According to the definition of P_c we have $V P_c = V$ and $V P_c$ is equal to the V_c belonging to s_c. It has trivial kernel and thus s_c is closable.

To apply the definition of a singular symmetric form we pick a $\xi \in \mathrm{dom}(s) = \mathrm{dom}(s_s)$ and approximate its component $P_c \hat{\xi}$ by the sequence $(\hat{\xi}_n)$. Then $\lim_{n \in \mathbb{N}} \hat{\xi}_n = \lim_{n \in \mathbb{N}} V \hat{\xi}_n = V P_c \hat{\xi} = V \hat{\xi} = \xi$. And $\lim_{n \in \mathbb{N}} s_s(\hat{\xi}_n, \hat{\xi}_n) = \lim_{n \in \mathbb{N}} \|P_s \hat{\xi}_n\|_s^2 = \|P_s P_c \hat{\xi}\|_s^2 = 0$. Thus, s_s is, in fact, singular.

(b) Let be t a positive form on $\mathcal{H}$, which is dominated by s as described in the theorem. Then $(\hat{\xi}|\hat{\psi})_t = (C^{1/2}\hat{\xi}|C^{1/2}\hat{\psi})_s \leq (\hat{\xi}|\hat{\psi})_s$, $\xi, \psi \in \mathrm{dom}(s)$, with an appropriate $0 \leq C \leq \mathbb{1}_{\mathcal{H}_s}$. For the decisive relation $P_c C^{1/2} = C^{1/2} P_c = C^{1/2}$ we refer to [Hon90a]. Then $(\hat{\xi}|\hat{\xi})_t = (C^{1/2}\hat{\xi}|C^{1/2}\hat{\xi})_s = (C^{1/2} P_c \hat{\xi}|C^{1/2} P_c \hat{\xi})_s \leq (\hat{\xi}|P_c\hat{\xi})_s = (\hat{\xi}|\hat{\xi})_{s_c}$.   □

The meaning of extracting a minimal singular form s_s from the positive sesquilinear form s will be further illustrated by the following examples. Part (a) of the first one coincides with the form considered in Example 43.5-9, but here we have chosen a smaller domain $\mathrm{dom}(s)$, consisting merely of absolutely continuous functions.

Example 43.5-16.

(a) [**Point Evaluation**] Let us here choose the domain $\mathrm{dom}(s) = \{\xi \in L^2([a,b], \mathbb{C}) \,|\, \xi \text{ absolutely continuous}\}$ (meaning that ξ be the integral of a locally integrable and measurable function $\xi' \in L^1([a,b], \mathbb{C})$, respectively that $d\xi(x)$ be absolutely continuous with respect to the Lebesgue measure dx) and define

$$s(\xi, \psi) = \overline{\xi(c)}\, \psi(c), \quad \text{for some fixed } c \in [a,b].$$

If we pick an arbitrary $\xi \in \mathrm{dom}(s)$, then intuitively it is plausible that there exists a sequence $(\xi_n) \subset \mathrm{dom}(s)$, which converges in norm to ξ, but the pointwise limit $\tilde{\xi}$ of which is discontinuous with $\tilde{\xi}(c) = 0$. Thus, according to Definition 43.5-12, s is singular.

(b) [**T. Kato**] Following [Kat84], Sec. VI.§1, we consider a symmetric sesquilinear form s with the same domain as in (a) and define

$$s(\xi, \psi) = \underbrace{\int_a^b \overline{\xi'(x)}\, \psi'(x)\, dx}_{=: \, s_1(\xi, \psi)} + \underbrace{\overline{\xi(c)}\, \psi(c)}_{=: \, s_2(\xi, \psi)}, \quad \text{for some fixed } c \in [a,b].$$

Then s_2 is singular by (a), and s_1 is closed. But s_2 is relatively bounded with respect to s_1 with s_1-bound zero. Thus s is closed, meaning $s = s_c$ and $s_s = 0$. Beside having the minimal singular part $s_s = 0$ in $s = s_c + s_s$, the defining sum $s = s_1 + s_2$ displays that s may exhibit also a different additive splitting into a closed part s_1 and a non-trivial singular part s_2.

Example 43.5-17. Generalizing the Examples 43.5-9 and 43.5-16, we choose an unbounded, densely defined linear form L on the complex Hilbert space $\mathcal{H}$, with which we define the positive sesquilinear form

$$s(\xi, \psi) := \overline{L(\xi)}L(\psi), \quad \forall \xi, \psi \in \mathrm{dom}(s) = \mathrm{dom}(L) \subseteq \mathcal{H}.$$

The unboundedness of L yields the form Hilbert space to coincide with the direct sum

$$\mathcal{H}_s = \overline{\mathrm{dom}(s)}^{\|\cdot\|_s} = \mathcal{H} \oplus \mathbb{C}, \quad (\xi \oplus \alpha | \psi \oplus \beta)_s = (\xi|\psi) + \overline{\alpha}\beta, \quad \hat{\xi} = \xi \oplus L(\xi),$$

and implies that the contraction $V : \mathcal{H}_s = \mathcal{H} \oplus \mathbb{C} \to \mathcal{H}$ (satisfying $V(\hat{\xi}) = \xi$) is given by

$$V(\xi \oplus \alpha) = \xi \quad \Rightarrow \quad \ker(V) = 0 \oplus \mathbb{C} = \{0 \oplus \alpha \,|\, \alpha \in \mathbb{C}\}.$$

Our simple proof below illustrates how the non-trivial part $\ker(V)$ is directly connected with the unboundedness of L, respectively of s.

It follows that P_c projects onto the left component $\mathcal{H} \oplus 0$, whereas P_s projects onto the right component $0 \oplus \mathbb{C}$ of the direct sum. The closable and singular parts s_c and s_s of s are according to Definition 43.5-14 (b),

$$s_c(\xi, \psi) = (\hat{\xi}|P_c\hat{\psi})_s - (\xi|\psi) = 0, \quad s_s(\xi, \psi) = (\hat{\xi}|P_s\hat{\psi})_s = \overline{L(\xi)}L(\psi) = s(\xi, \psi).$$

In this general manner, we verify the singular property of s and render the intuitive reasoning in Example 43.5-16 (a) rigorous (the unbounded linear form $L(\xi) = \xi(c)$ being there the evaluation at $c \in [a, b]$ of the functions $\xi : [a, b] \to \mathbb{C}$).

Proof. Since L is unbounded, there exists a norm-bounded sequence (ξ_n) in $\mathrm{dom}(L)$ with $0 \neq L(\xi_n) \to \infty$. Setting $\psi_n := \alpha\xi_n/L(\xi_n)$ for $\alpha \in \mathbb{C}$, we observe $\hat{\psi}_n = \psi_n \oplus L(\psi_n) \to 0 \oplus \alpha$. Thus all of $0 \oplus \mathbb{C}$ is contained in $\mathcal{H}_s$. This result combined with $\mathrm{dom}(s)$ being dense in $\mathcal{H}$, finally leads to $\mathcal{H}_s = \mathcal{H} \oplus \mathbb{C}$. $\qquad\square$

43.6. Unitary One-Parameter Groups

43.6.1. *Generator, SNAG Theorem*

A family $U \equiv \{U(t) \in \mathcal{L}(\mathcal{H}) \,|\, t \in \mathbb{R}\}$ of unitaries in a (complex) Hilbert space $\mathcal{H}$ is called a *unitary one-parameter group*, if

$$U(0) = \mathbb{1}, \quad U(s)U(t) = U(s + t), \quad \forall s, t \in \mathbb{R}.$$

That means that the mapping $t \mapsto U(t)$ is a unitary representation of the additive group $\mathbb{R}$. It follows that $U(t)^* = U(-t)$.

The one-parameter group U is called strongly continuous, if $t \mapsto U(t)$ is continuous in the strong operator topology, i.e., $\lim_{s \to t} \|(U_s - U_t)\psi\| = 0$ for all $\psi \in \mathcal{H}$ and every $t \in \mathbb{R}$ (cf. Definition 46.1-1 (3) on page 1671).

For a strongly continuous unitary one-parameter group $U = \{U(t) \in \mathcal{L}(\mathcal{H}) \mid t \in \mathbb{R}\}$ the (infinitesimal) *generator* B is defined by

$$\mathrm{dom}(B) := \left\{ \psi \in \mathcal{H} \mid \lim_{t \to 0} \tfrac{1}{t}(U(t) - \mathbb{1})\psi \text{ exists} \right\},$$

$$B\psi := -i \lim_{t \to 0} \tfrac{1}{t}(U(t) - \mathbb{1})\psi = -i \frac{dU(t)}{dt}\bigg|_{t=0} \psi, \quad \forall \psi \in \mathrm{dom}(B),$$

(43.6.1)

where the limits $\lim_{t \to 0} \tfrac{1}{t}(U(t) - \mathbb{1})\psi$ are taken with respect to the norm of $\mathcal{H}$.

Theorem 43.6-1 (Stone's Theorem). *Let $\mathcal{H}$ be an arbitrary Hilbert space.*

(a) *Let B be a self-adjoint operator in $\mathcal{H}$ with associated projection-valued measure P_B. Then $\{U(t) \in \mathcal{L}(\mathcal{H}) \mid t \in \mathbb{R}\}$ defined by*

$$U(t) := e^{itB} = \int_{\mathbb{R}} e^{it\lambda} \, dP_B(\lambda), \quad t \in \mathbb{R},$$

defines a strongly continuous one-parameter group of unitaries on $\mathcal{H}$.

(b) *Let $U = \{U(t) \in \mathcal{L}(\mathcal{H}) \mid t \in \mathbb{R}\}$ be a strongly continuous one-parameter group of unitaries on $\mathcal{H}$. Then the generator of U exists and is given by a unique self-adjoint (possibly unbounded) operator B on $\mathcal{H}$. We have $U(t) = e^{itB}$ for all $t \in \mathbb{R}$.*

(c) *Let B be a self-adjoint operator on $\mathcal{H}$, and suppose D to be a subspace of $\mathrm{dom}(B)$, which is invariant under the unitary group $\{e^{itB} \mid t \in \mathbb{R}\}$ and which is dense in $\mathcal{H}$. Then D is a core for B.*

Let us emphasize, that the self-adjointness, in the concise mathematical sense, of the generator of a unitary one-parameter group is the central topic of Stone's theorem. First, the generator's domain is precisely given by those vectors on which the derivative of the unitary operators exists (part (b)). Second, only a definitely self-adjoint operator is able to generate a unitary group (part (a)). That means for the Schrödinger dynamics, that the domain of the Hamiltonian has to be proved to be equal to that of the adjoint Hamiltonian in order to obtain a well defined time evolution. Third, if the unitary group is directly given, then a useful subdomain for its generator may be identified by invariance (part (c)).

Stone's theorem has the following generalization, which is named after the mathematicians Stone, Naimark, Ambrose, and Godement (e.g., [RN82]). $\mathcal{U}(\mathcal{H})$ denotes the unitaries acting on the Hilbert space $\mathcal{H}$.

Proposition 43.6-2 (The SNAG Theorem). *Let G be a locally compact Abelian group which has the strongly continuous unitary representation $G \ni g \mapsto U(g) \in \mathcal{U}(\mathcal{H})$ in some Hilbert space $\mathcal{H}$. Denote by $\hat{G}$ the topological dual group (of continuous characters $\chi : G \to \{z \in \mathbb{C} \mid |z| = 1\}$ with uniform convergence on compact subsets of G). Then there exists a unique projection-valued measure $P : \mathsf{B}(\hat{G}) \to \mathcal{P}(\mathcal{H})$, which maps the Borel sets $B \subset \hat{G}$ onto projections $P(B)$ in $\mathcal{H}$, such that we have the joint spectral representation*

$$U(g) = \int_{\hat{G}} \chi(g) dP(\chi), \quad \forall g \in G.$$

The $P(B)$ are weak limits of sequences from $\mathrm{LH}(U(G))$.

Let us remark, an operator $A \in \mathcal{L}(\mathcal{H})$ commutes with $U(G)$, if and only if A commutes with all spectral projections $P(B)$, $B \in \mathsf{B}(\hat{G})$.

43.6.2. *Analytic Vectors*

If the self-adjoint B is bounded, then the exponentials $U(t) = e^{itB}$ may be constructed by the series

$$U(t) = \exp\{itB\} = \sum_{n=0}^{\infty} \frac{(it)^n}{n!} B^n, \quad t \in \mathbb{R},$$

converging in the operator norm, what does not work for an unbounded generator B. For analytic vectors of the self-adjoint B, however, the exponential series is valid point-wise by the subsequent result.

If B is an operator on the Hilbert space $\mathcal{H}$, then an element $\psi \in \mathcal{H}$ is called an *analytic* vector for B, if $\psi \in \bigcap_{n=1}^{\infty} \mathrm{dom}(B^n)$ and if there is an $\varepsilon(\psi) > 0$ such that

$$\sum_{n=0}^{\infty} \frac{|z|^n}{n!} \|B^n \psi\| < \infty, \quad \text{for all } z \in \mathbb{C} \text{ with } |z| < \varepsilon(\psi). \tag{43.6.2}$$

The positive $\varepsilon(\psi) \in \,]0, \infty]$ is called the *radius of analyticity* associated with the analytic vector ψ. ψ is called an *entire analytic* vector for B, if $\varepsilon(\psi) = \infty$. From the triangle inequality $\|B^n(z_1\xi + z_2\psi)\| \leq |z_1| \|B^n\xi\| + |z_2| \|B^n\psi\|$, where $z_1, z_2 \in \mathbb{C}$ and ξ, ψ are (entire) analytic vectors for B, it follows that $z_1\xi + z_2\psi$ is an (entire) analytic vector for B, too. Consequently, the set of all entire analytic vectors as well as the set of all analytic vectors of an operator B constitute subspaces of $\bigcap_{n=1}^{\infty} \mathrm{dom}(B^n)$. Especially, if B is bounded, then every $\psi \in \mathcal{H}$ is an entire analytic vector for B, since $\|B^n\psi\| \leq \|B\|^n \|\psi\|$ and thus

$$\sum_{n=0}^{\infty} \frac{|z|^n}{n!} \|B^n\psi\| \leq \sum_{n=0}^{\infty} \frac{(|z| \|B\|)^n}{n!} \|\psi\| = \exp\{|z| \|B\|\} \|\psi\| < \infty, \quad \text{for all } z \in \mathbb{C}.$$

Proposition 43.6-3 (Analyticity and Self-adjointness). *Let $\mathcal{H}$ be a Hilbert space.*

(a) *Let B be a self-adjoint operator on $\mathcal{H}$, and suppose ψ to be an analytic vector for B. Then for all $z \in \mathbb{C}$ with $|z| < \varepsilon(\psi)$ we have $\psi \in \mathrm{dom}(\exp\{zB\})$ (the latter being defined by spectral theory) and we get the series expansion*

$$\exp\{zB\}\psi = \sum_{n=0}^{\infty} \frac{z^n}{n!} B^n \psi, \quad \text{for all } z \in \mathbb{C} \text{ with } |z| < \varepsilon(\psi),$$

which converges with respect to the norm of $\mathcal{H}$.

(b) *Let B be a symmetric operator on $\mathcal{H}$, and assume that a subset $\mathcal{V}$ of the analytic vectors for B is total in $\mathcal{H}$. Then B is essentially self-adjoint. Especially, a closed symmetric operator is self-adjoint, if and only if a subset of its analytic vectors is total.*

(c) *Let B be a self-adjoint operator on $\mathcal{H}$ and suppose $\mathcal{V}$ to be a total subset of its analytic vectors. Then*

$$\mathrm{LH}\{\mathcal{V}\} \subseteq \bigcap_{n=1}^{\infty} \mathrm{dom}(B^n)$$

and both linear subspaces are cores for B.

The self-adjointness criterion of part (b) is known in the literature as "Nelson's Theorem".

43.6.3. *Convergence in the Strong Resolvent Sense*

Let us turn to a certain kind of approximation by self-adjoint operators, which is equivalent to the approximation in terms of the unitary one-parameter groups. Recall, that for each complex z contained in the resolvent set $\rho(B)$ of a self-adjoint operator B, the so-called resolvent $(z\mathbb{1} - B)^{-1}$ is a bounded operator on $\mathcal{H}$ (see the beginning of Sec. 43.3). Especially, the self-adjointness of B ensures $\sigma(B) \subseteq \mathbb{R}$ for its spectrum, and thus $z \in \mathbb{C}$ with $\mathrm{Im}(z) \neq 0$ is an element of $\rho(B) = \mathbb{C}\backslash\sigma(B)$.

Definition 43.6-4 (Strong Resolvent Convergence). Let B be a self-adjoint operator on the Hilbert space $\mathcal{H}$. A sequence $\{B_n \mid n \in \mathbb{N}\}$ of self-adjoint operators in $\mathcal{H}$ is said to converge to B in the strong resolvent sense (written srs–$\lim_n B_n = B$), if it holds in the strong operator topology

$$\lim_{n\to\infty} (z\mathbb{1} - B_n)^{-1} = (z\mathbb{1} - B)^{-1}, \quad \forall z \in \mathbb{C}\backslash\mathbb{R}.$$

There are the following criteria for strong resolvent convergence.

Proposition 43.6-5 (Strong Resolvent Convergence). *Let B_n, $n \in \mathbb{N}$, and B be self-adjoint operators on the Hilbert space $\mathcal{H}$. Then it holds srs–$\lim_n B_n = B$ (strong resolvent limit), if one of the following assumptions is satisfied:*

(a) *There is a core D of B such that for each $\xi \in D$ there exists an $n_\xi \in \mathbb{N}$ with*

$$\xi \in \operatorname{dom}(B_n), \quad \forall n \geq n_\xi, \quad \text{and} \quad \lim_{n \to \infty} \|B_n \xi - B\xi\| = 0.$$

(b) *The operators B_n and B are bounded with $\lim_n B_n = B$ in the strong operator topology.*

(c) *There is a core D of B with $D \subseteq \operatorname{dom}(B_n)$ for all $n \in \mathbb{N}$, and there are null sequences (a_n) and (b_n) such that for each $\xi \in D$,*

$$\|B_n \xi - B\xi\| \leq a_n \|\xi\| + b_n \|B\xi\|, \quad \forall n \in \mathbb{N}.$$

(d) *$G(B) = \lim_n G(B_n)$ for the graphs in $\mathcal{H} \oplus \mathcal{H}$.*

For example, the core D in the preceding part (a) may be realized by a total set of vectors, which are analytic for each B_n and the limiting operator B. Then one only has to show that the B_n and B are symmetric on D to apply the proposition. A further application is found in proposition 44.3-3 below for the strong resolvent approximation of Dirichlet Laplacians.

Important for the limiting dynamics are the following equivalent conditions.

Proposition 43.6-6 (Strong Resolvent Convergence). *Let B_n, $n \in \mathbb{N}$, and B be self-adjoint operators on some Hilbert space $\mathcal{H}$. Then there are the following equivalent conditions:*

(a) *srs–$\lim_n B_n = B$ in the strong resolvent sense.*

(b) *$\lim_n (z\mathbb{1} - B_n)^{-1} = (z\mathbb{1} - B)^{-1}$ in the strong operator topology for a single $z \in \mathbb{C} \backslash \mathbb{R}$.*

(c) *$\lim_n e^{itB_n} = e^{itB}$ in the strong operator topology for each $t \in \mathbb{R}$.*

(d) *$\lim_n u(B_n) = u(B)$ in the strong operator topology for each continuous bounded function $u : \mathbb{R} \to \mathbb{C}$.*

43.7. Reduction, and C-Realness of Operators

We first consider specific restrictions of an operator. Let $\mathcal{H}_1$ and $\mathcal{H}_2$ be two Hilbert spaces. Let us consider a closed subspace $\mathcal{V}$ of $\mathcal{H}_1$, with orthogonal complement $\mathcal{V}^\perp$ in $\mathcal{H}_1$, and denote the orthogonal projection of $\mathcal{H}_1$ onto $\mathcal{V}$ by Q. Suppose for an operator B from $\mathcal{H}_1$ into $\mathcal{H}_2$ that

$$Q \operatorname{dom}(B) \subseteq \operatorname{dom}(B). \tag{43.7.1}$$

Then for $\psi \in \operatorname{dom}(B)$ we have $(\mathbb{1} - Q)\psi \in \operatorname{dom}(B)$, that is, ψ has the unique orthogonal decomposition within $\operatorname{dom}(B)$,

$$\psi = \xi \oplus \eta \in \operatorname{dom}(B), \quad \xi = Q\psi \in \mathcal{V} \cap \operatorname{dom}(B), \quad \eta = (\mathbb{1} - Q)\psi \in \mathcal{V}^\perp \cap \operatorname{dom}(B).$$

Thus by the following definition there are given an operator $B_\mathcal{V}$ from the (sub-) Hilbert space $\mathcal{V}$ into $\mathcal{H}_2$ as well as an operator $B_{\mathcal{V}^\perp}$ from the (sub-) Hilbert space

$\mathcal{V}^\perp$ into $\mathcal{H}_2$,

$$B_\mathcal{V}\xi := B\xi\,, \quad \forall \xi \in \mathrm{dom}(B_\mathcal{V}) := \mathcal{V} \cap \mathrm{dom}(B)\,,$$
$$B_{\mathcal{V}^\perp}\eta := B\eta\,, \quad \forall \eta \in \mathrm{dom}(B_{\mathcal{V}^\perp}) := \mathcal{V}^\perp \cap \mathrm{dom}(B)\,. \tag{43.7.2}$$

Hence, $\mathrm{dom}(B)$ has the orthogonal decomposition

$$\mathrm{dom}(B) = \mathrm{dom}(B_\mathcal{V}) \oplus \mathrm{dom}(B_{\mathcal{V}^\perp})\,, \quad \text{according to } \mathcal{H}_1 = \mathcal{V} \oplus \mathcal{V}^\perp\,.$$

Obviously, if B is densely defined, so are $B_\mathcal{V}$ and $B_{\mathcal{V}^\perp}$.

As a simple example, let us consider an operator B from the Hilbert space $\mathcal{H}_1$ into the Hilbert space $\mathcal{H}_2$ and choose a closed subspace $\mathcal{V}$ of $\mathcal{H}_1$ such that $\mathcal{V} \subseteq \mathrm{ker}(B)$. (Recall, the kernel $\mathrm{ker}(B)$ necessarily is closed, only if B is a closed operator.) Then $Q\,\mathrm{dom}(B) = \mathcal{V} \subseteq \mathrm{ker}(B) \subseteq \mathrm{dom}(B)$, and hence Eq. (43.7.1) is fulfilled. Clearly, $B_\mathcal{V} = 0$. Since only a part of the kernel of B is cut off, there is no loss of information, when treating instead of B the restricted operator $B_{\mathcal{V}^\perp}$, where $\mathrm{ran}(B) = \mathrm{ran}(B_{\mathcal{V}^\perp})$. So, when finally restricting $\mathcal{H}_2$ to the closure of the image, we obtain that $B_{\mathcal{V}^\perp}$ is an operator from the Hilbert space $\mathcal{V}^\perp$ into the Hilbert space $\overline{\mathrm{ran}(B)}$.

We now come to the situation, where $\mathcal{H}_1 = \mathcal{H}_2 = \mathcal{H}$. Let $\mathcal{V}$ be a closed subspace of $\mathcal{H}$, and suppose B to be an operator acting in $\mathcal{H}$. Here one wishes that $\mathrm{ran}(B_\mathcal{V}) \subseteq \mathcal{V}$ and $\mathrm{ran}(B_{\mathcal{V}^\perp}) \subseteq \mathcal{V}^\perp$, in order that $B_\mathcal{V}$ is an operator acting on the Hilbert space $\mathcal{V}$ and $B_{\mathcal{V}^\perp}$ acts on the Hilbert space $\mathcal{V}^\perp$.

Definition 43.7-1 (Reducing Subspace). Let $\mathcal{V}$ be a closed subspace of the Hilbert space $\mathcal{H}$, and denote by Q the orthogonal projection of $\mathcal{H}$ onto $\mathcal{V}$. We say that $\mathcal{V}$ is a reducing subspace for the operator B on $\mathcal{H}$, if

$$QB \subseteq BQ\,,$$

or equivalently, $Q\,\mathrm{dom}(B) \subseteq \mathrm{dom}(B)$ and $QB\psi = BQ\psi$ for all $\psi \in \mathrm{dom}(B)$.

The reduction condition $QB \subseteq BQ$ implies $(\mathbb{1} - Q)B \subseteq B(\mathbb{1} - Q)$. Thus, $\mathcal{V}$ is a reducing subspace for B, if and only if its orthogonal complement $\mathcal{V}^\perp$ is a reducing subspace for B, too. Then according to Eq. (43.7.2), the operator $B_\mathcal{V}$ acts on $\mathcal{V}$, and $B_{\mathcal{V}^\perp}$ on $\mathcal{V}^\perp$. $B_\mathcal{V}$ is called the *reduction* of B to $\mathcal{V}$, and $B_{\mathcal{V}^\perp}$ is the reduction of B to $\mathcal{V}^\perp$.

We now state a result concerning reducing subspaces for *self-adjoint* operators B on the Hilbert space $\mathcal{H}$.

Theorem 43.7-2 (Reducing Subspace). *Let B be a self-adjoint operator on the Hilbert space $\mathcal{H}$ with corresponding projection-valued measure P_B according to the spectral calculus in Theorem 43.3-3 on page 1536. Further let $\mathcal{V}$ be a closed subspace of $\mathcal{H}$ with associated orthogonal projection Q. Then the following assertions are equivalent:*

(i) *$\mathcal{V}$ is a reducing subspace for B.*
(ii) *$QP_B(\Lambda) = P_B(\Lambda)Q$ for all $\Lambda \in \mathsf{B}(\mathbb{R})$.*

(iii) $Qe^{itB} = e^{itB}Q$ for all $t \in \mathbb{R}$, or equivalently, $\mathcal{V}$ is left invariant by the unitary group e^{itB}, $t \in \mathbb{R}$, i.e., $e^{itB}\mathcal{V} \subseteq \mathcal{V}$ for all $t \in \mathbb{R}$.

Suppose the above equivalent conditions to be valid. Then the reductions $B_{\mathcal{V}}$ and $B_{\mathcal{V}^{\perp}}$ are self-adjoint operators on $\mathcal{V}$ respectively $\mathcal{V}^{\perp}$, and moreover, for the spectra we have $\sigma(B) = \sigma(B_{\mathcal{V}}) \cup \sigma(B_{\mathcal{V}^{\perp}})$.

Especially, the spectral image space $\mathcal{V}' := P_B(\Lambda')\mathcal{H}$ is a reducing subspace for B by (ii) for each Borel set $\Lambda' \in \mathsf{B}(\mathbb{R})$.

Let us consider also another kind of reduction.

Definition 43.7-3 (Conjugation, C-Realness). We shall employ the following notions:

(a) A *conjugation* C on the Hilbert space $\mathcal{H}$ is an antilinear mapping with domain $\mathrm{dom}(C) = \mathcal{H}$, satisfying $C^2 = \mathbb{1}$, and $\mathrm{Im}(C\xi|\psi) = \mathrm{Im}(C\psi|\xi)$ $\forall \xi, \psi \in \mathcal{H}$ or equivalently $C^* = C$. (Recall that the adjoint A^* of a bounded antilinear operator A on $\mathcal{H}$ with $\mathrm{dom}(A) = \mathcal{H}$ is defined by $(\xi|A\psi) = (\psi|A^*\xi)$ $\forall \xi, \psi \in \mathcal{H}$).

(b) Let C be a conjugation in the Hilbert space $\mathcal{H}$. Then an operator B on $\mathcal{H}$ is called *C-real*, if

$$CB \subseteq BC,$$

or equivalently, $C \, \mathrm{dom}(B) \subseteq \mathrm{dom}(B)$ and $CB\xi = BC\xi$ for all $\xi \in \mathrm{dom}(B)$.

The conjugation C decomposes uniquely the complex Hilbert space $\mathcal{H}$ into

$$\mathcal{H} = \mathcal{H}_r + i\mathcal{H}_r, \qquad (43.7.3)$$

where the real Hilbert space $\mathcal{H}_r$ is defined as the eigenspace of C corresponding to the eigenvalue $+1$,

$$\mathcal{H}_r := \{\xi \in \mathcal{H} \mid C\xi = \xi\} = \{\psi + C\psi \mid \psi \in \mathcal{H}\}. \qquad (43.7.4)$$

The eigenspace of C with eigenvalue -1 then is given by $i\mathcal{H}_r$. The real inner product on $\mathcal{H}_r$ arises by restricting the complex inner product $(.|.)$ from $\mathcal{H}$ to $\mathcal{H}_r$.

Since $C^2 = \mathbb{1}$ it follows from $C \, \mathrm{dom}(B) \subseteq \mathrm{dom}(B)$ that $\mathrm{dom}(B) = C^2 \, \mathrm{dom}(B) \subseteq C \, \mathrm{dom}(B)$, and thus $C \, \mathrm{dom}(B) = \mathrm{dom}(B)$. Hence C-realness of B yields $CB = BC$.

C-realness becomes important in the context of self-adjointness. For a self-adjoint operator B on the Hilbert space $\mathcal{H}$ there always exists a conjugation C on $\mathcal{H}$ such that B is C-real. This may be shown by going over to the spectral representation of B, where B is a multiplication operator on a direct sum of Hilbert spaces of type $\mathrm{L}^2(\mathbb{R}, \mu)$. There one has the natural complex conjugation of functions.

However, there also exists a converse statement: If for a symmetric operator B on $\mathcal{H}$ there exists a conjugation C on $\mathcal{H}$ such that B is C-real, then B possesses self-adjoint extensions, which in general are non-unique, cf. [Wei80] Theorem 8.9.

Proposition 43.7-4 (C-Realness and Spectral Calculus). *Let B be a self-adjoint operator on $\mathcal{H}$, which is C-real with respect to a conjugation C. Then it follows,*

$$C\operatorname{dom}(u(B)) = \operatorname{dom}(\bar{u}(B)), \qquad Cu(B) = \bar{u}(B)C$$

for every Borel measurable function $u : \mathbb{R} \to \mathbb{C}$.

Furthermore, the C-realness of the self-adjoint B on $\mathcal{H}$ allows its restriction to a self-adjoint operator B_r on the real Hilbert space $\mathcal{H}_r$, possessing the domain $\operatorname{dom}(B_r) = \operatorname{dom}(B) \cap \mathcal{H}_r$. Generally, for every Borel measurable $u : \mathbb{R} \to \mathbb{R}$ we have that $u(B)_r = u(B_r)$ with the domain

$$\operatorname{dom}(u(B_r)) = \operatorname{dom}(u(B)) \cap \mathcal{H}_r, \quad \operatorname{dom}(u(B)) = \operatorname{dom}(u(B_r)) + i\operatorname{dom}(u(B_r)).$$

The restrictions $u(B)_r = u(B_r)$ are called C-real restrictions.

Chapter 44

Laplace and Curlcurl Operators

A concise formulation of electrodynamics requires the introduction of *vectorial* differential operators, such as gradient, divergence, curl (also called rotation), curlcurl, and Laplacian, as densely defined, closed, respectively self-adjoint operators acting between L^2-Hilbert spaces. The precise handling of these operators, respectively of the associated forms, makes extensive use of Sobolev spaces, which are chosen according to the appropriate boundary conditions.

In our outline of the theory, we have only included selected proofs, to give to the reader an impression of how the mathematical machinery works. But we present also original results, needed in various parts of our photon theory. (For supplementary literature we refer e.g., to [CH62], [Ada75], [Wlo82], [GT83], [Cha84], [Lei86], [Zie89], [DL93], [Rau91], [Tay96], and [FK08], and references therein.)

Let us mention for clarity that we write $\mathbb{N}$ for the natural numbers $1, 2, 3, \ldots$, and set $\mathbb{N}_0 := \mathbb{N} \cup \{0\}$. If not specified otherwise, we mean by $r \in \mathbb{N}$ the dimension of the Euclidean space $\mathbb{R}^r$. The elements of $\mathbb{R}^r$ are written as the r-tuples $x = (x_1, \ldots, x_r)$.

Definition 44.0-1 (Domain, Interior, Exterior, Boundary). Throughout the book, Λ denotes an arbitrary domain or region, which is open and connected, but in general not simply connected subset of $\mathbb{R}^r$. Here "connected" means always "path connected", so that any pair of points in Λ may be connected via a continuous path within Λ, whereas "simply connected" means that any closed loop in Λ may be contracted within Λ to a point.

Λ is called an interior domain if Λ for itself is bounded, and an exterior domain if its complement $\mathbb{R}^r \setminus \Lambda$ is bounded.

By $\bar{\Lambda}$, we denote the closure of the domain Λ, and by $\partial \Lambda = \bar{\Lambda} \setminus \Lambda$ its boundary.

The connectedness of Λ is necessary for some of the elaborated results, especially for the compact embedding results, but not for all of them. Obviously, for a disconnected open set the results are valid in each of its connected components, and may be combined.

Throughout the present chapter, we use *complex* L^2-Hilbert spaces consisting of *complex-valued* square integrable functions, in which the differential vector operators act $\mathbb{C}$-linearly. In our electrodynamical applications, however, these operators act mostly in *real* L^2-Hilbert spaces, which poses no problem, since the operators commute with the component-wise complex conjugation C.

Definition 44.0-2 (C-Realness of Operators). The commutativity of an operator B from the Hilbert space $L^2(\Lambda, \mathbb{C}^n)$ into the Hilbert space $L^2(\Lambda, \mathbb{C}^m)$ with the component-wise complex conjugation C is called the C-realness of B.

C-realness implies for an $\mathbb{R}^n$-valued $\psi \in \mathrm{dom}(B)$ that the m components of $B\psi$ are also real, and so we may restrict B to map $L^2(\Lambda, \mathbb{R}^n)$ into $L^2(\Lambda, \mathbb{R}^m)$.

The general notion of C-realness and its consequences are elaborated in Sec. 43.7, see especially Proposition 43.7-4 on page 1556.

44.1.   Function Spaces

44.1.1.   *Square Integrable Weak Derivatives*

Let us first fix again some notation. If $k \in \mathbb{N}$, then for a function $\psi : \Lambda \to \mathbb{C}^k$ with component functions $\psi_j : \Lambda \to \mathbb{C}$ the complex conjugation C is defined component-wise and point-wise, which means $C\psi(x) = \overline{\psi}(x) = \overline{\psi(x)} = (\overline{\psi_1(x)}, \ldots, \overline{\psi_k(x)})$ for all $x \in \Lambda$. The standard inner product $(.|.)$ on the complex Hilbert space $L^2(\Lambda, \mathbb{C})$ of Lebesgue square integrable functions $\psi : \Lambda \to \mathbb{C}$ is given by $(\phi|\psi) = \int_\Lambda \overline{\phi}\psi \, d^r x$.

One may construct the direct sum Hilbert space $L^2(\Lambda, \mathbb{C}^k) = \bigoplus\limits_{j=1}^{k} L^2(\Lambda, \mathbb{C})$, the inner product of which is also denoted by $(.|.)$, that is, $(\phi|\psi) = \sum\limits_{j=1}^{k}(\phi_j|\psi_j) = \int_\Lambda \overline{\phi} \cdot \psi \, d^r x$.

Hereby $(a,b) \mapsto \overline{a} \cdot b := \sum\limits_{j=1}^{k} \overline{a_j} b_j$ stands for the familiar inner product on $\mathbb{C}^k$ with associated norm $|b| = \sqrt{\overline{b} \cdot b}$.

For a multi index $s = (s_1, \ldots, s_r) \in \mathbb{N}_0^r$ with $s_j \in \mathbb{N}_0$ for $j \in \{1, \ldots, r\}$ we write

$$|s| := s_1 + \cdots + s_r, \qquad \partial^s := \frac{\partial^{|s|}}{\partial x_1^{s_1} \cdots \partial x_r^{s_r}}. \qquad (44.1.1)$$

As usual, we put $\partial^0 \psi := \psi$ for the vanishing multi index $s = 0$.

Definition 44.1-1 (General Notations for Function Spaces). For the peculiar symbols for the function spaces of vector analysis one has to work through the present section, whereas the notions for the usual function spaces are listed here.

The function space $C^m(\Lambda, \mathbb{C})$ contains all m-times continuously differentiable functions, where $m \in \mathbb{N}_0 \cup \{\infty\}$. We write $C_b^m(\Lambda, \mathbb{C})$, if each derivative $\partial^s \psi$ in addition is bounded.

By $C_c^m(\Lambda, \mathbb{C})$, we denote the m-times continuously differentiable functions $\psi : \Lambda \to \mathbb{C}$ with compact support within Λ. The value $m = \infty$ leads to a popular test function space in the theory of distributions.

The elements of $C_c^\infty(\mathbb{R}^r, \mathbb{C})|_\Lambda$ are the restrictions $\phi|_\Lambda$ of $\phi \in C_c^\infty(\mathbb{R}^r, \mathbb{C})$ to Λ.

$C^m(\bar{\Lambda}, \mathbb{C})$ is the subspace consisting of those functions $\psi \in C^m(\Lambda, \mathbb{C})$ for which each derivative $\partial^s \psi$, with $|s| \leq m$, extends to a continuous function on $\bar{\Lambda}$, the extension of which is also denoted by $\partial^s \psi$.

As usual, for $m = 0$, we drop the upper index and write, e.g., $C_b^0(\Lambda, \mathbb{C}) \equiv C_b(\Lambda, \mathbb{C})$, meaning the bounded continuous functions on Λ.

The introduced function spaces also are considered for k components, in which case we write, e.g., $\psi = (\psi_1, \ldots, \psi_k) \in C_b^m(\Lambda, \mathbb{C}^k)$ whenever each component function satisfies $\psi_j \in C_b^m(\Lambda, \mathbb{C})$.

Let us make *two remarks*. (1) By construction $\psi \in C_c^\infty(\mathbb{R}^r, \mathbb{C})|_\Lambda$ is of type $\psi = \phi|_\Lambda$ for some $\phi \in C_c^\infty(\mathbb{R}^r, \mathbb{C})$. Thus each derivative $\partial^s \psi = \partial^s \phi|_\Lambda$ is bounded and extends uniquely to a continuous function on $\bar{\Lambda}$, precisely given by the restriction $\partial^s \phi|_{\bar{\Lambda}}$ of $\partial^s \phi$ to $\bar{\Lambda}$. So

$$C_c^\infty(\mathbb{R}^r, \mathbb{C})|_\Lambda \subseteq C^\infty(\bar{\Lambda}, \mathbb{C}) \cap C_b^\infty(\Lambda, \mathbb{C}).$$

(2) If Λ is not bounded, then there exist some $\psi \in C^m(\bar{\Lambda}, \mathbb{C})$ which are unbounded on the connection of Λ to infinity. Consequently it holds $C^m(\bar{\Lambda}, \mathbb{C}) \subseteq C_b^m(\Lambda, \mathbb{C})$, if and only if Λ is an interior domain.

Let $s \in \mathbb{N}_0^r$ be a multi index. Then for $|s| \leq m$, iterated partial integration yields

$$\int_\Lambda \overline{\varphi}(\partial^s \phi) \, d^r x = (-1)^{|s|} \int_\Lambda (\partial^s \overline{\varphi}) \phi \, d^r x, \tag{44.1.2}$$

if at least one of the functions $\varphi \in C^m(\Lambda, \mathbb{C})$ or $\phi \in C^m(\Lambda, \mathbb{C})$ has compact support, what implies its vanishing at the boundary of the open region Λ, together with that of all its derivatives. This relation gives rise to the definition of the *distributional, also called generalized or weak derivative*. For our treatment of Sobolev-like spaces, however, we do not use distribution theory and understand under the weak derivation ∂^s of a locally Lebesgue integrable function $\phi : \Lambda \to \mathbb{C}$, definitely, a locally Lebesgue integrable function $\phi_s : \Lambda \to \mathbb{C}$ with the property that $\int_\Lambda \overline{\varphi} \phi_s \, d^r x = (-1)^{|s|} \int_\Lambda (\partial^s \overline{\varphi}) \phi \, d^r x$ for all test function $\varphi \in C_c^\infty(\Lambda, \mathbb{C})$. (In distribution theory the derivative is in general not a function at all.) In case of existence, ϕ_s is unique up to Lebesgue zero sets, and then one puts $\partial^s \phi := \phi_s$ in order to obtain the formula

$$\int_\Lambda \overline{\varphi}(\partial^s \phi) \, d^r x = (-1)^{|s|} \int_\Lambda (\partial^s \overline{\varphi}) \phi \, d^r x, \quad \forall \varphi \in C_c^\infty(\Lambda, \mathbb{C}), \tag{44.1.3}$$

which resembles the partial integration in Eq. (44.1.2).

We shall generalize, e.g., the ordinary derivations occurring in the Laplacian $\Delta := \sum_{j=1}^r \frac{\partial^2}{\partial x_j^2}$ to that in the weak sense, for which we then use the same symbols, writing again Δ. If for $\phi : \Lambda \to \mathbb{C}$ the expression $\Delta\phi$ exists, this symbol means then a locally integrable function with

$$\int_\Lambda \overline{\varphi}(\Delta\phi)\, d^r x = \int_\Lambda (\Delta\overline{\varphi})\phi\, d^r x\,, \quad \forall \varphi \in C_c^\infty(\Lambda, \mathbb{C})\,. \qquad (44.1.4)$$

When considering vector fields $\psi : \Lambda \to \mathbb{C}^r$ one may also generalize the gradient, the divergence, and the curl to the corresponding differential operators in the weak sense. We recall at first the usual definition of these operators making use of the so-called nabla operator $\nabla = (\frac{\partial}{\partial x_1}, \ldots, \frac{\partial}{\partial x_r})$. As is well known, the gradient is defined by

$$\nabla\varphi := \left(\frac{\partial\varphi}{\partial x_1}, \ldots, \frac{\partial\varphi}{\partial x_r} \right), \quad \varphi \in C^1(\Lambda, \mathbb{C})\,,$$

and the divergence is given by

$$\nabla \cdot \phi := \sum_{j=1}^r \frac{\partial\phi_j}{\partial x_j}\,, \quad \phi = (\phi_1, \ldots, \phi_r) \in C^1(\Lambda, \mathbb{C}^r)\,.$$

The curl, however, is used only for $r = 3$, acting on 3-component functions on $\Lambda \subseteq \mathbb{R}^3$, (since we want it not to change the number of components):

$$\nabla \times \psi := \left(\frac{\partial\psi_3}{\partial x_2} - \frac{\partial\psi_2}{\partial x_3}, \frac{\partial\psi_1}{\partial x_3} - \frac{\partial\psi_3}{\partial x_1}, \frac{\partial\psi_2}{\partial x_1} - \frac{\partial\psi_1}{\partial x_2} \right), \quad \psi = (\psi_1, \psi_2, \psi_3) \in C^1(\Lambda, \mathbb{C}^3)\,.$$

The divergence $\nabla\cdot$ is the formal operator-adjoint to the negative gradient $-\nabla$. If at least one of the functions $\varphi \in C^1(\Lambda, \mathbb{C})$ or $\phi \in C^1(\Lambda, \mathbb{C}^r)$ has compact support, then partial integration leads to

$$\int_\Lambda \overline{\varphi}(\nabla \cdot \phi)\, d^r x = -\int_\Lambda (\nabla\overline{\varphi}) \cdot \phi\, d^r x\,. \qquad (44.1.5)$$

Note that in this and the following formula we employ, in fact, only the component-wise partial integration and do not need the conversion of volume into surface integrals (as in the Gauss law or in Green's theorems).

The rotation $\nabla\times$ appears as being formally self-adjoint, that is, we get by partial integration

$$\int_\Lambda \overline{\varphi} \cdot (\nabla \times \psi)\, d^3 x = \int_\Lambda (\nabla \times \overline{\varphi}) \cdot \psi\, d^3 x\,, \qquad (44.1.6)$$

whenever at least one of the functions $\varphi, \psi \in C^1(\Lambda, \mathbb{C}^3)$ has compact support.

As mentioned above, these connections give rise to the definition of the *weak divergence* and *weak curl*. Let us repeat explicitly, what this means: The weak divergence of a locally Lebesgue integrable function $\phi : \Lambda \to \mathbb{C}^r$ is defined to be a locally Lebesgue integrable function $\nabla \cdot \phi : \Lambda \to \mathbb{C}$ (provided existence) so that Eq. (44.1.5) is valid for all test functions $\varphi \in C_c^\infty(\Lambda, \mathbb{C})$. For $r = 3$ the weak curl of a locally Lebesgue integrable function $\psi : \Lambda \to \mathbb{C}^3$ is defined to be a locally Lebesgue integrable function $\nabla \times \psi : \Lambda \to \mathbb{C}^3$ (provided existence) so that Eq. (44.1.6) is valid for all test functions $\varphi \in C_c^\infty(\Lambda, \mathbb{C}^3)$.

If $\phi \in L^2(\Lambda, \mathbb{C})$, then ϕ is locally Lebesgue integrable, but the reverse conclusion is not valid. (The local singularities — in contradistinction to singularities at $|x| \to \infty$ — are damped by performing the square root.) For a multi index $s \in \mathbb{N}_0^r$ we briefly write $\partial^s \phi \in L^2(\Lambda, \mathbb{C})$, whenever the weak derivative $\partial^s \phi$ exists not only as a locally Lebesgue integrable function but in addition is Lebesgue square integrable. Analogously, for $\psi \in L^2(\Lambda, \mathbb{C}^r)$ we briefly write $\nabla \cdot \psi \in L^2(\Lambda, \mathbb{C})$, respectively $\nabla \times \psi \in L^2(\Lambda, \mathbb{C}^3)$ in case of $r = 3$, if the generalized divergence of ψ, respectively the generalized curl of ψ, exist even as a Lebesgue square integrable function.

The subsequent Lemma concerning the existence of weak derivatives under the additional condition of square integrability is an immediate consequence of the Riesz Theorem 43.1-1 on page 1522.

Lemma 44.1-2 (Square Integrable Weak Derivatives). *Let $\Lambda \subseteq \mathbb{R}^r$ be an arbitrary domain.*

(a) *Let $\phi \in L^2(\Lambda, \mathbb{C})$ and $s \in \mathbb{N}_0^r$ a multi index. We have $\partial^s \phi \in L^2(\Lambda, \mathbb{C})$, if and only if the linear form $C_c^\infty(\Lambda, \mathbb{C}) \ni \varphi \mapsto (\phi | \partial^s \varphi)$ is continuous with respect to the norm of $L^2(\Lambda, \mathbb{C})$, in which case it holds*

$$(\partial^s \phi | \varphi) = (-1)^{|s|} (\phi | \partial^s \varphi), \quad \forall \varphi \in C_c^\infty(\Lambda, \mathbb{C}).$$

In other words, for given $\phi \in L^2(\Lambda, \mathbb{C})$, verify the norm continuity of $C_c^\infty(\Lambda, \mathbb{C}) \ni \varphi \mapsto (\phi | \partial^s \varphi)$, and then you have the existence of the derivative $\partial^s \phi$ in the weak sense plus its square integrability.

This criterion is applied to the following three special cases:

(b) *Let $\phi \in L^2(\Lambda, \mathbb{C})$. From part (a) it immediately follows that $\nabla \phi \in L^2(\Lambda, \mathbb{C}^r)$, if and only if the linear form $C_c^\infty(\Lambda, \mathbb{C}^r) \ni \varphi \mapsto (\phi | \nabla \cdot \varphi)$ is continuous with respect to the norm of $L^2(\Lambda, \mathbb{C}^r)$, in which case it holds*

$$(\nabla \phi | \varphi) = -(\phi | \nabla \cdot \varphi), \quad \forall \varphi \in C_c^\infty(\Lambda, \mathbb{C}^r).$$

(c) *Let $\psi \in L^2(\Lambda, \mathbb{C}^r)$. Then $\nabla \cdot \psi \in L^2(\Lambda, \mathbb{C})$, if and only if the linear form $C_c^\infty(\Lambda, \mathbb{C}) \ni \varphi \mapsto (\psi | \nabla \varphi)$ is continuous with respect to the norm of $L^2(\Lambda, \mathbb{C})$, in which case it holds*

$$(\nabla \cdot \psi | \varphi) = -(\psi | \nabla \varphi), \quad \forall \varphi \in C_c^\infty(\Lambda, \mathbb{C}).$$

(d) *Suppose $r = 3$, and let $\psi \in L^2(\Lambda, \mathbb{C}^3)$. Then $\nabla \times \psi \in L^2(\Lambda, \mathbb{C}^3)$, if and only if the linear form $C_c^\infty(\Lambda, \mathbb{C}^3) \ni \varphi \mapsto (\psi | \nabla \times \varphi)$ is continuous with respect to the norm of $L^2(\Lambda, \mathbb{C}^3)$, in which case it holds*

$$(\nabla \times \psi | \varphi) = (\psi | \nabla \times \varphi), \quad \forall \varphi \in C_c^\infty(\Lambda, \mathbb{C}^3).$$

44.1.2. *Classical Sobolev Spaces*

The construction of Sobolev spaces appeals to the square integrability of weak derivatives treated in the foregoing Lemma 44.1-2.

Definition 44.1-3 (Sobolev Space $W^m(\Lambda, \mathbb{C})$). Suppose $m \in \mathbb{N}_0$. The Sobolev space $W^m(\Lambda, \mathbb{C})$ is defined as the complex vector space, the elements of which are classes of square integrable functions with the following properties

$$W^m(\Lambda, \mathbb{C}) := \{\phi \in L^2(\Lambda, \mathbb{C}) \mid \partial^s \phi \in L^2(\Lambda, \mathbb{C}) \text{ for } |s| \leq m\},$$

where here and in the rest of this chapter, the derivatives are meant in the weak sense. $W^m(\Lambda, \mathbb{C})$ is equipped with the **inner product**

$$(\psi|\phi)_m := \sum_{|s| \leq m} (\partial^s \psi | \partial^s \phi). \qquad (44.1.7)$$

In the literature, the Sobolev spaces $W^m(\Lambda, \mathbb{C})$ are also denoted by $H^m(\Lambda)$, or by $W^{m,2}(\Lambda)$ in order to indicate the assumed square integrability of the weak derivatives. We shall write for the associated Sobolev **norm** $\|\phi\|_m := \sqrt{(\phi|\phi)_m}$.

Proposition 44.1-4 (Completeness of the Sobolev Spaces). $W^m(\Lambda, \mathbb{C})$ *is a separable complex Hilbert space for every* $m \in \mathbb{N}_0$.

Proof. Let ϕ_ν, $\nu \in \mathbb{N}$, be a Cauchy sequence in $W^m(\Lambda, \mathbb{C})$. By construction of the norm $\|.\|_m$ we have $\|\partial^s \psi\| \leq \|\psi\|_m$ for $\psi \in W^m(\Lambda, \mathbb{C})$ and $|s| \leq m$, and so it follows that $\partial^s \phi_\nu$ is Cauchy with respect to the norm $\|.\|$ of $L^2(\Lambda, \mathbb{C})$. The completeness of $L^2(\Lambda, \mathbb{C})$ ensures the existence of $\phi^s \in L^2(\Lambda, \mathbb{C})$ with

$$\lim_{\nu \to \infty} \|\partial^s \phi_\nu - \phi^s\| = 0, \quad \forall |s| \leq m; \qquad \phi := \phi^0 = \lim_{\nu \to \infty} \phi_\nu.$$

This yields for $|s| \leq m$ the continuity of

$$C_c^\infty(\Lambda, \mathbb{C}) \ni \varphi \mapsto (\phi^s|\varphi) = \lim_{\nu \to \infty} (\partial^s \phi_\nu | \varphi) = \lim_{\nu \to \infty} (\phi_\nu | \partial^s \varphi) = (\phi | \partial^s \varphi).$$

With Lemma 44.1-2(a) we conclude that $\phi^s = \partial^s \phi$, that is $\phi \in W^m(\Lambda, \mathbb{C})$.

Separability follows from that of $L^2(\Lambda, \mathbb{C})$, since the mapping

$$W^m(\Lambda, \mathbb{C}) \to \bigoplus_{|s| \leq m} L^2(\Lambda, \mathbb{C}), \quad \phi \mapsto \bigoplus_{|s| \leq m} \partial^s \phi$$

constitutes an isometry onto a closed subspace of the direct sum $\bigoplus_{|s| \leq m} L^2(\Lambda, \mathbb{C})$. $\qquad \square$

For the case $r = 1$ we have a special situation, since for an open, possibly unbounded interval $I \subseteq \mathbb{R}$ the Sobolev space $W^1(I, \mathbb{C})$ is given by

$$W^1(I, \mathbb{C}) = \{\psi \in L^2(I, \mathbb{C}) \mid \psi \text{ is absolutely continuous with } \psi' = \tfrac{d\psi}{dx} \in L^2(I, \mathbb{C})\}. \qquad (44.1.8)$$

In the background of this connection stands the fact that each absolutely continuous function $\psi : I \to \mathbb{C}$ is differentiable almost everywhere (a.e.), and its a.e. derivative ψ' is integrable over all compact sub-intervals of I, but not necessarily square integrable (cf. [Wei80] and also [Coh80]). Of course, ψ' coincides with the weak derivative $\frac{d\psi}{dx}$ of ψ.

In boundary problems, often the vanishing of functions and some of their derivatives on the boundary is required. This is expressed in a more abstract and generalized manner by demanding that the functions be the elements of closed subspaces of the preceding Sobolev spaces.

Definition 44.1-5 (Sobolev Space $\mathrm{W}_0^m(\Lambda, \mathbb{C})$). Suppose $m \in \mathbb{N}_0$. The Sobolev space $\mathrm{W}_0^m(\Lambda, \mathbb{C})$ is defined as the closure of $\mathrm{C}_c^\infty(\Lambda, \mathbb{C})$ within the Sobolev Hilbert space $\mathrm{W}^m(\Lambda, \mathbb{C})$, that is,

$$\mathrm{W}_0^m(\Lambda, \mathbb{C}) := \overline{\mathrm{C}_c^\infty(\Lambda, \mathbb{C})}^{\|\cdot\|_m}.$$

Note that all derivatives of the elements in $\mathrm{C}_c^\infty(\Lambda, \mathbb{C})$ vanish on $\partial \Lambda$ and that the Sobolev norm $\|.\|_m$ provides a growth estimate for all derivatives up to order m. So we may say that all (weak) derivatives up to order m of the elements in $\mathrm{W}_0^m(\Lambda, \mathbb{C})$ vanish on $\partial \Lambda$ in a generalized sense. This is an example, how properties of smooth elements may be extended to analogous properties for general elements in a Sobolev space, by using continuity with respect to a Sobolev norm.

We first turn to properties of Sobolev spaces, which do not require certain smoothness conditions for the boundary $\partial \Lambda$, to be considered later on. Especially, the compactness result in part (g) below is of great importance for deducing the spectral properties of the Laplacian with Dirichlet boundary condition (if $\Lambda \subset \mathbb{R}^r$ is an interior domain).

Proposition 44.1-6. *The following assertions are valid:*

(a) $\mathrm{W}^m(\mathbb{R}^r, \mathbb{C}) = \mathrm{W}_0^m(\mathbb{R}^r, \mathbb{C})$ *for all* $m \in \mathbb{N}_0$.
(b) $\mathrm{W}^0(\Lambda, \mathbb{C}) = \mathrm{W}_0^0(\Lambda, \mathbb{C}) = \mathrm{L}^2(\Lambda, \mathbb{C})$.
(c) *For every* $m \in \mathbb{N}_0$ *one has,*

$$\mathrm{C}_b^\infty(\Lambda, \mathbb{C}) \cap \mathrm{W}^m(\Lambda, \mathbb{C}) = \{\phi \in \mathrm{C}_b^\infty(\Lambda, \mathbb{C}) \mid \partial^s \phi \in \mathrm{L}^2(\Lambda, \mathbb{C}) \text{ for } |s| \leq m\}$$

is dense in $\mathrm{W}^m(\Lambda, \mathbb{C})$ *(with respect to its norm* $\|.\|_m$*). Thus, one may define the Sobolev spaces* $\mathrm{W}^m(\Lambda, \mathbb{C})$ *independently from the notion of weak derivatives as the* $\|.\|_m$*-closure of* $\{\phi \in \mathrm{C}_b^\infty(\Lambda, \mathbb{C}) \mid \partial^s \phi \in \mathrm{L}^2(\Lambda, \mathbb{C}) \text{ for } |s| \leq m\}$.
(d) *Let* $\Lambda \subset \mathbb{R}^r$ *be interior (i.e., bounded), and* $m \in \mathbb{N}$. *Then there exists a constant* $c > 0$, *only dependent from the diameter of* Λ, *such that*

$$\|\phi\|_m^2 \leq c \sum_{|s|=m} \|\partial^s \phi(x)\|^2, \quad \forall \phi \in \mathrm{W}_0^m(\Lambda, \mathbb{C}).$$

For $m = 1$ *this inequality is known as* Poincaré *estimate.*
(e) *Let* $\Lambda \subset \mathbb{R}^r$ *be interior, and* $m \geq 1$. *Then* $\mathrm{W}_0^m(\Lambda, \mathbb{C})$ *is a proper subspace of* $\mathrm{W}^m(\Lambda, \mathbb{C})$. *(The constant functions are not contained in* $\mathrm{W}_0^m(\Lambda, \mathbb{C})$ *by part (d).)*
(f) *Let* Λ *and* Ω *be two domains of* $\mathbb{R}^r$ *such that* Λ *is a proper subset of* Ω. *Let* $m \geq 1$. *Then each* $\phi \in \mathrm{W}_0^m(\Lambda, \mathbb{C})$ *extends by zero to a unique element of* $\mathrm{W}_0^m(\Omega, \mathbb{C})$.

*This trivial extension is continuous with respect to the norms $\|.\|_m$. (This
follows immediately from Definition 44.1-5, since $C_c^\infty(\Lambda, \mathbb{C}) \subset C_c^\infty(\Omega, \mathbb{C})$.)
However, such a trivial continuation in general does not work for the spaces
$W^m(\Lambda, \mathbb{C})$ and $W^m(\Omega, \mathbb{C})$ for $m \geq 1$.*

(g) *Suppose $m > n$. Then the identical embeddings*

$$W_0^m(\Lambda, \mathbb{C}) \hookrightarrow W_0^n(\Lambda, \mathbb{C}), \qquad W^m(\Lambda, \mathbb{C}) \hookrightarrow W^n(\Lambda, \mathbb{C})$$

*are continuous and injective. If in addition Λ is interior, then the embedding
$W_0^m(\Lambda, \mathbb{C}) \hookrightarrow W_0^n(\Lambda, \mathbb{C})$ is compact.*

(h) *If $m - k > r/2$, then we have the inclusion (map) $W_0^m(\Lambda, \mathbb{C}) \subseteq C^k(\bar\Lambda, \mathbb{C})$, which
means the association of a unique, k-times continuously differentiable function
with a class of measurable functions, which make up an element of $W_0^m(\Lambda, \mathbb{C})$
(lifting of a class to a function).*

In order to state further properties of Sobolev spaces, one has the need for
smoothness conditions on the boundary $\partial\Lambda$ of the domain $\Lambda \subset \mathbb{R}^r$, which we state
now, consecutively ordered according to increasing strength.

Definition 44.1-7 (Smoothness Conditions for the Boundary). Let Λ be
an arbitrary, possibly unbounded domain in $\mathbb{R}^r$.

(a) Λ possesses the *segment property*, if $\partial\Lambda$ has a locally finite open covering $\{U_\alpha\}$
and corresponding vectors $\{a_\alpha\} \subset \mathbb{R}^r$, such that $y + ta_\alpha \in \Lambda$ for all $y \in \bar\Lambda \cap U_\alpha$
and all $0 < t < 1$.
(That means, in each (small set of full dimension, inside of $\bar\Lambda$) $\bar\Lambda \cap U_\alpha$ there is
a fixed direction a_α pointing into Λ.)

(b) Λ possesses the *uniform cone property*, if $\partial\Lambda$ has a locally finite open covering $\{U_\alpha\}$ and corresponding cones $\{K_\alpha\}$ with vertices at the origin (of finite
heights), such that $y + K_\alpha \subset \Lambda$ for all $y \in \Lambda \cap U_\alpha$. It follows that $\partial\Lambda$ is a zero
set with respect to the r-dimensional Lebesgue measure.
(That means, in each $\Lambda \cap U_\alpha$ there is not only a vector but a whole fixed cone
pointing into Λ.)

(c) Λ is called C^k-*smooth*, where $k \in \mathbb{N}$, if its boundary $\partial\Lambda$ is an $(r-1)$-dimensional
submanifold of $\mathbb{R}^r$ of class C^k, and if Λ is locally situated only on one side of
its boundary.

(d) Λ is called *piece-wise* C^k-*smooth*, if it has the uniform cone property (especially
necessary at the edges), and if — with the exception of the edges — its boundary
$\partial\Lambda$ consists of finitely many C^k-smooth pieces.

C^k-smoothness for $k \geq 1$ implies (d) and (b), whereas (b) yields (a).

The following inclusions depend on the smoothness of $\partial\Lambda$. Especially, the
compactness result in part (d) of the subsequent proposition is important for the

spectrum of the Laplacian on $L^2(\Lambda, \mathbb{C})$ with Neumann or mixed boundary conditions in interior domains $\Lambda \subset \mathbb{R}^r$.

Proposition 44.1-8. *The following assertions are valid:*

(a) *If $\Lambda \subseteq \mathbb{R}^r$ possesses the segment property, then $C_c^\infty(\mathbb{R}^r, \mathbb{C})|_\Lambda$ is dense in the Sobolev space $W^m(\Lambda, \mathbb{C})$ for each $m \in \mathbb{N}_0$.*

(b) *Let $\Lambda \subseteq \mathbb{R}^r$ have the uniform cone property, and let $m - k > r/2$. Then,*

$$W^m(\Lambda, \mathbb{C}) \subseteq C^k(\bar{\Lambda}, \mathbb{C}).$$

(Recall that by Proposition 44.1-6(h) this inclusion is valid for $W_0^m(\Lambda, \mathbb{C})$ without any smoothness condition for Λ.)

(c) *Let the interior $\Lambda \subset \mathbb{R}^r$ possess the segment property. Then there exists a constant $c > 0$ such that*

$$\|\phi\| \leq c(\|\nabla\phi\| + |(1|\phi)|), \quad \forall \phi \in W^1(\Lambda, \mathbb{C}),$$

where 1 means the constant unit function $1(x) = 1$ for all $x \in \Lambda$. Also this inequality is known as Poincaré estimate.

(d) *Let be $m > n$. By Proposition 44.1-6(g) the identical embedding $W^m(\Lambda, \mathbb{C}) \hookrightarrow W^n(\Lambda, \mathbb{C})$ is continuous and injective. If Λ is interior and possesses the uniform cone property, then the identical embedding $W^m(\Lambda, \mathbb{C}) \hookrightarrow W^n(\Lambda, \mathbb{C})$ in addition is compact.*

Furthermore, for the case $m = 1$ and $n = 0$ the segment property is sufficient for the compactness of $W^1(\Lambda, \mathbb{C}) \hookrightarrow L^2(\Lambda, \mathbb{C})$, provided Λ is interior.

44.1.3. *Boundary Evaluation and Boundary Operator*

In the formulation of boundary evaluations one deals with the "restrictions" of elements $\phi \in W^m(\Lambda, \mathbb{C})$ to the boundary $\partial\Lambda$ in terms of so-called *boundary operators*, also called *trace operators*. The direct definition of a "restriction" is only possible for Sobolev space elements, which correspond to smooth functions. More precisely, these functions, together with their derivatives up to a certain order — say $l \in \mathbb{N}_0 \cup \{\infty\}$ — must be continuous on $\bar{\Lambda}$. Let us exactly describe what this means.

By definition a Sobolev space element $\phi \in W^m(\Lambda, \mathbb{C})$ is a *class* of functions on the open region Λ with certain properties. It is said to correspond to a function in $C^l(\bar{\Lambda}, \mathbb{C})$, if its class contains such a function, which then is unique. As mentioned before, it is a common usage to identify in this case the Sobolev space element $\phi \in W^m(\Lambda, \mathbb{C})$ with this smooth function, also denoted by ϕ. In this agreement, each $\phi \in W^m(\Lambda, \mathbb{C}) \cap C^l(\bar{\Lambda}, \mathbb{C})$ means a function $\phi : \bar{\Lambda} \to \mathbb{C}$, for which each derivative $\partial^s\phi$, with $|s| \leq l$, is continuous on the closure $\bar{\Lambda} = \Lambda \cup \partial\Lambda$, especially on the boundary $\partial\Lambda$ (cf. Definition 44.1-1).

First one defines a boundary operator R by the direct restriction $R\phi := \phi|_{\partial\Lambda}$ to the boundary $\partial\Lambda$ for the functions $\phi \in W^m(\Lambda, \mathbb{C}) \cap C^l(\bar{\Lambda}, \mathbb{C})$. By construction, the map R is linear, and by Proposition 44.1-8(a) it is densely defined in $W^m(\Lambda, \mathbb{C})$ for every $l \in \mathbb{N}_0 \cup \{\infty\}$, whenever Λ possesses the segment property. If R is continuous with respect to the norm in $W^m(\Lambda, \mathbb{C})$ and to a certain Sobolev norm in the image space, it may be uniquely and continuously extended to the whole of $W^m(\Lambda, \mathbb{C})$.

The complicated part is the norm in the image space. For sufficiently smooth $\Lambda \subset \mathbb{R}^r$ there exists the Sobolev space $W^{m-1/2}(\partial\Lambda, \mathbb{C})$ on the boundary as image space for R. We omit its exact definition and only try to give an intuitive characterization.

Remark 44.1-9 (On the Boundary Sobolev Spaces $W^\kappa(\partial\Lambda, \mathbb{C})$ for $\kappa \in \mathbb{R}$).
We assume the boundary $\partial\Lambda$ to be a C^k-differentiable manifold. A surface integral $\int_{\partial\Lambda} \phi(x)\, dS(x)$ is then evaluated in the jth chart, $1 \le j \le N$, in terms of Cartesian coordinates $y = (y_1, \ldots, y_{r-1}) \in \mathbb{R}^{r-1}$. The resulting expression $g_j(y)$ is assumed to be in $W^\kappa(\mathbb{R}^{r-1}, \mathbb{C})$. This will say that, written in terms of its Fourier transform $\hat{g}_j(k)$, it has the finite norm

$$\|g_j\|_\kappa = \left[\int_{\mathbb{R}^{r-1}} (1 + |k|^2)^s |\hat{g}_j(k)|^2 d^{r-1}k\right]^{1/2} < \infty\,.$$

For integer $\kappa = m$ this coincides with the original Sobolev norm in $W^m(\mathbb{R}^{r-1}, \mathbb{C})$ (in which the norms of the position space derivatives up to order m are involved). The existence of $\|g_j\|_\kappa$ implies also the square integrability of certain of its position space derivatives. The norm $\|\phi\|_\kappa$ is composed of the $\|g_j\|_\kappa$. The $W^\kappa(\partial\Lambda, \mathbb{C})$, $\kappa \in \mathbb{R}$, are Hilbert spaces and have properties similar to the previously discussed Sobolev spaces.

In the literal sense, if $\phi|_{\partial\Lambda} = 0$, that is $\phi(x) = 0$ for all $x \in \partial\Lambda$, then $R\phi = 0$. But $R\phi$ as a Sobolev space element in $W^{m-1/2}(\partial\Lambda, \mathbb{C})$ vanishes, if and only if its Sobolev norm vanishes. Since in the Sobolev norms the norms of certain derivatives are involved, also the latter must vanish in some sense on the boundary for elements in $\ker(R)$, as is expressed in the following Proposition.

Proposition 44.1-10 (Boundary Operator). *Suppose $\Lambda \subset \mathbb{R}^r$ to be an interior C^k-smooth domain for some $k \in \mathbb{N}$, and let $m \in \{0, 1, \ldots, k\}$. Then there exists a unique $\mathbb{C}$-linear, continuous boundary operator R from $W^m(\Lambda, \mathbb{C})$ onto $W^{m-1/2}(\partial\Lambda, \mathbb{C})$, which continuously extends the above direct restriction R to the boundary. Also in its extension R is symbolically written*

$$R\phi = \phi|_{\partial\Lambda}\,, \quad \phi \in W^m(\Lambda, \mathbb{C})\,.$$

The kernel of the boundary operator R is given by

$$\ker(R) = W_0^m(\Lambda, \mathbb{C})\,.$$

For m = 1 this remains even valid, if Λ is an interior or exterior domain being only piece-wise C¹ *-smooth.*

According to the intuitive interpretation, given after Definition 44.1-5, the Sobolev space $W_0^m(\Lambda, \mathbb{C})$ expresses vanishing boundary values for its elements and their weak derivatives up to order m in a rather generalized sense. If $\partial \Lambda$ is sufficiently smooth so that a boundary operator exists, this fact is expressed in a somewhat more concrete sense by the above kernel expression.

For the proof of the preceding proposition one has to demonstrate, that — under the smoothness assumptions on $\partial \Lambda$ — the norm of $R\phi$ in the $W^{m-1/2}(\partial \Lambda, \mathbb{C})$-space is dominated by the norm of ϕ in $W^m(\Lambda, \mathbb{C})$. For this purpose, and for the continuity of embeddings of Sobolev spaces, Poincaré estimates are useful.

Let us sketch how to generalize the above notions to multi-component functions $\psi = (\psi_1, \ldots, \psi_k) : \Lambda \to \mathbb{C}^k$ with the component functions $\psi_j : \Lambda \to \mathbb{C}$. For every $m \in \mathbb{N}_0$ the Sobolev Hilbert space $W^m(\Lambda, \mathbb{C}^k)$ is constructed with the component-wise Sobolev inner product $(\phi|\psi)_m = \sum_{j=1}^{k} (\phi_j|\psi_j)_m$. For $b \in \mathbb{C}^k$ and $\varphi \in W^m(\Lambda, \mathbb{C})$ one obtains the special element $b\varphi := (b_1\varphi, \ldots, b_k\varphi) \in W^m(\Lambda, \mathbb{C}^k)$ with the Sobolev norm $\|b\varphi\|_m = |b| \|\varphi\|_m$. If $\{e_l \mid l \in \mathbb{N}\}$ is an orthonormal basis of the Sobolev Hilbert space $W^m(\Lambda, \mathbb{C})$ and $\{\epsilon_1, \ldots, \epsilon_k\}$ is an orthonormal basis of $\mathbb{C}^k$, then $\{\epsilon_j e_l \mid j = 1, \ldots, k; l \in \mathbb{N}\}$ constitutes an orthonormal basis of $W^m(\Lambda, \mathbb{C}^k)$.

44.1.4.   *Div and Curl Sobolev Spaces*

In general, we deal here with arbitrary Euclidean dimension $r \geq 2$, but set automatically $r = 3$ whenever the curl is treated.

Analogously to the previous classical Sobolev spaces $W^m(\Lambda, \mathbb{C})$ and $W_0^m(\Lambda, \mathbb{C})$ the operator-specific "div and curl Sobolev spaces" are defined by L^2-properties of weak derivatives, but now in the special combinations $(\nabla \cdot .)$ and $(\nabla \times .)$. They possess similar properties as the classical Sobolev spaces, which we describe now in corresponding succession.

Definition 44.1-11 (Sobolev Spaces $W(\mathrm{div}; \Lambda, \mathbb{C}^r)$ **and** $W(\mathrm{curl}; \Lambda, \mathbb{C}^3)$**).**
We define the div-Sobolev space $W(\mathrm{div}; \Lambda, \mathbb{C}^r)$ as the complex vector space

$$W(\mathrm{div}; \Lambda, \mathbb{C}^r) := \{\phi \in L^2(\Lambda, \mathbb{C}^r) \mid \nabla \cdot \phi \in L^2(\Lambda, \mathbb{C})\}$$

and equip it with the inner product

$$(\psi|\phi)_{\mathrm{div}} := (\psi|\phi) + (\nabla \cdot \psi | \nabla \cdot \phi). \qquad (44.1.9)$$

We introduce the curl-Sobolev space $W(\mathrm{curl}; \Lambda, \mathbb{C}^3)$ as the complex vector space

$$W(\mathrm{curl}; \Lambda, \mathbb{C}^3) := \{\phi \in L^2(\Lambda, \mathbb{C}^3) \mid \nabla \times \phi \in L^2(\Lambda, \mathbb{C}^3)\}$$

and equip it with the inner product

$$(\psi|\phi)_{\text{curl}} := (\psi|\phi) + (\nabla \times \psi|\nabla \times \phi).\tag{44.1.10}$$

In the literature these spaces are also denoted by $\text{H}(\text{div}, \Lambda)$ respectively $\text{H}(\text{curl}, \Lambda)$. The completeness of the L^2-spaces, applied also to the above mentioned sets of special weak derivatives, leads to:

Proposition 44.1-12 (Completeness of the Div and Curl Sobolev Spaces).
$\text{W}(\text{div}; \Lambda, \mathbb{C}^r)$ *and* $\text{W}(\text{curl}; \Lambda, \mathbb{C}^3)$ *are separable complex Hilbert spaces.*

Proof.   The proof works analogously to that of Proposition 44.1-4, what we briefly indicate for $\text{W}(\text{curl}; \Lambda, \mathbb{C}^3)$. Let ϕ_ν, $\nu \in \mathbb{N}$, be a Cauchy sequence in $\text{W}(\text{curl}; \Lambda, \mathbb{C}^3)$. Then both ϕ_ν and $\nabla \times \phi_\nu$ are Cauchy in $\text{L}^2(\Lambda, \mathbb{C}^3)$, thus converging there to ϕ respectively ϕ^c with respect to $\|.\|$ by its completeness. Hence

$$C_c^\infty(\Lambda, \mathbb{C}^3) \ni \varphi \mapsto (\phi^c|\varphi) = \lim_{\nu \to \infty} (\nabla \times \phi_\nu|\varphi) = \lim_{\nu \to \infty} (\phi_\nu|\nabla \times \varphi) = (\phi|\nabla \times \varphi)$$

is continuous, and Lemma 44.1-2(d) implies $\phi^c = \nabla \times \phi$, that is $\phi \in \text{W}(\text{curl}; \Lambda, \mathbb{C}^3)$.

Separability follows, since the map $\phi \mapsto \phi \oplus [\nabla \times \phi]$ is an isometry from $\text{W}(\text{curl}; \Lambda, \mathbb{C}^3)$ onto a closed subspace of the separable direct sum $\text{L}^2(\Lambda, \mathbb{C}^3) \oplus \text{L}^2(\Lambda, \mathbb{C}^3)$.   □

Since the L^2-property of all first weak derivatives is stronger a property than the L^2-property of certain of its combinations, it is not surprising that $\text{W}^1(\Lambda, \mathbb{C}^r)$ is a subspace, in fact a dense subspace, of $\text{W}(\text{div}; \Lambda, \mathbb{C}^r)$ and also of $\text{W}(\text{curl}; \Lambda, \mathbb{C}^3)$.

In order to formulate vanishing boundary conditions we introduce operator-specific closed subspaces.

Definition 44.1-13 (Sobolev Spaces $\text{W}_0(\text{div}; \Lambda, \mathbb{C}^r)$ and $\text{W}_0(\text{curl}; \Lambda, \mathbb{C}^3)$).
$\text{W}_0(\text{div}; \Lambda, \mathbb{C}^r)$ is defined as the closure of $C_c^\infty(\Lambda, \mathbb{C}^r)$ within the Sobolev Hilbert space $\text{W}(\text{div}; \Lambda, \mathbb{C}^r)$, and $\text{W}_0(\text{curl}; \Lambda, \mathbb{C}^3)$ is defined as the closure of $C_c^\infty(\Lambda, \mathbb{C}^3)$ within the Sobolev Hilbert space $\text{W}(\text{curl}; \Lambda, \mathbb{C}^3)$.

Analogously to Proposition 44.1-6(a), we have for the whole Euclidean space $\Lambda = \mathbb{R}^r$,

$$\begin{aligned}\text{W}(\text{div}; \mathbb{R}^r, \mathbb{C}^r) &= \text{W}_0(\text{div}; \mathbb{R}^r, \mathbb{C}^r)\,,\\ \text{W}(\text{curl}; \mathbb{R}^3, \mathbb{C}^3) &= \text{W}_0(\text{curl}; \mathbb{R}^3, \mathbb{C}^3)\,.\end{aligned}\tag{44.1.11}$$

Independently from smoothness properties for the domain boundary, the smooth Sobolev elements, with all derivatives bounded, are generally dense.

$$C_b^\infty(\Lambda, \mathbb{C}^r) \cap \text{W}(\text{div}; \Lambda, \mathbb{C}^r) = \{\phi \in C_b^\infty(\Lambda, \mathbb{C}^r) \mid \phi \in \text{L}^2(\Lambda, \mathbb{C}^r),\ \nabla \cdot \phi \in \text{L}^2(\Lambda, \mathbb{C})\}$$

is dense in $W(\mathrm{div}; \Lambda, \mathbb{C}^r)$, and

$$C_b^\infty(\Lambda, \mathbb{C}^3) \cap W(\mathrm{curl}; \Lambda, \mathbb{C}^3) =$$
$$= \{\phi \in C_b^\infty(\Lambda, \mathbb{C}^3) \mid \phi \in L^2(\Lambda, \mathbb{C}^3), \ \nabla \times \phi \in L^2(\Lambda, \mathbb{C}^3)\}$$

is dense in $W(\mathrm{curl}; \Lambda, \mathbb{C}^3)$.

Since for $\Lambda \subset \Omega$ each $\phi \in C_c^\infty(\Lambda, \mathbb{C}^r)$ extends by zero to an element in $C_c^\infty(\Omega, \mathbb{C}^r)$, the following result follows immediately from Definition 44.1-13.

Lemma 44.1-14. *Let Λ and Ω be two domains in $\mathbb{R}^r$ such that Λ is a proper subset of Ω. Then each $\phi \in W_0(\mathrm{div}; \Lambda, \mathbb{C}^r)$ extends by zero to a unique element of $W_0(\mathrm{div}; \Omega, \mathbb{C}^r)$. This trivial point-wise continuation is an embedding map, continuous with respect to the norm $\|.\|_{\mathrm{div}}$. Similarly, each $\phi \in W_0(\mathrm{curl}; \Lambda, \mathbb{C}^3)$ extends by zero to a unique element of $W_0(\mathrm{curl}; \Omega, \mathbb{C}^3)$, providing an embedding, which is continuous with respect to the norm $\|.\|_{\mathrm{curl}}$.*

In case of the spaces $W(\mathrm{div}; \Lambda, \mathbb{C}^r)$ and $W(\mathrm{curl}; \Lambda, \mathbb{C}^3)$ such a trivial continuation does not extend to continuous embedding operators.

For further properties of the div- and curl-Sobolev spaces one needs smoothness conditions for the boundary $\partial\Lambda$, such as given in Definition 44.1-7 on page 1564. Let us first state that there exist boundary operators for the div- and curl-Sobolev spaces similar to that in Proposition 44.1-10 on page 1566 for the ordinary Sobolev spaces $W^m(\Lambda, \mathbb{C})$.

Proposition 44.1-15 (Normal and Tangential Boundary Operators). *If Λ is interior or exterior and piece-wise C^1-smooth, then there exist the continuous boundary operators*

$$R_n : W(\mathrm{div}; \Lambda, \mathbb{C}^r) \to W^{-1/2}(\partial\Lambda, \mathbb{C}), \quad \psi \mapsto \psi \cdot n|_{\partial\Lambda}, \tag{44.1.12}$$
$$R_t : W(\mathrm{curl}; \Lambda, \mathbb{C}^3) \to W^{-1/2}(\partial\Lambda, \mathbb{C}^3), \quad \psi \mapsto \psi \times n|_{\partial\Lambda}, \tag{44.1.13}$$

where $n : \partial\Lambda \to \mathbb{R}^r$ means again the outer normal. That is, R_n gives the normal component at the boundary, and R_t evaluates the tangential component at the boundary, both in a generalized sense, so that the restriction symbol $|_{\partial\Lambda}$ may be taken literally only for smooth Sobolev elements.

For the kernels of the boundary operators one finds

$$\ker(R_n) = W_0(\mathrm{div}; \Lambda, \mathbb{C}^r), \quad \ker(R_t) = W_0(\mathrm{curl}; \Lambda, \mathbb{C}^3). \tag{44.1.14}$$

These boundary evaluations are involved in the following part (b).

Proposition 44.1-16. *The following relations are valid:*

(a) *If $\Lambda \subseteq \mathbb{R}^r$ possesses the segment property, then the set of restrictions from the whole space, $C_c^\infty(\mathbb{R}^r, \mathbb{C}^r)|_\Lambda$, is dense in the spaces $W(\mathrm{div}; \Lambda, \mathbb{C}^r)$ and $W(\mathrm{curl}; \Lambda, \mathbb{C}^3)$.*

(b) *The connection of the div- and curl-spaces* $W(\mathrm{div}; \Lambda, \mathbb{C}^3)$ *and* $W(\mathrm{curl}; \Lambda, \mathbb{C}^3)$
with the Sobolev space $W^1(\Lambda, \mathbb{C}^3)$ *is as follows. Let* Λ *be an interior or exterior*
domain of $\mathbb{R}^3$, *which is piece-wise* C^1*-smooth. Then*

$$W_0(\mathrm{div}; \Lambda, \mathbb{C}^3) \cap W(\mathrm{curl}; \Lambda, \mathbb{C}^3) = \{\psi \in W^1(\Lambda, \mathbb{C}^3) \mid \psi \cdot n|_{\partial\Lambda} = 0\},$$
$$W(\mathrm{div}; \Lambda, \mathbb{C}^3) \cap W_0(\mathrm{curl}; \Lambda, \mathbb{C}^3) = \{\psi \in W^1(\Lambda, \mathbb{C}^3) \mid \psi \times n|_{\partial\Lambda} = 0\}.$$

(*Note, by Proposition 44.1-10, the boundary operator* $R\psi = \psi|_{\partial\Lambda}$ *is well defined*
for $\psi \in W^1(\Lambda, \mathbb{C}^3)$, *leading the symbolic boundary restrictions* $\psi \cdot n|_{\partial\Lambda}$ *and*
$\psi \times n|_{\partial\Lambda}$.)
In these two spaces the Sobolev norm $\|.\|_1$ *and the norm* $\|.\|_{\mathrm{div,curl}}$ *are equiva-*
lent, where the latter norm is defined by

$$\|\psi\|^2_{\mathrm{div,curl}} := \|\psi\|^2 + \|\nabla \cdot \psi\|^2 + \|\nabla \times \psi\|^2. \qquad (44.1.15)$$

(c) *Let* Λ *be interior with the uniform cone property. Then the identical embeddings*

$$W_0(\mathrm{div}; \Lambda, \mathbb{C}^3) \cap W(\mathrm{curl}; \Lambda, \mathbb{C}^3) \hookrightarrow L^2(\Lambda, \mathbb{C}^3),$$
$$W(\mathrm{div}; \Lambda, \mathbb{C}^3) \cap W_0(\mathrm{curl}; \Lambda, \mathbb{C}^3) \hookrightarrow L^2(\Lambda, \mathbb{C}^3)$$

are compact.
Note, if the interior Λ *fulfills the stronger boundary condition of being piece-wise*
C^1*-smooth, this result follows from part* (b) *and Proposition 44.1-8(d).*

As a consequence of part (b) and Proposition 44.1-10 we obtain,

$$W_0(\mathrm{div}; \Lambda, \mathbb{C}^3) \cap W_0(\mathrm{curl}; \Lambda, \mathbb{C}^3) = W^1_0(\Lambda, \mathbb{C}^3). \qquad (44.1.16)$$

44.2. Laplacians with Classical Boundary Conditions

In this section, we use Sobolev spaces for discussing Laplacians with the most
common boundary conditions. If we have the need for the notion of an outer
normal derivative $\frac{\partial\psi}{\partial n} = \nabla\psi \cdot n$ at the boundary $\partial\Lambda$ of Λ (provided Λ is smooth
enough), we tacitly assume the position space dimension r greater than 1.

We treat self-adjoint Laplacians $-\Delta_\rho$ (the minus sign providing positivity) in
the Hilbert space $L^2(\Lambda, \mathbb{C})$. Acting on the functions in $C^\infty_c(\Lambda, \mathbb{C})$, these operators
all are equal to $-\sum_{j=1}^{r} \frac{\partial^2}{\partial x_j^2}$. They are discriminated from each other by their operator
domains, referred to by the index ρ. ρ may imagined as a formal function $\rho : \partial\Lambda \to$
$[0, +\infty]$ in the first three of the following boundary conditions. The mathematically
concise formulation of the boundary conditions, which we have given below, are the
characteristic features of the operator domains.

(1) The *Dirichlet* boundary condition means functions vanishing at the boundary,
that is $\psi(x) = 0$ for all $x \in \partial\Lambda$. This boundary condition is indexed by $\rho \equiv \infty$.

(2) The *Neumann* boundary condition means the vanishing of the normal derivative at the boundary, i.e., $\frac{\partial \psi}{\partial n}(x) = 0$ for all $x \in \partial\Lambda$. Here $\rho \equiv 0$.

(3) A *mixed* boundary condition is given in terms of a non-trivial boundary function $\rho : \partial\Lambda \to [0, \infty[$ so that $\rho(x)\psi(x) + \frac{\partial \psi}{\partial n}(x) = 0$ for all $x \in \partial\Lambda$. It is indexed, of course, by the function ρ. (In this manner the preceding two boundary conditions are special cases of the mixed one.)

(4) If Λ is a rectangular parallelepiped, then one may also introduce the *periodic* boundary condition, which is indicated by $\rho = $ per. This case is dealt with in Sec. 44.7.1.

44.2.1. *Self-adjoint Laplacians with Dirichlet, Neumann, or Mixed Boundary Conditions*

The Laplacians corresponding to one of the above boundary conditions are best described in terms of sesquilinear forms. So, instead of starting with the boundary condition for the operator domain, we first define the sesquilinear form h_ρ, corresponding to $-\Delta_\rho$, on its form domain. We apply then the general connection between sesquilinear forms and self-adjoint operators, as described in Sec. 43.5.1 on page 1540, and verify the appropriate boundary condition on the canonically deduced operator domain.

The sesquilinear form h_∞ on $L^2(\Lambda, \mathbb{C})$ corresponding to the Laplacian $-\Delta_\infty$ with *Dirichlet boundary condition* is defined by

$$h_\infty(\psi, \phi) := (\nabla \psi | \nabla \phi), \quad \forall \psi, \phi \in \text{dom}(h_\infty) := W_0^1(\Lambda, \mathbb{C}). \tag{44.2.1}$$

The sesquilinear form h_0 on $L^2(\Lambda, \mathbb{C})$ corresponding to the Laplacian $-\Delta_0$ with *Neumann boundary condition* is defined by

$$h_0(\psi, \phi) := (\nabla \psi | \nabla \phi), \quad \forall \psi, \phi \in \text{dom}(h_0) := W^1(\Lambda, \mathbb{C}). \tag{44.2.2}$$

Observe that the scalar product is in both cases that of $L^2(\Lambda, \mathbb{C})$ and that the only difference between the two sesquilinear forms lies in the altered domain of definition.

For mixed boundary conditions we suppose that $r \geq 2$ and that Λ is *interior* and at least piece-wise C^1-smooth (for unbounded Λ mixed boundary conditions are not so relevant). The boundary restriction $\psi \mapsto R\psi = \psi|_{\partial\Lambda}$ is a continuous operator from $W^1(\Lambda, \mathbb{C})$ into $W^{1/2}(\partial\Lambda, \mathbb{C})$ by Proposition 44.1-10. Thus the boundary sesquilinear form

$$b_\rho(\psi, \phi) := \int_{\partial\Lambda} \rho \, \overline{R\psi} \, R\phi \, dS \equiv \int_{\partial\Lambda} \rho \, \overline{\psi} \, \phi \, dS, \quad \forall \psi, \phi \in \text{dom}(b_\rho) := W^1(\Lambda, \mathbb{C}), \tag{44.2.3}$$

is well defined, where we require $\rho \in C^1(\bar{\Lambda}, \mathbb{C})$ with $\rho(x) \in [0, \infty[$ for all $x \in \partial\Lambda$, what implies the boundedness of ρ on $\bar{\Lambda}$ and thus on $\partial\Lambda$. (Note that for sufficiently smooth Λ every C^1-function on the boundary $\partial\Lambda$ may be extended — non-uniquely — to an element of $C^1(\bar{\Lambda}, \mathbb{C})$. For bounded ρ, the condition $R\psi, R\phi \in$

$W^{1/2}(\partial\Lambda, \mathbb{C})$ ensures then integrability in (44.2.3) also over an unbounded $\partial\Lambda$, what is not investigated further.)

Now the sesquilinear form h_ρ on $L^2(\Lambda, \mathbb{C})$ corresponding to the Laplacian $-\Delta_\rho$ with *mixed boundary conditions* is defined by the sum

$$h_\rho := h_0 + b_\rho, \qquad \text{dom}(h_\rho) := W^1(\Lambda, \mathbb{C}). \tag{44.2.4}$$

Proposition 44.2-1 (Existence of the Laplacians $-\Delta_\rho$). *Each sesquilinear form h_ρ from above is positive, closed, and unbounded. By Theorem 43.5-10 (a) on page 1543 there corresponds to h_ρ a unique (including the domain of definition $\text{dom}(-\Delta_\rho)$) self-adjoint operator $-\Delta_\rho$ on the Hilbert space $L^2(\Lambda, \mathbb{C})$ satisfying $\text{dom}(-\Delta_\rho) \subseteq \text{dom}(h_\rho)$ and $h_\rho(\psi, \phi) = (\psi|-\Delta_\rho\phi)$, $\forall\psi \in \text{dom}(h_\rho)$, $\forall\phi \in \text{dom}(-\Delta_\rho)$. We have $-\Delta_\rho \geq 0$, or equivalently, $\sigma(-\Delta_\rho) \subseteq [0, \infty[$ for its spectrum.*

Proof. [Sketch] For the constant functions $\rho \in \{0, \infty\}$ it is immediately checked that

$$h_\rho(\psi, \psi) + \|\psi\|^2 = \|\psi\|_1^2, \quad \forall\psi \in \text{dom}(h_\rho), \tag{44.2.5}$$

with the Sobolev norm $\|.\|_1$. Since $\text{dom}(h_\rho)$ is complete with respect to $\|.\|_1$ by Proposition 44.1-4, it follows that the form h_ρ is closed according to the definition given in Sec. 43.5.1.

Note that for interior Λ one has in the Dirichlet case $\rho = \infty$ a more stringent estimation than (44.2.5), namely

$$h_\infty(\psi, \psi) \geq c\|\psi\|_1^2, \quad \forall\psi \in \text{dom}(h_\infty) = W_0^1(\Lambda, \mathbb{C}), \tag{44.2.6}$$

with some constant $c > 0$ by the Poincaré estimate from Proposition 44.1-6(d).

For mixed boundary conditions ρ, we only note without proof that — by the continuity of the restriction map R — b_ρ is relatively bounded with respect to h_0, so that h_ρ is closed, too. $\qquad\square$

As an immediate consequence of the above proof it follows that each space, which is $\|.\|_1$-dense in $W_0^1(\Lambda, \mathbb{C})$ respectively $W^1(\Lambda, \mathbb{C})$, is a *form core* for h_ρ, but in general not for the Laplacian $-\Delta_\rho$ itself. Especially, $C_c^\infty(\Lambda, \mathbb{C})$ is a form core for h_∞. And if Λ possesses the segment property, then $C_c^\infty(\mathbb{R}^r, \mathbb{C})|_\Lambda$ is a form core for h_0. The latter is also valid for h_ρ with mixed boundary conditions, provided Λ is piece-wise C^1-smooth and interior.

Remark 44.2-2 (The Free Space Laplacian). In the case of $\Lambda = \mathbb{R}^r$, we have $h_0 = h_\infty$ by Proposition 44.1-6 (a). Hence in $\mathbb{R}^r$ there exists a *unique* self-adjoint Laplacian in $L^2(\mathbb{R}^r, \mathbb{C})$, which we denote by $-\Delta_{\mathbb{R}^r}$. The space $C_c^\infty(\mathbb{R}^r, \mathbb{C})$ is a core for $-\Delta_{\mathbb{R}^r}$.

By partial integration one immediately checks that the self-adjoint Laplacians $-\Delta_\rho$ act on twice continuously differentiable functions with compact support within

Λ by ordinary differentiation. But we note, if Λ is interior, then $C_c^2(\Lambda, \mathbb{C})$ is *not* a core for all the Laplacians $-\Delta_\rho$. Beside other things the following result ensures that the self-adjoint Laplacians $-\Delta_\rho$ on $L^2(\Lambda, \mathbb{C})$ indeed act on elements $\phi \in W^2(\Lambda, \mathbb{C}) \cap \mathrm{dom}(-\Delta_\rho)$ by weak differentiation (= differential operator Δ without index, cf. (44.1.4)),

$$-\Delta_\rho \phi = -\Delta \phi = -\sum_{j=1}^{r} \frac{\partial^2 \phi}{\partial x_j^2}, \quad \forall \phi \in W^2(\Lambda, \mathbb{C}) \cap \mathrm{dom}(-\Delta_\rho). \qquad (44.2.7)$$

For specific domains Λ (balls, cubes, etc.) this fact simplifies many applications, such as e.g., the search for eigenfunctions, or the search for concrete solutions ϕ of the abstract inhomogeneous Laplace equation $-\Delta_\rho \phi = \psi$ for given ψ.

Theorem 44.2-3 (Spectral Properties of Laplacians). *Let $\Lambda \subseteq \mathbb{R}^r$ be an arbitrary domain.*

(a) ***The Laplacian with Dirichlet Boundary Condition*** $-\Delta_\infty$: *It acts by twofold weak differentiation on the following Sobolev elements*

$$\mathrm{dom}(-\Delta_\infty) = \{\psi \in W_0^1(\Lambda, \mathbb{C}) \mid \nabla\psi \in W(\mathrm{div}; \Lambda, \mathbb{C}^r)\},$$
$$-\Delta_\infty \psi = -\nabla \cdot (\nabla\psi) = -\Delta\psi, \quad \forall \psi \in \mathrm{dom}(-\Delta_\infty).$$

This means nothing else than the existence of the product of the unbounded operators (introduced in Sec. 44.4 below)

$$-\Delta_\infty = -\,\mathrm{div}\,\mathrm{grad}_0,$$

where the domain of definition realizes the Dirichlet boundary condition.

- *If Λ is interior or exterior and piece-wise C^1-smooth, then $R\psi = \psi|_{\partial\Lambda} = 0$ for $\psi \in W_0^1(\Lambda, \mathbb{C})$ (by Proposition 44.1-10), expressing the Dirichlet boundary condition in terms of the boundary operator.*
- *If Λ is interior and C^2-smooth, then $\mathrm{dom}(-\Delta_\infty) = W_0^1(\Lambda, \mathbb{C}) \cap W^2(\Lambda, \mathbb{C})$.*
- *Provided Λ is interior (no smoothness necessary), then $-\Delta_\infty$ has a pure point spectrum accumulating only at infinity; more precisely, there exists an orthonormal basis $\{e_k \mid k \in \mathbb{N}\}$ of $L^2(\Lambda, \mathbb{C})$ of eigenvectors e_k for $-\Delta_\infty$ with associated eigenvalues $\lambda_k > 0$, $k \in \mathbb{N}$, (i.e., 0 is not an eigenvalue) satisfying*

$$0 < \lambda_1 \le \lambda_2 \le \lambda_3 \le \dots, \qquad \lim_{k \to \infty} \lambda_k = \infty. \qquad (44.2.8)$$

Every eigenspace of $-\Delta_\infty$ is of finite dimension, and $(-\Delta_\infty)^{-1}$ is a compact operator in $L^2(\Lambda, \mathbb{C})$.
- *If Λ is exterior (no smoothness necessary), then $-\Delta_\infty$ does not possess a point spectrum, it rather has a pure absolutely continuous spectrum given by $[0, \infty[$.*

(b) **The Laplacian with Neumann Boundary Condition** $-\Delta_0$: It acts by twofold weak differentiation on the following Sobolev elements

$$\mathrm{dom}(-\Delta_0) = \{\psi \in \mathrm{W}^1(\Lambda, \mathbb{C}) \mid \nabla\psi \in \mathrm{W}_0(\mathrm{div}; \Lambda, \mathbb{C}^r)\},$$
$$-\Delta_0\psi = -\nabla \cdot (\nabla\psi) = -\Delta\psi, \quad \forall\psi \in \mathrm{dom}(-\Delta_0).$$

This means nothing else than the existence of the product of the unbounded operators (described in Sec. 44.4 below)

$$-\Delta_0 = -\mathrm{div}_0\,\mathrm{grad},$$

where the domain of definition realizes the Neumann boundary condition, since div_0 requires vanishing normal component in its domain of definition.

- Provided $r \geq 2$ and Λ is interior or exterior and piece-wise C^1-smooth, then we have the explicit boundary condition $R_n\psi \equiv \frac{\partial\psi}{\partial n}|_{\partial\Lambda} = \nabla\psi \cdot n|_{\partial\Lambda} = 0$ for $\psi \in \mathrm{dom}(-\Delta_0)$.
- If Λ is interior with the segment property, then $-\Delta_0$ has a pure point spectrum accumulating only at infinity, where each eigenspace is finite-dimensional. Here, however, in contrast to the Dirichlet case, the lowest eigenvalue vanishes, i.e., $\lambda_1 = 0$, and the corresponding eigenspace is one dimensional and consists of the constant functions only. Thus, $\lambda_k > 0$ for the other eigenvalues, where the index runs through $k \geq 2$.
- If Λ is exterior with the segment property, then $-\Delta_0$ does not possess a point spectrum; it rather has an absolutely continuous spectrum covering all of $[0, \infty[$.

(c) **The Laplacian with Mixed Boundary Condition** $-\Delta_\rho$: Let $r \geq 2$, and suppose Λ to be interior and piece-wise C^1-smooth. Assume $\rho \in \mathrm{C}^1(\bar{\Lambda}, \mathbb{C})$ with $\rho(x) \in [0, \infty[$ for all $x \in \partial\Lambda$. Then $-\Delta_\rho$ acts by twofold weak differentiation only on a subspace of its domain,

$$\{\psi \in \mathrm{W}^2(\Lambda, \mathbb{C}) \mid \rho\psi + \tfrac{\partial\psi}{\partial n} = 0 \text{ on } \partial\Lambda\} = \mathrm{dom}(-\Delta_\rho) \cap \mathrm{W}^2(\Lambda, \mathbb{C}),$$
$$-\Delta_\rho\psi = -\Delta\psi, \quad \forall\psi \in \mathrm{dom}(-\Delta_\rho) \cap \mathrm{W}^2(\Lambda, \mathbb{C}).$$

The Laplacian $-\Delta_\rho$ has a pure positive point spectrum accumulating only at infinity, where again each eigenspace has finite multiplicity.

(d) **C-Realness:** Let C be the common complex conjugation in the Hilbert space $\mathrm{L}^2(\Lambda, \mathbb{C})$. Then all of the above Laplacians are C-real (see Sec. 43.7 on page 1553), implying for interior Λ that the eigenvectors may be chosen as $\mathbb{R}$-valued functions $e_k \in \mathrm{L}^2(\Lambda, \mathbb{R})$. (The projection on every eigenspace V commutes with C, and thus, $\mathrm{Re}(e) \in V$ and $\mathrm{Im}(e) \in V$ for every $e \in V$.)

Proof. [Sketch] We prove only some parts. We check first the Dirichlet and Neumann cases. By Proposition 44.4-2 on page 1585 the operators grad_0 and $-\mathrm{div}$ from Definition 44.4-1 are closed and adjoint to each other. Hence the operator product $-\mathrm{div}\,\mathrm{grad}_0 = \mathrm{grad}_0^*\,\mathrm{grad}_0$ is positive and self-adjoint in $\mathrm{L}^2(\Lambda, \mathbb{C})$, the domain of which is contained in $\text{dom}(h_\infty) = \text{dom}(\text{grad}_0)$. Now Theorem 43.5-10(a) ensures $-\Delta_\infty = -\text{div grad}_0$.

Analogously, $-\Delta_0 = -\text{div}_0 \text{grad} = \text{grad}^* \text{grad}$. $\nabla\psi \cdot n|_{\partial\Lambda} = \frac{\partial\psi}{\partial n}|_{\partial\Lambda} = 0$ for $\psi \in \text{dom}(-\Delta_0)$ follows with Eq. (44.1.12).

In all three cases the discrete spectra for interior Λ follow by means of the basic Proposition 43.5-11 on page 1544 since the identical embeddings of $W_0^1(\Lambda, \mathbb{C})$ and $W^1(\Lambda, \mathbb{C})$ into $L^2(\Lambda, \mathbb{C})$ are compact by the Propositions 44.1-6(g) and 44.1-8(d).

To characterize the domain of definition in case of a mixed boundary condition one starts with the sesquilinear form and applies Green's first formula to obtain

$$h_\rho(\psi, \phi) = (\psi| - \Delta\phi) + \int_{\partial\Lambda} \overline{\psi} \left(\rho\phi + \frac{\partial\phi}{\partial n} \right) dS$$

for all $\psi \in W^1(\Lambda, \mathbb{C})$ and all $\phi \in W^2(\Lambda, \mathbb{C})$. (Take first $\psi, \phi \in C^\infty(\bar{\Lambda}, \mathbb{C})$ and use then density arguments.) On the other hand, one has by the definition of $-\Delta_\rho$ that $h_\rho(\psi, \phi) = (\psi| - \Delta_\rho\phi)$ for $\psi \in W^1(\Lambda, \mathbb{C})$ and $\phi \in \text{dom}(-\Delta_\rho)$. Comparing both expressions of h_ρ proves the assertion, especially the boundary condition.

We show the C-realness. Because of $C\frac{\partial\psi}{\partial x_j} = \frac{\partial C\psi}{\partial x_j}$ it follows that $C(\text{dom}(h_\Lambda^\rho)) = \text{dom}(h_\Lambda^\rho)$. Moreover, $h_\rho(\psi, C\phi) = h_\rho(\phi, C\psi)$ and $(\psi|C\phi) = (\phi|C\psi)$. Thus we get for all $\psi, \phi \in \text{dom}(-\Delta_\rho) \subseteq \text{dom}(h_\rho)$,

$$(-\Delta_\rho\psi|C\phi) = h_\rho(\psi, C\phi) = h_\rho(\phi, C\psi) = (-\Delta_\rho\phi|C\psi) = (\psi| - C\Delta_\rho\phi).$$

From the definition of the adjoint $(-\Delta_\rho)^*$ (note $-\Delta_\rho$ is self-adjoint), we conclude that $C\phi \in \text{dom}(-\Delta_\rho)$ and thus $C(\text{dom}(-\Delta_\rho)) \subseteq \text{dom}(-\Delta_\rho)$, and $-\Delta_\rho C \supseteq -C\Delta_\rho$. Now use $C^2 = \mathbb{1}$ to obtain $C(-\text{dom}(\Delta_\rho)) = \text{dom}(-\Delta_\rho)$ and $-\Delta_\rho C = -C\Delta_\rho$. $\square$

Let us state a conclusion which refers to peculiarities of L^2-spaces, in which the boundary conditions are not valid in the naive sense, but are rather blurred.

Conclusion 44.2-4 (Basis Systems with Boundary Conditions). As a remarkable consequence of the above Theorem, it follows for interior (sufficiently smooth) Λ — for which $-\Delta_\rho$ has a pure point spectrum — that $\{(1 + \lambda_k)^{-1/2}e_k \mid k \in \mathbb{N}\}$ constitutes an orthonormal basis of the Sobolev Hilbert space $\text{dom}(h_\rho)$ with respect to the Sobolev inner product $(.|.)_1$.

Let us also draw an important conclusion for Dirichlet Laplacians in interior domains Λ. If we know that ψ is contained in the domain of $-\Delta_\infty$, then it vanishes on $\partial\Lambda$ (in the generalized sense, $R\psi = 0$, when no further smoothness properties for ϕ are specified). Since by the above Theorem $-\Delta_\infty$ does not possess the eigenvalue 0, it follows that $-\Delta_\infty\psi = 0$ implies $\psi = 0$.

Conclusion 44.2-5 (Uniqueness of Harmonic Functions). A solution $\phi \in C(\bar{\Lambda}, \mathbb{C}) \cap C^2(\Lambda, \mathbb{C})$ of $\Delta\phi = 0$ under some boundary condition is called a *harmonic function* on Λ.

Now let Λ be an interior domain. If two harmonic functions ϕ, ξ on Λ have the same boundary values, then $\phi - \xi \in \mathrm{dom}(-\Delta_\infty)$ with $-\Delta_\infty(\phi - \xi) = 0$, and thus $\phi = \xi$ which via continuity means $\phi(x) = \xi(x)$ for all $x \in \bar{\Lambda}$. That is, the harmonic functions are uniquely determined by their boundary values and are intimately connected with the geometry of the cavity Λ.

Without proof let us mention in this connection a further property: Each harmonic function on an interior Λ assumes its minimum and its maximum on the boundary $\partial\Lambda$.

44.2.2.   *Regularity of Solutions and Comparison of Eigenvalues in an Interior Domain*

As a classical result on the regularity of solutions in dependence of the smoothness of the inhomogeneous term we refer first *Weyl's lemma*. It concerns the Laplacian $\Delta = \sum_{j=1}^{r} \frac{\partial^2}{\partial x_j^2}$ in an arbitrary interior domain $\Lambda \subset \mathbb{R}^r$: Let be given $\phi \in C^m(\Lambda, \mathbb{C})$ and assume one has found a locally square integrable function $\psi : \Lambda \to \mathbb{C}$ which is a weak solution of the inhomogeneous equation $-\Delta\psi = \phi$, that is,

$$\int_\Lambda (-\Delta\bar{\varphi})\psi \, d^r x = \int_\Lambda \bar{\varphi}\phi \, d^r x, \quad \forall \varphi \in C_c^\infty(\Lambda, \mathbb{C}).$$

Then it follows that $\psi \in C^{m+2}(\Lambda, \mathbb{C})$.

Weyl's lemma does not tell anything about the behavior of the solution ψ at the boundary $\partial\Lambda$, nor about its square integrability. For stronger regularity statements one needs a smooth boundary.

Proposition 44.2-6 (Regularity Properties). *Let $\Lambda \subset \mathbb{R}^r$ be interior and C^{m+2}-smooth with $m \in \mathbb{N}_0$. For $\phi \in W^m(\Lambda, \mathbb{C})$ let $\psi \in \mathrm{dom}(h_\rho)$ be the weak solution of the inhomogeneous Laplace equation $-\Delta_\rho\psi = \phi$, that is, we have*

$$h_\rho(\varphi, \psi) = (\varphi|\phi), \quad \forall \varphi \in \mathrm{dom}(h_\rho).$$

Then it follows that $\psi \in W^{m+2}(\Lambda, \mathbb{C})$.

The above result has various consequences, especially on the regularity of eigenfunctions.

Corollary 44.2-7 (Regular Eigenfunctions). *Let $\Lambda \subset \mathbb{R}^3$ (i.e., $r = 3$) be interior and C^{m+2}-smooth with $m \in \mathbb{N}_0$. Then the eigenfunctions e_k of $-\Delta_\rho$ are contained in $W^{m+2}(\Lambda, \mathbb{C}) \cap \mathrm{dom}(h_\rho)$, implying $e_k \in C^m(\bar{\Lambda}, \mathbb{C})$ by Proposition 44.1-6 (h) on page 1564.*

The following result, comparing the eigenvalues of the different Laplacians for a fixed interior domain Λ, follows from the basic Proposition 43.5-11(b).

Proposition 44.2-8. *For $r \geq 2$ let Λ be interior and piece-wise C^1-smooth. Moreover, let $\rho_1, \rho_2 \in C^1(\bar{\Lambda}, \mathbb{C})$ with $0 \leq \rho_1(x) \leq \rho_2(x)$ for all $x \in \partial\Lambda$. By $(\lambda_k^\rho)_{k \in \mathbb{N}}$ we denote the eigenvalues of $-\Delta_\rho$ in increasing order (repeated according to their multiplicity). Then*

$$0 \leq \lambda_k^0 \leq \lambda_k^{\rho_1} \leq \lambda_k^{\rho_2} \leq \lambda_k^\infty, \quad \forall k \in \mathbb{N}.$$

The estimation $\lambda_k^0 \leq \lambda_k^\infty$ for all $k \in \mathbb{N}$ is valid under the weaker smoothness property of Λ being interior with the segment property in $\mathbb{R}^r$ (here also $r = 1$ is allowed).

44.2.3.   Dirichlet Laplacians in Interior Domains

We refer here some results from the literature without proof. Since we treat different domains Λ, we use here only the index Λ and write $-\Delta_\Lambda$ for the Dirichlet Laplacian and h_Λ for the associated form.

According to Proposition 44.1-6(f), we have the continuous embedding

$$W_0^1(\Lambda, \mathbb{C}) \subseteq W_0^m(\Omega, \mathbb{C}), \quad \Lambda \subseteq \Omega,$$

when each $\phi \in W_0^m(\Lambda, \mathbb{C})$ is extended by zero to a unique element of $W_0^m(\Omega, \mathbb{C})$. Consequently, the form h_Λ extends trivially to a form on $L^2(\Omega, \mathbb{C})$. The following result compares the eigenvalues of the Dirichlet Laplacians in different interior domains; it is proved similarly to Proposition 43.5-11(b) with the min–max principle [RS78].

Proposition 44.2-9. *Suppose two interior domains Λ and Ω of $\mathbb{R}^r$ with $\Lambda \subseteq \Omega$. By $(\lambda_k^\Lambda)_{k \in \mathbb{N}}$ respectively $(\lambda_k^\Omega)_{k \in \mathbb{N}}$, we denote the increasingly ordered eigenvalues (repeated according to their multiplicity) of the Dirichlet Laplacians $-\Delta_\Lambda$ respectively $-\Delta_\Omega$. Then*

$$\lambda_k^\Lambda \geq \lambda_k^\Omega, \quad \forall k \in \mathbb{N}. \tag{44.2.9}$$

In case of $\bar{\Lambda} \subseteq \Omega$, the inequalities in (44.2.9) are proper, i.e., $\lambda_k^\Lambda > \lambda_k^\Omega$ for all $k \in \mathbb{N}$.

For a physical illustration of the preceding eigenvalue relations assume that, up to a constant factor, $\omega_k := \sqrt{\lambda_k}$ is the kth eigenfrequency of an oscillating object (like the string of a guitar or the membrane of a drum), which is fixed at its boundary (Dirichlet boundary condition). Then the above result predicts that the smaller object oscillates with higher frequencies.

Let us finally refer some geometric properties of eigenvalues and eigenfunctions of the Laplacian $-\Delta_\Lambda$ with the Dirichlet boundary condition, where Λ is interior.

Proposition 44.2-10 (Geometric Properties). *Let Λ be a C^2-smooth interior domain in $\mathbb{R}^r$. We consider the Dirichlet Laplacian $-\Delta_\Lambda$ with eigenfunctions e_k and eigenvalues λ_k, $k \in \mathbb{N}$, ordered increasingly and repeated according to their multiplicity.*

(a) *The lowest eigenvalue $\lambda_1 > 0$ is given in the form $\lambda_1 = p(\Lambda)^{-2}$, where the purely geometric Poincaré constant $p(\Lambda)$ is defined by*

$$p(\Lambda)^2 = \sup\{\|\psi\|^2/h_\Lambda(\psi, \psi) \mid 0 \neq \psi \in W_0^1(\Lambda, \mathbb{C})\}.$$

Note that by means of the Poincaré estimate in Proposition 44.1-6(d) there exists a constant $c > 0$ (only dependent from the diameter of Λ) such that $c^{-1}\|\psi\|_1^2 \leq h_\Lambda(\psi, \psi) \leq \|\psi\|_1^2$ for all $\psi \in W_0^1(\Lambda, \mathbb{C})$. This ensures that $h_\Lambda(.,.)^{1/2}$ defines a norm in $W_0^1(\Lambda, \mathbb{C})$ equivalent to the Sobolev norm $\|.\|_1$. So $\lambda_1 = p(\Lambda)^{-2}$ gives the infimum over all these constants c, and hence the best Poincaré estimation.

(b) *The eigenspace corresponding to the lowest eigenvalue $\lambda_1 > 0$ is one-dimensional. An associated eigenfunction e_1 satisfies $e_1(x) \neq 0$ for all $x \in \Lambda$, but e_1 vanishes on the boundary $\partial\Lambda$ i.e., $Re_1 = e_1|_{\partial\Lambda} = 0$.*

(c) *For every $k \in \mathbb{N}$, the eigenfunction e_k has at most k different knot regions, where a knot region is defined as a maximal (connected) subdomain of Λ with $\{x \in \Lambda \mid e_k(x) \neq 0\}$.*

(d) *The r-dimensional volume $|\Lambda|$ of Λ may be gained as the limit*

$$|\Lambda| = \frac{(2\pi)^r}{|B_1|} \lim_{k \to \infty} \frac{k}{\lambda_k^{r/2}},$$

where $|B_1|$ is the volume of the r-dimensional unit ball $B_1 := \{x \in \mathbb{R}^r \mid |x| < 1\}$. That means that the volume of Λ can be calculated from the spectrum $\sigma(-\Delta_\Lambda) = \{\lambda_k \mid k \in \mathbb{N}\}$ (see [BH76]).

(e) *Let $B_R := \{x \in \mathbb{R}^r \mid |x| < R\}$ be the ball in $\mathbb{R}^r$, for which the radius $R > 0$ is chosen so that $|\Lambda| = |B_R|$ for the volume of the given r-dimensional Λ. Then it holds for the smallest eigenvalues λ_1^Λ respectively $\lambda_1^{B_R}$ of the Dirichlet Laplacians $-\Delta_\Lambda$ respectively $-\Delta_{B_R}$ that $\lambda_1^\Lambda \geq \lambda_1^{B_R}$.*

Part (c) is due to Courant, and part (d) is known as *Weyl's asymptotic formula*.

44.2.4. *Dirichlet and Neumann Laplacians for Parallelepipeds*

For fixed $a = (a_1, \ldots, a_r) \in \mathbb{R}^r$ with $a_j > 0$ let us consider in the present section the rectangular r-dimensional, open parallelepiped

$$\Lambda_a := \{x \in \mathbb{R}^r \mid -a_j < x_j < a_j, \, j = 1, \ldots, r\} =]-a_1, a_1[\times \cdots \times]-a_r, a_r[,$$
$$\text{(44.2.10)}$$

where $r \in \mathbb{N}$. Its volume is $|\Lambda_a| = 2^r a_1 \cdots a_r$. Obviously, Λ_a is bounded with a piece-wise C^∞-smooth boundary $\partial \Lambda_a$ including the uniform cone property.

According to Theorem 44.2-3, the Laplacians with Dirichlet and Neumann boundary conditions in $L^2(\Lambda_a, \mathbb{C})$, $-\Delta_\infty$ respectively $-\Delta_0$, have purely discrete spectra. Using the fact that the abstract Hilbert space Laplacians act by ordinary respectively weak differentiation as in Eq. (44.2.7), explicit calculations lead to the following spectral results. (Compare also with Example 4.4.5 on page 75 for $r = 3$.) For a concrete handling it is more useful to label the eigenvectors and eigenvalues by multi indices $n = (n_1, \ldots, n_r)$ from $\mathbb{N}^r$, or $\mathbb{N}_0^r$, respectively $\mathbb{Z}^r$, instead of using natural numbers $k \in \mathbb{N}$.

Laplacian $-\Delta_\infty$ with Dirichlet Boundary Condition

The eigenvectors of $-\Delta_\infty$, which constitute an orthonormal basis of $L^2(\Lambda_a, \mathbb{C})$, are given by functions $e_n \in \{\psi \in C^\infty(\bar{\Lambda}_a, \mathbb{R}) \mid \psi = 0 \text{ on } \partial \Lambda_a\}$ where $n = (n_1, \ldots, n_r) \in \mathbb{N}^r$ and

$$e_n(x) = \prod_{j=1}^r a_j^{-1/2} \phi_{n_j}(x_j/a_j), \quad \forall x = (x_1, \ldots, x_r) \in \Lambda_a.$$

Here, we have defined for $y \in \mathbb{R}$

$$\phi_k(y) := \cos(k\pi y/2), \quad \text{for} \quad k = 1, 3, 5, \ldots,$$
$$\phi_k(y) := \sin(k\pi y/2), \quad \text{for} \quad k = 2, 4, 6, \ldots.$$

The eigenvalue λ_n of e_n, $n \in \mathbb{N}^r$, is

$$\lambda_n = \frac{\pi^2}{4} \sum_{j=1}^r \frac{n_j^2}{a_j^2}. \tag{44.2.11}$$

Laplacian $-\Delta_0$ with Neumann Boundary Condition

The orthonormal eigenbasis of $-\Delta_0$ in $L^2(\Lambda_a, \mathbb{C})$ is given in terms of functions $e_n \in \{\psi \in C^\infty(\bar{\Lambda}_a, \mathbb{R}) \mid \frac{\partial \psi}{\partial n} = 0 \text{ on } \partial \Lambda_a\}$, $n = (n_1, \ldots, n_r) \in \mathbb{N}_0^r$, with

$$e_n(x) = \prod_{j=1}^r a_j^{-1/2} \psi_{n_j}(x_j/a_j), \quad \forall x = (x_1, \ldots, x_r) \in \Lambda_a.$$

Here, we have defined for $y \in \mathbb{R}$

$$\psi_0(y) := \tfrac{1}{2}\sqrt{2}, \quad \text{for} \quad k = 0,$$
$$\psi_k(y) := \sin(k\pi y/2), \quad \text{for} \quad k = 1, 3, 5, \ldots,$$
$$\psi_k(y) := \cos(k\pi y/2), \quad \text{for} \quad k = 2, 4, 6, \ldots.$$

The eigenvalue λ_n corresponding to e_n, $n \in \mathbb{N}_0^r$, is again determined by Eq. (44.2.11). For a proof of the two cases, observe that for all $k, l \in \mathbb{N}$, respectively

$k, l \in \mathbb{N}_0$, one has

$$\int_{-a_j}^{a_j} \phi_k(x_j/a_j)\phi_l(x_j/a_j)\,dx_j = a_j\delta_{k,l} = \int_{-a_j}^{a_j} \psi_k(x_j/a_j)\psi_l(x_j/a_j)\,dx_j$$

with the Kronecker delta, $\delta_{k,l} = 0$ for $k \neq l$ and $\delta_{k,l} = 1$ for $k = l$.

For further spectral properties in finite cavities Λ we refer again to [BH76].

44.3. Thermodynamic Limits of Dirichlet Laplacians

In this section, we are concerned with mathematical details for the problem, in how far the excitations and equilibrium states of a vibrating system, described by the negative Dirichlet Laplacian, respectively by its square root (for light), become independent of the shape of the volume in approaching the infinite volume limit (thermodynamic limit). Mathematically this requires convergence estimations for nets of unbounded, self-adjoint operators, which commonly are formulated in terms of bounded functions of these operators.

For the domain $\Lambda \subseteq \mathbb{R}^r$ the Laplacian with Dirichlet boundary condition is denoted (again) by $-\Delta_\Lambda$ (cf. Proposition 44.2-1); it is a positive, self-adjoint operator on $L^2(\Lambda, \mathbb{C})$. Recall that, for interior Λ, we have $-\Delta_\Lambda \geq \lambda_1^\Lambda \mathbb{1}$ with its smallest eigenvalue $\lambda_1^\Lambda > 0$. This especially implies that $\mathbb{1} - \exp\{-\beta\sqrt{-\Delta_\Lambda}\}$ and its inverse, as well as $\exp\{-\beta\sqrt{-\Delta_\Lambda}\}$ are bounded self-adjoint operators on $L^2(\Lambda, \mathbb{C})$ for each $\beta > 0$. In agreement with Remark 44.2-2, the unique Laplacian in $L^2(\mathbb{R}^r, \mathbb{C})$ is denoted by $-\Delta_{\mathbb{R}^r}$.

Notational Remark 44.3-1 (Trivial Extension from Λ to $\mathbb{R}^r$). Without changing the notation, we extend $-\Delta_\Lambda$ trivially to an operator on $L^2(\mathbb{R}^r, \mathbb{C})$ by means of the identification

$$-\Delta_\Lambda \equiv -\Delta_\Lambda \oplus 0\,, \quad \text{acting in} \quad L^2(\mathbb{R}^r, \mathbb{C}) = L^2(\Lambda, \mathbb{C}) \oplus L^2(\mathbb{R}^r \backslash \Lambda, \mathbb{C})\,.$$

In this way, we subsequently treat $-\Delta_\Lambda$ always as a positive, self-adjoint operator on the Hilbert space $L^2(\mathbb{R}^r, \mathbb{C})$. Observe, by means of this extension, 0 becomes a — let us say — artificial spectral value of $-\Delta_\Lambda$, arising from its trivial part 0 on the orthogonal complement $L^2(\mathbb{R}^r \backslash \Lambda, \mathbb{C})$.

Consequently, for an arbitrary Borel measurable function $u : [0, \infty[\to \mathbb{C}$, we obtain from the spectral calculus that

$$u(-\Delta_\Lambda) = u(-\Delta_\Lambda)P_\Lambda + u(0)(\mathbb{1} - P_\Lambda)\,, \quad \text{in} \quad L^2(\mathbb{R}^r, \mathbb{C}) = L^2(\Lambda, \mathbb{C}) \oplus L^2(\mathbb{R}^r \backslash \Lambda, \mathbb{C})\,.$$

Here, P_Λ is the orthogonal projection of $L^2(\mathbb{R}^r, \mathbb{C})$ onto the sub-Hilbert space $L^2(\Lambda, \mathbb{C})$, and hence $\mathbb{1} - P_\Lambda$ is the projection onto the orthogonal complement $L^2(\mathbb{R}^r \backslash \Lambda, \mathbb{C})$. The original operator on $L^2(\Lambda, \mathbb{C})$ is recovered by the part $u(-\Delta_\Lambda)P_\Lambda$.

In the subsequent exposition, we take over from [HH92a] and [HH92b] some results for thermodynamic limits of the type

$$\lim_{\Lambda \to \mathbb{R}^r} u(-\Delta_\Lambda) = ?, \quad \text{involving certain functions } u : [0, \infty[\to \mathbb{C}.$$

These works were performed for discussing the quantum mechanical black body radiation. But in our present elaboration we add some results appropriate for the classical black body radiation.

For describing the different possibilities of thermodynamic limits $\Lambda \to \mathbb{R}^r$ we introduce the following notions, consecutively ordered according to increasing strength.

Definition 44.3-2 (Nets of Interior Domains).

(a) Let $\mathcal{N}$ be a collection of interior domains $\Lambda \subset \mathbb{R}^r$, ordered by inclusion. $\mathcal{N}$ is called an *absorbing net* in $\mathbb{R}^r$, if for each bounded subset $M \subset \mathbb{R}^r$ there exists a $\Lambda \in \mathcal{N}$ with $M \subseteq \Lambda$.

(b) An absorbing net $\mathcal{N}_s$ is said to possess the *segment property*, if each $\Lambda \in \mathcal{N}_s$ has the segment property (indicated by the index "s").

(c) Let $\Sigma \subset \mathbb{R}^r$ be an interior domain and $x \in \mathbb{R}^r$. Then the collection

$$\mathcal{N}_\Sigma^x := \{\mu(\Sigma - x) \mid \mu \in [1, \infty[\},$$

of bounded domains of $\mathbb{R}^r$ is called a *monotonously dilated net* for Σ with stretching (fix) point $x \in \mathbb{R}^r$ (where $\mu(\Sigma - x) := \{\mu(y - x) \mid y \in \Sigma\}$). Note, the family $\mathcal{N}_\Sigma^x$ is an absorbing net if and only if $x \in \Sigma$.

We write $\lim_{\Lambda \in \mathcal{N}} \dots$, or $\lim_{\Lambda \in \mathcal{N}_s} \dots$, respectively $\lim_{\Lambda \in \mathcal{N}_\Sigma^x} \dots := \lim_{\lambda \to \infty} \dots$ for the associated net limits.

The function space $C_b([0, \infty[, \mathbb{C})$ consists of the bounded continuous functions on $[0, \infty[$; it is equipped with the supremum norm $\|u\|_{\sup} = \sup\{|u(\lambda)| \mid \lambda \in [0, \infty[\}$.

Proposition 44.3-3 (Strong Resolvent Limit). *For each absorbing net $\mathcal{N}$ in $\mathbb{R}^r$ it holds in the strong resolvent sense*

$$\text{srs-}\lim_{\Lambda \in \mathcal{N}}(-\Delta_\Lambda) = -\Delta_{\mathbb{R}^r}, \quad \text{srs-}\lim_{\Lambda \in \mathcal{N}} \sqrt{-\Delta_\Lambda} = \sqrt{-\Delta_{\mathbb{R}^r}}, \quad \text{in } L^2(\mathbb{R}^r, \mathbb{C}).$$

Thus $\lim_{\Lambda \in \mathcal{N}} u(-\Delta_\Lambda) = u(-\Delta_{\mathbb{R}^r})$ *in the strong operator topology for each* $u \in C_b([0, \infty[, \mathbb{C})$.

Proof. Let $\xi \in C_c^\infty(\mathbb{R}^r, \mathbb{C})$. Since $\mathcal{N}$ is absorbing, there exists an interior $\Lambda_\xi \in \mathcal{N}$ containing the compact support of ξ. Consequently, $\xi \in \text{dom}(-\Delta_\Lambda)$ for every $\Lambda \supseteq \Lambda_\xi$ and

$$-\Delta_\Lambda \xi = -\sum_{j=1}^r \frac{\partial^2 \xi}{\partial x_j^2} = -\Delta_{\mathbb{R}^r} \xi, \quad \forall \Lambda \supseteq \Lambda_\xi \supset \text{supp}(\xi),$$

that is $\| - \Delta_\Lambda \xi + \Delta_{\mathbb{R}^r} \xi \| = 0$ for each $\Lambda \supseteq \Lambda_\xi$. On the other side, $C_c^\infty(\mathbb{R}^r, \mathbb{C})$ is a core for the free space Laplacian $-\Delta_{\mathbb{R}^r}$, cf. Remark 44.2-2. Thus the sufficiency criterion (a) of Proposition 43.6-5 is fulfilled, implying srs–$\lim_\Lambda(-\Delta_\Lambda) = -\Delta_{\mathbb{R}^r}$.

By Proposition 43.6-6, this is equivalent to $\lim_\Lambda u(-\Delta_\Lambda) = u(-\Delta_{\mathbb{R}^r})$ strongly for every $u \in C_b([0, \infty[, \mathbb{C})$, especially for $u(\sqrt{.}\,)$, yielding the result. $\qquad\square$

The following trace class properties for certain functions of our Dirichlet Laplacians are deduced in [HH92a] with help of so-called "positivity preservation" of operators of type $\exp\{-\beta\sqrt{-\Delta_\Lambda}\}$. We state them to give the reader an impression of how complex the connections between the local Laplacians $-\Delta_\Lambda$, Λ interior, and the limiting Laplacian $-\Delta_{\mathbb{R}^r}$ are. We simply denote by $|\Omega|$ the r-dimensional volume of an interior $\Omega \subset \mathbb{R}^r$.

Lemma 44.3-4 (Trace Class Properties). *Let Λ and Ω be arbitrary interior domains of $\mathbb{R}^r$, but Λ with segment property. Then for each $u \in C_b([0, \infty[, \mathbb{C})$ and every $\beta > 0$ the following operators are of trace class on $L^2(\mathbb{R}^r, \mathbb{C})$ and fulfill the estimations*

$$\|P_\Omega P_\Lambda \exp\{-\beta\sqrt{-\Delta_\Lambda}\} P_\Lambda P_\Omega\|_{\mathrm{tr}} \le \|P_\Omega \exp\{-\beta\sqrt{-\Delta_{\mathbb{R}^r}}\} P_\Omega\|_{\mathrm{tr}} = c\frac{|\Omega|}{\beta^r},$$

$$\|P_\Omega u(\sqrt{-\Delta_{\mathbb{R}^r}}) \exp\{-\beta\sqrt{-\Delta_{\mathbb{R}^r}}\} P_\Omega\|_{\mathrm{tr}} \le 4\|u\|_{\sup}\|P_\Omega \exp\{-\beta\sqrt{-\Delta_{\mathbb{R}^r}}\} P_\Omega\|_{\mathrm{tr}},$$

$$\|P_\Omega P_\Lambda u(\sqrt{-\Delta_\Lambda})\exp\{-\beta\sqrt{-\Delta_\Lambda}\} P_\Lambda P_\Omega\|_{\mathrm{tr}} \le 4\|u\|_{\sup}\|P_\Omega P_\Lambda\exp\{-\beta\sqrt{-\Delta_\Lambda}\} P_\Lambda P_\Omega\|_{\mathrm{tr}}.$$

Here $\|.\|_{\mathrm{tr}}$ denotes the trace norm in $L^2(\mathbb{R}^r, \mathbb{C})$, and $c := (2^r/\pi)^{1/2}\, \Gamma((r+1)/2)$ with Γ meaning the Gamma function.

Let us mention that one may choose u of type $u(\lambda) = v(\lambda)\exp\{-\kappa\lambda\}$ for some $\kappa > 0$ with a possibly unbounded continuous function $v : [0, \infty[\to \mathbb{C}$ such as e.g., a polynomial.

Suppose in the above Lemma $\Lambda = \Omega$ to be interior with the segment property, then

$$\|P_\Lambda u(\sqrt{-\Delta_\Lambda})\exp\{-m\beta\sqrt{-\Delta_\Lambda}\} P_\Lambda\|_{\mathrm{tr}} \le 4\|u\|_{\sup}\, c\frac{|\Lambda|}{\beta^r}\frac{1}{m^r}, \quad \forall \beta > 0, \quad \forall m \in \mathbb{N}.$$

But $\sum_m \frac{1}{m^r} < \infty$ for $r \ge 2$, thus for all $\alpha, \beta > 0$ and $u \in C_b([0, \infty[, \mathbb{C})$, we have that

$$\sum_{m=0}^\infty P_\Lambda u(\sqrt{-\Delta_\Lambda})\exp\{-\alpha\sqrt{-\Delta_\Lambda}\}\exp\{-m\beta\sqrt{-\Delta_\Lambda}\} P_\Lambda$$

$$= P_\Lambda u(\sqrt{-\Delta_\Lambda})\exp\{-\alpha\sqrt{-\Delta_\Lambda}\}(\mathbb{1} - \exp\{-\beta\sqrt{-\Delta_\Lambda}\})^{-1} P_\Lambda$$

converges with respect to the trace norm, leading to a trace class operator in $L^2(\mathbb{R}^r, \mathbb{C})$. The term $\exp\{-\alpha\sqrt{-\Delta_\Lambda}\}$ is involved to ensure the trace class property for $m = 0$. This trace class property is the reason why in our subsequent result we have to assume $r \ge 2$.

By means of the foregoing trace relations and estimations we arrive at the following limiting results (generalizing those of [HH92a] and [HH92b]).

Summary 44.3-5 (Thermodynamic Limits). Let $r \geq 2$, and suppose $\alpha, \beta > 0$.

(a) Let $u_k \in C_b([0, \infty[, \mathbb{C})$ and $\psi_k \in L^2(\mathbb{R}^r, \mathbb{C})$ for $k \in \{1, \ldots, n\}$ for some $n \in \mathbb{N}$. Then it follows for every interior domain $\Omega \subset \mathbb{R}^r$ and each absorbing net $\mathcal{N}_s$ in $\mathbb{R}^r$ with segment property that

$$\lim_{\Lambda \in \mathcal{N}_s} \Big\| \sum_{k=1}^{n} u_k(\sqrt{-\Delta_\Lambda})(\mathbb{1} - \exp\{-\beta\sqrt{-\Delta_\Lambda}\})^{-1/2} P_\Lambda P_\Omega \psi_k \Big\|$$

$$= \Big\| \sum_{k=1}^{n} u_k(\sqrt{-\Delta_{\mathbb{R}^r}})(\mathbb{1} - \exp\{-\beta\sqrt{-\Delta_{\mathbb{R}^r}}\})^{-1/2} P_\Omega \psi_k \Big\|,$$

$$\lim_{\Lambda \in \mathcal{N}_s} \Big\| \sum_{k=1}^{n} u_k(\sqrt{-\Delta_\Lambda}) \sqrt{-\Delta_\Lambda}^{-1/2} P_\Lambda P_\Omega \psi_k \Big\|$$

$$= \Big\| \sum_{k=1}^{n} u_k(\sqrt{-\Delta_{\mathbb{R}^r}}) \sqrt{-\Delta_{\mathbb{R}^r}}^{-1/2} P_\Omega \psi_k \Big\|.$$

Here $P_\Omega \psi$ is contained in the domains of both unbounded self-adjoint operators $(\mathbb{1} - \exp\{-\beta\sqrt{-\Delta_{\mathbb{R}^r}}\})^{-1/2}$ and $\sqrt{-\Delta_{\mathbb{R}^r}}^{-1/2}$ for all $\psi \in \mathcal{H}$ and any interior Ω.

(b) Let Σ be an interior domain of $\mathbb{R}^r$ with segment property, such that its boundary $\partial\Sigma$ is a zero set with respect to the r-dimensional Lebesgue measure, and consider the monotonously dilated net $\mathcal{N}_\Sigma^x$ with stretching point $x \in \mathbb{R}^r$. Then it follows for each $u \in C_b([0, \infty[, \mathbb{C})$ that

$$\lim_{\Lambda \in \mathcal{N}_\Sigma^x} \frac{1}{|\Lambda|} \operatorname{tr}\Big[P_\Lambda u(\sqrt{-\Delta_\Lambda}) \exp\{-\alpha\sqrt{-\Delta_\Lambda}\} (\mathbb{1} - \exp\{-\beta\sqrt{-\Delta_\Lambda}\})^{-1} P_\Lambda \Big]$$

$$= \frac{r|B_1|}{(2\pi)^r} \int_0^\infty u(\lambda)\, \lambda^{r-1} \frac{\exp\{-\alpha\lambda\}}{1 - \exp\{-\beta\lambda\}}\, d\lambda,$$

$$\lim_{\Lambda \in \mathcal{N}_\Sigma^x} \frac{1}{|\Lambda|} \operatorname{tr}\Big[P_\Lambda u(\sqrt{-\Delta_\Lambda}) \exp\{-\alpha\sqrt{-\Delta_\Lambda}\} \sqrt{-\Delta_\Lambda}^{-1} P_\Lambda \Big]$$

$$= \frac{r|B_1|}{(2\pi)^r} \int_0^\infty u(\lambda)\, \lambda^{r-2} \exp\{-\alpha\lambda\}\, d\lambda.$$

Here, the operators $\#$ in the expressions $\operatorname{tr}[\#]$ are of trace class for any interior domain Λ possessing the segment property by the previous arguments (note, $\sqrt{-\Delta_\Lambda}^{-1}$ is bounded). $|B_1|$ means the volume of the unit ball $B_1 := \{x \in \mathbb{R}^r \mid |x| < 1\}$. Observe, the limits are independent of the stretching point $x \in \mathbb{R}^r$ and of Σ.

Proof. [Hint] In each part the first limit formula (including $\mathbb{1} - \exp\{-\beta\sqrt{-\Delta_\Lambda}\}$) follows similarly as in [HH92a] and [HH92b]. For proving the second formula, respectively, note that $u_0 \in C_b([0, \infty[, \mathbb{C})$ for $u_0(\lambda) := (1 - \exp\{-\beta\lambda\})/\lambda$, $\lambda \geq 0$.

Replacing in the first formula, respectively, u_k in part (a) by $u_k u_0^{1/2}$ and u in part (b) by $u u_0$ leads then to the stated second formula. $\square$

44.4.   The Grad, Div, and Curl Operators

As in Sec. 44.1, we deal here with general Euclidean dimension $r \geq 2$, but automatically set $r = 3$ when considering the curl operator.

In the defining equations below we employ the ∇ operator in certain, previously introduced Sobolev spaces as domains, where it exists in the weak sense. The domains imply L^2-properties for the (weak) first-order derivatives and express certain boundary conditions (cf. Sec. 44.1); the subscript 0 indicates the vanishing of certain derivatives on the boundary in the generalized sense of Sobolev spaces.

Definition 44.4-1 (Vectorial Differential Operators).   The concise definition of the vectorial differential operators, as densely defined operators from L^2-Hilbert spaces into (in general different) L^2-Hilbert spaces, is given as follows:

$$\text{grad}_0\colon \text{dom}(\text{grad}_0) := W_0^1(\Lambda, \mathbb{C}) \subset L^2(\Lambda, \mathbb{C}) \longrightarrow L^2(\Lambda, \mathbb{C}^r),\ \text{grad}_0\,\varphi := \nabla\varphi,$$
$$\text{grad}\colon \text{dom}(\text{grad}) := W^1(\Lambda, \mathbb{C}) \subset L^2(\Lambda, \mathbb{C}) \longrightarrow L^2(\Lambda, \mathbb{C}^r),\ \text{grad}\,\varphi := \nabla\varphi.$$

$$\text{div}_0\colon \text{dom}(\text{div}_0) := W_0(\text{div}; \Lambda, \mathbb{C}^r) \subset L^2(\Lambda, \mathbb{C}^r) \longrightarrow L^2(\Lambda, \mathbb{C}),\ \ \text{div}_0\,\phi := \nabla \cdot \phi,$$
$$\text{div}\colon \text{dom}(\text{div}) := W(\text{div}; \Lambda, \mathbb{C}^r) \subset L^2(\Lambda, \mathbb{C}^r) \longrightarrow L^2(\Lambda, \mathbb{C}),\ \ \text{div}\,\phi := \nabla \cdot \phi.$$

$$\text{curl}_0\colon \text{dom}(\text{curl}_0) := W_0(\text{curl}; \Lambda, \mathbb{C}^3) \subset L^2(\Lambda, \mathbb{C}^3) \longrightarrow L^2(\Lambda, \mathbb{C}^3),\ \text{curl}_0\,\psi := \nabla \times \psi,$$
$$\text{curl}\colon \text{dom}(\text{curl}) := W(\text{curl}; \Lambda, \mathbb{C}^3) \subset L^2(\Lambda, \mathbb{C}^3) \longrightarrow L^2(\Lambda, \mathbb{C}^3),\ \text{curl}\,\psi := \nabla \times \psi.$$

That is, if we replace in our notation the nabla symbol for a vectorial differential expression by the (abbreviated) name, we mean the Hilbert space operator with specified domain of definition.

There is a structural and physical necessity to discriminate between the two kinds of each vectorial differential operator. For physical intuition, let us consider the 1-component functions φ on dom(grad) as potentials and those on ran(div) as densities, whereas the multi-component ϕ's, and ψ's may be viewed as vector fields.

Let us give an overview over the following sections. In Sec. 44.4.1, we deduce the two kinds of Helmholtz–Hodge decompositions on $L^2(\Lambda, \mathbb{C}^3)$, where $\Lambda \subseteq \mathbb{R}^3$ is an *arbitrary* domain and may especially be unbounded. We achieve this by using pure operator theory in Hilbert space, in contradistinction to the more known analytic or differential geometric methods, which demand more restrictive Λ. In the following Secs. 44.4.2 to 44.4.6, we mainly refer results from the literature, especially from [DL93] Vol. 3, Chapter IX, Part A, § 1, from which we finally derive some additional results on the Helmholtz–Hodge decompositions and the global Poincaré lemma.

44.4.1. *Helmholtz–Hodge Decompositions*

The definition of the above operators leads to the operator inclusions

$$\text{grad}_0 \subseteq \text{grad}, \qquad \text{div}_0 \subseteq \text{div}, \qquad \text{curl}_0 \subseteq \text{curl}. \tag{44.4.1}$$

One verifies that for interior and exterior domains $\Lambda \subset \mathbb{R}^r$ (implying $\Lambda \neq \mathbb{R}^r$), with sufficiently smooth boundaries, these operator inclusions are proper. Also the inclusions

$$\ker(\text{div}_0) \subset \ker(\text{div}), \quad \ker(\text{curl}_0) \subset \ker(\text{curl}), \quad \Lambda \neq \mathbb{R}^r, \tag{44.4.2}$$

are proper.

For example, for bounded Λ the first inclusion in (44.4.1) is easily demonstrated by the observation that the non-constant potentials $\Lambda \in x \mapsto a \cdot x$, $0 \neq a \in \mathbb{C}^r$, with hyper-planes as graphs, are elements of $W^1(\Lambda, \mathbb{C})$. They possess the constant gradients $\text{grad}(a \cdot x) = a$, which — as the potentials for themselves — are square integrable over Λ. If the potential $a \cdot x$ is to be approximated by functions φ_n in $W_0^1(\Lambda, \mathbb{C})$ then the compactly supported φ_n acquire steeper and steeper slopes near the boundary $\partial\Lambda$ so that their gradients cannot approximate a constant. Thus the potentials $a \cdot x$ cannot be in $W_0^1(\Lambda, \mathbb{C})$. Only for the free space $\Lambda = \mathbb{R}^r$, we have the equalities in Eq. (44.4.1), cf. Sec. 44.8 on page 1619.

The usual denseness argument for Sobolev spaces employs the fact that the infinitely differentiable functions with compact support in the (open) region Λ are contained in the mentioned operator domains. From this it follows that the six operators from Definition 44.4-1 all are densely defined in the respective L^2-Hilbert spaces. The concise notions of closedness, adjointing, graph norm, core, etc., for operators acting from one Hilbert space into another, as recalled in Sec. 43.1 on page 1522, are used in the subsequent relations.

Proposition 44.4-2 (Closedness, Adjoints). *Each of the six differential operators of Definition 44.4-1 is closed and C-real with respect to the component-wise complex conjugation C. Every subspace in the domain of such differential operator, dense with respect to the pertinent Sobolev norm, is a core for the differential operator. We have the adjoints*

$$\text{grad}_0^* = -\text{div}, \qquad \text{div}^* = -\text{grad}_0,$$
$$\text{grad}^* = -\text{div}_0, \qquad \text{div}_0^* = -\text{grad},$$
$$\text{curl}_0^* = \text{curl}, \qquad \text{curl}^* = \text{curl}_0.$$

Notice that the adjointing relations require one operator with vanishing boundary condition (with index 0) to avoid boundary terms.

Proof. We check the result only for the pair grad_0 and div, since the other pairs of adjoint operators are treated analogously. The graph norm of div (see Eq. (43.1.4) on page 1524) is just the norm $\|.\|_{\text{div}}$ arising from Eq. (44.1.9). So div is closed, since $\text{dom}(\text{div}) = W(\text{div}; \Lambda, \mathbb{C}^r)$ is complete with respect to the norm $\|.\|_{\text{div}}$ by

Proposition 44.1-12. By the definition of a core, every subspace, which is $\|.\|_{\mathrm{div}}$-dense in $\mathrm{dom}(\mathrm{div}) = W(\mathrm{div}; \Lambda, \mathbb{C}^r)$, is a core for the operator div.

On the other side, the graph norm of grad_0 coincides with the Sobolev norm $\|.\|_1$ (see Eq. (44.1.7)). But $\mathrm{dom}(\mathrm{grad}_0) = W_0^1(\Lambda, \mathbb{C})$ is complete with respect to $\|.\|_1$ (cf. Definition 44.1-5), and so grad_0 is closed. Since $\mathrm{dom}(\mathrm{grad}_0) = W_0^1(\Lambda, \mathbb{C})$ is the closure of $C_c^\infty(\Lambda, \mathbb{C})$ with respect to the norm $\|.\|_1$, it follows that $C_c^\infty(\Lambda, \mathbb{C})$ is a core for grad_0.

According to the construction of the adjoint of an operator in Sec. 43.1, we have

$$\mathrm{dom}(\mathrm{grad}_0^*) = \{\psi \in L^2(\Lambda, \mathbb{C}^r) \mid W_0^1(\Lambda, \mathbb{C}) \ni \varphi \mapsto (\psi \mid \mathrm{grad}_0 \varphi) \text{ is } \|.\|\text{-continuous}\}.$$

Lemma 44.1-2(c) tells us that

$$\mathrm{dom}(\mathrm{div}) = \{\psi \in L^2(\Lambda, \mathbb{C}^r) \mid C_c^\infty(\Lambda, \mathbb{C}) \ni \varphi \mapsto -(\psi \mid \mathrm{grad}_0 \varphi) \text{ is } \|.\|\text{-continuous}\}.$$

The latter condition is equivalent to the foregoing since there $C_c^\infty(\Lambda, \mathbb{C})$ may be replaced by $W_0^1(\Lambda, \mathbb{C})$ (because $C_c^\infty(\Lambda, \mathbb{C})$ is a core for grad_0; use an $\varepsilon/3$-argument). Thus we have indeed $\mathrm{grad}_0^* = -\mathrm{div}$. With this the closedness of grad_0 gives $\mathrm{grad}_0 = \mathrm{grad}_0^{**} = -\mathrm{div}^*$. The C-realness is obvious. □

Let us remark that we have already used the above adjoints in the proof of Theorem 44.2-3 to show that the Dirichlet respectively Neumann Laplacians on $L^2(\Lambda, \mathbb{C})$ are given by the operator products

$$-\Delta_\infty = -\mathrm{div}\,\mathrm{grad}_0, \quad -\Delta_0 = -\mathrm{div}_0\,\mathrm{grad}. \tag{44.4.3}$$

Since $\ker(B^*) = \mathrm{ran}(B)^\perp = $ orthogonal complement of the image $\mathrm{ran}(B)$ of B for a densely defined operator B from one Hilbert space into another (cf. formula (43.1.3) on page 1524), we obtain from Proposition 44.4-2 for example the orthogonality relations

$$\ker(\mathrm{div}) = \mathrm{ran}(\mathrm{grad}_0)^\perp, \quad \ker(\mathrm{div}_0) = \mathrm{ran}(\mathrm{grad})^\perp,$$

or the analogue relations from permuting ker and $\mathrm{ran}^\perp$. Another type of orthogonality relations, based on Proposition 44.4-2, is

$$\ker(\mathrm{curl}_0) = \mathrm{ran}(\mathrm{curl})^\perp, \quad \ker(\mathrm{curl}) = \mathrm{ran}(\mathrm{curl}_0)^\perp.$$

As an immediate consequence of the orthogonality relations, we arrive thus at the following orthogonal decompositions of the Hilbert space $L^2(\Lambda, \mathbb{C}^r)$,

$$\begin{aligned}
L^2(\Lambda, \mathbb{C}^r) &= \overline{\mathrm{ran}(\mathrm{grad}_0)} \oplus \ker(\mathrm{div}) = \overline{\mathrm{ran}(\mathrm{grad})} \oplus \ker(\mathrm{div}_0), \\
L^2(\Lambda, \mathbb{C}^3) &= \ker(\mathrm{curl}_0) \oplus \overline{\mathrm{ran}(\mathrm{curl})} = \ker(\mathrm{curl}) \oplus \overline{\mathrm{ran}(\mathrm{curl}_0)}.
\end{aligned} \tag{44.4.4}$$

The remaining orthogonal decomposition has the form

$$L^2(\Lambda, \mathbb{C}) = \ker(\mathrm{grad}_0) \oplus \overline{\mathrm{ran}(\mathrm{div})} = \overline{\mathrm{ran}(\mathrm{div})} = \ker(\mathrm{grad}) \oplus \overline{\mathrm{ran}(\mathrm{div}_0)} \tag{44.4.5}$$

since the kernel of grad_0 vanishes, whereas $\ker(\text{grad})$ is non-trivial if and only if Λ is bounded (in which case $\ker(\text{grad})$ consists of the constant functions on Λ).

Let us concentrate on the case $r = 3$, recalling that the infinitely differentiable functions with compact support are cores for grad_0 and div_0. The well known equation $\nabla \times (\nabla\varphi) = 0$ is also valid in the weak sense. According to the two interpretations of $\nabla\varphi$ it can be translated into the operator language by letting φ run either through $\text{dom}(\text{grad}_0)$ or through $\text{dom}(\text{grad})$ and by choosing the smallest curl operator which annihilates the corresponding ranges of the gradient operators, so that the ranges of the gradients are contained in the kernel of the chosen curl. Since the kernel is a closed subspace, the closures of the mentioned gradient ranges are still contained in it. This leads to the first line of the subsequent inclusions.

The second line follows in an analogous manner from the equation $\nabla \cdot (\nabla \times \phi) = 0$, expressing that curl images have a vanishing divergence.

$$\overline{\text{ran}(\text{grad}_0)} \subseteq \ker(\text{curl}_0), \qquad \overline{\text{ran}(\text{grad})} \subseteq \ker(\text{curl}),$$
$$\overline{\text{ran}(\text{curl}_0)} \subseteq \ker(\text{div}_0), \qquad \overline{\text{ran}(\text{curl})} \subseteq \ker(\text{div}). \tag{44.4.6}$$

It depends on the cohomological properties of Λ, which is not necessarily simply connected, whether these inclusions are proper or not. Concerning the second line of (44.4.6) we check, using the second line of (44.4.4),

$$\ker(\text{div}_0) \ominus \overline{\text{ran}(\text{curl}_0)} = \ker(\text{div}_0) \cap \text{ran}(\text{curl}_0)^\perp = \ker(\text{div}_0) \cap \ker(\text{curl}) =: \mathbb{H}_1\,,$$
$$\ker(\text{div}) \ominus \overline{\text{ran}(\text{curl})} = \ker(\text{div}) \cap \text{ran}(\text{curl})^\perp = \ker(\text{div}) \cap \ker(\text{curl}_0) =: \mathbb{H}_2\,. \tag{44.4.7}$$

Definition 44.4-3 (First and Second Cohomology Space). For an arbitrary (open, connected) domain (= region) Λ in $\mathbb{R}^3$ let us introduce what we shall call *cohomology spaces*, namely

$$\mathbb{H}_1 \equiv \mathbb{H}_1(\Lambda) := \ker(\text{div}_0) \cap \ker(\text{curl}),$$
$$\mathbb{H}_2 \equiv \mathbb{H}_2(\Lambda) := \ker(\text{div}) \cap \ker(\text{curl}_0). \tag{44.4.8}$$

Being vector spaces $\mathbb{H}_1$ and $\mathbb{H}_2$ are additive groups, and they are in fact directly related to the cohomology groups of differential geometry as we shall describe below.

It is remarkable that we obtain by this general reasoning already a Hodge-type decomposition for vector fields over arbitrary, multiply connected domains $\Lambda \subseteq \mathbb{R}^3$, which may have rather irregular boundaries.

Theorem 44.4-4 (The Two Helmholtz–Hodge Decompositions). *For an arbitrary domain Λ in $\mathbb{R}^3$, we obtain immediately from the preceding considerations (see Definition 44.4-3 and Eqs. (44.4.4), (44.4.6), and (44.4.7)) the following two* *orthogonal decompositions*

$$
\mathrm{L}^2(\Lambda, \mathbb{C}^3) = \underbrace{\overline{\mathrm{ran}(\mathrm{grad})} \oplus \mathbb{H}_1 \oplus \overbrace{\overline{\mathrm{ran}(\mathrm{curl}_0)}}^{= \,\mathrm{ker}(\mathrm{div}_0)}}_{= \,\mathrm{ker}(\mathrm{curl})}, \tag{44.4.9}
$$

$$
\mathrm{L}^2(\Lambda, \mathbb{C}^3) = \underbrace{\overline{\mathrm{ran}(\mathrm{grad}_0)} \oplus \mathbb{H}_2 \oplus \overbrace{\overline{\mathrm{ran}(\mathrm{curl})}}^{= \,\mathrm{ker}(\mathrm{div})}}_{= \,\mathrm{ker}(\mathrm{curl}_0)}. \tag{44.4.10}
$$

In case of a sufficiently smooth boundary $\partial\Lambda$ and of closed ranges, the orthogonal decompositions (44.4.9) and (44.4.10) are called "Hodge–Morrey–Friedrichs decompositions" (e.g., [Sch95b]). We choose the name "Helmholtz–Hodge decompositions" to indicate the more general setup of a non-smooth boundary $\partial\Lambda$ and non-closed ranges.

In case of an interior Λ the ranges of our six differential operators from Definition 44.4-1 all are closed.

Lemma 44.4-5 (Closed Ranges for Interior Domains). *Let Λ be an interior domain. Then $\mathrm{ran}(\mathrm{grad}_0)$ is closed in $\mathrm{L}^2(\Lambda, \mathbb{C}^r)$.*

The segment property suffices for $\mathrm{ran}(\mathrm{grad})$ and $\mathrm{ran}(\mathrm{div}_0)$ to be closed in $\mathrm{L}^2(\Lambda, \mathbb{C}^r)$ and $\mathrm{L}^2(\Lambda, \mathbb{C})$, respectively.

The uniform cone property yields the closedness of $\mathrm{ran}(\mathrm{div})$, respectively of $\mathrm{ran}(\mathrm{curl}_0)$ and $\mathrm{ran}(\mathrm{curl})$ in $\mathrm{L}^2(\Lambda, \mathbb{C})$, respectively in $\mathrm{L}^2(\Lambda, \mathbb{C}^3)$.

Proof. [Hint] The result for grad_0 respectively grad is easily proved with the help of the Poincaré estimates from the Propositions 44.1-6(d) and 44.1-8(c), respectively. For the other ranges, see, e.g., [Lei86]. □

If one wants L^2-closedness of the images also for exterior domains Λ, then one has to leave the L^2-frame and to define the domains of definition of the six differential operators e.g., in terms of certain Beppo–Levi spaces (see [DL93] Vol. 3, Chapter IX, Part A, §1). We remain, however, within L^2-operator theory, what fits better to the L^2-photon wave functions.

44.4.2. *Description of the Cohomology Spaces $\mathbb{H}_1$ and $\mathbb{H}_2$*

Frequently the spaces $\mathbb{H}_1$ and $\mathbb{H}_2$, defined in Eq. (44.4.8), have finite dimensions. For bounded Λ this is an immediate consequence from the compact identical embeddings stated in Proposition 44.1-16(c).

Lemma 44.4-6. *Suppose the interior or exterior domain $\Lambda \subseteq \mathbb{R}^3$ to possess the uniform cone property. Then $\mathbb{H}_1$ and $\mathbb{H}_2$ both are finite-dimensional.*

If in addition Λ is simply connected, then $\mathbb{H}_1(\Lambda) = \{0\}$.

If Λ is interior with uniform cone property such that the exterior domain $\mathbb{R}^3\backslash\bar{\Lambda}$ is connected, then $\mathbb{H}_2(\Lambda) = \{0\}$.

Proof. We prove the first part for bounded Λ only, for the rest of the proof we refer to the literature, e.g., [Lei86] Secs. 8.5 and 9.3. Since $\mathbb{H}_1 = \ker(\mathrm{div}_0) \cap \ker(\mathrm{curl})$ is a subspace of $W_0(\mathrm{div};\Lambda,\mathbb{C}^3) \cap W(\mathrm{curl};\Lambda,\mathbb{C}^3)$, the identical embedding $\mathbb{H}_1 \hookrightarrow L^2(\Lambda,\mathbb{C}^3)$ is compact. However, on $\mathbb{H}_1$ the norm $\|.\|_{\mathrm{div,curl}}$ coincides with the common norm $\|.\|$ of $L^2(\Lambda,\mathbb{C}^3)$. Consequently, every $\|.\|$-bounded sequence in $\mathbb{H}_1$ contains a $\|.\|$-convergent subsequence, which implies $\mathbb{H}_1$ to be finite-dimensional. The proof for $\mathbb{H}_2$ works analogously. $\qquad\square$

In virtue of the boundary evaluations from Eq. (44.1.12) to Eq. (44.1.14) one immediately obtains:

Corollary 44.4-7. *Let the domain $\Lambda \subseteq \mathbb{R}^r$ be interior or exterior with piece-wise C^1-smooth boundary $\partial\Lambda$. Then*

$$\begin{aligned}
\ker(\mathrm{div}_0) &= \{\phi \in L^2(\Lambda,\mathbb{C}^r) \mid \nabla \cdot \phi = 0,\ \phi \cdot n|_{\partial\Lambda} = 0\},\\
\ker(\mathrm{curl}_0) &= \{\psi \in L^2(\Lambda,\mathbb{C}^3) \mid \nabla \times \psi = 0,\ \psi \times n|_{\partial\Lambda} = 0\},
\end{aligned} \tag{44.4.11}$$

where $n : \partial\Lambda \to \mathbb{R}^r$ is the outer normal. Consequently,

$$\begin{aligned}
\mathbb{H}_1 &= \{\phi \in L^2(\Lambda,\mathbb{C}^3) \mid \nabla \cdot \phi = 0,\ \nabla \times \phi = 0,\ \phi \cdot n|_{\partial\Lambda} = 0\} \subset W^1(\Lambda,\mathbb{C}^3),\\
\mathbb{H}_2 &= \{\psi \in L^2(\Lambda,\mathbb{C}^3) \mid \nabla \cdot \psi = 0,\ \nabla \times \psi = 0,\ \psi \times n|_{\partial\Lambda} = 0\} \subset W^1(\Lambda,\mathbb{C}^3),
\end{aligned} \tag{44.4.12}$$

where the inclusions on the right-hand sides follow from Proposition 44.1-16(b).

In order to get more details of $\mathbb{H}_1$ and $\mathbb{H}_2$, let us formulate the following assumptions on Λ, which may be considered standard for most physical applications.

Assumption 44.4-8 (Standard Assumption on the Domain Λ). Let Λ be an interior or exterior domain with piece-wise C^2-smooth boundary $\partial\Lambda$, such that:

(1) Λ can be made simply connected by a finite number of cuts $\Sigma_1, \Sigma_2, \dots, \Sigma_{b_1}$, where $b_1 \equiv b_1(\Lambda) \in \mathbb{N}_0$. ($b_1 = 0$, if Λ is already simply connected.) That is, the Σ_j are 2-dimensional submanifolds of $\mathbb{R}^3$, piece-wise of class C^k with $k \geq 2$, not tangential to $\partial\Lambda$, and such that $\Sigma_i \cap \Sigma_j = \emptyset$ for $i \neq j$. Then the resulting simply connected domain

$$\Lambda_{\mathrm{cut}} := \Lambda\backslash\Sigma, \quad \text{where} \quad \Sigma := \bigcup_{j=1}^{b_1} \Sigma_j,$$

with boundary $\partial\Lambda_{\mathrm{cut}} = \partial\Lambda \cup \Sigma$, is piece-wise of class C^2 (and $\partial\Lambda_{\mathrm{cut}}$ is thus a zero-set with respect to the three-dimensional Lebesgue measure). Note however, for $b_1 \geq 1$ the boundary $\partial\Lambda_{\mathrm{cut}}$ is no longer locally situated only on one side of Λ_{cut} (as demanded for C^2-smoothness in Definition 44.1-7(c)).

(2) The boundary $\partial\Lambda$ of our domain Λ possesses a finite number of connected components $\partial\Lambda_0, \partial\Lambda_1, \ldots, \partial\Lambda_{b_2}$, where $b_2 \equiv b_2(\Lambda) \in \mathbb{N}_0$. Hereby, $\partial\Lambda_0$ denotes the boundary of the infinite connected component of $\mathbb{R}^3 \backslash \bar{\Lambda}$ in case of interior Λ, and $\partial\Lambda_0 = \emptyset$ in case of exterior Λ.

Observation 44.4-9 (Concerning Assumption Part (2)). Let $\Lambda \subset \mathbb{R}^3$ be as in the above assumption with $b_2 \in \mathbb{N}_0$. Consider the complementary open set $\Omega := \mathbb{R}^3 \backslash \bar{\Lambda}$.

(a) Suppose Λ to be interior. Then Ω may be disconnected with connected components $\Omega_0, \Omega_1, \ldots, \Omega_{b_2}$, where Ω_0 is chosen as the part of Ω which is connected with infinity. (This is only a single connected component, because two of them could be separated from each other only by means of an unbounded Λ.) Then for each $k \in \{0, 1, \ldots, b_2\}$ the boundary $\partial\Omega_k$ of Ω_k coincides just with the connected component $\partial\Lambda_k$ of the boundary $\partial\Lambda$ of Λ.
(b) Now let Λ be exterior. Then Ω is bounded and not connected to infinity and thus $\partial\Lambda_0 = \emptyset$. The existing connected components $\Omega_1, \ldots, \Omega_{b_2}$ have the boundaries $\partial\Omega_k = \partial\Lambda_k$, for each $k \in \{1, \ldots, b_2\}$.

Altogether, $b_2 \equiv b_2(\Lambda)$ is just the number of connected components of the complementary open set $\Omega = \mathbb{R}^3 \backslash \bar{\Lambda}$, without counting the infinite connected component of Ω in case of interior Λ.

A cut Σ_j from part (1) of the Standard Assumption, interpreted as a part of $\partial\Lambda_{\mathrm{cut}}$, has two faces Σ_j^+ and Σ_j^-, and we orientate the normal n on Σ_j from Σ_j^+ to Σ_j^-. For a possibly smooth function $\phi : \Lambda_{\mathrm{cut}} \to \mathbb{C}^k$, $k \in \mathbb{N}$, which allows for a boundary evaluation, we may have that $\phi|_{\Sigma_j^+} \neq \phi|_{\Sigma_j^-}$, so that ϕ makes a jump across the cut. We denote the height of the jump by

$$[\phi]_{\Sigma_j} := \phi|_{\Sigma_j^+} - \phi|_{\Sigma_j^-}, \quad j = 1, \ldots, b_1.$$

Since a gradient field $\psi = \nabla\varphi$ of a harmonic function φ, which satisfies $\nabla \cdot \psi = \Delta\varphi = 0$, has both vanishing divergence and curl, it is a candidate for a cohomological vector field. The details are given in the following proposition, which we cannot prove in the present exposition.

Theorem 44.4-10 (Gradient Representation for Cohomological Fields). *Suppose $\Lambda \subseteq \mathbb{R}^3$ to satisfy the Standard Assumption 44.4-8.*
If Λ is an interior domain, then it holds:

(1) *The first cohomology space $\mathbb{H}_1 \equiv \mathbb{H}_1(\Lambda)$ consists of those $\psi \in \mathrm{L}^2(\Lambda, \mathbb{C}^3)$ which satisfy $\psi = \nabla\varphi$ within Λ_{cut} in the generalized sense, where $\varphi \in \mathrm{W}^1(\Lambda_{\mathrm{cut}}, \mathbb{C})$ is*

a solution of

$$\Delta\varphi = 0 \quad in \quad \Lambda_{\text{cut}}, \qquad \frac{\partial\varphi}{\partial n}\bigg|_{\partial\Lambda} = 0,$$

$$[\varphi]_{\Sigma_j} = \text{constant}_j, \qquad \left[\frac{\partial\varphi}{\partial n}\right]_{\Sigma_j} = 0, \quad \forall j \in \{1,\ldots,b_1\}.$$

The latter two relations mean that the jumps of the harmonic function φ across each cut are constant along the cut, and that the two normal components of the original $\psi = \nabla\varphi \in \mathbb{H}_1$ coincide, when ψ crosses the cut.

The dimension of $\mathbb{H}_1$ is just b_1, the number of cuts needed to render Λ simply connected. Furthermore, if in addition $\partial\Lambda$ is of class $\mathrm{C}^{k,\kappa}$ with $k \geq 2$ and $0 < \kappa < 1$, then $\mathbb{H}_1 \subset \mathrm{C}^{k-1,\kappa}(\bar{\Lambda}, \mathbb{C}^3)$, where κ means the order of Hölder continuity. So, when crossing the cuts, φ makes jumps, but $\psi = \nabla\varphi \in \mathbb{H}_1$ is continuous.

*$\mathbb{H}_1$ is isomorphic to the **first cohomology group** from differential geometry — the quotient of the closed differential 1-forms on Λ by the exact differential 1-forms on $\Lambda-$, and b_1 is the **first Betti number**.*

(2) *The second cohomology space $\mathbb{H}_2 \equiv \mathbb{H}_2(\Lambda)$ consists of those $\psi \in \mathrm{L}^2(\Lambda, \mathbb{C}^3)$ which satisfy $\psi = \nabla\varphi$ within Λ in the generalized sense (that is $\psi = \mathrm{grad}\,\varphi$), where $\varphi \in \mathrm{W}^1(\Lambda, \mathbb{C})$ is a solution of*

$$\Delta\varphi = 0 \quad in \quad \Lambda, \qquad \varphi|_{\partial\Lambda_j} = \text{constant}_j, \quad \forall j \in \{0,\ldots,b_2\}.$$

The dimension of $\mathbb{H}_2$ is just b_2, the number of connected components of $\partial\Lambda$ minus the infinite connected component $\partial\Lambda_0$. Furthermore, if in addition $\partial\Lambda$ is of class $\mathrm{C}^{k,\kappa}$ with $k \geq 2$ and $0 < \kappa < 1$, then $\mathbb{H}_2 \subset \mathrm{C}^{k-1,\kappa}(\bar{\Lambda}, \mathbb{C}^3)$.

*$\mathbb{H}_2$ is isomorphic to the **second cohomology group** — the quotient of the closed differential 2-forms in Λ by the exact differential 2-forms on Λ-, and b_2 is the **second Betti number**.*

If $\Lambda \subseteq \mathbb{R}^3$ is an exterior domain, then the parts (1) and (2) remain valid, when the first Sobolev spaces $\mathrm{W}^1(\Lambda_{\text{cut}}, \mathbb{C})$ respectively $\mathrm{W}^1(\Lambda, \mathbb{C})$ are replaced by the first Beppo–Levi spaces. The first Beppo–Levi space consists of (classes of) of functions φ, for which only $\nabla\varphi$ is assumed to be contained in $\mathrm{L}^2(\Lambda_{\text{cut}}, \mathbb{C}^3)$ respectively $\mathrm{L}^2(\Lambda, \mathbb{C}^3)$, but φ itself possibly may not be square integrable. For further details see, e.g., [DL93] Vol. 3, p. 230.

In the above two cases of an interior respectively exterior domain we have

$$\mathbb{H}_2 \subset \ker(\mathrm{curl}_0) = \overline{\mathrm{ran}(\mathrm{grad}_0)} \oplus \mathbb{H}_2 \subseteq \overline{\mathrm{ran}(\mathrm{grad})}. \tag{44.4.13}$$

The first inclusion follows simply from (44.4.10), but the second is new. It is a consequence of part (2), since each $\psi \in \mathbb{H}_2$ is of type $\psi = \nabla\varphi$ with $\varphi \in \mathrm{W}^1(\Lambda, \mathbb{C})$ for interior Λ, respectively for exterior Λ with $\varphi \in \mathrm{B}^1(\Lambda, \mathbb{C})$ for the first Beppo–Levi space $\mathrm{B}^1(\Lambda, \mathbb{C})$ and the fact $\overline{\mathrm{ran}(\mathrm{grad})} = \overline{\nabla\mathrm{B}^1(\Lambda, \mathbb{C})}$ for the closure of the *range of our L^2-operator* grad. *Note, by Lemma 44.4-5 for interior Λ the images* ran(grad$_0$) *and* ran(grad) *are already closed subspaces of $L^2(\Lambda, \mathbb{C}^3)$, thus the bar for the closures may be dropped in (44.4.13).*

We explicitly emphasize: By its definition in Eq. (44.4.8) the first cohomology space $\mathbb{H}_1$ is independent of the particular choice of cuts needed to render Λ simply connected. We deduce from Theorem 44.4-10, that C^∞-smoothness of Λ implies $\mathbb{H}_1 \subset C^\infty(\bar{\Lambda}, \mathbb{C}^3)$ and $\mathbb{H}_2 \subset C^\infty(\bar{\Lambda}, \mathbb{C}^3)$.

Corollary 44.4-11 (Trivial Cohomology). *Let the interior or exterior domain $\Lambda \subseteq \mathbb{R}^3$ satisfy the Standard Assumption 44.4-8. Then*

(1) $b_1 = 0$ $\Longleftrightarrow$ $\mathbb{H}_1 = \{0\}$ $\Longleftrightarrow$ Λ *is simply connected.*
(2) $b_2 = 0$ $\Longleftrightarrow$ $\mathbb{H}_2 = \{0\}$ $\Longleftrightarrow$ $\partial\Lambda$ *is connected.*

44.4.3. *Examples for Cohomology Spaces and Betti Numbers*

Let us turn here to some simple examples for interior and exterior domains with various Betti numbers b_1 and b_2.

The free Euclidean space $\Lambda = \mathbb{R}^3$ with its trivial cohomology is treated in detail in Sec. 44.8. The more interesting cases are of course $\Lambda \neq \mathbb{R}^3$.

44.4.3.1. *Open Radial Shell*

We choose the three-dimensional open radial shell

$$\Lambda \equiv \Lambda_{\alpha,\beta} := \{x \in \mathbb{R}^3 \mid \alpha < |x| < \beta\}$$

for some $0 < \alpha < \beta < \infty$. Clearly Λ satisfies the Standard Assumption 44.4-8 and is simply connected, leading to $\mathbb{H}_1 = \{0\}$. The boundary $\partial\Lambda$ has two connected components $\partial\Lambda_1 = \{x \in \mathbb{R}^3 \mid |x| = \alpha\}$ and $\partial\Lambda_0 = \{x \in \mathbb{R}^3 \mid |x| = \beta\}$, the latter being also the boundary of the infinite connected component of $\mathbb{R}^3 \backslash \bar{\Lambda}$. Hence the second Betti number is $b_2 = 1$, and $\dim(\mathbb{H}_2) = 1$.

Thus we know that $\mathbb{H}_2 = \mathbb{C}\psi$ with some almost uniquely given vector field ψ. We guess

$$\psi : \Lambda \to \mathbb{C}^3, \quad x \mapsto c\frac{x}{|x|^3}, \quad \text{with some} \quad 0 \neq c \in \mathbb{R}. \tag{44.4.14}$$

If we interpret this as part of the Coulomb field of a point charge q at the origin, then $c = \frac{q}{4\pi\varepsilon_0}$.

That ψ is indeed an element of $\mathbb{H}_2$ is already seen by Eq. (44.4.12) (since $\nabla \cdot \psi = 0$, $\nabla \times \psi = 0$, and $\psi \times n|_{\partial\Lambda} = 0$). Moreover, we have the gradient representation $\psi = \nabla\varphi$ with $\varphi(x) := -\frac{c}{|x|}$, $x \in \Lambda$. Hence φ is harmonic, $\Delta\varphi = 0$, and satisfies the correct boundary conditions $\varphi|_{\partial\Lambda_j} = \text{constant}_j$ for $j = 0, 1$. This also ensures that $\psi \in \mathbb{H}_2$ by part (2) of the above theorem and provides an example of a purely cohomological electric field without a longitudinal or transversal component.

If we perform a smooth deformation of the shell then still $\dim(\mathbb{H}_2) = 1$, since this is a topological invariant. Thus we know that there exists also for the deformed region always an up to a factor unique vector field ψ with $\nabla \cdot \psi = 0$, $\nabla \times \psi = 0$, and $\psi \times n|_{\partial\Lambda} = 0$.

44.4.3.2. *Pointed Open Ball*

If we choose the three-dimensional pointed open ball

$$\Lambda \equiv \Lambda_{0,\beta} := \{x \in \mathbb{R}^3 \mid 0 < |x| < \beta\}$$

for some $0 < \beta < \infty$, then this does not satisfy the Standard Assumption 44.4-8, since the point-like interior part of the boundary is not a 2-dimensional surface, and thus not piece-wise C^2-smooth. The vector field ψ of (44.4.14) is similar to an element of $\mathbb{H}_2$, since it satisfies $\nabla \cdot \psi = 0$, $\nabla \times \psi = 0$, and $\psi \times n|_{\partial\Lambda} = 0$ for the outer boundary. But ψ is not square integrable over $\Lambda_{0,\beta}$ and leads to an infinite selfenergy of the point charge. The singularity near 0 cannot be damped by smearing this field, because according to our strategy we smear only by elements of $\mathbb{H}_2$.

We modify the example in terms of an extended charge distribution.

44.4.3.3. *Open Ball*

We choose the three-dimensional open ball

$$\Lambda \equiv \Lambda_{[0,\beta} := \{x \in \mathbb{R}^3 \mid 0 \le |x| < \beta\}$$

for some $0 < \beta < \infty$ and insert a charge density with

$$\varrho(x) := \begin{cases} \varrho_0 > 0, & \text{for } 0 \le |x| \le \alpha < \beta, \\ 0 & \text{for } \alpha < |x| < \beta, \end{cases} \qquad \alpha > 0.$$

Then Λ and $\partial\Lambda = \partial\Lambda_0 = \{x \in \mathbb{R}^3 \mid |x| = \beta\}$ are simply connected and thus $\mathbb{H}_1 = \mathbb{H}_2 = \{0\}$, according to Corollary 44.4-11.

The electric field, generated by the radial symmetric charge distribution, is a vector field of the form

$$\psi(x) \equiv \mathbf{E}^{\|}(x) = \begin{cases} c\dfrac{x}{\alpha^3}, & \text{for } 0 \le |x| \le \alpha, \\ c\dfrac{x}{|x|^3}, & \text{for } \alpha < |x| < \beta. \end{cases}$$

Here $c = \frac{q}{4\pi\varepsilon_0}$ with charge $q = \frac{4}{3}\pi\alpha^3\varrho_0$.

This field is a purely longitudinal field. It has vanishing curl and vanishing tangential component at $\partial\Lambda$, but non-vanishing divergence, and its potential can be renormalized at $\partial\Lambda$ to zero (cf. the definition of $\mathbf{E}^{\|}$ in the Helmholtz–Hodge decomposition (44.4.10)). This is so in spite of its restriction to $\Lambda_{\alpha,\beta}$ having the same form as the field in Example 44.4.3.1 for the radial shell. $\Lambda_{\alpha,\beta}$ taken as cavity has another topological structure than the domain $\Lambda_{[0,\beta}$, and the potential at the two boundary components cannot simultaneously be renormalized to zero.

The cavity alone does of course not determine $\mathbf{E}^{\parallel}$, because the field depends also on the charge distribution. Thus a longitudinal field does not characterize the topological situation.

44.4.3.4. *Dirac Monopole, Pointed Open Ball*

To discuss the base space of the famous Dirac monopole we choose as in Example 44.4.3.2 the three-dimensional pointed open ball

$$\Lambda \equiv \Lambda_{0,\beta} := \{x \in \mathbb{R}^3 \mid 0 < |x| < \beta\}$$

for some $0 < \beta < \infty$. Λ does not satisfy our Standard Assumption 44.4-8, but Λ is simply connected, and $\Omega = \mathbb{R}^3\backslash\bar{\Lambda}$ is also simply connected, in sharp contrast to $\Lambda^c = \mathbb{R}^3\backslash\Lambda$ containing also the origin.

We interpret the vector field

$$\psi : \Lambda \to \mathbb{C}^3, \quad x \mapsto c\frac{x}{|x|^3}, \quad \text{with some} \quad 0 \neq c \in \mathbb{R}, \tag{44.4.15}$$

as the **B**-field of a hypothetical magnetic point-charge g at the origin, so that $c = \frac{g}{4\pi}$. This **B**-field satisfies in Λ the relations $\nabla \cdot \mathbf{B} = 0$, $\nabla \times \mathbf{B} = 0$, and is normal to the exterior boundary, in contradistinction to a **B**-field, generated by a surface current. Therefore, it is not a $\mathbf{B}^{\text{co}}$ of ED.

44.4.3.5. *Exterior Domain = Complement of a Simply Connected Interior Region*

Suppose the domain Λ to be a simply connected, C^2-smooth interior domain, so that the associated exterior domain $\Omega := \mathbb{R}^3\backslash\bar{\Lambda}$ is connected. It follows that Ω is a simply connected, C^2-smooth exterior domain. For the connected components of the boundaries of Λ and Ω we have

$$\partial\Omega_0 = \emptyset, \quad \partial\Omega = \partial\Omega_1 = \partial\Lambda_0 = \partial\Lambda \neq \emptyset,$$

from which we conclude that

$$\mathbb{H}_1(\Lambda) = \mathbb{H}_1(\Omega) = \{0\}, \quad \mathbb{H}_2(\Lambda) = \{0\}, \quad \dim \mathbb{H}_2(\Omega) = b_2(\Omega) = 1.$$

Let us take e.g.,

$$\Lambda := \{x \in \mathbb{R}^3 \mid |x| < 1\}, \quad \text{thus} \quad \Omega = \{x \in \mathbb{R}^3 \mid |x| > 1\}.$$

Then similarly to the Example 44.4.3.1, we have $\mathbb{H}_2(\Omega) = \mathbb{C}\psi$ with

$$\psi : \Omega \to \mathbb{C}^3, \quad x \mapsto c\frac{x}{|x|^3}, \quad \text{with some} \quad 0 \neq c \in \mathbb{R}.$$

Again it holds $\psi = \nabla\varphi$ with $\varphi(x) := -\frac{c}{|x|}$, $x \in \Omega$. Moreover, $\Delta\varphi = 0$ and $\varphi|_{\partial\Lambda} = \text{constant}$. Since Ω is exterior, the function φ is contained in the first Beppo–Levi space $\mathrm{B}^1(\Lambda, \mathbb{C})$, especially φ is not square integrable, but $\nabla\varphi$ is so.

In terms of an electric field we may realize the situation by a point charge, which is symmetrically surrounded by a conducting shell. The influence charge on the shell produces the exterior Coulomb field. By a smooth deformation of the shell we can deduce properties of the exterior field, the up to a factor unique field in $\mathbb{H}_2(\Omega)$, also in a non-symmetrical situation.

44.4.3.6. *Torus Ring with Constant Surface Current*

A typical situation for a cohomological **B**-field is the open interior Λ of a torus ring in $\mathbb{R}^3$, where a constant surface current is flowing in $\partial\Lambda$. In physics, $\partial\Lambda$ is realized by a tightly wound toroidal coil.

Since $\partial\Lambda = \partial\Lambda_0$ is also the infinitely extended connected component of the boundary of $\mathbb{R}^3 \backslash \bar{\Lambda}$ we have $\mathbb{H}_2(\Lambda) = \{0\}$.

Because a single cut Σ_1 is needed, perpendicular to the ring axis and to $\partial\Lambda$, in order to render Λ to the simply connected Λ_{cut}, we have $\dim(\mathbb{H}_1(\Lambda)) = b_1(\Lambda) = 1$.

The **B**-field in Λ is parallel to the ring axis and homogeneous, if the cross section of the coil is small. Thus we have the following relations, which identify **B** as a cohomological $\mathbf{B}^{\text{co}}$

$$\nabla \times \mathbf{B}_t^{\text{co}} = 0, \quad \underbrace{\nabla \cdot \mathbf{B}_t^{\text{co}} = 0, \quad \mathbf{B}_t^{\text{co}} \cdot n|_{\partial\Lambda} = 0}. \tag{44.4.16}$$

$$\Leftrightarrow \ \mathbf{B}_t^{\text{co}} \in \ker(\text{div}_0)$$

In Λ_{cut} there is a harmonic scalar function $\varphi \in W^1(\Lambda_{\text{cut}}, \mathbb{C})$ with $\mathbf{B} = \nabla\varphi$ in the weak sense. The jump $[\varphi]_{\Sigma_1} = \text{constant}_1$ is non-zero, whereas the left and right sided normal gradients at the cut coincide, giving the **B**-field. Also $\frac{\partial\varphi}{\partial n}\big|_{\partial\Lambda} = 0$.

44.4.3.7. *Cylinder Shell*

Now we choose for an interior domain Λ the finite cylindrical shell

$$\Lambda := \{x \in \mathbb{R}^3 \mid \alpha < \sqrt{x_1^2 + x_2^2} < \beta, \ |x_3| < \gamma\}$$

for some $0 < \alpha < \beta < \infty$ and $\gamma > 0$. Then a single cut Σ_1 is needed to render Λ to the simply connected Λ_{cut}. Hence $\dim(\mathbb{H}_1(\Lambda)) = b_1(\Lambda) = 1$. Since $\partial\Lambda = \partial\Lambda_0$ is also the infinite connected component of the boundary of $\mathbb{R}^3 \backslash \bar{\Lambda}$ we have $\mathbb{H}_2(\Lambda) = \{0\}$.

44.4.3.8. *Geometry for an Aharanov–Bohm Effect*

We arrive from the foregoing Λ to the situation of the Aharanov–Bohm effect, if we let $\alpha \to \beta$ and $\gamma \to \infty$. The cylindrical shell is interpreted as the tightly wound wire of a long current carrying coil, which produces a constant magnet field $\mathbf{B} = (0, 0, B_0)$ in its interior. Outside of the coil, the **B**-field is practically zero.

Our interest concerns the not-simply connected, open outside region $\{x \in \mathbb{R}^3 \mid \beta < \sqrt{x_1^2 + x_2^2}\}$, which is what we denote now by Λ. Λ is not an exterior domain in our sense, since the interior region of the coil is not bounded. But we can apply our previous notions by means of explicit calculations.

To make Λ to the simply connected Λ_{cut} we need one cut, which we choose as $\Sigma_1 := \{x \in \mathbb{R}^3 \mid x_1 \le 0, x_2 = 0\} \cap \Lambda$. Thus we expect for Λ a (generalized) one-dimensional cohomological space $\mathbb{H}_1(\Lambda)$.

For the interior **B**-field the simplest vector potential is $\mathbf{A}(x) = \frac{B_0}{2}(-x_2, x_1, 0) = \frac{1}{2}\mathbf{B} \times x$.

The exterior vector potential cannot be chosen zero, since a closed line integral around the coil is to give the non-vanishing magnetic flux. The physically appropriate exterior vector potential is

$$\mathbf{A}(x) = \frac{B_0\beta^2}{2}\left(-\frac{x_2}{x_1^2 + x_2^2}, \frac{x_1}{x_1^2 + x_2^2}, 0\right). \tag{44.4.17}$$

This follows from the following features: Its curl is zero, and it matches with the interior vector potential at the coil surface $x_1^2 + x_2^2 = \beta^2$.

Beside that, it has also vanishing divergence and vanishing normal component at the coil surface. Thus it satisfies all conditions of the first line in (44.4.12) to be an element of $\mathbb{H}_1(\Lambda)$.

Interesting is that its gradient representation $\mathbf{A} = \nabla\varphi$ (cf. Theorem 44.4-10) can be written down explicitly in terms of the scalar function:

$$\varphi(x) = \frac{B_0\beta^2}{2}\arctan\frac{x_2}{x_1}, \quad x \in \Lambda_{\text{cut}}. \tag{44.4.18}$$

Since $\varphi(x)$ is proportional to the polar angle it has its only discontinuity at the negative x_1-axis and is well defined on Λ_{cut}. Across Σ_1 it jumps from $\frac{B_0\beta^2\pi}{2}$ to $-\frac{B_0\beta^2\pi}{2}$. Its one-sided, normal gradients near the cut are well defined, coincide with the **A**-field, and are continuous.

We see that the physical meaning of the cohomological field in $\mathbb{H}_1(\Lambda)$ is here a vector potential, it is $\mathsf{A}_{\text{co}} = \mathsf{A}_{\text{co}}^0$. This field is according to our approach an index function in the Lagrangian and Hamilton functions, and stays classical after the field quantization. Especially in the (classical and quantum mechanical) Coulomb Hamiltonian it produces an interaction with the material particles (say electrons).

Because of the singularity on Σ_1 the gradient $\nabla\varphi$ can gauge away our vector potential only in Λ_{cut}. If this is executed then there remains a singular expression for the vector potential on Σ_1. The cross section of the half plane Σ_1 with the plane $x_3 = 0$ is similar to a *Dirac string* for a magnetic monopole. For more details see Sec. 55.1.4 on page 2041.

44.4.4. *Refined Helmholtz–Hodge Decomposition*

Let us suppose in the present section an interior or exterior, piece-wise C^2-smooth domain $\Lambda \subset \mathbb{R}^3$ fulfilling the Standard Assumption 44.4-8.

By Eq. (44.4.13), we have $\ker(\mathrm{curl}_0) \subseteq \overline{\mathrm{ran}(\mathrm{grad})}$. Taking orthogonal complements gives $\ker(\mathrm{div}_0) \subseteq \overline{\mathrm{ran}(\mathrm{curl})}$. This completes Eq. (44.4.6) to

$$\overline{\mathrm{ran}(\mathrm{grad}_0)} \subseteq \ker(\mathrm{curl}_0) \subseteq \overline{\mathrm{ran}(\mathrm{grad})} \subseteq \ker(\mathrm{curl}),$$

$$\overline{\mathrm{ran}(\mathrm{curl}_0)} \subseteq \ker(\mathrm{div}_0) \subseteq \overline{\mathrm{ran}(\mathrm{curl})} \subseteq \ker(\mathrm{div}).$$

(44.4.19)

We want to gain a more detailed insight into these relations. According to the inclusion $\ker(\mathrm{curl}_0) \subseteq \overline{\mathrm{ran}(\mathrm{grad})}$ let us define an in general infinite-dimensional, closed subspace of $\mathrm{L}^2(\Lambda, \mathbb{C}^3)$ by

$$\mathbb{V} := \overline{\mathrm{ran}(\mathrm{grad})} \ominus \ker(\mathrm{curl}_0) = \overline{\mathrm{ran}(\mathrm{grad})} \cap \ker(\mathrm{curl}_0)^\perp = \overline{\mathrm{ran}(\mathrm{grad})} \cap \overline{\mathrm{ran}(\mathrm{curl})},$$

(44.4.20)

which leads to the orthogonal decomposition

$$\overline{\mathrm{ran}(\mathrm{grad})} = \underbrace{\overline{\mathrm{ran}(\mathrm{grad}_0)} \oplus \mathbb{H}_2 \oplus \mathbb{V}}_{= \ker(\mathrm{curl}_0)}.$$

Thus the two Helmholtz–Hodge decompositions of Theorem 44.4-4 can be traced back to two different coarsenings of a unique refined decomposition.

Theorem 44.4-12 (Refined Helmholtz–Hodge Decomposition). *Suppose the interior or exterior domain $\Lambda \subseteq \mathbb{R}^3$ to satisfy the Standard Assumption 44.4-8. Then the following orthogonal decomposition is valid:*

$$\mathrm{L}^2(\Lambda, \mathbb{C}^3) = \overbrace{\overline{\mathrm{ran}(\mathrm{grad}_0)} \oplus \mathbb{H}_2 \oplus \mathbb{V}}^{= \overline{\mathrm{ran}(\mathrm{grad})}} \oplus \overbrace{\mathbb{H}_1 \oplus \overline{\mathrm{ran}(\mathrm{curl}_0)}}^{= \ker(\mathrm{div}_0)},$$

$$\underbrace{\qquad\qquad\qquad\qquad}_{= \ker(\mathrm{curl})}$$

$$\mathrm{L}^2(\Lambda, \mathbb{C}^3) = \underbrace{\overline{\mathrm{ran}(\mathrm{grad}_0)} \oplus \mathbb{H}_2}_{= \ker(\mathrm{curl}_0)} \oplus \overbrace{\underbrace{\mathbb{V} \oplus \mathbb{H}_1 \oplus \overline{\mathrm{ran}(\mathrm{curl}_0)}}_{= \overline{\mathrm{ran}(\mathrm{curl})}}}^{= \ker(\mathrm{div})}.$$

Recall from Lemma 44.4-5, that for interior Λ the images $\mathrm{ran}(\mathrm{grad}_0)$, $\mathrm{ran}(\mathrm{grad})$, $\mathrm{ran}(\mathrm{curl}_0)$, $\mathrm{ran}(\mathrm{curl})$ are already closed subspaces of $\mathrm{L}^2(\Lambda, \mathbb{C}^3)$, and thus the bar for the closures may be dropped.

The refined version discloses, that the two Helmholtz–Hodge decompositions from Eqs. (44.4.9) and (44.4.10) indeed are different for $\Lambda \neq \mathbb{R}^3$.

As already mentioned, the assumed piece-wise C^2-smoothness for the boundary $\partial\Lambda$ could be weakened.

From Theorem 44.4-10, we know that $\mathbb{H}_2$ consists of the gradients of harmonic fields φ, which are constant on each boundary component. But in the direct sum $\mathbb{H}_2 \oplus \mathbb{V}$ this boundary condition for the harmonic fields φ is dropped,

$$\mathbb{H}_2 \oplus \mathbb{V} = \{\psi = \nabla\varphi \mid \varphi \in \mathrm{W}^1(\Lambda, \mathbb{C}), \ \Delta\varphi = 0\}, \quad \text{for interior } \Lambda,$$

with $\Delta\varphi = 0$ generalized in Λ (by [DL93] Vol. 3). For exterior Λ, the analogous relation holds but with $\mathrm{W}^1(\Lambda, \mathbb{C})$ replaced by the first Beppo–Levi space $\mathrm{B}^1(\Lambda, \mathbb{C})$.

So, in virtue of (44.4.20) $\mathbb{V}$ for itself may be characterized by

$$\mathbb{V} = \operatorname{ran}(\operatorname{grad}) \cap \operatorname{ran}(\operatorname{curl})$$
$$= \{\psi = \nabla\varphi \mid \varphi \in W^1(\Lambda, \mathbb{C}), \; \Delta\varphi = 0\} \cap \operatorname{ran}(\operatorname{curl}), \qquad \text{for interior } \Lambda.$$

44.4.5. *Poincaré Lemma and Helmholtz–Hodge Decompositions*

Especially in ED one is confronted with the following two questions for an arbitrary domain $\Lambda \subseteq \mathbb{R}^3$:

(a) Starting from the relation $\nabla \times \psi = 0$ for a function $\psi : \Lambda \to \mathbb{C}^3$, is there a scalar potential $\varphi : \Lambda \to \mathbb{C}$ with $\psi = \nabla\varphi$?

(b) If $\nabla \cdot \psi = 0$ for a function $\psi : \Lambda \to \mathbb{C}^3$, does there exist a vector potential $\phi : \Lambda \to \mathbb{C}^3$ with $\psi = \nabla \times \phi$?

In differential geometry this problem is locally answered by the Poincaré Lemma, which we formulate here in terms of classical vector fields.

Lemma 44.4-13 (Local Poincaré Lemma). *Let Λ be a domain of $\mathbb{R}^3$, and suppose $\psi \in C^1(\Lambda, \mathbb{C}^3)$. Then the following assertions are valid:*

(a) *If $\nabla \times \psi = 0$, then for each open rectangular parallelepiped $\mathsf{P} \subseteq \Lambda$ there exists a function $\varphi \in C^2(\mathsf{P}, \mathbb{C})$ with $\psi = \nabla\varphi$ in P. φ is unique up to an additive constant.*

(b) *If $\nabla \cdot \psi = 0$, then for each open rectangular parallelepiped $\mathsf{P} \subseteq \Lambda$ there exists a function $\phi \in C^2(\mathsf{P}, \mathbb{C}^3)$ with $\psi = \nabla \times \phi$ in P.*

A rectangular parallelepiped is suited to construct the potentials by integration. In case of $\Lambda = \mathbb{R}^3$, one may choose the rectangular parallelepiped P as $\mathbb{R}^3$ itself, so that the Poincaré lemma holds globally. In part (a), one may paste together the various functions $\varphi \equiv \varphi_\mathsf{P}$ (for each parallelepiped P) simply by adding constants, in order to obtain a scalar potential $\varphi \in C^2(\Omega, \mathbb{C})$ with $\psi = \nabla\varphi$ within an arbitrary simply connected domain Ω contained in Λ.

Here, however, we intend a global Poincaré lemma, i.e., in all of Λ, in the context of L^2-functions. According to the two Helmholtz–Hodge decompositions in Theorem 44.4-4, we have

$$\ker(\operatorname{curl}) = \overline{\operatorname{ran}(\operatorname{grad})} \oplus \mathbb{H}_1, \quad \ker(\operatorname{div}) = \overline{\operatorname{ran}(\operatorname{curl})} \oplus \mathbb{H}_2,$$

for arbitrary domain Λ in $\mathbb{R}^3$. As mentioned before in Lemma 44.4-5, one may drop the closure bars for interior Λ with suitable smoothness conditions. Using Corollary 44.4-11 it is immediate to arrive at the desired global Poincaré result for interior Λ.

Corollary 44.4-14 (A Global Poincaré Lemma for Interior Domain). *Let $\Lambda \subset \mathbb{R}^3$ be an interior domain.*

(a) *If* Λ *possesses the segment property, then we have the following equivalence(s),*

$$\ker(\mathrm{curl}) = \mathrm{ran}(\mathrm{grad}) \quad \Longleftrightarrow \quad \mathbb{H}_1 = \{0\} \quad \left(\overset{St.Ass.}{\Longleftrightarrow} \ \Lambda \ \textit{is simply connected} \right),$$

where the equivalence in brackets needs the more stringent boundary condition of the Standard Assumption 44.4-8 abbreviated by "St.Ass." This means for trivial $\mathbb{H}_1$: *If* $\mathrm{curl}\,\psi = \nabla \times \psi = 0$ *for a* $\psi \in L^2(\Lambda, \mathbb{C}^3)$, *then there exists a* $\varphi \in W^1(\Lambda, \mathbb{C})$ *(unique up to an additive constant) with* $\psi = \mathrm{grad}\,\varphi = \nabla\varphi$.

(b) *If* Λ *possesses the uniform cone property, then we have the following equivalence(s),*

$$\ker(\mathrm{div}) = \mathrm{ran}(\mathrm{curl}) \quad \Longleftrightarrow \quad \mathbb{H}_2 = \{0\} \quad \left(\overset{St.Ass.}{\Longleftrightarrow} \ \partial\Lambda \ \textit{is connected} \right).$$

This means for trivial $\mathbb{H}_2$: *If* $\mathrm{div}\,\psi = \nabla \cdot \psi = 0$ *for a* $\psi \in L^2(\Lambda, \mathbb{C}^3)$, *then there exists some* $\phi \in W^1(\Lambda, \mathbb{C}^3)$ *with* $\psi = \mathrm{curl}\,\phi = \nabla \times \phi$. ϕ *is unique, when chosen from* $\mathrm{ran}(\mathrm{curl}_0) \cap W(\mathrm{curl}; \Lambda, \mathbb{C}^3)$ *(the latter space is specified further in Eq. (44.4.28) below).*

If for exterior Λ one wishes analogous assertions, one needs closed images. As mentioned before, then one has to leave partially the L^2-Hilbert space theory and has to define analogues to grad and curl on suitable Beppo–Levi spaces. We pursue, however, in the present book another strategy for physical reasons.

If Λ possesses e.g., a C^∞-smooth boundary $\partial\Lambda$, then in the above global Poincaré Lemma there hold all the regularity properties listed at the end of the next section: If $\psi \in W^m(\Lambda, \mathbb{C}^3)$, then $\varphi \in W^{m+1}(\Lambda, \mathbb{C})$ in part (a) respectively $\phi \in W^{m+1}(\Lambda, \mathbb{C}^3)$ in part (b), also in case where ϕ is uniquely chosen from $\mathrm{ran}(\mathrm{curl}_0) \cap W(\mathrm{curl}; \Lambda, \mathbb{C}^3)$.

In ED (cf. Sec. 6.2.3 on page 105) it is a basic question whether there exists also in not-simply connected cavities a vector potential for the cohomological magnetic field $\mathbf{B}^{\mathrm{co}} \in \mathbb{H}_1$, respectively for the total magnetic field $\mathbf{B} \in \ker(\mathrm{div}_0)$. Let us emphasize that we deal with a more restricted class $\mathbf{B} \in \ker(\mathrm{div}_0)$ of magnetic fields (by the second Maxwell equation with perfect conductor boundary condition), and *not* with the class $\mathbf{B} \in \ker(\mathrm{div})$. Thus this problem is *not* of type (b) of the above version of the global Poincaré Lemma, where a non-trivial $\mathbb{H}_2$ would prevent the existence of a global vector potential.

Because of its eminent physical importance, we formulate the following easy conclusion from the foregoing considerations as a theorem.

Theorem 44.4-15 (Existence of Global Vector Potentials). *Provided the interior domain* Λ *fulfills our Standard Assumption 44.4-8, we have in virtue of Eq. (44.4.19) respectively Theorem 44.4-12*

$$\mathbb{H}_1 \subset \ker(\mathrm{div}_0) \subseteq \mathrm{ran}(\mathrm{curl}). \tag{44.4.21}$$

Thus for both $\mathbf{B}^{\mathrm{co}} \in \mathbb{H}_1$ *and* $\mathbf{B} \in \ker(\mathrm{div}_0)$ *there exist vector potentials* $\mathsf{A}_{\mathrm{co}}, \mathsf{A} \in \mathrm{dom}(\mathrm{curl}) = W(\mathrm{curl}; \Lambda, \mathbb{C}^3)$, *satisfying*

$$\mathbf{B}^{\mathrm{co}} = \mathrm{curl}\,\mathsf{A}_{\mathrm{co}}, \quad \mathbf{B} = \mathrm{curl}\,\mathsf{A},$$

independently from $\mathbb{H}_2$ *(and* $\mathbb{H}_1$*) being trivial or not.*

44.4.6. *Density of Subspaces and Regular Functions*

44.4.6.1. *Dense Subspaces for* grad_0 *and* grad

We first turn to dense subspaces in $\overline{\mathrm{ran}(\mathrm{grad}_0)}$ and $\overline{\mathrm{ran}(\mathrm{grad})}$. Since $\|\nabla\varphi\| \le \|\varphi\|_1$ for all $\varphi \in \mathrm{W}^1(\Lambda,\mathbb{C})$ with respect to the Sobolev norm $\|.\|_1$ from Eq. (44.1.7) it follows that ∇V_0^1 is $\|.\|$-dense in $\overline{\mathrm{ran}(\mathrm{grad}_0)}$ for every subspace V_0^1 being $\|.\|_1$-dense in the Sobolev space $\mathrm{W}_0^1(\Lambda,\mathbb{C})$. For V_0^1 one may e.g., take the test functions $\mathrm{C}_c^\infty(\Lambda,\mathbb{C})$ from distribution theory. Analogously, ∇V^1 is $\|.\|$-dense in $\overline{\mathrm{ran}(\mathrm{grad})}$ for every subspace V^1 being $\|.\|_1$-dense in $\mathrm{W}^1(\Lambda,\mathbb{C})$. For V^1 one may e.g., choose the subspace $\mathrm{C}_b^\infty(\Lambda,\mathbb{C}) \cap \mathrm{W}^1(\Lambda,\mathbb{C})$ by Proposition 44.1-6(c), and, in case where Λ has the segment property, one may take $\mathrm{C}_c^\infty(\mathbb{R}^r,\mathbb{C})|_\Lambda$ by Proposition 44.1-8(a).

44.4.6.2. *Dense Subspaces for* div_0

To show that certain subspaces are dense in $\mathrm{ker}(\mathrm{div}_0)$ respectively in $\mathrm{ker}(\mathrm{div})$ is more complicated, and we have to refer to the literature (e.g., [DL93] Vol. 3). As a side remark let us mention that such density relations are also used to describe the flow in an incompressible fluid in terms of the Navier–Stokes equations (for Navier–Stokes, cf. e.g., [Lad63], [FK64], [Hen81], [Gol85], and [DL93] Vol. 6). There, divergence-free functions $\psi : \Lambda \to \mathbb{C}^3$ are called to be "solenoidal", and one has the need for Laplacians on solenoidal vector fields. We treat the divergence-free Dirichlet Laplacian in Sec. 44.6.2.

Proposition 44.4-16. *Let* $\Lambda \subset \mathbb{R}^r$ *be interior and piece-wise* C^1*-smooth. Then* $\{\psi \in \mathrm{C}_c^\infty(\Lambda,\mathbb{C}^r) \mid \nabla \cdot \psi = 0\}$ *is* $\|.\|_1$*-dense in the* $\|.\|_1$*-closed subspace* $\mathrm{ker}(\mathrm{div}_0) \cap \mathrm{W}_0^1(\Lambda,\mathbb{C}^r) = \{\psi \in \mathrm{W}_0^1(\Lambda,\mathbb{C}^r) \mid \nabla \cdot \psi = 0\}$ *of* $\mathrm{W}_0^1(\Lambda,\mathbb{C}^r)$ *and is also* $\|.\|$*-dense in* $\mathrm{ker}(\mathrm{div}_0)$.

44.4.6.3. *Regularity for Decompositions* "grad_0 & div" *and* "grad & div_0"

For most physical applications functions with some regular behavior are desirable.

Let again Λ be interior and C^{m+1}-smooth for some $m \in \mathbb{N}$. Then for the two orthogonal decompositions

$$\mathrm{L}^2(\Lambda,\mathbb{C}^r) = \mathrm{ran}(\mathrm{grad}_0) \oplus \mathrm{ker}(\mathrm{div}) = \mathrm{ran}(\mathrm{grad}) \oplus \mathrm{ker}(\mathrm{div}_0),$$
$$\psi = \nabla\varphi \oplus \phi, \quad \text{where } \varphi \in \mathrm{W}_0^1(\Lambda,\mathbb{C}) \text{ respectively } \varphi \in \mathrm{W}^1(\Lambda,\mathbb{C}),$$

from Eq. (44.4.4), it holds: $\psi \in \mathrm{W}^m(\Lambda,\mathbb{C}^r)$, if and only if $\varphi \in \mathrm{W}^{m+1}(\Lambda,\mathbb{C})$ and $\phi \in \mathrm{W}^m(\Lambda,\mathbb{C}^r)$. Especially, $\mathrm{ker}(\mathrm{div}) \cap \mathrm{W}^m(\Lambda,\mathbb{C}^r)$ is $\|.\|$-dense in $\mathrm{ker}(\mathrm{div})$. With C^2-smooth, interior Λ it follows for $\psi \in \mathrm{C}^2(\bar{\Lambda},\mathbb{C}^r)$ that $\varphi \in \mathrm{C}^1(\bar{\Lambda},\mathbb{C}) \cap \mathrm{C}^2(\Lambda,\mathbb{C})$, which implies that $\nabla\varphi \in \mathrm{C}^0(\bar{\Lambda},\mathbb{C}^r) \cap \mathrm{C}^1(\Lambda,\mathbb{C}^r)$ and $\phi \in \mathrm{C}^0(\bar{\Lambda},\mathbb{C}^r) \cap \mathrm{C}^1(\Lambda,\mathbb{C}^r)$. Especially,

$$\{\phi \in \mathrm{C}^0(\bar{\Lambda},\mathbb{C}^r) \cap \mathrm{C}^1(\Lambda,\mathbb{C}^r) \mid \nabla \cdot \phi = 0\}$$

is $\|.\|$-dense in $\ker(\mathrm{div})$. Note, for the first orthogonal decomposition $L^2 = \mathrm{ran}(\mathrm{grad}_0) \oplus \ker(\mathrm{div})$ we have $\varphi|_{\partial\Lambda} = 0$. (Concerning the proofs we remark: Since $\nabla \cdot \phi = 0$, φ is a weak solution of the inhomogeneous Laplace equation $-\Delta_\rho \varphi = -\nabla \cdot \psi$ for Dirichlet $[\rho = \infty]$ respectively Neumann $[\rho = 0]$ boundary conditions. Now use Regularity Proposition 44.2-6 on page 1576, and classical solution theory.)

44.4.6.4. *Images of* curl_0 *and* curl

According to the procedure presented in Sec. 43.7 on page 1553, we may restrict the operators curl and curl_0 to the orthogonal complement (in $L^2(\Lambda, \mathbb{C}^3)$) of closed subspaces of their kernels. From Eq. (44.4.9), we conclude that curl is an injective operator from the Hilbert space $\overline{\mathrm{ran}(\mathrm{curl}_0)}$ into the Hilbert space $\overline{\mathrm{ran}(\mathrm{curl})}$. By Eq. (44.4.10) and by curl_0 being the adjoint of curl, it follows that curl_0 is an injective operator from the Hilbert space $\overline{\mathrm{ran}(\mathrm{curl})}$ into the Hilbert space $\overline{\mathrm{ran}(\mathrm{curl}_0)}$. The domain of definition for this restriction of curl is $\overline{\mathrm{ran}(\mathrm{curl}_0)} \cap W(\mathrm{curl}; \Lambda, \mathbb{C}^3)$, and is $\overline{\mathrm{ran}(\mathrm{curl})} \cap W_0(\mathrm{curl}; \Lambda, \mathbb{C}^3)$ for curl_0. Consequently, for subsets V and V_0 with the below indicated specifications one has

$$\mathrm{ran}(\mathrm{curl}) = \nabla \times V, \quad \overline{\mathrm{ran}(\mathrm{curl}_0)} \cap W(\mathrm{curl}; \Lambda, \mathbb{C}^3) \subseteq V \subseteq W(\mathrm{curl}; \Lambda, \mathbb{C}^3),$$

$$\mathrm{ran}(\mathrm{curl}_0) = \nabla \times V_0, \quad \overline{\mathrm{ran}(\mathrm{curl})} \cap W_0(\mathrm{curl}; \Lambda, \mathbb{C}^3) \subseteq V_0 \subseteq W_0(\mathrm{curl}; \Lambda, \mathbb{C}^3).$$

$$(44.4.22)$$

Let us describe some candidates for V respectively V_0. For interior or exterior, piece-wise C^1-smooth domain $\Lambda \subseteq \mathbb{R}^3$, we conclude from Proposition 44.1-16(b) that

$$\overline{\mathrm{ran}(\mathrm{curl}_0)} \cap W(\mathrm{curl}; \Lambda, \mathbb{C}^3) \subseteq \ker(\mathrm{div}_0) \cap W(\mathrm{curl}; \Lambda, \mathbb{C}^3)$$
$$\subseteq W_0(\mathrm{div}; \Lambda, \mathbb{C}^3) \cap W(\mathrm{curl}; \Lambda, \mathbb{C}^3) = \{\psi \in W^1(\Lambda, \mathbb{C}^3) \mid \psi \cdot n|_{\partial\Lambda} = 0\}$$
$$\subseteq W^1(\Lambda, \mathbb{C}^3) \subseteq W(\mathrm{curl}; \Lambda, \mathbb{C}^3),$$

$$(44.4.23)$$

and that

$$\overline{\mathrm{ran}(\mathrm{curl})} \cap W_0(\mathrm{curl}; \Lambda, \mathbb{C}^3) \subseteq \ker(\mathrm{div}) \cap W_0(\mathrm{curl}; \Lambda, \mathbb{C}^3)$$
$$\subseteq W(\mathrm{div}; \Lambda, \mathbb{C}^3) \cap W_0(\mathrm{curl}; \Lambda, \mathbb{C}^3) = \{\psi \in W^1(\Lambda, \mathbb{C}^3) \mid \psi \times n|_{\partial\Lambda} = 0\}.$$

$$(44.4.24)$$

Proposition 44.4-17. *Let* $\Lambda \subset \mathbb{R}^3$ *satisfy the Standard Assumption 44.4-8, from which we use the notation. Then*

$$\overline{\mathrm{ran}(\mathrm{curl})} = \{\psi \in \ker(\mathrm{div}) \mid \int_{\partial\Lambda_j} \psi \cdot n\, dS = 0, \, j = 0, 1, \ldots, b_2\},$$

$$\overline{\mathrm{ran}(\mathrm{curl}_0)} = \{\phi \in \ker(\mathrm{div}_0) \mid \int_{\Sigma_j} \phi \cdot n\, dS = 0, \, j = 1, \ldots, b_1\}.$$

In case of interior Λ *one may drop the closure bars by Lemma 44.4-5, and one has* $\mathrm{ran}(\mathrm{curl}_0) = \nabla \times W_0^1(\Lambda, \mathbb{C}^3)$.

44.4.6.5. *Regularity for Helmholtz–Hodge Decompositions*

From now on assume Λ interior, fulfilling the Standard Assumption 44.4-8.

First let us consider the Helmholtz–Hodge decomposition in Eq. (44.4.9),

$$\mathrm{L}^2(\Lambda, \mathbb{C}^3) = \mathrm{ran}(\mathrm{grad}) \oplus \mathbb{H}_1 \oplus \mathrm{ran}(\mathrm{curl}_0), \quad \psi = \nabla\varphi \oplus h_1 \oplus \nabla \times \phi, \qquad (44.4.25)$$

where $\varphi \in \mathrm{W}^1(\Lambda, \mathbb{C})$ is unique up to an additive constant, and $\phi \in \mathrm{W}_0(\mathrm{curl}; \Lambda, \mathbb{C})$. ϕ is unique, when taken from

$$\mathrm{ran}(\mathrm{curl}) \cap \mathrm{W}_0(\mathrm{curl}; \Lambda, \mathbb{C}^3) \qquad (44.4.26)$$

$$= \{\phi \in \mathrm{W}^1(\Lambda, \mathbb{C}^3) \mid \nabla \cdot \phi = 0,\ \phi \times n|_{\partial\Lambda} = 0,\ \int_{\partial\Lambda_j} \phi \cdot n\, dS = 0,\ j = 0, 1, \ldots, b_2\}.$$

This follows from our above argumentation (in restriction curl_0 acts injectively from the space $\mathrm{ran}(\mathrm{curl}) \cap \mathrm{W}_0(\mathrm{curl}; \Lambda, \mathbb{C}^3)$ onto $\mathrm{ran}(\mathrm{curl}_0)$), Eq. (44.4.24), and from the above Proposition 44.4-17.

Let us also treat the second Helmholtz–Hodge decomposition Eq. (44.4.10).

$$\mathrm{L}^2(\Lambda, \mathbb{C}^3) = \mathrm{ran}(\mathrm{grad}_0) \oplus \mathbb{H}_2 \oplus \mathrm{ran}(\mathrm{curl}), \quad \psi = \nabla\varphi \oplus h_2 \oplus \nabla \times \phi, \qquad (44.4.27)$$

where $\varphi \in \mathrm{W}_0^1(\Lambda, \mathbb{C})$ is unique, and $\phi \in \mathrm{W}(\mathrm{curl}; \Lambda, \mathbb{C})$. Analogously to the above argumentation, we conclude that ϕ is unique, when taken from

$$\mathrm{ran}(\mathrm{curl}_0) \cap \mathrm{W}(\mathrm{curl}; \Lambda, \mathbb{C}^3) =\qquad (44.4.28)$$

$$= \{\phi \in \mathrm{W}^1(\Lambda, \mathbb{C}^3) \mid \nabla \cdot \phi = 0,\ \phi \cdot n|_{\partial\Lambda} = 0,\ \int_{\Sigma_j} \phi \cdot n\, dS = 0,\ j = 1, \ldots, b_1\}.$$

(Note that curl acts injectively from $\mathrm{ran}(\mathrm{curl}_0) \cap \mathrm{W}(\mathrm{curl}; \Lambda, \mathbb{C}^3)$ onto $\mathrm{ran}(\mathrm{curl})$, use Eq. (44.4.23) and Proposition 44.4-17.)

Let us finally turn to regularity properties for ψ, φ, ϕ, and h_1, h_2 in Eqs. (44.4.25) and (44.4.27). For simplicity, we assume C^∞-smoothness of Λ, also of the cuts. If $m \in \mathbb{N}$ is arbitrary, then $\psi \in \mathrm{W}^m(\Lambda, \mathbb{C}^3)$ implies that $\varphi \in \mathrm{W}^{m+1}(\Lambda, \mathbb{C})$ and that $\phi \in \mathrm{W}^{m+1}(\Lambda, \mathbb{C}^3)$. This is valid also in case that ϕ is uniquely chosen from $\mathrm{ran}(\mathrm{curl}) \cap \mathrm{W}_0(\mathrm{curl}; \Lambda, \mathbb{C}^3)$ respectively from $\mathrm{ran}(\mathrm{curl}_0) \cap \mathrm{W}(\mathrm{curl}; \Lambda, \mathbb{C}^3)$.

We already know for $h_l \in \mathbb{H}_l$ in Eq. (44.4.25) respectively Eq. (44.4.27), $l = 1, 2$, that $h_l \in \mathrm{C}^\infty(\bar{\Lambda}, \mathbb{C}^3)$, with $\nabla \cdot h_l = 0$, $\nabla \times h_l = 0$ in Λ, and $h_1 \cdot n|_{\partial\Lambda} = 0$ respectively $h_2 \times n|_{\partial\Lambda} = 0$ (cf. Eq. (44.4.12)). Thus by Proposition 44.4-10, it holds $h_1 = \nabla\varphi_1$ within Λ_{cut} for $\varphi_1 \in \mathrm{C}^\infty(\bar{\Lambda}_{\mathrm{cut}}, \mathbb{C})$, and $h_2 = \nabla\varphi_2$ for $\varphi_2 \in \mathrm{C}^\infty(\bar{\Lambda}, \mathbb{C})$. Observe that $\varphi_1 \in \mathrm{C}^\infty(\bar{\Lambda}_{\mathrm{cut}}, \mathbb{C})$ means that φ_1 is infinitely differentiable within Λ_{cut} and that each derivative $\partial^s\psi$ extends to a continuous function on the closure $\bar{\Lambda}_{\mathrm{cut}} = \Lambda_{\mathrm{cut}} \cup \partial\Lambda_{\mathrm{cut}}$. This condition still allows for jumps at each cut Σ_j, so that possibly $[\partial_s\varphi]_{\Sigma_j} \neq 0$.

44.5. **Self-adjoint Curlcurl Operators**

Especially for expressing the Maxwell dynamics in terms of the potentials and for the wave equations of the force fields, one needs the iterated curl operators. Recall that the force fields are most often calculated by means of wave equations. It is an essential message of the present approach that also for transversal fields the spatial part of the wave equation is in general not a Laplacian but a reduced curlcurl operator.

We assume in this section that Λ is an arbitrary domain in $\mathbb{R}^3$.

44.5.1. *Definition of the Two Curlcurl Operators*

We introduce two curlcurl operators which act in $L^2(\Lambda, \mathbb{C}^3)$ and are denoted by $\operatorname{curl}^2_{t0}$ and $\operatorname{curl}^2_{n0}$. The first acts on fields with vanishing tangential component at the boundary, whereas the second differentiates fields, the curl of which has vanishing tangential component at the boundary. Like for the Laplacians in Sec. 44.2.1, we define the two curlcurl operators in terms of sesquilinear forms on $L^2(\Lambda, \mathbb{C}^3)$, and verify later on their boundary conditions. Many arguments are similar to those for the Laplacians.

The sesquilinear form h_{t0} for $\operatorname{curl}^2_{t0}$ is defined by

$$h_{t0}(\psi, \phi) := (\nabla \times \psi | \nabla \times \phi), \quad \forall \psi, \phi \in \operatorname{dom}(h_{t0}) := W_0(\operatorname{curl}; \Lambda, \mathbb{C}^3). \quad (44.5.1)$$

Recall that $W_0(\operatorname{curl}; \Lambda, \mathbb{C}^3)$ is just the kernel of the tangential boundary operator R_t from Eq. (44.1.13).

The sesquilinear form h_{n0} for $\operatorname{curl}^2_{n0}$ is defined by

$$h_{n0}(\psi, \phi) := (\nabla \times \psi | \nabla \times \phi), \quad \forall \psi, \phi \in \operatorname{dom}(h_{n0}) := W(\operatorname{curl}; \Lambda, \mathbb{C}^3). \quad (44.5.2)$$

The two forms h_{t0} and h_{n0} are positive, unbounded, and closed (the latter is an immediate consequence of the closedness of the operators curl_0 and curl). By Theorem 43.5-10 (a) on page 1543 there correspond to h_{t0} respectively h_{n0} unique self-adjoint operators $\operatorname{curl}^2_{t0}$ and $\operatorname{curl}^2_{n0}$ satisfying the relations

$$h_\#(\psi, \phi) = (\psi | \operatorname{curl}^2_\# \phi), \quad \forall \psi \in \operatorname{dom}(h_\#), \quad \forall \phi \in \operatorname{dom}(\operatorname{curl}^2_\#),$$

where $\# \in \{t0, n0\}$.

Since the operators curl_0 and curl from Definition 44.4-1 are adjoint to each other according to Proposition 44.4-2, the operator products $\operatorname{curl}\operatorname{curl}_0 = \operatorname{curl}^*_0 \operatorname{curl}_0$ and $\operatorname{curl}_0 \operatorname{curl} = \operatorname{curl}^* \operatorname{curl}$ are positive and self-adjoint. For their domains, we have the inclusions

$$\operatorname{dom}(\operatorname{curl}\operatorname{curl}_0) \subseteq \operatorname{dom}(\operatorname{curl}_0) = \operatorname{dom}(h_{t0}),$$
$$\operatorname{dom}(\operatorname{curl}_0 \operatorname{curl}) \subseteq \operatorname{dom}(\operatorname{curl}) = \operatorname{dom}(h_{n0}).$$

Hence the uniqueness of self-adjoint operators representing the forms h_{t0} and h_{n0} ensures that the two curlcurls are given as the just mentioned operator products, namely

$$\operatorname{curl}^2_{t0} = \operatorname{curl}\operatorname{curl}_0, \qquad \operatorname{curl}^2_{n0} = \operatorname{curl}_0 \operatorname{curl}. \quad (44.5.3)$$

Consequently, we have $\mathrm{curl}^2_\# \psi = \nabla \times (\nabla \times \psi)$ with ψ from the domains

$$\mathrm{dom}(\mathrm{curl}^2_{t0}) = \{\psi \in W_0(\mathrm{curl}; \Lambda, \mathbb{C}^3) \mid \nabla \times \psi \in W(\mathrm{curl}; \Lambda, \mathbb{C}^3)\},$$
$$\mathrm{dom}(\mathrm{curl}^2_{n0}) = \{\psi \in W(\mathrm{curl}; \Lambda, \mathbb{C}^3) \mid \nabla \times \psi \in W_0(\mathrm{curl}; \Lambda, \mathbb{C}^3)\}. \qquad (44.5.4)$$

Since curl_0 and curl are C-real, the two curlcurl operators are also C-real.

44.5.2. Reduction of the Two Curlcurl Operators

In order to state further properties of the two curlcurl operators let us restrict them to the divergence-free sub-Hilbert spaces $\overline{\mathrm{ran}(\mathrm{curl})}$ respectively $\overline{\mathrm{ran}(\mathrm{curl}_0)}$ of $\ker(\mathrm{div})$ respectively $\ker(\mathrm{div}_0)$. (For restrictions of operators see Sec. 43.7 on page 1553.)

The two Helmholtz–Hodge decompositions in Theorem 44.4-4 yield that we may restrict curl to an operator from $\overline{\mathrm{ran}(\mathrm{curl}_0)}$ into $\overline{\mathrm{ran}(\mathrm{curl})}$, and curl_0 to an operator from $\overline{\mathrm{ran}(\mathrm{curl})}$ into $\overline{\mathrm{ran}(\mathrm{curl}_0)}$, simply by cutting of the associated closed kernels. The domains of definition for these restrictions are $\overline{\mathrm{ran}(\mathrm{curl}_0)} \cap W(\mathrm{curl}; \Lambda, \mathbb{C}^3)$ for curl, and $\overline{\mathrm{ran}(\mathrm{curl})} \cap W_0(\mathrm{curl}; \Lambda, \mathbb{C}^3)$ for curl_0. Consequently we have the following situation, *most important for the concise photon concept.*

Theorem 44.5-1 (Reduction of the Two Curlcurls). *The closed subspace* $\overline{\mathrm{ran}(\mathrm{curl})}$ *(and also the larger* $\ker(\mathrm{div})$*) is a reducing subspace for* curl^2_{t0}*, and* $\overline{\mathrm{ran}(\mathrm{curl}_0)}$ *(and also the larger* $\ker(\mathrm{div}_0)$*) is a reducing subspace for* curl^2_{n0}*.*

Also the associated sesquilinear forms are the restrictions of h_{t0} *respectively* h_{n0} *to the Hilbert spaces* $\overline{\mathrm{ran}(\mathrm{curl})}$ *respectively* $\overline{\mathrm{ran}(\mathrm{curl}_0)}$ *with the domains* $\overline{\mathrm{ran}(\mathrm{curl})} \cap W_0(\mathrm{curl}; \Lambda, \mathbb{C}^3)$*, respectively* $\overline{\mathrm{ran}(\mathrm{curl}_0)} \cap W(\mathrm{curl}; \Lambda, \mathbb{C}^3)$*.*

We use the following notations,

$$\begin{aligned} &\mathrm{curl}^2_{t0}| \quad \text{for the reduction of } \mathrm{curl}^2_{t0} \text{ to the sub-Hilbert space } \overline{\mathrm{ran}(\mathrm{curl})}, \\ &\mathrm{curl}^2_{n0}| \quad \text{for the reduction of } \mathrm{curl}^2_{n0} \text{ to the sub-Hilbert space } \overline{\mathrm{ran}(\mathrm{curl}_0)}. \end{aligned} \qquad (44.5.5)$$

By construction, we have $\ker(\mathrm{curl}^2_{t0}|) = \{0\} = \ker(\mathrm{curl}^2_{n0}|)$ for the reduced curlcurls, whereas for the unreduced curlcurl operators it holds

$$\ker(\mathrm{curl}^2_{t0}) = \ker(\mathrm{curl}_0) = \overline{\mathrm{ran}(\mathrm{grad}_0)} \oplus \mathbb{H}_2,$$
$$\ker(\mathrm{curl}^2_{n0}) = \ker(\mathrm{curl}) = \overline{\mathrm{ran}(\mathrm{grad})} \oplus \mathbb{H}_1.$$

Thus by construction the reductions $\mathrm{curl}^2_{t0}|$ and $\mathrm{curl}^2_{n0}|$ are *strictly positive, injective, self-adjoint* operators in the Hilbert spaces $\overline{\mathrm{ran}(\mathrm{curl})}$ and $\overline{\mathrm{ran}(\mathrm{curl}_0)}$, respectively. (For strict positivity cf. Sec. 43.1.)

We have already mentioned the vanishing tangential boundary value in the domain of curl^2_{t0}, that is, $\mathrm{dom}(\mathrm{curl}^2_{t0}) \subset \mathrm{dom}(h_{t0}) = W_0(\mathrm{curl}; \Lambda, \mathbb{C}^3)$ is contained in the kernel of the tangential boundary operator R_t. Concerning curl^2_{n0}, we consider an interior or exterior, piece-wise C^1-smooth domain Λ. A vanishing normal component at the boundary arises with Proposition 44.1-16 (b) on page 1570 from the fact that

$$\mathrm{dom}(\mathrm{curl}^2_{n0}|) = \overline{\mathrm{ran}(\mathrm{curl}_0)} \cap \mathrm{dom}(\mathrm{curl}^2_{n0}) \subseteq$$
$$\subseteq \ker(\mathrm{div}_0) \cap \mathrm{W}(\mathrm{curl}; \Lambda, \mathbb{C}^3) = \{\psi \in \mathrm{W}^1(\Lambda, \mathbb{C}^3) \mid \nabla \cdot \psi = 0, \ \psi \cdot n|_{\partial \Lambda} = 0\}.$$

Analogously we supplement for the reduction of the tangential curlcurl the argument

$$\mathrm{dom}(\mathrm{curl}^2_{t0}|) = \overline{\mathrm{ran}(\mathrm{curl})} \cap \mathrm{dom}(\mathrm{curl}^2_{t0}) \subseteq$$
$$\subseteq \ker(\mathrm{div}) \cap \mathrm{W}_0(\mathrm{curl}; \Lambda, \mathbb{C}^3) = \{\psi \in \mathrm{W}^1(\Lambda, \mathbb{C}^3) \mid \nabla \cdot \psi = 0, \ \psi \times n|_{\partial \Lambda} = 0\}.$$

Theorem 44.5-2 (Spectral Properties). *Let $\Lambda \subseteq \mathbb{R}^3$ be a domain with the uniform cone property, and let $\# \in \{t0, n0\}$.*

(a) *If Λ is interior then a reduced curlcurl operator $\mathrm{curl}^2_{\#}|$ has a pure point spectrum accumulating only at infinity. More precisely, there exists an orthonormal basis $\{e_k \mid k \in \mathbb{N}\}$ of $\overline{\mathrm{ran}(\mathrm{curl})}$ for $\# = t0$, respectively of $\overline{\mathrm{ran}(\mathrm{curl}_0)}$ for $\# = n0$, consisting of eigenvectors e_k of $\mathrm{curl}^2_{\#}|$. The associated eigenvalues $\lambda_k > 0$, $k \in \mathbb{N}$, (i.e., 0 is not an eigenvalue) satisfy*

$$0 < \lambda_1 \leq \lambda_2 \leq \lambda_3 \leq \ldots, \qquad \lim_{k \to \infty} \lambda_k = \infty.$$

Every eigenspace of $\mathrm{curl}^2_{\#}|$ is of finite dimensions, and $(\mathrm{curl}^2_{\#}|)^{-1}$ is a compact operator in $\overline{\mathrm{ran}(\mathrm{curl})}$ respectively in $\overline{\mathrm{ran}(\mathrm{curl}_0)}$.

(b) *If Λ is exterior, then a reduced operator $\mathrm{curl}^2_{\#}|$ has an absolutely continuous spectrum with range $[0, \infty[$.*

Proof. [Sketch] We only show the result for interior Λ and for $\# = t0$, since for interior Λ and $\# = n0$ the proof works analogously. To $\mathrm{curl}^2_{t0}|$ there corresponds the form h_{t0} restricted to the Hilbert space $\overline{\mathrm{ran}(\mathrm{curl})}$ with the form domain $\overline{\mathrm{ran}(\mathrm{curl})} \cap \mathrm{W}_0(\mathrm{curl}; \Lambda, \mathbb{C}^3)$. By Proposition 44.1-16(b), the identical embedding $\mathrm{W}(\mathrm{div}; \Lambda, \mathbb{C}^3) \cap \mathrm{W}_0(\mathrm{curl}; \Lambda, \mathbb{C}^3) \hookrightarrow \mathrm{L}^2(\Lambda, \mathbb{C}^3)$ is compact. However, on $\overline{\mathrm{ran}(\mathrm{curl})} \cap \mathrm{W}_0(\mathrm{curl}; \Lambda, \mathbb{C}^3) \subseteq \ker(\mathrm{div}) \cap \mathrm{W}_0(\mathrm{curl}; \Lambda, \mathbb{C}^3)$ the norm $\|.\|_{\mathrm{div,curl}}$ coincides with the norm $\|.\|_{\mathrm{curl}}$. Hence the spectral properties of the restricted curlcurl $\mathrm{curl}^2_{t0}|$ follow from Proposition 43.5-11 on page 1544. $\square$

44.5.3. Connection to the Restrictions of the Curl Operators

Let us write the reduced curlcurls in terms of the restrictions of the original curl operators curl_0 and curl, introduced at the beginning of Sec. 44.5.1. According to the orthogonal decompositions from Eq. (44.4.4),

$$\mathrm{L}^2(\Lambda, \mathbb{C}^3) = \ker(\mathrm{curl}_0) \oplus \overline{\mathrm{ran}(\mathrm{curl})} = \ker(\mathrm{curl}) \oplus \overline{\mathrm{ran}(\mathrm{curl}_0)},$$

the operator curl_0 may be restricted to the injective operator $\overline{\text{curl}_0|}$ from the Hilbert space $\ker(\text{curl}_0)^\perp = \overline{\text{ran}(\text{curl})}$ into the Hilbert space $\overline{\text{ran}(\text{curl}_0)}$, whereas the operator $\overline{\text{curl}}$ may be restricted to the injective $\text{curl}|$ from the Hilbert space $\ker(\text{curl})^\perp = \overline{\text{ran}(\text{curl}_0)}$ into the Hilbert space $\overline{\text{ran}(\text{curl})}$ with the dense domains of definition

$$\text{dom}(\text{curl}_0|) = \overline{\text{ran}(\text{curl})} \cap \text{dom}(\text{curl}_0), \quad \text{dom}(\text{curl}|) = \overline{\text{ran}(\text{curl}_0)} \cap \text{dom}(\text{curl}),$$

respectively.

Since the non-restricted curl_0 and curl are adjoint to each other, it follows that the restrictions $\text{curl}_0|$ and $\text{curl}|$ are adjoint to each other, too. Now it is immediately checked that the reduced curlcurls from above are given by

$$\text{curl}_{t0}^2| = \text{curl}| \, \text{curl}_0|, \qquad \text{curl}_{n0}^2| = \text{curl}_0| \, \text{curl}| \,. \tag{44.5.6}$$

44.6.   Self-adjoint Laplacians under Divergence-Freeness

We want to define positive, self-adjoint Laplacians in the divergence-free Hilbert spaces $\ker(\text{div}_0)$ respectively $\ker(\text{div})$, sub-Hilbert spaces of $L^2(\Lambda, \mathbb{C}^r)$. First, we consider Laplacians $-\Delta_\rho^{rc}$ acting component-wise in $L^2(\Lambda, \mathbb{C}^r)$, which, however, turn out not to be reducibly to the divergence-free Hilbert spaces. The upper index "rc" means r components, where $r \geq 2$. So, finally, divergence-free Laplacians have to be defined in terms of sesquilinear forms on $\ker(\text{div}_0)$ respectively $\ker(\text{div})$. Analogously to Sec. 44.2 for the 1-component Laplacians, ρ may imagined as a formal matrix function on the boundary $\partial\Lambda$.

44.6.1.   *Non-Reducibility to Divergence-Freeness*

In the r-component Hilbert space $L^2(\Lambda, \mathbb{C}^r)$, the Dirichlet and Neumann boundary conditions are treated component-wise. For $\rho \in \{\infty, 0\}$, the sesquilinear form h_ρ^{rc} on $L^2(\Lambda, \mathbb{C}^r)$ is given by

$$h_\rho^{rc}(\psi, \phi) := \sum_{j=1}^{r} (\nabla\psi_j | \nabla\phi_j) = \sum_{j=1}^{r} h_\rho(\psi_j, \phi_j), \quad \forall \psi, \phi \in \text{dom}(h_\rho^{rc}), \tag{44.6.1}$$

where $\text{dom}(h_\infty^{rc}) = W_0^1(\Lambda, \mathbb{C}^r)$ and $\text{dom}(h_0^{rc}) = W^1(\Lambda, \mathbb{C}^r)$, with the associated 1-component Dirichlet or Neumann form h_ρ on $L^2(\Lambda, \mathbb{C})$ from Eqs. (44.2.1), respectively (44.2.2). To the form h_ρ^{rc} there corresponds the r-component positive, self-adjoint Laplacian $-\Delta_\rho^{rc}$ on the Hilbert space $L^2(\Lambda, \mathbb{C}^r)$, given in each component by $-\Delta_\rho$ in $L^2(\Lambda, \mathbb{C})$. That is

$$-\Delta_\rho^{rc}\psi = (-\Delta_\rho\psi_1, \ldots, -\Delta_\rho\psi_r), \quad \psi = (\psi_1, \ldots, \psi_r) \in \text{dom}(-\Delta_\rho^{rc}), \tag{44.6.2}$$

with the domain of definition $\text{dom}(-\Delta_\rho^{rc}) = \bigoplus_{j=1}^{r} \text{dom}(-\Delta_\rho) \subset L^2(\Lambda, \mathbb{C}^r)$.

If we go over to mixed boundary conditions for interior Λ, we find a greater variety of boundary forms in terms of the surface integrals

$$b_\rho^{rc}(\psi, \phi) := \int_{\partial\Lambda} \overline{\psi(x)} \cdot \rho(x)\phi(x) \, dS(x), \quad \forall \psi, \phi \in \mathrm{dom}(b_\rho^{rc}) := \mathrm{W}^1(\Lambda, \mathbb{C}^r), \quad (44.6.3)$$

where for every $x \in \partial\Lambda$ the expression $\rho(x)$ is a positive $r \times r$-matrix. We assume a sufficiently smooth boundary $\partial\Lambda$. Then similarly to the 1-component case in Eq. (44.2.4) the form $h_\rho^{rc} = h_0^{rc} + b_\rho^{rc}$ defines the Laplacian $-\Delta_\rho^{rc}$ on $\mathrm{L}^2(\Lambda, \mathbb{C}^r)$.

Unfortunately, the divergence-free Hilbert spaces $\mathrm{ker}(\mathrm{div}_0)$ respectively $\mathrm{ker}(\mathrm{div})$ do not constitute in general reducing subspaces for the r-component self-adjoint Laplacians $-\Delta_\rho^{rc}$. Only in free space $\Lambda = \mathbb{R}^r$ (see Sec. 44.8) and for periodic boundary conditions, (see Proposition 44.7-4) the reduction is possible.

Observation 44.6-1 (No-Go Argument for Parallelepipeds). For $r \geq 2$ consider the rectangular parallelepiped Λ_a with $a \in \,]0, \infty[^r$ from Eq. (44.2.10) on page 1578. The r-component Dirichlet and Neumann Laplacians in $\mathrm{L}^2(\Lambda_a, \mathbb{C}^r)$, $-\Delta_\infty^{rc}$ respectively $-\Delta_0^{rc}$, are not reducible by the divergence-free sub-Hilbert spaces $\mathrm{ker}(\mathrm{div}_0)$ respectively $\mathrm{ker}(\mathrm{div})$.

Proof. We treat only the Dirichlet case since the Neumann case works analogously. In order that $\mathrm{ker}(\mathrm{div}_0)$ or $\mathrm{ker}(\mathrm{div})$ reduce $-\Delta_\infty^{rc}$, the orthogonal projections onto $\mathrm{ker}(\mathrm{div}_0)$ respectively $\mathrm{ker}(\mathrm{div})$ have to commute with all spectral projections of $-\Delta_\infty^{rc}$, especially with the projection onto the eigenspace E_{low} of the lowest eigenvalue. That means, E_{low} should decompose orthogonally according to either of the two orthogonal decompositions $\mathrm{L}^2(\Lambda, \mathbb{C}^r) = \mathrm{ran}(\mathrm{grad}_0) \oplus \mathrm{ker}(\mathrm{div}) = \mathrm{ran}(\mathrm{grad}) \oplus \mathrm{ker}(\mathrm{div}_0)$ from Eq. (44.4.4), where by Lemma 44.4-5, the images of grad_0 and grad are already closed.

From Sec. 44.2.4, we conclude that $E_{\mathrm{low}} = \{b e_{\mathrm{low}} \mid b \in \mathbb{C}^r\}$ with the lowest eigenfunction e_{low} of the 1-component Dirichlet Laplacian $-\Delta_\infty$,

$$e_{\mathrm{low}}(x) = \prod_{j=1}^r a_j^{-1/2} \phi_1(x_j/a_j) = \frac{1}{\sqrt{a_1 \cdots a_r}} \cos(\pi x_1/(2a_1)) \cdots \cos(\pi x_r/(2a_r))$$

for all $x \in \Lambda_a$. It is immediately checked that for $b \neq 0$ the divergence $\nabla \cdot (b e_{\mathrm{low}})$ does not vanish on the boundary $\partial\Lambda_a$ nor in Λ_a. Thus $b e_{\mathrm{low}} \notin \mathrm{ker}(\mathrm{div})$, respectively $E_{\mathrm{low}} \cap \mathrm{ker}(\mathrm{div}) = \{0\}$. In order that $b e_{\mathrm{low}} = \nabla \varphi$ for some $\varphi : \Lambda_a \to \mathbb{C}$, one would have component-wise $\frac{\partial \varphi}{\partial x_j} = b_j e_{\mathrm{low}}$ for every $j \in \{1, \ldots, r\}$, which is not possible for $r \geq 2$. Hence $E_{\mathrm{low}} \cap \mathrm{ran}(\mathrm{grad}) = \{0\}$.

Summarizing we conclude that none of the lowest eigenelements $b e_{\mathrm{low}}$, $b \neq 0$, is contained in one of the closed subspaces $\mathrm{ker}(\mathrm{div}_0) \subset \mathrm{ker}(\mathrm{div})$ and $\mathrm{ran}(\mathrm{grad}_0) \subset \mathrm{ran}(\mathrm{grad})$, a contradiction. $\qquad\square$

We recognize that it is not possible to restrict respectively to reduce the r-component Laplacians $-\Delta_\rho^{rc}$ from $L^2(\Lambda, \mathbb{C}^r)$ to the divergence-free Hilbert spaces in order to obtain *self-adjoint* divergence-free Laplace operators. Consequently, one has to define divergence-free Laplacians $-\Delta_\rho^{div}$ (acting on $\ker(div_0)$ respectively on $\ker(div)$) in terms of sesquilinear forms of the type

$$h_\rho^{div}(\phi, \psi) = \sum_{j=1}^{r} (\nabla\phi_j | \nabla\psi_j) + b_\rho^{rc}(\psi, \phi) \tag{44.6.4}$$

on suitable domains depending on the boundary condition ρ, given by sub-Sobolev spaces of order one, $\|.\|$-dense in the respective divergence-free Hilbert spaces.

44.6.2.   *Dirichlet Boundary Condition*

We suppose here that $\Lambda \subset \mathbb{R}^r$ is interior and piece-wise C^1-smooth.

For the definition of the divergence-free Dirichlet Laplacian $-\Delta_\infty^{div}$ we have to choose the divergence-free Hilbert space $\ker(div_0)$, part of the orthogonal decomposition

$$L^2(\Lambda, \mathbb{C}^r) = \overline{ran(grad)} \oplus \ker(div_0)$$

from Eq. (44.4.4). The reason for choosing $\ker(div_0)$ lies in the fact that only in this case the divergence-free Sobolev space $\ker(div_0) \cap W_0^1(\Lambda, \mathbb{C}^r)$ is $\|.\|$-dense in $\ker(div_0)$ by Proposition 44.4-16 on page 1600, and is a $\|.\|_1$-closed subspace of $W_0^1(\Lambda, \mathbb{C}^r)$. The associated sesquilinear form h_∞^{div} is defined, in accordance with the above considerations, as

$$h_\infty^{div}(\phi, \psi) = \sum_{j=1}^{r} (\nabla\phi_j | \nabla\psi_j) = \sum_{j=1}^{r} h_\infty(\psi_j, \phi_j), \tag{44.6.5}$$

with the 1-component Dirichlet form h_∞ from Eq. (44.2.1). We take $\phi = (\phi_1, \ldots, \phi_r)$ and $\psi = (\psi_1, \ldots, \psi_r)$ from the form domain

$$dom(h_\infty^{div}) := \ker(div_0) \cap W_0^1(\Lambda, \mathbb{C}^r) = \{\psi \in W_0^1(\Lambda, \mathbb{C}^r) \mid \nabla \cdot \psi = 0\}. \tag{44.6.6}$$

So the form h_∞^{div} is just the restriction of the r-component Dirichlet form h_∞^{rc} from $L^2(\Lambda, \mathbb{C}^r)$ to the divergence-free sub-Hilbert space $\ker(div_0)$. From the foregoing considerations it follows that the associated self-adjoint Dirichlet Laplacians are *not* obtainable simply by a restriction.

By construction, the densely defined divergence-free Dirichlet form h_∞^{div} is positive, closed, and unbounded on the Hilbert space $\ker(div_0)$. So similarly to the 1-component Laplacians and the curlcurls we may apply Theorem 43.5-10(a) to obtain the uniquely associated, positive, self-adjoint Laplace operator $-\Delta_\infty^{div}$ in the Hilbert space $\ker(div_0)$. $-\Delta_\infty^{div}$ has a pure point spectrum accumulating only at infinity, where its lowest eigenvalue is larger or equal to the lowest eigenvalue $\lambda_1 > 0$ of the 1-component Dirichlet Laplacian $-\Delta_\infty$ on $L^2(\Lambda, \mathbb{C})$. (This follows from Eq. (44.6.5), since $h_\infty^{div}(\psi, \psi) = \sum_j h_\infty(\psi_j, \psi_j) \geq \lambda_1 \|\psi\|^2$.)

Finally let us remark that $-\Delta_\infty^{\mathrm{div}}$ is the Friedrichs extension of the symmetric operator $-P_{\mathrm{div}_0}\Delta_\infty^{\mathrm{rc}}$ on $\ker(\mathrm{div}_0)$, where P_{div_0} denotes the orthogonal projection of $L^2(\Lambda, \mathbb{C}^r)$ onto $\ker(\mathrm{div}_0)$. In case of $\mathbb{C}^2$-smoothness of Λ one finds that

$$\mathrm{dom}(-\Delta_\infty^{\mathrm{div}}) = \mathrm{dom}(h_\infty^{\mathrm{div}}) \cap \mathrm{W}^2(\Lambda, \mathbb{C}^r),$$

which resembles the 1-component Dirichlet case where, according to Theorem 44.2-3 (a) on page 1573, we have $\mathrm{dom}(-\Delta_\infty) = \mathrm{dom}(h_\infty) \cap \mathrm{W}^2(\Lambda, \mathbb{C})$.

If $r = 3$, we may reduce the curlcurl operator curl_{n0}^2 to the divergence-free Hilbert space $\ker(\mathrm{div}_0) = \mathbb{H}_1 \oplus \overline{\mathrm{ran}(\mathrm{curl}_0)}$ in the form $\mathrm{curl}_{n0,\mathrm{div}}^2 := 0 \oplus \mathrm{curl}_{n0}^2|$. The associated form arises from the restriction of h_{n0} to $\ker(\mathrm{div}_0)$, with the $\|.\|$-dense domain

$$\ker(\mathrm{div}_0) \cap \mathrm{W}(\mathrm{curl}; \Lambda, \mathbb{C}^3) = \{\psi \in \mathrm{W}^1(\Lambda, \mathbb{C}^3) \mid \nabla \cdot \psi = 0, \ \psi \cdot n|_{\partial\Lambda} = 0\}.$$

Since Λ is supposed to be interior, it follows from Theorem 44.5-2 that $\mathrm{curl}_{n0,\mathrm{div}}^2$ has a pure point spectrum accumulating only at infinity. Here the finite-dimensional, possibly non-vanishing kernel

$$\ker(\mathrm{curl}_{n0,\mathrm{div}}^2) = \mathbb{H}_1 \tag{44.6.7}$$

has to be taken into account for numbering the increasing eigenvalues. Let us compare the eigenvalues of the divergence-free Dirichlet Laplacian $-\Delta_\infty^{\mathrm{div}}$ with those of the divergence-free curlcurl $\mathrm{curl}_{n0,\mathrm{div}}^2$.

Lemma 44.6-2. *For $r = 3$ let $\Lambda \subset \mathbb{R}^3$ be interior and piece-wise $\mathbb{C}^1$-smooth. Then we have $h_\infty^{\mathrm{div}}(\phi, \psi) = h_{n0}(\phi, \psi)$ for all $\phi, \psi \in \mathrm{dom}(h_\infty^{\mathrm{div}}) \subseteq \ker(\mathrm{div}_0) \cap \mathrm{W}(\mathrm{curl}; \Lambda, \mathbb{C}^3)$. Thus $\lambda_k^\infty \geq \lambda_k^{n0}$ for all $k \in \mathbb{N}$ by Corollary 43.5-11, where $(\lambda_k^\infty)_{k\in\mathbb{N}}$ denotes the eigenvalues of $-\Delta_\infty^{\mathrm{div}}$ and $(\lambda_k^{n0})_{k\in\mathbb{N}}$ those of $\mathrm{curl}_{n0,\mathrm{div}}^2$ in increasing order (repeated according to their multiplicity).*

Proof. From the well known relation $\nabla \times (\nabla \times \psi) = \nabla(\nabla \cdot \psi) - \Delta\psi$ it follows with partial integration that $(\nabla \times \phi|\nabla \times \psi) = -(\nabla \cdot \phi|\nabla \cdot \psi) + h_\infty^{\mathrm{div}}(\phi, \psi)$ for all $\phi, \psi \in \mathrm{W}_0^1(\Lambda, \mathbb{C}^3)$ (first take smooth functions and then use a density argument). Now observe Eq. (44.6.6). $\qquad \square$

44.6.3. *Neumann Boundary Condition*

For a $\mathbb{C}^2$-smooth interior domain $\Lambda \subset \mathbb{R}^r$ it follows that $\ker(\mathrm{div}) \cap \mathrm{W}^1(\Lambda, \mathbb{C}^r)$ is $\|.\|$-dense in $\ker(\mathrm{div})$ according to Sec. 44.4.6. Hence the divergence-free Neumann Laplacian $-\Delta_0^{\mathrm{div}}$ is well defined in the divergence-free Hilbert space $\ker(\mathrm{div})$ (also for mixed boundary conditions). The Neumann sesquilinear form on $\ker(\mathrm{div})$ is given by

$$h_0^{\mathrm{div}}(\phi, \psi) = \sum_{j=1}^{r} (\nabla \phi_j | \nabla \psi_j) = \sum_{j=1}^{r} h_0(\psi_j, \phi_j), \qquad (44.6.8)$$

with the one-component Neumann form h_0 from Eq. (44.2.2). We take $\phi = (\phi_1, \ldots, \phi_r)$ and $\psi = (\psi_1, \ldots, \psi_r)$ from the form domain

$$\mathrm{dom}(h_0^{\mathrm{div}}) := \ker(\mathrm{div}) \cap \mathrm{W}^1(\Lambda, \mathbb{C}^r), \qquad (44.6.9)$$

which is a $\|.\|_1$-closed subspace of $\mathrm{W}^1(\Lambda, \mathbb{C}^r)$. The form h_0^{div} is just the restriction of the r-component Neumann form h_0^{rc} from $\mathrm{L}^2(\Lambda, \mathbb{C}^r)$ to the divergence-free sub-Hilbert space $\ker(\mathrm{div})$. Again, in contrast to the forms, the associated self-adjoint Neumann Laplacians do *not* simply arise by restriction.

The same techniques as for the divergence-free Dirichlet Laplacian lead to the unique positive, self-adjoint Laplacian $-\Delta_0^{\mathrm{div}}$ acting in the divergence-free Hilbert space $\ker(\mathrm{div})$ with Neumann boundary conditions. Its spectrum is purely discrete and accumulates only at infinity. The lowest eigenvalue vanishes: it corresponds to the constant functions on Λ. $-\Delta_0^{\mathrm{div}}$ is just the Friedrichs extension of the symmetric operator $-P_{\mathrm{div}}\Delta_0^{\mathrm{rc}}$ on $\ker(\mathrm{div})$, where P_{div} indicates the orthogonal projection of $\mathrm{L}^2(\Lambda, \mathbb{C}^r)$ onto $\ker(\mathrm{div})$.

44.7. Operators with (Almost) Periodic Boundary Conditions

In physics, periodic boundary conditions over a parallelepiped are rather popular. We use them especially for radiation in a rectangular cavity and for electrons in a periodic crystal, where in both cases periodicity has a physical justification. The temptation (which we resist in the book) to use periodic boundary conditions also without physical motivation arises from their simplifying effect. One can use the theory of Fourier series and comfortably deal with explicit eigenvalues and eigenfunctions.

We introduce the so-called periodic Sobolev spaces to obtain vectorial differential operators with periodic boundary conditions as closed respectively self-adjoint operators. This makes these operators comparable with those under previously treated boundary conditions. Also we use explicit eigenfunctions in our arguments and earn a considerable simplification in comparison to the previous Sobolev theory. Our approach allows for an (almost) periodic Helmholtz–Hodge theory.

Up to the last Sec. 44.7.5, in the present section, we consider for the Euclidean dimension $r \geq 2$ the rectangular, open parallelepiped

$$\Lambda_a = \{x \in \mathbb{R}^r \mid -a_j < x_j < a_j, \ j = 1, \ldots, r\} =]-a_1, a_1[\times \cdots \times]-a_r, a_r[\,,$$

with fixed $a = (a_1, \ldots, a_r) \in]0, \infty[^r$. As before, we assume $r = 3$ if a rotation comes into play.

44.7.1.   *Periodic Sobolev Spaces*

A function $\tilde{\psi} : \mathbb{R}^r \to \mathbb{C}$ is called $2a$-*periodic*, if for every choice of $n_j \in \{0, 1\}$, $j = 1, \ldots, r$, and thus also for every $n = (n_1, \ldots, n_r) \in \mathbb{Z}^r$, one has

$$\tilde{\psi}(x_1 + n_1 2a_1, \ldots, x_r + n_r 2a_r) = \tilde{\psi}(x), \quad \forall x \in \mathbb{R}^r. \qquad (44.7.1)$$

If for fixed j, Eq. (44.7.1) is only valid for $n_j \in \mathbb{Z}$ and the special values $0 = n_l$ for $l \neq j$, the function $\tilde{\psi}$ is termed j-*partially* $2a$-*periodic*.

We denote by $\mathrm{C}_{\mathrm{per},a}^m(\mathbb{R}^r, \mathbb{C})$ the m-times continuously differentiable, $2a$-periodic functions $\tilde{\psi} : \mathbb{R}^r \to \mathbb{C}$. Their derivatives $\partial^s \tilde{\psi}$ are then also $2a$-periodic, for $|s| \leq m$.

An element $\psi \in \mathrm{C}(\bar{\Lambda}_a, \mathbb{C})$ is called $2a$-periodic, if it is the restriction of an $2a$-periodic function $\tilde{\psi} : \mathbb{R}^r \to \mathbb{C}$, that is

$$\{\psi \in \mathrm{C}(\bar{\Lambda}_a, \mathbb{C}) \mid \psi \text{ is } 2a\text{-periodic}\} = \mathrm{C}_{\mathrm{per},a}(\mathbb{R}^r, \mathbb{C})|_{\Lambda_a}.$$

Note that for $m \geq 1$ the set $\mathrm{C}_{\mathrm{per},a}^m(\mathbb{R}^r, \mathbb{C})|_{\Lambda_a}$ is only a proper subspace of $\{\psi \in \mathrm{C}^m(\bar{\Lambda}_a, \mathbb{C}) \mid \psi \text{ is } 2a\text{-periodic}\}$, since each $2a$-periodic $\psi \in \mathrm{C}^m(\bar{\Lambda}_a, \mathbb{C})$ may be extended uniquely to a $\tilde{\psi} \in \mathrm{C}_{\mathrm{per},a}(\mathbb{R}^r, \mathbb{C})$, the derivatives $\partial^s \tilde{\psi}$ of which, may be, however, discontinuous on the boundary $\partial\Lambda_a$. Observe that every $\psi \in \mathrm{C}(\bar{\Lambda}_a, \mathbb{C})$, which is constant on the boundary $\partial\Lambda_a$, is $2a$-periodic. So the test function space $\mathrm{C}_c^\infty(\Lambda_a, \mathbb{C})$ consists of $2a$-periodic functions, and we have for every $m \in \mathbb{N}_0 \cup \{\infty\}$ the proper inclusion

$$\mathrm{C}_c^m(\Lambda_a, \mathbb{C}) \subset \mathrm{C}_{\mathrm{per},a}^m(\mathbb{R}^r, \mathbb{C})|_{\Lambda_a}.$$

Analogously we say that for fixed $j \in \{1, \ldots, r\}$ a function $\psi \in \mathrm{C}(\bar{\Lambda}_a, \mathbb{C})$ is j-partially $2a$-periodic, if it is the restriction of a j-partially $2a$-periodic $\tilde{\psi} : \mathbb{R}^r \to \mathbb{C}$.

Let us define the *periodic Sobolev space* $\mathrm{W}_{\mathrm{per}}^1(\Lambda_a, \mathbb{C})$ by the following closure with respect to the Sobolev norm $\|.\|_1$, arising from the Sobolev inner product $(.|.)_1$ from Eq. (44.1.7),

$$\mathrm{W}_{\mathrm{per}}^1(\Lambda_a, \mathbb{C}) := \overline{\{\psi \in \mathrm{C}^1(\bar{\Lambda}_a, \mathbb{C}) \mid \psi \text{ is } 2a\text{-periodic}\}}^{\|.\|_1}. \qquad (44.7.2)$$

Thus, these "periodic" Sobolev elements are classes of functions, possessing locally square integrable, weak derivatives, which are also approximated by continuous periodic functions.

From Definition 44.1-5 and Proposition 44.1-8(a), we deduce that the following inclusions are proper

$$\mathrm{W}_0^1(\Lambda_a, \mathbb{C}) \subset \mathrm{W}_{\mathrm{per}}^1(\Lambda_a, \mathbb{C}) \subset \mathrm{W}^1(\Lambda_a, \mathbb{C}).$$

The identical embedding $\mathrm{W}^1(\Lambda_a, \mathbb{C}) \hookrightarrow \mathrm{L}^2(\Lambda_a, \mathbb{C})$ is compact by Proposition 44.1-8(d), and therefore the same is true for $\mathrm{W}_{\mathrm{per}}^1(\Lambda_a, \mathbb{C}) \hookrightarrow \mathrm{L}^2(\Lambda_a, \mathbb{C})$.

The *periodic div and curl Sobolev spaces* are defined as in Eq. (44.7.2) in analogy to the div and curl Sobolev spaces from Sec. 44.1.4,

$$W_{per}(div; \Lambda_a, \mathbb{C}^r) := \overline{\{\psi \in C^1(\bar{\Lambda}_a, \mathbb{C}^r) \mid \psi \text{ is } 2a\text{-periodic}\}}^{\|\cdot\|_{div}},$$

$$W_{per}(curl; \Lambda_a, \mathbb{C}^3) := \overline{\{\psi \in C^1(\bar{\Lambda}_a, \mathbb{C}^3) \mid \psi \text{ is } 2a\text{-periodic}\}}^{\|\cdot\|_{curl}}.$$

It is immediate to check that the following inclusions are proper

$$W_0(div; \Lambda_a, \mathbb{C}^r) \subset W_{per}(div; \Lambda_a, \mathbb{C}^r) \subset W(div; \Lambda_a, \mathbb{C}^r),$$

$$W_0(curl; \Lambda_a, \mathbb{C}^3) \subset W_{per}(curl; \Lambda_a, \mathbb{C}^3) \subset W(curl; \Lambda_a, \mathbb{C}^3).$$

Later on we shall see that $C^\infty_{per,a}(\mathbb{R}^r, \mathbb{C})|_{\Lambda_a}$ is $\|.\|_1$-dense in the periodic Sobolev space $W^1_{per}(\Lambda_a, \mathbb{C})$, and moreover, $C^\infty_{per,a}(\mathbb{R}^r, \mathbb{C}^r)|_{\Lambda_a}$ is dense in the div Sobolev space $W_{per}(div; \Lambda_a, \mathbb{C}^r)$ as well as in the curl Sobolev space $W_{per}(curl; \Lambda_a, \mathbb{C}^3)$ with respect to the associated norms $\|.\|_{div}$ respectively $\|.\|_{curl}$. Furthermore, we will find later

$$W_{per}(div; \Lambda_a, \mathbb{C}^3) \cap W_{per}(curl; \Lambda_a, \mathbb{C}^3) = W^1_{per}(\Lambda_a, \mathbb{C}^3),$$

as well as $\|\psi\|_{div,curl} = \|\psi\|_1$ for all $\psi \in W^1_{per}(\Lambda_a, \mathbb{C}^3)$, where the norm $\|.\|_{div,curl}$ is defined as in Eq. (44.1.15).

44.7.2.   *The Self-adjoint Periodic Laplacian*

The task to construct the positive, self-adjoint (one-component) Laplacian $-\Delta_{per}$ with periodic boundary condition on $L^2(\Lambda_a, \mathbb{C})$ is completely analogous to that in the Dirichlet and Neumann case. It is defined in terms of the sesquilinear form h_{per} on the Hilbert space $L^2(\Lambda_a, \mathbb{C})$, given by

$$h_{per}(\psi, \phi) := (\nabla\psi | \nabla\phi), \quad \forall \psi, \phi \in dom(h_{per}) := W^1_{per}(\Lambda_a, \mathbb{C}). \tag{44.7.3}$$

The only difference to the Dirichlet respectively Neumann forms (from Eqs. (44.2.1) and (44.2.2)) is seen to be the domain of definition. Analogously to Proposition 44.2-1, the form h_{per} leads to the Laplacian with periodic boundary conditions: By construction the form h_{per} is positive, closed, and unbounded, and thus Theorem 43.5-10 (a) on page 1543 ensures, in the standard way, the existence of a unique self-adjoint operator $-\Delta_{per}$ in $L^2(\Lambda_a, \mathbb{C})$ — denoted *periodic Laplacian* — satisfying $dom(-\Delta_{per}) \subseteq dom(h_{per})$ and

$$h_{per}(\psi, \phi) = (\psi | -\Delta_{per}\phi), \quad \forall \psi \in dom(h_{per}), \quad \forall \phi \in dom(-\Delta_{per}).$$

Since the identical embedding $W^1_{per}(\Lambda_a, \mathbb{C}) \hookrightarrow L^2(\Lambda_a, \mathbb{C})$ is compact, it again follows that $-\Delta_{per}$ has a pure point spectrum accumulating only at infinity (by Proposition 43.5-11). The eigenspace of the lowest eigenvalue $\lambda_1 = 0$ consists of the constant functions, as for the Neumann Laplacian.

The periodic Laplacian $-\Delta_{\text{per}}$ is C-real with respect to the common complex conjugation C on $\text{L}^2(\Lambda_a, \mathbb{C})$, and hence the eigenfunctions e_k may be chosen $\mathbb{R}$-valued (cf. Theorem 44.2-3(d)).

As in Proposition 44.2-8, one may compare the eigenvalues of the three different Laplacians over the parallelepiped Λ_a by applying Proposition 43.5-11.

Proposition 44.7-1. *We denote by $(\lambda_k^\rho)_{k \in \mathbb{N}}$ the eigenvalues of $-\Delta_\rho$ in increasing order, where $\rho \in \{\infty, 0, \text{per}\}$ indicate the three different Laplacians. Then we find*

$$0 \le \lambda_k^0 \le \lambda_k^{\text{per}} \le \lambda_k^\infty , \quad \forall k \in \mathbb{N}.$$

We now prove that, in application to twice continuously differentiable $2a$-periodic functions, $-\Delta_{\text{per}}$ acts by ordinary differentiation.

Lemma 44.7-2. *We have the inclusion $\text{C}^2_{\text{per},a}(\mathbb{R}^r, \mathbb{C})|_{\Lambda_a} \subseteq \text{dom}(-\Delta_{\text{per}})$, and find that $-\Delta_{\text{per}}$ operates on theses functions $\psi \in \text{C}^2_{\text{per},a}(\mathbb{R}^r, \mathbb{C})|_{\Lambda_a}$ by ordinary differentiation, $-\Delta_{\text{per}}\psi = -\Delta\psi$.*

Proof. For $2a$-periodic $\psi \in \text{C}^1(\bar{\Lambda}_a, \mathbb{C})$ and $\phi \in \text{C}^2_{\text{per},a}(\mathbb{R}^r, \mathbb{C})|_{\Lambda_a}$ Green's formula may be applied over the domain Λ_a, with a piece-wise smooth boundary, and leads to

$$h_{\text{per}}(\psi, \phi) = (\psi| - \Delta\phi) + \int_{\partial\Lambda_a} \overline{\psi}\, \frac{\partial\phi}{\partial n}\, dS.$$

Since $\nabla\phi$ is also $2a$-periodic and the outer normal n of the boundary has pair-wise opposite sign, it follows that the boundary integral vanishes. Hence $h_{\text{per}}(\psi, \phi) = (\psi| - \Delta\phi)$. On the other hand, one has $h_{\text{per}}(\psi, \phi) = (\psi| - \Delta_{\text{per}}\phi)$ for $\psi \in \text{W}^1_{\text{per}}(\Lambda_a, \mathbb{C})$ and $\phi \in \text{dom}(-\Delta_{\text{per}})$, which gives the result. □

With the foregoing Lemma in mind one may search for eigenfunctions $e_k \in \text{C}^2_{\text{per},a}(\mathbb{R}^r, \mathbb{C})|_{\Lambda_a}$ satisfying $-\Delta_{\text{per}}e_k = -\Delta e_k = \lambda_k e_k$ in the sense of ordinary differentiation. Labeled by the multi-indices $n = (n_1, \dots, n_r) \in \mathbb{Z}^r$, an orthonormal basis of eigenvectors for $\text{L}^2(\Lambda_a, \mathbb{C})$, is given by the following functions $e_n \in \text{C}^\infty_{\text{per},a}(\mathbb{R}^r, \mathbb{C})|_{\Lambda_a}$

$$e_n(x) = |\Lambda_a|^{-1/2} \exp\{i\pi \tfrac{n}{a} \cdot x\}, \quad \forall x = (x_1, \dots, x_r) \in \Lambda_a. \qquad (44.7.4)$$

We have written symbolically $\frac{n}{a}$ for the vector $(\frac{n_1}{a_1}, \dots, \frac{n_r}{a_r}) \in \mathbb{R}^r$, so that $\frac{n}{a} \cdot x = \sum_{j=1}^{r} a_j^{-1} n_j x_j$. $|\Lambda_a|$ denotes the r-dimensional volume of Λ_a. The eigenvalue λ_n of e_n has the form

$$\lambda_n = \pi^2 \sum_{j=1}^{r} \frac{n_j^2}{a_j^2} = \pi^2 \frac{n}{a} \cdot \frac{n}{a}. \qquad (44.7.5)$$

(From the theory of Fourier series we know that $\{y \mapsto (2\pi)^{-1} \exp\{iky\} \mid k \in \mathbb{Z}\}$ is an orthonormal basis in $\text{L}^2(]-\pi, \pi[, \mathbb{C})$ and can then rescale.)

As for the other classical boundary conditions, one immediately shows that $\{(1+\lambda_n)^{-1/2}e_n \mid n \in \mathbb{Z}^r\}$ constitutes an orthonormal basis of the Sobolev Hilbert space $W^1_{\text{per}}(\Lambda_a, \mathbb{C})$ (with respect to its inner product $(.|.)_1$). Since $e_n \in C^\infty_{\text{per},a}(\mathbb{R}^r, \mathbb{C})|_{\Lambda_a}$ it follows that $C^\infty_{\text{per},a}(\mathbb{R}^r, \mathbb{C})|_{\Lambda_a}$ is $\|.\|_1$-dense in $W^1_{\text{per}}(\Lambda_a, \mathbb{C})$.

Since $-\Delta_{\text{per}}$ is C-real, we may obtain a real orthonormal eigensystem. Explicitly, we conclude from $Ce_n = e_{-n}$ that $\text{Re}(e_{-n}) = \text{Re}(e_n)$ and $\text{Im}(e_{-n}) = -\text{Im}(e_n)$. With $[n] := \{-n, n\}$, we write for every $[n] \in \mathbb{Z}^r|_{\text{mod}\pm}$,

$$e^{\text{Re}}_{[n]} = \sqrt{2}\,\text{Re}(e_n) = \tfrac{1}{\sqrt{2}}(e_n + Ce_n), \quad e^{\text{Im}}_{[n]} = \sqrt{2}\,\text{Im}(e_n) = \tfrac{1}{i\sqrt{2}}(e_n - Ce_n),$$

and get $\{e^{\text{Re}}_{[n]}, e^{\text{Im}}_{[n]} \mid [n] \in \mathbb{Z}^r|_{\text{mod}\pm}\}$ as a real orthonormal eigensystem of $L^2(\Lambda_a, \mathbb{C})$.

44.7.3. *Periodic Grad, Div, and Curl Operators*

Because we have now different domains of definition we have to re-define the vectorial differential operators, what we carry out in close analogy to Definition 44.4-1. So we introduce the periodic gradient, divergence, and curl operators by

$$
\begin{aligned}
\text{grad}_{\text{per}}\,\varphi &:= \nabla\varphi, & \forall\varphi \in \text{dom}(\text{grad}_{\text{per}}) &:= W^1_{\text{per}}(\Lambda_a, \mathbb{C}), \\
\text{div}_{\text{per}}\,\phi &:= \nabla \cdot \phi, & \forall\phi \in \text{dom}(\text{div}_{\text{per}}) &:= W_{\text{per}}(\text{div}; \Lambda_a, \mathbb{C}^r), \quad (44.7.6) \\
\text{curl}_{\text{per}}\,\psi &:= \nabla \times \psi, & \forall\psi \in \text{dom}(\text{curl}_{\text{per}}) &:= W_{\text{per}}(\text{curl}; \Lambda_a, \mathbb{C}^3).
\end{aligned}
$$

It is plain that grad_{per} acts from $L^2(\Lambda_a, \mathbb{C})$ into $L^2(\Lambda_a, \mathbb{C}^r)$, div_{per} acts from $L^2(\Lambda_a, \mathbb{C}^r)$ into $L^2(\Lambda_a, \mathbb{C})$, and curl_{per} operates on $L^2(\Lambda_a, \mathbb{C}^3)$.

By construction, these three operator are closed and C-real. Since the periodic functions $e_n : \Lambda_a \to \mathbb{C}$, $n \in \mathbb{Z}^r$, from Eq. (44.7.4) constitute an orthonormal system for $L^2(\Lambda_a, \mathbb{C})$, it follows that with every orthonormal basis $\{\epsilon_1, \ldots, \epsilon_r\}$ of $\mathbb{C}^r$ we obtain the orthonormal basis $\{\epsilon_j e_n \mid j = 1, \ldots, r; \ n \in \mathbb{Z}^r\}$ of $L^2(\Lambda_a, \mathbb{C}^r)$. (Recall that $b\varphi(x) = (b_1\varphi(x), \ldots, b_r\varphi(x))$, $\forall x \in \Lambda_a$, for $b \in \mathbb{C}^r$ and $\varphi : \Lambda_a \to \mathbb{C}$.)

Obviously, we come up with the eigenvalue relations

$$\text{grad}_{\text{per}}\,e_n = i\pi\tfrac{n}{a}e_n, \quad \text{div}_{\text{per}}\,be_n = i\pi b \cdot \tfrac{n}{a}e_n, \quad \text{curl}_{\text{per}}\,be_n = i\pi b \times \tfrac{n}{a}e_n, \quad (44.7.7)$$

for each $b \in \mathbb{C}^r$ and every $n \in \mathbb{Z}^r$.

Now it is an easy matter to show that $\{\epsilon_j e_n \mid j = 1, \ldots, r; \ n \in \mathbb{Z}^r\}$ is a complete orthogonal system of $W_{\text{per}}(\text{div}; \Lambda_a, \mathbb{C}^r)$ respectively of $W_{\text{per}}(\text{curl}; \Lambda_a, \mathbb{C}^3)$ with respect to the inner products $(.|.)_{\text{div}}$ respectively $(.|.)_{\text{curl}}$. Since $e_n \in C^\infty_{\text{per},a}(\mathbb{R}^r, \mathbb{C})|_{\Lambda_a}$ we conclude that $C^\infty_{\text{per},a}(\mathbb{R}^r, \mathbb{C}^r)|_{\Lambda_a}$ is $\|.\|_{\text{div}}$-dense in the Sobolev space $W_{\text{per}}(\text{div}; \Lambda_a, \mathbb{C}^r)$ respectively $\|.\|_{\text{curl}}$-dense in $W_{\text{per}}(\text{curl}; \Lambda_a, \mathbb{C}^3)$, as already mentioned in Sec. 44.7.1.

As a further consequence of Eq. (44.7.7), we conclude that the ranges of grad_{per}, div_{per}, and curl_{per} are closed (since their inverses [defined on suitable subspaces] are compact).

With the help of (44.7.7), we check the now simplified adjoint relations

$$\text{grad}^*_{\text{per}} = -\,\text{div}_{\text{per}}, \qquad \text{div}^*_{\text{per}} = -\,\text{grad}_{\text{per}}, \qquad \text{curl}^*_{\text{per}} = \text{curl}_{\text{per}} \qquad (44.7.8)$$

and realize the self-adjointness of curl_{per}. So we derive for the periodic Laplacian on $L^2(\Lambda_a, \mathbb{C})$

$$-\Delta_{\text{per}} = \text{grad}^*_{\text{per}} \text{grad}_{\text{per}} = -\,\text{div}_{\text{per}} \text{grad}_{\text{per}}. \qquad (44.7.9)$$

Using the same argumentation, which leads to Eq. (44.4.4) on page 1586, we obtain similar orthogonal decompositions

$$L^2(\Lambda_a, \mathbb{C}^r) = \text{ran}(\text{grad}_{\text{per}}) \oplus \text{ker}(\text{div}_{\text{per}}) = \text{ker}(\text{curl}_{\text{per}}) \oplus \text{ran}(\text{curl}_{\text{per}}). \qquad (44.7.10)$$

Let us introduce the periodic "cohomology" space

$$\mathbb{H}_{\text{per}} := \text{ker}(\text{div}_{\text{per}}) \cap \text{ker}(\text{curl}_{\text{per}}) = \{be_0 \mid b \in \mathbb{C}^3\}, \qquad (44.7.11)$$

which consists just of the constant vector fields. We obtain then for $r = 3$ the following Hodge decomposition

$$L^2(\Lambda_a, \mathbb{C}^3) = \underbrace{\text{ran}(\text{grad}_{\text{per}}) \oplus \mathbb{H}_{\text{per}}}_{= \text{ker}(\text{curl}_{\text{per}})} \overset{= \text{ker}(\text{div}_{\text{per}})}{\oplus \text{ran}(\text{curl}_{\text{per}})}, \qquad (44.7.12)$$

which we in addition establish, using the e_n of Eq. (44.7.7), by means of the following orthonormal basis: We choose an orthonormal basis $\{\epsilon_1^0, \ldots, \epsilon_r^0\}$ of $\mathbb{C}^r$ and label it by the index $0 \in \mathbb{Z}^r$. For each $0 \neq n \in \mathbb{Z}^r$, we form the normalized vector $n_a := |\frac{n}{a}|^{-1} \frac{n}{a} \in \mathbb{C}^r$ and supplement it to an orthonormal basis $\{\epsilon_1^n, \ldots, \epsilon_{r-1}^n, n_a\}$ of $\mathbb{C}^r$. For $n = 0$, we set $e_0^j := \epsilon_j^0 e_0$, and for $n \neq 0$ we define the following functions in $L^2(\Lambda_a, \mathbb{C}^r)$

$$e_n^\nabla := n_a e_n, \qquad e_n^j := \epsilon_j^n e_n,, \qquad \forall j = 1, \ldots, r-1. \qquad (44.7.13)$$

Then $\{e_n^\nabla \mid n \in \mathbb{Z}^r \backslash \{0\}\}$ constitutes an orthonormal basis of $\text{ran}(\text{grad}_{\text{per}})$, whereas $\{e_n^j \mid j = 1, \ldots, r-1;\ n \in \mathbb{Z}^r \backslash \{0\}\} \cup \{e_0^j \mid j = 1, \ldots, r\}$ forms an orthonormal basis of its orthogonal complement $\text{ker}(\text{div}_{\text{per}})$. Since, $e_n^j \in C^\infty_{\text{per},a}(\mathbb{R}^r, \mathbb{C}^r)|_{\Lambda_a}$, it follows that $\{\psi \in C^\infty_{\text{per},a}(\mathbb{R}^r, \mathbb{C}^r)|_{\Lambda_a} \mid \nabla \cdot \psi = 0\}$ is $\|.\|$-dense in $\text{ker}(\text{div}_{\text{per}})$. Finally, specializing to $r = 3$, we obtain that $\{e_0^1, e_0^2, e_0^3,\}$ is an orthonormal basis of $\mathbb{H}_{\text{per}}$, and $\{e_n^j \mid j = 1, 2;\ n \in \mathbb{Z}^r \backslash \{0\}\}$ accomplishes an orthonormal basis of $\text{ran}(\text{curl}_{\text{per}})$.

Lemma 44.7-3.

(a) *For $\psi \in C^1(\Lambda_a, \mathbb{C}^r) \cap C(\bar{\Lambda}_a, \mathbb{C}^r)$ it holds: $\psi \in \text{ker}(\text{div}_{\text{per}})$, if and only if $\nabla \cdot \psi = 0$ and for each $j = 1, \ldots, r$ the component function ψ_j is j-partially $2a$-periodic.*

(b) *We have the proper inclusions* $\ker(\mathrm{div}_0) \subset \ker(\mathrm{div}_{\mathrm{per}}) \subset \ker(\mathrm{div})$, *what implies that the following three orthogonal decompositions are mutually different,*

$$L^2(\Lambda_a, \mathbb{C}^r) = \mathrm{ran}(\mathrm{grad}_0) \oplus \ker(\mathrm{div})$$
$$= \mathrm{ran}(\mathrm{grad}_{\mathrm{per}}) \oplus \ker(\mathrm{div}_{\mathrm{per}})$$
$$= \mathrm{ran}(\mathrm{grad}) \oplus \ker(\mathrm{div}_0).$$

Proof. Part (a). Suppose $\psi \in \ker(\mathrm{div}_{\mathrm{per}})$. Then $\nabla \cdot \psi = 0$ leads to $\nabla \cdot (\eta\psi) = \eta(\nabla \cdot \psi) + \psi \cdot (\nabla \eta) = \psi \cdot (\nabla \eta)$ for all $\eta \in \mathrm{C}^1(\Lambda_a, \mathbb{C})$. On the other side, the orthogonal decomposition $L^2(\Lambda_a, \mathbb{C}^r) = \mathrm{ran}(\mathrm{grad}_{\mathrm{per}}) \oplus \ker(\mathrm{div}_{\mathrm{per}})$ yields $0 = (\nabla \overline{\eta} | \psi)$ for all $\eta \in \mathrm{C}^\infty_{\mathrm{per},a}(\mathbb{R}^r, \mathbb{C})|_{\Lambda_a}$. Now the Gauss theorem gives

$$0 = (\nabla \overline{\eta} | \psi) = \int_{\Lambda_a} \nabla \cdot (\eta\psi) d^r x = \int_{\partial\Lambda_a} \eta\psi \cdot n\, dS, \quad \forall \eta \in \mathrm{C}^\infty_{\mathrm{per},a}(\mathbb{R}^r, \mathbb{C})|_{\Lambda_a}.$$

With the specific form of Λ_a this is valid, if and only if each ψ_j is j-partially $2a$-periodic. Conversely we conclude that $\nabla \cdot \psi = 0$ and $\int_{\partial\Lambda_a} \eta\psi \cdot n\, dS = 0$ implies $(\nabla \overline{\eta} | \psi) = 0$ for all $\eta \in \mathrm{C}^\infty_{\mathrm{per},a}(\mathbb{R}^r, \mathbb{C})|_{\Lambda_a}$. Because $\mathrm{C}^\infty_{\mathrm{per},a}(\mathbb{R}^r, \mathbb{C})|_{\Lambda_a}$ is $\|.\|_1$-dense in $\mathrm{W}^1_{\mathrm{per}}(\Lambda_a, \mathbb{C})$, we obtain $\psi \perp \mathrm{ran}(\mathrm{grad}_{\mathrm{per}})$, or equivalently $\psi \in \ker(\mathrm{div}_{\mathrm{per}})$.

Part (b). For $\psi \in \mathrm{C}^1(\bar{\Lambda}_a, \mathbb{C}^r)$ one has: $\psi \in \ker(\mathrm{div})$, if and only if $\nabla \cdot \psi = 0$. $\psi \in \ker(\mathrm{div}_0)$, if and only if $\nabla \cdot \psi = 0$ and $\psi \cdot n|_{\partial\Lambda_a} = 0$, where the boundary condition is equivalent to: For every $j = 1, \ldots, r$ one has $\psi_j(x) = 0$ for $x \in \{x \in \partial\Lambda_a \mid x_j = \pm a_j\}$. For the periodic case, see part (a). Now it is immediate to verify that $\ker(\mathrm{div}_0) \subset \ker(\mathrm{div}_{\mathrm{per}}) \subset \ker(\mathrm{div})$ by constructing examples. □

44.7.4. *Periodic Multi-component Laplacian and Curlcurl*

The r-component periodic Laplacian $-\Delta^{rc}_{\mathrm{per}}$ on $L^2(\Lambda, \mathbb{C}^r)$ is defined component-wise, analogously to the r-component Dirichlet and Neumann Laplacians in Sec. 44.6.1. It corresponds to the r-component sesquilinear form h^{rc}_{per} with domain $\mathrm{W}^1_{\mathrm{per}}(\Lambda_a, \mathbb{C}^r)$. By construction the function be_n is an eigenvector for $-\Delta^{rc}_{\mathrm{per}}$ for every $b \in \mathbb{C}^r$ and each $n \in \mathbb{Z}^r$, fulfilling

$$-\Delta^{rc}_{\mathrm{per}}(be_n) = -b\Delta_{\mathrm{per}}e_n = \lambda_n(be_n), \quad \forall b \in \mathbb{C}^r, \quad \forall n \in \mathbb{Z}^r,$$

with the eigenvalue λ_n from Eq. (44.7.5). Consequently, the e^∇_n, e^j_n from Eq. (44.7.13) are eigenvectors for $-\Delta^{rc}_{\mathrm{per}}$. This proves the next result.

Proposition 44.7-4. $\mathrm{ran}(\mathrm{grad}_{\mathrm{per}})$, *and* $\ker(\mathrm{div}_{\mathrm{per}})$, *as well as* $\mathrm{ran}(\mathrm{curl}_{\mathrm{per}})$ *are reducing subspaces for the r-component periodic Laplacian* $-\Delta^{rc}_{\mathrm{per}}$ *on* $L^2(\Lambda_a, \mathbb{C}^r)$.

The periodic curlcurl operator is defined as the square of the self-adjoint curl operator $\mathrm{curl}_{\mathrm{per}}$ (we do not require a sesquilinear form here). With Eq. (44.7.12), we conclude from Sec. 43.7 that $\ker(\mathrm{div}_{\mathrm{per}})$ and $\mathrm{ran}(\mathrm{curl}_{\mathrm{per}})$ are reducing subspaces for $\text{curl}_{\text{per}}^2$. In each reduction to one of these spaces the periodic curlcurl operator has a pure point spectrum accumulating only at infinity.

Replacing in the well known formula $\nabla \times (\nabla \times \psi) = \nabla(\nabla \cdot \psi) - \Delta\psi$ the differentiations by our periodic operators curl_{per}, grad_{per}, div_{per}, $\Delta_{\text{per}} = \text{div}_{\text{per}}\,\text{grad}_{\text{per}}$ for each component, and taking into account that these operators leave $C_{\text{per},a}^\infty(\mathbb{R}^3, \mathbb{C}^3)|_{\Lambda_a}$ invariant, we arrive at

$$\text{curl}_{\text{per}}^2 \psi = \text{grad}_{\text{per}}\,\text{div}_{\text{per}}\,\psi - \Delta_{\text{per}}^{3c}\psi, \quad \forall\psi \in C_{\text{per},a}^\infty(\mathbb{R}^3, \mathbb{C}^3)|_{\Lambda_a}.$$

Performing adjoints and using a $\|.\|_1$-density argument leads to

$$(\text{curl}_{\text{per}}\,\phi|\,\text{curl}_{\text{per}}\,\psi) + (\text{div}_{\text{per}}\,\phi|\,\text{div}_{\text{per}}\,\psi) = h_{\text{per}}^{3c}(\phi, \psi), \quad \forall\phi, \psi \in W_{\text{per}}^1(\Lambda_a, \mathbb{C}^3).$$
(44.7.14)

The latter implies $\|\psi\|_{\text{div,curl}} = \|\psi\|_1$ for all $\psi \in W_{\text{per}}^1(\Lambda_a, \mathbb{C}^3)$. As an immediate consequence of Eq. (44.7.14) it follows that the reductions to $\text{ker}(\text{div}_{\text{per}})$ or to $\text{ran}(\text{curl}_{\text{per}})$, either of the curlcurl or of the negative, 3-component Laplacian, coincide. Since the reduction of an A is indicated by $A|$ we write

$$\text{curl}_{\text{per}}^2| = -\Delta_{\text{per}}^{3c}|, \quad \text{in reduction to } \text{ker}(\text{div}_{\text{per}}) \text{ or to } \text{ran}(\text{curl}_{\text{per}}). \quad (44.7.15)$$

Especially, $\text{dom}(\text{curl}_{\text{per}}^2|) = V \cap \text{dom}(\text{curl}_{\text{per}}^2) = V \cap \text{dom}(-\Delta_{\text{per}}^{3c}) = \text{dom}(-\Delta_{\text{per}}^{3c}|)$ with $V = \text{ker}(\text{div}_{\text{per}})$ or $V = \text{ran}(\text{curl}_{\text{per}})$. Observe, however, that in the total space $L^2(\Lambda_a, \mathbb{C}^3)$ the periodic curlcurl and Laplacian do not coincide, as demonstrates

$$\text{ker}(\text{curl}_{\text{per}}^2) = \text{ker}(\text{curl}_{\text{per}}) = \text{ran}(\text{grad}_{\text{per}}) \oplus \mathbb{H}_{\text{per}}, \quad \text{ker}(-\Delta_{\text{per}}^{3c}) = \mathbb{H}_{\text{per}}.$$
(44.7.16)

44.7.5. *Almost Periodic Boundary Conditions*

We sketch in the present section the generalization of the theory of vector differential operators — previously on a fixed finite volume Λ_a with periodic boundary conditions — to those on infinite volume with almost periodic boundary conditions. We consider only the case of Euclidean dimension $r = 3$.

We employ in Chapter 32 on page 925 on electronic Bloch theory direct definitions of almost periodic gradients and Laplacians in terms of a special basis. That is sufficient for the band theory of electrons in a crystal (where the Laplacians are perturbed by periodic potentials).

For the description of photons coupled to band electrons, one needs also almost periodic boundary conditions. There the dynamical generator of the free photon dynamics must be given by the transversal part of a curlcurl operator with almost periodic boundary conditions.

To construct an appropriate test function space we introduce an increasing sequence of cubes Λ_m, with edge lengths $L_m = 2^m a$, $m \in \mathbb{N}_0$, where a is the lattice constant of the Bloch theory. Note, $a > 0$, as well as L_m, denote here *a single positive number* each. For fixed m, the present Λ_m corresponds to the parallelepiped which would be designated Λ_{a_m} in the preceding sections with $a_m = \frac{1}{2}(L_m, L_m, L_m)$.

A plane wave $e_k(x) = \exp\{ik \cdot x\}$, $x \in \Lambda_m$, satisfies the pertinent periodic boundary conditions if the wave vector has the form $k = (2\pi n/L_m)$, $n \in \mathbb{Z}^3$. The set of these k be denoted by $\mathcal{K}_m$. If m varies in $\mathbb{N}_0$, then one cannot number an independent set of plane waves by the indices $k \in \mathcal{K} := \bigcup_{m \in \mathbb{N}_0} \mathcal{K}_m$ but restricts the k to $\mathcal{B} := \{k \in \mathcal{K} \mid -\frac{\pi}{a} \le k_j < \frac{\pi}{a}, 1 \le j \le 3\}$. $\mathcal{B}$ is the denumerable first Brillouin zone (see Eq. (32.2.2) on page 930).

These plane wave functions constitute an orthonormal basis system, if — as in Chapter 32 on page 925 — the scalar product $(e_k|e_{k'})$ is formed in an $\mathrm{L}^2(\Lambda_m, \mathbb{C})$ which contains the two $e_k(x)$ and $e_{k'}(x)$ under consideration, and if one uses the renormalized Lebesgue measure $dV(x) := d^3x/|\Lambda_m|$ (with the volume $|\Lambda_m|$ of Λ_m) for integration, rather than to renormalize the e_k, as in the preceding sections.

Let us denote the linear hull $\mathrm{LH}\{e_k \mid k \in \mathcal{B}\}$ by $\mathrm{B}_0^2(\mathbb{R}^3, \mathbb{C})$. In $\mathrm{B}_0^2(\mathbb{R}^3, \mathbb{C})$, the introduced scalar product implements a norm, and the norm completion of $\mathrm{B}_0^2(\mathbb{R}^3, \mathbb{C})$ is called the "space of B^2-almost periodic functions" in [Bes32]. We denote it by $\mathrm{B}^2(\mathbb{R}^3, \mathbb{C})$.

In the position space realization, the elements of $\mathrm{B}^2(\mathbb{R}^3, \mathbb{C})$ are large classes of functions. The usual property of being "almost periodic" is displayed by the $x \in \mathbb{R}^3$ uniformly converging Fourier series $\psi(x) = \sum_{k \in \mathcal{B}} c_k e_k(x)$, $c_k \in \mathbb{C}$. Let us recall that "almost periodic" for these continuous $\psi(x)$ means the following: For each $\varepsilon > 0$ there is an $l(\varepsilon) > 0$ such that each cube in $\mathbb{R}^3$ of length $l(\varepsilon)$ contains at least one $y \in \mathbb{R}^3$ with

$$|\psi(x + y) - \psi(x)| < \varepsilon, \quad \forall x \in \mathbb{R}^3 . \tag{44.7.17}$$

We introduce now a basis for 3-component test functions by the set of vector plane waves $\{\epsilon_j e_k \mid k \in \mathcal{B}, 1 \le j \le 3\}$, where $\epsilon_1, \epsilon_2, \epsilon_3$ constitute a basis of $\mathbb{C}^3$. (Recall that $b\varphi(x) = (b_1\varphi(x), b_2\varphi(x), b_3\varphi(x))$ for all $x \in \Lambda_m$ with $b = (b_1.b_2, b_3) \in \mathbb{C}^3$ and $\varphi : \Lambda_m \to \mathbb{C}$, according to the first paragraphs of Sec. 44.7.3.) Repeating the preceding construction, we form first $\mathrm{LH}\{\epsilon_j e_k \mid k \in \mathcal{B}, 1 \le j \le 3\} =: \mathrm{B}_0^2(\mathbb{R}^3, \mathbb{C}^3)$ and arrive by norm completion at the complex Hilbert space $\mathrm{B}^2(\mathbb{R}^3, \mathbb{C}^3)$ of 3-component B^2-almost periodic functions.

For our test function space we use, however, only $E := \mathrm{B}_0^2(\mathbb{R}^3, \mathbb{C}^3)$. Equation (44.7.7) demonstrates, how E transforms under the vectorial differential operators, which we identify by a subscript "ap" when acting on E. In the same vein, we introduce the almost periodic "cohomology" space

$$\mathbb{H}_{\mathrm{ap}} := \ker(\mathrm{div}_{\mathrm{ap}}) \cap \ker(\mathrm{curl}_{\mathrm{ap}}) = \{be_0 \mid b \in \mathbb{C}^3\}, \tag{44.7.18}$$

which consists just of the constant vector fields.

We obtain the following Hodge decomposition

$$E = \underbrace{\mathrm{ran}(\mathrm{grad}_{\mathrm{ap}})}_{=:\, E^{\|}} \oplus \underbrace{\mathbb{H}_{\mathrm{ap}}}_{=:\, E^{\mathrm{co}}} \oplus \underbrace{\mathrm{ran}(\mathrm{curl}_{\mathrm{ap}})}_{=:\, E^{\top}}, \qquad (44.7.19)$$

which decomposes a test function $E \ni f = f^{\|} \oplus f^{0} \oplus f^{\top}$ uniquely into gradients, constants, and curls.

Especially important is the validity of

$$\mathrm{curl}_{\mathrm{ap}}^{2} f = \mathrm{grad}_{\mathrm{ap}} \mathrm{div}_{\mathrm{ap}} f - \Delta_{\mathrm{ap}}^{3\mathrm{c}} f, \qquad \forall f \in E, \qquad (44.7.20)$$

involving the component-wise acting Laplacian. That leads to

$$\mathrm{curl}_{\mathrm{ap}}^{2}| = -\Delta_{\mathrm{ap}|}^{3\mathrm{c}}, \qquad \text{in reduction to } E^{\top}. \qquad (44.7.21)$$

So far, we have the positive symmetric operators $\mathrm{curl}_{\mathrm{ap}}$ and $-\Delta_{\mathrm{ap}}^{3\mathrm{c}}$ defined only on E. Since they both generate one-parametric unitary groups which leave E invariant they have a unique extension to self-adjoint operators on $\mathrm{B}^{2}(\mathbb{R}^{3}, \mathbb{C}^{3})$, which we denote by the same symbol.

The norm closure $\mathrm{B}^{2\top}(\mathbb{R}^{3}, \mathbb{C}^{3})$ of $E^{\top}$ reduces $-\Delta_{\mathrm{ap}}^{3\mathrm{c}}$ to $-\Delta_{\mathrm{ap}|}^{3\mathrm{c}}$, and the latter is a strictly positive self-adjoint operator on $\mathrm{B}^{2\top}(\mathbb{R}^{3}, \mathbb{C}^{3})$ (which contains 0 in its spectrum, but 0 is not an eigenvalue). We get then $\hbar c \sqrt{-\Delta_{\mathrm{ap}|}^{3\mathrm{c}}}$ as the *one-photon Hamiltonian*, if the quantized electromagnetic field interacts with the Bloch electrons.

Let us end with a **notational remark**: We have, in the chapters on semiconductor theory, denoted the Bloch space for almost periodic electron wave functions with spin by $\mathfrak{h} \oplus \mathfrak{h}$, what would write in the present notation as $\mathrm{B}^{2}(\mathbb{R}^{3}, \mathbb{C}^{2})$. Analogously we have used for the present almost periodic one-photon Hilbert space $\mathrm{B}^{2\top}(\mathbb{R}^{3}, \mathbb{C}^{3})$ previously the notation $P^{\top}(\mathfrak{h} \oplus \mathfrak{h} \oplus \mathfrak{h})$.

44.8. Operators over the Whole Euclidean Space

The situation $\Lambda = \mathbb{R}^{r}$ plays of course a dominant role in Physics, especially since it allows for the application of the Fourier transform. We proceed to investigate the curl, div, and related operators over the free space $\mathbb{R}^{r}$, $r \in \mathbb{N}$, and set $r = 3$ if curl occurs.

Since we have $\mathrm{W}^{1}(\mathbb{R}^{r}, \mathbb{C}) = \mathrm{W}_{0}^{1}(\mathbb{R}^{r}, \mathbb{C})$, and analogous identifications for the div and curl Sobolev spaces, it follows from Definition 44.4-1 on page 1584 that

$$\mathrm{grad}_{0} = \mathrm{grad}, \qquad \mathrm{div}_{0} = \mathrm{div}, \qquad \mathrm{curl}_{0} = \mathrm{curl}. \qquad (44.8.1)$$

This implies trivial cohomological fields,

$$\mathbb{H}_{1}(\mathbb{R}^{3}) = \{0\} = \mathbb{H}_{2}(\mathbb{R}^{3}).$$

Consequently, the formulas treated in Sec. 44.4 simplify, and resemble the situation for the periodic boundary condition in the foregoing section. Let us summarize,

$$\text{grad}^* = -\text{div}, \qquad \text{div}^* = -\text{grad}, \qquad \text{curl}^* = \text{curl},$$
$$-\Delta_{\mathbb{R}^r} = \text{grad}^* \, \text{grad} = -\text{div} \, \text{grad}, \tag{44.8.2}$$

with the unique self-adjoint Laplacian $-\Delta_{\mathbb{R}^r}$ in $L^2(\mathbb{R}^r, \mathbb{C})$ (cf. Remark 44.2-2 on page 1572). The interesting spaces specialize to

$$\ker(\text{grad}) = \{0\}, \qquad L^2(\mathbb{R}^r, \mathbb{C}) = \overline{\text{ran}(\text{div})}, \tag{44.8.3}$$
$$L^2(\mathbb{R}^r, \mathbb{C}^r) = \underbrace{\overline{\text{ran}(\text{grad})}}_{= \ker(\text{curl})} \oplus \underbrace{\ker(\text{div})}_{= \overline{\text{ran}(\text{curl})}}. \tag{44.8.4}$$

Since the Laplacian $-\Delta_{\mathbb{R}^r}$ is injective, we conclude that U from the polar decomposition $\text{grad} = U(-\Delta_{\mathbb{R}^r})^{1/2}$ is an isometry from $L^2(\mathbb{R}^r, \mathbb{C})$ onto $\overline{\text{ran}(\text{grad})}$, and that UU^* is the projection onto $\overline{\text{ran}(\text{grad})}$. But U is just the closure of $\text{grad} \, (-\Delta_{\mathbb{R}^r})^{-1/2}$ and its adjoint U^* is the closure of $(-\Delta_{\mathbb{R}^r})^{-1/2} \, \text{div}$ (cf. Proposition 43.3-5 on page 1537 for the polar decomposition). Thus the orthogonal projection of $L^2(\mathbb{R}^r, \mathbb{C}^r)$ onto the divergence-free (sub)-Hilbert space $\ker(\text{div})$ is given by

$$P_{\text{div}} = \mathbb{1} - UU^* = \mathbb{1} - \overline{\text{grad}(-\Delta_{\mathbb{R}^r})^{-1/2}(-\Delta_{\mathbb{R}^r})^{-1/2} \, \text{div}}. \tag{44.8.5}$$

Obviously, P_{div} as well as grad, div, curl, and $-\Delta_{\mathbb{R}^r}$ are C-real with respect to the common complex conjugation C.

For treating differential operators on $L^2(\mathbb{R}^r, \mathbb{C})$ respectively on $L^2(\mathbb{R}^r, \mathbb{C}^r)$ we introduce the Fourier transformation

$$\hat{\varphi}(k) \equiv \mathbb{F}\varphi(k) := (2\pi)^{-r/2} \int_{\mathbb{R}^r} \exp\{-ik \cdot x\}\varphi(x) \, d^r x, \qquad \varphi \in L^2(\mathbb{R}^r_x, \mathbb{C}), \tag{44.8.6}$$

which we lift to the m-component Hilbert space $L^2(\mathbb{R}^r, \mathbb{C}^m)$, $m \in \mathbb{N}$, by putting in each component $\hat{\psi} \equiv \mathbb{F}\psi := (\hat{\psi}_1, \ldots, \hat{\psi}_m)$ for $\psi = (\psi_1, \ldots, \psi_m) \in L^2(\mathbb{R}^r, \mathbb{C}^m)$. It is well known that the Fourier transformation is a unitary on $L^2(\mathbb{R}^r, \mathbb{C}^m)$ with inverse

$$\check{\phi}(x) \equiv \mathbb{F}^{-1}\phi(x) := (2\pi)^{-r/2} \int_{\mathbb{R}^r} \exp\{ik \cdot x\}\phi(k) \, d^r k, \qquad \phi \in L^2(\mathbb{R}^r_k, \mathbb{C}). \tag{44.8.7}$$

From a physical point of view, $L^2(\mathbb{R}^r, \mathbb{C}^m)$ contains functions on position space with variable x, and $\mathbb{F}(L^2(\mathbb{R}^r, \mathbb{C}^m)) = L^2(\mathbb{R}^r, \mathbb{C}^m)$ functions of the wave vectors k (indicated by the indices in $\mathbb{R}^r_x$ respectively in $\mathbb{R}^r_k$).

The Fourier transform of an operator A from $L^2(\mathbb{R}_x^r, \mathbb{C}^m)$ into $L^2(\mathbb{R}_x^r, \mathbb{C}^n)$ (we treat here only $m, n \in \{1, r, r = 3\}$) is given by

$$\widehat{A} := \mathbb{F}A\mathbb{F}^{-1}, \qquad \text{dom}(\widehat{A}) = \mathbb{F}(\text{dom}(A)),$$

and acts from $L^2(\mathbb{R}_k^r, \mathbb{C}^m)$ into $L^2(\mathbb{R}_k^r, \mathbb{C}^n)$. Thus the Fourier transforms of the differential operators from Eq. (44.8.2) are the multiplication operators

$$
\begin{aligned}
-i\,\widehat{\text{grad}}\varphi(k) &= k\varphi(k), & \varphi &\in \text{dom}(\widehat{\text{grad}}) \subset L^2(\mathbb{R}_k^r, \mathbb{C}), \\
-i\,\widehat{\text{div}}\phi(k) &= k \cdot \phi(k), & \phi &\in \text{dom}(\widehat{\text{div}}) \subset L^2(\mathbb{R}_k^r, \mathbb{C}^r), \\
-i\,\widehat{\text{curl}}\psi(k) &= k \times \psi(k), & \psi &\in \text{dom}(\widehat{\text{curl}}) \subset L^2(\mathbb{R}_k^3, \mathbb{C}^3), \\
-\widehat{\Delta}_{\mathbb{R}^r}\varphi(k) &= |k|^2\varphi(k), & \varphi &\in \text{dom}(-\widehat{\Delta}_{\mathbb{R}^r}) \subset L^2(\mathbb{R}_k^r, \mathbb{C}).
\end{aligned}
\tag{44.8.8}
$$

Especially, divergence-freeness rewrites simply as

$$\mathbb{F}(\ker(\text{div})) = \ker(\widehat{\text{div}}) = \{\phi \in L^2(\mathbb{R}_k^r, \mathbb{C}^r) \mid k \cdot \phi(k) = 0 \text{ for almost all } k \in \mathbb{R}^r\}.$$
$$\tag{44.8.9}$$

This leads to the Fourier transform $\widehat{P}_{\text{div}}$ of the orthogonal projection P_{div} from Eq. (44.8.5), which is given for every $\phi \in L^2(\mathbb{R}_k^r, \mathbb{C}^r)$ by

$$\widehat{P}_{\text{div}}\phi(k) = \phi(k) - \frac{k}{|k|}\left(\frac{k}{|k|} \cdot \phi(k)\right), \qquad \text{for almost all } k \in \mathbb{R}^r. \tag{44.8.10}$$

This means that for almost every momentum $k \in \mathbb{R}^r$, $\widehat{P}_{\text{div}}\phi(k)$ is the projection of $\phi(k) \in \mathbb{C}^r$ into the direction orthogonal to k. Obviously, $\widehat{P}_{\text{div}}$ is the orthogonal projection from $L^2(\mathbb{R}_k^r, \mathbb{C}^r)$ onto $\ker(\widehat{\text{div}})$.

The r-component Laplacian $-\Delta_{\mathbb{R}^r}^{rc}$ in $L^2(\mathbb{R}_x^r, \mathbb{C}^r)$ acts component-wise like $-\Delta_{\mathbb{R}^r}$ (cf. Sec. 44.6.1 on page 1606). $-\Delta_{\mathbb{R}^r}$ as well as $-\Delta_{\mathbb{R}^r}^{rc}$ have absolutely continuous spectra given by $[0, \infty[$. The Fourier transformed unitary group $\exp\{-it\widehat{\Delta}_{\mathbb{R}^r}^{rc}\}$ is just the multiplication by the function $k \mapsto \exp\{it|k|^2\}$ in each component. Using Eq. (44.8.10), we conclude then that $\exp\{-it\widehat{\Delta}_{\mathbb{R}^r}^{rc}\}$ commutes with $\widehat{P}_{\text{div}}$:

$$\exp\{-it\Delta_{\mathbb{R}^r}^{rc}\}P_{\text{div}} = P_{\text{div}}\exp\{-it\Delta_{\mathbb{R}^r}^{rc}\}, \qquad \forall t \in \mathbb{R}.$$

From the results for reducing subspaces, stated in Theorem 43.7-2 on page 1554, we deduce:

Proposition 44.8-1. $\overline{\text{ran}(\text{grad})}$ *and* $\ker(\text{div})$ *are reducing subspaces for the* r-*component free space Laplacian* $-\Delta_{\mathbb{R}^r}^{rc}$ *on* $L^2(\mathbb{R}_x^r, \mathbb{C}^r)$.

The free space curlcurl operator is defined as the square of the self-adjoint curl operator curl (we do not need a sesquilinear form here). From Eq. (44.8.4) and Sec. 43.7 it follows that $\ker(\text{div}) = \overline{\text{ran}(\text{curl})}$ is a reducing subspace for curl^2.

It turns out that $\nabla \times (\nabla \times \psi) = \nabla(\nabla \cdot \psi) - \Delta\psi$ on smooth functions extends to

$$\mathrm{curl}^2\,\psi = \mathrm{grad}\,\mathrm{div}\,\psi - \Delta^{3c}_{\mathbb{R}^3}\psi\,, \quad \forall\psi \in \mathrm{W}^2(\mathbb{R}^3, \mathbb{C}^3)\,.$$

Performing adjoints and using a density argument finally gives

$$(\mathrm{curl}\,\phi|\,\mathrm{curl}\,\psi) + (\mathrm{div}\,\phi|\,\mathrm{div}\,\psi) = h^{3c}_0(\phi, \psi), \quad \forall\phi, \psi \in \mathrm{W}^1(\mathbb{R}^3, \mathbb{C}^3)\,. \qquad (44.8.11)$$

Consequently,

$$\|\psi\|_{\mathrm{div,curl}} = \|\psi\|_1, \quad \forall\psi \in \mathrm{W}^1(\mathbb{R}^3, \mathbb{C}^3) = \mathrm{W}(\mathrm{div}; \mathbb{R}^3, \mathbb{C}^3) \cap \mathrm{W}(\mathrm{curl}; \mathbb{R}^3, \mathbb{C}^3),$$
$$(44.8.12)$$

cf. Proposition 44.1-16 (b) on page 1570. A further consequence of Eq. (44.8.11) is that — reduced to divergence-freeness — the curlcurl and the 3-component Laplacian coincide:

$$\mathrm{curl}^2| = -\Delta^{3c}_{\mathbb{R}^3}|, \quad \text{in reduction to } \mathrm{ker}(\mathrm{div}) = \overline{\mathrm{ran}(\mathrm{curl})}\,. \qquad (44.8.13)$$

Especially, $\mathrm{dom}(\mathrm{curl}^2|) = \mathrm{ker}(\mathrm{div}) \cap \mathrm{dom}(\mathrm{curl}^2) = \mathrm{ker}(\mathrm{div}) \cap \mathrm{dom}(-\Delta^{3c}_{\mathbb{R}^3}) = \mathrm{dom}(-\Delta^{3c}_{\mathbb{R}^3}|)$. Hence the reduced curlcurl operator $\mathrm{curl}^2|$ has a pure absolutely continuous spectrum. Clearly in the whole of $\mathrm{L}^2(\mathbb{R}^3, \mathbb{C}^3)$ curlcurl and Laplacian do not coincide, having, e.g., different null spaces

$$\mathrm{ker}(\mathrm{curl}^2) = \mathrm{ker}(\mathrm{curl}) = \overline{\mathrm{ran}(\mathrm{grad})}\,, \qquad \mathrm{ker}(-\Delta^{3c}_{\mathbb{R}^3}) = \{0\}\,.$$

44.9.   A Note on Further Boundary Conditions

Suppose the spatial domain $\Lambda \subset \mathbb{R}^r$, $r \geq 2$, to be interior or exterior with a sufficiently smooth boundary (at least piece-wise C^1-smooth).

In virtue of Proposition 44.1-10 we have for the restriction to the boundary that $\varphi|_{\partial\Lambda} = 0$ for all $\varphi \in \mathrm{W}^1_0(\Lambda, \mathbb{C})$. But $\varphi|_{\partial\Lambda}$ may be arbitrary for $\varphi \in \mathrm{W}^1(\Lambda, \mathbb{C})$. So it is interesting to demand $\varphi|_{\partial\Lambda_{b1}} = 0$ for a suitable part $\partial\Lambda_{b1}$ of the boundary, e.g., if the boundary $\partial\Lambda$ decomposes into two disconnected $\partial\Lambda_{b1}$ and $\partial\Lambda_{b2}$. From now on let us suppose that the boundary of Λ decomposes as

$$\partial\Lambda = \partial\Lambda_{b1} \cup \partial\Lambda_{b2} \qquad (44.9.1)$$

with two non-trivial parts $\partial\Lambda_{b1}$ and $\partial\Lambda_{b2}$, which are indicated by the indices "$b1$" and "$b2$" standing for "boundary part one" and "boundary part two".

Let us first give the definition of the Sobolev space corresponding to the first boundary part $\partial\Lambda_{b1}$,

$$\mathrm{W}^1_{b1}(\Lambda, \mathbb{C}) := \overline{\{\varphi \in \mathrm{C}^1(\bar{\Lambda}, \mathbb{C}) \cap \mathrm{C}^1_b(\Lambda, \mathbb{C}) \mid \varphi|_{\partial\Lambda_{b1}} = 0\}}^{\|\cdot\|_1}$$
$$= \{\varphi \in \mathrm{W}^1(\Lambda, \mathbb{C}) \mid \varphi|_{\partial\Lambda_{b1}} = 0\}\,.$$

The div and curl Sobolev spaces for the first boundary part $\partial\Lambda_{b1}$ are defined by

$$W_{b1}(\mathrm{div};\Lambda,\mathbb{C}^r) := \overline{\{\phi \in C^1(\bar{\Lambda},\mathbb{C}^r)\, C_b^1(\Lambda,\mathbb{C}^r) \mid \phi|_{\partial\Lambda_{b1}} = 0\}}^{\,\|\cdot\|_{\mathrm{div}}},$$

$$W_{b1}(\mathrm{curl};\Lambda,\mathbb{C}^3) := \overline{\{\psi \in C^1(\bar{\Lambda},\mathbb{C}^3)\, C_b^1(\Lambda,\mathbb{C}^3) \mid \psi|_{\partial\Lambda_{b1}} = 0\}}^{\,\|\cdot\|_{\mathrm{curl}}}.$$

This leads to the following proper inclusions

$$W_0^1(\Lambda,\mathbb{C}) \subset W_{b1}^1(\Lambda,\mathbb{C}) \subset W^1(\Lambda,\mathbb{C}),$$
$$W_0(\mathrm{div};\Lambda,\mathbb{C}^r) \subset W_{b1}(\mathrm{div};\Lambda,\mathbb{C}^r) \subset W(\mathrm{div};\Lambda,\mathbb{C}^r),$$
$$W_0(\mathrm{curl};\Lambda,\mathbb{C}^3) \subset W_{b1}(\mathrm{curl};\Lambda,\mathbb{C}^3) \subset W(\mathrm{curl};\Lambda,\mathbb{C}^3).$$

In addition to the classical boundary conditions for the 1-component Laplacians of Sec. 44.2, one may now turn to a mixture of the Dirichlet and Neumann boundary conditions, called *mixed boundary conditions*. Define on $L^2(\Lambda,\mathbb{C})$ the sesquilinear form

$$h_{b1}(\varphi,\phi) = (\nabla\varphi|\nabla\phi), \quad \varphi,\phi \in \mathrm{dom}(h_{b1}) := W_{b1}^1(\Lambda,\mathbb{C}),$$

which corresponds to a Laplacian $-\Delta_{b1}$ on $L^2(\Lambda,\mathbb{C})$ with $\varphi = 0$ on the first boundary part $\partial\Lambda_{b1}$ (Dirichlet boundary condition) and $\frac{\partial\varphi}{\partial n} = 0$ on the second boundary part $\partial\Lambda_{b2}$ (Neumann boundary condition). Also a mixed boundary condition may be introduced by adding to h_{b1} a positive, relatively bounded boundary form which lives on the second boundary part $\partial\Lambda_{b2}$, only. For interior Λ the identical embedding $W_{b1}^1(\Lambda,\mathbb{C}) \hookrightarrow L^2(\Lambda,\mathbb{C})$ is compact by Proposition 44.1-8(d), and hence the Laplacian $-\Delta_{b1}$ has a purely discrete spectrum accumulating only at infinity.

Gradient, divergence, and curl operators corresponding to boundary part one are defined by

$$\begin{aligned}
\mathrm{grad}_{b1}\,\varphi &:= \nabla\varphi, & \forall\varphi \in \mathrm{dom}(\mathrm{grad}_{b1}) &:= W_{b1}^1(\Lambda,\mathbb{C}), \\
\mathrm{div}_{b1}\,\phi &:= \nabla\cdot\phi, & \forall\phi \in \mathrm{dom}(\mathrm{div}_{b1}) &:= W_{b1}(\mathrm{div};\Lambda,\mathbb{C}^r), \\
\mathrm{curl}_{b1}\,\psi &:= \nabla\times\psi, & \forall\psi \in \mathrm{dom}(\mathrm{curl}_{b1}) &:= W_{b1}(\mathrm{curl};\Lambda,\mathbb{C}^3).
\end{aligned} \tag{44.9.2}$$

The gradient grad_{b1} is an operator from the Hilbert space $L^2(\Lambda,\mathbb{C})$ into the Hilbert space $L^2(\Lambda,\mathbb{C}^r)$, the divergence div_{b1} acts from the Hilbert space $L^2(\Lambda,\mathbb{C}^r)$ into $L^2(\Lambda,\mathbb{C})$, whereas the curl operator curl_{b1} acts on the Hilbert space $L^2(\Lambda,\mathbb{C}^3)$. By construction these three operators are closed and C-real with respect to the common complex conjugation C.

For the second boundary part $\partial\Lambda_{b2}$ the gradient, divergence, and curl operators are given by replacing the index "$b1$" by the index "$b2$" in Eq. (44.9.2). Partial integration gives $(\frac{\partial\varphi}{\partial x_j}|\phi) = -(\varphi|\frac{\partial\phi}{\partial x_j})$ for $\varphi,\phi \in C^1(\bar{\Lambda},\mathbb{C})$ with $\varphi|_{\partial\Lambda_{b1}} = 0$ and $\phi|_{\partial\Lambda_{b2}} = 0$. Consequently, by construction we obtain

$$\mathrm{grad}_{b1}^* = -\,\mathrm{div}_{b2}, \quad \mathrm{div}_{b1}^* = -\,\mathrm{grad}_{b2}, \quad \mathrm{curl}_{b1}^* = \mathrm{curl}_{b2},$$

and conversely when replacing "$b1$" by "$b2$". For the Laplacians $-\Delta_{b1}$ and $-\Delta_{b2}$ we have

$$-\Delta_{b1} = \operatorname{grad}_{b1}^* \operatorname{grad}_{b1} = -\operatorname{div}_{b2} \operatorname{grad}_{b1}, \quad -\Delta_{b2} = \operatorname{grad}_{b2}^* \operatorname{grad}_{b2} = -\operatorname{div}_{b1} \operatorname{grad}_{b2}.$$

We now turn to orthogonal Hilbert space decompositions, which follow from the same argumentation as in Sec. 44.4.1 on page 1585. The proper inclusions $W_0^1(\Lambda, \mathbb{C}) \subset W_{b1/2}^1(\Lambda, \mathbb{C}) \subset W^1(\Lambda, \mathbb{C})$ imply the proper inclusions $\operatorname{ran}(\operatorname{grad}_0) \subset \operatorname{ran}(\operatorname{grad}_{b1}) \subset \operatorname{ran}(\operatorname{grad})$. Thus, in general the four orthogonal decompositions

$$\begin{aligned}
L^2(\Lambda, \mathbb{C}^r) &= \overline{\operatorname{ran}(\operatorname{grad}_0)} \oplus \ker(\operatorname{div}) = \overline{\operatorname{ran}(\operatorname{grad})} \oplus \ker(\operatorname{div}_0) \\
&= \overline{\operatorname{ran}(\operatorname{grad}_{b1})} \oplus \ker(\operatorname{div}_{b2}) = \overline{\operatorname{ran}(\operatorname{grad}_{b2})} \oplus \ker(\operatorname{div}_{b1})
\end{aligned} \tag{44.9.3}$$

are mutually different. Consequently, taking different decompositions (44.9.1) of the boundary, one obtains a continuum of mutually different orthogonal decompositions and thus of mutually different divergence-free sub-Hilbert spaces $\ker(\operatorname{div}_{b1/2})$ of $L^2(\Lambda, \mathbb{C}^r)$.

In case $r = 3$, that is for $\Lambda \subset \mathbb{R}^3$, we finally arrive with the cohomology spaces

$$\mathbb{H}_1^b := \ker(\operatorname{div}_{b1}) \cap \ker(\operatorname{curl}_{b2}), \quad \mathbb{H}_2^b := \ker(\operatorname{div}_{b2}) \cap \ker(\operatorname{curl}_{b1})$$

at the orthogonal Hilbert space decompositions

$$L^2(\Lambda, \mathbb{C}^3) = \overline{\operatorname{ran}(\operatorname{grad}_{b2})} \oplus \mathbb{H}_1^b \oplus \overbrace{\operatorname{ran}(\operatorname{curl}_{b1})}^{= \ker(\operatorname{div}_{b1})}, \tag{44.9.4}$$
$$\underbrace{\phantom{L^2(\Lambda,\mathbb{C}^3)}}_{= \ker(\operatorname{curl}_{b2})}$$

$$L^2(\Lambda, \mathbb{C}^3) = \overline{\operatorname{ran}(\operatorname{grad}_{b1})} \oplus \mathbb{H}_2^b \oplus \overbrace{\operatorname{ran}(\operatorname{curl}_{b2})}^{= \ker(\operatorname{div}_{b2})}. \tag{44.9.5}$$
$$\underbrace{\phantom{L^2(\Lambda,\mathbb{C}^3)}}_{= \ker(\operatorname{curl}_{b1})}$$

In general, the spaces $\mathbb{H}_1^b$ and $\mathbb{H}_2^b$ seem to have finite dimensions. And for interior Λ the ranges of grad_{b1}, grad_{b2}, div_{b1}, div_{b2}, curl_{b1}, and curl_{b2} are closed, especially, then the previous orthogonal decompositions are Hodge decompositions again.

The two self-adjoint curlcurl operators

$$\operatorname{curl}_{b2} \operatorname{curl}_{b1} = \operatorname{curl}_{b1}^* \operatorname{curl}_{b1}, \quad \operatorname{curl}_{b1} \operatorname{curl}_{b2} = \operatorname{curl}_{b2}^* \operatorname{curl}_{b2} \tag{44.9.6}$$

on the Hilbert space $L^2(\Lambda, \mathbb{C}^3)$ correspond to the two forms $(\phi, \psi) \mapsto (\nabla \times \phi | \nabla \times \psi)$ with domains $W_{b1}(\operatorname{curl}; \Lambda, \mathbb{C}^3)$ respectively $W_{b2}(\operatorname{curl}; \Lambda, \mathbb{C}^3)$. The reductions of the curlcurl operators in Eq. (44.9.6) to $\overline{\operatorname{ran}(\operatorname{curl}_{b2})}$ respectively $\overline{\operatorname{ran}(\operatorname{curl}_{b1})}$ have pure discrete spectra accumulating only at infinity in case of interior Λ (implying the closedness of the ranges of $\mathrm{curl}_{b1/2}$, since the inverses of the curlcurls are compact), and pure absolutely continuous spectra in case of exterior Λ.

Let us finally mention, that as for the Laplacians one may possibly add to the curlcurl forms some suitable relatively bounded boundary forms, in order to obtain further boundary conditions (with discrete spectra in case of interior Λ for the associated curlcurls).

Chapter 45

C^*-Algebras and their Representations

The theory of C^*-algebras arose mathematically as an abstraction of the norm closed *-algebras of bounded operators in Hilbert space. The latter, in which the *-operation is realized as the Hermitian adjointing, are sometimes called "concrete C^*-algebras". C^*-algebras generalize also the "rings of operators", earlier developed by J. von Neumann and now named after him. These are closed even in a weaker-than-norm topology and provided the basic connections between algebraic and topological notions.

Our overview starts with (abstract) *-algebras, which do not necessarily own a norm or another topology. It deepens the structural insight to know, which of the algebraic notions are already possible in the setup of *-algebras. Besides this, there are physical applications of *-algebras of their own value (especially to describe unbounded observables).

For a short overview on Hilbert space operators we refer to our Chapter 43, and references given there. An elementary introduction to functional analysis including Hilbert space theory is found in [Kre78] and [Con85]. For an introduction to C^*-algebras let us mention again [Tak79] and [BR87].

Notational Remark 45.0-1. Throughout the present Chapter "linearity" is always meant over the complex field $\mathbb{C}$.

For a given Hausdorff topological space X (cf. Sec. 49.1) we denote by $C(X)$ the vector space of the continuous, $\mathbb{C}$-valued functions on X and by $C_b(X)$ the subspace of the bounded ones. If X is locally compact, then $C_\infty(X)$ denotes the functions in $C_b(X)$ which vanish at infinity (along a sequence of points, leaving each compact). Recall that if X is compact, then $C_\infty(X) = C_b(X) = C(X)$.

45.1. *-Algebras

45.1.1. *Elementary Definitions and Properties*

An *algebra* $\mathcal{A}$ is a (complex) vector space, which is equipped with an associative, but possibly non-commutative, distributive product, denoted mostly without a multiplication symbol. Thus, one assumes for all $A, B, C \in \mathcal{A}$

$$A(BC) = (AB)C,$$
$$A(B+C) = AB + AC, \qquad (A+B)C = AC + BC,$$
$$uv(AB) = (uA)(vB), \qquad \forall u, v \in \mathbb{C}.$$

If $\mathcal{A}$ possesses a unit $\mathbb{1}$ (satisfying $\mathbb{1}A = A\mathbb{1} = A$ for all $A \in \mathcal{A}$), then $\mathcal{A}$ is called *unital*. An algebra $\mathcal{A}$ is called *commutative* or *Abelian*, if

$$AB = BA, \qquad \forall A, B \in \mathcal{A}.$$

A mapping $A \mapsto A^*$ on an algebra $\mathcal{A}$ is called a **-operation*, if it satisfies the following properties:

$$A^{**} \equiv (A^*)^* = A, \quad (AB)^* = B^* A^*, \quad (uA + vB)^* = \bar{u}A^* + \bar{v}B^*,$$

for all $A, B \in \mathcal{A}$ and all $u, v \in \mathbb{C}$ ($\bar{u}$ is the complex conjugate to $u \in \mathbb{C}$). An algebra with a *-operation is called a **-algebra*.

If a *-algebra $\mathcal{A}$ contains a unit $\mathbb{1}$, it follows that $\mathbb{1}^* = \mathbb{1}$, and if A is invertible, then A^* is invertible with the inverse $(A^*)^{-1} = (A^{-1})^*$.

Example 45.1-1 (Two typical *-algebras). Let us consider the Weyl system $(W, \mathcal{H})$ over one degree of freedom from Sec. 17.3 on page 376 with its associated field operators $\Phi(z)$, where $W(z) = \exp\{i\Phi(z)\}$ for all $z \in \mathbb{C}$. In terms of these quantities we formulate two typical cases of a *-algebra.

(a) Consider the space $\mathcal{A}$ of all polynomials of the $\Phi(z)$, $z \in \mathbb{C}$. Since the field operators are unbounded, they are only densely defined. By Proposition 17.3-2 on page 378 there exists a dense subspace D of $\mathcal{H}$, which is a common core for, and invariant by, each of the field operators. Then every polynomial in the field operators leaves D invariant. Also the CCR are understood on D only, and provide the unit element for $\mathcal{A}$. Consequently, every element of $\mathcal{A}$ may be considered as an operator on $\mathcal{H}$ with domain D, and in this sense $\mathcal{A}$ is closed under the *-algebraic operations. Thus, $\mathcal{A}$ is a (concrete) *-algebra, in which most elements do not possess a (finite) norm at all.

(b) Because the Weyl operators $W(z)$, $z \in \mathbb{C}$, satisfy the Weyl relations in the form (17.3.2) on page 376, it follows that the linear hull $\mathrm{LH}\{W(z) \mid z \in \mathbb{C}\}$ gives a *-algebra with the unit $\mathbb{1} := W(0)$.

This *-algebra consists entirely of elements with a (finite) norm, but is not closed in the norm topology. Its norm closure constitutes the C^*-Weyl algebra (with "test function space" $\mathbb{C}$).

The *center* $\mathcal{Z}(\mathcal{A})$ of a *-algebra $\mathcal{A}$ consists by definition of those elements, which commute with every other element of $\mathcal{A}$,

$$\mathcal{Z}(\mathcal{A}) := \{A \in \mathcal{A} \mid AB = BA \text{ for all } B \in \mathcal{A}\}. \tag{45.1.1}$$

If $\mathcal{A}$ is unital, then we have $\mathbb{C}\mathbb{1} \subseteq \mathcal{Z}(\mathcal{A})$, what is called the *trivial part* of the center.

A subspace $\mathcal{J}$ is called a **-ideal* of the *-algebra $\mathcal{A}$, if $\mathcal{J}$ contains I^* and AI for all $I \in \mathcal{J}$ and all $A \in \mathcal{A}$. (Then also IA is in $\mathcal{A}$ by *-conjugation, so that $\mathcal{J}$ is automatically a 2-sided ideal.)

Especially it follows that $\mathcal{J}$ is a sub-*-algebra of $\mathcal{A}$. If $\mathcal{A}$ is a *-algebra with a *-ideal $\mathcal{J}$, then the quotient space $\mathcal{A}/\mathcal{J}$ is a *-algebra, too, in which linear combination, multiplication, and *-operation are implemented by $z\widetilde{A} + \widetilde{B} := \widetilde{zA + B}$, $\widetilde{A}\widetilde{B} := \widetilde{AB}$, and $(\widetilde{A})^* := \widetilde{A^*}$, using the quotient map $A \mapsto \widetilde{A} := \{A + I \mid I \in \mathcal{J}\}$.

As for bounded operators in Hilbert space one distinguishes the following special elements in a *-algebra.

Definition 45.1-2 (Specific elements in a *-algebra). Let $\mathcal{A}$ be a *-algebra.

(a) $A \in \mathcal{A}$ is called *self-adjoint*, if $A = A^*$. We denote by $\mathcal{A}_{\mathrm{sa}}$ the real subspace of $\mathcal{A}$ consisting of all self-adjoint element of $\mathcal{A}$. $P \in \mathcal{A}$ is called a *projection*, if $P^2 = P = P^*$ (but has nothing to project).

(b) $A \in \mathcal{A}$ is called a *partial isometry*, if A^*A is a projection. If in addition $\mathcal{A}$ contains a unit $\mathbb{1}$, then an $A \in \mathcal{A}$ with $A^*A = \mathbb{1}$ is called an *isometry*.

(c) $A \in \mathcal{A}$ is called *normal*, if $A^*A = AA^*$.

(d) If $\mathcal{A}$ is unital, then $A \in \mathcal{A}$ is called *unitary*, if $A^*A = AA^* = \mathbb{1}$. (In Example 45.1-1(a) the only unitary elements are $e^{i\theta}\mathbb{1}$ with $\theta \in \mathbb{R}$.)

(e) $A \in \mathcal{A}$ is called *positive*, if there exists a $D \in \mathcal{A}$ with $A = D^*D$. The set of all positive elements of $\mathcal{A}$ is denoted by $\mathcal{A}_+$. The positivity of A is indicated by $A \geq 0$. Whenever $A - B \geq 0$ for two elements $A, B \in \mathcal{A}$ (for what we say "A *dominates* B"), we also write $A \geq B$ or $B \leq A$, specializing to $A > B$ or $B < A$, if $A \neq B$. Note that then $A \leq 0$ means $-A = 0 - A \in \mathcal{A}_+$.

Every element A of a *-algebra $\mathcal{A}$ decomposes into two unique self-adjoint elements $A_1, A_2 \in \mathcal{A}_{\mathrm{sa}}$,

$$A = A_1 + iA_2, \quad A_1 = \frac{1}{2}(A + A^*), \quad A_2 = \frac{1}{2i}(A - A^*). \tag{45.1.2}$$

A_1 and A_2 are called the *real* and the *imaginary* part of A. Thus, we have the decomposing set relation

$$\mathcal{A} = \mathcal{A}_{\mathrm{sa}} + i\mathcal{A}_{\mathrm{sa}}. \tag{45.1.3}$$

Since $A^*A = A_1^2 + A_2^2 + i(A_1 A_2 - A_2 A_1)$ and $AA^* = A_1^2 + A_2^2 - i(A_1 A_2 - A_2 A_1)$, it follows that A is normal, if and only if the real part A_1 and the imaginary part A_2 commute with each other. Positive elements are self-adjoint, $\mathcal{A}_+ \subseteq \mathcal{A}_{\mathrm{sa}}$.

Every projection $P \in \mathcal{A}$ satisfies $P = P^2 = P^*P$ and thus is positive and dominates the projection 0. If $\mathbb{1} \in \mathcal{A}$, then $\mathbb{1} - P$ is, with P, a projection and hence is positive. So the projection $\mathbb{1}$ dominates each other projection.

Note, however, that the domination relation $A \geq B$ does in general not define an order relation, since generally one cannot conclude from $A \geq 0$ and $A \leq 0$ that $A = 0$, and neither can conclude from $A \geq B$ and $B \geq C$ that $A \geq C$. In Lemma 45.2-10, we obtain, however, for the self-adjoint part of a C^*-algebra such an order structure based on positivity. Nevertheless positivity (respectively domination) is also a useful concept for general *-algebras.

For an unital *-algebra $\mathcal{A}$ we obtain that every $A \in \mathcal{A}$ decomposes into a linear combination of four positive elements

$$A = \frac{1}{4} \sum_{n=0}^{3} i^n \, (A + i^n \mathbb{1})^* (A + i^n \mathbb{1}), \quad \forall A \in \mathcal{A}.$$

Thus, the real part A_1 of A is given by summing over $n = 0, 2$ and the imaginary part A_2 by summing over $n = 1, 3$. Consequently, in addition to (45.1.3), we obtain the further set decomposition

$$\mathcal{A}_{\text{sa}} = \mathcal{A}_+ - \mathcal{A}_+, \quad \text{provided } \mathcal{A} \text{ has a unit } \mathbb{1}. \tag{45.1.4}$$

Proposition 45.1-3. *Let $\mathcal{A}$ be a *-algebra and $A, B \in \mathcal{A}$. If $A \geq B$, then it follows that also $A + C \geq B + C$ and $C^* AC \geq C^* BC$ for all $C \in \mathcal{A}$.*

45.1.2.   *-Homomorphisms, *-Isomorphisms, *-Automorphisms

An *-*homomorphism* from a *-algebra $\mathcal{A}$ into a *-algebra $\mathcal{B}$ is a mapping $\alpha : \mathcal{A} \to \mathcal{B}$, which respects the *-algebraic structures:

$$\alpha(A + zB) = \alpha(A) + z\alpha(B), \quad \alpha(AB) = \alpha(A)\alpha(B), \quad \alpha(A^*) = \alpha(A)^*,$$

for all $A, B \in \mathcal{A}$ and all $z \in \mathbb{C}$. (This implies that the domain of definition of α is all of $\mathcal{A}$.)

An *-homomorphism $\alpha : \mathcal{A} \to \mathcal{B}$ is called *onto* $\mathcal{B}$, if $\alpha(\mathcal{A}) = \mathcal{B}$ (surjectivity). An *-homomorphism α from $\mathcal{A}$ into $\mathcal{B}$ is called an *-*isomorphism*, if α is injective (what means a trivial kernel $\ker(\alpha) = \{0\}$). If a *-isomorphism is also onto, it must be mentioned.

An *-isomorphism from a *-algebra $\mathcal{A}$ onto itself is called a *-*automorphism* or sometimes simply an automorphism. The set *-aut$(\mathcal{A})$ of all *-automorphisms of $\mathcal{A}$ constitutes a group with respect to the multiplication $(\alpha \circ \beta)(A) := \alpha(\beta(A))$, $A \in \mathcal{A}$ and $\alpha, \beta \in$ *-aut$(\mathcal{A})$.

Proposition 45.1-4 (Properties of *-homomorphisms). *For a *-homomorphism α from the *-algebra $\mathcal{A}$ into the *-algebra $\mathcal{B}$ the following assertions are valid:*

(a) *Its kernel $\ker(\alpha)$ is a *-ideal in $\mathcal{A}$, and its image $\alpha(\mathcal{A})$ is a sub-*-algebra of $\mathcal{B}$.*
(b) *α preserves self-adjointness, that is $\alpha(\mathcal{A}_{sa}) \subseteq \mathcal{B}_{sa}$.*
(c) *If $A \in \mathcal{A}$ is normal, or a projection, or a partial isometry, then also $\alpha(A) \in \mathcal{B}$ is normal, or a projection, or a partial isometry.*

(d) α *is positivity preserving, that is* $\alpha(\mathcal{A}_+) \subseteq \mathcal{B}_+$. *Thus, also* $A \geq B$ *in* $\mathcal{A}$ *gives* $\alpha(A) \geq \alpha(B)$ *in* $\mathcal{B}$.

Notice that if $\mathcal{A}$ possesses a unit, then in general $\alpha(\mathbb{1})$ is only a projection in $\mathcal{B}$ and not necessarily the unit of $\mathcal{B}$ (if $\mathcal{B}$ has one). If in fact $\alpha(\mathbb{1}) \neq \mathbb{1}$, it follows for an isometry $A \in \mathcal{A}$ that $\alpha(A)$ is only a partial isometry, and for a unitary $A \in \mathcal{A}$ that $\alpha(A)$ and $\alpha(A)^*$ are only partial isometries. (Only if $\alpha(\mathbb{1}) = \mathbb{1} \in \mathcal{B}$, an α-transformed isometry remains an isometry and an α-transformed unitary remains a unitary.)

The kernel $\ker(\alpha)$ being a *-ideal, we may go over to the quotient *-algebra $\mathcal{A}/\ker(\alpha)$. The *-homomorphism α induces then a *-isomorphism $\widetilde{\alpha}$ from $\mathcal{A}/\ker(\alpha)$ into $\mathcal{B}$ by setting $\widetilde{\alpha}(\widetilde{A}) := \alpha(A)$ for all equivalence classes $\widetilde{A} = \{A + I \mid I \in \ker(\alpha)\}$.

45.1.3. *Representations in Hilbert Spaces*

We need some basic notions.

Let $\mathcal{H}$ be a Hilbert space, and $\mathcal{M}$ a subset of the *-algebra $\mathcal{L}(\mathcal{H})$ (being in fact a most important C^*-algebra) of all bounded operators in $\mathcal{H}$. The commutant $\mathcal{M}'$ of $\mathcal{M}$ is defined

$$\mathcal{M}' := \{A \in \mathcal{L}(\mathcal{H}) \mid AM = MA, \ \forall M \in \mathcal{M}\}. \tag{45.1.5}$$

If $\mathcal{M}$ is invariant under adjointing (i.e., $M \in \mathcal{M}$ implies $M^* \in \mathcal{M}$), then the commutant $\mathcal{M}'$ of $\mathcal{M}$ is a sub-*-algebra of $\mathcal{L}(\mathcal{H})$. By the functional calculus, every bounded function of a self-adjoint $A = A^* \in \mathcal{M}'$ is also contained in the commutant $\mathcal{M}'$, especially so are its spectral projections. The bicommutant $\mathcal{M}'' := (\mathcal{M}')'$ of $\mathcal{M}$ (the commutant of the commutant $\mathcal{M}'$) is also a sub-*-algebra of $\mathcal{L}(\mathcal{H})$ with

$$\mathcal{M} \subseteq \mathrm{LH}\{A_1 A_2 \cdots A_m \mid A_j \in \mathcal{M}, \ m \in \mathbb{N}\} \subseteq \mathcal{M}''.$$

A subspace $\mathcal{H}_0$ is called an *invariant subspace* of $\mathcal{M}$, if $\mathcal{H}_0$ is a *closed* subspace of $\mathcal{H}$ satisfying $M\mathcal{H}_0 \subseteq \mathcal{H}_0$ for all $M \in \mathcal{M}$. The subset $\mathcal{M} \subseteq \mathcal{L}(\mathcal{H})$ is called *irreducible* in $\mathcal{H}$, if its invariant subspaces are only the trivial ones, namely $\{0\}$ and $\mathcal{H}$.

Proposition 45.1-5 (Irreducibility). *Let $\mathcal{M}$ be a nontrivial subset of the C^*-algebra $\mathcal{L}(\mathcal{H})$ (where non-trivial means that $\mathcal{M}$ contains a non-zero element $M \neq 0$), which is invariant under adjointing. Then the following conditions are equivalent:*

(i) $\mathcal{M}$ *is irreducible in* $\mathcal{H}$.
(ii) *The commutant* $\mathcal{M}'$ *consists of the multiples of the identity only, that is* $\mathcal{M}' = \mathbb{C}\mathbb{1}$.

(iii) *Every non-zero $\psi \in \mathcal{H}$ is cyclic for $\mathcal{M}$, meaning $\mathcal{M}\psi$ is total in $\mathcal{H}$ (which means that $\mathrm{LH}\{M\psi \mid M \in \mathcal{M}\}$ is dense in $\mathcal{H}$).*

For more results concerning commutants, bicommutants, and higher commutants we refer to Sec. 46.1.2 below.

We mention the following definitions of representation theory.

Definition 45.1-6 (Representations of *-algebras). A representation of a *-algebra $\mathcal{A}$ is a tuple $(\Pi, \mathcal{H}_\Pi)$, with $\mathcal{H}_\Pi$ a (complex) Hilbert space and Π a *-homomorphism from $\mathcal{A}$ into the **bounded operators** $\mathcal{L}(\mathcal{H}_\Pi)$.

For a representation $(\Pi, \mathcal{H}_\Pi)$ of $\mathcal{A}$ there are the following qualifications:

(a) $(\Pi, \mathcal{H}_\Pi)$ is *faithful*, if Π is injective.
(b) $(\Pi, \mathcal{H}_\Pi)$ is *non-degenerate*, if $\Pi(\mathcal{A})\mathcal{H}_\Pi$ is dense in $\mathcal{H}_\Pi$.
(c) $\mathcal{H}_0$ is an *invariant subspace* of the representation $(\Pi, \mathcal{H}_\Pi)$, if $\mathcal{H}_0$ is an invariant subspace for $\Pi(\mathcal{A})$.
(d) $(\Pi, \mathcal{H}_\Pi)$ is *irreducible*, if $\Pi(\mathcal{A})$ is irreducible in $\mathcal{L}(\mathcal{H}_\Pi)$.

For denoting a representation $(\Pi, \mathcal{H}_\Pi)$, one often drops the $\mathcal{H}_\Pi$ and only writes Π. The representation $(\Pi, \mathcal{H}_\Pi)$ is called *trivial*, if $\Pi(A) = 0$ for every $A \in \mathcal{A}$.

Examples of invariant subspaces may be constructed by applying the represented *-algebra to arbitrary subsets of the representation Hilbert space: If $K \subseteq \mathcal{H}_\Pi$ is an arbitrary subset, then the closure of the linear hull $\mathrm{LH}\{\Pi(\mathcal{A})K\}$ is an invariant subspace of the representation $(\Pi, \mathcal{H}_\Pi)$. A representation $(\Pi, \mathcal{H}_\Pi)$ of a *-algebra $\mathcal{A}$ in the complex field $\mathcal{H}_\Pi = \mathbb{C}$, is always irreducible, since the only invariant subspaces of $\mathcal{H}_\Pi$ are $\{0\}$ and $\mathcal{H}_\Pi = \mathbb{C}$.

Lemma 45.1-7 (Sub-Representations of *-algebras). *Let $(\Pi, \mathcal{H}_\Pi)$ be a representation of the *-algebra $\mathcal{A}$. Suppose $\mathcal{H}_1$ to be a closed subspace of $\mathcal{H}_\Pi$ with associated orthogonal projection P_1 from $\mathcal{H}_\Pi$ onto $\mathcal{H}_1$. Then $\mathcal{H}_1$ is an invariant subspace of $(\Pi, \mathcal{H}_\Pi)$, if and only if $P_1\Pi(A) = \Pi(A)P_1$ for all $A \in \mathcal{A}$, i.e., P_1 is contained in the commutant $\Pi(\mathcal{A})'$.*

In case of an invariant subspace $\mathcal{H}_1$ we have that the orthogonal complement $\mathcal{H}_2 := (\mathbb{1} - P_1)\mathcal{H}_\Pi$ is an invariant subspace of $(\Pi, \mathcal{H}_\Pi)$, too. Then

$$\Pi_1(A) := P_1\Pi(A), \quad \Pi_2(A) := (\mathbb{1} - P_1)\Pi(A), \quad \forall A \in \mathcal{A},$$

defines two representations $(\Pi_1, \mathcal{H}_1)$ and $(\Pi_2, \mathcal{H}_2)$ of $\mathcal{A}$ such that

$$\mathcal{H}_\Pi = \mathcal{H}_1 \oplus \mathcal{H}_2, \quad \Pi(A) = \Pi_1(A) \oplus \Pi_2(A), \quad \forall A \in \mathcal{A},$$

where $\mathcal{H}_2 := (\mathbb{1} - P_1)\mathcal{H}$ is the orthogonal complement of $\mathcal{H}_1$.

The two representations $(\Pi_1, \mathcal{H}_1)$ and $(\Pi_2, \mathcal{H}_2)$ are called sub-representations *of $(\Pi, \mathcal{H}_\Pi)$, indicated by*

$$\Pi_j \leq \Pi, \qquad (\text{notion for sub-representation}). \tag{45.1.6}$$

In addition one finds: If the original representation $(\Pi, \mathcal{H}_\Pi)$ *is non-degenerate, then so are the above constructed sub-representations* $(\Pi_1, \mathcal{H}_1)$ *and* $(\Pi_2, \mathcal{H}_2)$.

Since $\mathcal{A}$ is a *-algebra, the represented algebra $\mathcal{M} := \Pi(\mathcal{A}) \subseteq \mathcal{L}(\mathcal{H}_\Pi)$ is invariant under adjointing. Thus, as an application of Proposition 45.1-5, we arrive at the following.

Proposition 45.1-8 (Irreducible Representations of *-Algebras). Let $(\Pi, \mathcal{H}_\Pi)$ be a nontrivial representation of the *-algebra $\mathcal{A}$. Then the following statements are equivalent:

(i) *The representation* $(\Pi, \mathcal{H}_\Pi)$ *is irreducible.*
(ii) *The commutant* $\Pi(\mathcal{A})'$ *of the represented* *-algebra $\Pi(\mathcal{A})$ *consists of multiples of the identity only, that is* $\Pi(\mathcal{A})' = \mathbb{C}\mathbb{1}$.
(iii) *Every non-zero* $\psi \in \mathcal{H}_\Pi$ *is cyclic for the representation* $(\Pi, \mathcal{H}_\Pi)$.

Moreover, every non-trivial irreducible representation is automatically non-degenerate.

Proposition 45.1-9 (Non-degenerate representations). *Let* $(\Pi, \mathcal{H}_\Pi)$ *be a representation of the *-algebra $\mathcal{A}$. Then the following statements are equivalent:*

(i) $(\Pi, \mathcal{H}_\Pi)$ *is non-degenerate.*
(ii) *For every non-zero* $\psi \in \mathcal{H}_\Pi$ *there exists an element* $A \in \mathcal{A}$ *with* $\Pi(A)\psi \neq 0$.

If $\mathcal{A}$ possesses an unit $\mathbb{1}$, then (i) and (ii) are equivalent to

(iii) Π *is identity preserving, that is* $\Pi(\mathbb{1}) = \mathbb{1}$.

Note that there exist *-algebras, which do not have any non-trivial representation (by bounded operators). One case is given by Example 45.1-1(a), since the CCR require unbounded field operators $\Phi(z)$, $z \in \mathbb{C}$.

45.1.4. Unitary Implementation of *-Automorphisms

For applications, a unitary implementation of a *-automorphism in a representation space is often useful.

Definition 45.1-10 (Unitary implementation of *-automorphisms). Let α be a *-automorphism of the *-algebra $\mathcal{A}$. Then α is said to be unitarily implementable in $(\Pi, \mathcal{H}_\Pi)$ of $\mathcal{A}$, if there exists a unitary operator U in $\mathcal{H}_\Pi$, such that

$$\Pi(\alpha(A)) = U\Pi(A)U^*, \quad \forall A \in \mathcal{A}.$$

Provided existence, the implementing unitary U is in general non-unique. This is formulated in the following proposition, for which we give the proof as an exercise.

Proposition 45.1-11 (Unitary implementations and commutant). *Let α be a *-automorphism of the *-algebra $\mathcal{A}$ and $(\Pi, \mathcal{H}_\Pi)$ a representation of $\mathcal{A}$, in which*

α *is implemented by the unitary* $U \in \mathcal{L}(\mathcal{H}_\Pi)$. *Then the following assertions are valid:*

(a) *The inverse *-automorphism* α^{-1} *is implemented in* $(\Pi, \mathcal{H}_\Pi)$ *by* $U^{-1} = U^*$.

(b) *If* V *is a further unitary implementing* α *in* $(\Pi, \mathcal{H}_\Pi)$, *then both* V^*U *and* UV^* *are contained in the commutant* $\Pi(\mathcal{A})'$.

(c) *If* W *is a unitary contained in the commutant* $\Pi(\mathcal{A})'$, *then — with* U — *also* WU *and* UW *implement* α *in* $(\Pi, \mathcal{H}_\Pi)$. *The set* $\mathcal{I}(\alpha, \Pi)$ *of all those implementing unitaries is given by*

$$\mathcal{I}(\alpha, \Pi) = \{WU \mid W \text{ is a unitary from } \Pi(\mathcal{A})'\}$$
$$= \{UW \mid W \text{ is a unitary from } \Pi(\mathcal{A})'\}$$
$$= \{W_1 U W_2 \mid W_1, W_2 \text{ are unitaries from } \Pi(\mathcal{A})'\}.$$

(d) *If the representation* $(\Pi, \mathcal{H}_\Pi)$ *is irreducible, then the implementing unitary* U *is unique up to a phase* $w \in U(1) = \{z \in \mathbb{C} \mid |z| = 1\}$ *so that*

$$\mathcal{I}(\alpha, \Pi) = \{wU \mid w \in U(1)\}.$$

Proof. Part (a). From $\Pi(\alpha(A)) = U\Pi(A)U^*$ for all $A \in \mathcal{A}$ it follows with $B = \alpha(A)$ that $\Pi(B) = U\Pi(\alpha^{-1}(B))U^*$, thus $U^*\Pi(B)U = \Pi(\alpha^{-1}(B))$ for all $B \in \mathcal{A}$.

Part (b). Both V^* and U^* implement α^{-1} by part (a). Hence for all $A \in \mathcal{A}$ it follows that

$$V^*U\Pi(A)(V^*U)^* = \Pi(\alpha^{-1}(\alpha(A))) = \Pi(A) = \Pi(\alpha(\alpha^{-1}(A))) = UV^*\Pi(A)(UV^*)^*.$$

Part (c). Because $W \in \Pi(\mathcal{A})'$, it holds $\Pi(B) = W\Pi(B)W^*$ for all $B \in \mathcal{A}$. Thus,

$$WU\Pi(A)(WU)^* = W\Pi(\alpha(A))W^* = \Pi(\alpha(A)) = U\Pi(A)U^* = UW\Pi(A)(UW)^*$$

for all $A \in \mathcal{A}$, showing that both UW and WU implement α in $(\Pi, \mathcal{H}_\Pi)$. If $X = V^*U, Y = UV^* \in \Pi(\mathcal{A})'$ in part (b), then $U = VX = YV$ and $V = UX^* = Y^*U$, which shows how $\mathcal{I}(\alpha, \Pi)$ looks like.

For proving part (d) note that by Proposition 45.1-8 on the preceding page we have $\Pi(\mathcal{A})' = \mathbb{C}\mathbb{1}$ for the commutant of the irreducible $(\Pi, \mathcal{H}_\Pi)$. □

45.1.5. *Kolmogorov Decomposition*

We refer at several places in our developments to the Kolmogorov decomposition, which also in other fields of mathematical sciences acquires more and more importance.

Let X be any set. A mapping $K : X \times X \to \mathbb{C}$, $(x, y) \mapsto K(x, y)$ is called a *kernel* on X, whereas a mapping $C : X \to \mathbb{C}$, $x \mapsto C(x)$ is named a *function* on X.

A kernel K on X is called *positive-definite*, if for every number $n \in \mathbb{N}$ and all $z_1, \ldots, z_n \in \mathbb{C}$ and all $x_1, \ldots, x_n \in X$ we have $\sum_{i,j=1}^n \overline{z_i} z_j K(x_i, x_j) \geq 0$. Every positive-definite kernel K on X admits a *Kolmogorov decomposition* [Kol41], [EL77], that is a mapping $v : X \to \mathcal{H}_v$ from X into a complex Hilbert space $\mathcal{H}_v$, which satisfies

$$K(x, y) = (v(x)|v(y)), \quad \forall x, y \in X, \tag{45.1.7}$$

where $(.|.)$ is the right-linear complex scalar product on $\mathcal{H}_v$. Conversely, a kernel is positive-definite, if it possesses a Kolmogorov decomposition. The Kolmogorov decomposition $v : X \to \mathcal{H}_v$ of K is called minimal, if the set $\{v(x) \mid x \in X\}$ is total in $\mathcal{H}_v$. If the Kolmogorov decomposition $v : X \to \mathcal{H}_v$ is not minimal, then one constructs a minimal Kolmogorov decomposition by restricting $\mathcal{H}_v$ to the closure of the linear hull of $\{v(x) \mid x \in X\}$. It is immediately checked that the minimal Kolmogorov decomposition is unique up to unitary equivalence [EL77].

45.1.6. *Positive Linear Functionals and the GNS Representation*

As a vector space, a *-algebra $\mathcal{A}$ owns linear functionals $\omega : \mathcal{A} \to \mathbb{C}$, $A \mapsto \langle \omega; A \rangle$ (where we express the duality relation by the bracket $\langle .; . \rangle$).

Definition 45.1-12 (Linear functionals and states). Let $\mathcal{A}$ be a *-algebra.

(a) A linear functional ω on $\mathcal{A}$ is called *Hermitian*, if $\langle \omega; A^* \rangle = \overline{\langle \omega; A \rangle}$ for every $A \in \mathcal{A}$, or equivalently, if $\langle \omega; A \rangle \in \mathbb{R}$ for all $A \in \mathcal{A}_{\mathrm{sa}}$ (use the Decomposition (45.1.2) into real and imaginary part).

(b) A linear functional ω on $\mathcal{A}$ is called *positive*, if $\langle \omega; A \rangle \geq 0$ for every $A \in \mathcal{A}_+$. (If $\mathcal{A}$ is unital, apply (45.1.4) to show its Hermiticity, or apply in case of a possibly non-unital C^*-algebra $\mathcal{A}$ the Jordan decomposition in Theorem 45.2-9 below.)

(c) For two Hermitian functionals φ and ω we say "φ is smaller than ω" and write $\varphi \leq \omega$, if $\omega - \varphi$ is positive.

(d) If the positive linear functional ω satisfies $\langle \omega; A \rangle > 0$ for all $A > 0$, then it is called *faithful*.

(e) A positive linear functional ω on a unital $\mathcal{A}$ is called a *state*, if it fulfills the normalization condition $\langle \omega; \mathbb{1} \rangle = 1$.

Every linear functional ω defines a sesquilinear form $s_\omega(A, B) := \langle \omega; A^* B \rangle$ on $\mathcal{A}$. s_ω is a semi-inner product and a positive-definite kernel on $\mathcal{A}$, if ω is a *positive* linear functional. If the positive ω is faithful, then s_ω is strictly positive and constitutes a scalar product on $\mathcal{A}$.

For the following basic relations we recall the well-known proof in order to realize the direct implications of linearity and positivity.

Lemma 45.1-13 (Cauchy–Schwarz Inequality). *Let ω be a positive linear functional on the *-algebra $\mathcal{A}$. Then one knows for all $A, B \in \mathcal{A}$ that*

$$\langle \omega; A^* B \rangle = \overline{\langle \omega; B^* A \rangle}, \quad |\langle \omega; A^* B \rangle|^2 \leq \langle \omega; A^* A \rangle \langle \omega; B^* B \rangle.$$

If in addition $\mathcal{A}$ is unital, that implies for every $A \in \mathcal{A}$ (and $B := \mathbb{1}$) the relations

$$\langle \omega; A^* \rangle = \overline{\langle \omega; A \rangle}, \quad |\langle \omega; A \rangle|^2 \le \langle \omega; \mathbb{1} \rangle \langle \omega; A^* A \rangle.$$

Proof. By the assumed linearity and positivity we obtain

$$0 \le \langle \omega; (A + zB)^*(A + zB) \rangle = \langle \omega; A^* A \rangle + z \langle \omega; A^* B \rangle + \bar{z} \langle \omega; B^* A \rangle + |z|^2 \langle \omega; B^* B \rangle.$$

The sum of the two terms in the middle of the right-hand side must be real for arbitrary $z \in \mathbb{C}$, thus we obtain the first of the asserted relations.

If $\langle \omega; B^* B \rangle = 0$ and $\langle \omega; A^* B \rangle$ would be non-vanishing, then a large negative value of z would lead to a contradiction in the preceding inequality. Thus, then $\langle \omega; A^* B \rangle = 0$, too.

For $\langle \omega; B^* B \rangle > 0$ choose $z = -\langle \omega; B^* A \rangle / \langle \omega; B^* B \rangle$, multiply by $\langle \omega; B^* B \rangle$, and arrive at the Cauchy–Schwarz inequality. □

We now discuss the connection between Hilbert space representations of a *-algebra $\mathcal{A}$ and its positive linear functionals. Let $(\Pi, \mathcal{H}_\Pi)$ be a given representation of the *-algebra $\mathcal{A}$. Then for every $\psi \in \mathcal{H}_\Pi$ the map $\omega_\psi : \mathcal{A} \to \mathbb{C}$, defined by

$$\langle \omega_\psi; A \rangle := (\psi | \Pi(A)\psi), \quad \forall A \in \mathcal{A}, \tag{45.1.8}$$

is a linear functional on $\mathcal{A}$. Since, in virtue of the *-homomorphic properties of Π, we have

$$\langle \omega_\psi; A^* A \rangle = (\psi | \Pi(A^* A)\psi) = (\psi | \Pi(A)^* \Pi(A)\psi) = \|\Pi(A)\psi\|^2 \ge 0, \quad \forall A \in \mathcal{A},$$

and ω_ψ is positive. Clearly $\mathcal{H}_\psi := \overline{\Pi(\mathcal{A})\psi}$ is an invariant subspace of $(\Pi, \mathcal{H}_\Pi)$. By Lemma 45.1-7 the associated projection P_ψ from $\mathcal{H}_\Pi$ onto $\mathcal{H}_\psi$ is contained in the commutant $\Pi(\mathcal{A})'$, and the prescription $\Pi_\psi(A) := P_\psi \Pi(A)$, $A \in \mathcal{A}$, defines a cyclic representation $(\Pi_\psi, \mathcal{H}_\psi)$ of $\mathcal{A}$. Representations of this kind are called *GNS representations*, where GNS stands for the mathematicians Gelfand, Naimark, and Segal.

Definition 45.1-14 (GNS representations). Let ω be a positive linear functional on the *-algebra $\mathcal{A}$. A GNS representation over ω is a triple $(\Pi_\omega, \mathcal{H}_\omega, \Omega_\omega)$ consisting of a representation $(\Pi_\omega, \mathcal{H}_\omega)$ of $\mathcal{A}$ and a cyclic vector $\Omega_\omega \in \mathcal{H}_\omega$, such that

$$\langle \omega; A \rangle = (\Omega_\omega | \Pi_\omega(A)\Omega_\omega), \quad \forall A \in \mathcal{A}. \tag{45.1.9}$$

According to Definition 45.1-6(b), GNS representations are non-degenerate. Two different GNS representations $(\Pi_\omega, \mathcal{H}_\omega, \Omega_\omega)$ and $(\tilde{\Pi}_\omega, \tilde{\mathcal{H}}_\omega, \tilde{\Omega}_\omega)$ over the same positive linear functional ω are unitarily equivalent in the following sense: There exists a unitary $U : \mathcal{H}_\omega \to \tilde{\mathcal{H}}_\omega$ with $\tilde{\Omega}_\omega = U\Omega_\omega$ and $\tilde{\Pi}_\omega(A) = U\Pi_\omega(A)U^*$ for all $A \in \mathcal{A}$. This U is constructed and uniquely determined by $\tilde{\Pi}_\omega(A)\tilde{\Omega}_\omega = U\Pi_\omega(A)\Omega_\omega$ for all $A \in \mathcal{A}$. Since unitary equivalent notions in Hilbert space theory are identified, we speak of *the* GNS representation $(\Pi_\omega, \mathcal{H}_\omega, \Omega_\omega)$ over ω.

For an arbitrary *-algebra $\mathcal{A}$, the GNS representation does not exist over every positive linear functional ω, whereas the minimal Kolmogorov decomposition v_ω : $\mathcal{A} \to \mathcal{H}_\omega$, $A \mapsto v_\omega(A)$, satisfying

$$s_\omega(A, B) = \langle \omega; A^*B \rangle = (v_\omega(A)|v_\omega(B)), \quad \forall A, B \in \mathcal{A},$$
$$\text{LH}\{v_\omega(A) \mid A \in \mathcal{A}\} \text{ dense in } \mathcal{H}_\omega, \tag{45.1.10}$$

exists via the positive-definite kernel s_ω (= semi-inner product) on $\mathcal{A}$. A general existence theorem of the GNS representation is e.g., possible for the so-called U^*-algebras.

Theorem 45.1-15 (Existence of GNS representations of U^*-algebras). *Let $\mathcal{A}$ be a U^*-algebra, that is a unital *-algebra, in which each element decomposes into a linear combination of unitaries. Then the GNS representation exists over every positive linear functional ω on $\mathcal{A}$.*

Proof. (Cf. [BHR04a]) For any unitary $U \in \mathcal{A}$ let us consider the mapping v^U : $\mathcal{A} \to \mathcal{H}_\omega$ defined by $v^U(A) := v_\omega(UA)$ for all $A \in \mathcal{A}$. Then with (45.1.10) we obtain that $s_\omega(A, B) = (v^U(A)|v^U(B))$ for all $A, B \in \mathcal{A}$, implying v^U to constitute a further minimal Kolmogorov decomposition for s_ω. But minimal Kolmogorov decompositions are unitarily equivalent, that is, there exists a unique unitary $\Pi_\omega(U)$ in $\mathcal{H}_\omega$ with $v^U(A) = v_\omega(UA) = \Pi_\omega(U)v_\omega(A)$ for all $A \in \mathcal{A}$.

ω being linear implies the minimal Kolmogorov decomposition $v_\omega : \mathcal{A} \to \mathcal{H}_\omega$ to be linear, too. So we may extend Π_ω linearly to a representation of the whole U^*-algebra $\mathcal{A}$ such that $\Pi_\omega(B)v_\omega(A) = v_\omega(BA)$ for all $A, B \in \mathcal{A}$, which implies the independence of $\Pi_\omega(A)$ from the linear decomposition of B into unitaries. Finally, set $\Omega_\omega := v_\omega(\mathbb{1})$. $\qquad\qquad\qquad\qquad\qquad\qquad\qquad\qquad\qquad\qquad\qquad\qquad\qquad$ □

Observe that every unital C^*-algebra is a U^*-algebra, since each of its elements decomposes into a linear combination of four unitaries (cf. below).

45.2. C^*-Algebras

45.2.1. *Elementary Definitions and Properties*

An algebra $\mathcal{A}$ is *normed*, if it is a normed vector space, in which the product inequality $\|AB\| \leq \|A\|\|B\|$ is valid for all $A, B \in \mathcal{A}$ (making the product bi–continuous).

In a *-algebra $\mathcal{A}$ also the *-operation should be continuous.

Definition 45.2-1 (*-Algebra Norm, Banach-*-algebra, C^*-Algebra).

(a) If in a *-algebra $\mathcal{A}$ there is a norm with $\|A\| = \|A^*\|$ for all $A \in \mathcal{A}$, then $\|.\|$ is called a *-algebra norm. (Since $A^{**} = A$ this follows from the apparently weaker condition $\|A^*\| \leq \|A\|$.)

(b) A *-algebra $\mathcal{A}$ with a *-algebra norm is called a *Banach-*-algebra*, if it is complete in the norm topology.

(c) A Banach-*-algebra is called a *C*-algebra*, if the norm satisfies

$$\|A^*A\| = \|A\|^2\,, \quad \forall A \in \mathcal{A}\,, \qquad (C\text{*-}norm\ property)\,. \qquad (45.2.1)$$

We find $\|A\|^2 = \|A^*A\| \leq \|A^*\|\|A\|$, and hence $\|A\| \leq \|A^*\|$, and by interchanging the roles of A and A^* we obtain also $\|A^*\| \leq \|A\|$. So we conclude $\|A\| = \|A^*\|$ for all $A \in \mathcal{A}$. Thus, the C*-norm property is stronger than the *-algebra norm condition.

A norm on a *-algebra $\mathcal{A}$ is called a *C*-norm*, or $\mathcal{A}$ is termed a *pre-C*-algebra*, if the product inequality and the C*-norm property are fulfilled. By going over to its norm completion, every pre-Banach-*-algebra respectively pre-C*-algebra is extensible to a Banach-*-algebra respectively C*-algebra.

A sub-*-algebra of the C*-algebra $\mathcal{A}$, which is closed in the norm topology, is called a *sub-C*-algebra* of $\mathcal{A}$. Similarly, a sub-Banach-*-algebra is defined.

If the pre-C*-algebra $\mathcal{A}$ has a unit $\mathbb{1}$, then the C*-norm property gives $\|\mathbb{1}\| = \|\mathbb{1}^*\mathbb{1}\| = \|\mathbb{1}\|^2$ and implies that $\|\mathbb{1}\| = 1$ or that $\|\mathbb{1}\| = 0$. Throughout the book we ignore the trivial case and always assume $\|\mathbb{1}\| = 1$.

Our main concern are C*-algebras, but we refer some necessary results on Banach-*-algebras in the Secs. 45.2.4 and 45.2.5.

Let $\mathcal{J}$ be a closed *-ideal of a C*-algebra $\mathcal{A}$. Then the equivalence classes $\widetilde{A}$ of the quotient *-algebra $\mathcal{A}/\mathcal{J}$ may be normed (without using representations) by setting

$$\|\widetilde{A}\| := \inf\{\|A + I\| \mid I \in \mathcal{J}\}\,, \quad A \in \mathcal{A}\,. \qquad (45.2.2)$$

It turns out that this norm is a C*-norm on $\mathcal{A}/\mathcal{J}$, for which $\mathcal{A}/\mathcal{J}$ is complete, so that $\mathcal{A}/\mathcal{J}$ becomes a C*-algebra.

Every C*-algebra $\mathcal{A}$ contains the trivial closed *-ideals $\{0\}$ and $\mathcal{A}$. If, beside these, a C*-algebra does not contain any non-trivial closed *-ideal, it is called *simple*.

Example 45.2-2 (*C*-algebras and closed *-ideals*).

(a) The set $\mathcal{L}(\mathcal{H})$ of all bounded operators acting in the Hilbert space $\mathcal{H}$ constitutes a C*-algebra, if the norm is given by the operator norm from Eq. (43.1.1) on page 1522, which in fact satisfies the C*-norm property. As already mentioned, the * is realized in $\mathcal{L}(\mathcal{H})$ by the Hermitian adjointing and the product by the iterated operator application. The identity mapping $\mathbb{1} : \mathcal{H} \rightarrow \mathcal{H}$, $\psi \mapsto \psi$ constitutes then the unit of $\mathcal{L}(\mathcal{H})$.

A sub-C*-algebra of $\mathcal{L}(\mathcal{H})$ is called *concrete* (since its algebraic operations are given explicitly).

(b) Let $\mathcal{H}$ be a Hilbert space. Then the *-algebras of the finite-rank operators $\mathcal{FL}(\mathcal{H})$, the trace class operators $\mathcal{T}(\mathcal{H})$, the Hilbert–Schmidt operators $\mathrm{HS}(\mathcal{H})$, and the compact operators $\mathcal{C}(\mathcal{H})$ constitute *-ideals in $\mathcal{L}(\mathcal{H})$ (their definitions may be found in Sec. 43.2 on page 1525). For finite-dimensional $\mathcal{H}$, all these operator classes coincide with $\mathcal{L}(\mathcal{H})$. For infinite-dimensional $\mathcal{H}$, we have the proper inclusions

$$\mathcal{FL}(\mathcal{H}) \subset \mathcal{T}(\mathcal{H}) \subset \mathrm{HS}(\mathcal{H}) \subset \mathcal{C}(\mathcal{H}) \subset \mathcal{L}(\mathcal{H}) . \qquad (45.2.3)$$

However, for infinite-dimensional $\mathcal{H}$, the only *-ideal from the mentioned ones which is closed in the operator norm, is $\mathcal{C}(\mathcal{H})$. Observe that the $\mathbb{1}$-operator is compact, if and only if $\mathcal{H}$ has finite-dimension. Hence the sub-C*-algebra $\mathcal{C}(\mathcal{H})$ does not contain a unit if $\mathcal{H}$ is infinite-dimensional.

(c) Suppose X to be a topological space and let $C_b(X)$ denote the bounded continuous functions (cf. Notational Remark 45.0-1.) With the point-wise *-algebraic operations

$$(f+ug)(x) := f(x)+ug(x) , \quad (fg)(x) := f(x)g(x) , \quad f^*(x) := \overline{f(x)} , \quad \forall x \in X , \qquad (45.2.4)$$

for all $f, g \in C_b(X)$ and every $u \in \mathbb{C}$, and with the sup-norm

$$\|f\|_{\mathrm{sup}} \equiv \|f\|_\infty := \sup\{|f(x)| \mid x \in X\} , \quad f \in C_b(X) , \qquad (45.2.5)$$

$C_b(X)$ becomes a commutative C*-algebra. Its unit is given by the unit function $\mathbb{1}(x) = 1$, $\forall x \in X$. The self-adjoint elements of $C_b(X)$ are just its real-valued functions, collected in $C_b(X)_{\mathrm{sa}}$.

If X is locally compact, then $C_\infty(X)$ consists of the continuous functions f, which vanish at infinity. (That means: For $\varepsilon > 0$ there is a compact $X_\varepsilon \subset X$, with $|f(x)| < \varepsilon$ for all $x \in X \backslash X_\varepsilon$.) $C_\infty(X)$ is a sub-C*-algebra of $C_b(X)$. Since the unit function $\mathbb{1}$ does not vanish at infinity, we conclude that $C_\infty(X)$ contains a unit, if and only if X is compact, in which case $C_\infty(X) = C_b(X) = C(X)$.

(d) Consider the situation of part (c) for $X = \mathbb{R}^m$. $\mathcal{H} := \mathrm{L}^2(\mathbb{R}^m)$ is the Hilbert space of all Lebesgue-square integrable functions. For $f \in C_b(\mathbb{R}^m)$ the multiplication operator $M_f : \mathcal{H} \to \mathcal{H}$, $\psi \mapsto f\psi$ is bounded having the norm

$$\|M_f\| = \sup\{\|f\psi\| \mid \psi \in \mathcal{H} , \ \|\psi\| \leq 1\} = \sup\{|f(x)| \mid x \in \mathbb{R}^m\} = \|f\|_{\mathrm{sup}}.$$

Thus, according to the *-isomorphic embedding $f \mapsto M_f$, we may interpret $C_b(\mathbb{R}^m)$ as a commutative sub-C*-algebra of $\mathcal{L}(\mathcal{H})$ (providing in Physics a classical part in the set of quantum observables).

In this connection, let us state a general Theorem.

Theorem 45.2-3 (Gelfand representation of Abelian C*-algebras). *Let $\mathcal{A}$ be an arbitrary commutative C*-algebra. Then there is a locally compact Hausdorff space X such that $\mathcal{A}$ is *-isomorphic to $C_\infty(X)$ (the Gelfand representation).*

Furthermore, X is compact, if and only if $\mathcal{A}$ is unital (in which case $C_\infty(X) = C_b(X) = C(X)$, see part (c) of the preceding Example).

Let us here only mention that a locally compact Hausdorff space X for the Gelfand representation is constructed by means of the multiplicative states, the characters χ, on $\mathcal{A}$. The product property $\chi(AB) = \chi(A)\chi(B)$ ensures that χ is a pure state, and is then identified with a point $x \in X$ (e.g., [KR86]).

45.2.2. *Spectrum and Functional Calculus*

The spectrum of C^*-algebra elements is introduced in the same way as for Hilbert space operators (cf. Sec. 43.3 on page 1532) and leads to similar results.

Definition 45.2-4 (Resolvent set and spectrum). Let $\mathcal{A}$ be a C^*-algebra with $\mathbb{1}$. Then the *resolvent set* $\rho_{\mathcal{A}}(A)$ of $A \in \mathcal{A}$ consists of all $z \in \mathbb{C}$ for which $z\mathbb{1} - A$ is invertible (in $\mathcal{A}$). The inverse $(z\mathbb{1} - A)^{-1}$ is called the *resolvent* of A at $z \in \rho_{\mathcal{A}}(A)$. The *spectrum* $\sigma_{\mathcal{A}}(A)$ is by definition $\sigma_{\mathcal{A}}(A) := \mathbb{C} \backslash \rho_{\mathcal{A}}(A)$.

If the C^*-algebra $\mathcal{A}$ does not contain a unit, then the spectrum $\sigma_{\mathcal{A}}(A)$ of $A \in \mathcal{A}$ is defined as the spectrum $\sigma_{\mathcal{A}_{\mathbb{1}}}(A)$, with A regarded as an element of the C^*-algebra $\mathcal{A}_{\mathbb{1}} := \mathbb{C}\mathbb{1} + \mathcal{A}$, obtained by adjoining a unit to $\mathcal{A}$.

The adjoining of $\mathbb{1}$ to a non-unital C^*-algebra is a frequently invoked standard procedure which deserves a comment.

Remark 45.2-5 (Adjoining a unit). If $\mathcal{A}$ is a non-unital C^*-algebra, then the direct sum $\mathcal{A}_{\mathbb{1}} := \mathbb{C}\mathbb{1} + \mathcal{A} \ni (c, A)$ constitutes a *-algebra if endowed with the product $(c, A)(c', A') := (cc', cA' + c'A + AA')$ and with the *-operation $(c, A)^* := (\bar{c}, A^*)$. Clearly $(1, 0)$ is the (left and right) unit for this product. We also see that $\mathcal{A}$ is *-isomorphic to $(0, \mathcal{A})$ and constitutes a *-ideal of $\mathcal{A}_{\mathbb{1}}$.

Furtheron one can demonstrate the C^*-norm property of

$$\|(c, A)\| := \sup\{\|cB + AB\| \mid B \in \mathcal{A}, \|B\| = 1\}, \tag{45.2.6}$$

by observing that on the right-hand side (c, A) acts as a left multiplication operator on $B \equiv (0, B) \in \mathcal{A}$. In this norm $\mathcal{A}_{\mathbb{1}}$ is complete and thus constitutes a C^*-algebra. Since this norm of $\mathcal{A}_{\mathbb{1}}$ coincides on $(0, \mathcal{A})$ with the original norm of $\mathcal{A}$, $\mathcal{A}$ is a norm closed *-ideal of $\mathcal{A}_{\mathbb{1}}$, and the quotient C^*-algebra $\mathcal{A}_{\mathbb{1}}/\mathcal{A}$ is *-isomorphic to $\mathbb{C}\mathbb{1}$. Moreover, $\mathcal{A}$ is an *essential* ideal of $\mathcal{A}_{\mathbb{1}}$, what means that any other norm closed, non-trivial *-ideal of $\mathcal{A}_{\mathbb{1}}$ has non-zero intersection with it.

If the C^*-algebra $\mathcal{A}$ contains the sub-C^*-algebra $\mathcal{B}$, then there are two possibly different spectra $\sigma_{\mathcal{A}}(A)$ and $\sigma_{\mathcal{B}}(A)$ for $A \in \mathcal{B}$. Different spectra arise from different units in $\mathcal{A}$ and $\mathcal{B}$. If $\mathcal{B}$ possesses, however, the same unit as $\mathcal{A}$, then $\sigma_{\mathcal{A}}(A) = \sigma_{\mathcal{B}}(A)$. So we write, under these circumstances, simply $\sigma(A)$, and also $\rho(A)$.

Let $\alpha : \mathcal{A} \to \mathcal{A}'$ be a surjective *-isomorphism between two unital C^*-algebras. Then clearly $\alpha(\mathbb{1}) = \mathbb{1}'$, and $\sigma_{\mathcal{A}}(A) = \sigma_{\mathcal{A}'}(\alpha(A))$ for all $A \in \mathcal{A}$. This expresses the algebraic invariance of the spectrum *as a subset of* $\mathbb{C}$. Further spectral properties of concrete C^*-algebras, as e.g., multiplicity, are not algebraically invariant (under general surjective *-isomorphisms). If e.g., $A \in \mathcal{A}$ — where $\mathcal{A}$ is a simple C^*-algebra — means physically a positive, bounded Hamiltonian, then its eigenvalue 0 for the ground state may in some faithful representations be degenerate and in others not, what is essential for understanding spontaneous symmetry break down.

Proposition 45.2-6 (Algebraic spectral and norm properties). *If $\mathcal{A}$ is a C^*-algebra with unit, then we have for an $A \in \mathcal{A}$:*

(a) $\sigma(A)$ *is a non-empty, compact subset of $\mathbb{C}$ with $|z| \leq \|A\|$ for all $z \in \sigma(A)$.*
(b) $\sigma(z\mathbb{1} - A) = z - \sigma(A)$ *for all $z \in \mathbb{C}$, and $\sigma(A^*) = \overline{\sigma(A)}$.*
(c) *If A is invertible, then $\sigma(A^{-1}) = \{\frac{1}{z} \mid z \in \sigma(A)\} = \sigma(A)^{-1}$.*
(d) *If A is normal (i.e., A commutes with A^*), then $\|A\| = \sup\{|z| \mid z \in \sigma(A)\}$. If A is isometric, then $\|A\| = 1$.*
(e) *If $A \in \mathcal{A}_{sa}$ (hence normal), then $\sigma(A) \subseteq [-\|A\|, \|A\|] \subset \mathbb{R}$, and $\sigma(A^2) \subseteq [0, \|A\|^2] \subset \mathbb{R}_+$.*
(f) *If A is unitary (hence normal and isometric), then $\sigma(A) \subseteq U(1)$. Especially, we then have $\|AB\| = \|B\| = \|BA\|$ for all $B \in \mathcal{A}$.*
(g) *For general $A \in \mathcal{A}$ and each polynomial $p(A) = \sum_{k=0}^{n} z_k A^k$, with $A^0 := \mathbb{1}$ and $z_k \in \mathbb{C}$, we have $\sigma(p(A)) = p(\sigma(A))$.*

Let us now turn to the spectral functional calculus of normal, especially self-adjoint, elements in an abstract C^*-algebra $\mathcal{A}$. In the physical, applications, it describes those spectral properties of bounded observables which are independent of any representation in Hilbert space.

We denote by $C_0(\sigma(A))$ the C^*-algebra of continuous functions on the spectrum $\sigma(A)$ of $A \in \mathcal{A}$ vanishing at zero. $C_0(\sigma(A))$ is a proper sub-C^*-algebra of $C(\sigma(A))$, if and only if $0 \in \sigma(A)$, equivalently, if and only if A is not invertible.

Theorem 45.2-7 (Continuous spectral mapping theorem). *Let $\mathcal{A}$ be a unital C^*-algebra and choose a normal $A \in \mathcal{A}$.*

(a) *The smallest sub-C^*-algebra $\mathcal{A}_{\{A\}}$ of $\mathcal{A}$ containing A and the smallest sub-C^*-algebra $\mathcal{A}_{\{\mathbb{1},A\}}$, which contains both $\mathbb{1}$ and A, are commutative.*
(b) *There exists a unique *-isomorphism, the* spectral mapping,

$$\Psi_A : C(\sigma(A)) \xrightarrow{\text{onto}} \mathcal{A}_{\{\mathbb{1},A\}}, \quad \text{with} \quad \Psi_A(p(u)) = p(A), \tag{45.2.7}$$

mapping any polynomial function

$$u \mapsto p(u) := \sum_{k,l=0}^{n} z_{k,l} \overline{u}^k u^l \in C(\sigma(A)) \quad \text{onto} \quad p(A) := \sum_{k,l=0}^{n} z_{k,l}(A^*)^k A^l \in \mathcal{A}_{\{\mathbb{1},A\}}$$

(where $n \in \mathbb{N}$, $z_{k,l} \in \mathbb{C}$ and $A^0 = \mathbb{1}$).
(c) *For $f \in C(\sigma(A))$ we write $f(A) := \Psi_A(f) \in \mathcal{A}_{\{\mathbb{1},A\}}$. Then $\sigma(f(A)) = f(\sigma(A))$ and $\|f(A)\| = \|f\|_{\sup}$ for every $f \in C(\sigma(A))$.*

*Summarizing we have the following *-isomorphic connections (the $\leftrightarrow$ relations being onto)*

$$
\begin{array}{ccccc}
C_0(\sigma(A)) & \subseteq & C(\sigma(A)) & & \\
\updownarrow \Psi_A & & \updownarrow \Psi_A & & \\
\mathcal{A}_{\{A\}} & \subseteq & \mathcal{A}_{\{\mathbb{1},A\}} & \subseteq \mathcal{A} & \textit{(unital)}.
\end{array}
$$

If $\mathcal{A}$ does not contain a unit, then one adjoins one and the spectral mapping takes its values in $\mathcal{A}_{\mathbb{1}} = \mathbb{C}\mathbb{1} + \mathcal{A}$. In this case, $0 \in \sigma(A)$ for every $A \in \mathcal{A}$, since otherwise $A^{-1} = -(0\mathbb{1} - A)^{-1}$ would exist, and $A^{-1}A = \mathbb{1}$ would be already in $\mathcal{A}$. Then $f \in C_0(\sigma(A))$, i.e., $f(0) = 0$, yields $f(A) = \Psi_A(f) \in \mathcal{A}$, which ensures the restriction of Ψ_A to be a *-isomorphism from $C_0(\sigma(A))$ onto the sub-C*-algebra $\mathcal{A}_{\{A\}} \subseteq \mathcal{A} \subsetneq \mathcal{A}_{\mathbb{1}}$.

For illustration of the last part of the foregoing theorem, recall that 0 is always in the spectrum of a compact operator $A \in \mathcal{C}(\mathcal{H})$ and that only a continuous function f from $C_0(\sigma(A))$ ensures $f(A) \in \mathcal{C}(\mathcal{H})$.

We obtain an interesting conclusion if we combine the spectral mapping theorem with the Riesz–Markov theorem 48.1-6 on page 1783 respectively with Example 45.2-24 given below.

Proposition 45.2-8 (Spectrum as Dispersion-Free Expectations). *Let A be a normal element of the unital C*-algebra $\mathcal{A}$. Then $z \in \sigma(A)$, if and only if $z = \langle \omega; A \rangle$ is the dispersion-free expectation value of a state $\omega \in \mathcal{S}(\mathcal{A})$ (meaning that A has a sharp value in ω).*

Proof. [Sketch] Let us map the C*-algebra $\mathcal{A}_{\{A\}}$ generated by A onto $C(\sigma(A))$. The dispersion-free states on $C(\sigma(A))$ are the point measures on $\sigma(A)$. If now $z \in \sigma(A)$, we form the point measure δ_z and extend it from $C(\sigma(A))$ to $\mathcal{A}$ by Hahn–Banach and obtain a dispersion-free (pure) state (e.g., [KR86]).

If there is a state ω with $\langle \omega; A \rangle = z$ such that its restriction to $C(\sigma(A))$ is dispersion-free, then this restriction must be the point measure at z, what is only possible if $z \in \sigma(A)$. $\hfill\square$

Proposition 45.2-8 belongs to the basic features, allowing to interpret the self-adjoint elements of a C*-algebra as observables in the narrow sense. It has a direct empirical implication: Whereas an experimenter has difficulties to look on the singular values of $(z\mathbb{1} - A)^{-1}$, if given a measurement apparatus for the self-adjoint A, he may much better detect dispersion-free values.

45.2.3.   The Positive Elements

In Definition 45.1-2(e), an element A of a *-algebra $\mathcal{A}$ was defined *positive* in a purely algebraic manner, namely that there exist a $D \in \mathcal{A}$ with $A = D^*D$. For a C*-algebra $\mathcal{A}$ we now want to relate the algebraic positivity of $A \in \mathcal{A}$ with the positivity of its spectrum $\sigma(A)$, what belongs to the deep results in C*-algebraic theory and took a long time to be proved (by Vaught and Kelley).

If $A \in \mathcal{A}$ is self-adjoint, then $\sigma(A) \subset \mathbb{R}$ (cf. Proposition 45.2-6), and the absolute value function over $\sigma(A)$ is an element of the commutative C*-algebra $C_0(\sigma(A))$; (as required, the function $|.|$ satisfies $|z| = 0$ at $z = 0$). According to the functional calculus of Theorem 45.2-7 the absolute value of A may then be defined in terms of the spectral mapping by $|A| := \Psi_A(|.|) \in \mathcal{A}_{\{A\}}$.

Theorem 45.2-9 (Positivity, Jordan decomposition, square root). *Let $\mathcal{A}$ be a C*-algebra. For $A \in \mathcal{A}$, the following three conditions are equivalent:*

(i) *$A = D^*D$ for some $D \in \mathcal{A}$, i.e., $A \in \mathcal{A}_+$.*
(ii) *$A = C^2$ for some $C \in \mathcal{A}_{sa}$.*
(iii) *A is self-adjoint and $\sigma(A) \subset [0, \infty[$.*

Hence for every $A \in \mathcal{A}_+$ we have $\sigma(A) \subseteq [0, \|A\|]$ and $\|A\| \in \sigma(A)$ by Proposition 45.2-6(e).

The set $\mathcal{A}_+$ of all positive elements of $\mathcal{A}$ is a closed subset in $\mathcal{A}$ satisfying $A + \lambda B \in \mathcal{A}_+$ for $A, B \in \mathcal{A}_+$ and $\lambda \geq 0$. It holds $\mathcal{A}_+ \cap (-\mathcal{A}_+) = \{0\}$.

If $A \in \mathcal{A}_{sa}$, then there exist unique elements $A_\pm \in \mathcal{A}_+$ such that

$$A = A_+ - A_- , \quad A_+A_- = 0 = A_-A_+ ,$$

which is called the Jordan decomposition *of A. The positive elements $A_\pm$ are given by $A_+ := \frac{1}{2}(|A| + A)$ and $A_- := \frac{1}{2}(|A| - A)$.*

Furthermore, if one demands $C \in \mathcal{A}_+$, then the decomposition in part (ii) is unique: For $A \in \mathcal{A}_+$ there exists a unique $C \in \mathcal{A}_+$ satisfying $A = C^2$, and this unique positive C is given by the square root $C = \sqrt{A} := \Psi_A(\sqrt{.})$.

Observe that the Jordan decomposition $\mathcal{A}_{sa} = \mathcal{A}_+ - \mathcal{A}_+$ is also valid (as in Eq. (45.1.4)) if the C*-algebra $\mathcal{A}$ does not contain a unit. Since $A^*A \in \mathcal{A}_+$, for every $A \in \mathcal{A}$, it follows from the above theorem that the absolute value is uniquely connected with the square root according to

$$|A| = \sqrt{A^*A}, \quad \forall A \in \mathcal{A}. \tag{45.2.8}$$

Recall the relation $B \leq A$ (or $A \geq B$), if $A - B \in \mathcal{A}_+$, as introduced for general *-algebras. This relation is obviously reflexive, i.e., $A \leq A$. In the case of C*-algebras $A \geq 0$ and $A \leq 0$ implies $A = 0$, what follows immediately from $\mathcal{A}_+$ being a pointed cone, that is $\mathcal{A}_+ \cap (-\mathcal{A}_+) = \{0\}$. Thus, $B \leq A$ is an antisymmetric binary relation (cf. Definition 47.2-3 on page 1731).

As a consequence of $\mathcal{A}_+ + \mathcal{A}_+ \subseteq \mathcal{A}_+$ we conclude: $A \geq B$ and $B \geq C$ means $A - B \in \mathcal{A}_+$ and $B - C \in \mathcal{A}_+$, which leads to $A - C = (A - B) + (B - C) \in \mathcal{A}_+$, that is $A \geq C$. Thus, $B \leq A$ is a transitive binary relation.

Within $\mathcal{A}$ the condition $A \geq B$ means that the imaginary parts of A and B coincide ($A - B \in \mathcal{A}_+$ implying $A - B$ self-adjoint). Thus, one employs the relation $\geq$ only on the real vector space $\mathcal{A}_{sa}$ of self-adjoint elements.

Lemma 45.2-10. *The relation $\geq$ on the real vector space $\mathcal{A}_{\mathrm{sa}}$ is an order relation (cf. Definition 47.2-3 on page 1731).*

Positivity of elements of a C^*-algebra leads to some less obvious inequalities.

Proposition 45.2-11 (Positivity and norm). *Let A and B be self-adjoint elements of a C^*-algebra $\mathcal{A}$. Then the following assertions are valid:*

(a) *If $0 \leq A \leq B$, then $\|A\| \leq \|B\|$.*
(b) *If $0 \leq A$, then $0 \leq A^2 \leq \|A\|A$.*
(c) *If $\mathcal{A}$ has a unit, then $A \in \mathcal{A}_+$ implies $0 \leq A \leq \|A\|\mathbb{1}$.*

If $\mathcal{A}$ contains a unit and A is invertible, then it follows that $|A|$ is invertible with $|A|^{-1} = \sqrt{(A^*A)^{-1}}$ by the spectral calculus. But then we have

$$A = U|A|, \quad \text{(invertible polar decomposition)},$$

where $U := A|A|^{-1} \in \mathcal{A}$. In fact, we have $U^*U = \mathbb{1}$, and U is invertible with $U^{-1} = |A|A^{-1}$, which implies U to be unitary.

This is a special polar decomposition, which we treated more generally for Hilbert space operators in Proposition 43.3-5 on page 1537. To obtain that general form in the algebraic setting one needs σ-weakly closed C^*-algebras (von Neumann algebras resp. W*-algebras, cf. Sec. 46.1).

From Theorem 45.2-9, Lemma 45.2-10, and Proposition 45.2-11, we draw a structurally important conclusion, which expresses the algebra norm in terms of order relations.

Corollary 45.2-12 (Algebraic Order-Unit). *If the C^*-algebra $\mathcal{A}$ possess a unit $\mathbb{1}$, then its self-adjoint part $\mathcal{A}_{\mathrm{sa}}$ is a (complete) order-unit space as introduced before Definition 47.2-8 on page 1735, with the order-unit $\mathbb{1}$. That is*

$$\|A\| = \inf\{\lambda \geq 0 \,|\, -\lambda\mathbb{1} \leq A \leq \lambda\mathbb{1}\}, \quad \forall A \in \mathcal{A}_{\mathrm{sa}}. \tag{45.2.9}$$

If the C^*-algebra $\mathcal{A}$ is not unital, then nevertheless the norm relation 45.2.9 is valid, if $\mathbb{1}$ is taken from $\mathcal{A}_{\mathbb{1}} = \mathbb{C}\mathbb{1} + \mathcal{A}$, cf. Remark 45.2-5. Since $\mathcal{A}_{\mathbb{1}}$ is the smallest C^*-algebra containing $\mathcal{A}$ and $\mathbb{1}$ one could then term $\mathcal{A}_{sa}$ alone an almost order-unit space.

45.2.4. *Properties of Algebraic Homomorphisms*

For *-homomorphisms from Banach-*-algebras into C^*-algebras, we have in addition to Proposition 45.1-4 on page 1630 some results concerning their continuity.

Theorem 45.2-13. *The following assertions are valid:*

(a) *Let α be a *-homomorphism from a Banach-*-algebra $\mathcal{A}$ into a C^*-algebra $\mathcal{B}$. Then $\|\alpha(A)\| \leq \|A\|$ for all $A \in \mathcal{A}$.*
    *If $\mathcal{A}$ is even a C^*-algebra, then the kernel $\ker(\alpha)$ is a closed *-ideal in $\mathcal{A}$, and the range $\mathrm{ran}(\alpha)$ of α is a sub-C^*-algebra of $\mathcal{B}$. Especially, if the C^*-algebra $\mathcal{A}$ is simple, then either $\ker(\alpha) = \{0\}$, i.e., α is injective, or $\alpha = 0$.*

(b) *Let α be a *-isomorphism from a C*-algebra $\mathcal{A}$ into a C*-algebra $\mathcal{B}$. Then α is norm preserving, i.e., $\|\alpha(A)\| = \|A\|$ for all $A \in \mathcal{A}$.*

Recall, if α is a *-isomorphism from a C*-algebra $\mathcal{A}$ onto itself it is called a **-automorphism*. That is the most popular case of a *symmetry* in the physical sense. One knows, however, already from Wigner's Theorem in traditional quantum mechanics, that certain physical symmetries, e.g., time inversion, are to be represented by an *anti-*-automorphism*. In algebraic quantum theory, both cases are generalized to Jordan automorphisms.

Definition 45.2-14. Let α be a (complex) linear map from a C*-algebra $\mathcal{A}$ into a C*-algebra $\mathcal{B}$.

(a) α is an anti-*-homomorphism if
$$\alpha(A^*) = \alpha(A)^* \quad \text{and} \quad \alpha(AB) = \alpha(B)\alpha(A), \quad \forall A, B \in \mathcal{A}. \qquad (45.2.10)$$
(b) α is a Jordan homomorphism if
$$\alpha(A^*) = \alpha(A)^* \quad \text{and} \quad \alpha([A, B]_+) = [\alpha(A), \alpha(B)]_+, \quad \forall A, B \in \mathcal{A}, \qquad (45.2.11)$$
where $[A, B]_+ := AB + BA$.

If the inverse α^{-1} exists, then we speak of the corresponding isomorphisms, and if in that case $\mathcal{A} = \mathcal{B}$ and α is onto, we speak of an anti-*-automorphism or of a Jordan automorphism, respectively.

Let us call in a physical context the Jordan automorphisms of a C*-algebra $\mathcal{A}$ also the *algebraic symmetries* of $\mathcal{A}$, or the *symmetries* in the abstract Heisenberg picture.

Theorem 45.2-15 (Properties of Jordan Homomorphisms).

(a) *A Jordan homomorphism α from a C*-algebra $\mathcal{A}$ into a C*-algebra $\mathcal{B}$ is positive (since it is square preserving) and norm decreasing (continuous). If it is a Jordan isomorphism, it is norm preserving (an isometry).*
(b) *If α is a Jordan automorphism of the C*-algebra $\mathcal{A}$, then the dual map α^* : $\mathcal{A}^* \to \mathcal{A}^*$ (given by $\langle\alpha^*(\omega); A\rangle = \langle\omega; \alpha(A)\rangle$) is a positive isometry "onto". This implies beside other things that α is weakly continuous. (For the dual space cf. also Definition 45.2-19 on page 1647.)*
(c) *Let α be a Jordan homomorphism α from a C*-algebra $\mathcal{A}$ into a concrete C*-algebra $\mathcal{B}$ (concrete means $\mathcal{B} \subseteq \mathcal{L}(\mathcal{H})$ for some Hilbert space $\mathcal{H}$). Then there exists a projection $P \in \mathcal{B}' \cap \mathcal{B}'' \subset \mathcal{L}(\mathcal{H})$ such that $A \mapsto \alpha(A)P$ is a *-homomorphism, and $A \mapsto \alpha(A)P^\perp$ is an anti-*-homomorphism.*
(d) *Consider the situation of part (c). If $\mathcal{B} \subseteq \mathcal{L}(\mathcal{H})$ is irreducible (i.e., $\mathcal{B}' = \mathbb{C}\mathbb{1}$, thus $P = 0$ or $P = \mathbb{1}$), then either α is a *-homomorphism or an anti-*-homomorphism.*

The involved proof of (c) is sketched in [BR87] and some more details are elaborated in [Rie80].

45.2.5. *Representations in Hilbert Spaces*

If $\mathcal{A}$ is a Banach-*-algebra, then Theorem 45.2-13(a) ensures the norm continuity of every representation Π of $\mathcal{A}$ (since $\|\Pi(A)\| \leq \|A\|$ for all $A \in \mathcal{A}$). Being *-homomorphic every representation $(\Pi, \mathcal{H}_\Pi)$ is positive (what means "positivity preserving": $A \geq 0$ implies $\Pi(A) \geq 0$).

Proposition 45.2-16 (Faithful Representation). *For a representation $(\Pi, \mathcal{H}_\Pi)$ of the C*-algebra $\mathcal{A}$ we have the following three equivalent conditions:*

(i) $(\Pi, \mathcal{H}_\Pi)$ *is faithful, i.e.,* $\ker(\Pi) = \{0\}$.
(ii) Π *is norm preserving.*
(iii) Π *is strict-positivity preserving, i.e.,* $\Pi(A) > 0$ *for all $A > 0$.*

Furthermore, the C*-algebra $\mathcal{A}$ is simple, if and only if every non-trivial representation is faithful (and thus norm preserving).

In Lemma 45.1-7 on page 1632 we introduced already a direct sum of two representations of *-algebras. By the continuity of C*-algebra representations, we are now able to construct infinite direct sum representations as follows. Let $\{(\Pi_\alpha, \mathcal{H}_\alpha) \mid \alpha \in I\}$ be a family of representations of the C*-algebra $\mathcal{A}$ indexed by an arbitrary (finite, countable, or over-countable) set I. The direct sum Hilbert space $\mathcal{H}_\Pi := \bigoplus_{\alpha \in I} \mathcal{H}_\alpha$ consists of those vectors $\psi = \bigoplus_{\alpha \in I} \psi_\alpha$ which have a finite norm $\|\psi\|^2 = \sum_{\alpha \in I} \|\psi_\alpha\|^2 < \infty$. This implies that only a countable number of the $\psi_\alpha \in \mathcal{H}_\alpha$ is non-zero. The scalar product in the direct sum Hilbert space $\mathcal{H}_\Pi$ is given by

$$(\xi|\psi) = \sum_{\alpha \in I} (\xi_\alpha | \psi_\alpha)\,, \quad \xi = \bigoplus_{\alpha \in I} \xi_\alpha \in \mathcal{H}_\Pi\,, \quad \psi = \bigoplus_{\alpha \in I} \psi_\alpha \in \mathcal{H}_\Pi\,.$$

For each $A \in \mathcal{A}$ and every vector $\psi = \bigoplus_{\alpha \in I} \psi_\alpha \in \mathcal{H}_\Pi$ we make the ansatz

$$\Pi(A)\psi := \bigoplus_{\alpha \in I} \Pi_\alpha(A)\psi_\alpha\,.$$

The inequality $\|\Pi_\alpha(A)\| \leq \|A\|$, for all $A \in \mathcal{A}$, implies that $\Pi(A)$ is a well-defined, bounded operator in $\mathcal{H}_\Pi$ with the operator norm

$$\|\Pi(A)\| = \sup_{\alpha \in I} \|\Pi_\alpha(A)\| \leq \|A\|\,.$$

Since the *-algebraic operations go component-wise for direct sum operators, Π is a *-homomorphism. Hence the tuple of direct sums

$$\mathcal{H}_\Pi := \bigoplus_{\alpha \in I} \mathcal{H}_\alpha\,, \quad \Pi := \bigoplus_{\alpha \in I} \Pi_\alpha\,,$$

constitutes a representation of $\mathcal{A}$, the *direct sum representation*, written

$$(\Pi, \mathcal{H}_\Pi) = \bigoplus_{\alpha \in I} (\Pi_\alpha, \mathcal{H}_\alpha) . \tag{45.2.12}$$

Whereas every C^*-algebra possesses a faithful representation (see Theorem 45.2-31 on page 1657), this is not true for Banach-*-algebras.

Definition 45.2-17 (Enveloping C*-algebra). A Banach-*-algebra is called an *A*-algebra*, if it admits a faithful representation (and so every C^*-algebra is an A*-algebra).

Let $\mathcal{A}$ be an arbitrary A*-algebra. We define a new norm $\|.\|_*$ on $\mathcal{A}$ by

$$\|A\|_* := \sup\{\|\Pi(A)\| \mid \Pi \text{ runs over all representations of } \mathcal{A}\} , \quad A \in \mathcal{A} . \tag{45.2.13}$$

Since $\|\Pi(A)\| \le \|A\|$, it follows that $\|A\|_* \le \|A\|$ for every $A \in \mathcal{A}$. By construction $\|.\|_*$ is a C^*-norm on $\mathcal{A}$ (since it is non-degenerate and since the operator norms in the representation spaces satisfy the C^*-norm property). The completion of $\mathcal{A}$ in $\|.\|_*$ is then a C^*-algebra, the *enveloping C*-algebra*, denoted by $C^*(\mathcal{A})$.

45.2.6. State Space, Pure States, GNS Representation

According to Definition 45.1-12 on page 1635, a linear functional ω on a *-algebra $\mathcal{A}$ is positive, if $\langle \omega; A^*A \rangle \ge 0$ for all $A \in \mathcal{A}$.

Assume now $\mathcal{A}$ to be a C^*-algebra. Because of the Jordan decomposition $A = A_+ - A_-$ from Theorem 45.2-9 and the decomposition (45.1.2) it follows that the positivity of the linear functional ω on $\mathcal{A}$ ensures the so-called *self-adjointness condition* $\overline{\langle \omega; A \rangle} = \langle \omega; A^* \rangle$, $\forall A \in \mathcal{A}$, to be valid also if $\mathcal{A}$ does not contain an identity (cf. also Lemma 45.1-13 on page 1635).

Besides self-adjointness, the positivity of a linear functional ω on a C^*-algebra has a less obvious but very important consequence.

Theorem 45.2-18 (Continuity of positive linear functionals). *Let ω be a positive linear functional on the C*-algebra $\mathcal{A}$. Then ω is continuous (in norm, what is by linearity equivalent to $|\langle \omega; A \rangle| \le c\|A\|$ with some $c > 0$). Furthermore, we have*

$$|\langle \omega; A \rangle|^2 \le \langle \omega; A^*A \rangle \|\omega\| , \quad \forall A \in \mathcal{A} ,$$
$$|\langle \omega; A^*BA \rangle| \le \langle \omega; A^*A \rangle \|B\| , \quad \forall A, B \in \mathcal{A} ,$$
$$\|\omega\| = \sup\{\langle \omega; A^*A \rangle \mid A \in \mathcal{A} , \ \|A\| = 1\} .$$

If in addition $\mathcal{A}$ possesses a unit, then $\|\omega\| = \langle \omega; \mathbb{1} \rangle$.

Definition 45.2-19 (Topologies in the dual space). We denote by $\mathcal{A}^*$ the topological dual of the C^*-algebra $\mathcal{A}$ with respect to its C^*-norm, which is by definition the Banach space of all bounded linear functionals on (the Banach space)

$\mathcal{A}$ (recall that, in contradistinction, $\mathcal{A}'$ means the commutant). We introduce in $\mathcal{A}^*$ the following two topologies:

The *norm topology* is determined by neighborhoods of the form

$$\mathcal{U}(\omega; \varepsilon) = \{\varphi \in \mathcal{A}^* \mid \|\omega - \varphi\| < \varepsilon\}, \quad \varepsilon > 0. \tag{45.2.14}$$

The second important topology in $\mathcal{A}^*$ is the *weak* topology*. That is the locally convex Hausdorff topology $\sigma(\mathcal{A}^*, \mathcal{A})$, the neighborhoods of which are indexed by a finite number $A_1, \ldots A_n \in \mathcal{A}$ and $\varepsilon > 0$, and have the form

$$\mathcal{U}(\omega; A_1, \ldots, A_n, \varepsilon) = \{\varphi \in \mathcal{A}^* \mid |\langle \omega; A_k \rangle - \langle \varphi; A_k \rangle| < \varepsilon, \ k = 1, 2, \ldots, n\} \tag{45.2.15}$$

for some $n \in \mathbb{N}$. Hence a net $\omega_\alpha \to \omega$ converges in $\mathcal{A}^*$ with respect to the weak* topology, if and only if it converges point-wise, that is

$$\langle \omega; A \rangle = \lim_\alpha \langle \omega_\alpha; A \rangle, \quad \forall A \in \mathcal{A}.$$

Since each $\sigma(\mathcal{A}^*, \mathcal{A})$-neighborhood contains a small open ball $\{\varphi \in \mathcal{A}^* \mid \|\omega - \varphi\| < \varepsilon\}$ the norm topology is stronger (finer) than the weak* topology.

Because a positive linear functional on $\mathcal{A}$ is automatically norm continuous, it is an element of $\mathcal{A}_+^* \subset \mathcal{A}_{\mathrm{sa}}^* \subset \mathcal{A}^*$. $\mathcal{A}_+^*$ is a pointed (with vertex 0) weak* closed cone and hence also norm closed.

In algebraic quantum theory, the set of bounded observables (in the loose sense which includes also complex numbers as a result of measurement) is the primary object and supposed to be given by a C^*-algebra $\mathcal{A}$. The normalized positive linear functionals, which have the meaning of expectation values, constitute then the state space as the derived object.

Definition 45.2-20 (State space). Let $\mathcal{A}$ be a C^*-algebra. Then every positive linear functional ω on $\mathcal{A}$ satisfying $\|\omega\| = 1$ is called a *state* on $\mathcal{A}$.

The set of all states on $\mathcal{A}$ is denoted by $\mathcal{S}(\mathcal{A})$ and is called the *state space* of $\mathcal{A}$. Thus, $\mathcal{S}(\mathcal{A}) \subset \mathcal{A}_+^* \subset \mathcal{A}_{\mathrm{sa}}^* \subset \mathcal{A}^*$.

The elements of the extreme boundary $\partial_e \mathcal{S}(\mathcal{A})$ are called the *pure states* of the C^*-algebra $\mathcal{A}$. In other words, ω is a pure state of $\mathcal{A}$, if and only if a convex decomposition $\omega = \lambda\omega_1 + (1 - \lambda)\omega_2$, with a $0 < \lambda < 1$ and $\omega_1, \omega_2 \in \mathcal{S}(\mathcal{A})$, implies $\omega_1 = \omega_2 = \omega$.

The physical term *state*, in the above sense, is also used in purely mathematical context. If the C^*-algebra $\mathcal{A}$ is associated with a physical system in a model discussion, then the value

$$\langle \omega; A \rangle, \qquad \text{(expectation value)},$$

means in the physical interpretation the *expectation* of the *observable* $A \in \mathcal{A}$ in the *state* $\omega \in \mathcal{S}(\mathcal{A})$. To identify in such a physical model treatment a calculated expectation functional as "state", one has — beside linearity and normalization — to only verify positivity to profit from norm continuity and the further inequalities, expounded in the present survey. Since positivity concerns the expectations of certain products of observables it is a special form of a "correlation inequality". Also the most useful second inequality of Theorem 45.2-18 is a kind of factorization, which is achieved without assuming mutual independence for the "observables" A and B.

As for any state space, the various convexity relations and the facial structure (cf. Chapter 47) are important also for the $C*$-algebraic state space $\mathcal{S}(\mathcal{A})$. We analyze these features, which are rather subtle e.g., for antiliminary $C*$-algebras, in much detail at the end of Sec. 46.1 and state here only some general aspects.

Proposition 45.2-21 (The convex state space). *Let $\mathcal{A}$ be a $C*$-algebra.*

(a) *The state space $\mathcal{S}(\mathcal{A})$ of $\mathcal{A}$ is a convex subset of the dual space $\mathcal{A}^*$.*

(b) *The convex hull of the pure states $\mathrm{Conv}(\partial_e \mathcal{S}(\mathcal{A}))$ is weak* dense in $\mathcal{S}(\mathcal{A})$. Moreover, each $\mathcal{S}_0 \subset \mathcal{S}(\mathcal{A}))$, for which $\mathrm{Conv}(\mathcal{S}_0)$ is weak* dense in $\mathcal{S}(\mathcal{A}))$, contains $\partial_e \mathcal{S}(\mathcal{A})$.*

(c) *If $\mathcal{A}$ contains a unit, then $\mathcal{S}(\mathcal{A})$ is weak* compact. If $\mathcal{A}$ is not unital, then $\mathcal{S}(\mathcal{A})$ is not weak* closed and hence not weak* compact. (Its weak* closure contains 0.)*

Proof. [Sketch] Part (a). Convexity of $\mathcal{S}(\mathcal{A})$ is easily checked: For $\omega_1, \omega_2 \in \mathcal{S}(\mathcal{A})$ and $\lambda_1, \lambda_2 \in \mathbb{R}_+$ the linear combination $\lambda_1 \omega_1 + \lambda_2 \omega_2$ is in $\mathcal{A}_+^*$. According to the third relation of Theorem 45.2-18 $\|\lambda_1 \omega_1 + \lambda_2 \omega_2\| = \sup\{(\lambda_1 \omega_1 + \lambda_2 \omega_2)(A) \mid A \geq 0, \|A\| = 1\} = \lambda_1 \|\omega_1\| + \lambda_2 \|\omega_2\|$. Thus, $\lambda_1 + \lambda_2 = 1$ provides normalization.

Part (c). As we have argued after Proposition 45.2-12, the formula $\|\omega\| = \langle \omega; \mathbb{1} \rangle$ defines a weak* closed set and leads — as a subset of the weak* compact unit ball in $\mathcal{A}^*$ (Banach–Alaoglu) — to the weak* compactness of the state space of a unital $C*$-algebra. For the reverse conclusion cf. [BR87].

Part (b). If $\mathcal{A}$ is unital, the Krein–Milman Theorem 48.1-8 ensures sufficiently many pure states. If $\mathcal{A}$ is not unital, the normalization condition makes $\mathcal{S}(\mathcal{A})$ only to a norm closed (convex) subset of $\mathcal{A}^*$. We may extend $\mathcal{A}$ to $\mathcal{A}_{\mathbb{1}} = \mathbb{C}\mathbb{1} + \mathcal{A}$, for which the dual $\mathcal{A}_{\mathbb{1}}^*$ is equal to $\mathbb{C} + \mathcal{A}^*$. As we explain at the beginning of Sec. 45.3 for the special case $\mathcal{A} = \mathcal{C}(\mathcal{H})$, each state in $\mathcal{S} \equiv \mathcal{S}(\mathcal{A})$ has a unique extension to a state in $\mathcal{S}_{\mathbb{1}} \equiv \mathcal{S}(\mathcal{A}_{\mathbb{1}})$ and $\mathcal{S}_{\mathbb{1}}$ is the convex hull of $\mathcal{S}$ and the unique pure state $\omega_{\mathbb{1}}$, which vanishes on $\mathcal{S}$. $\mathcal{S}$ is a norm closed split face of $\mathcal{S}_{\mathbb{1}}$ with complementary split face $\{\omega_{\mathbb{1}}\}$. ($\omega_{\mathbb{1}}$ is pure since its GNS representation is 1-dimensional and hence irreducible.)

Due to the Krein–Milman theorem, $\mathrm{Conv}(\partial_e \mathcal{S}_{\mathbb{1}})$ is weak* dense in $\mathcal{S}_{\mathbb{1}}$. Since $\mathcal{S}$ is a face of $\mathcal{S}_{\mathbb{1}}$, its pure states are also extremal in $\mathcal{S}_{\mathbb{1}}$. $\mathrm{Conv}(\partial_e \mathcal{S})$ must then be weak* dense in $\mathcal{S}$, since only the convex combinations including $\omega_{\mathbb{1}}$ are missing.

The last part of (b) is proved in [Mur90]. $\qquad\square$

If $\mathcal{A}$ is a unital $C*$-algebra then $\mathcal{A}_{\mathrm{sa}}$ is an order-unit space by Proposition 45.2-12. Thus, we may apply Proposition 47.2-9 on page 1735 and know for $\mathcal{A}_{\mathrm{sa}}^* = (\mathcal{A}_{\mathrm{sa}})^*$

the relations of a base-normed space. Especially we have

$$A^*_{\mathrm{sa}} = A^*_+ - A^*_+ = \mathbb{R}_+ \mathcal{S}(A) - \mathbb{R}_+ \mathcal{S}(A). \qquad (45.2.16)$$

Since $A^* = A^*_{\mathrm{sa}} + iA^*_{\mathrm{sa}}$ we conclude, by the way, that for the weak convergence of observables $\langle \omega; A_i \rangle \to \langle \omega; A \rangle$ for all $\omega \in A^*$, the convergence of the expectation values (of states) is necessary and sufficient.

As we explain in Chapter 47, and exploit more intensively at the end of the present chapter, the most important characteristic feature of the C^*-algebraic state space is the following (cf. [ASH80]).

Proposition 45.2-22 (Orientable State Space). *If A is a C^*-algebra then its state space $\mathcal{S}(A)$ has the 3-ball property: Each pair of its pure states span by coherent and incoherent superpositions either a qubit space (affinely isomorphic to a 3-dimensional ball) or a 1-dimensional simplex (isomorphic to the real interval $[0, 1]$, demonstrating disjointness of the states).*

Hence $\mathcal{S}(A)$ is orientable, by choosing in its overlapping qubit spaces always a right- or left-handed coordinate system.

If A is an element of the C^*-algebra $\mathcal{A}$, then it defines on $\mathcal{S}(A)$ the affine function $\hat{A}(\omega) := \langle \omega; A \rangle$, which obviously is weak* continuous. Since $\hat{A}$ determines A, we can say that $A \mapsto \hat{A}$ is a strict positivity and norm preserving, linear bijection from $\mathcal{A}$ onto $\mathrm{Aff}_c(\mathcal{S}(A))$. This observation enables the characterization of algebraic symmetries in the Schrödinger picture. Because a Jordan isomorphism α in $\mathcal{A}$ is according to Theorem 45.2-15 positivity and norm preserving, its dual map $\langle \alpha^*(\omega); A \rangle := \langle \omega; \alpha(A) \rangle$ constitutes an affine weak* continuous bijection of $\mathcal{S}(A)$. Remarkable is the reverse conclusion.

Theorem 45.2-23 (Algebraic Symmetries in the Schrödinger picture). *Let $\mathcal{A}$ denote an arbitrary C^*-algebra.*

(a) *A map $\alpha : A \to A$ is a Jordan automorphism, if and only if the dual map α^* restricted to the state space (then denoted by ν) is an affine weak* continuous bijection of $\mathcal{S}(A)$.*

(b) *$\alpha : A \to A$ is a *-automorphism (an anti-*-automorphism), if and only if the dual map ν is an affine weak* continuous bijection of $\mathcal{S}(A)$, which preserves (reverses) the orientation of $\mathcal{S}(A)$.*

Note that for an arbitrary affine bijection ν of $\mathcal{S}(A)$, the dual transformation ν^* acts in the space $\mathrm{Aff}_b(\mathcal{S}(A)) \supset \mathrm{Aff}_c(\mathcal{S}(A))$ of bounded affine functions (which is order isomorphic to the universal enveloping von Neumann algebra of $\mathcal{A}$), so that $\nu^*(\hat{A})$ is not necessarily in $\mathrm{Aff}_c(\mathcal{S}(A))$, if $A \in \mathcal{A}$. We shall present later on arguments, that these more general affine bijections of $\mathcal{S}(A)$ preserve already the physically relevant structure of the theory.

Let us consider the state space in the classical case, which is described in terms of a commutative C^*-algebra.

Example 45.2-24 (The State Space of a Commutative C*-algebra). From Theorem 45.2-3, we know that every commutative C*-algebra is *-isomorphic to $C_\infty(X)$, where X is a locally compact Hausdorff space (cf. also Example 45.2-2(c)). According to the Riesz–Markov theorem, the topological dual of $C_\infty(X)$ consists just of the finite complex regular Borel measures $M(X)$ on X ([Coh80] Theorem 7.3.5), where the duality relation is realized by

$$\langle \mu; f \rangle := \int_X f(x)\, d\mu(x), \quad \forall f \in C_\infty(X), \quad \forall \mu \in M(X) = C_\infty(X)^*.$$

The norm of an element in $M(X) = C_\infty(X)^*$, now called the *total variation* of the measure, is given by

$$\|\mu\| = |\mu|(X) = \sup\{|\langle \mu; f \rangle| \mid f \in C_\infty(X), \ \|f\|_{\sup} \le 1\}.$$

The weak* topology on $M(X)$ is also called the *vague topology*.

The positive elements of $C_\infty(X)$ are just the $[0, \infty[$-valued functions, and thus the state space of $C_\infty(X)$ coincides with the probability measures $M_p(X)$ on X (the positive regular Borel measure μ on X with $\mu(X) = 1$). Thus,

$$\mathcal{S}(C_\infty(X)) = M_p(X).$$

The extreme boundary of the convex state space $\mathcal{S}(C_\infty(X)) = M_p(X)$ — that are the pure states —, is given by

$$\partial_e M_p(X) = \{\delta_x \mid x \in X\}.$$

Here $\delta_x \in M_p(X)$ designates the point evaluation (point measure) at $x \in X$, so that $f(x) = \langle \delta_x; f \rangle = \int_X f(y) d\delta_x(y)$ for all $f \in C_\infty(X)$, ([Tak79] Sec. 1.4, [BR87] Sec. 2.3.5). It is easily checked that the mapping $x \mapsto \delta_x$ is a homeomorphism from X onto $\partial_e M_p(X)$ with respect to the weak* topology (vague topology) on $M(X)$.

Now suppose X to be compact. Then $C_\infty(X) = C_b(X) = C(X)$ contains an identity, namely the unit function $\mathbb{1}(x) = 1$ for all $x \in X$, and thus by the above Proposition the state space $\mathcal{S}(C(X)) = M_p(X)$ is a compact convex set within the dual $C(X)^* = M(X)$ with respect to the weak* topology. Moreover, $M_p(X)$ constitutes a Bauer simplex, since the extreme boundary $\partial_e M_p(X)$ is homeomorphic to the compact configuration space X. (The notion of a Bauer simplex is introduced in Sec. 47.3.1 on page 1748.)

Remark 45.2-25 (Unitizations and compactifications).

(a) As in the previous example, let X be a locally compact Hausdorff space. Then the space $C_b(X)$ of all bounded continuous functions constitutes an Abelian C*-algebra with unit $\mathbb{1}(x) = 1$, $\forall x \in X$, as having been described before in Example 45.2-2(c).

Consequently, according to Theorem 45.2-3, there should be a compact Hausdorff space Y, so that $C_b(X) \cong C(Y)$, in the sense of a Gelfand representation. This condition determines Y as the Stone–Čech compactification βX of X.

If X is not already compact, $C_\infty(X)$ is not unital and $C(\beta X)$ may be considered as a unitization of $C_\infty(X)$ according to Remark 45.2-5, i.e.,

$$C(\beta X) \cong C_b(X) \cong \mathbb{C}\mathbb{1} + C_\infty(X). \qquad (45.2.17)$$

The compactification βX is distinguished in that any $f \in C_\infty(X)$ may be continuously extended to an element in $C(\beta X)$, and thus may be considered as an element of $C(\beta X)$. As such the set $C_\infty(X)$ is characterized within $C(\beta X)$ by vanishing function values at infinity, which constitutes a maximal ideal of $C(\beta X)$. Since any other ideal in $C(\beta X)$ is characterized by the vanishing of its functions on a set $X_0 \subset \beta X$, it has non-vanishing intersection with $C_\infty(X)$, in which there are also functions which vanish in X_0. Thus, $C_\infty(X)$ is an essential ideal, as it should be by Remark 45.2-5.

(In Eq. (45.2.17) $C_\infty(X)$ is supplemented by a one-dimensional space, but βX is different from the one-point compactification.)

(b) A somewhat analogous compactification occurs in connection with the classical, commutative Weyl algebra $\mathcal{W}(E_\tau, 0)$, with $\hbar = 0$, which was introduced on the one side purely algebraically as a special case of the Weyl algebra $\mathcal{W}(E_\tau, \hbar \,\mathrm{Im}(.|.))$ with arbitrary $\hbar \in \mathbb{R}$, and on the other side as the set of all τ-continuous, almost periodic functions on the test function space E_τ, where τ is a locally convex topology, stronger than the norm, in which E_τ is complete. The Gelfand representation of the classical Weyl algebra, which owns already a unit, is here given by $C(\hat{E})$, where $\hat{E}$ denotes the group of all (also non-continuous) characters on E_τ. E_τ is compact in the topology of point-wise convergence, being the dual group of the locally compact Abelian group E_τ in the discrete topology. $\hat{E}$ coincides with the Bohr compactification bE_τ of this group E_τ, a compactification which is independent of the locally convex topology τ. (According to [HR70], the Bohr compactification consists of a direct product of one-dimensional tori, which is compact by Tychonoff's theorem [RS73b].)

(c) Let us mention in the Bosonic context still another useful compactification. Given a $\mathbb{C}$-linear form $L : E_\tau \to \mathbb{C}$, which is τ-continuous, but *unbounded* in the (weaker) norm topology, we have discussed in Sec. 26.4 on page 719 the set of all macroscopic, first-order coherent states $\mathcal{S}_L^{(1)}$, the pure ones of which are indexed by $z \in \mathbb{C}$ (since their normally ordered characteristic functions are provided by continuous characters on $\mathbb{C}$).

Since $\mathcal{S}_L^{(1)}$ is a simplex with extreme boundary indexed by $\mathbb{C}$, we have here a classical subtheory, corresponding to an observable algebra $C_b(\mathbb{C})$. It is, however, much nicer to frame the optical coherence theory with $C(b\mathbb{C})$, where the Bohr compactification $b\mathbb{C} = \hat{\mathbb{C}}$ of $\mathbb{C}$ parameterizes now the set of all so-called L-distributed states. $C(b\mathbb{C})$ is so to speak the Gelfand representation of the Abelian subalgebra of Bosonic observables, identifying the macroscopic first-order coherent states by phase and amplitude. By compactification, ideal states with infinite amplitudes are added.

As in Sec. 45.1.6, we now turn to special states given by vectors in suitable Hilbert space representations. Let $(\Pi, \mathcal{H}_\Pi)$ be a non-degenerate representation of the C^*-algebra $\mathcal{A}$. For simplicity we assume that $\mathcal{A}$ possesses a unit. Then $\Pi(\mathbb{1}) = \mathbb{1}$ is the identity operator in $\mathcal{H}_\Pi$ by Proposition 45.1-9. For every $\psi \in \mathcal{H}_\Pi$, the mapping $\omega_\psi : \mathcal{A} \to \mathbb{C}$, $\langle \omega_\psi; A \rangle = (\psi | \Pi(A) \psi)$ (cf. Eq. (45.1.8)) defines a positive linear functional on $\mathcal{A}$. Since $\|\omega_\psi\| = \langle \omega_\psi; \mathbb{1} \rangle = (\psi | \Pi(\mathbb{1}) \psi) = \|\psi\|^2$ we have $\|\omega_\psi\| = 1$, if and only if $\|\psi\| = 1$, in which case ω_ψ is a state on $\mathcal{A}$.

The converse situation, that a state ω on $\mathcal{A}$ is representable in terms of a scalar product with a normalized vector of a suitable representation, is provided by the GNS construction (from Definition 45.1-14 on page 1636). Since a C^*-algebra $\mathcal{A}$ with unit is a U^*-algebra, the existence of the GNS representation for every $\omega \in \mathcal{S}(\mathcal{A})$ is already ensured by Theorem 45.1-15. However, this result is also valid for C^*-algebras without a unit, and we indicate the constructive existence proof because we permanently appeal to it.

The main idea is that we can equip the Banach space $\mathcal{A}$ with a semi-inner product, by using the linearity and positivity of the given state, defining

$$(A|B) := \langle \omega; A^* B \rangle, \quad \forall A, B \in \mathcal{A}.$$

To remove the degeneration of the semi-inner product, we form equivalence classes with respect to the subspace

$$I_\omega := \{ A \in \mathcal{A} \mid \langle \omega; A^* A \rangle = 0 \}. \tag{45.2.18}$$

If $C \in I_\omega$ and $A \in \mathcal{A}$, then we obtain by the second relation in Theorem 45.2-18

$$0 \leq \langle \omega; (AC)^* AC \rangle \leq \|A\|^2 \langle \omega; C^* C \rangle = 0,$$

and so $AC \in I_\omega$, too. Thus, I_ω is a *left ideal*, which is clearly norm closed. It is the so-called *left kernel* of ω. The fundamental vectors in the desired representation space are now introduced as the equivalence classes

$$\Omega_A := A + I_\omega = \{ A + C \mid C \in I_\omega \}, \quad A \in \mathcal{A}. \tag{45.2.19}$$

By setting $z\Omega_A + \Omega_B := \Omega_{zA+B}$ for all $z \in \mathbb{C}$ and $A, B \in \mathcal{A}$, the set Ω_A becomes a linear space. Now the left-ideal property of I_ω makes

$$(\Omega_A | \Omega_B) := \langle \omega; A^* B \rangle, \quad \forall A, B \in \mathcal{A},$$

independent from the representatives, and $(\Omega_A | \Omega_A) = 0$ is equivalent to $A \in I_\omega$, or to $\Omega_A = 0 + I_\omega$, that is the 0 in Ω_A. The norm completion of $\{\Omega_A \mid A \in \mathcal{A}\}$ is a Hilbert space, which we denote by $\mathcal{H}_\omega$.

Theorem 45.2-26 (GNS representation). *Let ω be a state on the C^*-algebra $\mathcal{A}$. Then the GNS representation $(\Pi_\omega, \mathcal{H}_\omega, \Omega_\omega)$ of ω exists. The GNS representation is non-degenerate and unique up to unitary equivalence.*

Therefore, if α is a *-automorphism on $\mathcal{A}$ such that $\langle w; \alpha(A)\rangle = \langle w; A\rangle$ for all $A \in \mathcal{A}$, it follows that there exists a unique *unitary U_w in $\mathcal{H}_w$ such that*

$$U_w \Omega_w = \Omega_w, \quad U_w \Pi_w(A)U_w^* = \Pi_w(\alpha(A)), \quad \forall A \in \mathcal{A}. \qquad (45.2.20)$$

(Note that the second relation means that U_w implements α. Also $U_w V$ implements α, for all unitaries V in $\Pi_w(\mathcal{A})'$ different from $\mathbb{1}$, but then violates the invariance of the cyclic vector Ω_w. So, the invariance for Ω_w does not even allow to change a phase of the implementing U_w.)

Proof.   We refer to the preceding construction of $\mathcal{H}_w$ and define the represented algebra element by $\Pi_w(A)\Omega_B := \Omega_{AB}$ for all $A, B \in \mathcal{A}$, checking that this is independent of the representative B for Ω_B. We estimate by means of Theorem 45.2-18

$$\|\Pi_w(A)\Omega_B\|^2 = (\Pi_w(A)\Omega_B|\Pi_w(A)\Omega_B) = \langle w; B^*A^*AB\rangle \le \|A\|^2\|\Omega_B\|^2. \quad (45.2.21)$$

(This estimation is neither possible for general *-algebras nor for the representation $\Pi'_w(A)$ by right multiplication — see text preceding Theorem 46.3-3 on page 1708 — so that there may arise unbounded operators by the analogous construction.) Thus, $\Pi_w(A)$ is bounded on its dense domain $\{\Omega_A \mid A \in \mathcal{A}\}$ and is uniquely extensible to a bounded operator in $\mathcal{H}_w$, denoted by the same symbol.

The map $\mathcal{A} \ni A \mapsto \Pi_w(A) \in \mathcal{L}(\mathcal{H}_w)$ is obviously linear and multiplicative. It is instructive to verify its *-preservation: $(\Omega_{B'}|\Pi_w(A^*)\Omega_B) = \langle w; (AB')^*B\rangle = (\Pi_w(A)\Omega_{B'}|\Omega_B) = (\Omega_{B'}|\Pi_w(A)^*\Omega_B)$, where in the first expression * is the abstract involution and in the last it means the Hermitian adjoint of Hilbert space operators. Thus, $(\Pi_w, \mathcal{H}_w)$ is a *-representation.

If $\mathcal{A}$ is unital we set $\Omega_w := \Omega_{\mathbb{1}}$ and verify $(\Omega_w|\Pi(A)\Omega_w) = \langle w; A\rangle$ for all $A \in \mathcal{A}$. Since $\{\Pi(A)\Omega_w = \Omega_A \mid A \in \mathcal{A}\}$ is dense in $\mathcal{H}_w$ by the construction of the latter, Ω_w is a cyclic vector for $(\Pi_w, \mathcal{H}_w)$.

If $\mathcal{A}$ is not unital, we join a unit and go over to $\mathcal{A}_{\mathbb{1}} = \mathbb{C}\mathbb{1} + \mathcal{A}$. Then w is linearly extended, so that $\langle w; z\mathbb{1} + A\rangle = z + \langle w; A\rangle$ for all $z \in \mathbb{C}$ and $A \in \mathcal{A}$. The extended w is a state on $\mathcal{A}_{\mathbb{1}}$ and we repeat the foregoing GNS construction for $\mathcal{A}_{\mathbb{1}}$. The subtle part is now to show that already the represented $\mathcal{A}$ is cyclic for the vector $\Omega_{\mathbb{1}}$. (This follows from the closed *-ideal $\mathcal{A} \subset \mathcal{A}_{\mathbb{1}}$ possessing an approximate unit for $\mathbb{1}$, e.g., [BR87].) This completes the existence proof for the GNS representation, which is non-degenerate by cyclicity.

The important feature of the GNS representation, to be unique up to unitary equivalence for a given w, is provided — as we have already mentioned for *-algebras — by the map $U\Omega_B := \tilde{\Omega}_B$ for all $B \in \mathcal{A}$, if there is another GNS triple $(\tilde{\Pi}_w, \tilde{\mathcal{H}}_w, \tilde{\Omega}_w)$ with which we define the vectors $\tilde{\Omega}_B := \tilde{\Pi}_w(B)\tilde{\Omega}_w$.

This applies immediately to the situation where α is a *-automorphism of $\mathcal{A}$ with $w \circ \alpha = w$ since then $(\Pi_w \circ \alpha, \mathcal{H}_w, \Omega_w)$ is also a GNS triple. The above connecting unitary U satisfies thus (45.2.20) (there called U_w). $\qquad \square$

Proposition 45.2-27 (Majorized States). *If $\mathcal{A}$ is a C^*-algebra, $\omega \in \mathcal{S}(\mathcal{A})$, and $\lambda \geq 0$, then we say that ω λ-majorizes a positive linear functional φ on $\mathcal{A}$ if $\langle \varphi; A^*A \rangle \leq \lambda \langle \omega; A^*A \rangle$ for all $A \in \mathcal{A}$. (Following Definition 45.1-12 we may express this by $\varphi \leq \lambda \omega$.)*

Then there is a one-one correspondence between these λ-majorized φ and the operators $T \in \Pi_\omega(\mathcal{A})'$ with $0 \leq T \leq \lambda \mathbb{1}$, such that

$$\langle \varphi; A \rangle = (T\Omega_\omega | \Pi_\omega(A)\Omega_\omega) = (\Omega_\omega | T^{1/2}\Pi_\omega(A)T^{1/2}\Omega_\omega), \quad \forall A \in \mathcal{A}. \quad (45.2.22)$$

This bijective correspondence is order preserving. Thus, the set of positive functionals φ, which are λ-majorized by ω is order isomorphic to the order interval $[0, \lambda \mathbb{1}] \subset \Pi_\omega(\mathcal{A})'_+$.

If in the above context φ is a state, which implies $\overline{(\Omega_\omega | T\Omega_\omega)} = 1$ and $\lambda \geq 1$, then its GNS triple $(\Pi_\varphi, \mathcal{H}_\varphi, \Omega_\varphi)$ is realizable by $(\Pi_\omega, \overline{\Pi_\omega(\mathcal{A})T^{1/2}\Omega_\omega}, T^{1/2}\Omega_\omega)$ and constitutes a sub-representation of $(\Pi_\omega, \mathcal{H}_\omega)$.

Proof. By the Cauchy–Schwartz inequality, for φ we find $|\langle \varphi; B^*A \rangle|^2 \leq \langle \varphi; B^*B \rangle \langle \varphi; A^*A \rangle \leq \lambda^2 \langle \omega; B^*B \rangle \langle \omega; A^*A \rangle = \lambda^2 \|\Pi_\omega(B)\Omega_\omega\|^2 \|\Pi_\omega(A)\Omega_\omega\|^2$. Thus, the mapping $\Pi_\omega(B)\Omega_\omega \times \Pi_\omega(A)\Omega_\omega \mapsto \langle \varphi; B^*A \rangle$ is a bounded, densely defined sesquilinear form over $\mathcal{H}_\omega \times \mathcal{H}_\omega$. In virtue of the Riesz Representation Theorem (Proposition 43.5-5 on page 1541) there exists a unique $T \in \mathcal{L}(\mathcal{H}_\omega)$ so that

$$\langle \varphi; B^*A \rangle = (\Pi_\omega(B)\Omega_\omega | T\Pi_\omega(A)\Omega_\omega), \quad \forall A, B \in \mathcal{A}. \quad (45.2.23)$$

Especially

$$0 \leq \langle \varphi; A^*A \rangle = (\Pi_\omega(A)\Omega_\omega | T\Pi_\omega(A)\Omega_\omega) \leq \lambda^2 \|\Pi_\omega(A)\Omega_\omega\|^2, \quad \forall A \in \mathcal{A},$$

gives $0 \leq T$ and $\|T\| \leq \lambda$, which is for the positive T equivalent to $0 \leq T \leq \lambda \mathbb{1}$ (cf. the spectral calculus in Sec. 43.3.2 and Proposition 45.2-6). Furtheron we have

$$(\Pi_\omega(B)\Omega_\omega | T\Pi_\omega(C)\Pi_\omega(A)\Omega_\omega) = \langle \varphi; B^*CA \rangle$$
$$= \langle \varphi; (C^*B)^*A \rangle = (\Pi_\omega(B)\Omega_\omega | \Pi_\omega(C)T\Pi_\omega(A)\Omega_\omega)$$

for all $A, B, C \in \mathcal{A}$. Thus, $T \in \Pi_\omega(\mathcal{A})'$.

To invert the reasoning, let be given $\omega \in \mathcal{S}(\mathcal{A})$ and a $T \in \Pi_\omega(\mathcal{A})'$, with $0 \leq T \leq \lambda \mathbb{1}$, so that $\|T\| \leq \lambda$. We define the positive functional $\langle \varphi; A \rangle := (\Omega_\omega | T\Pi_\omega(A)\Omega_\omega) = (T^{1/2}\Omega_\omega | \Pi_\omega(A)T^{1/2}\Omega_\omega)$ and estimate $\langle \varphi; A^*A \rangle = \|T^{1/2}\Pi_\omega(A)\Omega_\omega\|^2 \leq \|T\| \langle \omega; A^*A \rangle \leq \lambda \langle \omega; A^*A \rangle$.

If the φ is a state, then the normalized vector $T^{1/2}\Omega_\omega$ in $\langle \varphi; A \rangle = (T^{1/2}\Omega_\omega | \Pi_\omega(A)T^{1/2}\Omega_\omega)$ is cyclic for Π_ω, restricted to the invariant subspace $\overline{\Pi_\omega(\mathcal{A})T^{1/2}\Omega_\omega} \subseteq \mathcal{H}_\omega$ (cf. Lemma 45.1-7). We obtain thus the GNS representation over φ as a sub-representation of the GNS representation over ω. $\square$

Let be given a state $\omega \in \mathcal{S}(\mathcal{A})$ and a positive linear functional $\varphi > 0$ with $\varphi < \lambda\omega = \omega$ for $\lambda = 1$. Then there is a $T \in \Pi_\omega(\mathcal{A})'$ with $0 < T < \mathbb{1}$, such that $\langle \varphi; A \rangle = (T\Omega_\omega | \Pi_\omega(A)\Omega_\omega)$, for all $A \in \mathcal{A}$, by the preceding proposition. We split

$$\langle \omega; A \rangle = \underbrace{(T\Omega_\omega | \Omega_\omega)}_{=: \; \lambda_1} \underbrace{\frac{(T\Omega_\omega | \Pi_\omega(A)\Omega_\omega)}{(T\Omega_\omega | \Omega_\omega)}}_{=: \; \langle \varphi_1; A \rangle} + \underbrace{((\mathbb{1} - T)\Omega_\omega | \Omega_\omega)}_{=: \; \lambda_2} \underbrace{\frac{((\mathbb{1} - T)\Omega_\omega | \Pi_\omega(A)\Omega_\omega)}{((\mathbb{1} - T)\Omega_\omega | \Omega_\omega)}}_{=: \; \langle \varphi_2; A \rangle}$$

$$(45.2.24)$$

and obtain a convex decomposition of ω into two states φ_1 and φ_2. The GNS representations of the majorized states take place in the subspaces $\mathcal{H}_{\varphi_1} = \overline{\Pi_\omega(\mathcal{A})T^{1/2}\Omega_\omega} \subseteq \mathcal{H}_\omega$ and $\mathcal{H}_{\varphi_2} = \overline{\Pi_\omega(\mathcal{A})(\mathbb{1} - T)^{1/2}\Omega_\omega} \subseteq \mathcal{H}_\omega$. Since the scalar product $(\Pi_\omega(A_1)T^{1/2}\Omega_\omega | \Pi_\omega(A_2)(\mathbb{1} - T)^{1/2}\Omega_\omega)$ does in general not vanish for arbitrary $A_1, A_2 \in \mathcal{A}$, the two representing subspaces are not always orthogonal to each other. The latter is, however, the case if T is a projection in $\Pi_\omega(\mathcal{A})'$ (since then the relation $T^{1/2} = T \perp (\mathbb{1} - T)^{1/2} = (\mathbb{1}_\omega - T)$ makes the scalar products vanishing).

We make the important conclusion: By means of projections from the commutant $\Pi_\omega(\mathcal{A})'$ a state ω may be decomposed into "finer", that are "purer", states with mutually orthogonal GNS Hilbert spaces (taken as subspaces of $\mathcal{H}_\omega$). This is the origin of the theory of *orthogonal decompositions* of states, which we expound in Chapter 48.

It is of interest to know when this purification of a state ω comes to an end.

Proposition 45.2-28. *Let ω be a state on the C^*-algebra $\mathcal{A}$. The following assertions are equivalent:*

(i) $\omega \in \partial_e \mathcal{S}(\mathcal{A})$, *signifying by definition a pure state.*
(ii) ω λ-*majorizes, for any $\lambda \geq 1$, no other state than itself.*
(iii) *The GNS representation $(\Pi_\omega, \mathcal{H}_\omega, \Omega_\omega)$ of $\mathcal{A}$ is irreducible.*

Proof. (i)$\Leftrightarrow$(ii): If for two states φ_1, φ_2 we have $\omega = \lambda\varphi_1 + (1 - \lambda)\varphi_2$ with $\lambda \in]0, 1[$, then $\varphi_1 \leq \lambda^{-1}\omega$. If (ii) is valid then follows $\varphi_1 = \omega$ and ω is pure. If, on the other side, ω is pure and λ^{-1}-majorizes a state φ_1, then we may construct the given convex decomposition with $\varphi_2 := (\omega - \lambda\varphi_1)/(1 - \lambda)$, from which follows by purity that $\varphi_1 = \omega$, so that (ii) is demonstrated.

(ii)$\Leftrightarrow$(iii): By Proposition 45.2-27 (ii) is valid if and only if any order interval $[0, \lambda\mathbb{1}] \subset \Pi_\omega(\mathcal{A})'$ contains only scalars. (Otherwise we could construct a state majorized by ω different from it.) Since each positive operator in $\Pi_\omega(\mathcal{A})'$ is by the last relation in Proposition 45.2-11 contained in an order interval $[0, \lambda\mathbb{1}]$ we know by the Jordan decomposition that all of $\Pi_\omega(\mathcal{A})'$ equals $\mathbb{C}\mathbb{1}$. But this is equivalent to the irreducibility of $(\Pi_\omega, \mathcal{H}_\omega)$ according to Proposition 45.1-8 on page 1633. $\square$

If $(\Pi, \mathcal{H}_\Pi)$ is an irreducible representation of the C^*-algebra $\mathcal{A}$ and $\langle \omega_\psi; A \rangle = (\psi | \Pi(A)\psi)$ for a normalized vector ψ in $\mathcal{H}_\Pi$, then the Π–invariant subspace $\overline{\Pi(\mathcal{A})\psi} \subseteq \mathcal{H}_\Pi$ must equal all of $\mathcal{H}_\Pi$, so that any vector state ω_ψ in an irreducible representation is pure.

If $(\Pi, \mathcal{H}_\Pi)$ is reducible and ω_ψ a vector state as above, then $\overline{\Pi(\mathcal{A})\psi}$ has a non-trivial complementary space, which gives another sub-representation of $(\Pi, \mathcal{H}_\Pi)$. In the latter, we may choose again a vector state ω', and so forth. By Zorn's lemma, we exhaust $\mathcal{H}_\Pi$ in this manner, if the representation is non-degenerate, and we may announce the following.

Proposition 45.2-29 (Decomposition into GNS representations). *Let $(\Pi, \mathcal{H}_\Pi)$ be a non-degenerate representation of the C^*-algebra $\mathcal{A}$. Then there exists a family $\{\omega_i \mid i \in I\}$ of states on $\mathcal{A}$, such that $(\Pi, \mathcal{H}_\Pi)$ is the direct sum of the associated GNS representations, that is, $(\Pi, \mathcal{H}_\Pi) = \bigoplus_{i \in I}(\Pi_{\omega_i}, \mathcal{H}_{\omega_i})$.*

If $(\Pi, \mathcal{H}_\Pi)$ is irreducible, then every vector state is pure, and the preceding decomposition into cyclic representations consists of one term only.

By means of a Hahn–Banach argument (for extending a state from a small algebra containing a given A to all of $\mathcal{A}$) one may prove:

Lemma 45.2-30. *Let A be an arbitrary, non-vanishing element of a C^*-algebra $\mathcal{A}$. Then there exists a pure state $\omega \in \partial_e \mathcal{S}(\mathcal{A})$ such that*

$$\langle \omega; A^*A \rangle = \|A\|^2 = \|\Pi_\omega(A)\|^2 . \tag{45.2.25}$$

(This follows already from $\mathcal{A}$ being an order unit space.)

Taking the direct sum representation over the GNS representations of all (pure) states on a C^*-algebra, then each $A \in \mathcal{A}$ finds in the direct sum a representation with (45.2.25), and we deduce the subsequent result.

Theorem 45.2-31 (Existence of faithful representations). *The so-called* universal representation

$$(\Pi_u, \mathcal{H}_u) := \bigoplus_{\omega \in \mathcal{S}(\mathcal{A})} (\Pi_\omega, \mathcal{H}_\omega) \tag{45.2.26}$$

of a C^*-algebra $\mathcal{A}$ is faithful.

Also the so-called atomic representation

$$(\Pi_a, \mathcal{H}_a) := \bigoplus_{\omega \in \partial_e \mathcal{S}(\mathcal{A})} (\Pi_\omega, \mathcal{H}_\omega) \tag{45.2.27}$$

of a C^*-algebra $\mathcal{A}$ is faithful.

Thus, every C^*-algebra $\mathcal{A}$ admits a faithful representation.

By definition, a faithful representation of a C^*-algebra $\mathcal{A}$ consists of bounded operators in a Hilbert space with a $*$-isomorphic algebraic structure, so that the preceding theorem confirms the appropriate choice of the axioms (especially the C^*-norm property) for a C^*-algebra in order to abstract the concrete operator algebras.

The universal and atomic representations take place in "large", non-separable Hilbert spaces, but may be continuously transferred, in some sense (quasi–equivalently), to more accessible representation spaces, if one applies the formalism of von Neumann algebras.

45.3.   Special Types of C^*-Algebras

In Chapter, 47 we emphasize the direct empirical meaning of the convex state spaces, with their convex superpositions and decompositions, where their affine functions, express mean values of observables. In algebraic quantum mechanics, on the other side, one starts usually with the choice of a C^*-algebra and derives therefrom the properties of the state space.

45.3.1.   *C*-Algebras Containing Compact Operators in Traditional Hilbert Space Quantum Mechanics*

In traditional Hilbert space quantum mechanics, where the (symmetries of the) particles determine a (mostly separable) Hilbert space $\mathcal{H}$, one considers the concrete C^*-algebra $\mathcal{L}(\mathcal{H})$ as describing the bounded observables (where we again include also the non-self-adjoint elements into the notion of an "observable algebra"). In Sec. 43.2.3, we have deduced $\mathcal{L}(\mathcal{H})$ from determining the bounded affine functions on the traditional state space $\mathcal{T}_1^+(\mathcal{H})$. The set of all states on $\mathcal{L}(\mathcal{H})$, in the sense of the general mathematical Definition 45.2-20, is, however, larger than $\mathcal{T}_1^+(\mathcal{H})$.

To analyze this situation more closely, we consider the norm closed *-ideal of compact operators $\mathcal{C}(\mathcal{H}) \subset \mathcal{L}(\mathcal{H})$, which is for infinite-dimensional $\mathcal{H}$ — what we always assume in the following — a genuine sub-C^*-algebra of $\mathcal{L}(\mathcal{H})$. Observe that $\mathcal{C}(\mathcal{H})$ is irreducible (being weakly dense in $\mathcal{L}(\mathcal{H})$) and does not contain a non-trivial, norm closed *-ideal.

(The *-ideals $\mathcal{T}(\mathcal{H})$ and $\mathrm{HS}(\mathcal{H})$ of $\mathcal{L}(\mathcal{H})$ are closed in stronger norms, i.e., in finer norm topologies.)

Proposition 45.3-1. *The dual space $\mathcal{C}(\mathcal{H})^*$ is Banach space isomorphic to $\mathcal{T}(\mathcal{H})$, and thus $\mathcal{T}_1^+(\mathcal{H})$ is the total state space $\mathcal{S}(\mathcal{C}(\mathcal{H}))$ of $\mathcal{C}(\mathcal{H})$.*

Since we have shown in Proposition 43.2-8 that $\mathcal{T}(\mathcal{H})^*$ is Banach space isomorphic to $\mathcal{L}(\mathcal{H})$ (what typifies $\mathcal{L}(\mathcal{H})$ as a W^*-algebra, cf. the following Chapter), we have in the Banach space sense $\mathcal{C}(\mathcal{H})^{**} = \mathcal{L}(\mathcal{H})$.

Proof. If $T \in \mathcal{T}(\mathcal{H})$, then $|\mathrm{tr}(TA)| \leq \|T\|_{\mathrm{tr}}\|A\|$ (cf. Proposition 43.2-3) and $\mathrm{tr}(T.)$ is a bounded linear functional ω on $\mathcal{C}(\mathcal{H})$, with $\|\omega\| := \sup\{|\langle\omega; A\rangle| \,|\, \|A\| \leq 1\} \leq \|T\|_{\mathrm{tr}}$.

Reversely, a given functional $\omega \in \mathcal{C}(\mathcal{H})^*$ is by definition continuous in the $\|.\|$-norm, and thus also in the stronger $\|.\|_{\mathrm{HS}}$-norm. Since $\mathrm{HS}(\mathcal{H})$ is a Hilbert space, with inner product given by tracing the operator product, there is by the Riesz representation theorem a $T \in \mathrm{HS}(\mathcal{H})$ with $\langle \omega; A \rangle = \mathrm{tr}(TA) = \mathrm{tr}(AT)$ for all $A \in \mathrm{HS}(\mathcal{H}) \subset \mathcal{C}(\mathcal{H})$. If $T = U|T|$ is the polar decomposition and P a finite projection then

$$0 \le \mathrm{tr}(P\,|T|\,P) = \mathrm{tr}(P\,|T|) = \mathrm{tr}(PU^*T) = \langle \omega; PU^* \rangle \le \|\omega\|,$$

because PU^* is compact with $\|PU^*\| \le 1$. Since this holds for all finite P, it equally is valid for the supremum $\mathbb{1}$ over these P, giving a finite $\mathrm{tr}(|T|) \le \|\omega\|$. Because $\mathrm{HS}(\mathcal{H})$ is $\|.\|$-dense in $\mathcal{C}(\mathcal{H})$, we have also $\langle \omega; A \rangle = \mathrm{tr}(TA)$ for all $A \in \mathcal{C}(\mathcal{H})$ and so, by the first paragraph, $\|T\|_{\mathrm{tr}} = \mathrm{tr}(|T|) \ge \|\omega\|$, which leads to $\omega \mapsto T$ being an isometry. $\qquad\square$

Because of $\mathcal{T}_1^+(\mathcal{H}) = \mathcal{S}(\mathcal{C}(\mathcal{H}))$ one may be inclined to consider $\mathcal{C}(\mathcal{H})$, instead of $\mathcal{L}(\mathcal{H})$, as the appropriate observable algebra for traditional Quantum Mechanics. A disadvantage of this observable algebra is, that the unit operator $\mathbb{1} \in \mathcal{L}(\mathcal{H})$ is not included in $\mathcal{C}(\mathcal{H})$. (This may e.g., be seen from the fact that the spectrum $\sigma(\mathbb{1}) = \{1\}$ does not include 0, which would be necessary for a compact operator.) So $\mathcal{S}(\mathcal{C}(\mathcal{H}))$ is not weak* compact and one cannot apply e.g., Choquet theory for the decomposition of states. (That $\mathcal{T}_1^+(\mathcal{H})$ contains sufficiently many pure states to generate all states by convex combination and norm closure follows e.g., from the spectral decomposition of density operators, without appealing to the non-applicable Krein–Milman theorem.)

Thus, the next best proposal for the traditional observable algebra, which has in fact been put forward, is to take the C^*-algebra $\mathcal{C}(\mathcal{H})_{\mathbb{1}} = \mathbb{C}\mathbb{1} + \mathcal{C}(\mathcal{H})$, obtained by adjoining the unit to $\mathcal{C}(\mathcal{H})$ by the mentioned standard procedure of Remark 45.2-5. Here $\mathcal{C}(\mathcal{H})_{\mathbb{1}}$ may also be defined as the smallest sub-C^*-algebra of $\mathcal{L}(\mathcal{H})$ containing $\mathcal{C}(\mathcal{H})$ and $\mathbb{1}$.

Since each $\omega \in \mathcal{S}(\mathcal{C}(\mathcal{H}))$, with density operator T_ω, has a unique linear continuation to a state in $\mathcal{S}_{\mathbb{1}} \equiv \mathcal{S}(\mathcal{C}(\mathcal{H})_{\mathbb{1}})$ (given by the same density operator), the essential new element in $\mathcal{S}_{\mathbb{1}}$ is the state $\omega_{\mathbb{1}}$, which vanishes on $\mathcal{C}(\mathcal{H})$ (i.e., $\langle \omega_{\mathbb{1}}; z\mathbb{1} + A \rangle = z$ for all $A \in \mathcal{C}(\mathcal{H})$ and $z \in \mathbb{C}$), and for which there is no density operator. Since the dual of $\mathcal{C}(\mathcal{H})_{\mathbb{1}}$ is Banach space isomorphic to $\mathbb{C} \oplus \mathcal{T}(\mathcal{H})$, we conclude that $\mathcal{S}_1 = \mathrm{Conv}(\omega_{\mathbb{1}} \cup \mathcal{T}_1^+(\mathcal{H}))$, and is now weak* compact, but contains the physically strange state $\omega_{\mathbb{1}}$.

Example 45.3-2 (The convex set $\mathcal{S}(\mathcal{C}(\mathcal{H})_{\mathbb{1}})$). As an exercise for convex sets we analyze $\mathcal{S}_{\mathbb{1}} = \mathcal{S}(\mathcal{C}(\mathcal{H})_{\mathbb{1}})$, referring to notions of the convex state space approach in Chapter 47.

Linearity gives for $\omega \in \mathcal{S}_{\mathbb{1}}$ that $\langle \omega; (z\mathbb{1} + A)^*(z\mathbb{1} + A) \rangle = |z|^2 + \bar{z}\langle \omega; A \rangle + z\langle \omega; A^* \rangle + \langle \omega; A^*A \rangle \ge (z\mathbb{1} + \langle \omega; A \rangle)^*(z\mathbb{1} + \langle \omega; A \rangle) \ge 0$, where we used the Cauchy–Schwarz inequality for ω applied to $\mathcal{C}(\mathcal{H})$ (cf. Lemma 45.1-13). This demonstrates, by the way, the positivity of the linear extension of an $\omega \in \mathcal{S}(\mathcal{C}(\mathcal{H}))$ to a functional on $\mathcal{C}(\mathcal{H})_{\mathbb{1}}$.

For $\omega = \omega_{\mathbb{1}}$ the above evaluation reduces to $|z|^2$. If we make the ansatz $\omega_{\mathbb{1}} = \lambda \omega' + (1 - \lambda)\omega''$ with $\lambda \in]0, 1[$ and $\omega', \omega'' \in \mathcal{S}_{\mathbb{1}}$, then the above evaluation leads to $\langle \omega_{\mathbb{1}}; (z\mathbb{1} + A)^*(z\mathbb{1} + A)\rangle = |z|^2 \geq \lambda(z\mathbb{1} + \langle\omega'; A\rangle)^*(z\mathbb{1} + \langle\omega'; A\rangle) + (1 - \lambda)(z\mathbb{1} + \langle\omega''; A\rangle)^*(z\mathbb{1} + \langle\omega''; A\rangle)$, where the last expression is larger than $|z|^2$ if $A > 0$ and if one of the component states does not vanish on A. Thus, the component states have to vanish on all positive $A \in \mathcal{C}(\mathcal{H})$ and, therefore, on all of $\mathcal{C}(\mathcal{H})$, what makes them equal to $\omega_{\mathbb{1}}$. Thus, $\omega_{\mathbb{1}}$ is pure. (Another proof for the purity of $\omega_{\mathbb{1}}$ is the irreducibility of its one-dimensional GNS representation.)

If $\{P_n \in \mathcal{C}(\mathcal{H}) \,|\, n \in \mathbb{N}\}$ is an increasing sequence of finite projections converging strongly to $\mathbb{1} \in \mathcal{L}(\mathcal{H})$, then $\{\langle \omega_{\mathbb{1}}; P_n\rangle = 0 \,|\, n \in \mathbb{N}\}$ does not converge to 1, and $\omega_{\mathbb{1}}$ is not a normal state (in the sense of Definition 46.1-13).

Since each state $\omega \in \mathcal{S}_{\mathbb{1}}$ has a unique decomposition $\omega = \lambda \omega_{\mathbb{1}} + (1 - \lambda)\omega_n \in \mathbb{C} \oplus \mathcal{T}(\mathcal{H})$, with ω_n a normal state, the tuple $(\{\omega_{\mathbb{1}}\}, \mathcal{T}_1^+(\mathcal{H}))$ constitutes a pair of norm closed, complementary split faces of $\mathcal{S}_{\mathbb{1}}$.

The classical F–property, given by the face $\{\omega_{\mathbb{1}}\}$, is the image of the renormalized version of the (unrenormalized, classical) P–filter projection $Q_{\mathbb{1}} \in \mathcal{Q}(\mathcal{S}_{\mathbb{1}})$ defined by $Q_{\mathbb{1}}(\omega) = Q_{\mathbb{1}}(\lambda \omega_{\mathbb{1}} + (1 - \lambda)\omega_n) := \lambda \omega_{\mathbb{1}}$ (where ω is decomposed according to the mentioned split faces).

Since the unital affine function $e \in \mathrm{Aff}_b(\mathcal{S}_{\mathbb{1}})$ is realized by $e(\omega) = \langle\omega; \mathbb{1}\rangle$, we find for the projective unit, which corresponds to $Q_{\mathbb{1}}$, the affine function $\mathcal{S}_{\mathbb{1}} \ni \omega \mapsto p_{\mathbb{1}}(\omega) = e(Q_{\mathbb{1}}(\omega)) = \langle Q_{\mathbb{1}}(\omega); \mathbb{1}\rangle = \lambda$ (using the same splitting of ω). By linear extension, $p_{\mathbb{1}}$ becomes an element in $(\mathbb{C} \oplus \mathcal{T}(\mathcal{H}))^* = \mathbb{C} \oplus \mathcal{L}(\mathcal{H})$. Since there is no projection operator in $\mathcal{L}(\mathcal{H})$ to realize $p_{\mathbb{1}}$, we have an illustration, how projective units generalize the projections.

We conclude that the classical P-filtering projection $Q_{\mathbb{1}}$, which filters the singular state $\omega_{\mathbb{1}}$, has no empirical meaning.

Since $\mathcal{S}(\mathcal{C}(\mathcal{H})_{\mathbb{1}})$ contains an unphysical enlargement of $\mathcal{T}_1^+(\mathcal{H})$, one adheres for microphysical systems, with infinitely many degrees of freedom, better to the traditional scheme, namely to employ $\mathcal{L}(\mathcal{H})$ as observable algebra, but to use only its normal states.

Because the mentioned observable algebras $\mathcal{C}(\mathcal{H})$, $\mathcal{C}(\mathcal{H})_{\mathbb{1}}$, $\mathcal{L}(\mathcal{H})$ are considered as C^*-algebras, it is interesting to know their (further) Hilbert space representations. The fact that $\mathcal{C}(\mathcal{H})$ contains all 1-dimensional projections, the atoms of the projection lattice $\mathcal{P}(\mathcal{H})$, leads to a severe restriction of its irreducible representations.

Proposition 45.3-3 (Irreducible representations of $\mathcal{C}(\mathcal{H})$). *Let $\mathcal{H}$ be any complex Hilbert space. All non-trivial irreducible representations of $\mathcal{C}(\mathcal{H})$ are unitarily equivalent.*

The proof of the unitary equivalence consists roughly speaking in realizing that a non-trivial representation morphism of the simple $\mathcal{C}(\mathcal{H})$ must map all 1-dimensional projections onto 1-dimensional projections and thus gives rise to a unitary operator, if the image representation space is not too large (cf. [Mur90]). This easily understandable effect of one-dimensional projections, respectively of compact operators, lies generally at the heart of determining unitarily equivalent representations and discloses, on the other side, under which conditions non-equivalent representations may come into play.

Theorem 45.3-4 (*C*-*Algebras containing a compact operator). *If there is a single compact operator, different from 0, in an irreducible operator C*-algebra $\mathcal{B} \subseteq \mathcal{L}(\mathcal{H})$, then this C*-algebra contains all of the compact operators in the Hilbert space $\mathcal{H}$, that is,*

$$\mathcal{C}(\mathcal{H}) \subseteq \mathcal{B} \subseteq \mathcal{L}(\mathcal{H}).$$

A C*-algebra $\mathcal{A}$, which in every non-trivial irreducible representation gives the compact operators alone is called liminary. *Each commutative C*-algebra (with its one-dimensional irreducible representations) as well as $\mathcal{C}(\mathcal{H})$ are liminary.*

If each non-trivial irreducible representation of a C*-algebra $\mathcal{A}$ contains a non-trivial compact operator (and hence all of them), it is termed postliminary.

Two non-trivial irreducible representations of a postliminary C*-algebra are unitarily equivalent, if and only if they have the same kernel (especially if they are faithful with kernel $\{0\}$).

Each liminary C*-algebra is postliminary.

$\mathcal{C}(\mathcal{H})_1$ is postliminary: If the kernel of a representation is $\{0\}$, then the representation represents also faithfully $\mathcal{C}(\mathcal{H})$ and contains all compact operators. If the kernel is $\mathcal{C}(\mathcal{H})$ then the representation gives a faithful image of the commutative quotient $\mathcal{C}(\mathcal{H})_1/\mathcal{C}(\mathcal{H}) = \mathbb{C}\mathbb{1}$ which in its irreducible representations contains the scalars; that are compact operators in the one-dimensional representation space.

45.3.2. *Antiliminary C*-Algebras and Inequivalent Representations*

$\mathcal{L}(\mathcal{H})$ is not postliminary if $\dim(\mathcal{H}) = \infty$: There are many irreducible representations with kernel $\mathcal{C}(\mathcal{H})$, which faithfully represent $\mathcal{L}(\mathcal{H})/\mathcal{C}(\mathcal{H})$ and do not contain any non-zero compact operator. In fact we have:

Proposition 45.3-5 (Calkin Algebra). *If $\mathcal{H}$ is an infinite-dimensional complex Hilbert space and $\mathcal{C}(\mathcal{H})$ the norm closed *-ideal of compact operators in $\mathcal{L}(\mathcal{H})$, then the quotient*

$$\text{Calk}(\mathcal{H}) := \mathcal{L}(\mathcal{H})/\mathcal{C}(\mathcal{H}). \qquad (45.3.1)$$

is a simple C*-algebra, which is called Calkin algebra.

If $\aleph_1$ is the cardinal of the continuum then there are $\aleph_2 = 2^{\aleph_1}$ pair-wise (unitarily) inequivalent irreducible representations of $\text{Calk}(\mathcal{H})$, which do not contain any non-zero compact operator (cf. [KR86]).

For $B \in \mathcal{L}(\mathcal{H})$, the equivalence class $[B] = B + \mathcal{C}(\mathcal{H}) \in \mathrm{Calk}(\mathcal{H})$ embodies operator features, which are "essential" in the sense of being stable against the "perturbation" by a compact operator. Especially the *essential spectrum* $\sigma_{\mathrm{ess}}(B)$ may be defined as the spectrum of $[B]$ in $\mathrm{Calk}(\mathcal{H})$.

The opposite to postliminary C^*-algebras constitutes the following class of C^*-algebras.

Definition 45.3-6 (Antiliminary C^*-algebras). A C^*-algebra, for which no irreducible representation contains a non-zero compact operator is called *antiliminary* (cf. [BR87]).

For infinite-dimensional $\mathcal{H}$, the C^*-algebra $\mathcal{L}(\mathcal{H})$, which is not postliminary, is neither antiliminary, since it contains the norm closed *-ideal of compact operators $\mathcal{C}(\mathcal{H})$ in its irreducible identity representation.

Proposition 45.3-7 (Simple antiliminary C^*-algebras). *Let $\mathcal{A} \subset \mathcal{L}(\mathcal{H})$ be a simple, irreducible, concrete C^*-algebra, which contains a non-trivial non-compact operator. Then $\mathcal{A}$ is antiliminary.*

Proof. If $\mathcal{A}$ would contain a non-zero compact operator it would contain all of them by Theorem 45.3-4. Then $\mathcal{C}(\mathcal{H})$ would constitute a non-trivial *-ideal of $\mathcal{A}$, different from $\mathcal{A}$, because of the non-compact element. That would contradict simplicity.

Thus $\mathcal{A}$ does not contain a non-zero compact operator and is antiliminary according to Definition 45.3-6. □

Theorem 45.3-8 (Many inequivalent representations). *Every C^*-algebra, which is not postliminary (especially any antiliminary C^*-algebra), has an uncountable family of pair-wise inequivalent representations, even if one fixes the kernel of the representations. That gives especially an uncountable family of pair-wise unitarily inequivalent irreducible representations (possibly with kernel $\{0\}$).*

45.3.3. *Inductive Limits of C^*-Algebras*

As we elaborate in the next Chapter, many inequivalent representations arise from a rich split face structure of the state space. The standard way to construct observable algebras in a physical meaningful procedure with non-trivial classical features (given by their split faces), is the inductive limit (may be over traditional algebras).

Definition 45.3-9 (C^*-inductive limit). Let Υ be an arbitrary index set, directed by the (partial) order $\preceq$, and let be given a family of unital C^*-algebras $\{\mathcal{A}_J \mid J \in \Upsilon\}$ with $\mathbb{1}_J \in \mathcal{A}_J$, $\forall J \in \Upsilon$. We assume that there are *-isomorphisms $\eta_{J',J} : \mathcal{A}_J \xrightarrow{\mathrm{into}} \mathcal{A}_{J'}$ for all comparable pairs $J \preceq J'$, $J, J' \in \Upsilon$, so that the following relations are satisfied

$$\mathbb{1}_{J'} = \eta_{J',J}(\mathbb{1}_J), \quad \eta_{J'',J'} \circ \eta_{J',J} = \eta_{J'',J}, \quad \text{for all} \quad J \subseteq J' \subseteq J'' \in \Upsilon. \quad (45.3.2)$$

The inductive limit algebra for $\{\mathcal{A}_J \,|\, J \in \Upsilon\}$ is constructed in terms of families $(A_J) := \{A_J \in \mathcal{A}_J \,|\, J \in \Upsilon\}$, where one starts with families which become stationary for indices J, larger than a certain J_0; the latter are families of the form

$$A \equiv (A_J) := \{A_J \in \mathcal{A}_J \,|\, A_J = \eta_{J,J_0}(A_{J_0}), \; \forall J \succeq J_0 \text{ for a } J_0 \in \Upsilon \text{ depending on } A\}$$

(where nothing is said of the $A_J, J \not\succeq J_0$). Under component-wise *-algebraic relations, the stationary A constitute a *-algebra. $\|A\| := \lim_J \|A_J\|$ exists in the stationary sense and constitutes a C^*-semi-norm (that is a semi-norm which fulfills the C^*-norm condition $\|A^*A\| = \|A\|^2$). The stationary A with vanishing semi-norm form a (2-sided) *-ideal. Performing the quotient to this ideal and the completion in the (now) norm leads to a unique C^*-algebra

$$\mathcal{A} = \lim_\Upsilon \{\mathcal{A}_J; \eta_{J',J}\}, \quad (45.3.3)$$

called the C^*-inductive limit of the C^*-algebras $\{\mathcal{A}_J \,|\, J \in \Upsilon\}$.

The families $(A_{J'}) \in \mathcal{A}$, which are stationary beginning with a fixed $A_J \in \mathcal{A}_J$ for a $J \in \Upsilon$ (i.e., $A_{J'} = \eta_{J',J}(A_J)$ for $J' \succeq J$), constitute the *-isomorphic image of $\mathcal{A}_J$, denoted by $\eta_J(\mathcal{A}_J) \subseteq \mathcal{A}$. The stationary family $(\mathbb{1}_{J'})$ of the units $\mathbb{1}_{J'} \in \mathcal{A}_{J'}$ is in each $\eta_J(\mathcal{A}_J)$. Thus,

$$\mathcal{A} \supset \eta_J(\mathcal{A}_J) \ni \mathbb{1} \equiv (\mathbb{1}_{J'}) = \eta_J(\mathbb{1}_J), \quad \forall J \in \Upsilon. \quad (45.3.4)$$

The embedding maps $\eta_J, J \in \Upsilon$, satisfy the compatibility relations

$$\eta_{J'} = \eta_{J',J} \circ \eta_J, \quad \text{for } J, J' \in \Upsilon \text{ with } J \succeq J'. \quad (45.3.5)$$

By construction we have for the C^*-inductive limit $\mathcal{A}$

$$\mathcal{A} = \overline{\bigcup_{J \in \Upsilon} \eta_J(\mathcal{A}_J)}^{\|\cdot\|}. \quad (45.3.6)$$

The last formula typifies a C^*-inductive limit, as demonstrated in the following example.

Example 45.3-10 (Simple C^*-Inductive Limit). A simple case of a C^*-inductive limit starts from Eq. (45.3.6). That is, one assumes a C^*-algebra of the form

$$\mathcal{A} = \overline{\bigcup_{J \in \Upsilon} \mathcal{A}_J}^{\|\cdot\|}, \quad (45.3.7)$$

where Υ is a directed set indexing a family of C^*-algebras, with $\mathcal{A}_{J'} \supset \mathcal{A}_J$ for $J' \succeq J$, and $\mathcal{A} \ni \mathbb{1} \in \mathcal{A}_J$ for all $J \in \Upsilon$.

If we take for the *-isomorphisms $\eta_{J',J}$, $J' \succeq J$, the pertinent inclusion maps, then all of the above-stated requirements for a C^*-inductive limit are satisfied and we have $\mathcal{A} = \lim_\Upsilon \{\mathcal{A}_J; \eta_{J',J}\}$. (Strictly speaking, the described C^*-inductive limit provides an algebra which is only *-isomorphic to $\mathcal{A}$, but we mostly identify *-isomorphic algebras.)

Because of this consideration, one often uses a formula like (45.3.7) to indicate a C^*-inductive limit, where we stick to the condition that the sub-C^*-algebras have to contain the unit.

Definition 45.3-11 (Various cases of C^*-inductive limits). Let us consider a C^*-inductive limit $\mathcal{A}$ in the form (45.3.7).

(a) If Υ is a denumerable order chain and if the $\mathcal{A}_J$, $J \in \Upsilon$ all are simple finite-dimensional sub-C^*-algebras (and thus *-isomorphic to some full matrix algebra), then $\mathcal{A}$ is called a *UHF-algebra* (short for "uniformly hyperfinite").

(b) If Υ is a denumerable order chain and if the $\mathcal{A}_J$, $J \in \Upsilon$ all are finite-dimensional sub-C^*-algebras (and thus *-isomorphic to a finite sum of some full matrix algebras), then $\mathcal{A}$ is called an *AF–algebra* (short for "approximately finite").

(c) We assume that Υ is a certain set of subsets $J \subset X$, directed by inclusion $J \subset J'$ (i.e., the ordering is given by the set inclusion $\subseteq$, and for two given finite sets there is a third finite set, containing the two given ones), and that there is an additional symmetric binary relation $J' \perp J$ which satisfies

(1) if $J \in \Upsilon$ then there is $J' \in \Upsilon$, with $J \perp J'$;
(2) if $J \subset J'$ and $J' \perp J''$ then also $J \perp J''$;
(3) if $J \perp J'$ and $J \perp J''$ then there is a $J_0 \in \Upsilon$, with $J', J'' \subset J_0$ and $J \perp J_0$.

If then $\mathcal{A}_J$ and $\mathcal{A}'_J$ commute with each other for $J \perp J'$, then $\mathcal{A}$ is called a *quasilocal algebra*.

For our so-called *quasilocal cluster structure* (of Sec. 33.4) we have $X = \mathbb{S} \approx \mathbb{N}$, $\Upsilon = F(\mathbb{S})$ is the finite subsets, and $\perp$ is the disjointness of sets. The $\mathcal{A}_J$ are full matrix algebras.

For *non-relativistic Boson algebras*, one has $X = \mathbb{R}^d$, $d = 1, 2, 3$, the J are (open, connected,) bounded regions in $\mathbb{R}^d$ and the $\mathcal{A}_J$ are (infinite-dimensional) Weyl algebras.

(d) For *continuous non-relativistic Fermions* we have for Υ the subspaces of the one-Fermion space, and the commutation rules for even local algebras are supplemented by the anti-commutation rules involving odd subalgebras (see Proposition 33.3-7 on page 989).

(e) For *continuous relativistic quantum field systems*, $X = \mathbb{R}^4$ and Υ is the (open, connected,) bounded regions in $\mathbb{R}^4$, $\perp$ is the disjointness of sets in space-like separation, and the $\mathcal{A}_J$ are W*-algebras (see [Haa92]).

45.3.4. *Infinite Tensor Products of Matrix Algebras*

Important examples of C^*-inductive limits are realized by infinite C^*-tensor products. We discuss the products of matrix algebras first.

The observable algebra of a *spin system or of a finite-level atom* is a full matrix algebra $\mathbb{M}_n = \mathcal{L}(\mathbb{C}^n)$. Two such systems have the algebra $\mathbb{M}_n \otimes \mathbb{M}_m$, defined as follows: The tensor product of $A = (a_{i,j}) \in \mathbb{M}_n$ with $B = (b_{k,l}) \in \mathbb{M}_m$ is directly defined as consisting of the m^2 blocks of the $n \times n$-matrices $b_{k,l}A$. The linear hull $\mathbb{M}_n \otimes \mathbb{M}_m$ of all the (tensor) product matrices, called the *tensor product of* $\mathbb{M}_n$ and $\mathbb{M}_m$, equals the full matrix algebra $\mathbb{M}_{n \cdot m} = \mathcal{L}(\mathbb{C}^n \times \mathbb{C}^m)$.

Since the product vectors $\xi = \xi_1 \times \xi_2$, with $\|\xi\| = \|\xi_1\| \|\xi_2\|$, are total in $\mathbb{C}^n \times \mathbb{C}^m$, we find $\|A \otimes B\| = \sup\{\|A\xi_1 \times B\xi_2\| \,|\, \xi_1, \xi_2$ the unit vectors in $\mathbb{C}^n$ and $\mathbb{C}^m$ respectively$\} = \|A\| \|B\|$. That is the product of two C^*-norms. Clearly $\mathbb{M}_n \otimes \mathbb{1}_m$, is a set of $n \cdot m$-matrices, *-isomorphic to $\mathbb{M}_n$. By iteration we can construct $\bigotimes_{i \in J} \mathbb{M}_{n(i)}$, where J is a finite index set.

Definition 45.3-12 (Infinite tensor product of matrix algebras). Consider the set of finite subsets of an infinite index set I, namely $F(I) := \{J \subseteq I \,|\, |J| < \infty\}$. $F(I)$ is directed by inclusion. For each $i \in I$, let be given an integer $n(i) > 1$. For each $J \in F(I)$ form the tensor product algebra $\mathcal{M}_J = \bigotimes_{i \in J} \mathbb{M}_{n(i)}$. Thus, $\mathcal{M}_J$ will be discriminated from $\mathcal{M}_{J'}$ if $J \neq J'$, also if the two product algebras are (factor-wise) *-isomorphic to each other.

If $J \subset J'$, and if we denote by $\mathbb{1}_J$ the unit of $\mathcal{M}_J$, the mapping

$$\eta_{J',J} : \mathcal{M}_J \longrightarrow \mathcal{M}_{J'}, \quad \text{defined by} \quad \eta_{J',J}(A) = A \otimes \mathbb{1}_{J' \setminus J}, \quad \forall A \in \mathcal{M}_J, \quad (45.3.8)$$

is introduced. For $J = J'$ the mapping $\eta_{J,J}$ is the identity on $\mathcal{M}_J$. The family $\{\eta_{J',J} \,|\, J', J \in F(I), J' \supseteq J\}$ consists obviously of *-isomorphisms, satisfying the relations (45.3.2). This allows to construct the inductive limit over the matrix algebras $\mathcal{M}_J$, which we term an *infinite matrix product*, and write

$$\bigotimes_{i \in I} \mathbb{M}_{n(i)} := \lim_{J \in F(I)} \{\mathcal{M}_J; \eta_{J',J}\}. \quad (45.3.9)$$

The embedding morphisms into the infinite product may now be written

$$\eta_J : \mathcal{M}_J \to \bigotimes_{i \in I} \mathbb{M}_{n(i)}, \quad \eta_J(A) = A \otimes \mathbb{1}_{I \setminus J}, \; \forall A \in \mathcal{M}_J. \quad (45.3.10)$$

Proposition 45.3-13 (On infinite matrix products). *An infinite matrix product* $\bigotimes_{i \in I} \mathbb{M}_{n(i)}$, $n(i) \in \mathbb{N}$, $n(i) \geq 2$, *is unital, has the trivial center $\mathbb{C}\mathbb{1}$, and is a simple C^*-algebra. It is separable, if and only if the index set I is countable, and in this case it is a UHF-algebra.*

An infinite matrix product is antiliminary.

(For the proof see e.g., [Ped79] and plausibility arguments below.)

Remark 45.3-14 (Classification of infinite matrix products). For our mesoscopic Fermionic systems we have infinite tensor products of finite-dimensional cluster observables, taken over the countable index set of cluster indices $\mathbb{S}$, mostly order-isomorphic to $\mathbb{N}$; that are elements from $\bigotimes_{\sigma \in \mathbb{S}} \mathbb{M}_{n(\sigma)}$ (see Sec. 33.4).

Denote by $n(\sigma)!$ the product $\prod_{\sigma'=1}^{\sigma} n(\sigma')$, characterizing the dimension of the matrix product up to σ, and decompose it into prime numbers. $n(\sigma)!$ may be divided by those prime numbers, which occur. Define for each prime number p the supremum $\epsilon(p)$ of exponents $\epsilon \in \mathbb{R}$ such that the ratio $\frac{n(\sigma)!}{p^\epsilon}$ is an integer, for some $\sigma \in \mathbb{S}$:

$$\epsilon(p) := \sup\left\{\epsilon \in \mathbb{R} \mid \tfrac{n(\sigma)!}{p^\epsilon} \in \mathbb{N} \text{ for a } \sigma \in \mathbb{S}\right\}.$$

The signature of the infinite matrix product $\{\epsilon(p) \mid p \text{ a prime number}\}$ provides only a necessary criterion for algebraic isomorphy. If there is another tensor product algebra of the form $\bigotimes_{\sigma \in \mathbb{S}'} \mathbb{M}_{n'(\sigma)}$ over a possibly different countable index set $\mathbb{S}'$, which is *-isomorphic to the first one, then necessarily $\epsilon(p)' = \epsilon(p)$ for each prime number p, [Ped79]. (A necessary and sufficient criterion for algebraic isomorphy for AF-algebras may be formulated in the frame of K-theory [Mur90].)

For our CAR algebra $\mathcal{A}(\mathfrak{h})$ with any infinite separable $\mathfrak{h}$ we have always

$$\epsilon(2) = \infty, \qquad \epsilon(p) = 0, \quad \forall p \neq 2, \tag{45.3.11}$$

as follows from Eq. (33.4.7) in Theorem 33.4-1. Thus, the necessary $\epsilon(p)$-criterion (45.3.11) allows for the *-isomorphy of all infinite, separable CAR algebras. That they are indeed *-isomorphic says e.g., Theorem 33.3-2, since all infinite separable Hilbert spaces are unitarily isomorphic. (The corresponding statement holds for Hilbert spaces with equal finite-dimensions.)

This is, of course, independent of any cluster realization. If, however, in a cluster realization certain degrees of freedom of the clusters are discarded, then we arrive at more general signatures. If, e.g., the σ-th cluster has the one-electron space $\mathfrak{k}_\sigma$, spanned by $N = \dim(\mathfrak{k}_\sigma)$ energy terms, which are occupied by a fixed number $M \leq N$ of electrons, then the pertinent Hilbert space is not equal to the Fock space $F_-(\mathfrak{k}_\sigma)$ (in which the electron number varies) but of lower dimension, say m.

Consider the case of equal clusters with an m-dimensional Hilbert space for the M electrons. If $m = p_1^{\epsilon_1} \cdots p_k^{\epsilon_k}$ is the unique prime number decomposition of m, then $\bigotimes_{\sigma \in \mathbb{S}} \mathbb{M}_m$ (which may be used as the material algebra for an infinite Dicke model of m-level atoms) has the signature

$$\epsilon(p_l) = \infty \text{ for } 1 \leq l \leq k, \quad \text{and} \quad \epsilon(p) = 0 \text{ for } p \neq p_l.$$

Thus, in dependence of the allowed number of states for the atomic shell electrons, there are infinitely many, non-*-isomorphic, material algebras for Dicke models.

On hand of infinite matrix products (including CAR algebras) typical features of antiliminary C^*-algebras may be elucidated. Especially the embedding morphism (45.3.10) discloses that finite operators go over to non-compact operators by being tensorized with the infinite-dimensional unit. By this elimination of the compact operators, the obstruction against inequivalent representations is ruled out.

An analogous effect takes place for the local density operators. As we have expounded for a Fermionic cluster algebra, each state ω on an inductive limit algebra (45.3.3) $\mathcal{A} = \lim_{\Upsilon} \{\mathcal{A}_J; \eta_{J',J}\}$, with embedding morphisms η_J, is uniquely characterized by a family $\{\omega_J \in \mathcal{S}(\mathcal{A}_J) \mid J \in \Upsilon\}$ of local states, which satisfy the compatibility conditions $\omega_J = \eta_{J,J'}^*(\omega_{J'})$ for $J \preceq J'$. For a UHF-algebra, $\mathcal{A}_J$ is the matrix algebra $\mathcal{M}_J$, and ω_J is given in terms of a density operator ϱ_J. Considering the diagonal representation of $\varrho_J = \sum_{i=1}^{|J|} \lambda_i |\xi_i)(\xi_i|$, the state ϱ_J may be purified to a state $\omega_{J'}$ in $\mathcal{S}(\mathcal{A}_{J'})$, if J' is large enough. This proceeds by tensoring the vectors ξ_i of the eigenbasis in $\mathbb{C}^{|J|}$ by orthonormal vectors χ_i in $\mathbb{C}^{|J_0|}$, $J_0 = J' \backslash J$, and forming the vector $\Omega' = \sum_{i=1}^{|J|} \lambda_i^{1/2} \xi_i \otimes \chi_i \in \mathbb{C}^{|J'|}$. Then take $\omega_{J'}$ as the vector state with Ω'. Performing in $\eta_{J,J'}^*(\omega_{J'})$ the partial trace over the $\mathbb{C}^{|J_0|}$ leads back to ω_J. Since $\omega_{J'}$ may be extended to a pure state on $\mathcal{A}$ we may say that any local state is the restriction of a pure global state. But all states are the weak* limits of local states, and thus — in this case — of pure states.

Proposition 45.3-15 (State spaces of infinite matrix products). *The state space $\mathcal{S}(A)$ of an infinite matrix product $\mathcal{A} = \bigotimes_{i \in I} \mathbb{M}_{n(i)}$, $n(i) \in \mathbb{N}$, $n(i) \geq 2$, is a weak* compact convex set, in which the pure states for themselves (and not only their convex combinations) are weak* dense. (The assertion is true for the states of any antiliminary C*-algebra.)*

Since there seems to be some confusion on the empirical meaning of weak* denseness let us emphasize, that it would be physically completely inadequate to substitute a mixed state of a many body system by a pure state from a weak* neighborhood. This is expressed, among other things, by the totally different structures of the F-properties connected with the two types of states (cf. Sec. 46.2.3 of the following chapter). That means in other words, that not the *topological weak* neighborhoods* but the *facial $\|.\|$-neighborhoods* express physical similarity of states. (Recall that a mixed state may have a temperature, a pure state does not.) Convexity relations must supplement topology!

The notion of antiliminarity for a C^*-algebra reduces the origin of inequivalent representations to a general concept. This becomes clear in the opposite case of a postliminary C^*-algebra, whose irreducible representations contain always all of the compact operators, including the one-dimensional projections, special Abelian elements.

Remark 45.3-16 (Abelian elements and CAR algebra). The abstract generalization of one-dimensional projections are the so-called Abelian elements [Dix77], [Ped79]. A positive element A of a C^*-algebra $\mathcal{A}$ is called *Abelian*, if the norm closure of the subalgebra $A\mathcal{A}A$ is commutative (what is the case, e.g., for $A = 0$, or for one-dimensional projections $A = |\psi)(\psi|$, $\psi \in \mathcal{H}$, contained in C^*-algebras $\mathcal{A} \subseteq$

$\mathcal{L}(\mathcal{H})$ acting in a Hilbert space $\mathcal{H}$). A is Abelian, if and only if $\dim(\Pi(A)\mathcal{H}_\Pi) \leq 1$ for each irreducible representation $(\Pi, \mathcal{H}_\Pi)$.

An antiliminary C^*-algebra may be characterized by possessing no non-trivial Abelian elements. In his classification of inductive limits of matrix algebras, this characteristic has been used by Glimm [Gli60]. In [Sak71], a C^*-algebra $\mathcal{A}$ is said to satisfy the *condition of Glimm*, if for every $0 < A \in \mathcal{A}$ there exists an irreducible representation $(\Pi, \mathcal{H}_\Pi)$ of $\mathcal{A}$ such that $\dim(\Pi(A)\mathcal{H}_\Pi) \geq 2$. This harmless appearing condition implies already antiliminarity (and thus infinite-dimensionality of $\Pi(A)\mathcal{H}_\Pi$).

In [Ped79], it is proved that each separable, antiliminary C^*-algebra contains the CAR algebra $\mathcal{A}(\mathfrak{h})$ over a separable pre-Hilbert space $\mathfrak{h}$.

45.3.5. *(Infinite) Tensor Products of C*-Algebras*

For the construction of *composite systems*, we have to say a word on general C^*-*tensor products*, which generalize the matrix tensor products employed above. Let $\mathcal{A}$ and $\mathcal{B}$ be two given C^*-algebras. Their algebraic tensor product $\mathcal{A} \odot \mathcal{B}$ consists of the finite linear combinations $\sum_i c_i A_i \odot B_i$ with $c_i \in \mathbb{C}$, $A_i \in \mathcal{A}$ and $B_i \in \mathcal{B}$. ($\mathcal{A} \odot \mathcal{B}$ means here the Cartesian product $A \times B$ with the componentwise algebraic product and *-conjugation.) Forming $\mathcal{A} \odot \mathcal{B}$ is the first step for constructing the C^*-algebra of observables for a composed system.

The second step is to find a suitable C^*-norm on $\mathcal{A} \odot \mathcal{B}$, that means a norm $\|.\|_\beta$ which satisfies besides the C^*-property Eq. (45.2.1) on page 1638 also the *cross norm property*

$$\|A \odot B\|_\beta = \|A\|_\beta \|B\|_\beta, \quad \forall A \in \mathcal{A}, \quad \forall B \in \mathcal{B}. \qquad (45.3.12)$$

The completion of $\mathcal{A} \odot \mathcal{B}$ with respect to $\|.\|_\beta$ would give the desired tensor product C^*-algebra, denoted by $\mathcal{A} \otimes_\beta \mathcal{B}$. (For the theory of tensor products of C^*-algebras we refer to [Sak71], [Tak79], [Ped79], and [KR86].) The problem is that there are in fact many C^*-norms $\|.\|_\beta$ on $\mathcal{A} \odot \mathcal{B}$, which satisfy these conditions.

The minimal C^*-cross norm $\|A \odot B\|_{\min}$ is gained by realizing $\mathcal{A}$ and $\mathcal{B}$ in Hilbert spaces $\mathcal{H}_\mathcal{A}$ and $\mathcal{H}_\mathcal{B}$ and taking the norm of the operator $A \otimes B$ as an element of $\mathcal{L}(\mathcal{H}_\mathcal{A} \otimes \mathcal{H}_\mathcal{B})$. (The tensor product of finitely many Hilbert spaces is a special case of the complete tensor product from Definition 48.4-23 on page 1854.) In formulas

$$\|C\|_{\min} := \sup \|\Pi_\mathcal{A} \odot \Pi_\mathcal{B}(C)\|, \quad C \in \mathcal{A} \odot \mathcal{B}, \qquad (45.3.13)$$

where $\Pi_\mathcal{A}$ runs through all representations of $\mathcal{A}$ and $\Pi_\mathcal{B}$ runs through all representations of $\mathcal{B}$. By completion in this norm one gets $\mathcal{A} \otimes_{\min} \mathcal{B}$, which is called the *injective* or *spatial* C^*-tensor product.

There exists also the largest C^*-cross norm

$$\|C\|_{\max} := \sup \|\Pi(C)\|, \quad C \in \mathcal{A} \odot \mathcal{B}, \tag{45.3.14}$$

where Π runs through all representations of the *-algebra $\mathcal{A} \odot \mathcal{B}$, leading to $\mathcal{A} \otimes_{\max} \mathcal{B}$. For every other C^*-cross norm $\|.\|_\beta$ on $\mathcal{A} \odot \mathcal{B}$ it follows that

$$\|C\|_{\min} \le \|C\|_\beta \le \|C\|_{\max}, \quad \forall C \in \mathcal{A} \odot \mathcal{B}.$$

The spatial tensor product $\mathcal{A} \otimes_{\min} \mathcal{B}$ is of main interest in Physics, and one often writes merely $\mathcal{A} \otimes \mathcal{B}$ for it. One of the reasons is that *it is associative*, i.e., if $\mathcal{A}_1, \ldots, \mathcal{A}_{m+n}$ are C^*-algebras, then

$$\mathcal{A}_1 \otimes \cdots \otimes \mathcal{A}_{m+n} = (\mathcal{A}_1 \otimes \cdots \otimes \mathcal{A}_m) \otimes (\mathcal{A}_{m+1} \otimes \cdots \otimes \mathcal{A}_n), \quad \text{for arbitrary } m, n \in \mathbb{N}.$$

For physical applications, however, it is desirable that the C^*-algebras $\mathcal{A}$ and $\mathcal{B}$ admit only a unique C^*-norm on their algebraic tensor product $\mathcal{A} \odot \mathcal{B}$.

Definition 45.3-17 (Nuclear C^*-Algebras). A C^*-algebra $\mathcal{A}$ is said to be *nuclear*, if $\mathcal{A} \otimes_{\min} \mathcal{B} = \mathcal{A} \otimes_{\max} \mathcal{B}$ for any other C^*-algebra $\mathcal{B}$, that is, if all C^*-cross norms coincide.

It is satisfying that every commutative and every finite-dimensional C^*-algebra is nuclear. More generally, all postliminary C^*-algebras are nuclear, and the inductive limits of nuclear C^*-algebras are also nuclear. Thus, there are also many antiliminary C^*-algebras, as e.g., the CAR and Weyl algebras of infinite systems, which are nuclear.

We are now ready to generalize the infinite C^*-algebraic tensor product. So, let for each $i \in I$, where I is an arbitrary index set, $\mathcal{A}_i$ be an arbitrary unital C^*-algebra and form the injective C^*-tensor product $\bigotimes_{i \in J} \mathcal{A}_i =: \mathcal{A}_J$ for all finite sets $J \in F(I)$.

Definition 45.3-18 (General infinite C^*-tensor products). Consider the preceding C^*-algebras $\mathcal{A}_i$, $i \in I$, with the injective C^*-tensor products $\mathcal{A}_J$. If $J \subset J'$, and if we denote by $\mathbb{1}_J$ the unit of $\mathcal{A}_J$, we introduce, as for the matrix algebras, the mapping

$$\eta_{J',J} : \mathcal{A}_J \longrightarrow \mathcal{A}_{J'}, \quad \text{defined by} \quad \eta_{J',J}(A) = A \otimes \mathbb{1}_{J' \setminus J}, \quad \forall A \in \mathcal{A}_J. \tag{45.3.15}$$

For $J = J'$ the mapping $\eta_{J,J}$ is the identity transformation in $\mathcal{A}_J$. These $\eta_{J',J}$ satisfy the relations (45.3.2) to construct the *infinite C^*-product* as the C^*-inductive limit

$$\mathcal{A} \equiv \bigotimes_{i \in I} \mathcal{A}_i := \lim_{J \in F(I)} \{\mathcal{A}_J; \eta_{J',J}\}. \tag{45.3.16}$$

Also the embeddings from $\mathcal{A}_J$ into $\mathcal{A}$ are given by $\eta_J(A) = A \otimes \mathbb{1}_{I \setminus J}$, in complete analogy to the tensor products of matrix algebras.

Chapter 46

von Neumann Algebras

46.1. Basics of von Neumann Algebras

46.1.1. *Locally Convex Topologies on* $\mathcal{L}(\mathcal{H})$

Let $\mathcal{H}$ be a Hilbert space, and $\mathcal{L}(\mathcal{H})$ the C*-algebra of all bounded operators in $\mathcal{H}$. The norm topology on $\mathcal{L}(\mathcal{H})$ is also termed *uniform topology*. For many purposes one needs a weaker topology, which, however, is not so canonically given as the norm topology. We are going to consider six topologies on $\mathcal{L}(\mathcal{H})$, which are weaker than the uniform topology. Each of these six topologies is a locally convex (LC) Hausdorff vector space topology, which is defined in terms of a family $\mathcal{P}$ of semi-norms (as we describe in Chap. 49). So, a neighborhood base at 0 for an LC topology is given by sets of the form

$$\mathcal{N}(p_1, \ldots, p_n; \varepsilon) = \{ A \in \mathcal{L}(\mathcal{H}) \mid p_k(A) < \varepsilon, \ k = 1, 2, \ldots, n \},$$

indexed by arbitrary finite subsets of semi-norms $p_1, \ldots, p_n \in \mathcal{P}$ and $\varepsilon > 0$. A net $A_\alpha \to A$ converges in $\mathcal{L}(\mathcal{H})$, if and only if $p(A_\alpha - A) \to 0$ for every semi-norm $p \in \mathcal{P}$.

It is easy to check that the expressions in the following definition are indeed semi-norms.

Definition 46.1-1 (Weak Topologies on $\mathcal{L}(\mathcal{H})$). There are the following topologies on $\mathcal{L}(\mathcal{H})$, which are used in the theory of operator algebras:

(1) The weak topology on $\mathcal{L}(\mathcal{H})$ is given by the semi-norms $A \mapsto |(\xi | A\eta)|$ for arbitrary $\xi, \eta \in \mathcal{H}$.

(2) The σ-weak topology on $\mathcal{L}(\mathcal{H})$ is given by the semi-norms $A \mapsto |\sum_n (\xi_n | A\eta_n)|$, where the sequences $(\xi_n)_{n \in \mathbb{N}}$ and $(\eta_n)_{n \in \mathbb{N}}$ in the Hilbert space $\mathcal{H}$ satisfy $\sum_n \|\xi_n\|^2 < \infty$ and $\sum_n \|\eta_n\|^2 < \infty$.

(3) The strong topology on $\mathcal{L}(\mathcal{H})$ is given by the semi-norms $A \mapsto \|A\xi\|$ for arbitrary $\xi \in \mathcal{H}$.

(4) The σ-strong topology on $\mathcal{L}(\mathcal{H})$ is given by the semi-norms $A \mapsto \left(\sum_n \|A\xi_n\|^2 \right)^{1/2}$, where the sequences $(\xi_n)_{n \in \mathbb{N}} \subset \mathcal{H}$ satisfy $\sum_n \|\xi_n\|^2 < \infty$.

(5) The strong* topology on $\mathcal{L}(\mathcal{H})$ is given by the semi-norms $A \mapsto \|A\xi\| + \|A^*\xi\|$ for arbitrary $\xi \in \mathcal{H}$.

(6) The σ-strong* topology on $\mathcal{L}(\mathcal{H})$ is given by the semi-norms $A \mapsto \left(\sum_n \|A\xi_n\|^2 + \sum_n \|A^*\xi_n\|^2\right)^{1/2}$, where the sequences $(\xi_n)_{n \in \mathbb{N}} \subset \mathcal{H}$ satisfy $\sum_n \|\xi_n\|^2 < \infty$.

Let the expression $\tau_1 \prec \tau_2$ mean that the topology τ_1 is finer than the topology τ_2. According to the "finer than" relation the mentioned topologies on $\mathcal{L}(\mathcal{H})$ are ordered as follows:

$$\text{uniform} \prec \sigma\text{-strong}^* \prec \sigma\text{-strong} \prec \sigma\text{-weak}$$

$$\wedge \qquad\qquad \wedge \qquad\qquad \wedge$$

$$\text{strong}^* \prec \text{strong} \prec \text{weak}\,.$$

We describe further properties of these locally convex topologies.

Proposition 46.1-2 (Properties of Locally Convex Topologies). *Let $\mathcal{L}_r(\mathcal{H})$ be the norm closed ball of radius $r > 0$ in $\mathcal{L}(\mathcal{H})$, i.e., $\mathcal{L}_r(\mathcal{H}) = \{A \in \mathcal{L}(\mathcal{H}) \mid \|A\| \leq r\}$. The following assertions are valid for every $r > 0$:*

(a) *The weak and the σ-weak topologies coincide on $\mathcal{L}_r(\mathcal{H})$. $\mathcal{L}_r(\mathcal{H})$ is compact in these topologies. The mappings $A \mapsto AB$, $A \mapsto BA$, and $A \mapsto A^*$ are continuous in these topologies, but the multiplication is not jointly continuous for infinite-dimensional Hilbert spaces $\mathcal{H}$.*

(b) *The strong and the σ-strong topologies coincide on $\mathcal{L}_r(\mathcal{H})$. $\mathcal{L}_r(\mathcal{H})$ is complete in these topologies. The multiplication $(A, B) \mapsto AB$ is jointly continuous in these topologies on $\mathcal{L}_r(\mathcal{H}) \times \mathcal{L}(\mathcal{H}) \to \mathcal{L}(\mathcal{H})$. For infinite-dimensional $\mathcal{H}$, the multiplication is not jointly continuous on all of $\mathcal{L}(\mathcal{H}) \times \mathcal{L}(\mathcal{H})$, and the *-operation $A \mapsto A^*$ is not continuous.*

(c) *The strong* and the σ-strong* topologies coincide on $\mathcal{L}_r(\mathcal{H})$. In these topologies the multiplication $(A, B) \mapsto AB$ is jointly continuous on $\mathcal{L}_r(\mathcal{H}) \times \mathcal{L}_r(\mathcal{H}) \to \mathcal{L}(\mathcal{H})$, and the *-operation $A \mapsto A^*$ is continuous. For infinite-dimensional $\mathcal{H}$ the multiplication is not jointly continuous on all of $\mathcal{L}(\mathcal{H}) \times \mathcal{L}(\mathcal{H})$.*

Let $\mathcal{FL}(\mathcal{H})$ and $\mathcal{T}(\mathcal{H})$ be the *-ideals of the finite rank, and of the trace class operators in $\mathcal{L}(\mathcal{H})$, respectively (for these *-ideals, see Example 45.2-2 (b) on page 1638 and Sec. 43.2 on page 1525). Every $T \in \mathcal{T}(\mathcal{H})$ is of the form

$$T = \sum_{k \in I} \lambda_k |\eta_k\rangle\langle\xi_k|, \tag{46.1.1}$$

where I is a countable index set, and $(\xi_k)_{k \in I}$ and $(\eta_k)_{k \in I}$ are normalized families of vectors in $\mathcal{H}$, respectively, and the complex numbers λ_k are absolutely summable, i.e., $\sum_k |\lambda_k| < \infty$. We have $T \in \mathcal{FL}(\mathcal{H}) \subseteq \mathcal{T}(\mathcal{H})$, if and only if I is finite. It is always possible to choose each of the two families $(\xi_k)_{k \in I}$ and $(\eta_k)_{k \in I}$ to consist of orthonormalized vectors, in which case one obtains with the usual trace $\text{tr}(\cdot)$ on $\mathcal{H}$,

$$\text{tr}(TA) = \sum_{k \in I} \lambda_k \langle\xi_k|A\eta_k\rangle, \quad \forall A \in \mathcal{L}(\mathcal{H}).$$

For a self-adjoint $T \in \mathcal{T}(\mathcal{H})_{\mathrm{sa}}$ its spectral decomposition is a special case of Eq. (46.1.1) as outlined in Proposition 43.3-1 on page 1534: There exists an orthonormalized family $(\xi_k)_{k \in I} \subset \mathcal{H}$ and unique $\lambda_k \in \mathbb{R}$ such that we have the spectral decomposition

$$T = \sum_{k \in I} \lambda_k |\xi_k)(\xi_k|. \qquad (46.1.2)$$

Proposition 46.1-3 (Linear Functionals). *The following assertions are valid:*

(a) *The linear functionals ω on $\mathcal{L}(\mathcal{H})$, which are continuous with respect to the weak, strong, and strong* topologies coincide. They are in linear bijection $\omega \leftrightarrow T_\omega$ with the finite rank operators $\mathcal{FL}(\mathcal{H})$ according to $\langle \omega; A \rangle = \mathrm{tr}(T_\omega A)$ for all $A \in \mathcal{L}(\mathcal{H})$.*

(b) *The linear functionals ω on $\mathcal{L}(\mathcal{H})$, which are continuous with respect to the σ-weak, σ-strong, and σ-strong* topologies, coincide. They are in linear bijection $\omega \leftrightarrow T_\omega$ with the trace class operators $\mathcal{T}(\mathcal{H})$ according to $\langle \omega; A \rangle = \mathrm{tr}(T_\omega A)$ for all $A \in \mathcal{L}(\mathcal{H})$.*

46.1.2. *Definition and Some Elementary Properties of General von Neumann Algebras*

Let $\mathcal{H}$ be a Hilbert space. The commutant $\mathcal{M}'$ of a subset $\mathcal{M} \subseteq \mathcal{L}(\mathcal{H})$ consists of all bounded operators, which commute with all members of $\mathcal{M}$ (as has been already defined in Eq. (45.1.5)).

Theorem 46.1-4 (Bicommutant Theorem). *Provided a subset $\mathcal{M} \subseteq \mathcal{L}(\mathcal{H})$ is invariant under the *-operation, its commutant $\mathcal{M}'$ is a (norm closed) sub-C*-algebra of $\mathcal{L}(\mathcal{H})$, which in addition is closed under each of the six locally convex topologies of the previous subsection (that are the weak, strong, strong*, σ-weak, σ-strong, and σ-strong* topology).*

Concerning the higher commutants, one has the following stationary behavior of iterated bicommuting operations

$$\mathcal{M} \subseteq \mathcal{M}'' = \mathcal{M}^{(\mathrm{iv})} = \mathcal{M}^{(\mathrm{vi})} = \mathcal{M}^{(\mathrm{viii})} = \cdots, \qquad (46.1.3)$$

$$\mathcal{M}' = \mathcal{M}''' = \mathcal{M}^{(\mathrm{v})} = \mathcal{M}^{(\mathrm{vii})} = \mathcal{M}^{(\mathrm{ix})} = \cdots. \qquad (46.1.4)$$

Evidently, a commutant algebra contains always the identity operator $\mathbb{1}$ in $\mathcal{H}$ as unit.

Definition 46.1-5 (von Neumann Algebras). A sub-*-algebra $\mathcal{M}$ of $\mathcal{L}(\mathcal{H})$, satisfying $\mathcal{M} = \mathcal{M}''$ (implying closedness under the six weaker-than-norm topologies), is called a *von Neumann algebra* in the Hilbert space $\mathcal{H}$.

Clearly, each von Neumann algebra $\mathcal{M}$ is also a C*-algebra (since norm closedness is weaker a condition than weak closedness), and we denote its *state space* (cf. Definition 45.2-20) again by $\mathcal{S}(\mathcal{M})$.

The *center* $\mathcal{Z}(\mathcal{M})$ of a von Neumann algebra $\mathcal{M}$ (as already introduced in Eq. (45.1.1)) is given by the intersection

$$\mathcal{Z}(\mathcal{M}) = \mathcal{M} \cap \mathcal{M}' \quad \text{(center of a von Neumann algebra } \mathcal{M}), \qquad (46.1.5)$$

and thus consists of those elements in $\mathcal{M}$, which commute with all other elements of $\mathcal{M}$. Each member of $\mathcal{Z}(\mathcal{M})$ is called a *central element* of $\mathcal{M}$.

For every subset $\mathcal{M} \subseteq \mathcal{L}(\mathcal{H})$ invariant under the *-operation (especially, for every concrete C*-algebra) it follows from (46.1.3) and (46.1.4) that both its commutant $\mathcal{M}'$ and its bicommutant $\mathcal{M}''$ are von Neumann algebras in $\mathcal{H}$. So, the algebraic manipulation of bicommutation leads to a topological closing procedure in the weaker-than-norm topologies. For operator algebras this constitutes in general to a natural extension process, which especially may provide new central elements.

Definition 46.1-6 (Factors). A von Neumann algebra $\mathcal{M}$ is called a factor, if its center is trivial, that is, if $\mathcal{Z}(\mathcal{M}) = \mathbb{C}\mathbb{1}$.

Example 46.1-7. $\mathcal{L}(\mathcal{H})$ is a von Neumann algebra and even a factor.

If $\mathcal{H}$ is infinite-dimensional, then the C*-algebra of all compact operators $\mathcal{C}(\mathcal{H})$ is not a von Neumann algebra. This follows from $\mathcal{C}(\mathcal{H})' = \mathbb{C}\mathbb{1}$, and thus the bicommutation gives $\mathcal{C}(\mathcal{H})'' = \mathcal{L}(\mathcal{H}) \supsetneq \mathcal{C}(\mathcal{H})$.

If one starts from an abstract C*-algebra $\mathcal{A}$, then one needs a representation $(\Pi, \mathcal{H}_\Pi)$ to form the bicommutant $\Pi(\mathcal{A})'' =: \mathcal{M}_\Pi$. The resulting von Neumann algebra $\mathcal{M}_\Pi$ depends, for fixed $\mathcal{A}$, in an essential manner on the representation.

Like most of the here stated results, also the following two topologically subtle assertions go back to von Neumann (cf. [vN61]).

Theorem 46.1-8 (Bicommutant and Density).

(a) *Let $\mathcal{M}$ be a sub-*-algebra of $\mathcal{L}(\mathcal{H})$ so that $\mathcal{M}\mathcal{H}$ is dense in the Hilbert space $\mathcal{H}$ (especially, this is valid if $\mathbb{1} \in \mathcal{M}$). Then $\mathcal{M}$ is closed with respect to any (and thus all) of the six locally convex topologies, if and only if $\mathcal{M} = \mathcal{M}''$, i.e., if and only if $\mathcal{M}$ is a von Neumann algebra in $\mathcal{H}$.*

(b) *Let $(\Pi, \mathcal{H}_\Pi)$ be a non-degenerate representation of an *-algebra $\mathcal{A}$. Then $\Pi(\mathcal{A})$ is dense in the von Neumann algebra $\Pi(\mathcal{A})'' = \mathcal{M}_\Pi$ with respect to each of the six weaker-than-norm topologies, that is,*

$$\mathcal{M}_\Pi := \overline{\Pi(\mathcal{A})}^{\text{-weak}} = \Pi(\mathcal{A})'' \subseteq \mathcal{L}(\mathcal{H}_\Pi) \quad \text{(representation von Neumann algebra)},$$

where $\overline{\Pi(\mathcal{A})}^{\text{-weak}}$ denotes the closure with respect to any of the six locally convex topologies of $\mathcal{L}(\mathcal{H}_\Pi)$.

Finally we remark some basic facts about von Neumann algebras.

Theorem 46.1-9 (Projections and Unitaries in von Neumann algebras). *Let $\mathcal{M}$ be a von Neumann algebra in the Hilbert space $\mathcal{H}$.*

(a) *The orthogonal projections $\mathcal{P}(\mathcal{M})$ in $\mathcal{M}$ span a norm dense subspace of $\mathcal{M}$.*
(b) *If $A \in \mathcal{M}$ is self-adjoint with associated projection-valued measure P_A, then each spectral projection $P_A(\Lambda)$ is contained in $\mathcal{M}$, $\Lambda \in \mathsf{B}(\mathbb{R})$.*
(c) *If $A = U|A|$ is the polar decomposition of $A \in \mathcal{M}$, then the partial isometry U and the absolute value $|A|$ are elements of $\mathcal{M}$.*
(d) *For an operator $A \in \mathcal{L}(\mathcal{H})$ we have $A \in \mathcal{M}$, if and only if $UAU^* = A$ for all unitaries $U \in \mathcal{M}'$.*

In the function realization of a commutative von Neumann algebra the projections are given by the indicator functions of measurable sets. They may viewed as σ-weak limits of continuous functions, which gives us an intuitive idea, how weaker-than-norm limits may lead to sufficiently many projections.

For commutative C*-algebras in representations, the weak closure is already sufficient to give the needed projections for spectral representations. That is worked out, e.g., in [KR86, Chap. 5], from which we select the following theorem, *basic for our radiation formulas.*

Theorem 46.1-10 (Joint Spectral Representation). *Let $\mathcal{A}$ be a unital Abelian C*-Algebra (if not unital, join a unit). According to the Gelfand representation (Theorem 45.2-3 on page 1639), we may identify $\mathcal{A}$ with the subsequent function algebra.*

Let $\mathrm{C}(X) \equiv \mathrm{C}(X, \mathbb{C})$ be the commutative C-algebra of continuous $\mathbb{C}$-valued functions on the compact Hausdorff space X and $(\Pi, \mathcal{H})$ any non-degenerate representation of it in the Hilbert space $\mathcal{H}$. The closure of $\Pi(\mathrm{C}(X))$ in a weaker-than-norm topology is a commutative von Neumann algebra denoted by $\mathcal{M}_\Pi$.*

Then there exists a projection-valued measure $P : \mathsf{B}(X) \to \mathcal{P}(\mathcal{M}_\Pi)$ from the Borel subsets $\mathsf{B}(X)$ of X into the projection lattice of $\mathcal{M}_\Pi$ such that for each $f \in \mathrm{C}(X)$ we have a spectral representation of its operator representative

$$\Pi(f) = \int_X f(x)\, dP(x). \tag{46.1.6}$$

That is, we have a joint spectral representation for all elements in $\Pi(C(X))$, which has the analogous form in all non-degenerate representations.

46.1.3. *Predual and Normal States*

Let us first agree on calling the six weaker-than-norm topologies henceforth simply the *weaker topologies.*

Every linear functional ω on a von Neumann algebra $\mathcal{M}$ in the Hilbert space $\mathcal{H}$, which is continuous with respect to one of the weaker topologies, extends to a linear functional on all of $\mathcal{L}(\mathcal{H})$ with the same continuity property, due to the Hahn–Banach theorem. Thus by Proposition 46.1-3 there exists a finite rank or a trace class operator $T_\omega \in \mathcal{T}(\mathcal{H})$ with

$$\langle \omega; A \rangle = \text{tr}(T_\omega A), \quad \forall A \in \mathcal{M}. \tag{46.1.7}$$

If $\mathcal{M}$ is a proper sub-*-algebra of $\mathcal{L}(\mathcal{H})$, then the finite rank or trace class operator T_ω may be non-unique.

The set of functionals, which are continuous in the σ-weak (equivalently σ-strong or σ-strong*) topology, obtains a special terminology.

Definition 46.1-11 (σ-Weak Continuous Functionals). The predual $\mathcal{M}_*$ of a von Neumann algebra $\mathcal{M}$ is the vector space of all σ-weak continuous linear functionals on $\mathcal{M}$.

Recall that the dual $\mathcal{M}^*$ of $\mathcal{M}$, a von Neumann algebra as a special Banach space, is the Banach space of all norm continuous linear functionals on $\mathcal{M}$. Clearly, the predual $\mathcal{M}_*$ is a subspace of $\mathcal{M}^*$, which is a proper subspace for infinite-dimensional $\mathcal{M}$ (the norm then being strictly stronger than the σ-weak topology).

Proposition 46.1-12 (Predual). *The predual $\mathcal{M}_*$ of a von Neumann algebra $\mathcal{M}$ is a sub-Banach space of the dual $\mathcal{M}^*$, and $\mathcal{M}$ is the dual of $\mathcal{M}_*$ in the duality*

$$\mathcal{M} \times \mathcal{M}_* \ni (A, \omega) \longmapsto \langle \omega; A \rangle.$$

So we have $\mathcal{M} = (\mathcal{M}_*)^*$, which justifies the terminology for $\mathcal{M}_*$.

This result tells that every von Neumann algebra is the dual of a Banach space. There exists also the converse statement: A C*-algebra is *-isomorphic to a von Neumann algebra, if and only if it is the dual of a Banach space.

Let $(A_\alpha) \equiv (A_\alpha)_{\alpha \in I}$ be an increasing net in $\mathcal{L}(\mathcal{H})_+$ with an upper bound $\mathcal{L}(\mathcal{H})_+ \ni B \geq A_\alpha$ for all $\alpha \in I$. Then there exists a least upper bound $A = \text{lub}_\alpha A_\alpha \in \mathcal{L}(\mathcal{H})_+$, and the net (A_α) converges σ-strongly to A. If $A_\alpha \in \mathcal{M}_+$ for every index α, where $\mathcal{M}$ is a von Neumann algebra in $\mathcal{H}$, then one knows that the limit $A = \text{lub}_\alpha A_\alpha$ stays in $\mathcal{M}_+$.

Definition 46.1-13 (Normal Mappings on a von Neumann Algebra). A positive linear mapping β from a von Neumann algebra $\mathcal{M}$ into a partially ordered Banach space $\mathcal{B}$ is called *normal*, if $\beta(\text{lub}_\alpha A_\alpha) = \text{lub}_\alpha \beta(A_\alpha)$ for every bounded increasing net $(A_\alpha) \subset \mathcal{M}_+$.

This applies especially to positive linear functionals and states on $\mathcal{M}$ (where the partially ordered Banach space $\mathcal{B}$ is $\mathbb{C}$), or to *-homomorphisms from $\mathcal{M}$ into a C*-algebra $\mathcal{A}$ (where $\mathcal{B} = \mathcal{A}$).

Observe that the given definition of a normal mapping avoids the choice of a weaker topology on $\mathcal{M}$.

Proposition 46.1-14 (Normal States). *Let $\mathcal{M}$ be a von Neumann algebra $\mathcal{M}$ in the Hilbert space $\mathcal{H}$. Then for a state $\omega \in \mathcal{S}(\mathcal{M})$ the following assertions are equivalent:*

(i) ω is normal.

(ii) $\omega \in \mathcal{M}_*$, i.e., ω is σ-weakly continuous.

(iii) There exists a density operator T_ω in $\mathcal{T}_1^+(\mathcal{H})$ such that ω is expressed in terms of the trace formula Eq. (46.1.7).

So the normal states on $\mathcal{M}$ are given by the intersection

$$\mathcal{S}_n(\mathcal{M}) = \mathcal{M}_* \cap \mathcal{S}(\mathcal{M}). \tag{46.1.8}$$

In the situation of $\mathcal{M} = \mathcal{L}(\mathcal{H})$ the mapping

$$\mathcal{L}(\mathcal{H})_* \cap \mathcal{S}(\mathcal{L}(\mathcal{H})) \longrightarrow \mathcal{T}_1^+(\mathcal{H}), \quad \omega \longmapsto T_\omega$$

is an affine bijection, in virtue of Proposition 46.1-3(b).

Recall from Definition 43.2-5 that the density operators in $\mathcal{H}$, which are exclusively used in traditional quantum mechanics to describe (pure and mixed) states, are just the normalized, positive trace class operators $\mathcal{T}_1^+(\mathcal{H})$ in $\mathcal{H}$. The identification of a normal state functional with a density operator is only possible for $\mathcal{M} = \mathcal{L}(\mathcal{H})$. For a general von Neumann algebra $\mathcal{M}$ in $\mathcal{H}$ a normal state is described by an equivalence class of density operators.

It is remarkable that von Neumann introduced the density operators from the axiom of σ-weak continuous expectation values for observables in $\mathcal{L}(\mathcal{H})$ already in [vN32].

For Jordan homomorphisms α of von Neumann algebras there arise — in addition to the norm continuity $\|\alpha(A)\| \leq \|A\|$ (cf. Theorem 45.2-13 on page 1644) — continuity properties with respect to certain weaker topologies.

Theorem 46.1-15 (Jordan Homomorphisms and Their (Pre-) Duals).
Notice first that the notion of a Jordan homomorphism from a von Neumann algebra $\mathcal{M}$ into a von Neumann algebra $\mathcal{N}$ is covered by Definition 45.2-14, since they are special C*-algebras. The following assertions are valid:

(a) Let α be a Jordan homomorphism from the von Neumann algebra $\mathcal{M}$ onto the von Neumann algebra $\mathcal{N}$. Then α is σ-weakly and σ-strongly continuous.

(b) Let ω be a normal state on a von Neumann algebra $\mathcal{M}$ with associated GNS representation $(\Pi_\omega, \mathcal{H}_\omega, \Omega_\omega)$. It follows that $\Pi_\omega(\mathcal{M})$ is a von Neumann algebra, (i.e., $\Pi_\omega(\mathcal{M}) = \Pi_\omega(\mathcal{M})''$) and that Π_ω is normal.

(c) For each Jordan homomorphism α from the von Neumann algebra $\mathcal{M}$ onto the von Neumann algebra $\mathcal{N}$ there exists an central projection $P \in \mathcal{N}' \cap \mathcal{N}$ such that $A \mapsto \alpha(A)P$ is a *-homomorphism, and $A \mapsto \alpha(A)P^\perp$ is an *-anti-homomorphism.

(d) If α is a Jordan isomorphism from the von Neumann algebra $\mathcal{M}$ onto the von Neumann algebra $\mathcal{N}$, then its inverse α^{-1} is also a Jordan isomorphism "onto". In this case α is an isometry.

(e) *If α is a Jordan isomorphism from the von Neumann algebra $\mathcal{M}$ onto the von Neumann algebra $\mathcal{N}$, then the dual map $\alpha^* : \mathcal{N}^* \longrightarrow \mathcal{M}^*$ is a positive isometry. Its restriction α_* to $\mathcal{N}_*$ has the image $\mathcal{M}_*$.*
The restriction ν of α_*^{-1} to $\mathcal{S}_n(\mathcal{M})$ constitutes, especially, an affine bijection of $\mathcal{S}_n(\mathcal{M})$ onto $\mathcal{S}_n(\mathcal{N})$.

(f) *Let reversely $\nu : \mathcal{S}_n(\mathcal{M}) \to \mathcal{S}_n(\mathcal{N})$ be an affine bijection. Then its dual $\nu^* : \mathcal{N} \to \mathcal{M}$ (is uniquely defined and) constitutes a Jordan isomorphism.*

A state ω on a C*-algebra $\mathcal{A}$ is called *factorial*, if the associated von Neumann algebra $\mathcal{M}_\omega := \Pi_\omega(\mathcal{A})''$, obtained via the GNS representation $(\Pi_\omega, \mathcal{H}_\omega, \Omega_\omega)$, is a factor (meaning trivial center). For every pure state ω on $\mathcal{A}$, especially, we have that Π_ω is irreducible, or equivalently, that $\Pi_\omega(\mathcal{A})' = \mathbb{C}\mathbb{1}$ (by Theorem 45.2-26 and Proposition 45.1-8). This implies $\mathcal{M}_\omega = \Pi_\omega(\mathcal{A})''$ to be a factor. Hence the extreme boundary $\partial_e\mathcal{S}(\mathcal{A})$ is a subset of the factorial states on $\mathcal{A}$.

From Theorem 46.1-15 (c) it follows that a Jordan automorphism in a factor is either an *-automorphism or an *-anti-automorphism.

Many features of von Neumann algebras $\mathcal{M}_i \subset \mathcal{L}(\mathcal{H}_i)$ are invariant under *-isomorphisms $\alpha : \mathcal{M}_1 \xrightarrow{\text{onto}} \mathcal{M}_2$, where the latter provide homeomorphisms not only with respect to the norm topology but also with respect to the weaker topologies. In this sense, those features do not depend on the special Hilbert spaces $\mathcal{H}_i$.

It holds, especially, $\alpha(\mathcal{P}(\mathcal{M}_1)) = \mathcal{P}(\mathcal{M}_2)$, and α preserves the ordering and orthocomplementation for projections. From the σ-weak continuity of α it follows that the spectral projections $P_A(\Lambda)$, $\Lambda \in B(\mathbb{R})$ of $A \in \mathcal{M}_{1,\mathrm{sa}}$ are mapped onto the spectral projections of $\alpha(A) \in \mathcal{M}_{2,\mathrm{sa}}$ (cf. Theorem 46.1-9 (b)). Remark, however, that the dimension of $\alpha(P_A(\Lambda)) = P_{\alpha(A)}(\Lambda)$ differs in general from the dimension of $P_A(\Lambda)$, so that the degeneration of eigenvalues is not preserved under α.

Thus *-isomorphic von Neumann algebras are *not physically equivalent*!

The equivalence class of *-isomorphic Neumann algebras can be characterized in abstract terms: If a C*-algebra $\mathcal{B}$ possesses a predual Banach space $\mathcal{B}_*$, then the predual is unique. Thus the abstract $\mathcal{B}$ owns, besides the norm topology, a distinguished weaker topology, the $\sigma(\mathcal{B}, \mathcal{B}_*)$- or σ-weak topology. Such a C*-algebra $\mathcal{B}$ displays all features of a von Neumann algebra, which do not depend on the Hilbert space, and has a faithful σ-weak continuous representation as a von Neumann algebra.

Definition 46.1-16 (W*-Algebras). A C*-algebra $\mathcal{B}$ which possesses a predual Banach space $\mathcal{B}_*$ (i.e., $\mathcal{B}$ is isomorphic to $(\mathcal{B}_*)^*$ in the sense of ordered Banach spaces) is called a *W*-algebra*.

Its normal state space is of course $\mathcal{S}_n(\mathcal{B}) := \mathcal{S}(\mathcal{B}) \cap \mathcal{B}_*$ and consists of the σ-weak continuous states.

In the Hilbert space representation of W*-algebras (as von Neumann algebras), the implementation of Jordan isomorphisms is of interest. It can always be accomplished in form of a pair of partial isometries, one being complex linear the other antilinear, which are related to a decomposing central projection P from Theorem 46.1-15(c). More precisely, we have the following (see [RR89]).

Theorem 46.1-17 (Implementation of Jordan Isomorphisms). *For each Jordan isomorphism α from the von Neumann algebra $\mathcal{M}_1 \subset \mathcal{L}(\mathcal{H}_1)$ onto the von Neumann algebra $\mathcal{M}_2 \subset \mathcal{L}(\mathcal{H}_2)$, with decomposing central projection $P_2 \in \mathcal{Z}_2$, there exists a pair of operators (V, W) such that*

(a) V *and* W *are partial isometries from* $\mathcal{H}_1$ *into* $\mathcal{H}_2$, V *linear,* W *antilinear;*
(b)

$$VV^* = P_2, \qquad V^*V = \alpha^{-1}(P_2),$$
$$WW^* = P_2^\perp, \qquad W^*W = \alpha^{-1}(P_2^\perp);$$

(c)

$$\alpha(M) = VMV^* + WM^*W^*, \quad \forall M \in \mathcal{M}_1.$$

The foregoing implementations V and W are not unique; they may be required to give the so-called standard implementations, as treated in [RR89] and in Theorem 46.3-13 on page 1714.

If $\mathcal{M}_2$ is a factor, then the decomposing projection $P_2 \in \mathcal{Z}_2$ of the Jordan isomorphism α is either $\mathbb{1}$ or 0, and either V is unitary (and $W = 0$) or W is antiunitary (and $V = 0$). If $\mathcal{M}_2 = \mathbb{M}_2$, the first case implies that α^* preserves the orientation of the qubit space $\mathcal{S}(\mathbb{M}_2)$, and the second case makes α^* orientation reversing (cf. Sec. 47.3.2 on page 1750).

46.2. Spectral and Classificatory Notions

46.2.1. *Arveson Spectrum and Borchers–Arveson Theorem*

For discussing equilibrium states, we need, especially, more detailed information on spectra of *-automorphisms and their unitary implementations.

Let us therefore compile some basic concepts of the *Arveson spectral theory* [Arv74]. This theory has been elaborated for locally compact groups, which act via isometries in general Banach spaces, continuously with respect to certain weaker-than-norm topologies. This setup is, especially, appropriate for W*-dynamical systems.

Definition 46.2-1 (W*-Dynamical Systems). Let G be a locally compact group which is represented by *-automorphisms $\alpha_g \in$ *-aut$(\mathcal{M})$, $g \in G$, in a W*-algebra $\mathcal{M}$. If $G \ni g \mapsto \alpha_g(M)$ is σ-weakly continuous for all $M \in \mathcal{M}$, then the triple $(\mathcal{M}, \alpha, G)$ is said to constitute a W*-*dynamical system*.

(Considering $\mathcal{M}$ as a C*-algebra, a W*-dynamical system $(\mathcal{M}, \alpha, G)$ has a weakened continuity property in comparison to a C*-dynamical system, as is discussed in Proposition 48.3-4.)

We use often the following continuity criterion, important especially for the Schrödinger picture of W*-dynamical systems (see [BR87, Corollary 2.5.23]).

Lemma 46.2-2 (Weak Continuity of Isometry Groups). *Let X be any Banach space and X^* its dual space. If $\mathbb{R} \ni t \mapsto \alpha_t$ is a $\sigma(X, X^*)$-continuous group of isometries in X then it is point-wise norm continuous (that is strongly continuous).*

We specialize in this subsection to the additive group $\mathbb{R}$ (the real time axis with usual topology), with the dual group $\hat{\mathbb{R}}$ of continuous characters. Each element of $\hat{\mathbb{R}}$ is characterized by a real $E \in \mathbb{R}$, and we identify $\hat{\mathbb{R}}$ with the real energy axis E. Thus we write the general group-theoretic duality relation

$$\langle E; t \rangle = \mathrm{e}^{itE}, \quad \forall E \in \hat{\mathbb{R}}, \quad \forall t \in \mathbb{R}.$$

We assume that $(\mathcal{M}, \tau, \mathbb{R})$ constitutes a W*-dynamical system.

The Arveson spectral theory employs the left regular representation of $\mathbb{R}$ on the group algebra $\mathrm{L}^1(\mathbb{R})$ (with convolution as multiplication), using the latter functions to "smear" the time dependence of the *-automorphisms. More precisely, for every $f \in \mathrm{L}^1(\mathbb{R})$ one forms the map

$$\tau_f : \mathcal{M} \longrightarrow \mathcal{M}, \quad \tau_f(A) := \int_{\mathbb{R}} \tau_t(A) f(t)\, dt, \quad \forall A \in \mathcal{M}, \qquad (46.2.1)$$

where the integral exists in the σ-weak topology. This gives rise to the norm decreasing homomorphism $\bar{\tau}$ from $\mathrm{L}^1(\mathbb{R})$ into the σ-weakly continuous operators acting in $\mathcal{M}$

$$\bar{\tau} : \mathrm{L}^1(\mathbb{R}) \longrightarrow \mathcal{L}_\sigma(\mathcal{M}), \quad \bar{\tau}(f) := \tau_f. \qquad (46.2.2)$$

One has the estimation

$$\|\tau_f(A)\| \leq \|f\|_1 \|A\|, \quad \forall f \in \mathrm{L}^1(\mathbb{R}), \quad \forall A \in \mathcal{M}.$$

Definition 46.2-3 (Arveson Spectrum). Let $t \mapsto \tau_t$ be a $\sigma(\mathcal{M}, \mathcal{M}_*)$-continuous representation of $\mathbb{R}$ by automorphisms in the W*-algebra $\mathcal{M}$ (constituting a W*-dynamical system), and choose an arbitrary subset $\mathcal{Y}$ of $\mathcal{M}$. Then we introduce the following:

(a) The closed *-ideal $\mathcal{I}_{\mathcal{Y}}^\tau$ of functions in $\mathrm{L}^1(\mathbb{R})$ by

$$\mathcal{I}_{\mathcal{Y}}^\tau := \{ f \in \mathrm{L}^1(\mathbb{R}) \mid \tau_f(A) = 0, \ \forall A \in \mathcal{Y} \}.$$

(b) The (local) Arveson spectrum (with respect to τ) of the subset of operators $\mathcal{Y}$ by

$$\mathrm{Sp}^\tau(\mathcal{Y}) := \{ E \in \mathbb{R} \mid \hat{f}(E) = 0, \ \forall f \in \mathcal{I}_{\mathcal{Y}}^\tau \},$$

where $\hat{f}(E) := \int_{\mathbb{R}} f(t) e^{itE} dt$, $E \in \mathbb{R}$, denotes the Fourier transform of $f \in L^1(\mathbb{R})$. If $\mathcal{Y} = \{A\}$ consists of a single operator $A \in \mathcal{M}$ we write $\mathrm{Sp}^\tau(A)$, and term it the τ-*spectrum of* A.

(c) The (total) Arveson spectrum of the W*-dynamical system by

$$\mathrm{Sp}(\tau) := \mathrm{Sp}^\tau(\mathcal{M}).$$

(d) The spectral subspace of $\mathcal{M}$ for a closed set $\Sigma \subseteq \hat{\mathbb{R}}$ by

$$\mathcal{M}^\tau(\Sigma) := \overline{\{A \in \mathcal{M} \mid \mathrm{Sp}^\tau(A) \subseteq \Sigma\}}^\sigma,$$

performing the closure in the $\sigma \equiv \sigma(\mathcal{M}, \mathcal{M}_*)$-topology.

(e) The set of τ-invariant operators

$$\mathcal{M}^\tau := \{A \in \mathcal{M} \mid \tau_t(A) = A, \, \forall t \in \mathbb{R}\}.$$

In the first two steps of the preceding definition we remark that the Arveson spectrum is introduced via something like a doubled negation (which may be the reason for its poor acceptance). Loosely speaking, the Arveson spectrum of an operator set $\mathcal{Y}$ consists of those E-values which support the test functions, for which τ_f does not map $\mathcal{Y}$ onto the set $\{0\}$.

For illustration choose $\mathcal{Y} = \{A\}$ for a non-zero $A \in \mathcal{M}$ such that $\tau_t(A) = e^{itE} A$. Then $\tau_f(A) = \hat{f}(E) A = 0$, if and only if $\hat{f}(E) = 0$. Thus $\mathrm{Sp}^\tau(A) = \{E\}$. Then also $\tau_t(A^*) = e^{-itE} A^*$, and $\mathrm{Sp}^\tau(A^*) = \{-E\}$. This confirms that $\mathrm{Sp}(\tau) = \mathrm{Sp}^\tau(\mathcal{M})$ is *always reflection invariant.*

In general, the τ-spectrum $\mathrm{Sp}^\tau(A)$ of $A \in \mathcal{M}$ has nothing to do with its algebraic spectrum $\sigma(A)$ (the complement of the resolvent set). There is, however, a noteworthy relationship between the two spectra, if A is the generator of a unitary implementation of τ, as is given in Proposition 46.2-6 below.

The ideal property of $\mathcal{I}_{\mathcal{Y}}^\tau$ is seen by forming the Fourier transforms. The total Arveson spectrum may also be formulated in terms of the polar set of a kernel, expressing the doubled negation in a concise manner

$$\mathrm{Sp}(\tau) = (\ker \overline{\tau})^\circ.$$

We list some properties of the Arveson spectrum which follow immediately from the above definitions.

Lemma 46.2-4. *Let* $(\mathcal{M}, \tau, \mathbb{R})$ *be a W*-dynamical system as above and* $A, B \in \mathcal{M}$. *Then we have the following:*

(a) $\mathrm{Sp}^\tau(\tau_t(A)) = \mathrm{Sp}^\tau(A)$ *for each* $t \in \mathbb{R}$.
(b) $\mathrm{Sp}^\tau(A + B) \subseteq \mathrm{Sp}^\tau(A) \cup \mathrm{Sp}^\tau(B)$.
(c) $\mathrm{Sp}^\tau(\tau_f(A)) \subseteq \mathrm{Sp}^\tau(A) \cap \mathrm{supp}(\hat{f})$.
(d) *Let* $f, g \in L^1(\mathbb{R})$ *satisfy in a neighborhood of* $\mathrm{Sp}^\tau(A)$ *the relation* $\hat{f} = \hat{g}$. *Then* $\tau_f(A) = \tau_g(A)$.

Lemma 46.2-5. *For a W*-dynamical system* $(\mathcal{M}, \tau, \mathbb{R})$, *the following criteria for the τ-spectrum of an $A \in \mathcal{M}$ are easily derived from its definition.*

(a) *$E \in \hat{\mathbb{R}}$ is in* $\mathrm{Sp}^\tau(A)$, *if and only if the following implication is valid:*

$$\hat{f}(E) \neq 0 \implies \tau_f(A) \neq 0, \quad \text{if } f \in \mathrm{L}^1(\mathbb{R}).$$

(b) *If Σ is a closed subset of $\hat{\mathbb{R}}$ then*

$$\mathrm{Sp}^\tau(A) \subseteq \Sigma, \text{ if and only if } \mathrm{supp}\, \hat{f} \cap \Sigma = \varnothing \Rightarrow \tau_f(A) = 0, \text{ if } f \in \mathrm{L}^1(\mathbb{R}).$$

If the locally compact Abelian group $\mathbb{R}$ has a strongly continuous, unitary representation $U : \mathbb{R} \longrightarrow \mathcal{L}(\mathcal{H})$ in a Hilbert space $\mathcal{H}$, the Arveson spectral theory can also be applied, dealing quite generally with groups of isometries in a Banach space [Arv74], and we are concerned with the *Arveson spectrum in Hilbert Space*.

In complete analogy to the case of W*-automorphisms we introduce for the unitary dynamics $\mathbb{R} \ni t \mapsto U_t$ the notions of time-smeared unitaries U_f, for $f \in \mathrm{L}^1(\mathbb{R})$, the (total) Arveson spectrum of the unitary group $\mathrm{Sp}(U)$, the spectrum $\mathrm{Sp}^U(\mathcal{K})$ of vector sets $\mathcal{K} \subset \mathcal{H}$, and the spectral subspace $\mathcal{H}^U(\Sigma)$ for a closed $\Sigma \subseteq \hat{\mathbb{R}}$.

Proposition 46.2-6. *Let the W*-dynamical system $(\mathcal{M}, \tau, \mathbb{R})$ be unitarily implemented in a Hilbert space $\mathcal{H}$ by a strongly continuous, unitary group U, that is*

$$\tau_t(A) = U_t A U_t^*, \quad \forall t \in \mathbb{R}, \quad \forall A \in \mathcal{M},$$

and assume an invariant vector $U_t \Omega = \Omega$, $\forall t \in \mathbb{R}$, $\Omega \neq 0$. Then we have the following facts:

(a) *There exists an associated projection-valued measure (see Definition 43.3-2 on page 1535)*

$$P_U : \mathsf{B}(\mathbb{R}) \longrightarrow \mathcal{P}(\mathcal{H}), \quad \Sigma \mapsto P_U(\Sigma),$$

from the Borel sets $\mathsf{B}(\mathbb{R})$ of $\mathbb{R}$ into the set of orthogonal projections $\mathcal{P}(\mathcal{H})$ on $\mathcal{H}$, such that we have the following:

   (1) *$\mathcal{H}^U(\Sigma) = P_U(\Sigma)\mathcal{H}$ for all closed $\Sigma \subseteq \mathbb{R}$.*

   (2) *$U_f = \int_{\mathbb{R}} \hat{f}(E)\, dP_U(E)$ holds in the strong operator topology for all Fourier transforms $\hat{f}$ of bounded measures on $\mathbb{R}$ and may be generalized to all bounded measurable functions $\hat{f}$ on $\hat{\mathbb{R}}$. For the special function $\hat{f}(E) = \mathrm{e}^{itE}$, which is the Fourier transform of the Dirac delta measure $f(t) = \delta(t)$, we obtain $U_t = \int_{\mathbb{R}} \mathrm{e}^{itE} dP_U(E)$.*

   (3) *$E \in \mathrm{Sp}(U)$, if and only if $P_U(\Sigma) \neq 0$ for all closed neighborhoods Σ of E.*

(4) P_U *is the resolution of the identity in Stone's theorem: Defining*

$$K := \int_{\mathbb{R}} E \, dP_U(E) \quad with \quad \mathrm{dom}(K) := \left\{ \psi \in \mathcal{H} \mid \int_{\mathbb{R}} E^2 (\psi | dP_U(E) \psi) < \infty \right\},$$
(46.2.3)

we obtain a self-adjoint operator K in $\mathcal{H}$ by the spectral calculus, according to Sec. 43.3.2. Then it holds

$$U_f = \hat{f}(K), \quad especially, \quad U_t = \mathrm{e}^{itK} \ for \ each \ t \in \mathbb{R}.$$
(46.2.4)

by the definition of a function of K and by property (a)(2). *One finds for the Arveson spectrum of the unitary group*

$$\mathrm{Sp}(U) = \sigma(K),$$
(46.2.5)

where the right-hand side denotes the Hilbert space spectrum of the self-adjoint operator K as introduced in Sec. 43.3.1 on page 1532.

(b) $\mathrm{Sp}^{\tau}(A) \supseteq \mathrm{Sp}^{U}(\{A\Omega\})$ *for all $A \in \mathcal{M}$ (where the right-hand side is the spectrum of a set of a vector).*
   (*For illustration note that $\tau_t(A) = \mathrm{e}^{itE} A$ implies $U_t A\Omega = U_t A U_t^* \Omega = \mathrm{e}^{itE} A\Omega$.*)
(c) $A \in \mathcal{M}^{\tau}(\Sigma) \implies A\Omega \in P_U(\Sigma)\mathcal{H}$, *for all closed $\Sigma \subseteq \mathring{\mathbb{R}}$.*
(d) *If Ω is also cyclic for $\mathcal{M}$, then*

$$\mathrm{Sp}(\tau) \supseteq \mathrm{Sp}(U).$$

   (*For illustration assume that $\{A_i \mid i \in I\}$ is a total set in $\mathcal{M}$ of eigen elements $\tau_t(A_i) = \mathrm{e}^{itE_i} A_i$, then cyclicity ensures that $\{A_i\Omega \mid i \in I\}$ is a total set of eigenvectors for U in $\mathcal{H}$.*)
(e) *If Ω is cyclic and separating for $\mathcal{M}$, then also the reverse relations are valid in* (b)–(d). *It holds, especially,*

$$\mathrm{Sp}(\tau) = \mathrm{Sp}(U).$$

Since the last assertion is basic for thermal equilibrium states, we formulate the following.

Corollary 46.2-7 (Spectrum in Faithful–State Representations). *Let the automorphism group $(\mathcal{A}, \tau_{\mathbb{R}})$ of the C*-algebra $\mathcal{A}$ have a faithful invariant state $\omega \in \mathcal{S}(\mathcal{A})$. Assume that the standard unitary implementation $U_t \Pi_\omega(A)\Omega_\omega := \Pi(\tau_t(A))\Omega_\omega$ in the GNS representation $(\Pi_\omega, \mathcal{H}_\omega, \Omega_\omega)$ of ω is strongly continuous with self-adjoint generator K, that is, $U_t = \mathrm{e}^{itK}$, and $\Pi_\omega(\tau_t(A)) = U_t \Pi_\omega(A) U_t^*$ for all $A \in \mathcal{A}$, and $U_t \Omega_\omega = \Omega_\omega$, for all $t \in \mathbb{R}$.*

Then we know that Ω_ω is a separating vector for the representation von Neumann algebra $\mathcal{M}_\omega = \Pi_\omega(\mathcal{A})''$ (see Corollary 46.2-27 on page 1696 below) and from Proposition 46.2-6(e) we have

$$\mathrm{Sp}(\tau) = \mathrm{Sp}(U) = \sigma(K),$$
(46.2.6)

so that $\sigma(K) \subseteq \mathbb{R}$ is reflection invariant, i.e., $\lambda \in \sigma(K) \Leftrightarrow -\lambda \in \sigma(K)$. Provided K is not bounded, the Hilbert space spectrum $\sigma(K)$ of K is, especially, a two-sided unbounded subset of $\mathbb{R}$.

We recognize, a ground state ω, with lower bounded, but unbounded energy $\sigma(K)$, is never faithful, and thus never represented by a separating vector Ω_ω.

More information concerning ground states is provided by the following theorem.

Theorem 46.2-8 (Borchers–Arveson Theorem). *Let $(\mathcal{M}, \mathbb{R}, \tau)$ be a W^*-dynamical system, where $\mathcal{M}$ is a von Neumann algebra in the Hilbert space $\mathcal{H}$. The following conditions are equivalent:*

(i) *There is a strongly continuous unitary one-parameter group $t \mapsto U_t \in \mathcal{L}(\mathcal{H})$ with positive spectrum $\mathrm{Sp}(U) \subseteq [0, \infty[$, such that*

$$\tau_t(A) = U_t A U_t^*, \quad \forall A \in \mathcal{M}, \ \forall t \in \mathbb{R}.$$

(ii) *There is a strongly continuous unitary one-parameter group $t \mapsto U_t \in \mathcal{M}$ with positive spectrum such that*

$$\tau_t(A) = U_t A U_t^*, \quad \forall A \in \mathcal{M}, \quad \forall t \in \mathbb{R}.$$

(iii) $\bigcap_{E \in \mathbb{R}} [\mathcal{M}^\tau([E, \infty[)\mathcal{H}] = 0$, *where the notation (linear subspace of $\mathcal{H}$) stands also for the projection onto the closure of the linear subspace. (The condition says, especially, that for $E \to \infty$ the set of operators with τ-spectrum in $[E, \infty[$ becomes empty.)*

Moreover, if (respectively, one of) these conditions (respectively, is) are satisfied, one may take for the unitary group U the special elements

$$U_t^{\mathrm{BA}} = \int_{\mathbb{R}} e^{itE} dP(E) \in \mathcal{M}, \quad \forall t \in \mathbb{R}.$$

(the upper index "BA" stands for Borchers–Arveson), where the spectral measure is obtained as follows: Define for each $E \in \mathbb{R}$

$$Q([E, \infty[) := \bigcap_{E' \leq E} [\mathcal{M}^\tau([E', \infty[)\mathcal{H}],$$

which is a projection in $\mathcal{M}$, and take account of the — here vanishing — spectral intersection

$$Q_\infty := \lim_{E \to \infty} Q([E, \infty[) = 0.$$

Define then the distinguished partition of unity

$$P(]-\infty, E[) := \mathbb{1} - Q([E, \infty[) \in \mathcal{M}, \quad \forall E \in \mathbb{R}.$$

The latter defines the projection-valued measure P on $\mathbb{R}$ with values in $\mathcal{M}$, and which is normalized in virtue of $Q_\infty = 0$. That measure P is employed in the above spectral representation of U_t^{BA}.

According to Theorem 43.6-1, the self-adjoint generator of the special unitary implementation $U_t^{BA} \in \mathcal{M}$ of τ_t has the form

$$H^{BA} = \int_{\mathbb{R}} E \, dP(E)$$

and is, of course, affiliated with $\mathcal{M}$ (cf. Definition 19.1-2 on page 460).

Observe that in the case, where there exists a unitary implementation of the W*-dynamical system $(\mathcal{M}, \mathbb{R}, \tau)$ with both-sided unbounded generator, it is not excluded that $Q_\infty = 0$, which in turn then would imply that there exists also a lower bounded implementation. If, however, $Q_\infty \neq 0$, then all unitary implementations of τ (if they exist) have both-sided unbounded generators, which may be, or may not be, affiliated with $\mathcal{M}$.

46.2.2. *Quasiequivalence, Disjointness, and Folia*

In the present subsection we want to compare different representations of a C*-algebra $\mathcal{A}$. With "unitarily equivalent" representations we were already concerned in the discussion of GNS constructions (cf. Definition 45.1-10 on page 1633). Since representations are largely characterized by their normal states, the notion of state folia comes into play.

Definition 46.2-9 (Comparison of Representations). For the C*-algebra $\mathcal{A}$ let the two representations $(\Pi_1, \mathcal{H}_1)$ and $(\Pi_2, \mathcal{H}_2)$ be given.

(a) The representations are called *unitarily equivalent*, if there exists a unitary mapping U from $\mathcal{H}_1$ onto $\mathcal{H}_2$ such that $U\Pi_1(A)U^* = \Pi_2(A)$ for all $A \in \mathcal{A}$.

(b) The representations are called *quasiequivalent*, if there exists an *-isomorphism α from the von Neumann algebra $\Pi_1(\mathcal{A})''$ onto the von Neumann algebra $\Pi_2(\mathcal{A})''$ such that $\alpha(\Pi_1(A)) = \Pi_2(A)$ for all $A \in \mathcal{A}$. Note that by Theorem 46.1-15(a) α is then automatically σ-weakly continuous.

(c) $(\Pi_1, \mathcal{H}_1)$ is *quasicontained* in $(\Pi_2, \mathcal{H}_2)$, or a quasi-subrepresentation of $(\Pi_2, \mathcal{H}_2)$, if $(\Pi_1, \mathcal{H}_1)$ is quasiequivalent to a subrepresentation of $(\Pi_2, \mathcal{H}_2)$.

(d) The two representations are called *disjoint*, if there is no subrepresentation of $(\Pi_1, \mathcal{H}_1)$ which is quasicontained in $(\Pi_2, \mathcal{H}_2)$, and vice versa.

(e) The two representations are called *inequivalent*, if they are not quasiequivalent. So, if, e.g., $(\Pi_1, \mathcal{H}_1)$ is properly quasicontained in $(\Pi_2, \mathcal{H}_2)$, then $(\Pi_1, \mathcal{H}_1)$ is inequivalent to $(\Pi_2, \mathcal{H}_2)$.

If an *-automorphism α of the C*-algebra $\mathcal{A}$ is unitarily implementable in the representation $(\Pi, \mathcal{H}_\Pi)$, then this amounts to unitary equivalence of the two representations $(\Pi \circ \alpha, \mathcal{H}_\Pi)$ and $(\Pi, \mathcal{H}_\Pi)$ of $\mathcal{A}$.

Remark 46.2-10. Unitary equivalence implies quasiequivalence, since the sandwiching by a unitary $\alpha(\Pi_1(A)) = U\Pi_1(A)U^* = \Pi_2(A)$ is per se a σ-weakly continuous map, which may be uniquely extended to an *-isomorphism α from $\Pi_1(A)''$ onto $\Pi_2(A)''$. The converse, however, is valid, if and only if both representations are irreducible.

In general, quasiequivalence of representations implies unitary equivalence of multiples of the representations.

The various concepts of comparing representations may be neatly expressed in term of their normal states.

Definition 46.2-11 (Π-Normal States). Let $(\Pi, \mathcal{H}_\Pi)$ be a representation of the C*-algebra A. A state ω on A is said to be Π-*normal*, if there exists a normal state $\dot{\omega}$ on the von Neumann algebra $\mathcal{M}_\Pi = \Pi(A)''$ so that

$$\langle \omega; A \rangle = \langle \dot{\omega}; \Pi(A) \rangle, \quad \forall A \in A.$$

If $(\Pi, \mathcal{H}_\Pi)$ is non-degenerate, then $\Pi(A)$ is σ-weakly dense in $\mathcal{M}_\Pi$, and the Π-normal state ω extends by σ-weak continuity uniquely to a normal state $\dot{\omega}$ on $\overline{\Pi(A)}^{\text{weak}} = \mathcal{M}_\Pi = \Pi(A)''$.

The set of the Π-normal states on A is denoted by $\mathcal{F}_\Pi(A)$ or simply by $\mathcal{F}_\Pi$, if the C*-algebra is understood.

For non-degenerate $(\Pi, \mathcal{H}_\Pi)$ one often identifies the affine isomorphic sets

$$\mathcal{F}_\Pi(A) \cong \mathcal{S}_n(\mathcal{M}_\Pi) \cong \mathcal{T}_1^+(\mathcal{H}_\Pi)/\approx \quad (\leftarrow \text{see subsequent text}). \quad (46.2.7)$$

According to Proposition 46.1-14 *each* state $\omega \in \mathcal{F}_\Pi(A)$ is realizable in terms of a (in general non-unique) density operator $T = T_\omega \in \mathcal{T}_1^+(\mathcal{H}_\Pi)$ by means of the trace formula

$$\langle \omega; A \rangle = \text{tr}[T\Pi(A)], \quad \forall A \in A. \quad (46.2.8)$$

Conversely, if $(\Pi, \mathcal{H}_\Pi)$ is non-degenerate, every density operator $T \in \mathcal{T}_1^+(\mathcal{H}_\Pi)$ provides by Eq. (46.2.8) a normal state $\omega = \omega_T \in \mathcal{F}_\Pi(A)$. The mapping $T \mapsto \omega_T$ from the density operators $\mathcal{T}_1^+(\mathcal{H}_\Pi)$ onto $\mathcal{F}_\Pi(A)$ is affine but in general not injective. Bijectivity can be achieved by forming the equivalence classes $\mathcal{T}_1^+(\mathcal{H}_\Pi)/\approx$, where two density operators are equivalent, if they give the same normal state on $\mathcal{M}_\Pi$.

Bijectivity of $\mathcal{T}_1^+(\mathcal{H}_\Pi) \to \mathcal{F}_\Pi(A)$ is directly valid for an irreducible representation $(\Pi, \mathcal{H}_\Pi)$, since there $\mathcal{M}_\Pi = \Pi(A)'' = \mathcal{L}(\mathcal{H}_\Pi)$, which separates the density operators.

The normal states of a general representation, $\mathcal{F}_\Pi(A)$, form a norm closed convex subset of the state space $\mathcal{S}(A)$. If $T \in \mathcal{T}_1^+(\mathcal{H}_\Pi)$ and $B \in \mathcal{L}(\mathcal{H}_\Pi)$ then $B^*TB \in$

$\mathcal{T}^+(\mathcal{H}_\Pi)$, and after renormalization defines a state $\tilde\omega \in \mathcal{F}_\Pi(\mathcal{A})$,

$$\langle \tilde\omega; A \rangle = \frac{\mathrm{tr}[B^*TB\,\Pi(A)]}{\mathrm{tr}[B^*TB]}, \quad \forall A \in \mathcal{A}, \quad \text{provided } \mathrm{tr}[B^*TB] \neq 0,$$

so that the set of normal states $\mathcal{F}_\Pi(\mathcal{A})$ is invariant under perturbations.

Definition 46.2-12 (Perturbed States, Folium). Let $\mathcal{A}$ be a C*-algebra.

(a) If $\omega \in \mathcal{S}(\mathcal{A})$ and $B \in \mathcal{A}$, then we define the perturbed state ω_B as the state on $\mathcal{A}$, which is given by $\langle \omega_B; \cdot \rangle = \langle \omega; B^* \cdot B \rangle \langle \omega; B^*B \rangle^{-1}$, if the denominator does not vanish, and by $\omega_B = \omega$ in the other case.

(b) A folium $\mathcal{F}$ of the C*-algebra $\mathcal{A}$ is a norm closed, convex subset of its state space $\mathcal{S}(\mathcal{A})$, which is invariant under "perturbations", that is $\omega \in \mathcal{F}$ implies $\omega_B \in \mathcal{F}$ for all $B \in \mathcal{A}$.

With the observation preceding Definition 46.2-12 we arrive at statement (a) of the following lemma.

Lemma 46.2-13 (Folium = Π-Normal States). *Let $\mathcal{A}$ be a C*-algebra.*

(a) *If Π is a representation of $\mathcal{A}$, then the Π-normal states $\mathcal{F}_\Pi(\mathcal{A})$ constitute a folium of $\mathcal{A}$.*

(b) *Let $\mathcal{F}$ be a folium of $\mathcal{A}$. Then there exists a representation Π of $\mathcal{A}$ such that $\mathcal{F}$ coincides with the Π-normal states on $\mathcal{A}$, that is $\mathcal{F} = \mathcal{F}_\Pi(\mathcal{A})$.*

(c) *Let us denote by $\mathcal{F}_\omega \subset \mathcal{S}(\mathcal{A})$ the smallest folium containing $\omega \in \mathcal{S}(\mathcal{A})$ and by Π_ω, as usual, the GNS representation of ω. Then we have*

$$\mathcal{F}_\omega = \mathcal{F}_{\Pi_\omega}. \tag{46.2.9}$$

Concerning part (b) of the preceding lemma one may, e.g., choose the representation $(\Pi_\mathcal{F}, \mathcal{H}_\mathcal{F})$ for a given folium $\mathcal{F}$, described in the subsequent observation, in which also part (c) is proved.

Observation 46.2-14 (Partially Universal Representations). For a given folium $\mathcal{F} \subset \mathcal{S} \equiv \mathcal{S}(\mathcal{A})$ we form the direct sum of GNS triples $\bigoplus_{\omega \in \mathcal{F}} (\Pi_\omega, \mathcal{H}_\omega, \Omega_\omega)$, which we call the *partially universal representation* over $\mathcal{F}$ and denote it by $(\Pi_\mathcal{F}, \mathcal{H}_\mathcal{F})$. (Concerning the direct sum of representations cf. the text after Proposition 45.2-16.) Then each $\omega \in \mathcal{F}$ is realized as a vector state corresponding to Ω_ω.

Note that we identify Ω_ω with $\bigoplus_{\omega' \in \mathcal{F}} \delta_{\omega,\omega'} \Omega_{\omega'} \in \mathcal{H}_\mathcal{F}$. In this sense one says that the $\{\Omega_\omega \mid \omega \in \mathcal{F}\}$ constitute a cyclic set of vectors for $\Pi_\mathcal{F}(\mathcal{A})$, and that $\{\Pi_\omega(A)\Omega_\omega \mid \omega \in \mathcal{F}, A \in \mathcal{A}\}$ is total in $\mathcal{H}_\mathcal{F}$.

$|\Omega_\omega)(\Omega_\omega|$ is certainly not the only realization of $\omega \in \mathcal{F}$ in terms of a density operator in $\mathcal{T}_1^+(\mathcal{H}_\mathcal{F})$. In any case, ω is by the representative $|\Omega_\omega)(\Omega_\omega|$ an element of $\mathcal{F}_{\Pi_\mathcal{F}}(\mathcal{A})$, the normal states of $\Pi_\mathcal{F}$.

Reversely, each $T \in \mathcal{T}_1^+(\mathcal{H}_\mathcal{F})$ is the denumerable convex sum of one-dimensional projections, in which each vector is the denumerable direct sum of components $\xi_\omega \in \mathcal{H}_\omega \subset \mathcal{H}_\mathcal{F}$. By the GNS construction there is a sequence $\Pi_\omega(B_i)\Omega_\omega$, $B_i \in \mathcal{A}$, which converges to ξ_ω. We have given in the proof of Theorem 47.5-2 an argument that the corresponding projections $|\Pi_\omega(B_i)\Omega_\omega)(\Pi_\omega(B_i)\Omega_\omega|$, which describe perturbations of $\omega \in \mathcal{F}$, converge in trace norm to $|\xi_\omega)(\xi_\omega|$. The corresponding states in $\mathcal{S}_n$ converge then in norm, and thus $|\xi_\omega)(\xi_\omega|$ represents a state in $\mathcal{F}$, by the norm closedness of the folium. The total T describes also a state in $\mathcal{F}$, due to the closedness of $\mathcal{F}$ under denumerable convex sums of states, converging in norm.

So we have proved (b) of the preceding lemma.

Our reasoning shows also that the folium $\mathcal{F}_{\Pi_\omega}(\mathcal{A})$ of the normal states of the GNS representation is generated by the convex sums of perturbations of $\omega \in \mathcal{S}(\mathcal{A})$ and therefore is the smallest folium containing ω, which proves part (c) of the preceding lemma.

The GNS folium $\mathcal{F}_\omega$ for $\omega \in \mathcal{S}(\mathcal{A})$ is represented by equivalence classes of the density operators $\mathcal{T}_1^+(\mathcal{H}_\omega)$ in the representation Hilbert space $\mathcal{H}_\omega$, where $\mathcal{H}_\omega$ is, e.g., separable, if $\mathcal{A}$ is separable. The folium $\mathcal{F}_\omega$ gives in turn rise to the partially universal representation $\Pi_{\mathcal{F}_\omega}$ in the highly non-separable Hilbert space $\mathcal{H}_{\mathcal{F}_\omega} = \bigoplus_{\omega \in \mathcal{F}_\omega} \mathcal{H}_\omega$. The equivalence classes of density operators in this big Hilbert space realize again only $\mathcal{F}_\omega$. In each equivalence class of a density operator, is always a one-dimensional projection operator, describing a vector state. This demonstrates drastically the possible non-uniqueness of the realization of normal states in terms of density operators (and also how inadequate it may be to deal with "wave functions" in general representation spaces to uncover quantum features like coherence).

There arises also the question about the relationship between $(\Pi_\omega, \mathcal{H}_\omega)$ and $(\Pi_{\mathcal{F}_\omega}, \mathcal{H}_{\mathcal{F}_\omega})$, an example of two representations with the same folium of normal states. Since quite generally the normal states $\mathcal{F}_\Pi$ coincide with the σ-weakly continuous states on $\Pi(\mathcal{A})$, it follows immediately that quasiequivalent representations provide the same folium of normal states.

The reverse, that the same folium $\mathcal{F}$ of normal states implies the quasiequivalence of two representations $(\Pi_1, \mathcal{H}_1)$ and $(\Pi_2, \mathcal{H}_2)$, is seen as follows: Since $\mathcal{F}_{\Pi_1}$ is identical to the folium $\mathcal{F} \subset \mathcal{S}(\mathcal{A})$, as is $\mathcal{F}_{\Pi_2}$, we may introduce an orientation-preserving bijection ν between $\mathcal{S}_n(\Pi_2(\mathcal{A})'')$ and $\mathcal{S}_n(\Pi_1(\mathcal{A})'')$ so that $\langle \omega; A \rangle = \langle \omega_1; \Pi_1(A) \rangle = \langle \nu(\omega_2); \Pi_1(A) \rangle = \langle \omega_2; \Pi_2(A) \rangle$ for all $A \in \mathcal{A}$, where for all $\omega \in \mathcal{F}$ the normal states ω_1 and ω_2 are uniquely determined. By Theorem 46.1-15(f), ν^* is then a Jordan isomorphism from $\Pi_1(\mathcal{A})''$ onto $\Pi_2(\mathcal{A})''$, and it satisfies $\nu^*(\Pi_1(A)) = \Pi_2(A)$ for all $A \in \mathcal{A}$. Thus ν^* is an *-isomorphism, demonstrating the quasi-equivalence of the two representations.

Altogether we found, by the foregoing reasoning, relation (a) of the subsequent theorem, in which the further assertions follow readily by the definitions and by the biunivocal connection between folia and quasiequivalence classes of representations.

In (e) we use that irreducible representations have no proper subrepresentations and that an *-isomorphism between entire $\mathcal{L}(\mathcal{H})$-algebras is unitarily implementable.

Theorem 46.2-15 (Folia and Quasiequivalent Representations). *Let $(\Pi_1, \mathcal{H}_1)$ and $(\Pi_2, \mathcal{H}_2)$ be two representations of the C^*-algebra $\mathcal{A}$. Then the following assertions are valid:*

(a) *The representations are quasi-equivalent, if and only if $\mathcal{F}_{\Pi_1} = \mathcal{F}_{\Pi_2}$.*

(b) *Each representation Π is, especially, quasiequivalent to the partially universal representation $\Pi_{\mathcal{F}_\Pi}$ over the folium $\mathcal{F}_\Pi$ of the Π-normal states.*

(c) *$(\Pi_1, \mathcal{H}_1)$ is a quasicontained in $(\Pi_2, \mathcal{H}_2)$, if and only if $\mathcal{F}_{\Pi_1} \subseteq \mathcal{F}_{\Pi_2}$. Moreover, $(\Pi_1, \mathcal{H}_1)$ is a proper quasi-subrepresentation of $(\Pi_2, \mathcal{H}_2)$, if and only if $\mathcal{F}_{\Pi_1}$ is a proper subset of $\mathcal{F}_{\Pi_2}$.*

(d) *The representations are disjoint, if and only if $\mathcal{F}_{\Pi_1} \cap \mathcal{F}_{\Pi_2} = \emptyset$.*

(e) *Let both representations be irreducible. Then they are either disjoint or quasiequivalent. That is, we either have $\mathcal{F}_{\Pi_1} \cap \mathcal{F}_{\Pi_2} = \emptyset$, or $\mathcal{F}_{\Pi_1} = \mathcal{F}_{\Pi_2}$. If they are quasiequivalent, then they are even unitarily equivalent.*

In the mathematical literature "equivalent" is often the abbreviation for "unitarily equivalent".

Corollary 46.2-16 (Ordering of Folia and Representations). *In virtue of the foregoing results the one-to-one correspondence between the folia of a C^*-algebra $\mathcal{A}$ and the quasiequivalence classes $\hat{\Pi}$ of representations $(\Pi, \mathcal{H}_\Pi)$ of $\mathcal{A}$ preserves the respective partial orderings:*

If $\hat{\Pi}_j$, for $j = 1, 2$, is the quasiequivalence class of a representation Π_j of $\mathcal{A}$, uniquely corresponding to the folium $\mathcal{F}_j \equiv \mathcal{F}_{\Pi_j}$, then

$$\mathcal{F}_1 \subseteq \mathcal{F}_2 \subseteq \mathcal{S}(\mathcal{A}) \quad \Longleftrightarrow \quad \hat{\Pi}_1 \leq \hat{\Pi}_2 \leq \hat{\Pi}_u \,,$$

where the ordering among the folia is the set inclusion, and the representations are ordered by being quasicontained.

The symbol Π_u indicates the universal representation (cf. Theorem 45.2-31 on page 1657), with corresponding von Neumann algebra $\mathcal{M}_u := \Pi_u(\mathcal{A})''$, the universal enveloping von Neumann algebra. Since Π_u is the direct sum of GNS representations over the whole state space (a special folium), we know the following:

$$\mathcal{S}(\mathcal{A}) = \mathcal{F}_{\Pi_u}(\mathcal{A}) \stackrel{\text{affine bijection}}{\longleftrightarrow} \mathcal{S}_n(\mathcal{M}_u) \,. \tag{46.2.10}$$

Note that a quasiequivalence class $\hat{\Pi}$ of representations $(\Pi, \mathcal{H}_\Pi)$ of $\mathcal{A}$ has lost the affiliation with a Hilbert space and is thus associated with a W-algebra (and not with a special von Neumann algebra $\Pi(\mathcal{A})''$). The partially universal von Neumann algebra $\mathcal{M}_\mathcal{F}$ of a folium $\mathcal{F}$ may then be considered as a distinguished representation of the W*-algebra, which is uniquely associated with $\mathcal{F}$.*

The notions of quasiequivalence and disjointness are taken over to states via their respective GNS representations.

Definition 46.2-17 (Equivalence and Disjointness of States). Let ω and φ be two states on the C*-algebra $\mathcal{A}$ with associated GNS triples $(\Pi_\omega, \mathcal{H}_\omega, \Omega_\omega)$ and $(\Pi_\varphi, \mathcal{H}_\varphi, \Omega_\varphi)$, and GNS folia $\mathcal{F}_\omega$ and $\mathcal{F}_\varphi$.

(a) ω and φ are called *quasiequivalent*, denoted $\omega \approx \varphi$, if the representations $(\Pi_\omega, \mathcal{H}_\omega)$ and $(\Pi_\varphi, \mathcal{H}_\varphi)$ are quasiequivalent, or equivalently, if $\mathcal{F}_\omega = \mathcal{F}_\varphi$.
(b) ω and φ are called disjoint, denoted $\omega \,\flat\, \varphi$, if the representations $(\Pi_\omega, \mathcal{H}_\omega)$ and $(\Pi_\varphi, \mathcal{H}_\varphi)$ are disjoint, or equivalently, if $\mathcal{F}_\omega \cap \mathcal{F}_\varphi = \emptyset$.

There are various results concerning quasiequivalence and disjointness of states. We give an example, in which the states are compared within a minimal conceptual setup. The following assertions are easily derived from later results on supporting folia.

Proposition 46.2-18 (Special Disjointness Criteria). *Let ω and φ be two states on the C*-algebra $\mathcal{A}$ and let $\varrho := \frac{1}{2}(\omega + \varphi)$ be a special convex combination.*

(a) *ω and φ are disjoint, if and only if there exists a orthogonal projection $C \in \mathcal{Z}(\Pi_\varrho(\mathcal{A})'')$ (center of the von Neumann algebra $\Pi_\varrho(\mathcal{A})''$) with*

$$\langle \omega; A \rangle = (\Omega_\varrho | C \Pi_\varrho(A) \Omega_\varrho), \quad \langle \varphi; A \rangle = (\Omega_\varrho | (\mathbb{1} - C) \Pi_\varrho(A) \Omega_\varrho), \quad \forall A \in \mathcal{A},$$

where $(\Pi_\varrho, \mathcal{H}_\varrho, \Omega_\varrho)$ denotes the GNS triple of ϱ.
(b) *Let ω and φ be factorial. Then ω and φ are quasiequivalent, if and only if $\varrho := \frac{1}{2}(\omega + \varphi)$ is factorial. (Sufficiency follows from (a).)*
(c) *Since the preceding criterion is an alternative, two factor states are either quasi-equivalent or disjoint.*
(d) *For ω and φ being pure states, i.e., $\omega, \varphi \in \partial_e \mathcal{S}(\mathcal{A})$ (and thus are factorial), we may discriminate the two cases as follows:*

  • *They are quasiequivalent if and only if ω can be represented by a normalized vector within the GNS representation of φ.*
  • *They are disjoint if and only if they have the maximal norm distance of the value $\|\omega - \varphi\| = 2$. (According to Sec. 48.4 below the norm distance increases with decreasing transition probability, reaching 2 if the latter reaches 0.)*

The transition from algebraic representation theory to convex analysis is initiated by realizing the facial structure of folia as subsets of the convex state space. Let us recall two pertinent definitions from Chap. 47.

Definition 46.2-19 (Face, Split Face). A convex subset F of the state space $\mathcal{S}(\mathcal{A})$ is called a *face*, if the following is true: If one has for two states $\omega, \varphi \in \mathcal{S}(\mathcal{A})$ the relation $\lambda \omega + (1 - \lambda)\varphi \in F$, for some $\lambda \in]0, 1[$, then one knows that ω and φ are elements of F.

A face F of the state space $\mathcal{S}(\mathcal{A})$ is called a *split face*, if there exists another face F^C of $\mathcal{S}(\mathcal{A})$ such that each $\omega \in \mathcal{S}(\mathcal{A})$ possesses a unique convex decomposition $\omega = \lambda\varphi + (1 - \lambda)\varphi^C$, with a $0 \leq \lambda \leq 1$, where $\varphi \in F$ and $\varphi^C \in F^C$. F and F^C are called *complementary* split faces.

There is a physically very satisfying relationship between the perturbational stability of a convex state set and the classicality of its F-property, the classicality being here expressed by splitting the state space to form a classical negation without quantum correlations. (For F-properties, cf. Sec. 47.2.1 on page 1729 and the following investigations.)

Proposition 46.2-20 (Split Face = Folium). *The folia of a C*-algebra $\mathcal{A}$ are the only norm closed split faces of the state space $\mathcal{S}(\mathcal{A})$.*

We deepen and derive that result in the subsequent considerations.

46.2.3.   *Faces, Projections, Supports, and Equivalence*

Besides the split faces of $\mathcal{S} \equiv \mathcal{S}(\mathcal{A})$ also the total set $\mathcal{E}(\mathcal{S})$ of norm closed faces is of physical importance. We argue in Chap. 47 that the $F \in \mathcal{E}(\mathcal{S})$ represent the "properties" of a physical system in a statistical theory, the so-called *F-properties*. Since $\mathcal{S} \equiv \mathcal{S}(\mathcal{A})$ is affine isomorphic to the normal state space $\mathcal{S}_n(\mathcal{M}_u)$, we cover also that case by investigating $\mathcal{S}_n(\mathcal{M})$ for an arbitrary von Neumann algebra $\mathcal{M} \subset \mathcal{L}(\mathcal{H})$. The arguments for the following, physically basic theorem are usually spread over many pages in the operator algebraic text books (involving left ideals and hereditary subcones, as, e.g., in [Tak79]), and so we are trying to accomplish a more direct reasoning, referring to the well-known concepts of Sec. 47.5.

Theorem 46.2-21 (Support Projections of Faces in Normal State Space).
Let $\mathcal{S}_n \equiv \mathcal{S}_n(\mathcal{M})$ be the normal state space of the von Neumann algebra $\mathcal{M} \subset \mathcal{L}(\mathcal{H})$ and denote by $\mathcal{E}(\mathcal{S}_n)$ the set of all norm closed faces of $\mathcal{S}_n$.
   Then the set $\mathcal{P}(\mathcal{M})$ of all projections in $\mathcal{M}$ is a complete orthomodular lattice and the mapping

$$\mathcal{P}(\mathcal{M}) \ni P \mapsto F_P := \{\omega \in \mathcal{S}_n \mid \langle\omega; P\rangle = 1\} \subseteq \mathcal{S}_n \qquad (46.2.11)$$

is a lattice isomorphism between $\mathcal{P}(\mathcal{H})$ and $\mathcal{E}(\mathcal{S}_n)$, where the inverse map is given by

$$\mathcal{E}(\mathcal{S}_n) \ni F \mapsto P_F := \inf\{P \in \mathcal{P}(\mathcal{M}) \mid \langle\omega; P\rangle = 1, \ \forall\omega \in F\}. \qquad (46.2.12)$$

(One defines $P_F := 0$ for $F = \emptyset \in \mathcal{E}(\mathcal{S}_n)$.) The projection P_F is called the support projection *of the face $F \in \mathcal{E}(\mathcal{S}_n)$.*
   By introducing the orthocomplementation $(F_P)^\perp := F_{P^\perp}$, the set $\mathcal{E}(\mathcal{S}_n)$ becomes a complete orthomodular lattice.

$F \in \mathcal{E}(\mathcal{S}_n)$ *is a split face of* $\mathcal{S}_n$, *if and only if it represents a classical F-property* (*that is an element of* $\mathcal{E}_c(\mathcal{S}_n)$, *the set of norm closed faces which are compatible with all other F-properties in the lattice theoretic sense*), *and this is true if and only if its support projection* P_F *is in the center* $\mathcal{Z}(\mathcal{M})$. *In formulas*

$$F \in \mathcal{E}_c(\mathcal{S}_n) \iff P_F \in \mathcal{P}_c(\mathcal{M}) := \mathcal{P}(\mathcal{M}) \cap \mathcal{Z}(\mathcal{M}). \qquad (46.2.13)$$

Proof. Since each $\omega \in \mathcal{S}_n$ may be realized by a (non-unique) density operator $T_\omega \in \mathcal{T}_1^+(\mathcal{H})$ we can take over many parts from the proof for Theorem 47.5-2, concerning $\mathcal{T}_1^+(\mathcal{H})$. The argument that F_P is a norm closed face and that the map $P \mapsto F_P$ is order preserving goes, especially, as for $\mathcal{T}_1^+(\mathcal{H})$.

For given $F \in \mathcal{E}(\mathcal{S}_n)$ we introduce the closed subspace

$$\mathcal{H}_F := \{\xi \in \mathcal{H} \mid \omega_\xi \in F\} \cup \{0\}, \text{ with } \omega_\xi \text{ the vector state for } \xi, \qquad (46.2.14)$$

as in Theorem 47.5-2 (where ξ need not be normalized, but ω_ξ must be normalized) and denote the projection operator onto $\mathcal{H}_F$ by $P \in \mathcal{P}(\mathcal{H})$. But we have now to show that $P \in \mathcal{P}(\mathcal{M})$. For this we choose an arbitrary unitary $U \in \mathcal{M}'$ and calculate

$$(U\hat{\xi} \mid AU\hat{\xi}) = (U\hat{\xi} \mid UA\hat{\xi}) = (\hat{\xi} \mid A\hat{\xi}), \quad \forall A \in \mathcal{M},$$

which shows that with $\hat{\xi}$ also $U\hat{\xi}$ is in $\mathcal{H}_F$. Since the same holds for $\mathcal{H}_F^\perp$, we conclude that $UP = PU$. Since the commutant of all unitaries in $\mathcal{M}'$ (which span linearly $\mathcal{M}'$) coincides with $\mathcal{M}'' = \mathcal{M}$ it follows that $P \in \mathcal{M}$.

Since the convex state decomposition $F \ni \omega = \sum_{k \in \mathbb{N}} \lambda_k \omega_{\xi_k}$, with the states ω_{ξ_k} given by the one-dimensional projections $|\xi_k)(\xi_k|$, is anyhow non-unique, the non-uniqueness of the vectors does not prevent the reasoning in Theorem 47.5-2 leading to $F = F_P$ and implying $P = P_F$.

A projection P is in $\mathcal{P}_c(\mathcal{M})$, if and only if it is compatible in the lattice theoretic sense with all $P \in \mathcal{P}(\mathcal{M})$, and this is true if and only if $F_P \in \mathcal{E}_c(\mathcal{S}_n)$. According to Theorem 47.2-20 each norm closed split face F is in $\mathcal{E}_c(\mathcal{S}_n)$ and then $P_F \in \mathcal{P}_c(\mathcal{M})$, due to the preceding argument. If, reversely, $P \in \mathcal{P}_c(\mathcal{M})$, each $\omega \in \mathcal{S}_n$ is uniquely split according to $\langle \omega; A \rangle = \langle \omega; PAP \rangle + \langle \omega; P^\perp AP^\perp \rangle$, and $\langle \omega; PAP \rangle / \langle \omega; P \rangle \in F_P$, if defined. Thus F_P is a split face. □

From the duality between $\mathcal{M}_*$ and $\mathcal{M}$ we know that $\mathcal{M}_{*,\mathrm{sa}}$ is the real predual of the real Banach space $\mathcal{M}_{\mathrm{sa}}$. Thus $\mathcal{M}_{\mathrm{sa}}$ is isomorphic as ordered Banach space to the bounded, real, affine functions $\mathrm{Aff}_b(\mathcal{S}_n)$ and has the order unit $\mathbb{1} \in \mathcal{L}(\mathcal{H})$. Explicitly

$$\mathcal{M}_{\mathrm{sa}} \ni A \longmapsto \hat{A} \equiv (\mathcal{S}_n \ni \omega \mapsto \langle \omega; A \rangle) \in \mathrm{Aff}_b(\mathcal{S}_n). \qquad (46.2.15)$$

Obviously the projections $\mathcal{P}(\mathcal{M})$ are part of $\mathcal{M}_{\mathrm{sa}}$ and define the affine functions $\hat{P}$.

Theorem 46.2-22 (The Normal State Space is Projective and Spectral).
Let again S_n be the normal state space of the von Neumann algebra $M \subset L(\mathcal{H})$ and $\mathcal{E}(S_n)$ the set of all norm closed faces of S_n.

(a) *Let $F \in \mathcal{E}(S_n)$, and $P \in \mathcal{P}(M)$ be its unique support projection. Define the filtering projection $Q_P \in \mathcal{Q}(S_n)$ by $\langle Q_P(\omega); A \rangle := \langle \omega; PAP \rangle$ for all $\omega \in M_{*,\mathrm{sa}}$ and all $A \in M_{\mathrm{sa}}$. Then Q_P is the unique filtering projection with $Q_P(M_{*,\mathrm{sa}}) \cap S_n = F$.*

(b) *Let $F \in \mathcal{E}(S_n)$, and $P \in \mathcal{P}(M)$ be its unique support projection. Then F is detected by the projective unit $\omega \mapsto \hat{P}(\omega) := \langle Q_P(\omega); \mathbb{1} \rangle$, that is $\hat{P}(\omega) = 1$ for $\omega \in F$ and $\hat{P}(\omega) < 1$ for $\omega \in S_n \backslash F$.*

(c) *From the foregoing two assertions we conclude that $\mathcal{Q}(S_n)$ and $\mathcal{P}(S_n)$ are ortholattice isomorphic to $\mathcal{P}(M)$, and thus to $\mathcal{E}(S_n)$. (For a more detailed formulation cf. Proposition 47.2-24.)*

Therefore, each norm closed face of S_n is detectable and filtered and S_n is a projective convex set.

(d) *By the spectral theorem in M_{sa} (cf. Theorem 46.1-9) each $a \in \mathit{Aff}_b(S_n)$, represented by $\hat{A}$, $A \in M_{\mathrm{sa}}$, has a spectral representation and S_n is thus a spectral convex set.*

The spectral family $\{P_t \in \mathcal{P}(M) \mid t \in \mathbb{R}\}$, biunivocally associated with an $\hat{A}$, $A \in M_{\mathrm{sa}}$, defines a spectral family $\{F_t \in \mathcal{E}(S_n) \mid t \in \mathbb{R}\}$ of F-properties, which constitutes a metric observable in the sense of Definition 47.2-24.

Since for any C*-algebra $\mathcal{A}$ its state space $\mathcal{S}(\mathcal{A})$ is affinely isomorphic to $S_n(M_u)$, we immediately transfer the foregoing results to $\mathcal{S}(\mathcal{A})$. We discuss these conclusions separately because in algebraic quantum theory one starts from an abstract $\mathcal{A}$. In some sense, we consider the C*-algebraic state space physically (even mathematically) more basic than the observable algebra $\mathcal{A}$, the convex state operations being empirically executable without introducing any numerical scale (see e.g., Stern–Gerlach experiment Example 47.2-14 on page 1737).

Recall that the weak* continuous affine functions on $\mathcal{S}(\mathcal{A})$ are given by elements from $\mathcal{A}$, in which algebra we have the spectral theory of continuous functions. This brings us to an illustration of a notion from Sec. 47.2.4.

Theorem 46.2-23 (The C*-Algebraic State Space is Strongly Spectral).
The state space $\mathcal{S} \equiv \mathcal{S}(\mathcal{A})$ of a C*-algebra $\mathcal{A}$ is projective (i.e., the norm closed faces from all $\mathcal{E}(\mathcal{S})$ are detected by a $\hat{P}$, $P \in \mathcal{P}(M_u)$), and $\mathcal{S}$ is strongly spectral.

For given $a \in \mathit{Aff}_b(\mathcal{S}) \equiv M_u$ there is biunivocally associated a spectral family $\{F_t \in \mathcal{E}(\mathcal{S}) \mid t \in \mathbb{R}\}$ of F-properties, which constitutes a metric empirical observable in the sense of Definition 47.2-24.

The facial structure $\mathcal{E}(\mathcal{S})$ of a C*-algebraic state space $\mathcal{S}$ allows one to formulate the empirical statements within the abstract C*-algebraic frame, without recourse to a representation. As is expounded in Remark 47.2-25, the empirical meaning of the spectral resolution may be entirely expressed in terms of the F_t-properties. This is perhaps achieved even clearer than in terms of projection operators, since the states are the notions which exhibit the empirical spectral values. The thermo-dynamic observables refer, especially, only to the macro states of the system, what microscopic-algebraically leads to state folia. On the other side, the reference to projection operators in a representation is of course a valuable technical assistance.

In a global discussion one refers mostly to the universal representation $(\Pi_u, \mathcal{H}_u)$. We give the support properties of C*-algebraic states both in $\mathcal{E}(\mathcal{S})$ and $\mathcal{P}(\mathcal{M}_u)$. Let us in before make the following remarks concerning the largeness of state sets.

Remark 46.2-24 (Full sets of states).   Let $\mathcal{A}$ be a C*-algebra and $\mathcal{S} \equiv \mathcal{S}(\mathcal{A})$ its state space.

(a) According to [BR87] a convex subset $\mathcal{S}_0 \subset \mathcal{S}$ is called *full*, if $\langle \varphi; A \rangle \geq 0$ for all $\varphi \in \mathcal{S}_0$, implies $A \geq 0$, for any $A \in \mathcal{A}$.
   If now $\mathcal{S}_0$ is full and $\langle \varphi; A \rangle = 0$, $\forall \varphi \in \mathcal{S}_0$, then this implies $A \geq 0$ and $A \leq 0$, so that $A = 0$.

(b) Quite generally, a convex set $\mathcal{S}_0$ of states on a C*-algebra $\mathcal{A}$ is full, if and only if it is weak* dense (that is $\sigma(\mathcal{S}(\mathcal{A}), \mathcal{A})$-dense) in $\mathcal{S}(\mathcal{A})$. (The proof of this assertion is not simple cf. [BR87].)

(c) If $\mathcal{S}_0$ is full, and we form the representation $(\Pi_{\mathcal{S}_0}, \mathcal{H}_{\mathcal{S}_0}) := \bigoplus_{\varphi \in \mathcal{S}_0} (\Pi_\varphi, \mathcal{H}_\varphi)$, then $\Pi_{\mathcal{S}_0}(A) = 0$ implies $\langle \varphi; A \rangle = (\Omega_\varphi | \Pi_\varphi(A)\Omega_\varphi) = (\Omega_\varphi | \Pi_{\mathcal{S}_0}(A)\Omega_\varphi) = 0$, $\forall \varphi \in \mathcal{S}_0$, so that $A = 0$. Then $\Pi_{\mathcal{S}_0}$ is faithful (and therefore is an invertible map on its image).

(d) If on the other side $\mathcal{S}_0$ is a folium and if the representation $(\Pi_{\mathcal{S}_0}, \mathcal{H}_{\mathcal{S}_0})$ is faithful, we conclude from $\langle \varphi; A \rangle \geq 0$ for all $\varphi \in \mathcal{S}_0$, that also

$$\langle \varphi; C^* A C \rangle = (\Pi_\varphi(C)\Omega_\varphi | \Pi_\varphi(A) \, \Pi_\varphi(C)\Omega_\varphi) \geq 0, \quad \forall \varphi \in \mathcal{S}_0, \quad \forall C \in \mathcal{A}$$

(since a folium is invariant under perturbations by C). Thus the expectations of $\Pi_{\mathcal{S}_0}(A)$ in a dense set of vectors in $\mathcal{H}_{\mathcal{S}_0}$ are positive and hence $\Pi_{\mathcal{S}_0}(A) \geq 0$. Since $\Pi_{\mathcal{S}_0}$ is invertible we deduce $\Pi_{\mathcal{S}_0}^{-1} \circ \Pi_{\mathcal{S}_0}(A) = A \geq 0$, proving fullness of $\mathcal{S}_0$. Note that we used in the preceding argument only the stability of a folium under a sufficiently large (norm dense) set of perturbations $C \in \mathcal{A}$, and did not need norm closedness for this set of C's.

(e) From the foregoing results we infer for a given folium $\mathcal{F} \subseteq \mathcal{S}$ that faithfulness of the (partially universal) representation $(\Pi_{\mathcal{F}}, \mathcal{H}_{\mathcal{F}})$ is equivalent to fullness of $\mathcal{F}$ and this is equivalent to the weak* density of $\mathcal{F}$ in $\mathcal{S}$.

(f) For just one state we have the following notion: A state $\omega \in \mathcal{S}$ is called *faithful*, if $\mathcal{A} \ni A > 0$ implies $\langle \omega; A \rangle > 0$. Equivalently ω is faithful, if and only if $A \geq 0$ combined with $\langle \omega; A \rangle = 0$ implies $A = 0$. (The same definition applies, of course, if $\mathcal{A}$ is a von Neumann algebra.)
   We conclude: If ω is faithful and $\Pi_\omega(A) = 0$ then $(\Omega_\omega | \Pi_\omega(A)^* \Pi_\omega(A)\Omega_\omega) = \langle \omega; A^* A \rangle = 0$. Thus by faithfulness of ω we have $A^* A = 0$, and therefore $A = 0$. So Π_ω, as well as the quasi-equivalent $\Pi_{\mathcal{F}_\omega}$, is faithful.

(g) From the two preceding results we infer: If $\omega \in \mathcal{S}$ is faithful, then its GNS folium $\mathcal{F}_\omega$ is full. (The reverse is not true.)

(h) If $\mathcal{A} = \mathcal{L}(\mathcal{H})$ then a normal state $T \in \mathcal{T}_1^+(\mathcal{H})$ is faithful, if and only if T^{-1} exists as a (densely defined, positive) self-adjoint operator in $\mathcal{H}$ (see, e.g., [BR87]). In terms of its spectral representation $T = \sum_{k \in I} \lambda_k |\xi_k)(\xi_k|$ the density operator T is faithful if and only if $\lambda_k > 0$ for all $k \in I$, provided $\{\xi_k \mid k \in I\}$ constitutes an orthonormal basis of $\mathcal{H}$. (The space $\mathcal{H}$, especially, has to be separable.) In this manner one derives the faithfulness for thermal states, given in terms of canonical density operators.

It seems useful to apply the attribute "full" also to certain (non-convex) sets of pure states. The following lemma is proved in [KR86] for unital C*-algebras only, but it can be extended to arbitrary C*-algebras by adjoining a unit.

Lemma 46.2-25 (Full Sets of Pure States). *Let $\mathcal{A}$ be an arbitrary C*-algebra with state space $\mathcal{S}$ and fix a subset $\mathcal{S}_0 \subset \partial_e \mathcal{S}$ of pure states. Extending the Definition 46.2-24(a), $\mathcal{S}_0$ is called* full, *if $\langle \varphi; A \rangle \geq 0$ for all $\varphi \in \mathcal{S}_0$, implies $A \geq 0$, for any $A \in \mathcal{A}$.*

Note that $\partial_e \mathcal{S}$ is always full in this sense, and that the vector states in a faithful irreducible representation of $\mathcal{A}$ are also full (generating all normal states by convex combinations).

The following assertions are equivalent:

(a) *$\mathcal{S}_0$ is full.*

(b) *The convex hull $\mathrm{Conv}(\mathcal{S}_0)$ is weak* dense in the total state space $\mathcal{S}$. (Here convexity is put into play.)*

(c) *All pure states $\partial_e \mathcal{S}$ are contained in the weak* closure of $\mathcal{S}_0$ (where the latter is in general strictly larger than $\partial_e \mathcal{S}$, also for unital C*-algebras).*

(d) *For $A \in \mathcal{A}_{\mathrm{sa}}$ one can compute the norm via states in $\mathcal{S}_0$,*

$$\|A\| = \sup\{|\langle \omega; A \rangle| \mid \omega \in \mathcal{S}_0\}. \qquad (46.2.16)$$

The proofs of the assertions in the subsequent lemma employ frequently used operator algebraic manipulations and are executed for exercise.

Lemma 46.2-26 (Cyclic and Separating Projections). *Let $\mathcal{H}$ be a Hilbert space.*

(a) *Let $\mathcal{B}$ be a sub-*-algebra of $\mathcal{L}(\mathcal{H})$, and $\mathcal{H}_0$ a closed subspace of $\mathcal{H}$, which is invariant under $\mathcal{B}$, i.e., $\mathcal{B}\mathcal{H}_0 \subseteq \mathcal{H}_0$. Then the projection P_0 onto $\mathcal{H}_0$ is in the commutant $\mathcal{B}'$ of $\mathcal{B}$. (The set $\mathcal{B}'$ is of all $A \in \mathcal{L}(\mathcal{H})$, which commute with all $B \in \mathcal{B}$, and is a von Neumann algebra if $\mathcal{B}$ contains the identity $\mathbb{1} \in \mathcal{L}(\mathcal{H})$.)*
Indeed: For $B \in \mathcal{B}$, invariance of $\mathcal{H}_0$ gives $BP_0\mathcal{H} \subseteq P_0\mathcal{H}$, thus $P_0BP_0 = BP_0$. Therefore, $P_0B = (B^*P_0)^* = (P_0B^*P_0)^* = P_0BP_0 = BP_0$, demonstrating $P_0 \in \mathcal{B}'$.
Reversely, if a projection $P_0 \in \mathcal{P}(\mathcal{H})$ is in $\mathcal{B}'$, then its range $\mathcal{H}_0$ is $\mathcal{B}$-invariant.

Indeed: If $\xi \in \mathcal{H}_0$, then $B\xi = BP_0\xi = P_0B\xi$, proving $B\xi \in \mathcal{H}_0$.

(b) *Note by the way that a closed subspace $\mathcal{H}_0$ of $\mathcal{H}$ is invariant under a sub-$*$-algebra $\mathcal{B}$ of $\mathcal{L}(\mathcal{H})$, if and only if the orthogonal space $\mathcal{H}_0^\perp$ is so. For:* $\eta \in \mathcal{H}_0^\perp \Leftrightarrow (\eta|\xi) = 0, \forall \xi \in \mathcal{H}_0$. *Thus for such η it holds* $(B\eta|\xi) = (\eta|B^*\xi) = 0, \forall \xi \in \mathcal{H}_0, B \in \mathcal{B}$ *(where the $*$-invariance of $\mathcal{B}$ is employed). Hence also $B\eta \in \mathcal{H}_0^\perp, \forall B \in \mathcal{B}$, and the reverse reasoning runs analogously.*

(c) *If $\mathcal{V}$ is, especially, a subset of vectors in $\mathcal{H}$, then $[\mathcal{B}\mathcal{V}]$ is invariant under the action of the $*$-algebra $\mathcal{B}$. (We use the symbol $[\mathcal{V}]$ quite generally for the smallest closed subspace containing the set of vectors $\mathcal{V}$, as well as for the projection operator on it.)*

Indeed: $\xi \in \mathcal{H}$ *is in* $[\mathcal{B}\mathcal{V}]$, *if and only if* $\xi = \lim B_n\xi_n$, $\xi_n \in \mathcal{V}, B_n \in \mathcal{B}$. *Thus $B\xi = \lim BB_n\xi_n \in [\mathcal{B}\mathcal{V}]$ for all $B \in \mathcal{B}$.*

A projection of the form $[\mathcal{B}\mathcal{V}]$ is sometimes called a cyclic projection of $\mathcal{B}'$.

(d) *Let $\mathcal{B}$ be a sub-$*$-algebra of $\mathcal{L}(\mathcal{H})$, which contains the unit $\mathbb{1} \in \mathcal{L}(\mathcal{H})$. Then $[\mathcal{B}\mathcal{V}]$ is the smallest of all those projections in $\mathcal{B}'$, which contain $\mathcal{V}$ in their ranges.*

Indeed: $\mathcal{V} \subseteq [\mathcal{B}\mathcal{V}]$, *since $\mathbb{1} \in \mathcal{B}$. On the other hand, if $\mathcal{V} \subseteq P_0\mathcal{H}$, for a projection $P_0 \in \mathcal{B}'$, then $P_0\mathcal{H}$ is invariant under $\mathcal{B}$ and $[\mathcal{B}\mathcal{V}] \subseteq P_0\mathcal{H}$.*

(e) *Let $\mathcal{B}$ be a sub-$*$-algebra of $\mathcal{L}(\mathcal{H})$. A set of vectors $\mathcal{V} \subseteq \mathcal{H}$ is called cyclic for $\mathcal{B}$ if $[\mathcal{B}\mathcal{V}] = \mathbb{1}$. A set of vectors $\mathcal{V} \subseteq \mathcal{H}$ is called separating for $\mathcal{B}$ if $B\mathcal{V} = 0$ implies $B = 0$, for $B \in \mathcal{B}$.*

We have the following equivalence: If $\mathcal{V} \subseteq \mathcal{H}$ is cyclic for the $*$-algebra $\mathcal{B} \ni \mathbb{1}$, then $\mathcal{V}$ is separating for $\mathcal{B}'$, and reversely. So, by the bicommutant theorem we may also state: If $\mathcal{V}$ is separating for a von Neumann algebra $\mathcal{M}$ (may be $\mathcal{M} = \mathcal{B}'' = \overline{\mathcal{B}}^{weak}$) if and only if $\mathcal{V}$ is cyclic for $\mathcal{M}'$.

In fact: If $A' \in \mathcal{B}'$ with $A'\mathcal{V} = 0$ then $A'B\xi = BA'\xi = 0$ for all $B \in \mathcal{B}$ and all $\xi \in \mathcal{V}$. If we know the cyclicity $[\mathcal{B}\mathcal{V}] = \mathbb{1}$, this means that $A' = 0$, and thus $\mathcal{V}$ is proved to be separating for $\mathcal{B}'$.

If reversely $\mathcal{V}$ is separating for $\mathcal{B}'$, we set $P' = [\mathcal{B}\mathcal{V}]$, and know $P' \in \mathcal{B}'$. Since all $\xi \in \mathcal{V}$ are eigenvectors to P' we have $(\mathbb{1} - P')\mathcal{V} = 0$. Hence the separating property gives $P' = \mathbb{1}$ and $[\mathcal{B}\mathcal{V}] = \mathbb{1}$, expressing the cyclicity of $\mathcal{V}$ for $\mathcal{B}$.

Basic for the theory of standard von Neumann algebras are the following considerations.

Corollary 46.2-27 (Separating and Cyclic Vector). *Let $\mathcal{A}$ be a C^*-algebra and $\mathcal{S} \equiv \mathcal{S}(\mathcal{A})$ its state space.*

(a) *If $\omega \in \mathcal{S}$ is faithful, then Ω_ω is separating for $\Pi_\omega(\mathcal{A})$, even for $\mathcal{M}_\omega$.*

For: If ω is faithful and $\Pi_\omega(\mathcal{A})\Omega_\omega = 0$, for an $A \in \mathcal{A}$, then $\langle \omega; A^*A \rangle = 0$, and then $A^*A = 0$ as well as $A = 0$. Hence Ω_ω is separating for $\Pi_\omega(\mathcal{A})$.

If $B\Omega_\omega = 0$ for some $B \in \mathcal{M}_\omega$, then also $B^*B\Omega_\omega = 0$. We approximate B^*B σ-weakly from below by a net $\Pi_\omega(A_i^*A_i)$, $A_i \in \mathcal{A}$, so that $\langle \omega; A_i^*A_i \rangle = 0$ and $A_i = B = 0$. Hence Ω_ω is separating for $\mathcal{M}_\omega$, too.

(b) *The reverse of the preceding implication holds if for the given $\omega \in \mathcal{S}$ its GNS representation $(\Pi_\omega, \mathcal{H}_\omega, \Omega_\omega)$ is faithful (e.g., if $\mathcal{A}$ is simple). If Ω_ω is separating for $\mathcal{M}_\omega$, then it is also separating for $\Pi_\omega(\mathcal{A})$. In the latter case $\langle \omega; A^* A \rangle = 0 = \|\Pi_\omega(A)\Omega_\omega\|^2$ implies $\Pi_\omega(A) = 0$ and this gives $A^* A = 0$ in virtue of the faithfulness of Π_ω. Hence ω is faithful.*

(c) *If $\omega \in \mathcal{S}$ is faithful then the GNS von Neumann algebra $\mathcal{M}_\omega = \Pi_\omega(\mathcal{A})''$ has Ω_ω as a cyclic and separating vector. (So Ω_ω is cyclic and separating also for $\mathcal{M}'_\omega$.) One says that $\mathcal{M}_\omega$ (also $\mathcal{M}'_\omega$) is in* standard representation.

Since the folia (split faces) are in one-to-one correspondence with quasiequivalence classes of representations, the following facts are also important for representation theory.

Observation 46.2-28 (Supporting Faces and Projections). Let $\mathcal{A}$ be a C*-algebra, $\mathcal{S}$ its state space, and $\mathcal{M}_u$ its universal enveloping von Neumann algebra. We denote $\tilde{\mathcal{S}}_n := \mathcal{S}_n(\mathcal{M}_u)$ and designate by $\tilde{\omega}$ the unique state in $\tilde{\mathcal{S}}_n$ associated with $\omega \in \mathcal{S}$.

We keep in mind the ortho-lattice isomorphism between the norm closed faces $F \in \mathcal{E}(\mathcal{S})$ and the projection operators $P_F \in \mathcal{P}(\mathcal{M}_u)$.

For $\omega \in \mathcal{S}$ we define its support F_ω as the smallest face in $\mathcal{E}(\mathcal{S})$ containing ω and define its support projection S_ω as the corresponding projection in $\mathcal{P}(\mathcal{M}_u)$.

Likewise we define the central support $\mathcal{F}_\omega$ as the smallest folium in $\mathcal{E}_c(\mathcal{S})$ containing ω and define its support projection C_ω as the corresponding central projection in $\mathcal{P}_c(\mathcal{M}_u) = \mathcal{P}(\mathcal{Z}_u)$.

Obviously $F_\omega \subseteq \mathcal{F}_\omega$, and $\mathcal{F}_\omega$ is the smallest folium containing F_ω.

(a) For the support projection we have the further characterizing relations

$$S_\omega = \inf\{P \in \mathcal{P}(\mathcal{M}_u) \,|\, \langle \tilde{\omega}; A \rangle = \langle \tilde{\omega}; PAP \rangle = \langle \tilde{\omega}; PA \rangle, \forall A \in \mathcal{M}_u\}. \quad (46.2.17)$$

Analogously we obtain for the central support projection

$$C_\omega = \inf\{P \in \mathcal{P}_c(\mathcal{M}_u) \,|\, \langle \tilde{\omega}; A \rangle = \langle \tilde{\omega}; PAP \rangle = \langle \tilde{\omega}; PA \rangle, \forall A \in \mathcal{M}_u\}. \quad (46.2.18)$$

(b) It holds: $\omega \in \mathcal{S}$ is pure, if and only if F_ω is an atom in $\mathcal{E}(\mathcal{S})$ (S_ω an atom in $\mathcal{P}(\mathcal{M}_u)$). (For "atom" cf. Definition 47.2-3 (e) on page 1731.)

Indeed: If ω is pure $F_\omega = \{\omega\}$, and this is an atom.

If reversely F_ω is not an atom in $\mathcal{E}(\mathcal{S})$ then S_ω is not an atom in $\mathcal{P}(\mathcal{M}_u)$. Thus, there is a $P \in \mathcal{P}(\mathcal{M}_u)$ with $0 < P < S_\omega$. Then $\langle \tilde{\omega}; P \rangle > 0$, since otherwise $S_\omega - P < S_\omega$ would also support ω. Since $\mathcal{Q}(\mathcal{S}) = \mathcal{Q}(\tilde{\mathcal{S}}_n)$ is ortho-lattice isomorphic to $\mathcal{P}(\mathcal{M}_u)$ we know $\langle\tilde{\omega}; P. P\rangle \leq \langle\tilde{\omega}; . \rangle$ and $\langle\omega'; .\rangle := \langle\tilde{\omega}; P. P\rangle/\langle\tilde{\omega}; P\rangle \leq \lambda\langle\omega; .\rangle$, with $\lambda = \langle\tilde{\omega}; P\rangle^{-1} \geq 1$. According to proposition 45.2-28 ω cannot be pure, since ω can be decomposed into $\omega' \neq \omega$ and another state.

(c) $\omega \in \mathcal{S}$ is factorial (a factor state), if and only if $\mathcal{F}_\omega$ is an atom in $\mathcal{E}_c(\mathcal{S})$ (C_ω an atom in $\mathcal{P}_c(\mathcal{M}_u)$).

From the subsequent Proposition we know that $\mathcal{M}_\omega$ is isomorphic to $C_\omega\mathcal{M}_u$, and the latter is a factor, if and only if C_ω is an atom in $\mathcal{P}_c(\mathcal{M}_u)$.

(d) It holds: If $\omega \in \mathcal{S}$ is faithful, then $F_\omega = \mathcal{F}_\omega$ ($S_\omega = C_\omega$).

For: If ω is faithful, then Ω_ω is separating for $\mathcal{M}_\omega$. Thus the relation $\langle\tilde{\omega}; C_\omega - S_\omega\rangle = \|(C_\omega - S_\omega)\Omega_\omega\|^2 = 0$ implies $C_\omega = S_\omega$ (at first for the faithful images of C_ω, S_ω in $\mathcal{M}_\omega \cong \mathcal{M}_{\mathcal{F}_\omega}$).

It holds on the other side: If $F_\omega = \mathcal{F}_\omega$ and Π_ω is faithful, then ω is faithful.

For: There is then no $P \in \mathcal{P}(\mathcal{M}_u)$, $0 < P \leq C_\omega$, with $\langle\tilde{\omega}; P\rangle = 0$, since otherwise $C_\omega - P < S_\omega$ would support $\tilde{\omega}$ which contradicts the definition of S_ω. If $A > 0$, we know $\Pi_\omega(A) > 0$ and of course $\langle\omega; A\rangle = (\Omega_\omega|\Pi_u(A)C_\omega\Omega_\omega) \geq 0$, where we work in $\mathcal{H}_u$. If the equality would be valid, then all spectral projections of $\Pi_u(A)C_\omega$ would vanish and hence also $\Pi_\omega(A)C_\omega$ and $\Pi_\omega(A)$ would vanish. To avoid this contradiction it is necessary that $\langle\omega; A\rangle > 0$, and thus ω must be faithful.

Thus for a simple C*-algebra, $F_\omega = \mathcal{F}_\omega$ is necessary and sufficient for ω to be faithful.

It follows from (d) of the preceding observation, that no pure state ω, where $F_\omega = \{\omega\}$, may be faithful if $\dim(\mathcal{A}) > 1$. This F_ω is then certainly not invariant under perturbations and so differs from $\mathcal{F}_\omega$. This implies that no vector state in an irreducible representation may be faithful, whereas a separating vector in a faithful (then necessarily reducible) representation provides a faithful state.

From Lemma 46.2-26(d) we may calculate, especially, the support projections, if we observe that $(S_\omega\Omega_\omega|\Pi_\omega(A)\Omega_\omega) = (\Omega_\omega|\Pi_\omega(A)\Omega_\omega)$, $\forall A \in \mathcal{A}$, implies $S_\omega\Omega_\omega = \Omega_\omega$ (in $\mathcal{H}_\omega$ or larger representation spaces). (Look on Eq. (46.2.17).) This may be used to prove some of the following assertions.

Proposition 46.2-29 (Partially Universal von Neumann Algebras). *Let $\mathcal{A}$ be a C*-algebra, and $\mathcal{S}$ its state space.*

For a given folium $\mathcal{F} \in \mathcal{E}_c(\mathcal{S})$, denote again by $(\Pi_{\mathcal{F}}, \mathcal{H}_{\mathcal{F}}) = \bigoplus_{\omega\in\mathcal{F}}(\Pi_\omega, \mathcal{H}_\omega)$ the partially universal representation with the associated von Neumann algebras $\mathcal{M}'_{\mathcal{F}} = \Pi_{\mathcal{F}}(\mathcal{A})'$ and $\mathcal{M}_{\mathcal{F}} = \Pi_{\mathcal{F}}(\mathcal{A})''$. For $\mathcal{F} = \mathcal{S}$ we have the corresponding universal notions, indexed by u.

(a) *For given folium $\mathcal{F} \subseteq \mathcal{S}$ its support projection $P_{\mathcal{F}} \equiv C_{\mathcal{F}}$ in $\mathcal{M}_u$ is the projection onto $\mathcal{H}_{\mathcal{F},u} \subseteq \mathcal{H}_u$, by which we mean the subspace specified in Eq. (46.2.14). According to its definition $\mathcal{H}_{\mathcal{F},u}$ contains those vectors which give states in $\mathcal{F}$, that are especially all $\Pi_u(A)\Omega_\omega = \Pi_\omega(A)\Omega_\omega$ with $A \in \mathcal{A}$ and $\omega \in \mathcal{F}$. (Cf. also the conventions of Observation 46.2-14.) The corresponding states constitute a* *norm dense set in $\mathcal{F}$, and $\mathcal{H}_{\mathcal{F},u}$ is the closure of the mentioned vectors. Thus $\mathcal{H}_{\mathcal{F},u} = \bigoplus_{\omega \in \mathcal{F}} \mathcal{H}_\omega = \mathcal{H}_\mathcal{F}$, and $C_\mathcal{F} = \bigoplus_{\omega \in \mathcal{F}} \mathbb{1}_\omega \in \mathcal{P}_c(\mathcal{M}_u)$.*

(b) *We see directly that $(\Pi_\mathcal{F}, \mathcal{H}_\mathcal{F}) = (C_\mathcal{F} \Pi_u, C_\mathcal{F} \mathcal{H}_u)$ and thus $\mathcal{M}_\mathcal{F} = \overline{\Pi_\mathcal{F}(\mathcal{A})}^{\text{-weak}} = C_\mathcal{F} \mathcal{M}_u$ (and not only in the sense of quasiequivalence, if we still omit the natural inclusion maps $\mathcal{H}_\omega \to \mathcal{H}_\mathcal{F}$, $\omega \in \mathcal{F}$.)*

Since the support projections of the states in $\mathcal{F}$ are all smaller than $C_\mathcal{F}$, we may calculate them in $\mathcal{M}_\mathcal{F} \subseteq \mathcal{L}(\mathcal{H}_\mathcal{F})$.

(c) *For each $\omega \in \mathcal{F}$ the cyclic projection $P_\omega \in \mathcal{P}(\mathcal{H}_\mathcal{F})$, defined by $P_\omega := [\Pi_\mathcal{F}(\mathcal{A})\Omega_\omega] = [\Pi_\omega(\mathcal{A})\Omega_\omega] = [\mathcal{H}_\omega]$, is the smallest projection in $\mathcal{M}'_\mathcal{F}$ leaving Ω_ω invariant. We identify it with $\mathbb{1}_\omega \in \mathcal{L}(\mathcal{H}_\omega)$ embedded into $\mathcal{L}(\mathcal{H}_\mathcal{F})$.*

Obviously $\bigoplus_{\omega \in \mathcal{F}} P_\omega = \mathbb{1}_\mathcal{F}$ is an orthogonal decomposition of the identity in $\mathcal{H}_\mathcal{F}$, which decomposes the representation $(\Pi_\mathcal{F}, \mathcal{H}_\mathcal{F})$ (but not $\mathcal{M}_\mathcal{F}$) back into its original subrepresentations.

(d) *For each $B \in \mathcal{M}_\mathcal{F} \supset \Pi_\mathcal{F}(\mathcal{A})$ we have*

$$\|B\| = \sup_{\omega \in \mathcal{F}} \|B P_\omega\| = \sup_{\omega \in \mathcal{F}} \|P_\omega B\|. \qquad (46.2.19)$$

(e) *For given subfolium $\mathcal{F}_0 \subseteq \mathcal{F}$ its support projection $P_{\mathcal{F}_0} \equiv C_0$ in $\mathcal{M}_\mathcal{F}$ is the projection onto $\mathcal{H}_0 \subseteq \mathcal{H}_\mathcal{F}$, by which we mean the subspace Eq. (46.2.14). According to its definition $\mathcal{H}_0$ contains $\Pi_\omega(A)\Omega_\omega$ for all $A \in \mathcal{A}$, if and only if $\omega \in \mathcal{F}_0$. (Cf. also the conventions of Remark 46.2-14.) Thus $\mathcal{H}_0 = \bigoplus_{\omega \in \mathcal{F}_0} \mathcal{H}_\omega$, and $C_0 = \bigoplus_{\omega \in \mathcal{F}_0} P_\omega \in \mathcal{P}_c(\mathcal{M}_\mathcal{F})$.*

(f) *In the same way the support projection of a folium $\mathcal{F} \subseteq \mathcal{S}$ in $\mathcal{M}_u$ is given by $C_\mathcal{F} = \bigoplus_{\omega \in \mathcal{F}} P_\omega \in \mathcal{P}_c(\mathcal{M}_u)$.*

The central support projection of $\omega \in \mathcal{F}$, that is the support projection of $\mathcal{F}_\omega$, equals, especially, $C_\omega = \bigoplus_{\omega' \in \mathcal{F}_\omega} P_{\omega'}$.

(g) *By means of Zorn's lemma we may select a family of states $\mathcal{S}_0 \subseteq \mathcal{F}$ such that $\bigoplus_{\omega \in \mathcal{S}_0} C_\omega = \mathbb{1}_\mathcal{F}$. (Note that this implies $C_\omega \perp C_{\omega'}$ for $\omega \neq \omega'$, and remark that $\mathcal{S}_0$ is not uniquely given and that the $\omega \in \mathcal{S}_0$ cannot all be chosen factorial, if $\mathcal{E}_c(\mathcal{F})$ is not an atomic lattice.) Then we have*

$$\mathcal{M}_\mathcal{F} \overset{*-\text{isomorphic}}{\cong} \bigoplus_{\omega \in \mathcal{S}_0} \mathcal{M}_\omega, \qquad (46.2.20)$$

and we see that any von Neumann algebra (which is always *-isomorphic to a $\mathcal{M}_\mathcal{F}$) possesses a discrete subcentral decomposition into von Neumann algebras with a cyclic vector (where "subcentral" means pair-wise orthogonality of the supporting central projections, cf. also Sec. 48.1 on page 1777).

As mentioned before, the structure of $\mathcal{E}_c(\mathcal{S})$ determines the variety of representations and vice versa. From Theorem 45.3-8 we know that antiliminary C*-algebras give rise to many inequivalent representations, which leads to the following conclusions.

Proposition 46.2-30 (Antiliminary State Spaces). *If $\mathcal{A}$ is an antiliminary C^*-algebra with state space $\mathcal{S}$, then the Boolean lattice of folia $\mathcal{E}_c(\mathcal{S})$ has overcountably many elements.*

$\mathcal{E}_c(\mathcal{S})$ has especially overcountably many atoms and overcountably many (pairwise disjoint) full folia, each of the latter being weak* dense in $\mathcal{S}$.

The completion of the structural analysis requires the theory of orthogonal measures and decompositions, see Sec. 48.1.

Since also weak* dense, mutually disjoint folia correspond to classically different state preparations they may, by no means, physically be identified with each other (what seems to have been suggested at the early stage of Algebraic Quantum Field Theory by some authors under the headline of "physically equivalent representations").

Proposition 46.2-31 (Function Representation of the Universal Center). *Let a unital C^*-algebra $\mathcal{A}$ with state space $\mathcal{S}$ be given, and denote by $x = [\varphi]$ a quasiequivalence class (according to Definition 46.2-17 on page 1690) of a factorial state $\varphi \in \mathcal{S}$. The set of all factorial quasi-equivalence classes is denoted by $X \equiv X(\mathcal{A})$.*

We know that there is a bijection between the $x \in X$ and the atoms C_x of the complete Boolean lattice $\mathcal{P}(\mathcal{Z}_u) \equiv \mathcal{P}_c$. We introduce now functions

$$\check{Z} : X \to \mathbb{C}, \quad \check{Z}(x)C_x := ZC_x, \quad \forall Z \in \mathcal{Z}_u, \tag{46.2.21}$$

which are well defined, since Z cannot vary on an atomic projection (spectral representation!). If $C \in \mathcal{P}_c$, then $\check{C}$ assumes only the values 0 and 1.

A subset $Y \subseteq X$ is called "measurable" if and only if there is a projection $C_Y \in \mathcal{P}_c$ such that $\check{C}_Y$ is the indicator function 1_Y of Y. Inversely, each $C \in \mathcal{P}_c$ determines a (measurable) set $Y_C \subset X$, to which $\check{C}$ is the indicator function.

Then it holds that the set $\mathsf{B}(X)$ of all measurable Y's in X is a σ-algebra and that $\mathcal{Z}_u$ is *-isomorphic to a sub-*-algebra of $\mathsf{F}_B(X, \mathbb{C})$, the $\mathsf{B}(X)$-measurable, bounded functions equipped with the point-wise *-algebraic operations.

Proof. The connection $\mathcal{P}_c \ni C \mapsto Y_C \in \mathsf{B}(X)$ is clearly a lattice ortho-isomorphism, and $\mathsf{B}(X)$ only another realization of the complete Boolean lattice $\mathcal{P}_c$. Thus $\mathsf{B}(X)$ is a σ-algebra.

The map $\mathcal{Z}_u \ni Z \mapsto \check{Z} \in \mathsf{F}_B(X, \mathbb{C})$ is an *-isomorphism "into". This can be directly verified for $Z = \sum c_i C_i, c_i \in \mathbb{C}$, which maps onto $\check{Z} = \sum c_i 1_{Y_i}$, say. For an arbitrary $Z \in \mathcal{Z}_u$ (which is a bounded normal operator in the universal Hilbert space $\mathcal{H}_u$), we have the spectral representation within $\mathcal{Z}_u$, since $\mathcal{Z}_u$ is a von Neumann algebra, and the spectral mapping is still an *-isomorphism into $\mathsf{F}_B(X, \mathbb{C})$. $\quad\square$

Remark 46.2-32 (Spectra of Algebras). For an arbitrary C^*-algebra $\mathcal{A}$ the set of quasiequivalence classes of factor representations is called the "quasispectrum" or "factor spectrum" of $\mathcal{A}$ (see, e.g., [Ped79], which considers only separable C^*-algebras). It contains as subset the set of quasiequivalence classes of cyclic factor representations, which is isomorphic to our $X(\mathcal{A})$ (see Definition 46.2-17 on page 1690).

The "spectrum" of $\mathcal{A}$ consists of quasiequivalence classes of irreducible representations and is a subset of the factor spectrum. If $\mathcal{A}$ is Abelian, then the just mentioned "spectrum" coincides with the usual definition of a spectrum for an Abelian algebra (given by the set of non-trivial *-homomorphisms of $\mathcal{A}$ into $\mathbb{C}$). And also the factor spectrum reduces to the spectrum.

Conclusion 46.2-33 (F-Properties of a Universal Quantum Theory). Let us consider a mesoscopic system, made up of microscopic constituents (with finite mass for clusters or vanishing mass for photons), the observable algebra of which is a quasi-local C*-algebra $\mathcal{A}$. If $\mathcal{S}$ is the state space, then the F-properties, i.e., the properties of the system in the statistical (and not deterministic) description, all are collected in $\mathcal{E}(\mathcal{S})$, the complete orthomodular lattice of the norm closed faces of $\mathcal{S}$. We claim that $\mathcal{E}(\mathcal{S})$ represents the conceptual frame of the total quantum theory of the system, including all its classical features.

The classical features are abundant! Even if we restrict the degrees of freedom of the kth constituent to a finite number $n(k)$, the observable algebra (which is typically $\bigotimes_{k \in \mathbb{N}} \mathbb{M}_{n(k)}$) is antiliminary, and there are overcountably many classical properties in $\mathcal{E}_c(\mathcal{S})$. This mathematical fact is of basic significance for the quantum mechanical explanation of (directly) observable phenomena, which always take place in the macroscopic or mesoscopic world. The large Boolean lattice $\mathcal{E}_c(\mathcal{S})$ comprises empirical classical observables, given in terms of increasing families of folia $(\mathcal{F}_\lambda)_{\mathbb{R}}$ with a continuum of scale values, collected in the support of the spectral family $(\mathcal{F}_\lambda)_{\mathbb{R}}$ (that is the set of increment points of the spectral family).

Each classical F-property $\mathcal{F}$ covers the quantum properties in the non-Boolean sublattice $\mathcal{F} \wedge \mathcal{E}(\mathcal{S})$, which turn up as additional features of the states in the folium $\mathcal{F}$. If $\mathcal{F}_\lambda$ is an atom in $\mathcal{E}_c(\mathcal{S})$, signifying a sharp classical property with scale value $\lambda \in \mathbb{R}$, then $\mathcal{F}_\lambda \wedge \mathcal{E}(\mathcal{S})$ contains only quantum properties, which in some sense "fluctuate" about the classical property. From the signal theoretic point of view, $\mathcal{F}_\lambda \wedge \mathcal{E}(\mathcal{S})$ is the collection of the quantum noise, possibly accompanying the communication of λ (see Eq. (48.4.49) on page 1878).

In the framework of the F-properties of statistical states there is no conceptual discrepancy between the classical and quantum aspects. To see the classical features of the system, the quantum aspects have not to be given up, no limit $\hbar \to 0$ has to be performed. The classical F-properties $\mathcal{F}$ represent rather a coarse–grained view on the system states, without excluding later looks on the fine-grained subproperties. The atomic $\mathcal{F}$ may be viewed as the points of a classical configuration space $X(\mathcal{A})$, and the central observables from $\mathcal{Z}_u$ as numerical functions on it (as is formalized in Proposition 46.2-31).

In this context, representation theory of the abstract C*-algebra $\mathcal{A}$ appears as a convenient exposition of this structure, which may be totally subsumed under the universal representation $(\Pi_u, \mathcal{H}_u)$. This is, however, made explicit only when one goes over to the huge universal enveloping von Neumann algebra $\mathcal{M}_u$, where the set of its projection operators $\mathcal{P}(\mathcal{M}_u)$ is ortho-lattice isomorphic to $\mathcal{E}(\mathcal{S})$.

This picture is further completed and confirmed by introducing the transition probabilities, which also in the abstract setting may be defined in terms of the state language alone (see Sec. 48.4 on page 1841) and gives especially vanishing probability for the transition between different classical properties.

Formulated in terms of this theoretical frame, Maxwell theory is embedded into the universal photonic quantum theory, but deals only with the classical structure $\mathcal{E}_c(\mathcal{S})$ of the state space $\mathcal{S}$, which is mathematically the state space of a Weyl algebra $\mathcal{W}(E,\sigma)$, with infinite-dimensional pre-symplectic test function space (E,σ). In statistical ED not even the atoms of $\mathcal{E}_c(\mathcal{S})$, the minimal folia, are known to the observer, which sees only classically mixed F-properties.

For the classification of universal quantum theories with state space $\mathcal{S}$, it is of course not only the distributive lattice $\mathcal{E}_c(\mathcal{S})$, but the whole of $\mathcal{E}(\mathcal{S})$, relevant. We investigate that again in terms of the projection lattice $\mathcal{P}(\mathcal{M})$ of von Neumann algebras $\mathcal{M} \subset \mathcal{L}(\mathcal{H})$. The normal states appear there mostly in the form of density operators, and we have to determine their support projections.

Remark 46.2-34 (Support Projections of Density Operators). Consider the von Neumann algebra $\mathcal{M} \subseteq \mathcal{L}(\mathcal{H})$. If the normal state $\varphi \in \mathcal{S}_n(\mathcal{M})$ has the density operator $\varrho_\varphi = \sum_n \lambda_n P_n \in \mathcal{T}_1^+(\mathcal{H})$, then the support projection $S_\varphi \in \mathcal{P}(\mathcal{M})$ is in general not directly given by $\vee_n P_n$, since the P_n need not be in $\mathcal{P}(\mathcal{M})$ (not even so, if the P_n are the spectral projections of ϱ_φ, in contradistinction to the spectral projections of an observable $A \in \mathcal{M}_{\mathrm{sa}}$).

Following the strategy of Eq. (46.2.14), one may determine S_φ as the projection onto the subspace $\mathcal{H}_{S_\varphi}$, which is in $\mathcal{P}(\mathcal{M})$, where

$$\mathcal{H}_{S_\varphi} = \{\xi \in \mathcal{H} \mid \mathrm{tr}_{\mathcal{H}}[\varrho_\varphi \, \hat{\xi}] = 1, \ \hat{\xi} := \xi/\|\xi\|\} \cup \{0\}. \tag{46.2.22}$$

Another formula is (cf. [Dix69, p. 5])

$$S_\varphi = [\mathcal{M}'(\vee_n P_n)\mathcal{H}], \tag{46.2.23}$$

where $[\cdot]$ means the projection onto the smallest closed subspace containing the set in the bracket.

Only if $\mathcal{M}$ is irreducible in $\mathcal{H}$, Eq. (46.2.23) reduces to $S_\varphi = \vee_n P_n$.

Up to now we did not make much use from the fact that the orthomodular lattice $\mathcal{P}(\mathcal{M})$ originates from an algebra. The algebraic structure provides, however, a basic equivalence relation in $\mathcal{P}(\mathcal{M})$, which leads at last to a dimension function.

Definition 46.2-35 (Von Neumann's Equivalence of Projections). Let $\mathcal{M}$ be a W*-algebra with projection lattice $\mathcal{P}(\mathcal{M})$.

Two projections $P, Q \in \mathcal{P}(\mathcal{M})$ are called *equivalent*, written $P \sim Q$ if there is a $W \in \mathcal{M}$ with $P = W^*W$ and $Q = WW^*$, which automatically implies that W can be chosen as a partial isometry.

If there is also an $R \in \mathcal{P}(\mathcal{M})$ with $Q \sim R$, realized by $Q = V^*V$ and $R = VV^*$, then $U = VW$ realizes $P \sim R$, so that $\sim$ is transitive. $P \sim P$ is realized by P and the symmetry of $\sim$ is obvious. Thus $\sim$ is in fact an equivalence relation.

If $0 = W^*W$ then $W = 0$, and the equivalence class of 0 contains only 0.

If $P = W^*W$ and $Q = WW^*$ and if there is a $C \in \mathcal{P}_c(\mathcal{M})$ with $CP = P$ and $C^\perp Q = Q$, then $Q = C^\perp QQ = C^\perp WCPW^* = 0 = P$. More generally, each $C \in \mathcal{P}_c(\mathcal{M})$ reduces the $\sim$-relation.

One writes $P \prec Q$, if there is an $R \in \mathcal{P}(\mathcal{M})$ with $R \leq Q$ and $P \sim R$. If $P \prec Q$ and $Q \prec P$ then follows $P \sim Q$. Thus $\prec$ is an *order relation* for the $\sim$-classes in $\mathcal{P}(\mathcal{M})$.

If $\mathcal{M}$ is a factor, then its $\sim$-classes are *totally ordered* by $\prec$. This total order may be mapped order-isomorphically by a so-called dimension function D into the extended nonnegative reals $[0, \infty]$. Such a *dimension function* D is uniquely characterized (up to a positive dilation) by the following properties, in which we use the relation $P \perp Q \Leftrightarrow P \leq Q^\perp$ and the definition: P is *finite* $\Leftrightarrow P \sim Q$ and $P \leq Q$ imply $P = Q$:

$$D(P) = 0 \iff P = 0; \tag{46.2.24}$$

$$P \perp Q \implies D(P + Q) = D(P) + D(Q); \tag{46.2.25}$$

$$P \text{ finite } \iff D(P) < \infty; \tag{46.2.26}$$

$$P \sim Q \iff D(P) = D(Q). \tag{46.2.27}$$

A dimension function can especially be realized by a *faithful, normal, tracial weight* $D(P) = \text{tr}(P)$, which satisfies (46.2.24) to (46.2.26) by definition of a faithful weight.

More precisely a *weight* on a W*-algebra $\mathcal{M}$ is a map $w : \mathcal{M}_+ \to [0, \infty]$ satisfying $w(A + B) = w(A) + w(B)$ for all $A, B \in \mathcal{M}_+$ and $w(cA) = cw(A)$ for $c \geq 0$ and $A \in \mathcal{M}_+$. A weight w is called *semi-finite* if the set $\mathcal{M}_+^w := \{A \in \mathcal{M}_+ \,|\, w(A) < \infty\}$ is σ-weakly dense in $\mathcal{M}_+$. The normality for w is defined as for states (see Definition 46.1-13 on page 1676).

A weight with $w(U^*AU) = w(A)$ for all $A \in \mathcal{M}_+$ and all unitaries $U \in \mathcal{M}$ is called a *trace*. It follows by an extension procedure that $w(AB) = w(BA)$ for all $A, B \in \text{LH}(\mathcal{M}_+^w)$.

If we choose a trace tr to get a dimension function, the trace property implies $\text{tr}(W^*W) = \text{tr}(WW^*)$ — where for W^*W not contained in $\mathcal{M}_+^w$ this holds by definition — and we see that tr is in fact constant on equivalence classes as required by (46.2.27). It follows then that tr transforms the $\prec$-order in $\mathcal{P}(\mathcal{M})$ into the $\leq$-order in $[0, \infty]$.

If one applies a dimension function $D : \mathcal{P}(\mathcal{M}) \to [0, \infty]$ on the supports S_φ of normal states φ on a von Neumann algebra, one obtains a numerical degree for the *mixedness of the states*. In an appropriate scaling one gets in fact $D(S_\varphi) = \dim[\text{Im}(\varrho_\varphi)]$, if ϱ_φ is a density operator for φ.

Theorem 46.2-36. *For all W*-algebras $\mathcal{M}$ there is a dimension function, given by a normal, faithful trace, which maps the chain of equivalence classes in $\mathcal{P}(\mathcal{M})$ order-isomorphically onto a chain in $[0, \infty]$, and which is unique up to a positive scale factor.*

Reversely, for each chain C in $[0, \infty]$, which is of one of the subsequently described types, there is a factor $\mathcal{M}$ and a dimension function D, such that $D(\mathcal{P}(\mathcal{M})) = C \subseteq [0, \infty]$.

That leads to a complete classification of the factors $\mathcal{M}$ as follows:

(a) *$\mathcal{M}$ is of type III, if and only if there exists a D with $D(\mathcal{P}(\mathcal{M})) = \{0, \infty\}$.*
(b) *$\mathcal{M}$ is of type II_1, if and only if there exists a D with $D(\mathcal{P}(\mathcal{M})) = [0, 1]$.*
(c) *$\mathcal{M}$ is of type II_∞, if and only if there exists a D with $D(\mathcal{P}(\mathcal{M})) = [0, \infty]$.*
(d) *$\mathcal{M}$ is of type I_n, if and only if there exists a D with $D(\mathcal{P}(\mathcal{M})) = \{0, 1, 2, \ldots, n\}$.*
(e) *$\mathcal{M}$ is of type I_∞, if and only if there exists a D with $D(\mathcal{P}(\mathcal{M})) = \mathbb{N}_0$.*

To read our table, notice that in the type III-case all non-zero projections acquire an infinite dimension since D is faithful. By the uniqueness up to dilation, there is then no semi-finite trace. Since a finite projection must have a finite dimension, there neither is then a finite projection, beside 0. Each of the latter two assertions provides for itself a characterization of III-factors.

On the other side, in II_1- and I_n-factors there are only finite projections. Since also in II_∞- and I_∞-factors there are sufficiently many finite projections (the infinite are approximated by the finite ones since the trace is normal), all factors, beside III-factors, have a semi-finite trace, and are called *semi-finite* for themselves (what covers the case being *finite*).

The continuous dimension for a II_1-factor has led von Neumann to introduce "continuous geometries". In II_1- and II_∞-factors there are no atoms. Thus, on these, as well as on III-factors, there are no pure states. From the C*-algebraic point of view, these factors may arise as GNS von Neumann algebras, corresponding to a state φ, and their normal states are affinely isomorphic to $\mathcal{F}_\varphi$. Then $\mathcal{F}_\varphi$ represents an *atomic classical F-property of φ, which no pure state is capable to exhibit*. (Think on a finite or infinite absolute temperature!)

In traditional Quantum Mechanics only I_n-factors, including $n = \infty$, have been used, the only factors with pure states. The I_2-factor is, especially, the observable algebra of the qubit space. The III- and I_1-factors have in common to possess only two equivalence classes, but the I_1-factor is commutative.

A sub-classification of III-factors uses Arveson spectral theory and the modular formalism and is sketched at the end of the following section.

In order to analyze the *coherence relation* of Definition 47.4-4 on page 1761 for three normal states φ_i, $i = 1, 2, 3$, on a W*-algebra $\mathcal{M}$ we use here the supports of the states in terms of their support projections S_i, $i = 1, 2, 3$ (and not in terms of the supporting faces). We then formulate: The coherence relation $K(\varphi_1, \varphi_2, \varphi_3)$

is valid, if and only if

$$S_1 \wedge S_2 = S_2 \wedge S_3 = S_3 \wedge S_1 = \emptyset,$$
$$S_1 \vee S_2 = S_2 \vee S_3 = S_3 \vee S_1. \tag{46.2.28}$$

For the states on a C*-algebra we use the same relation, where the support projections are, of course, taken from the universal enveloping von Neumann algebra $\mathcal{M}_u$.

We employ now the so-called parallelogram law for $P, Q \in \mathcal{P}(\mathcal{M})$

$$(P \vee Q) \wedge P^\perp = (P \vee Q) - P \sim Q - (P \wedge Q) = Q \wedge (P^\perp \vee Q^\perp). \tag{46.2.29}$$

Applying to this a dimension function gives us

$$D(P) + D(Q) = D(P \wedge Q) + D(P \vee Q). \tag{46.2.30}$$

Using that for the S_i in Eq. (46.2.28), leads to $D(S_1) = D(S_2) = D(S_3)$ as a necessary condition for quantum coherence. It means that the degree of mixedness must be the same for all three states from a coherent triple. Referring to results in [Fil65] there are elaborated in [RR83] further criteria and relations for quantum coherence.

Proposition 46.2-37 (Coherent Superposability). *Consider only normal states on a W*-algebra $\mathcal{M}$. Two states φ_i, $i = 1, 2$, are called "coherent superposable", if there is a φ_3 with $K(\varphi_1, \varphi_2, \varphi_3)$.*

Recall from Eq. (47.2.2) on page 1732 and subsequent definition that two projections P, Q are called maximal incompatible *if and only if $C(P, Q) \equiv (P \wedge Q) \vee (P \wedge Q^\perp) \vee (P^\perp \wedge Q) \vee (P^\perp \wedge Q^\perp) = 0$.*

(a) *Necessary and sufficient for two states φ_i, $i = 1, 2$, to be coherent superposable is that their support projections are equivalent ($S_1 \sim S_2$) and intersectionless ($S_1 \wedge S_2 = 0$).*
(b) *Necessary and sufficient for a state φ to have a coherent superposable partner is $S_\varphi \prec S_\varphi^\perp$.*
(c) *A projection $P \in \mathcal{P}(\mathcal{M})$ has a maximal incompatible partner projection Q, if and only if $P \sim P^\perp$.*
   Thus, a state φ, with $S_\varphi \sim S_\varphi^\perp$ and with $S_\varphi^\perp$ being σ-finite (i.e., having at most countable infinitely many mutually orthogonal subprojections), has a coherent superposable partner state, with maximal incompatible support.
(d) *If for a given triple of states one of the supports commutes with the other two, the coherence relation is not valid. Thus there are no coherent state superpositions in Abelian von Neumann algebras.*

Somewhat surprising may be that a qubit space and a III-factor have in some sense analogous coherence properties.

Proposition 46.2-38 (Uniform Coherent Superposability). *Consider only normal states on a σ-finite W*-algebra $\mathcal{M}$ (which is defined in Proposition 46.3-2* *below). The following conditions are equivalent:*

(i) $\mathcal{M}$ *is a factor of type* I_2 *or* III.
(ii) *For each* $P \in \mathcal{P}(\mathcal{M})$ *with* $0 < P < \mathbb{1}$ *there exists a* $Q \in \mathcal{P}(\mathcal{M})$ *which is maximal incompatible.*
(iii) *Each non-faithful state has a coherent superposable partner state (even one with maximal incompatible support).*
(iv) *Each pair of states, with intersection-free supports is coherent superposable.*

Notice that the coherent superposable states on the I_2-*factor all are pure, and those on the* III-*factor all are very mixed, having infinite-dimensional supports.*

The quantum coherence structure of a qubit space is basic for its intended use for quantum computing. The coherence structure of a III-factor seems not to have been discussed in Physics, in spite of occurring, e.g., in the black body radiation.

Example 46.2-39 (Quantum Coherence for Thermal Radiation Noise).
We consider the thermal GNS representation $(\Pi_\beta, \mathcal{H}_\beta, \Omega_\beta)$ of the black body radiation, for which the associated von Neumann algebra $\Pi_\beta(\mathcal{W}(E, \hbar \mathrm{Im}(.|.)))'' = \mathcal{M}_\beta$ is a III-factor (see the discussion following Theorem 46.3-21 on page 1720). We assume that the normalized vectors $M_1\Omega_\beta$ and $M_2\Omega_\beta$ with $0 \neq M_1, M_2 \in \mathcal{M}_\beta$ represent two disturbances $\varphi_1, \varphi_2 \in \mathcal{S}_n(\mathcal{M}_\beta)$ of the thermal vacuum, which belong to different parts of the spectrum of a self-adjoint operator K^β, affiliated with $\mathcal{M}_\beta$, and therefore are vectors which are orthogonal to each other in $\mathcal{H}_\beta$.
    For any $N_1, N_2 \in \mathcal{M}_\beta$ the vectors $j(N_1)M_1\Omega_\beta$ and $j(N_2)M_2\Omega_\beta$ belong still to the same different parts of the spectrum, since $K^\beta j(N_i)M_i\Omega_\beta = j(N_i)K^\beta M_i\Omega_\beta$ (where j maps $\mathcal{M}_\beta$ onto the commutant, see Theorem 46.3-3). We conclude that all vectors of $\mathcal{M}_\beta' M_1\Omega_\beta$ are orthogonal to all vectors of $\mathcal{M}_\beta' M_2\Omega_\beta$. By formula Eq. (46.2.23) it means that the support projections S_1, S_2 for φ_1, φ_2 are orthogonal to each other.
    We deduce now, e.g., from Proposition 46.2-38(iv) that φ_1 and φ_2 are coherent superposable.
    We form the normalized vector $c_1 M_1\Omega_\beta + c_2 M_2\Omega_\beta =: M_3\Omega_\beta$, with $0 \neq c_i \in \mathbb{C}$, which represents the normal state φ_3. One can now deduce that there is no intersection of $\mathcal{M}_\beta' M_3\Omega_\beta$ with $\mathcal{M}_\beta' M_1\Omega_\beta$ and neither with $\mathcal{M}_\beta' M_2\Omega_\beta$ by studying the linear combinations of the vectors. Thus all three support projections are mutually intersection-less, and they are equivalent as normal states of a III-factor, so that $K(\varphi_1, \varphi_2, \varphi_3)$ is valid.
    It turns out that also for these very mixed states a (special) coherent superposition of φ_1 and φ_2, namely φ_3, is expressible in terms of a linear combination of some state vectors, in quite the same manner as for pure states in traditional Hilbert space quantum theory.
    Recall that the 3-ball property, intimately connected with the coherent superposability for vector states in traditional quantum theory, refers only to pure states

on general C*-algebras. Thus one may say that $K(\varphi_1, \varphi_2, \varphi_3)$, obtained above for very (incoherently) mixed states, is a means to express the additional quantum diffuseness of the states in cases where the 3-ball property does not work.

The relation between quantum coherence and quantum optical coherence for photons is discussed in Sec. 26.3.10 on page 715.

46.3. Modular Theory and Thermal Fields

46.3.1. *Standard von Neumann Algebras*

The structure of the folia is intimately connected with the structure of the von Neumann algebras, for which they constitute the normal states.

Definition 46.3-1 (Standard von Neumann Algebras). Modular theory is concerned with W*-algebras in a so-called *standard representation*, where they appear as von Neumann algebras with a *cyclic and separating vector*.

We briefly write the couple $(\mathcal{M}, \Omega)$ for the standard represented von Neumann algebra $\mathcal{M}$ in the Hilbert space $\mathcal{H}$, where Ω denotes a cyclic and separating vector $\Omega \in \mathcal{H}$.

Not all W*-algebras may be cast into a standard form of that kind.

Proposition 46.3-2 (σ-Finite W*-Algebras). *Let $\mathcal{M}$ be a W*-algebra. Then the following conditions are equivalent:*

(i) *$\mathcal{M}$ is σ-finite: It admits only an at most countable infinite family of mutually orthogonal projections.*
(ii) *The normal state space of $\mathcal{M}$ admits only an at most countable infinite family of mutually orthogonal subfaces.*
(iii) *$\mathcal{M}$ owns a faithful normal state.*
(iv) *$\mathcal{M}$ is W*-isomorphic to a von Neumann algebra in standard form (possessing a separating and cyclic vector).*

In order to overcome the restriction of σ-finiteness, one has developed a more general modular theory, referring to a faithful weight. We are, however, concerned in our applications only with faithful *states*. Most often we start from a faithful state ω on a C*-algebra $\mathcal{A}$ (so that $\mathcal{F}_\omega$ is full) and obtain by the GNS construction the cyclic and separating vector Ω_ω for $\mathcal{M}_\omega = \Pi_\omega(\mathcal{A})''$, arriving automatically at the representation von Neumann algebra in standard form.

For a W*-algebra in standard form there exists a remarkable isomorphy to its commutant, which is related with a basic antiunitary involution J in the representation space. As a motivating remark, let us recall the finite-temperature formalism for Bosons with a discrete energy spectrum, starting from Fock space (see Sec. 31.2.1). There the basic antiunitary involution J is the Hermitian conjugation of Hilbert–Schmidt operators, where the latter constitute the vectors of the thermal representation space (making up the most popular example of a *Hilbert algebra*).

Thus, for generalizing that ansatz, one could be inclined to proceed as follows. For any faithful state $\omega \in \mathcal{S}(\mathcal{A})$ its left kernel is trivial, i.e., $I_\omega = \{0\}$, where we use the general GNS notation of Theorem 45.2-26 on page 1653. Thus there is an injection $\mathcal{A} \ni C \mapsto \Omega_C \in \mathcal{H}_\omega$. That is, the GNS scalar product may be viewed as taking place on the original C*-algebra $\mathcal{A}$ for itself, which then would form a Hilbert algebra. In this case there is also a biunivocal connection between $\Pi_\omega(A)$ and the linear operator $\Pi'_\omega(A)$, densely defined in $\mathcal{H}_\omega$, by setting

$$\Pi'_\omega(A)\Omega_C := \Omega_{CA^*} \equiv CA^*\Omega_\omega, \quad \forall A, C \in \mathcal{A}. \tag{46.3.1}$$

This definition employs the one-to-one connection between Ω_C and C and defines an antilinear *-homomorphism on the domain $\mathcal{A}$. Clearly, the images $\Pi'_\omega(A)$ commute with all $\Pi_\omega(B)$, $B \in \mathcal{A}$, but the $\Pi'_\omega(A)$ are in general *not bounded* operators in $\mathcal{H}_\omega$ (since the inequality (45.2.21) is not satisfied; compare, however, Eq. (31.2.12) in the Hilbert–Schmidt case, due to the trace commutativity).

One basic point of the so-called *Tomita–Takesaki theory* of Hilbert algebras is to construct a similar bijective connection between the $\Pi_\omega(A)$ and *bounded* operators, which commute with all of the representation operators (see [Tak02]).

The starting point for this important construction is the densely defined, antilinear operator S^0_ω

$$S^0_\omega \Omega_C := \Omega_{C^*}, \quad \forall C \in \mathcal{A}, \tag{46.3.2}$$

using again the one-to-one connection between Ω_C and C. With that, Eq. (46.3.1) writes

$$\Pi'_\omega(A)C\Omega_\omega = CA^*\Omega_\omega = S^0_\omega A S^0_\omega C\Omega_\omega, \quad \forall A, C \in \mathcal{A}, \tag{46.3.3}$$

and we have a new expression for Π'_ω. Evidently $S^0_\omega = (S^0_\omega)^{-1}$. But S^0_ω is in general not bounded, from which just originates the unboundedness of $\Pi'_\omega(A)$. By means of the polar decomposition one splits off the unbounded part of the closure $\overline{S^0_\omega}$.

Theorem 46.3-3 (Modular Quantities). *Let, as above, ω denote a faithful state on the C*-algebra $\mathcal{A}$, leading to the GNS triple $(\Pi_\omega, \mathcal{H}_\omega, \Omega_\omega)$, with the standard von Neumann algebra $\Pi_\omega(\mathcal{A})'' = \mathcal{M}_\omega$ with cyclic and separating vector Ω_ω.*

Then S^0_ω, defined in Eq. (46.3.2), is closable and its closure S_ω is invertible, leaves Ω_ω invariant, and possesses the polar decomposition $S_\omega = J_\omega \Delta_\omega^{1/2}$, consisting of the antiunitary involution J_ω and the positive, invertible, self-adjoint $\Delta_\omega^{1/2}$.

S_ω is often named "Tomita map", J_ω is called the "modular conjugation" and satisfies (beside $J_\omega^* = J_\omega^{-1} = J_\omega$) the relation $J_\omega \Omega_\omega = \Omega_\omega$.

Δ_ω is called the modular operator of the faithful state $\omega \in \mathcal{S}(\mathcal{A})$, or of the pair $(\mathcal{M}_\omega, \Omega_\omega)$ (see, e.g., [Tak02, BR87]).

The family of transformations

$$\mathbb{R} \ni t \longmapsto \sigma_t^\omega, \quad \sigma_t^\omega(M) := \Delta_\omega^{it} M \Delta_\omega^{-it}, \quad M \in \mathcal{M}_\omega, \qquad (46.3.4)$$

*constitutes a weakly continuous group of *-automorphisms in* $\mathcal{M}_\omega$, *the* modular automorphism group *of* ω. *It is the unique automorphism group, for which* ω *satisfies the KMS condition (see* (35.1.28) *and* (46.3.9)) *with* $\beta = -1$. *One has for the implementing unitaries* $\Delta_\omega^{it}\Omega_\omega = \Omega_\omega$ *for all* $t \in \mathbb{R}$.

The mapping

$$j_\omega(M) =: J_\omega M J_\omega, \quad \forall M \in \mathcal{M}_\omega, \qquad (46.3.5)$$

*constitutes an antilinear *-isomorphism*

$$j_\omega : \mathcal{M}_\omega \longrightarrow \Pi_\omega(\mathcal{A})' = \mathcal{M}_\omega{}' \qquad (46.3.6)$$

between the indicated von Neumann algebras. This implies that j_ω *is weakly continuous (and has, of course, bounded image operators, so that the unboundedness of the *-operation, applied to vectors, is in fact deposited into* Δ_ω).

Since $j_\omega(\Pi_\omega(\mathcal{A})) \subset j_\omega(\mathcal{M}_\omega) = \Pi_\omega(\mathcal{A})'$, *the commutant is even "larger" than the faithfully represented algebra for itself, expressing a high reducibility of* Π_ω.

Notice that the foregoing notions and relations are valid for any standard von Neumann algebra $(\mathcal{M}, \Omega)$, *independent from a GNS representation, so that the dependence on the* ω *is replaced by that on* Ω, *and often omitted, writing simply* $J, \Delta, \ldots$ *for the modular quantities.*

Remark 46.3-4 (Modular Quantities in the Abelian Case). Let $(\mathcal{M}, \Omega)$ be an Abelian standard von Neumann algebra, which we assume — without restriction in generality — in the form $L^\infty(X, \mu, \mathbb{C})$, acting as multiplication operators in $L^2(X, \mu, \mathbb{C})$. Let μ be a probability measure on the Borel space $(X, \mathcal{B})$. If $\mathrm{supp}(\mu) = X$, then $\Omega := 1 \in L^2(X, \mu, \mathbb{C})$ is in fact a cyclic and separating vector.

For each $f \in L^\infty(X, \mu, \mathbb{C})$ we obtain $Sf1 = Jf1 = \bar{f}1$, where the bar denotes complex conjugation. Because Ω is cyclic, $\mathcal{M}$ is maximal Abelian. Then $J : \mathcal{M} \to \mathcal{M} = \mathcal{M}'$ is directly seen to be an antilinear *-isomorphism. The modular automorphisms are the identity map, what conforms to their leaving the center point-wise invariant.

If $\kappa : X \to X$ is a measure-preserving mapping, the pullback $(\kappa^\star f)(x) = f(\kappa x)$ constitutes an *-automorphism in $\mathcal{M}$, which is unitarily implemented by $Uf1 := (\kappa^\star f)1, \forall f \in \mathcal{M}$, the latter giving the unique implementation which leaves the cyclic vector 1 invariant and coincides with the standard implementation, described below. (That observation leads to Remark 46.3-14 below and is, e.g., of interest for a limiting mean field dynamics with a classical flow.)

We need also the modular formalism associated with tensor products of standard von Neumann algebras. The pertinent construction is indicated in [Tak02, Chap. VIII Proposition 4.3], together with its preceding lemmata.

Proposition 46.3-5 (Tensor Product of Modular Quantities). *For two given standard von Neumann algebras* $(\mathcal{M}_1, \Omega_1)$ *and* $(\mathcal{M}_2, \Omega_2)$ *one may form the standard tensor product von Neumann algebra* $(\mathcal{M}_1 \overline{\otimes} \mathcal{M}_2, \Omega_1 \otimes \Omega_2) =: (\mathcal{M}, \Omega)$.

Then the modular operator Δ *of* $(\mathcal{M}, \omega)$ *is obtained as the closure* $\Delta_1 \otimes \Delta_2$ *of the algebraic tensor product* $\Delta_1 \circ \Delta_2$ *on* $\mathrm{dom}(\Delta_1) \otimes \mathrm{dom}(\Delta_2)$ *and has the polar decomposition* $\Delta = (J_1 \otimes J_2)(|\Delta_1| \otimes |\Delta_2|)$.

It follows that the modular automorphisms for $(\mathcal{M}, \Omega)$ *are the tensor products of those for* $(\mathcal{M}_1, \Omega_1)$ *and* $(\mathcal{M}_2, \Omega_2)$.

Remark 46.3-6 (Thermal Fermion Fields). If $(\mathcal{A}, \tau, \mathbb{R})$ is any C*-dynamical system (see Definition 48.3-3 on page 1808) in the CAR algebra $\mathcal{A} \equiv \mathcal{A}(\mathfrak{h})$ and ω^β any KMS state for it (satisfying (35.1.28)), then ω^β is faithful and the modular quantities are defined in its GNS representation $(\Pi_\beta, \mathcal{H}_\beta, \Omega_\beta)$. The automorphism group τ_t may be continuously extended to $\mathcal{M}_\omega$ and one has $\sigma_t^\omega = \tau_{-t\beta}$.

In Quantum Field Theory thermal equilibrium states are described by a set of Green's functions — that are expectations of field products in a special ordering — satisfying the KMS condition. From these, in the so-called *thermal field theory* [Ume95], the GNS representation and part of the modular quantities had been derived, independently from the Tomita–Takesaki theory, in a heuristic manner. The cyclic vector Ω_β there is called "thermal vacuum" and the (unsmeared) fields $c_\sigma^{(*)}(x)$ (in the representation) have been found to be "doubled", which expresses in some way the occurrence of the $j_\beta(c_\sigma^{(*)}(x))$.

The additional fields are mostly called "formal" in the physical literature. They acquired, however, much interest in the formalism of finite temperature Feynman integrals. (There is given an overview in [Oji81], where also the connection with the modular quantities is worked out and applications in gauge theory are indicated.) Constructions like the representation in the doubled Fock space (see Eq. (35.1.33) on 1076) are used to realize the additional field operators.

The additional fields are also used for constructing special operators, especially for the "Bosonization" of Fermion theories. In our investigations we use them in first line for the renormalization of Hamiltonians, in both cases of Fermion and Boson models. These Hamiltonians would lead in perturbation theory to the thermal Feynman integrals (see also Sec. 37.1.2 on page 1151), the basic quantities of thermal field theory. Since we sum up the Dyson series in the weak coupling limit of our mesoscopic radiation models, we do not follow this aspect further.

As a first exercise with the modular quantities we derive an important commutativity relation. For this we use the fact that for any *-automorphism group $\{\alpha_t \in {}^*\text{-aut}(\mathcal{A}) \,|\, t \in \mathbb{R}\}$ of a C*-algebra $\mathcal{A}$ (which may be a W*-algebra) there is a norm dense set $\mathcal{A}_\alpha \ni A$ of analytic elements on which $\alpha_t(A)$ may be analytically continued to complex t-values. We treat the analyticity relations in our sketch of the modular theory only sloppily and refer to more refined analyticity arguments, which may be deduced from the modular quantities, to the literature (see, e.g., [BR87, Bor99]).

Observation 46.3-7 (Modular Relation and KMS Condition). Let $(\mathcal{M}, \Omega)$ be a standard von Neumann algebra with the modular automorphisms σ_t. For analytic elements $A, B \in \mathcal{M}_\sigma$ one calculates in the state ω, defined by $\Omega \in \mathcal{H}$,

$$
\begin{aligned}
\langle \omega; \sigma_{i/2}(A)\sigma_{-i/2}(B) \rangle &= (\Omega | \Delta^{-1/2} A \Delta^{1/2} \Delta^{1/2} B \Delta^{-1/2} \Omega) \\
&= (\Delta^{1/2} A^* \Delta^{-1/2} \Omega | \Delta^{1/2} B \Delta^{-1/2} \Omega) \\
&= (J \Delta^{1/2} B \Omega | J \Delta^{1/2} A^* \Omega) = \langle \omega; BA \rangle.
\end{aligned} \tag{46.3.7}
$$

For this result one has applied only the relations mentioned in Theorem 46.3-3.

The equality of the first with the last term in Eq. (46.3.7) constitutes the "modular relation". If we use $\omega = \omega \circ \sigma_{-i/2}$ in application to analytic elements we obtain the KMS condition at $\beta = -1$,

$$
\langle \omega; A\sigma_{-i}(B) \rangle = \langle \omega; A\sigma_{i\beta}(B) \rangle |_{\beta = -1} = \langle \omega; BA \rangle. \tag{46.3.8}
$$

In this manner the KMS condition arises as an asymmetric form of the modular relation and reveals its connection with basic algebraic structures.

Notice that, by replacing B with $\sigma_t(B)$, we get from Eq. (46.3.8), generalized to arbitrary $\beta \in]0, \infty[$, the usual form of the KMS condition

$$
\langle \omega^\beta; A\, \sigma_{t+i\beta}(B) \rangle = \langle \omega^\beta; \sigma_t(B)A \rangle, \quad \forall B \in \mathcal{A}_\sigma, \quad \forall A \in \mathcal{A}, \quad \forall t \in \mathbb{R}. \tag{46.3.9}
$$

($\mathcal{A}_\sigma$ are the analytic elements for σ.) Specializing Eq. (46.3.9) to $A = \mathbb{1}$ (if $\mathcal{A}$ is unital, which we assume in most parts of the book, but which is not necessary for the hitherto cited results of the Tomita–Takesaki theory), we get for $B \in \mathcal{A}_\sigma$ the expectation as a periodic analytic function, which is bounded and thus a constant. Thus each β-KMS state is necessarily time invariant.

If we assume in Eq. (46.3.8) that B is in the center of $\mathcal{M}$, then we find $(A^*\Omega | \sigma_{-i}(B)\Omega) = (A^*\Omega | B\Omega)$ for all $A \in \mathcal{M}$, leading — by the cyclic and separating property of Ω and by analyticity arguments — to the following conclusion.

Corollary 46.3-8. *In a finite temperature representation over a KMS state ω^β for a C^*-dynamical system $(\mathcal{A}, \alpha, \mathbb{R})$, the extended dynamics leaves the center $\mathcal{Z}_\beta = \mathcal{M}_\beta \cap \mathcal{M}'_\beta$ of the temperature von Neumann algebra $\mathcal{M}_\beta = \Pi_\beta(\mathcal{A})''$ point-wise invariant, i.e., $\alpha_t(A) = A$ for all $A \in \mathcal{Z}_\beta$ and every $t \in \mathbb{R}$.*

Since for a grand canonical equilibrium state the original (not reduced) dynamics does not provide the KMS condition for that state, one may obtain a nontrivial dynamics in the center of its representation von Neumann algebra. This may explain important physical time-dependent equilibrium effects (cf. [Rie84]), as, e.g., the Josephson relations (cf. [RU85b, RU85a]). Recall that the grand canonical equilibrium state represents thermal equilibrium under coupling to a particle reservoir.

The modular quantities enable a distinguished realization of normal states on the standard von Neumann algebra $(\mathcal{M}_\omega, \Omega_\omega)$ by vectors from a certain cone in $\mathcal{H}_\omega$.

Definition 46.3-9 (Natural Positive Cone). Let ω be a faithful state on the C*-algebra $\mathcal{A}$, with associated standard von Neumann algebra $(\mathcal{M}_\omega, \Omega_\omega)$. The natural positive cone $\mathcal{P}_\omega$ is defined as the (norm) closure

$$\mathcal{P}_\omega := \overline{\{Aj_\omega(A)\Omega_\omega \mid A \in \mathcal{M}_\omega\}} \subset \mathcal{H}_\omega. \qquad (46.3.10)$$

Obviously a natural positive cone $\mathcal{P}$ is associated with any standard von Neumann algebra $(\mathcal{M}, \Omega)$ (independently from being viewed as representing a C*-algebra).

The cone property "$\xi \in \mathcal{P}$ implies $\lambda\xi \in \mathcal{P}$ for all $\lambda > 0$" is evidently satisfied. Since in Eq. (46.3.10) the variables A run in a von Neumann algebra, they include the unit operator of the representation space. Thus always $\Omega_\omega \in \mathcal{P}_\omega$.

Proposition 46.3-10 (Properties of the Natural Positive Cone). *Let* $\mathcal{P} \subset \mathcal{H}$ *be the natural positive cone of the standard von Neumann algebra* $(\mathcal{M}, \Omega)$.

(a) *$\mathcal{P}$ is a convex cone.*
(b) *$\mathcal{P}$ is a pointed cone, i.e., $\mathcal{P} \cap (-\mathcal{P}) = \{0\}$.*
(c) *$\mathcal{P}$ linearly spans $\mathcal{H}$.*
(d) *If $\xi \in \mathcal{P}$ then $J\xi = \xi$.*
(e) *If $A \in \mathcal{M}$ then $Aj(A)\mathcal{P} \subseteq \mathcal{P}$.*
(f) *For $\xi, \eta \in \mathcal{P}$ we have $(\xi|\eta) \geq 0$, especially $(Aj(A)\Omega|\Omega) \geq 0$ for all $A \in \mathcal{M}$.*
(g) *There holds the following "self-duality relation": if for a vector $\eta \in \mathcal{H}$ one has $(\xi|\eta) \geq 0$ for all $\xi \in \mathcal{P}$, then $\eta \in \mathcal{P}$.*
(h) *$\mathcal{P}$ is invariant under the unitaries Δ^{it}, i.e., $\Delta^{it}\mathcal{P} = \mathcal{P}$ for all $t \in \mathbb{R}$.*

Proof. [Sketch] For exercise we play with the modular quantities as follows: $J(AJAJ)\Omega = (JAJ)A\Omega = AJAJ)\Omega$, since $J\Omega = \Omega$ and $[j(A), A] = 0$. Thus J leaves $AJAJ\Omega \in \mathcal{P}$ invariant, which illustrates (d). Further, if $A, B \in \mathcal{M}$ then $Aj(A)Bj(B)\Omega = ABj(A)j(B)\Omega = ABj(AB)\Omega \in \mathcal{P}$, where we used $[j(A), B] = 0$ and the product homomorphy of j. This illustrates (e). Concerning (f) we multiply first $S\Omega = J\Delta^{1/2}\Omega = \Omega$ by J, observe again $J\Omega = \Omega$, and obtain the generally interesting equalities

$$\Delta^{1/2}\Omega = \Omega, \quad \text{and} \quad \Delta^{-1/2}\Omega = \Omega. \qquad (46.3.11)$$

Then we calculate

$$(Aj(A)\Omega|\Omega) = (JA\Omega|A^*\Omega) = (J\Delta^{1/2}\Delta^{-1/2}A^*\Delta^{1/2}\Omega|A\Omega)$$
$$= (\Delta^{1/2}A\Delta^{-1/2}\Omega|A\Omega) = (\Delta^{1/4}A\Omega|\Delta^{1/4}A\Omega) \geq 0.$$

Observing for all $A, B \in \mathcal{M}$ the relations

$$(Aj(A)\Omega|Bj(B)\Omega) = (B^*j(B^*)Aj(A)\Omega|\Omega) = (B^*Aj(B^*A)\Omega|\Omega) \geq 0,$$

and executing limits to arbitrary cone vectors, the preceding relation, not only illustrates, but proves (f). $\square$

One should mention that, by analyticity arguments, Eq. (46.3.11) generalizes to

$$\Delta^z \Omega = \Omega, \quad \forall z \in \mathbb{C}, \tag{46.3.12}$$

so that Ω is especially an entire analytic vector for the self-adjoint Δ (see the defining Eq. (43.6.2)).

Proposition 46.3-11 (Universality of the Natural Positive Cone). *For a standard von Neumann algebra* $(\mathcal{M}, \Omega)$ *with natural positive cone* $\mathcal{P} \subset \mathcal{H}$ *let* $\xi \in \mathcal{P}$ *be another cyclic vector for* $\mathcal{M}$. *Then one knows that* ξ *is separating for* $\mathcal{M}$, *and one knows that* $(\mathcal{M}, \xi)$ *leads to the same modular involution* J *and the same positive cone* $\mathcal{P}$ *as* $(\mathcal{M}, \Omega)$ *(see, e.g., [BR87]).*

In this sense $\mathcal{P}$ *is related to the normal state space in the whole and not to peculiar vectors or states.*

(The corresponding assertion for faithful normal weights follows from [Tak02, Chap. IX, Theorem 1.14].)

As a further geometrical feature, the natural positive cone $\mathcal{P}$ allows for a peculiar form of an *orientation*, as has been expounded in [Con74]. This additional quality leads also from the normal positive cone of a standard Jordan algebra to that of a standard W*-algebra, as we have discussed it for states in terms of the 3-ball orientation and constitutes, so to speak, a kind of complexification of the Jordan algebra. (The technical result of [Con74] says that in a given Hilbert space the standard von Neumann algebras are in one-to-one correspondence with the self-dual, oriented, facially homogeneous cones. In [BI79] for those cones a spectral theory is developed, illustrating again the power of the state space approach.) In [AS98b] the 3-ball orientation and the Connes orientation have been subsumed under the more general concept of a *dynamical correspondence* (see also [AS98a]).

Since we relate an orientation of the state space with the occurrence of transition operators in the dual space, we find it interesting that vectors of the natural positive cone enable the introduction of a transition probability in terms of a scalar product [Rag82]. (One defines $(\xi(\omega)|\xi(\varphi))$ — and not its square — as transition probability between the two normal states $\omega, \varphi \in \mathcal{S}_n(\mathcal{M})$, using the subsequent theorem.)

In this connection observe also that — according to Proposition 46.3-16 — the vectors in the natural positive cone alone are only able to discriminate a Jordan automorphism from an *-automorphism, if the orientation concept is employed.

The following basic theorem requires an involved proof (see [BR87, Tak02]).

Theorem 46.3-12 (Standard State Implementation). *Let* $\mathcal{P} \subset \mathcal{H}$ *be the natural positive cone of the standard von Neumann algebra* $(\mathcal{M}, \Omega)$. *For any* $\xi \in \mathcal{P}$ *we introduce the normal scaled state* $\omega_\xi \in \mathcal{M}_{*,+}$ *by* $\langle \omega_\xi; A \rangle := (\xi | A \xi)$, $\forall A \in \mathcal{M}$.

It holds: *For any* $\omega \in \mathcal{M}_{*,+}$ *there is a unique* $\xi \in \mathcal{P}$, *with* $\omega = \omega_\xi$, *and the following inequalities are valid:*

$$\|\xi - \eta\|^2 \le \|\omega_\xi - \omega_\eta\| \le \|\xi - \eta\| \, \|\xi + \eta\| \, . \tag{46.3.13}$$

Thus the mapping $\mathcal{P} \ni \xi \mapsto \omega_\xi \in \mathcal{M}_{*,+}$ *has an inverse* $\mathcal{M}_{*,+} \ni \omega \mapsto \xi(\omega) \in \mathcal{P}$, *and constitutes a norm–norm homeomorphism.*

To construct the $\xi(\omega) \in \mathcal{P}$, for a given $\omega \in \mathcal{M}_{*,+}$, is a science for itself, but nevertheless the general relationships of the preceding theorem are very important.

46.3.2.　*Standard Implementation of Automorphisms*

As a corollary from Theorem 46.3-12 we obtain the following most powerful result.

Theorem 46.3-13 (Standard Implementation of Automorphisms). *Let* $\mathcal{P} \subset \mathcal{H}$ *be the natural positive cone of the standard von Neumann algebra* $(\mathcal{M}, \Omega)$.

For each α *in* *-aut$(\mathcal{M})$ *there exists a unitary implementation* $\alpha(A) = U(\alpha)AU(\alpha)^*$ *for all* $A \in \mathcal{M}$ *with the following properties:*

(a) *The operator* $U(\alpha)$ *is the only implementing unitary in* $\mathcal{H}$ *with* $U(\alpha)\mathcal{P} \subseteq \mathcal{P}$.

(b) *-aut$(\mathcal{M}) \ni \alpha \mapsto U(\alpha) \in U(\text{*-aut}(\mathcal{M}))$ *is a homeomorphism in the norm topologies. (Notice that the unique images* $U(\alpha) \in U(\mathcal{H})$, $\alpha \in$ *-aut$(\mathcal{M})$, *are unitaries in* $\mathcal{H}$ *with special properties.)*

(c) *-aut$(\mathcal{M})^*|_{\mathcal{M}_*} \ni \alpha^* \mapsto U(\alpha) \in U(\text{*-aut}(\mathcal{M}))$ *is a homeomorphism in the strong topologies.*
   (The α^* *are the Schrödinger picture transformations, restricted to the normal functionals, which converge strongly if they converge point-wise in the norm of the normal functionals.)*

(d) *For each* $\alpha \in$ *-aut$(\mathcal{M})$ *we have* $[U(\alpha), J] = 0$.

(e) *For each* $\alpha \in$ *-aut$(\mathcal{M})$ *we have* $U(\alpha)\xi(\omega) = \xi((\alpha^*)^{-1}\omega)$ *for all* $\omega \in \mathcal{M}_{*,+}$.

Proof.　[Sketch] We *assume* first the existence of an implementing unitary $U(\alpha) \equiv U$ for $\alpha \in$ *-aut$(\mathcal{M})$ such that it leaves $\mathcal{P}$ invariant.

Define $\xi := U\Omega \in \mathcal{P}$. Thus $(\Omega|\alpha^{-1}(A)\Omega) = (\xi|A\xi)$, $\forall A \in \mathcal{M}$. Since we have $A\xi = U\alpha^{-1}(A)\Omega$, and $\alpha^{-1}(A)$ runs through $\mathcal{M}$ with A, we see that ξ is cyclic for $\mathcal{M}$ (and separating).

For $B \in \mathcal{M}$ we form the scaled normal state $\mathcal{M} \ni A \mapsto (B\Omega|\alpha^{-1}(A)B\Omega) = (UB\Omega|AUB\Omega)$. Since α^{-1} is an *-automorphism, the scalar product writes

$$(\Omega|\alpha^{-1}[\alpha(B^*)A\alpha(B)]\Omega) = (\xi|[\alpha(B^*)A\alpha(B^*)]\xi) = (\alpha(B)\xi|A\alpha(B)\xi) \, .$$

Thus we get the explicit and unique characterization of the implementing unitary

$$U B\Omega \equiv U(\alpha)B\Omega = \alpha(B)\xi, \quad \forall B \in \mathcal{M}. \tag{46.3.14}$$

For any $\eta \in \mathcal{P}$ we have $U\eta = JUJ\eta \in \mathcal{P}$, or, by $J^2 = \mathbb{1}$, $JU\eta = UJ\eta$. By linear extension we get (d), since $\mathcal{H} = \text{LH}(\mathcal{P})$.

For any $\omega \in \mathcal{M}_{*,+}$ we have

$$(U\xi(\omega)|AU\xi(\omega)) = (\xi(\omega)|U^*AU\xi(\omega)) = (\xi(\omega)|\alpha^{-1}(A)\xi(\omega)) = \langle\omega;\alpha^{-1}(A)\rangle$$
$$= \langle\alpha^{-1^*}(\omega);A\rangle = (\xi(\alpha^{-1^*}(\omega))|A\,\xi(\alpha^{-1^*}(\omega))), \quad \forall A \in \mathcal{M}.$$

From the uniqueness of the representing vector in $\mathcal{P}$ we deduce (e).

The proof for the *existence* of $U(\alpha)$, for given $\alpha \in *\text{-aut}(\mathcal{M})$, starts with Eq. (46.3.14) as definition, where ξ is introduced by $(\Omega|\alpha^{-1}(A)\Omega) = (\xi|A\xi)$. One then proves the unitarity and implementing property for $U(\alpha)$ and shows the invariance of $\mathcal{P}$ under that operator. The further consequences (d) and (e) follow then as above.

For this and the continuity properties of $\alpha \mapsto U(\alpha)$ we refer to [BR87, Corollary 2.5.32]. □

Remark 46.3-14 (Standard Implementation in the Abelian Case). In the situation of Remark 46.3-4, where one has the standard implementation of an Abelian von Neumann algebra $\mathcal{M} = \text{L}^\infty(X,\mu,\mathbb{C})$ in a function representation, the natural positive cone $\mathcal{P}$ is generated by the $f1$, where the $f \in \mathcal{M}$ vary over the positive functions. The implementing U of a pullback *-automorphism κ^* leaves obviously $\mathcal{P}$ invariant and is thus the standard implementation of κ^*.

In terms of the above notation, we get a useful corollary.

Corollary 46.3-15 (Extended Automorphisms). *For the standard implementing unitary of $\alpha \in *\text{-aut}(\mathcal{M})$ we obtain by (d) of the foregoing theorem*

$$U(\alpha)Aj(B)\Omega = \alpha(A)j(\alpha(B))U(\alpha)\Omega, \quad \forall A, B \in \mathcal{M}. \tag{46.3.15}$$

If $U(\alpha)\Omega = \Omega$ and $A = B$ this illustrates the invariance of $\mathcal{P}$ under $U(\alpha)$.

Dropping the separating Ω, Eq. (46.3.15) indicates the possibility to define with $\alpha \in *\text{-aut}(\mathcal{M})$ naturally an automorphism in $(\mathcal{M} \cup \mathcal{M}')''$.

Proposition 46.3-16 (From Unitaries to Automorphisms). *Assume the modular setup as in the previous Theorem, but stipulate that we have reversely a unitary U with $U\mathcal{P} = \mathcal{P}$. Then there exists a unique Jordan automorphism $\alpha : \mathcal{M} \to \mathcal{M}$ with*

$$(\xi|\alpha(A)\xi) = (\xi|UAU^*\xi), \quad \forall A \in \mathcal{M}, \ \forall\xi \in \mathcal{P}. \tag{46.3.16}$$

*To guarantee the *-automorphism property for α, requires additional assumptions on U, as leaving invariant the Connes orientation of $\mathcal{P}$.*

If now, for $\alpha \in *\text{-aut}(\mathcal{M})$, the normal state $\omega \in \mathcal{S}(\mathcal{M})$ is invariant under α^*, and thus under α^{-1^*} (replace A in $\langle\omega;\alpha(A)\rangle = \langle\omega;A\rangle$ by $\alpha^{-1}(B)$), then Proposition 46.3-13(e) specializes to $U(\alpha)\xi(\omega) = \xi(\omega)$ and Eq. (46.3.14) to $U(\alpha)B\Omega = \alpha(B)\Omega$, which provides nothing else than the usual *GNS implementation* U_ω (see Theorem 45.2-26 on page 1653). Because of uniqueness we know all properties of the preceding $U(\alpha)$ to hold also for U_ω in the case of a faithful invariant state ω on the C*-algebra $\mathcal{A}$, where $(\Pi_\omega(\mathcal{A})'', \Omega_\omega)$ plays the role of the standard von Neumann algebra.

Proposition 46.3-17 (Modular Renormalization). *Let $(\mathcal{M}, \Omega)$ be a von Neumann algebra in standard representation in the Hilbert space $\mathcal{H}$, with $\mathcal{P} \subset \mathcal{H}$ the self-dual positive cone.*

Let K be a self-adjoint operator in $\mathcal{H}$, affiliated with $\mathcal{M}$, and $\alpha_t(M) := e^{itK} M e^{-itK}$ the corresponding W-automorphisms in $\mathcal{M}$ for all $t \in \mathbb{R}$. Then we have the following conditions:*

(a) *The subtracted operator $\tilde{K}_0 := K - JKJ$ is essentially self-adjoint on $\mathrm{dom}(K) \cap \mathrm{dom}(JKJ)$, where we denote its self-adjoint closure by $\tilde{K}$. We name $\tilde{K}$ the modular renormalization of K.*

(b) *The standard implementation of α_t is achieved by the unitaries*

$$U(\alpha_t) = e^{it\tilde{K}} = e^{itK} J e^{itK} J = e^{it(K-JKJ)}, \quad \forall t \in \mathbb{R}. \tag{46.3.17}$$

(These are the only implementing unitaries of the α_t which leave $\mathcal{P}$ invariant.)

(c) *If $\varphi \in \mathcal{M}_{*+}$ is any scaled state with $\varphi = \varphi \circ \alpha_t$ for all $t \in \mathbb{R}$, and $\xi(\varphi) \in \mathcal{P}$ is the corresponding standard implementing vector, then $\xi(\varphi) \in \mathrm{dom}(\tilde{K})$ and $\tilde{K}\xi(\varphi) = 0$.*

Proof. Since $K^* = K$, $J = J^*$, and $J^2 = \mathbb{1}$, we find $\mathrm{dom}(JKJ) = J \mathrm{dom}(K)$, and get there the self-adjointness $(JKJ)^* = JKJ$.

If $(P_\lambda)_\mathbb{R}$ is the spectral family of K (recall $P_\lambda = P(] - \infty, \lambda])$), then $(JP_\lambda J)_\mathbb{R}$ is that of JKJ. Since K is affiliated with $\mathcal{M}$ we know $P(\Lambda) \in \mathcal{M}$, $\forall \Lambda \in \mathcal{B}(\mathbb{R})$. Then $JP(\Lambda)J \in \mathcal{M}'$. Thus K and JKJ commute in the sense that their spectral projections commute.

On $\mathrm{ran}(P([-a,a])JP([-a,a])J) \subset \mathcal{H}$ the operator $\tilde{K}_0 = K - JKJ$ is bounded, so that $\bigcup_{a>0} \mathrm{ran}(P([-a,a])JP([-a,a])J)$ is a dense linear family of analytic vectors for $\tilde{K}_0$. By Nelsons's theorem on analytic vectors (see Proposition 43.6-3) we conclude that $\tilde{K}_0$ is essentially self-adjoint with a unique self-adjoint extension $\tilde{K}$, which shows (a).

By differentiation one sees on $\mathrm{dom}(K) \cap \mathrm{dom}(JKJ)$ that $\tilde{K}$ generates the unitary group $V_t := e^{itK} J e^{itK} J$, $t \in \mathbb{R}$, where $Je^{itK}J \in \mathcal{M}'$ is essential for the group law. Also by the last relation, one checks that V_t implements α_t. Since by Proposition 46.3-10 (e) $V_t \mathcal{P} \subset \mathcal{P}$, we know $V_t = U(\alpha_t)$, proving (b).

For the last statement (c) we invoke Theorem 46.3-13 (e) and get $e^{it\tilde{K}}\xi(\varphi) = \xi(\varphi)$ for all $t \in \mathbb{R}$, which can be differentiated to t. From Stone's theorem we obtain the assertion. $\qquad\square$

In the situation of Proposition 46.3-17 the state belonging to the reference vector Ω is in general not invariant under the considered $\{\alpha_t \mid t \in \mathbb{R}\} \equiv \alpha$. Since the triple

$(\mathcal{M}, \alpha, \mathbb{R})$ constitutes a W*-dynamical system, with the amenable group $\mathbb{R}$, one knows, however, that there exists a normal invariant state φ on $\mathcal{M}$ (see Proposition 48.3-9). Its standard representative $\xi(\varphi) \in \mathcal{P}$ is then an eigenvector for the modular renormalized Hamiltonian $\tilde{K}$ with zero eigenvalue.

Remark 46.3-18 (On Modular Limiting Dynamics and its Perturbation).
In order to illustrate modular renormalization we sketch in the following paragraphs the construction of a dynamics in the thermodynamic limit, and its perturbation, in a way which constitutes the ideal case. Among the model discussions of the book, the ideal case is executed for ideal thermal Bosons and sketched for ideal thermal Fermions. The mean field and radiation models require additional techniques.

The starting point is usually a quasi-local C*-algebra $\mathcal{A} = \overline{\bigcup_{\Lambda \in \mathcal{L}} \mathcal{A}_\Lambda}^{\|\cdot\|} = \overline{\mathcal{A}_0}$, where most commonly each local $\mathcal{A}_\Lambda \in \mathcal{A}_0$ is isomorphic to $\mathcal{L}(\mathcal{H}_\Lambda)$, for some Hilbert space $\mathcal{H}_\Lambda$. The unperturbed model is specified by a family $\{H_\Lambda \mid \Lambda \in \mathcal{L}\}$ of local, self-adjoint Hamiltonians (in $\mathcal{H}_\Lambda$) which lead to local automorphisms $e^{itH_\Lambda} \cdot e^{-itH_\Lambda} = \alpha_t^\Lambda(\cdot) \in *\text{-aut}(\mathcal{A}_\Lambda)$.

Let us at first assume that the limiting dynamics $\alpha_t = \lim_{\Lambda \in \mathcal{L}} \alpha_t^\Lambda$ exists in the point-wise norm topology and constitutes a C*-dynamical system $(\mathcal{A}, \alpha, \mathbb{R})$ (where $\alpha := \{\alpha_t \mid t \in \mathbb{R}\}$).

We consider a (faithful) KMS state ω^β for α at the natural temperature $\beta \in]0, \infty[$. We form via the (faithful) GNS construction the thermal standard von Neumann algebra $(\mathcal{M}_\beta, \Omega_\beta)$, $\mathcal{M}_\beta = \Pi_\beta(\mathcal{A})''$, and embed $\mathcal{A}$ into $\mathcal{M}_\beta$ (so that the unit $\mathbb{1}_\Lambda = \mathbb{1} \in \mathcal{A}$ is identified with $\mathbb{1} \in \mathcal{M}_\beta$, the identity operator in the thermal representation space $\mathcal{H}_\beta$). The embedded $\mathcal{A}_\Lambda$ are sub-von Neumann algebras $\mathcal{M}_\Lambda \subset \mathcal{M}_\beta$, for all of which Ω_β is separating, but not necessarily cyclic. The modular involution and natural positive cone for $(\mathcal{M}_\beta, \Omega_\beta)$ are denoted by J_β and $\mathcal{P}_\beta$.

By unitary implementation, the α_t^Λ and the α_t are uniquely extended to elements of $*\text{-aut}(\mathcal{M}_\beta)$. As such, we may apply Proposition 46.3-13 to each of the mentioned automorphisms to obtain the standard unitary implementation $U_\beta(\alpha_t^{(\Lambda)})$, with $U_\beta(\alpha_t^{(\Lambda)})\mathcal{P}_\beta \subseteq \mathcal{P}_\beta$, which only for α_t coincides with the GNS implementation, since in general $U_\beta(\alpha_t^\Lambda)\Omega_\beta \neq \Omega_\beta$. For the group $U_\beta(\alpha_t)$, $t \in \mathbb{R}$, we may, e.g., invoke Proposition 48.3-5 on page 1808 to get strong continuity in dependence of t, which provides us with the self-adjoint generator $\tilde{H}_\beta$.

As described above, originally we have locally another unitary implementation in terms of the $e^{itH_\Lambda} \in \mathcal{M}_\Lambda \subset \mathcal{M}_\beta$, with which the application of Proposition 46.3-17 gives $U_\beta(\alpha_t^\Lambda) = e^{itH_\Lambda} J_\beta e^{itH_\Lambda} J_\beta$. These unitaries depend strongly on t by construction and possess the modular renormalized self-adjoint generators $\tilde{H}_\Lambda = H_\Lambda - J_\beta H_\Lambda J_\beta$ (also for unbounded H_Λ, see Proposition 46.3-17).

If the convergence to the limit automorphisms — for each t — would be valid even in the norm topology (as operators in $\mathcal{M}_\beta$), then Proposition 46.3-13(b) would deliver automatically the norm convergence of the corresponding standard implementing unitaries (as operators in the GNS Hilbert space $\mathcal{H}_\beta$). This convergence to the limiting dynamics is too a strong one for interesting applications, but it gives us the insight, that the modular renormalized $\tilde{H}_\Lambda$ are properly adjusted so that they might converge to $\tilde{H}_\beta$, in some sense. Without a unifying renormalization prescription, in each local region Λ, that would not be feasible.

Thus, to prove constructively the limiting dynamics in a temperature representation, one might try to begin the dynamical discussion with studying the convergence properties of modular renormalized Hamiltonians in the temperature representation. In fact, to characterize the temperature states one does not necessarily need the KMS condition, which presupposes the limiting automorphism group. One may instead determine those states which display minimal free energy, where for the convergence of the local free energy densities in the thermodynamic limit there exist powerful methods of convex analysis. In our long range cluster models the self-consistency equations provide the (stable and unstable) temperature states. (For special long range models one succeeded even to calculate directly the limiting Gibbs states in their central decompositions [Rie86].)

The direct handling of the net of local Hamiltonians $\tilde{H}_\Lambda$ for deducing a limiting dynamics seems, however, unexplored, and thus it appears more favorable to use for the local expectation values the identity

$$(B\Omega_\beta|\tilde{H}_\Lambda A\Omega_\beta) - (B\Omega_\beta|A\tilde{H}_\Lambda\Omega_\beta) = (B\Omega_\beta|[H_\Lambda, A]\Omega_\beta), \quad A, B \in \mathcal{A}_0, \quad (46.3.18)$$

to shift the convergence problem to $\lim_{\Lambda\in\mathcal{L}}(B\Omega_\beta|[H_\Lambda, A]\Omega_\beta)$. That leads to the limit of the $\tilde{H}_\Lambda$ if $\lim_{\Lambda\in\mathcal{L}}(B\Omega_\beta|A\tilde{H}_\Lambda\Omega_\beta) = 0$ may be verified. In that case one has in some sense

$$\tilde{H}_\beta A\Omega_\beta = \lim_{\Lambda\in\mathcal{L}} \tilde{H}_\Lambda A\Omega_\beta = \lim_{\Lambda\in\mathcal{L}}[H_\Lambda, A]\Omega_\beta, \quad A, B \in \mathcal{A}_0. \quad (46.3.19)$$

That strategy may be applied to *short range* material models, as that is treated in [BR97] and in references cited therein. Let us assume, that for a model $\tilde{H}_\beta = \text{srs-lim}_{\Lambda\in\mathcal{L}} \tilde{H}_\Lambda$ has been proved. According to Corollary 46.3-8, the limiting dynamics leaves the center $\mathcal{Z}(\mathcal{M})_\beta$ point-wise invariant; there are no moving collective observables.

Within the described setup, including the assumed strong resolvent convergence, consider now local, bounded, *self-adjoint perturbations* $\{P_\Lambda \mid \Lambda \in \mathcal{L}\}$ which converge strongly in $\mathcal{H}_\beta$ to $P \in \mathcal{M}_\beta$. Then $\text{srs-lim}_{\Lambda\in\mathcal{L}}[\tilde{H}_\beta^\Lambda + P_\Lambda - J_\beta P_\Lambda J_\beta] = \tilde{H}_\beta + P - J_\beta P J_\beta$ and gives us the perturbed limiting dynamics α'_t in the same manner as the unperturbed one. From perturbed KMS theory (see [BR97]) one knows that the perturbed KMS state ω'_β is still normal to $\mathcal{M}_\beta$. Its standard representation $\xi(\omega'_\beta) = \Omega'_\omega$ is a cyclic and separating vector in $\mathcal{H}_\beta$.

We have then for the perturbed automorphisms α'_t the situation outlined in the text preceding the present remark. The modular involution and natural positive cone with respect to $(\mathcal{M}_\beta, \Omega'_\omega)$ equal that for $(\mathcal{M}_\beta, \Omega_\omega)$ but the modular operators Δ_β and Δ'_β (as well as the associated modular automorphisms) differ from each other.

For the perturbed limiting dynamics α'_t also the Hamiltonians $\tilde{H}_\beta + P - J_\beta \hat{P} J_\beta$, with arbitrary $\hat{P} \in \mathcal{M}_{\beta,\mathrm{sa}}$, all are well-defined (differently renormalized) self-adjoint operators in $\mathcal{H}_\beta$ and generate implementing unitaries. Thus it is at first not clear, which one produces the "correct" energy values.

We think that the *Arveson spectral theory*, which associates the spectral values with the dynamical automorphism group for itself (or with its dual transformation group in the state space), provides valuable insights into that problem. We know from Proposition 46.2-6 on page 1682 that just the $\tilde{H}_\beta + P - J_\beta P J_\beta$, which gives the cyclic and separating Ω'_ω zero energy (and whose operator spectrum coincides with the Arveson spectrum of the unitary group it generates) provides us with the Arveson spectrum $\mathrm{Sp}(\alpha')$. And that spectrum is independent from special implementations of α'.

Let us again emphasize, that not Hilbert state vectors but the algebraic states (expectation functionals) characterize physical states. Since the algebraic Schrödinger dynamics $\nu'_t = \alpha'_{-t}{}^*$ is also implementation independent, and $\mathrm{Sp}(\nu') = \mathrm{Sp}(\alpha')$, it should be this *spectrum of energy differences* which counts physically. (Even the Third Law of thermodynamics gives no absolute energy value for $\beta = +\infty$, but only a coordination of the energy and entropy values [SR76]. For the modification of the Third Law in case of solids, compare also the discussion in the vicinity of Eq. (35.1.60) on page 1087.) Thus it is favorable that $\mathrm{Sp}(\alpha')$ may be evaluated by means of the operator spectrum of the modular renormalized Hamiltonian.

According to the Borchers–Arveson Theorem 46.2-8 on page 1684 a *positive spectrum* implies the possibility of an implementation of the automorphism group in terms of unitaries taken from the von Neumann algebra (whereas the standard implementation involves also operators from the commutant). For an infinite system that is never possible for finite temperature states. Rather the *both-sided unbounded spectrum* describes it as an unlimited energy reservoir, seen from the microscopic point of view.

The general strategy — in contrast to the convergence investigation — for *long range models* is more involved. For the material cluster models of Sec. 36.1 the long-range interaction, already in its homogeneous form, enforces mean field operators in the limiting Hamiltonian. That is why one needs the classical extension of the CAR algebra $\mathcal{A}$ to $\mathcal{A}_e$. One can show that Eq. (46.3.19) is valid with fixed $A \in \mathcal{A}_0$, as well as with $A_\Lambda \in \mathcal{A}_0$, which converge strongly to an $A \in \mathcal{A}_e$. In the latter case, central elements of $\mathcal{M}_\beta$ may be moved, what then prevents strong resolvent convergence for the local renormalized Hamiltonians, according to Theorem 36.1-11.

In a finite temperature representation, one may formulate a perturbation theory, which leads from the homogeneous to the weakly inhomogeneous cluster dynamics in terms of standard implementing unitaries, similarly to the described scheme, in spite of the perturbations $P_\Lambda \equiv P_\mathsf{K}$ becoming unbounded in the thermodynamic limit. The corresponding perturbed equilibrium states may leave $\mathcal{S}_n(\mathcal{M}_\beta)$.

The argumentation for *radiation models* in the weak coupling limit is even more complicated since the photon observables are in general not related to a standard von Neumann algebra (as is the case for $(\mathcal{M}_\beta, \Omega_\beta)$ of the Planck radiation) and the matter–field interaction is unbounded. Nevertheless, we have described for the radiating semiconductor in Sec. 37.1 a construction of the limiting dynamics via materially renormalized Hamiltonians, a strategy which is generalized by Corollary 51.3-6 on page 1937.

Let us in the present context already refer to the limiting Hamiltonian of Theorem 52.2-3. There occurs an explicit renormalization term $\int_{\mathsf{P}} \lambda(\varrho)\, dP(\varrho)$ composed of numerical renormalization constants $\lambda(\varrho)$ in each material sector $\varrho \in \mathsf{P}$. It is due to collective phases arising in the Trotter product for the implementing unitaries. In spite of the Arveson spectrum of the limiting dynamics depending not on these renormalization parameters, one should perhaps not exclude completely a physical meaning of these phases which arise also in coupling models for material Bosons.

We *conclude our sketch of the modular formalism* with the definition of the Connes invariant and its use to classify factors of type *III*, following [Con73, Ped79].

Definition 46.3-19 (Connes Invariant).   Let φ be any normal state on the W*-algebra $\mathcal{M}$, with support projection S_φ. Then φ is a faithful normal state on the W*-algebra $S_\varphi \mathcal{M} S_\varphi$. As such, φ induces a faithful GNS representation of $S_\varphi \mathcal{M} S_\varphi$ in the Hilbert space $\mathcal{H}^\varphi$, with cyclic and separating vector Ω^φ, where the represented algebra is denoted $\mathcal{M}^\varphi$. The corresponding modular operator is written Δ^φ and the modular automorphisms $\sigma_t^\varphi(\cdot) = (\Delta^\varphi)^{it} \cdot (\Delta^\varphi)^{-it}$. The spectrum of Δ^φ (as an operator in $\mathcal{H}^\varphi$) is designated by $\sigma(\Delta^\varphi)$. If φ is a faithful normal state on $\mathcal{M}$, then the restricted modular quantities reduce to the usual ones.

The *Connes invariant* of the W*-algebra $\mathcal{M}$ is then defined

$$S(\mathcal{M}) := \bigcap \{ \sigma(\Delta^\varphi) \mid \varphi \in \mathcal{S}_n(\mathcal{M}) \}. \tag{46.3.20}$$

The Connes invariant distinguishes the factors of type *III* from other factors as follows.

Proposition 46.3-20. *Let $\mathcal{M}$ be a factorial W*-algebra. If $\mathcal{M}$ is of type III, then $0 \in S(\mathcal{M})$. Otherwise $S(\mathcal{M}) = \{1\}$.*

Theorem 46.3-21. *The Connes invariant $S(\mathcal{M})$ provides a complete classification of σ-finite III-factors $\mathcal{M}$ by specifying the following cases:*

(a) $S(\mathcal{M}) = \{0, 1\}$, *characterizing III_0-factors.*
(b) $S(\mathcal{M}) = \{\lambda^n \mid n \in \mathbb{N}\}$, $0 < \lambda < 1$, *characterizing III_λ-factors.*
(c) $S(\mathcal{M}) = \mathbb{R}$, *characterizing III_1-factors.*

According to [Con73, Corollary 3.2.5] it is sufficient to perform the intersection in Eq. (46.3.20) over all normal *faithful* states, if one knows that the factor is not of type I_∞ or II_∞. It is even enough to calculate $S(\mathcal{M})$ with a single normal faithful state φ, i.e., $S(\mathcal{M}) = \sigma(\Delta_\varphi)$, if the invariant algebra $\mathcal{M}_\varphi^{\mathbb{R}}$ for the modular automorphism group is a factor (see [Con73, Corollary 3.2.7]), which we denote the "factorial invariant case".

If the normal state is faithful, the logarithm of the operator spectrum $\sigma(\Delta_\varphi)$ is equal to the Arveson spectrum of the modular automorphism group (by Corollary 46.2-7), and gives by rescaling the dynamical spectrum of the effective Heisenberg dynamics over a KMS state. Being an algebraic invariant, such a dynamical spectrum exhibits a great stability against perturbations.

The "factorial invariant case" is especially realized for faithful ergodic states φ of an asymptotic Abelian dynamics. Then the dynamics is also $G = \mathbb{R}$-Abelian and the $\mathbb{R}$-invariant GNS subspace is $\mathcal{H}_\varphi^{\mathbb{R}} = \mathbb{C}\Omega_\varphi$ (see Proposition 48.3-21 on page 1823), which implies $\mathcal{M}_\varphi^{\mathbb{R}} = \mathbb{C}\mathbb{1}_\varphi$. In this manner we can conclude that the von Neumann algebra for the black body radiation in an infinite cavity is a factor of type III_1. (Notice that also there the GNS von Neumann algebra is σ-finite, acting in a separable Hilbert space.) Therefore, there are no normal pure states in the temperature representation, a typically thermodynamic feature.

PART N

States and their Decomposition Measures

Chapter 47

Convex Sets

Convex sets turn up in our book mainly as state spaces and distinguished subsets of them. The first section of this overview treats basic notions of geometric convexity. In the second section, we outline some general features of state spaces and characterize quantum mechanical state spaces by their 3-ball property. For deeper insight into quantum mechanical notions, we mention in the third Section state spaces with n-ball property. For $n > 3$, they are even more non-classical than quantum mechanical state spaces. This leads in following sections to a rather general formulation and interpretation of "properties", coherent superpositions of states, and of transition probabilities.

Some connections of convexity with topology and measure theory are given in Sec. 48.1.1.

47.1. Fundamentals of Convex Sets and Faces

Let $\mathcal{V}$ be a vector space over the scalar field $\mathbb{R}$ or $\mathbb{C}$. A *convex combination* of elements $v_1, \ldots, v_n$ of $\mathcal{V}$ is defined as

$$\sum_{j=1}^{n} \lambda_j v_j \in \mathcal{V}, \quad \text{with} \quad \lambda_j \geq 0 \quad \text{and} \quad \sum_{j=1}^{n} \lambda_j = 1, \tag{47.1.1}$$

where the number $n \in \mathbb{N}$ of elements is always finite.

The set of all convex combinations of two elements $v_1, v_2 \in \mathcal{V}$ produces the line $L(v_1, v_2)$ between v_1 and v_2:

$$L(v_1, v_2) := \{\lambda v_1 + (1 - \lambda)v_2 \in \mathcal{V} \mid \lambda \in [0, 1]\}.$$

The convex combination $v = \lambda v_1 + (1 - \lambda)v_2$ of $v_1, v_2 \in \mathcal{V}$ is called *proper*, if $0 < \lambda < 1$ and $v_1 \neq v_2$, that is, if v is an interior point of the line $L(v_1, v_2)$. If V is any subset of $\mathcal{V}$, then the *convex hull* $\mathrm{Conv}(V)$ consists of all convex combinations involving elements from V.

Definition 47.1-1 (Convex Set). Let $\mathcal{V}$ be a real or complex vector space. Then a subset $K \subseteq \mathcal{V}$ is *convex*, if K contains all convex combinations of its elements, that is, if K contains the lines $L(v_1, v_2)$ between all elements $v_1, v_2 \in K$.

The element $v \in K$ is called an *extreme element* of the convex set K, if there exists no proper convex decomposition of v within K: If $v = \lambda v_1 + (1 - \lambda)v_2$ for some $0 < \lambda < 1$ and some $v_1, v_2 \in K$, then this implies $v_1 = v_2 = v$.

The *extreme boundary* $\partial_e K$ of the convex set K consists of all extreme points of K.

Usually it is assumed that $\mathcal{V}$ is a Hausdorff locally convex topological vector space, an LC-space, as we describe them in Chapter 49, and the convex subset $K \subset \mathcal{V}$ is equipped with the induced topology. Since a point v in the interior $\dot{K}$ of K is surrounded by a convex neighborhood, it cannot belong to the extreme boundary $\partial_e K$. Thus $\partial_e K$ is contained in the topological boundary ∂K.

For example, if K is a closed (hence compact) tetrahedra T in $\mathcal{V} = \mathbb{R}^3$, then the extreme boundary $\partial_e T$ consists of the four vertices of T and is much smaller than the topological boundary ∂T of T. Note that the topological interior $\dot{T}$ of the tetrahedra is also a convex set, the extreme boundary of which is empty.

As another example, we consider a closed 3-ball $B = \{x \in \mathbb{R}^3 = \mathcal{V} \mid |x - x_0| \leq r\}$ with radius $r > 0$ and center point $x_0 \in \mathbb{R}^3$. Obviously B is convex, and its extreme boundary is just the 2-sphere $\partial_e B = \{x \in \mathbb{R}^3 \mid |x - x_0| = r\}$, what here agrees with the topological boundary ∂B of B.

The compact tetrahedra and compact 3-ball may serve to illustrate the *Krein–Milman Theorem* 48.1-8 on page 1783 for a compact convex set K. They are the (topological) closures of $\text{Conv}(\partial_e K)$, what implies especially the non-voidness of $\partial_e K$.

Examples of non-compact convex sets are provided by hyper-planes (affine subspaces) of a vector space $\mathcal{V}$. So $H := \{v_0 + v \mid v \in \mathcal{V}_0\}$, $\mathcal{V}_0$ a linear subspace of $\mathcal{V}$, is a frequent example of a convex set, which is not a linear subspace if $v_0 \neq 0$.

Definition 47.1-2 (Faces). A subset F of a convex set K is called a *face*, if $v \in F$, and $v = \lambda v_1 + (1 - \lambda)v_2$ with $v_1, v_2 \in K$ and $\lambda \in [0, 1]$, implies $v_1, v_2 \in F$.

A face F of K is called *proper* if it is different from K itself and from the empty subset $\emptyset \subset K$, the latter being considered as an improper face of K, for completeness.

Thus, the quality to be an element of a face preserves under convex decompositions: The components of the convex decompositions are still in the face. (Only special faces lead to that preservation of their element relation under infinite or even continuous convex decompositions.)

Observation 47.1-3. Let K be a convex set.

Each one-point set (singleton) $\{v\}$, with $v \in \partial_e K$, is a face, allowing only the trivial decomposition.

For each face F of K, the extreme boundary $\partial_e F$ is contained in $\partial_e K$. Indeed, if $v \in \partial_e F$ is convex decomposed in K, then the decomposition stays in F and is thus trivial.

In the same manner, it follows that a subface F' of F is also a face of K.

For a closed 3-ball B the only proper faces are the singletons in ∂B.

Definition 47.1-4 (Split Faces). If F is a face of the convex set K, then the *complementary set* F^C is by definition the union of all faces of K, non-intersecting with F (and thus F^C is different from $K \backslash F$). F^C is not convex in general, but if so, it is a face.

A face F of the convex set K is said to be a *split face*, if F^C is a face and if K is the direct convex sum of F and F^C. That is, for each $v \in K$ there are unique elements $v_1 \in F$, $v_2 \in F^C$ and a unique number $\lambda \in [0,1]$ such that $v = \lambda v_1 + (1 - \lambda)v_2$.

If F is a split face, then F^C is also a split face, and we call (F, F^C) a pair of complementary split faces. Sometimes K for itself is considered an improper split face with complementary face $K^C = \emptyset$.

Let again T be a closed tetrahedra and F the closed line between two vertices. Then F^C is the closed line between the remaining two vertices. Clearly (F, F^C) constitutes a pair of complementary split faces of the tetrahedra. Since the points on the mentioned two lines are unique convex combinations of their end points, each point of T is a unique convex combination of the four vertices: T is a *simplex*. From this fact alone follows, that each closed face of T is a split face.

For a 3-ball B consider the face $\{v\}$, $v \in \partial_e B$. The complementary set $\{v\}^C$ is the union of the disjoint faces and equals $\partial_e B \backslash \{v\}$, which is no face. There is no proper split face in B. For arbitrary two different elements $v_1, v_2 \in \partial_e B$ every proper convex combination $\lambda v_1 + (1 - \lambda)v_2$, $0 < \lambda < 1$, gives an element in the interior $\dot{B}$ of B. In fact, B is the convex hull $\mathrm{Conv}(\partial_e B)$ of $\partial_e B$. But each $v \in \dot{B}$ can be obtained by various proper convex combinations of two different extreme elements, and B is not a simplex.

Already in this general context we discover a feature, which in the statistical interpretation is characteristic for two so-called disjoint physical states:

Proposition 47.1-5 (Disjoint Extreme Points). *Let (F, F^C) be a pair of proper complementary split faces of a convex set K and let be given two extreme points $v_1 \in \partial_e F$ and $v_2 \in \partial_e F^C$. Then the smallest face $F(v_1, v_2)$ containing v_1 and v_2 is the line $L(v_1, v_2)$ between the two points.*

Proof. Let $v = \lambda' w_1 + (1 - \lambda')w_2$ be a convex decomposition in K of an arbitrary $v = \lambda v_1 + (1 - \lambda)v_2 \in L(v_1, v_2)$. Substitute in the first decomposition of v the unique split decompositions of w_1 and of w_2. This gives a split decomposition of v, which must coincide with the second originally given decomposition of v, which is already split. From this, one concludes that w_1 and w_2 are both in $L(v_1, v_2)$ and that $L(v_1, v_2)$ is a face of K. Since $\{v_1\}$ and $\{v_2\}$ are the only proper subfaces of $L(v_1, v_2)$, the latter is the smallest face containing v_1 and v_2. $\qquad\square$

Definition 47.1-6 (Affine Mappings). Let K and K' be two convex sets. A mapping $\phi : K \to K'$ is called *affine*, if ϕ preserves convex combinations, that is, if

$$\phi(\lambda v_1 + (1-\lambda)v_2) = \lambda\phi(v_1) + (1-\lambda)\phi(v_2), \quad \forall v_1, v_2 \in K, \quad \forall \lambda \in [0,1]. \quad (47.1.2)$$

In general, ϕ is, of course, not injective. For example, the affine ϕ may map a K of arbitrary dimension into $K' = \mathbb{R}$, what we then call an *affine function* on K. The set of affine functions on K is denoted by $\mathrm{Aff}(K)$.

The image $\phi(K)$ of an affine mapping between the convex sets K and K' is always a convex subset of K'.

Let the affine mapping $\phi : K \to K'$ be injective. If $v' = \lambda v_1' + (1-\lambda)v_2'$ is a convex combination within the convex image $\phi(K)$, then we get $\phi(\lambda\phi^{-1}(v_1') + (1-\lambda)\phi^{-1}(v_2')) = v_1' + (1-\lambda)v_2' = v'$ since ϕ is affine. Thus $\phi^{-1}(v') = \lambda\phi^{-1}(v_1') + (1-\lambda)\phi^{-1}(v_2')$, and we see that also $\phi^{-1} : \phi(K) \to K$ is affine.

We observe that an affine bijection $\phi : K \to K'$ maps the convex combinations bijectively onto each other. Thus F is a face of K, if and only if $\phi(F)$ is a face of K'. As a consequence we have the following result.

Lemma 47.1-7 (Affine Isomorphisms). *Let ϕ be a bijective affine map from the convex set K onto the convex set K'.*

(a) *Then ϕ maps the faces, especially the extreme elements, of K bijectively onto the faces, especially onto the extreme elements, of K'.*

(b) *We also have for a face $F \subset K$ that the complementary set F^C is mapped onto the complementary set $\phi(F)^C$ of $\phi(F)$. Thus F is a split face of K, if and only $\phi(F)$ is a split face of K'.*

If $K' = K$, then the affine bijections constitute a group, which may be viewed as the convex structure group *of K.*

The special mathematical importance of real affine functions $\mathrm{Aff}(K)$ and their meaning in the statistical interpretation is discussed in the following section. Here, we compile preparatory properties of affine functions.

Observation 47.1-8 (Affine Functions). Let K be a convex subset of the real vector space $\mathcal{V}$.

(a) $\mathrm{Aff}(K)$ is a real vector space under the point-wise linear combinations.

(b) If $a \in \mathrm{Aff}(\mathcal{V})$ and $a(0) = a_0 \in \mathbb{R}$, then $a - a_0 \in \mathrm{Aff}_0(\mathcal{V})$, the subvector space of affine functions on $\mathcal{V}$ vanishing at $v = 0$.

(c) Each $a \in \mathrm{Aff}_0(\mathcal{V})$ is a real linear function on $\mathcal{V}$, and each real linear function is in $\mathrm{Aff}_0(\mathcal{V})$. Thus $\mathrm{Aff}(\mathcal{V})$ contains the real linear functions as a genuine subspace.

(d) Let $\mathcal{V}$ be generated by K, and 0 not contained in K. That is, $\mathcal{V} = \mathbb{R}_+ K - \mathbb{R}_+ K$, and assume that each $w \in \mathcal{V}$ has a unique (Jordan like) representation $w = \alpha_1 v_1 - \alpha_2 v_2$, with $\alpha_1, \alpha_2 \in \mathbb{R}_+$ and $v_1, v_2 \in K$. Then each $a \in \mathrm{Aff}(K)$ has by dilation and additivity, $a(w) := \alpha_1 a(v_1) - \alpha_2 a(v_2)$, a unique extension to a function in $\mathrm{Aff}_0(\mathcal{V})$.

(e) Not only the restrictions of the functions in $\mathrm{Aff}_0(\mathcal{V})$ to functions on K, but also those of $\mathrm{Aff}(\mathcal{V})$, constitute in general a subspace of $\mathrm{Aff}(K)$.

47.2. Convex State Spaces

Let us now interpret the points of a convex set K as the (statistical) states of a physical system. In order to have sufficiently many extreme points we mostly assume K to be compact (referring again to the Krein–Milman Theorem 48.1-8 on page 1783). Since, in the sense of the *convex state space approach*, we want to develop the statistical theory from K as the primary notion, we assume its topology given intrinsically (without considering at first an enclosing LC space $\mathcal{V}$). As a general assumption, we require the topology of the compact convex set K to be Hausdorff.

We need further mathematical concepts for the set of faces of K and for the affine functions on K, but consider all that from the viewpoint of a statistical theory.

47.2.1. *Statistical Interpretation of Convexity*

Definition 47.2-1 (Statistical Interpretation of Convex Operations). The operations of convex composition respectively decomposition in the given compact convex set K are viewed as the *mixing* respectively *purification* of *states*. If the statistical state is visualized as an *ensemble of systems*, then one-point in the convex set means a whole ensemble in a special preparation, and the fundamental convex operations correspond to the weighted combinations respectively weighted splittings of the ensembles.

This interpretation of the convex operations is considered universally valid for classical, quantum mechanical, and even more general statistical theories.

Thus, the concept of a *pure state*, defined as an element of the extreme boundary $\partial_e K$, is a universal notion (independent of considering a classical or a non-classical theory). The purity of a state means that it cannot be made less mixed. In general, however, pure states do not describe *individual states*, where we define the latter as those, in which all qualities of the system are actualized.

If e.g., K is the closed tetrahedra $T \subset \mathbb{R}^3$, then its four vertices $v_i \in \partial_e T$ are its pure states, and each point $v \in T$ is a unique convex mixture $v = \sum_{i=1}^4 \lambda_i v_i$ of them (with $\lambda_i \in [0,1]$ and $\sum_{i=1}^4 \lambda_i = 1$). Thus T describes a statistical experiment with four outcomes, and the λ_i give the probabilities, where the uniqueness of the extremal decomposition is a very special feature of that convex set. This feature characterizes a simplex and is typical for classical theories only.

If we restrict our interests entirely to the given statistical system, then the v_i come along as individuals. Each "property" of the system is given by a subset $f \subseteq \partial_e T$ of individuals which "have" that "property". A subset $f' \subset f$ signifies a more specific "property" than f, including still f (corresponding to the implication of classical proposition calculus). The finest "properties" are represented by the singletons of the individuals for themselves. Since in a deterministic description one deals directly with the individuals, one is concerned only with $P(\partial_e T)$, the set of all subsets of the extreme boundary.

Since a statistical description includes the mixtures of the pure states, one has to form the statistical notions in reference to the convex body created by the extreme points. On hand of the tetrahedra T, one remarks directly, that the $f \in P(\partial_e T) = P(\{v_1, \ldots, v_4\})$ are in bijective, inclusion preserving correspondence, with those closed faces F of T, for which $\partial_e F = f$. If one knows $v \in F$, then one knows the unique set $\{v_i, \ldots, v_k\} \subseteq \{v_1, \ldots, v_4\}$ of pure states in the extreme decomposition of v. Since these own the "property" represented by $\{v_1, \ldots, v_4\}$ we may say that also v has this "property". Thus we may say that faces F *per se* represent "properties" in the ensemble language. It is the latter formulation of a "property", *which shows us how to generalize "properties" also to statistical theories with non-simplicial convex state spaces.*

Definition 47.2-2 (F-Properties of Convex State Spaces). For a statistical state space, given by the convex set K, let us speak of an F-*property* the state $v \in K$ is displaying, if the state is an element of the face F.

The F'-property implies the F-property, if F' is a subface of F, and we have the traditional inferential ordering by inclusion also for F-properties.

A decisive aspect is, that the relation $v \in F$ takes over to the components in a convex decomposition $v = \lambda v' + (1 - \lambda)v''$ of v, so that also any (less mixed) component states v' and v'' possess the F-property. The inclusion relation for sets of individuals is in this manner replaced for ensembles by "being less mixed" (defined as being a component of a convex decomposition).

For general convex K, the F-property constitutes an essential generalization of the notion of a "property", given as a set of individuals. There are (non-compact) faces F (of compact K) without extreme points, so that no pure state in $\partial_e K$ displays then the F-property (cf. in this context Observation 47.1-3). This situation is independent from the pure state describing an individual or not, and is abundant in (quantum) statistical mechanics, where the temperature is the most known example. (For infinite systems, the F-property "temperature" is given by a split face without an extreme boundary: No pure classical or quantum state has a finite temperature, and neither has an internal energy or another property depending on the temperature.)

Another generalization consists in the fact that F-properties are often not "compatible" with each other, in a sense which can be expressed in terms of "logical operations", that are the lattice relations. For discussing this let us list here, once and for all, the definitions of some general comparative and lattice relations (cf. [Kal83]).

47.2.2. *Partially Ordered Sets and Lattices*

The deterministic and statistical inclusion relation is a partial ordering for the set of faces of a convex set. Complementary faces should lead to a complementation relation.

Definition 47.2-3 (Posets, Chains, and Lattices). Let M be a set.

(a) M is *(partially) ordered*, if it owns a binary (order) relation $\leq$, which is reflexive $(a \leq a, \forall a \in M)$, transitive $(a \leq b$ and $b \leq c$ imply $a \leq c)$, and antisymmetric $(a \leq b$ and $b \leq a$ imply $a = b)$.

The tuple $(M, \leq)$ is then often called a *poset*. Let us verbalize $a \leq b$ by "b is greater than a" or by "b dominates a" or by "a is smaller than b".

If antisymmetry is omitted "$\leq$" is called a *pre-order*.

(b) Two elements a, b of a poset M are called *comparable*, if $a \leq b$ or $b \leq a$. A poset M is called a *chain* if every two of its elements are comparable.

(c) A subset X of a poset M has the upper (lower) bound b, if $a \leq b$ $(a \geq b)$, $\forall a \in X$.

A poset M is *lower bounded*, if M has a lower bound (denoted $0 \in M$) and *upper bounded* if it has an upper bound (denoted $1 \in M$).

(d) If a poset M contains a and b with $a \leq b$, the *order interval* $[a, b]$ consists of all $c \in M$ with $a \leq c \leq b$. (Notice that $[a, b]$ is not always a chain.)

(e) If for a, b in a poset M, the order interval $[a, b]$ equals the 2-element set $\{a, b\}$, then we say that b *covers* a (since there is no third element in between).

If a in a lower bounded poset M covers 0, then it is called an *atom*.

(f) Let M again be a poset. The *supremum* $\vee X$ of $X \subset M$ is, if it exists (in M), defined as the least upper bound of X, and the *infimum* $\wedge X$ of $X \subset M$ is, if it exists, defined as the greatest lower bound of X.

For a 2-element set, we write $\vee \{a, b\} \equiv a \vee b$ and $\wedge \{a, b\} \equiv a \wedge b$, and get in this manner binary relations, which may be iterated.

(g) A *lattice* L is a poset, for which each *finite* subset has a supremum and an infimum.

A lattice L is *complete*, if the supremum and infimum exist for all subsets.

(h) A lattice L is *atomic*, if it is lower bounded and each $a \in L, a \neq 0$, dominates an atom.

For the elements a, b, c of a lattice L there holds associativity $a \vee (b \vee c) = (a \vee b) \vee c$ and $a \wedge (b \wedge c) = (a \wedge b) \wedge c$, commutativity $a \vee b = b \vee a$ and $a \wedge b = b \wedge a$, as well as the absorption laws $a \vee (a \wedge b) = a$ and $a \wedge (a \vee b) = a$.

Reversely, a lattice may be defined as a set L equipped with two binary relations $\vee$ and $\wedge$, which satisfy the preceding three types of laws. L is made to a poset by setting $a \leq b \Leftrightarrow a = a \wedge b$.

Definition 47.2-4 (Special Lattices). Let L be a lattice.

(a) An ordered triple $(a, b, c) \subset L$ is called *distributive*, if $a \wedge (b \vee c) = (a \wedge b) \vee (a \wedge c)$. L is called *distributive*, if all its triples $(a, b, c) \subset L$ are distributive and also satisfy $a \vee (b \wedge c) = (a \vee b) \wedge (a \vee c)$.

(b) A map $^\perp : L \to L$ in a bi-bounded L is an *orthocomplementation*, if $a^{\perp\perp} = a$, $a \leq b \Rightarrow b^\perp \leq a^\perp$, $a \wedge a^\perp = 0$, $a \vee a^\perp = 1$ for all $a, b \in L$.
One concludes that $0^\perp = 1$, the relation $^\perp$ is one-to-one, and $(a \vee b)^\perp = a^\perp \wedge b^\perp$. An L endowed with an orthocomplementation is called *orthocomplemented*. The notion of orthocomplementation is also applied to bi-bounded posets.

(c) A distributive orthocomplemented L is called *Boolean*.

(d) An orthocomplemented L is called *orthomodular*, if for two comparable elements the *orthomodular law*

$$a \leq b \implies a \vee (a^\perp \wedge b) = b \left(\Leftrightarrow (a \wedge b) \vee (a^\perp \wedge b) = (a \vee a^\perp) \wedge b \right) \quad (47.2.1)$$

is valid. (The version within the brackets reveals orthomodularity as a special distributivity law.)

In an arbitrary orthocomplemented lattice one may formulate the *compatibility relation*

$$a \overset{c}{\sim} b \quad \Leftrightarrow \quad (a, b, b^\perp) \text{ is distributive}.$$

In an arbitrary orthocomplemented lattice L the compatibility relation is *symmetric*, if and only if L is orthomodular.
Let us define the symbol

$$C(a, b) := (a \wedge b) \vee (a \wedge b^\perp) \vee (a^\perp \wedge b) \vee (a^\perp \wedge b^\perp), \quad a, b \in L. \quad (47.2.2)$$

One has in an orthomodular lattice

$$a \overset{c}{\sim} b \quad \Leftrightarrow \quad C(a, b) = 1. \quad (47.2.3)$$

One also deduces in an orthomodular lattice that $a \overset{c}{\sim} b$ is valid, if and only if the smallest sublattice containing a and b is distributive.

This suggests the following definition: Two elements in an orthomodular lattice are called *maximal incompatible*, if and only if $C(a, b) = 0$. (It is an interesting problem whether all non-trivial spectral projections of the position operator of traditional quantum mechanics are maximal incompatible with all non-trivial spectral projections of the momentum operator.)

We return now to the F-properties of the convex state space K and observe the following.

Observation 47.2-5 (Lattice of General Faces). Let be K an arbitrary convex set and denote by $\mathcal{F}(K)$ the set of all its faces. The inclusion relation as ordering (logical implication) makes $\mathcal{F}(K)$ to a complete lattice. Indeed, the set-intersection

$$\bigwedge \{F_i \in \mathcal{F}(K) \,|\, i \in I\} := \bigcap \{F_i \in \mathcal{F}(K) \,|\, i \in I\} \in \mathcal{F}(K) \qquad (47.2.4)$$

is stable against convex combinations and convex decompositions, for arbitrary index sets I, and is so an element of $\mathcal{F}(K)$, which is clearly the largest lower bound. This leads also to the existence of the supremum of an arbitrary family of faces

$$\bigvee \{F_i \in \mathcal{F}(K) \,|\, i \in I\} := \bigcap \{F' \in \mathcal{F}(K) \,|\, \bigcup_I F_i \subseteq F'\} \in \mathcal{F}(K), \qquad (47.2.5)$$

which is again an infimum of the faces F' (those which contain the given family).

The lattice $\mathcal{F}(K)$ has the lowest element $\emptyset \equiv 0$ and the greatest element $K \equiv 1$. In general $\mathcal{F}(K)$ is not *distributive*.

In order to define "compatibility" as a special distributivity, and also for an adequate filter interpretation, we need still an important feature for a face lattice $\mathcal{F}(K)$, namely an *orthocomplementation*. This requires the introduction of surprisingly much more mathematical formalism.

Before we engulf into the somewhat involved mathematics let us mention that a major purpose of the present discussion of F-properties is to connect the notion of an *observable* as an algebra element, used all over the book, with an operational content. We want to illustrate that the so-called "abstract" mathematical descriptions of states and observables may nevertheless be near to the experimental handling.

A physical "observable" is certainly a concept, which associates each individual state with a real numerical value, or more generally, which associates each statistical state (prepared ensemble) with an expectation value. A class of states associated with a fixed value of an observable should represent a "property" of the system, also in the formalized sense, which means in our context an F-property. The special numerical scale of an observable is, however, of less empirical significance than the ordering among the states, expressed by that of the real scale values. To be precise, the scale expresses only a pre-ordering among the states, but produces a chain ordering for the classes of states with fixed observable value, that is by our assumption a chain of "properties".

For example, the classes of equal temperature are arranged by thermal contact and waiting for equilibrium, and their ordering by the direction of heat flow. We still suffer, however, under the different temperature scales. Concerning the entropy, one knows that under adiabatic enclosure each transition of states leads to a higher-or-equal value of this observable, and each entropy scale has to represent this ordering. (By the extensivity of the entropy its possible scales are much more restricted than the temperature scales.)

Conceptually it is more elegant to employ in the beginning not the state classes of equal values of an observable, but to work with those state classes which represent lower values of the observable than a given one. Thus an *empirical observable* is in first line a family of "properties", which is ordered by inclusion, that is, in the convex state space approach, an ordered family $\{F\}_{\leq} \subset \mathcal{F}(K)$. A *metric empirical observable* can then be defined as an observable $\{F\}_{\leq}$ with a numerical scale, and can be identified with an order preserving mapping $A : \{F\}_{\leq} \to \mathbb{R}$.

If the lattice $\mathcal{F}(K)$ is non-distributive, the members of an empirical observable $\{F\}_{\leq}$ have to satisfy an additional compatibility assumption. We have to introduce into $\mathcal{F}(K)$ a "compatibility" concept so that two comparable F-properties, $F \leq F'$ say, are compatible with each other.

The ultimate aim is, to relate a metric empirical observable A with an expectation value functional, that is, with an affine function $a : K \to \mathbb{R}$. That is the inverse point of view to algebraic quantum theory, where the algebra of observables (where the observables already have a scale, cf. the commutation relations) is the primary notion, and the states are linear (positive, normalized) functionals on it. In the convex state space approach, one starts with the apparently much simpler notion of a convex set and has then to do some work to get the metric empirical observables.

We examine first the mathematical features of these intended expressions for observables.

47.2.3. *Affine Functions on Convex Sets*

The relations discussed in the following pertain also to C*-algebraic quantum theory. What is lacking is the algebraic product.

Definition 47.2-6 (Bounded Affine Functions). Let the convex set K be equipped with a topology τ, in which it is compact and where the convex combinations $\lambda v_1 + (1 - \lambda)v_2$ are jointly continuous in $\lambda \in [0, 1]$, $v_1, v_2 \in K$.

We denote by $\text{Aff}_c(K)$ the continuous, and by $\text{Aff}_b(K)$ the bounded, real-valued, affine functions on K. (Since over the compact K a continuous function is bounded, we have $\text{Aff}_c(K) \subset \text{Aff}_b(K)$.) These are real vector spaces under point-wise linear combinations.

We define a norm in $\text{Aff}_b(K)$ by

$$\|a\| := \sup\{|a(v)| \,|\, v \in K\}, \quad a \in \text{Aff}_b(K). \tag{47.2.6}$$

We set up an order relation by

$$a \leq b \Leftrightarrow a(v) \leq b(v), \quad \forall v \in K, \quad a, b \in \text{Aff}_b(K). \tag{47.2.7}$$

We introduce the unit function

$$e \in \text{Aff}_b(K), \quad e(v) := 1, \ \forall v \in K. \tag{47.2.8}$$

It is of great importance that e is also in $\text{Aff}_c(K)$.

(Hint for the C*-algebraic conditioned reader: One may compare $\mathrm{Aff}_c(K)$ with a unital C*-algebra $\mathcal{A}$, K with the state space $\mathcal{S}(\mathcal{A})$, and $\mathrm{Aff}_b(K)$ with $\mathcal{A}^{**} \cong \mathcal{M}_u$, as will be confirmed by the subsequent results.)

Observation 47.2-7. For the ordering in $\mathrm{Aff}_b(K)$, induced by the (pointed, convex) cone $\mathrm{Aff}_b(K)^+ = \{a \in \mathrm{Aff}_b(K) \,|\, a(v) \geq 0, \forall v \in K\}$, we clearly have $a \leq b$ implies $a + c \leq b + c$ and implies $\lambda a \leq \lambda b$, for $a, b, c \in \mathrm{Aff}_b(K)$ and $\lambda \in \mathbb{R}_+$. This makes $\mathrm{Aff}_b(K)$ to an ordered vector space.

Since the unit-ball $\mathrm{Aff}_b(K)_1$ consists of those affine functions a with $\sup\{|a(v)| \,|\, v \in K\} \leq 1$, it equals the order interval $[-e, e]$. The ordering in $\mathrm{Aff}_b(K)$, is therefore Archimedian, i.e., $-\mathbb{R}_+ a$ is upper bounded, if and only if $a \geq 0$. These facts qualify $\mathrm{Aff}_b(K)$ to be an ordered vector space with *order unit* e.

In such space, formula (47.2.9) below (the Minkowsky gauge) is known to make the space to a normed vector space, which is termed *order-unit space* (see [Alf71]).

Taking into account the norm completeness of $\mathrm{Aff}_b(K)$, and of $\mathrm{Aff}_c(K)$, we may state the following.

Proposition 47.2-8 (Order-Unit Spaces of Affine Functions). *Endowed with the above relations, $\mathrm{Aff}_b(K)$ is an order-unit space with order unit e, so that we have*

$$\|a\| := \inf\{\lambda \geq 0 \,|\, -\lambda e \leq a \leq \lambda e\}, \quad \forall a \in \mathrm{Aff}_b(K). \qquad (47.2.9)$$

The subspace of continuous affine functions $\mathrm{Aff}_c(K) \subset \mathrm{Aff}_b(K)$ is for itself an order-unit space with the same order unit e.

Both spaces are ordered Banach spaces.

By the standard procedure, we introduce the dual Banach space of all bounded, real-valued, linear functionals, acting on the continuous affine functions,

$$\mathcal{V} := \mathrm{Aff}_c(K)^* \ni \hat{v}, \quad \|\hat{v}\| := \sup\{|\hat{v}(a)| \,|\, a \in \mathrm{Aff}_c(K), \|a\| \leq 1\}. \qquad (47.2.10)$$

In $\mathcal{V}$, one has the (partial) ordering $\hat{v} \leq \hat{w} \Leftrightarrow \hat{v}(a) \leq \hat{w}(a), \forall a \in \mathrm{Aff}_c(K)^+$. This leads us back to the original K, enriched with a norm topology.

Proposition 47.2-9 (Dual Banach Space of $\mathrm{Aff}_c(K)$). *Assume, as before, the convex K to be τ-compact. Note that, as a dual Banach space, $\mathcal{V} = \mathrm{Aff}_c(K)^*$ inherits also the weak* topology of point-wise convergence. The canonical embedding*

$$K \ni v \mapsto \hat{v} \in \mathcal{V} = \mathrm{Aff}_c(K)^*, \quad \text{given by } \hat{v}(a) := a(v), \ \forall a \in \mathrm{Aff}_c(K), \qquad (47.2.11)$$

constitutes an affine homeomorphism between K and $\mathcal{V}_1^+ := \{\hat{v} \in \mathcal{V}^+ \,|\, \|\hat{v}\| = 1\}$, the latter being equipped with the induced weak* topology (where $\mathcal{V}^+$ consists of those $\hat{v}$, for which $\hat{v}(a) \geq 0, \forall a \in \mathrm{Aff}_c(K)^+$).

In $\mathcal{V}$, we have the following relations.

(a) *The positive cone $\mathcal{V}^+$ is generated by K, i.e., $\mathcal{V}^+ = \cup_{\lambda \geq 0} \lambda K$.*
(b) *For all $\hat{v} \in \mathcal{V}^+$ the norm is expressible by $\|\hat{v}\| = \hat{v}(e)$.*

(c) *The unit ball* $B := \{\hat{v} \in \mathcal{V} \mid \|\hat{v}\| \leq 1\}$ *equals the convex hull* $\mathrm{Conv}(K \cup (-K))$.

(d) *The base normed property is valid for all* $\hat{v} \in \mathcal{V}$: $\|\hat{v}\| = \inf\{\lambda \geq 0 \mid \hat{v} \in \lambda B\}$.

(e) *A Hahn–Jordan decomposition holds for all* $\hat{v} \in B$: $\hat{v} = \hat{v}_+ - \hat{v}_-$ *for uniquely determined* $\hat{v}_+, \hat{v}_- \in \mathcal{V}^+$, *and one has then* $\|\hat{v}\| = \|\hat{v}_+\| + \|\hat{v}_-\|$.

(f) *The whole of* $\mathcal{V}$ *is linearly generated by the original state space* K: $\mathcal{V} = \mathcal{V}^+ - \mathcal{V}^+ = \mathrm{LH}(K)$ ($\mathbb{R}$-*linear hull*).

Of structural interest are also the following isomorphisms between ordered Banach spaces, which we mostly treat as identifications:

$$\mathrm{Aff}_b(K) \quad \longleftrightarrow \quad \mathcal{V}^* \quad \longleftrightarrow \quad \mathrm{Aff}_c(K)^{**}. \tag{47.2.12}$$

The first identification in (47.2.12) says that each bounded affine function a on K has a unique extension $\tilde{a}$ to a *linear, norm continuous function on* $\mathcal{V}$.

Definition 47.2-10 (Linear Extension of Affine Functions). The extension of the function $a \in \mathrm{Aff}_b(K)$ acts on $\mathcal{V} \ni \hat{w} = t_1\hat{v}_1 - t_1\hat{v}_2$, $t_1, t_2 \geq 0$, $v_{1,2} \in K$, (cf. Proposition 47.2-9 (a) and (f)) by

$$\tilde{a}(\hat{w}) := t_1 a(v_1) - t_2 a(v_2), \quad \text{especially} \quad \tilde{e}(\hat{w}) := t_1 - t_2, \tag{47.2.13}$$

and is linear in $\hat{w} \in \mathcal{V}$. (This follows from $\tilde{a}$ being affine on $\mathcal{V}$ and vanishing for $\hat{w} = 0$.)

Reversely, the restriction to K of a linear function $\tilde{a}$ on $\mathcal{V}$ is clearly affine. (We stick here to real functions, but the extension to complex linear functions, as is appropriate for quantum mechanics, is of course also uniquely given.)

The second identification in (47.2.12) follows from the definition of $\mathcal{V}$.

The decisive fact is, that the original topology τ on the compact convex K corresponds to the $\sigma(\mathcal{V}_1^+, \mathrm{Aff}_c(K))$-topology (the latter being equal to the induced weak* topology). The set of positive normalized functionals $\mathcal{V}_1^+$ is called in [Alf71] the *state space* of $\mathrm{Aff}_c(K)$, what conforms with our statistical interpretation of its affine homeomorphic counterpart K.

Corollary 47.2-11. *Each compact convex K is (affine homeomorphic to) the mathematical state space of a complete order-unit space.*

The compactness of $\mathcal{V}_1^+$ may bee seen as follows. By the Banach–Alaoglu theorem the unit ball $\mathcal{V}_1$ is weak* compact by duality, and the positive cone $\mathcal{V}^+$ is easily seen to be weak* closed. The state space $\mathcal{V}_1^+$ is, however, weak* compact only because $\mathrm{Aff}_c(K)$ contains an order unit e. By Proposition 47.2-9(b), $\mathcal{V}_1^+$ is the intersection of the weak* closed hyper-plane $\{\hat{v} \in \mathcal{V} \mid \hat{v}(e) = 1\}$ with $\mathcal{V}^+$ and with $\mathcal{V}_1$, and is thus compact.

Notational Remark 47.2-12 (Ensembles are Scaled States). According to the above identification, the state space K may now be viewed as a subset of $\mathcal{V}$

and we **drop the hat** for designating elements $v \in \mathcal{V}_1^+$. Extending this notation we denote henceforth all elements of $\mathcal{V}$ by characters like v, w etc.

The elements in $\mathcal{V}^+$ may be interpreted as *unnormalized states* that are *scaled states*, which let us call simply *ensembles*, to have a name for them. The norm $\|w\| = w(e)$ of an ensemble $w \in \mathcal{V}^+$ indicates its *size*, and one may say that the unit function $e \in \mathrm{Aff}_b(K)$ tests the size of the ensemble.

The map

$$\mathcal{F}(K) \ni F \to \mathbb{R}_+ F \in \mathcal{F}(\mathcal{V}^+) \qquad (47.2.14)$$

constitutes a *lattice isomorphism* from the faces of K (including the improper face $\emptyset$) onto the faces of the positive cone $\mathcal{V}^+$, if one associates $\emptyset \in \mathcal{F}(K)$ with $\{0\} \in \mathcal{F}(\mathcal{V}^+)$.

There are two desirable physical operations concerning F-properties, which restrict the mathematical nature of the corresponding faces. The first is, that each F-property should be retrieved by the fact that a certain observable assumes a given real value, what is called a detectable F-property. If we anticipate that an (metric, empirical) observable may in fact be represented by a bounded affine function, that means the following (cf. [Rüt83]).

Definition 47.2-13 (Detectable Faces). A face $F \in \mathcal{F}(K)$ is called *detectable*, if there is an $a \in \mathrm{Aff}_b(K)$ and a real $t \in \mathbb{R}$ so that

$$a(v) = t, \ \forall v \in F, \quad \text{and} \quad a(v) < t, \ \forall v \in K \backslash F. \qquad (47.2.15)$$

For any $a \in \mathrm{Aff}_b(K)$ and $t \in \mathbb{R}$, the pre-image $a^{-1}(t) =: F$ is certainly a face of K, if $a \leq te$, which by the norm continuity of a is *norm closed*. Because of that, detectable faces are also called "norm exposed". Geometrically, a face, detectable by $a \in \mathrm{Aff}_b(K)$, is the contact region between the norm closed hyper-plane $H = \tilde{a}^{-1}(t)$ (with $\tilde{a}$ the linear extension of a) and K.

The second idea, which restricts the faces of K, namely that the physically most interesting faces should be the result of a filtering operation, is best formulated in terms of scaled states, viz. ensembles.

Example 47.2-14 (Stern–Gerlach Experiment). As an empirical paradigm for a filtering let us consider an ensemble of microscopic particles in the Stern–Gerlach experiment. The initial ensemble is split by the transversal magnetic field into subensembles, spatially separated in the direction of the field, say in the 3-direction. If one eliminates all sub-ensembles up to a single one and repeats the experiment, there is no further splitting of the sub-ensemble.

If one applies further, already known, measurement devices, which decompose the filtered subensemble in the convex sense (measuring e.g., the electric charge or the energy), the again repeated Stern–Gerlach experiment does still not give a new splitting. That means that the newly created subensembles (with sharp electric charge and energy, say) retain the quality, which has led to the first splitting in the Stern–Gerlach experiment. So the Stern–Gerlach filtering leads to a family of scaled states, which has a facial structure.

The Stern–Gerlach splitting is thus the kind of filtering we have in mind: It is idempotent and filters out a face of scaled states.

If we associate numerical values with the Stern–Gerlach filtered subensembles, and call them "spin in 3-direction", a subensemble "has" now a spin in 3-direction. Thus, to have a sharp spin in 3-direction is an F-property, and that F-property is detectable.

We remark, by the way, that the introduction of (affine) numerical functions is a secondary process, after the convex decomposition properties of system states having been analyzed.

In the general frame of the convex state space approach one simply assumes a generalized version of such filtering projections, specifying — an thus clarifying — its characteristic features.

Definition 47.2-15 (Filtering Projections).   Consider the dual $\mathcal{V}$ of $\mathrm{Aff}_c(K)$ for a compact convex K. A linear mapping $Q : \mathcal{V} \to \mathcal{V}$ is called a *filtering projection*, if it owns the following six features:

(1) It is positive: $Q(\mathcal{V}^+) \subset \mathcal{V}^+$.
(2) It is idempotent: $Q \circ Q = Q$.
(3) It has unit norm: $\|Q\| := \sup\{\|Qv\| \mid \|v\| = 1\} = 1$.
(4) There exists a complementary map $Q^\perp$, which owns also the properties (1)–(3), and for which one has

$$\mathrm{ran}^+ Q \;=\; \ker^+ Q^\perp \quad \text{and} \quad \mathrm{ran}^+ Q^\perp = \ker^+ Q\,,$$

   where $\mathrm{ran}^+ Q \equiv \mathrm{ran}\, Q \cap \mathcal{V}^+ = \mathrm{ran}\, Q|_{\mathcal{V}^+}$ etc.
(5) The dual transformation $Q^* \;:\; \mathrm{Aff}_b(K) \;\to\; \mathrm{Aff}_b(K)$ (uniquely given by $[Q^*(a)](v) := a(Qv),\ \forall v \in \mathcal{V}_1^+ = K$) possesses also the properties (1)–(4) (where now $\mathcal{V}^+$ has to be replaced by $\mathrm{Aff}_b(K)^+$).
   The set of all filtering projections is denoted by $\mathcal{Q}(K)$. It includes the 0-map and its complementary map, the identity map.
(6) If $Q \in \mathcal{Q}(K)$, then it defines also a filtering projection Q_1 in K by renormalization: $Q_1(v) = Q(v)/\|Q(v)\| \Leftrightarrow Q(v) \neq 0$, the latter condition indicating $\mathrm{dom}\, Q_1 \subset K$.
   For $0 \in \mathcal{Q}(K)$, we write 0_1 for the improper filtering map in K with range $\emptyset \in \mathcal{F}(K)$.

As a little exercise let us demonstrate that a filtered set of ensembles $\mathrm{ran}^+ Q = Q(\mathcal{V}^+)$ is a norm closed face in $\mathcal{F}(\mathcal{V}^+)$: $v \in \mathrm{ran}^+ Q \Leftrightarrow Q^\perp v = 0$. The latter relation is clearly preserved under convex combinations, but also under convex decompositions as $v = \lambda v_1 + (1 - \lambda)v_2$, since $Q^\perp(v) = 0 = \lambda Q^\perp(v_1) + (1 - \lambda)Q^\perp(v_2) \Leftrightarrow \lambda Q^\perp(v_1) = -(1 - \lambda)Q^\perp(v_2) \Rightarrow Q^\perp(v_1) \in \mathcal{V}^+ \cap -\mathcal{V}^+ \Leftrightarrow Q^\perp(v_1) = 0 \Leftrightarrow v_1 \in \mathrm{ran}^+ Q$. Since Q and $Q^\perp$ are linear and norm continuous (with norm closed kernels), and since $\mathcal{V}^+$ is norm closed, the filtered set $\mathrm{ran}^+ Q = \ker Q^\perp \cap \mathcal{V}^+$ is also norm closed. The corresponding result is valid for Q_1 acting in K. If $Q \in \mathcal{Q}(K)$ and if for

$w \in \mathrm{dom}(Q_1)$, we have $v = Q_1(w) \in \mathrm{ran}\, Q_1 \subset K$ then there is exactly one $\hat{w} = w/\|Q(w)\|$ in $\mathcal{V}^+$ with $Q(\hat{w}) = v$.

A more profound result is, that the norm closed face $\mathrm{ran}\, Q_1 = Q(\mathcal{V}^+) \cap K$ of K determines already Q. And this enables us to introduce an orthocomplementation into the set of filtered faces, which means a special negation in the set of F-properties.

Proposition 47.2-16 (Orthocomplementation of Filtered Faces). *Let be given the filtering projection $Q \in \mathcal{Q}$ acting as Q_1 in K (cf. Definition 47.2-15(6)), where K is a compact convex set.*

(a) *We have*

$$F_Q := \mathrm{ran}\, Q_1 = Q(\mathcal{V}^+) \cap K \text{ is a norm closed face in } \mathcal{F}(K) \text{ for all } Q \in \mathcal{Q}(K).$$
$$(47.2.16)$$

(b) **Definition.** *Let us denote a face of the form F_Q for some $Q \in \mathcal{Q}(K)$ a filtered face (being also called* projective*). The set of filtered faces is denoted $\mathcal{E}(K)$. It is a subset of $\mathcal{F}(K)$.*

(c) *For given $F_Q \in \mathcal{E}(K)$, each other filtering projection $Q' \in \mathcal{Q}(K)$, with $Q'(\mathcal{V}^+) \cap K = F_Q$, equals Q.*

(d) *As a consequence of the foregoing assertion, each filtering projection $Q \in \mathcal{Q}(K)$ has just one complementary filtering projection $Q^\perp \in \mathcal{Q}(K)$.*

(e) *As a consequence of the two preceding assertions, we are able to define the relation*

$$\perp : \mathcal{E}(K) \to \mathcal{E}(K),\ F_Q \mapsto F_Q^\perp := F_{Q^\perp},\quad \forall Q \in \mathcal{Q}(K). \qquad (47.2.17)$$

This relation in $\mathcal{E}(K)$ satisfies $\mathcal{E}(K) \ni F = F^{\perp\perp}$. And if we introduce in $\mathcal{Q}(K)$ the ordering $Q \le Q' \Leftrightarrow Q \circ Q' = Q$ (and the set inclusion in $\mathcal{E}(K)$), then $Q \mapsto F_Q$ is order preserving and $\perp : \mathcal{E}(K) \to \mathcal{E}(K)$ is order reversing.

(f) *Up to now, we do not know whether the infima and suprema exist in $\mathcal{E}(K)$ so that $\mathcal{E}(K)$ would be a lattice. But we may already conclude that $Q \wedge Q^\perp = 0$, and from this that $F_Q \wedge F_{Q^\perp} = \emptyset$ and $F_Q \vee F_{Q^\perp} = K$, so that "$\perp$" is an orthocomplementation in the bi-bounded poset $\mathcal{E}(K)$ (cf. Definition 47.2-4).*

The special negation in $\mathcal{E}(K)$ given by $F \mapsto F^\perp$ does in general not agree with the usual ("classical") negation "not to have F" for a state in $F^\perp$. If F means e.g., to have the sharp spin value $1/2$ in 3-direction, then "not to have a sharp spin value $1/2$ in 3-direction" is not an F-property at all. Rather $F^\perp$ means that a state in $F^\perp$ has a sharp spin in 3-direction (a truly positive statement) and its value is the complementary value $-1/2$.

If $F \in \mathcal{F}(K)$ is a split face, we have the unique convex decomposition $K \ni v = \lambda v_1 + (1 - \lambda)v_2$, $v_1 \in F$, $v_2 \in F^C$, and we may define explicitly the renormalized filtering projection $Q_1(v) := v_1$, as well as $Q_1^\perp(v) := v_2$. Then $F_Q = F$ and $F_Q^\perp = F^C$. Since F^C is by definition the union of all faces (F-properties), which have no overlap with F, the peculiar negation $F_Q^\perp$ coincides in this case with the usual negation of classical proposition calculus. If $F \in \mathcal{F}(K)$ is a norm closed split face, it is therefore in $\mathcal{E}(K)$.

To complete the theory of filtered faces, we need still another kind of quantities.

Definition 47.2-17 (Projective Units).   If $Q \in \mathcal{Q}(K)$ is a filtering projection and $\tilde{e}$ the linearly extended order unit of (47.2.13), then

$$K \ni v \mapsto p_Q(v) := \tilde{e}(Q(v)) \equiv Q^*(\tilde{e})(v) \qquad (47.2.18)$$

defines an affine function in $\mathrm{Aff}_b(K)$ with values in $[0,1] \subset \mathbb{R}$.

(Recall that Q acts linearly on the whole of $\mathcal{V}^+$, even on $\mathcal{V}$. Restricted to K, Q produces values in the finite, pointed cone $[0,1]K$, including 0. This contrasts the range $\mathrm{ran}\, Q_1$ of the renormalized filtering projection which is contained in the state space K.)

The p_Q are called *projective units* and are combined into the set $\mathcal{P}(K) := \{p_Q \,|\, Q \in \mathcal{Q}\}$.

If $p \in \mathcal{P}(K)$, we define the affine function $p^\perp := 1 - p$, which assumes also its values in $[0,1] \subset \mathbb{R}$.

If $Q = 0$, then $p_Q = 0$, since $\tilde{e}(0) = 0$, and if $Q = \mathrm{id}$, then $p_Q = 1 = 0^\perp$.

Since the filtering projections $Q \in \mathcal{Q}(K)$ are only characterized axiomatically, the given definition of the projective units is neither a constructive one. More concrete is the formula (47.2.19) below for a projective unit associated with a given filtered face.

In traditional Hilbert space quantum mechanics (in which the state space $\mathcal{T}_1^+(\mathcal{H})$ is, however, not compact but a norm closed split face of a compact set (see Sec. 47.5), the projective units p_Q are given by the projection operators $P \in \mathcal{L}(\mathcal{H})$, so that $v \mapsto p_Q(v) = \tilde{e}(Q(v))$ corresponds to $T \mapsto \mathrm{tr}[TP] = \mathrm{tr}[\mathbb{1}PTP]$ (because $\tilde{e}(v)$ corresponds to $\mathrm{tr}[\mathbb{1}T]$ and $Q(v)$ corresponds to PTP).

Proposition 47.2-18 (Properties of Projective Units). *Let K be a compact convex set.*

(a) *For $Q \in \mathcal{Q}(K)$, the projective unit $p_Q \in \mathcal{P}(K) \subset \mathrm{Aff}_b(K)$ detects the (norm closed) filtered face $F_Q = Q(\mathcal{V}^+) \cap K$. That means $p_Q(v) = 1$ for $v \in F_Q$, and $p_Q(v) < 1$ for all other $v \in K$.*

(b) *We have $p_Q^\perp = p_{Q^\perp}$. Thus $p_Q(v) = 1 - p_{Q^\perp}(v) = 0$ for all $v \in F_Q^\perp$.*

(c) *If F_Q is given, then we have a direct characterization of p_Q by a physically interesting maximality property:*

$$p_Q = \sup\{a \in \mathrm{Aff}_b(K) \,|\, 0 \le a \le e,\ a \text{ vanishes on } F_Q^\perp\}. \qquad (47.2.19)$$

This makes the relation $F_Q = p_Q^{-1}(1)$ to an order- and $\perp$-preserving bijection between $\mathcal{P}(K)$ and $\mathcal{E}(K)$.

The proof of the lattice structure of $\mathcal{E}(K)$ proceeds by showing that feature for $\mathcal{P}(K)$, since the infima and suprema of these special affine functions can be shown to exist. (This contrasts the fact that the infima and suprema for two general functions $a, b \in \mathrm{Aff}_b(K)$ do not always exist in $\mathrm{Aff}_b(K)$, so that also the existence of the supremum in (47.2.19) is a remarkable exception.) We consider the lattice properties of $\mathcal{E}(K)$ only for special compact convex sets K.

Definition 47.2-19 (Projective Convex Sets). The compact convex set K is called *projective* if each face $F \in \mathcal{F}(K)$, which is detectable, is also a filtered set, and thus in $\mathcal{E}(K)$ (meaning that there is a unique filtering projection $Q \in \mathcal{Q}(K)$ with $F = F_Q$).

Theorem 47.2-20 (Orthomodular Lattice of Filtered F-Properties). *Let K be a projective convex set. Then the following is valid:*

(a) *Equipped with the previous ordering (by inclusion) and orthocomplementation the set of filtered faces $\mathcal{E}(K)$ is a complete orthomodular lattice. The infimum is gained as in $\mathcal{F}(K)$ by set intersection, whereas the supremum is slightly modified to $\bigvee_{i \in I} F_i := \bigcap \{ F \in \mathcal{E}(K) \mid \bigcup_{i \in I} F_i \subseteq F \}$.*

(b) *Like in every orthomodular lattice, the following relation, called* compatibility *relation,*

$$F \overset{c}{\sim} F' \Leftrightarrow F' = (F' \wedge F) \vee (F' \wedge F^{\perp}), \quad F, F' \in \mathcal{E}(K), \qquad (47.2.20)$$

is a symmetric and transitive relation in $\mathcal{E}(K)$. If $F \overset{c}{\sim} F'$ is valid the two faces, respectively the corresponding F-properties, are called compatible. *(Thus by the orthomodular law (47.2.1) two order-comparable faces are always compatible.)*

(c) *The subset of split faces $\mathcal{E}_c(K) \subset \mathcal{E}(K)$ is a complete distributive orthocomplemented sublattice of $\mathcal{E}(K)$ (and thus orthomodular), in which the orthocomplement $F^{\perp}$ of $F \in \mathcal{E}_c(K)$ coincides with the complementary split face F^C. $\mathcal{E}_c(K)$ is called the* center *of $\mathcal{E}(K)$.*

Each $C \in \mathcal{E}_c(K)$ is compatible with all other faces, that is $C \overset{c}{\sim} F$ for all $F \in \mathcal{E}(K)$.

(d) *By means of the mappings*

$$\mathcal{Q}(K) \ni Q \mapsto Q^*(\tilde{e}) = p_Q \in \mathcal{P}(K) \ni p_Q \mapsto p_Q^{-1}(1) = F_Q \in \mathcal{E}(K), \qquad (47.2.21)$$

the complete orthomodular lattice $\mathcal{E}(K)$ is ortho-lattice isomorphic to $\mathcal{P}(K)$ and $\mathcal{Q}(K)$ (and makes the latter complete).

For the filtered F-properties in $\mathcal{E}(K)$, K projective, we have now a suitable orthogonal decomposition theory, both for the classical and the non-classical cases. The concept of compatibility between F and F' in $\mathcal{E}(K)$ means something like that the splitting of $K = F \vee F^{\perp}$ takes over to a corresponding splitting of F', and vice versa. So the splitting of $K = C \vee C^{\perp}$ by means of a *classical property* $C \in \mathcal{E}_c(K)$ induces a corresponding splitting of all other properties in the form $F = (F \wedge C) \vee (F \wedge C^{\perp})$. This means that each F decomposes into a unique subproperty, which displays also C and into another unique subproperty which displays also non-C. This splitting is orthogonal in the sense that each subproperty is contained in the complement of the other subproperty.

Example 47.2-21 (Classical F-Properties of Electrons). For illustration consider a material ray (ensemble) consisting of electrons and positrons. The application of a transversal electric field induces a splitting, which is empirically compatible with all decompositions connected with any other quality of the particles: Already with the concepts of the general convex state space approach one can in this manner describe the classical F-property to have a positive or negative electric charge. (So we need not argue in terms of individual charged particles as in the introduction of "charge" in classical electrodynamics, using macroscopic charged specimen.)

In the more detailed Hilbert space quantum mechanics, the underlying state space K may be realized by the trace-norm completion of $\mathrm{Conv}(\mathcal{T}_1^+(\mathcal{H}_{\mathrm{pos}}) \oplus \mathcal{T}_1^+(\mathcal{H}_{\mathrm{el}}))$, and all these density operators commute with the projections onto the sub-Hilbert spaces and thus split uniquely into sub-density operators with a definite charge value.

That the sub-Hilbert spaces may be viewed as representation spaces of the gauge group $U(1)$ with different values of a Casimir operator is, of course, a theoretical refinement, which is important for the dynamics and for incorporating positrons and electrons into the scheme of all elementary particles. But it is in first line the split face structure of the charge–property, operationally realized by applying an electric field, which expresses the classical character of the charge. Usually it is said, that charge is (or induces) a *superselection rule* (see also Sec. 48.2.4 on page 1804).

In reference to Example 47.2-14 let us modify the Stern–Gerlach filtering, in that the direction of the magnetic field is arbitrary. Then the filtered subensembles of microscopic particles are spatially separated always in the varying direction of the magnetic field, but retain, beside that, all other qualities described previously. This realizes the filtering of the classical F-property to have "a spin with a given absolute value".

A more sophisticated classical quality of an electron ray, traveling from one electrode to another (as in the Josephson junction), is its originating from the left (or right) electrode. This is commonly indicated by giving the electron states an additional index l or r, without caring about the undistinguishability principle. We see no other way to formulate this quality mathematically than to express it as a classical F-property in a non-classical theory.

If one has introduced already the CAR algebra for the electrons, one may formalize the classical property "left–right" by a spatially structured thermodynamic limit, specifying subnets for the right and left electronic subsystems. One introduces, so to speak, two infinite electronic clusters. The anti–symmetrization goes nevertheless over the total system in virtue of the CAR relations. The gain is the introduction of two types of observables at infinity, which decompose the center of the universal enveloping von Neumann algebra into two parts. By that decomposition of the center the classical splitting of the state space may be achieved. Being bound to limiting concepts for many degrees of freedom, "left–right" can be observed only for large lumps of electrons.

For superconductors, the two types of observables at infinity lead to two types of condensed Cooper pairs, as we explain it in Chapter 41. These are connected with a decomposition of the center in low–temperature representations (a part of the universal center). Without the involved C*-algebraic formalism one could imagine to test the lack of EPR correlations between "left" and "right" condensed Cooper pairs, in contrast to the case of non-condensed Cooper pairs. Since a condensed Cooper pair is characterized by its phase correlations with many other pairs, we deal again with a many–particle concept.

Definition 47.2-22 (Supporting Faces respectively F-Properties). Let K be a projective convex set.

Since $\mathcal{E}(K)$ is a complete lattice, there exists for each state $v \in K$, the smallest property $F_v := \inf\{F \in \mathcal{E}(K) \,|\, v \in F\}$, containing v. We call F_v the *supporting face (supporting property)* of v.

Likewise we define $\mathcal{F}_v := \inf\{C \in \mathcal{E}_c(K) \,|\, v \in C\}$ and obtain so the *supporting split face (supporting classical property)* of v.

As mentioned in Definition 47.2-3 (e), an *atom* is a lattice element different from the lowest element 0, which dominates (covers) only 0 (where here $0 = \emptyset \in \mathcal{E}(K)$).

If $\mathcal{F}_v$ is an atom in $\mathcal{E}_c(K)$ then v is called *classically pure* or *factorial*.

If $v \in \partial_e K$ and if the (norm closed) face $\{v\}$ is detectable, then $F_v = \{v\}$, which gives just the form of the atoms in $\mathcal{E}(K)$.

The lattice isomorphism between $\mathcal{E}(K)$ and $\mathcal{Q}(K)$ enables the transcription of the compatibility relation for F-properties into the set of filtering projections. Here arises already the relationship to algebraic commutativity.

Lemma 47.2-23 (Compatible Filter Projections). *Let K be a projective convex set and $Q, Q' \in \mathcal{Q}(K)$. Then the following relations are equivalent.*

(i) *Q and Q' are compatible, that is $Q' = (Q' \wedge Q) \vee (Q' \wedge Q^\perp)$.*
(ii) *Their product is again a filtering projection: $Q \circ Q' \in \mathcal{Q}(K)$.*
(iii) *Their infimum equals the product: $Q \wedge Q' = Q \circ Q'$.*
(iv) *Their successive application to ensembles (scaled states) is commutative: $Q \circ Q' = Q' \circ Q$.*
(v) *They decompose the other's projective unit: $Q^* u_{Q'} + Q^{*\perp} u_{Q'} = u_{Q'}$.*

A filtering projection Q is classical *if it filters a classical F-property, that is $F_Q \in \mathcal{E}_c(K)$. Thus — by lattice isomorphism — Q is classical, if and only if it is compatible with all other filtering projections. This is also equivalent to $Q + Q^\perp = $ identity map in $\mathcal{V}$.*

47.2.4. *Observables over Spectral Convex Sets*

We may now characterize a metric observable as follows:

(As is common in probability theory, we employ the *Stieltjes integral* for integrating by means of statistical distribution functions $t \mapsto F_t$ over the real line $\mathbb{R}$. This is only a special case of the general Lebesgue integral, recalled in Eq. (48.1.2) on page 1779, where the probability measure is now given on intervals by $\mu(]a, b]) = F_b - F_a$.)

Definition 47.2-24 (Metric Observable and its Affine Function). Let K be a projective convex set, describing the statistical states of a system, and $\mathcal{E}(K)$ the complete orthomodular lattice of its filtered faces.

(a) Under a *metric observable* A we understand an ordered chain of F-properties, parameterized by its real scale values, with the following features:

$$A = \{F_t \in \mathcal{E}(K) \,|\, t \in \mathbb{R} \text{ with } F_t \leq F_{t'} \text{ for } t \leq t', \textstyle\bigwedge_{t \in \mathbb{R}} F_t = \emptyset, \bigvee_{t \in \mathbb{R}} F_t = K\}, \tag{47.2.22}$$

where we add also the right-continuity assumption $F_t = \bigwedge_{s > t} F_s$ (preferring it over the also possible left-continuity assumption $F_t = \bigvee_{s < t} F_s$).
We use also the shorthand notation $A = (F_t)_{\mathbb{R}}$.

(b) The *spectrum* of a metric observable $A = (F_t)_{\mathbb{R}}$ is defined as

$$\operatorname{spec} A \equiv \operatorname{spec}(F_t)_{\mathbb{R}} := \{t \in \mathbb{R} \,|\, F_{t+\epsilon} \wedge F_{t-\epsilon}^{\perp} \neq \emptyset, \forall \epsilon > 0\}. \tag{47.2.23}$$

The elements of $\operatorname{spec} A$ give the scale values, which may be assumed by the metric observable A. Notice that $\operatorname{spec} A$ is here defined without any algebraic notions, usually raised for an operator spectrum.
The metric observable $A = (F_t)_{\mathbb{R}}$ is defined bounded, if $\operatorname{spec} A$ is a bounded subset of $\mathbb{R}$. In the general convex state space approach, we restrict ourselves to bounded A.

(c) By lattice isomorphism, we may express the same structure in terms of the associated family of projective units $p_t(v) := \tilde{e}(Q_t(v)) \in \mathcal{P}(K)$, $t \in \mathbb{R}$, where $Q_t \in \mathcal{Q}(K)$ are the filter projections for F_t, $t \in \mathbb{R}$. (Observe that $\lim_{t \to -\infty} Q_t = 0$ and $\lim_{t \to +\infty} Q_t = \text{identity in } \mathcal{V}$.) Thus, we also denote for convenience

$$A = \{p_t \in \mathcal{P}(K) \,|\, t \in \mathbb{R} \text{ with } p_t \leq p_{t'} \text{ for } t \leq t', \textstyle\bigwedge_{t \in \mathbb{R}} p_t = 0, \bigvee_{t \in \mathbb{R}} p_t = e\}, \tag{47.2.24}$$

where the right-continuity relation $p_t = \bigwedge_{s > t} p_s$ is additionally required.
We use also the shorthand notation $A = (p_t)_{\mathbb{R}}$.

(d) We observe that for each $v \in K$ the function $t \mapsto p_t(v)$ is a statistical distribution function, rising monotonically from 0 to 1 and displaying the usual right-continuity. This leads us to the following statistical interpretation: If $B \subseteq \mathbb{R}$ is a

Borel set, the probability to measure a value in B for the observable $A = (p_t)_{\mathbb{R}}$, if the system is in the state $v \in K$, is defined by the Stieltjes integral,

$$v^A(B) \equiv \operatorname{prob}_v^A(B) := \int_B dp_t(v), \quad B \in \mathsf{B}(\mathbb{R}). \tag{47.2.25}$$

(In the theory of generalized — also algebraic — transition probabilities a notation like $v^A(B)$ is common, which emphasizes the state dependence.)

(e) For a given bounded metric observable $A = (p_t)_{\mathbb{R}}$, we define now the associated affine function $a \in \operatorname{Aff}_b(K)$ as the expectation value over the preceding probability distribution. So we are led to define a in terms of a Stieltjes integral as follows:

$$a : K \to \mathbb{R}, \quad a(v) := \int_{\mathbb{R}} t\, dp_t(v) \text{ for all } v \in K. \tag{47.2.26}$$

The family $(p_t)_{\mathbb{R}}$ (satisfying the relations in Equation (47.2.24)) is now called the *spectral family of* a (a rather new concept in Mathematics). Observe that the range of a is given by the closed convex hull

$$\operatorname{ran} a = \overline{\operatorname{Conv}}(\operatorname{spec} A) = \overline{\operatorname{Conv}}(\operatorname{spec}(p_t)_{\mathbb{R}}) \subset \mathbb{R}, \tag{47.2.27}$$

which is indeed a bounded set for bounded A.

The probability ansatz (47.2.25) implies already in the general frame of projective convex sets the following interpretational observations, which then take over to all more special theories as Jordan algebraic, C*-algebraic, and Hilbert space quantum mechanics.

Observation 47.2-25 (Probabilities for Observable Values). Over the projective convex state space K, let be given the metric observable $A = \{F_t \in \mathcal{E}(K) \,|\, t \in \mathbb{R}\}$, which may possess a continuous or discrete scale. We define $F_{<t} := \bigcup_{s<t} F_s$, for which we have from the increasing ordering that $F_{<t} \leq F_t$. In virtue of the orthomodular identity (47.2.1), we know that $F_t = F_{<t} \vee (F_t \wedge F_{<t}^{\perp})$.

If $F_t^D := F_t \wedge F_{<t}^{\perp}$ is non-empty, and $v \in F_t^D$, then the distribution function $t' \mapsto p_{t'}(v) = e(Q_{t'}(v))$ jumps from 0 to 1, the only assumed values, while crossing $t' = t$. (At $t' = t$ the state v is for the first time completely — with all its filtered subrays — in a face $F_{t'}$, which remains true also for all larger t', while for $t' < t$, v is completely not in $F_{t'}$.) Then prob_v^A equals the point measure δ_t, and the value t is assumed with certainty from the observable A, if the system is in the state $v \in F_t^D$.

If F_t^D is again non-empty, a more general $v \in F_t$ may have components both in F_t^D and in $F_{<t}$, the jump of $p_{t'}(v)$ at $t' = t$ is diminished, and the probability $\operatorname{prob}_v^A(\{t\})$ is smaller than 1.

If F_t^D is empty, then the distribution function $t' \mapsto p_{t'}(v)$ is for all $v \in K$ two-sided continuous at $t' = t$, and $\operatorname{prob}_v^A(\{t\}) = 0$, in spite of $t' \mapsto p_{t'}(v)$ possibly having a non-vanishing slope at $t' = t$. (If K means the state space of a microscopic system and A is the energy, such a value $t = E$ characterizes the so-called scattering region, and $v \in F_{t+\epsilon} \wedge F_{t-\epsilon}^{\perp}$ are scattering states.)

If A has a discrete scale, $t' \mapsto p_{t'}(v)$ may increase for any $v \in K$ only at the countably many jump points.

We see that we have also in a very general, mostly non-classical, theory the usual notions of probability theory, if we deal with the values of a *fixed* observable A.

The non-classical character is e.g., expressed by the occurrence of observables $A = \{F_t \in \mathcal{E}(K) \mid t \in \mathbb{R}\}$ and $A' = \{F_t' \in \mathcal{E}(K) \mid t \in \mathbb{R}\}$ with mutually incompatible face families, so that there exists no common probability distribution for A and A'. (The lack of common probability distributions for incompatible observables is discussed in [Dav76].)

Example 47.2-26 (The One-Filter Observable). Let be given in the projective convex state space K the single face $F \in \mathcal{E}(K)$. We want to construct the corresponding metric observable $A_F = \{F_t \in \mathcal{E}(K) \mid t \in \mathbb{R}\}$ and define

$$
F_t := \begin{cases}
\emptyset & : \quad t < 0 \\
F^{\perp} & : \quad 0 \leq t < 1 \\
F \vee F^{\perp} = K & : \quad 1 \leq t < \infty
\end{cases}.
$$

We see that $F_t^D \equiv F_t^{\perp} \wedge F_{<t}^{\perp} = F_t^{\perp} \wedge \emptyset^{\perp} = F^{\perp}$ for $t = 0$ and $F_t^D = K \wedge (F^{\perp})^{\perp} = F$ for $t = 1$, whereas $F_t^D = \emptyset$ for all other t-values. These are the discrete scale values which may be assumed by A_F.

For calculating the probabilities and mean values we need the projective units $p_F(v) := \tilde{e}(Q_F(v)) \in \mathcal{P}(K)$, for a given $F \in \mathcal{E}(K)$, where Q_F denotes the filtering projection associated with F. For the special F_t from the spectral family we — as before — simply write p_t respectively Q_t, and obtain for the corresponding mean value $a_F(v) := \int_{\mathbb{R}} t \, dp_t(v)$, $v \in K$. From the preceding paragraph we know that formally $dQ_t = [\delta(t) Q_{F^{\perp}} + \delta(t-1) Q_F] \, dt$ so that the affine function associated with the one-filter observable A_F is given by

$$
a_F : K \to \mathbb{R}, \quad a_F(v) := \int_{\mathbb{R}} t \, \tilde{e}(dQ_t(v)) = \tilde{e}(Q_F(v)) = p_F(v), \quad \forall v \in K.
$$
(47.2.28)

This equals the projective unit directly associated with F. We evaluate the probability Eq. (47.2.25) for the one-filter observable, if the system is in the state v, $\text{prob}_v^F(B) \equiv v^F(B)$, as

$$
v^F(B) = \int_B \tilde{e}(dQ_t(v)) = \tilde{e}(Q_F^{\perp}(v)) \int_B \delta(t) \, dt + \tilde{e}(Q_F(v)) \int_B \delta(t-1) \, dt
$$
(47.2.29)

for all $B \in \mathsf{B}(\mathbb{R})$.

For the incoherent superposition $v = \lambda v_1 + (1 - \lambda)v_2$, with $v_1 \in F$, $v_2 \in F^\perp$ and $\lambda \in [0, 1]$, we find the universal expression

$$v^F(B) = (1 - \lambda) \int_B \delta(t)\, dt + \lambda \int_B \delta(t - 1)\, dt = (1 - \lambda)\delta_0(B) + \lambda\delta_1(B). \quad (47.2.30)$$

We conclude that for incoherent superpositions v of v_1 and v_2 those probabilities $\mathrm{prob}_v^F(B)$ do not depend on the theory (C*-algebraic, Jordan algebraic, or more general theory).

For later use, we calculate the probability density as formal derivation of the distribution function $v_t^F := v^F(]-\infty, t])$

$$dv_t^F = \tilde{e}(Q_F(v))\delta(t)\, dt + \tilde{e}(Q_F^\perp(v))\delta(t - 1)\, dt. \quad (47.2.31)$$

Whereas the construction of an affine function a by the expectations $a(v)$ (for the values of a given metric observable A in the state $v \in K$) has, in principle, a straightforward character, the possibility of a reverse procedure appears, in such generality, rather unexpected. One has, in fact, to sharpen a bit the conditions on the convex state space to reach this goal. If a has the form (47.2.26) the spectral family induces for each $t \in \mathbb{R}$ a splitting of a into two parts, which are supported by mutually orthogonal faces. The same is valid for the positive and negative parts of a. In [AS79] it is elaborated, that assuming just this feature leads to a general spectral theory for affine functions.

Definition 47.2-27 (Spectral Convex Sets). Two positive affine functions $a, a' \in \mathrm{Aff}_b^+(K)$ are called *orthogonal* to each other ($a \perp a'$), if there is a filtered face $F \in \mathcal{E}(K)$ such that

$$a(v) = 0 \text{ for } v \in F, \text{ and } a'(v) = 0 \text{ for } v \in F^\perp. \quad (47.2.32)$$

A convex set K is called *spectral*, if it is projective and if each $a \in \mathrm{Aff}_b(K)$ may be decomposed as follows:

$$a = a^+ - a^-, \text{ with } a^+, a^- \in \mathrm{Aff}_b^+(K) \text{ and } a^+ \perp a^-. \quad (47.2.33)$$

A spectral convex set K is called *strongly spectral*, if for $a \in \mathrm{Aff}_c(K)$ there is a decomposition of the form (47.2.33) with $a^+, a^- \in \mathrm{Aff}_c^+(K)$.

Again we simply add a new requirement, the spectrality, to the convex state space in order to complete the general theory of observables, and demonstrate this feature later on for special state spaces (for C*-algebras cf. Theorem 46.2-23).

Theorem 47.2-28 (Spectral Representation of Affine Functions). *Let K be a spectral convex set. Then each $a \in \mathrm{Aff}_b(K)$ determines a unique spectral family of projective units $(p_t)_\mathbb{R} \subset \mathcal{P}(K)$ (in the sense of Definition 47.2-24), such that one* *has the spectral representation, and by this the metric observable A, as follows:*

$$a := \int_{\mathbb{R}} t \, dp_t \quad \text{respectively} \quad A = \{F_t \in \mathcal{E}(K) \, | \, F_t \text{ is detected by } p_t, \ t \in \mathbb{R}\}.$$

$$(47.2.34)$$

In the same manner as described between Observation 47.5-4 on page 1772 and Proposition 47.5-6, a metric observable $A = (F_t)_{\mathbb{R}}$ leads to a lattice homomorphism $\mathsf{B}(\mathbb{R}) \to \mathcal{E}(K)$, what occasionally is considered the characteristic feature of a metric observable. Since sometimes the scale of the observable is irrelevant (as for "temperature"), we define the following.

Definition 47.2-29 (Observables With and Without a Scale). Let $\mathcal{E}(K)$ be the orthomodular lattice of filtered faces in a spectral convex set K.

A metric observable may also be defined as a lattice ortho-isomorphism from the real Borel sets $\mathsf{B}(\mathbb{R})$ onto a σ-complete distributive sublattice of $\mathcal{E}(K)$, which maps $\mathbb{R}$ onto K.

A non-metric observable may then be considered as a class of the mentioned lattice ortho-isomorphisms $\mathsf{B}(\mathbb{R}) \to \mathcal{E}(K)$, which arise from each other by applying a homeomorphism in $\mathbb{R}$ (as a, possibly not order preserving, scale transformation).

We sketch in the following the intrinsic characterization of some convex state spaces, from which the structure and a special algebraic realization of the affine functions follows as a mere consequence and begin with special types of convex sets.

47.3. Special Convex State Spaces

47.3.1. *Bauer Simplices*

To begin with a most simple example, we repeat that for the tetraeder T all its faces split T, and a convex decomposition of an interior point into extremal elements is unique. These features are typical also for more general simplices, what we formulate here in a preliminary version. If we consider not only convex decompositions into pure states $v = \sum_{j=1}^{n} \lambda_j v_j \in \text{Conv}(\partial_e K)$, but also limits of these with fixed $v \in K$, then we arrive roughly speaking at the notion of a *boundary measure with barycenter v*. Boundary measures are special probability measures from $M_p(K)$ on K, which in some sense are supported by the extreme boundary $\partial_e K$ (cf. Sec. 48.1.2). For a general compact convex set K, there may exist different boundary measures $\mu \neq \mu'$ with the same barycenter $v \in K$. In the statistical interpretation this means, that the splitting of the ensemble $v \in K$ into pure cases is non-unique.

Definition 47.3-1 (Simplex). The compact convex set K is a *(Choquet) simplex*, if every $v \in K$ is the barycenter of a unique boundary measure $\mu \in M_p(K)$.

The compact simplex K is called a *Bauer simplex*, if K is metrizable and if its extreme boundary $\partial_e K$ is a closed (hence compact) subset of K.

For the statistical interpretation it is fundamental that a Bauer simplex is uniquely characterized as a set of probability measures on a certain compact Hausdorff space Γ. (see, e.g., [Alf71] § II.4). The regular probability measures $M_p(\Gamma)$ constitute a convex subset of the real vector space of all signed regular Borel measures $\mathcal{V} := M(\Gamma)$ on Γ (cf. Sec. 48.1.1). $M(\Gamma)$ is equipped with the so-called *vague topology*, defined by the convergence of measures if integrated over continuous functions on Γ (integrated as in (47.3.1) below).

Theorem 47.3-2 (Bauer Simplices). *Let Γ be a compact Hausdorff space. Then the singletons $\{\gamma\}$, $\gamma \in \Gamma$, belong to the Borel σ-algebra $\mathsf{B}(\Gamma)$, and the corresponding point measures δ_γ belong to the regular Borel probability measures $M_p(\Gamma)$. $M_p(\Gamma)$, equipped with the vague topology, is a Bauer simplex K with extreme boundary $\partial_e K = \{\delta_\gamma \mid \gamma \in \Gamma\}$.*

If reversely K is a Bauer simplex, then there is a compact Hausdorff space Γ, such that there is an affine homeomorphism from K onto $M_p(\Gamma)$ (mapping $\partial_e K$ bijectively onto $\{\delta_\gamma \mid \gamma \in \Gamma\}$). The set of continuous affine functions $\mathrm{Aff}_c(K)$ is then linear homeomorphic to $\mathrm{C}(\Gamma, \mathbb{R})$, the set of real continuous functions on Γ.

In the second part of the theorem, the points v of a given Bauer simplex K are biunivocally (homeomorphically) associated with their extremal decompositions (in terms of boundary measures). This identification is only possible because such a boundary measure μ is uniquely determined by its barycenter, due to the simplex property. That an arbitrary real continuous function f on $\partial_e K$ may be extended to a continuous affine function $a \in \mathrm{Aff}_c(K)$ on the total K is due to the fact that the dimension of K is large enough in comparison to the cardinality of $\partial_e K$. In finite dimensions this means that the dimension of K must be equal to the number of vertices minus 1.

In the statistical interpretation, the extreme boundary $\partial_e K$ of a Bauer simplex K plays the role of a classical configuration space Γ (in the sense of a general sample space), and each statistical state $v \in K$ can be identified with a (regular Borel) probability measure on $\partial_e K$.

In this manner we obtain, however, only compact phase spaces from Bauer simplices. In our analysis of (Q)ED, we have to surpass considerable mathematical difficulties to deal directly with statistical distributions on non-compact, infinite-dimensional phase spaces, which leads to the concept of so-called *weak distributions* (cf. Chapter 50). (On the other hand, this is one of the reasons for the occupation in the present treatise with compactifications.)

Concerning the observables, we arrive by Theorem 47.3-2 at a realization of the affine functions $\mathrm{Aff}_c(K)$ by functions in $\mathrm{C}(\Gamma, \mathbb{R})$ with $\Gamma = \partial_e K$. This realization of the affine functions fits completely to the usual formulation of classical observables in (statistical) mechanics. To be explicit, Theorem 47.3-2 associates with each

$v \in K$ a measure $\mu \in M_p(K)$ and with each $a \in \mathrm{Aff}_c(K)$ a function $f \in \mathrm{C}(\Gamma, \mathbb{R})$ such that

$$\hat{v}(a) \equiv a(v) = \mu(f) \equiv \int_\Gamma f(\gamma)\, d\mu(\gamma)\,. \qquad (47.3.1)$$

(The definition of the general Lebesgue integral is sketched in Sec. 48.1.1 on page 1777.) In particular, equipped with the supremum norm, $\mathrm{C}(\Gamma, \mathbb{R})$ constitutes the self-adjoint part of the commutative C*-algebra $\mathrm{C}(\Gamma, \mathbb{C}) := \mathrm{C}(\Gamma, \mathbb{R}) + i\, \mathrm{C}(\Gamma, \mathbb{R})$. Thus we may say that each Bauer simplex K determines a unique commutative C*-algebra, to which it is the state space. (We say more on the state spaces of commutative C*-algebras in Example 45.2-24.)

Let us finally mention an interesting connection between simplices and lattice theory. For intuitive motivation consider a triangle which, as a proper face of our tetrahedra, is also a simplex. A baby carriage with three wheels touches a plain bottom always with all wheels, in contradistinction to a carriage with four wheels (too many vertices!). For the latter it may happen that the contact with the plain bottom is performed with equal probability by two different sets of three wheels, so that the vehicle is wobbling. The mathematical reason for this effect is that the two affine functions, determined by the two sets of three contact points, have no infimum.

More generally, two continuous functions $f, g \in \mathrm{C}(\Gamma, \mathbb{R})$, Γ compact, have always a continuous upper and lower envelope, which constitute $f \vee g, f \wedge g \in \mathrm{C}(\Gamma, \mathbb{R})$, with respect to the usual point-wise ordering in $\mathrm{C}(\Gamma, \mathbb{R})$. Thus $\mathrm{C}(\Gamma, \mathbb{R})$ is a lattice, but mostly not a complete lattice. If Γ is the compact boundary of a Bauer simplex K, then the bijection between $\mathrm{C}(\Gamma, \mathbb{R})$ and $\mathrm{Aff}_c(K)$ is order preserving, so that $\mathrm{Aff}_c(K)$ is also a lattice. This argument can be inverted [Alf71].

Theorem 47.3-3 (Lattice of Affine Functions). *Let K be a compact convex set. Then K is a Bauer simplex, if and only if the order-unit space $\mathrm{Aff}_c(K)$ is a lattice.*

Since every unital commutative C*-algebra is by its Gelfand representation *-isomorphic to a $\mathrm{C}(\Gamma, \mathbb{C})$, where the compact Γ is homeomorphic to its set of pure states, the foregoing result provides also an order-theoretic foundation of commutative C*-algebras.

47.3.2. *Qubit Space*

In a rather recent mathematical development, the algebraic properties of $\mathrm{Aff}_c(K)$ and $\mathrm{Aff}_b(K)$ have been derived from intrinsic features of K, also for more general compact convex sets K than simplices.

Whereas the statistical state space of one (or no) bit is the interval $[0, 1] \subset \mathbb{R}$, and constitutes the smallest (non-trivial) classical state space, it will turn out that the smallest non-classical state space is isomorphic to a 3-dimensional ball, if we require rather basic statistical assumptions. It is commonly called the space of "quantum bits" or simply the "qubit space".

Let us therefore study the compact 3-ball of radius $1/2$, with center point 0, denoted $B_{1/2} \equiv B_{1/2}^3$, which has a compact extreme boundary, but is not a simplex. We introduce an affine map ϕ of $B_{1/2}$ into the set $\mathcal{S} = T_1^+(\mathbb{C}^2)$ of 2×2-density matrices $\tilde{\varrho}$ (positive matrices with trace 1). Let σ^i, $1 \le i \le 3$, denote the (self-adjoint and unitary) Pauli spin matrices

$$\sigma^1 = \begin{pmatrix} 0 & 1 \\ 1 & 0 \end{pmatrix}, \qquad \sigma^2 = \begin{pmatrix} 0 & -i \\ i & 0 \end{pmatrix}, \qquad \sigma^3 = \begin{pmatrix} 1 & 0 \\ 0 & -1 \end{pmatrix}, \qquad (47.3.2)$$

and recall the product formulas

$$\sigma^i \sigma^j = -\sigma^j \sigma^i = i\,\sigma^k, \quad (i, j, k) \text{ a cyclic permutation of } (1, 2, 3). \qquad (47.3.3)$$

We define

$$\phi(\vec{\varrho}) := \frac{1}{2}\mathbb{1} + \vec{\varrho} \cdot \vec{\sigma} = \begin{pmatrix} \frac{1}{2} + \varrho_3 & \varrho_1 - i\varrho_2 \\ \varrho_1 + i\varrho_2 & \frac{1}{2} - \varrho_3 \end{pmatrix} \in M_2\,, \quad \vec{\varrho} \in B_{1/2} \subset \mathbb{R}^3. \qquad (47.3.4)$$

Each $\phi(\vec{\varrho})$ is self-adjoint, and since the σ^i have vanishing trace, $\phi(\vec{\varrho})$ has trace 1. Also $\phi(\vec{\varrho})$ has a non-negative determinant $\det \phi(\vec{\varrho}) = \frac{1}{4} - \vec{\varrho}^2$, for $\vec{\varrho} \in B_{1/2}$. Since the self-adjoint matrix $\phi(\vec{\varrho})$ has two real eigenvalues λ_1 and λ_2, its determinant is $\lambda_1 \lambda_2$. Because of the positive trace at least one eigenvalue must be positive. Since the determinant is non-negative the second eigenvalue must be non-negative. Thus each $\phi(\vec{\varrho})$ is positive and, being also normalized, is a density matrix.

$\phi : B_{1/2} \to \mathcal{S} = T_1^+(\mathbb{C}^2)$ is obviously an affine bijection: Since the Pauli matrices, supplemented by the unit matrix, constitute a basis in M_2, ϕ is injective, and since each density operator can be represented as in Eq. (47.3.4), ϕ is "onto" $T_1^+(\mathbb{C}^2) = \mathcal{S}$.

As ϕ maps $\partial_e B_{1/2}$ bijectively onto $\partial_e \mathcal{S}$, we know that $\phi(\vec{\varrho}) \in \partial_e \mathcal{S}$, if and only if $\|\vec{\varrho}\| = 1/2$, that is if and only if $\det \phi(\vec{\varrho}) = 0$. Each extremal $\phi(\vec{\varrho})$ has, therefore, the eigenvalues 0 and 1, constituting a 1-dimensional projection. This property is equivalent to $\phi(\vec{\varrho})^2 = \phi(\vec{\varrho})$, if $\phi(\vec{\varrho}) \in \mathcal{S}$ is pre-supposed. On the other side, each 1-dimensional projection in $\mathbb{C}^2$ is a density matrix and we have

$$\phi(\partial_e B_{1/2}) = \left\{ \begin{pmatrix} \frac{1}{2} + \varrho_3 & \varrho_1 - i\varrho_2 \\ \varrho_1 + i\varrho_2 & \frac{1}{2} - \varrho_3 \end{pmatrix} \,\Big|\, \|\vec{\varrho}\| = \frac{1}{2} \right\} = \{ |\chi\rangle\langle\chi| \,|\, \chi \in \mathbb{C}^2, \|\chi\| = 1 \}.$$
$$\qquad (47.3.5)$$

If a is an affine function, i.e., $a \in \mathrm{Aff}(B_{1/2})$, then $\vec{\varrho} \mapsto a(\vec{\varrho}) - x_0$, $x_0 := a(0)$, is linear and there is an $\vec{x} \in \mathbb{R}^3$ such that $a(\vec{\varrho}) - x_0 = \vec{\varrho} \cdot \vec{x}$. Thus each $a \in \mathrm{Aff}(B_{1/2})$ is linearly parameterized by a real quadruple: $a = a_x$, $x = (x_0, \vec{x}) \in \mathbb{R}^4$, so that

$a_x(\vec{\varrho}) = \vec{\varrho} \cdot \vec{x} + x_0$ for all $\vec{\varrho} \in B_{1/2}$). We observe

$$a_x(\vec{\varrho}) = \text{tr}[\phi(\vec{\varrho}) \, m_x], \quad \text{with} \quad m_x = x_0 \mathbb{1} + \vec{x} \cdot \vec{\sigma}/2 \in \mathbb{M}_{2,\text{sa}}. \quad (47.3.6)$$

We get all of $\text{Aff}(B_{1/2}) \ni a_x$ by varying x in $\mathbb{R}^4$, and the corresponding m_x run exactly through $\mathbb{M}_{2,\text{sa}}$. This follows from $\{\mathbb{1}, \vec{\sigma}\}$ being a self-adjoint basis of $\mathbb{M}_2$. Since the correspondence is bijective and continuous in both directions we have

$$\phi^{-1*} : \text{Aff}(B_{1/2}) \stackrel{\text{linear homeomorphism}}{\longrightarrow} \mathbb{M}_{2,\text{sa}}, \quad \phi^{-1*}(a_x) = m_x. \quad (47.3.7)$$

The algebraic product which leaves $\mathbb{M}_{2,\text{sa}}$ invariant is the symmetrized matrix product

$$a \circ b := \frac{ab + ba}{2}, \quad a, b \in \mathbb{M}_{2,\text{sa}}. \quad (47.3.8)$$

With this distributive, but not associative product, $\mathbb{M}_{2,\text{sa}}$ is a Jordan algebra (cf. the following section), for which $\mathcal{S}$ is the state space $\mathcal{S}(\mathbb{M}_{2,\text{sa}})$. (We identify for the moment a density matrix $\tilde{\varrho} \in \mathcal{T}_1^+(\mathbb{C}^2)$ with the positive, linear, normalized functional $\mathbb{M}_{2,\text{sa}} \ni m \to \text{tr}[\tilde{\varrho}\, m]$.)

Thus, in first line, the map ϕ discloses $B_{1/2}$ as the state space of the Jordan algebra $\mathbb{M}_{2,\text{sa}}$.

But $B_{1/2}$, besides being a compact convex set, has a further structure: It is also an *orientable* manifold (where the positive orientation is given by the class of all right-handed coordinate systems). If ν is an affine bijection of the ball $B_{1/2}$, with center point 0, it extends to a linear transformation T which preserves not only the norm of $\vec{\varrho} \in \partial_e B_{1/2}$ but also the norm of all points in $\text{Conv}(\partial_e B_{1/2})$. Therefore, the convex structure group of $B_{1/2}$, consisting of all affine bijections, is $O(3)$. Each $T \in O(3)$ is equal either to a pure rotation $R \in SO(3)$ or to a product $C_2 R$ of a pure rotation R and a reflection C_2, say across the 1-3-plane. The affine transformation ν preserves the orientation of $B_{1/2}$, if and only if it belongs to a pure rotation.

Each $R \in SO(3)$ is given by a rotation $\exp\{i\vartheta \vec{n} \cdot \vec{\ell}\}$ about the axis $\vec{n}$, $\|\vec{n}\| = 1$, by the angle ϑ. (The components of $\vec{\ell} \equiv \mathbf{I}$ are specified in Sec. 11.3.1.) We find

$$\phi(R\vec{\varrho}) = \frac{1}{2}\mathbb{1} + \vec{\varrho} \cdot R^T \vec{\sigma} = \exp\{i\tfrac{\vartheta}{2}\vec{n} \cdot \vec{\sigma}\}\phi(\vec{\varrho})\exp\{-i\tfrac{\vartheta}{2}\vec{n} \cdot \vec{\sigma}\} =: \alpha_{R^T}(\phi(\vec{\varrho})). \quad (47.3.9)$$

To the rotation $R \in SO(3)$ in the state space $B_{1/2}$ belongs thus the transformation α_R in the observable algebra $\mathbb{M}_{2,\text{sa}}$, which is expressed in terms of a unitary implementation

$$\alpha_R(m) = \exp\{-i\tfrac{\vartheta}{2}\vec{n} \cdot \vec{\sigma}\}\, m \exp\{i\tfrac{\vartheta}{2}\vec{n} \cdot \vec{\sigma}\}, \quad \forall m \in \mathbb{M}_{2,\text{sa}},$$

and clearly preserves the Jordan product. This type of a Jordan automorphism has a unique extension to an automorphism in $\mathbb{M}_2$:

$$\alpha_R(m_1 + im_2) := \alpha_R(m_1) + i\alpha_R(m_2), \quad m_1, m_2 \in \mathbb{M}_{2,\text{sa}}.$$

For the reflection C_2, we obtain

$$\phi(C_2 \vec{\varrho}) = \frac{1}{2}\mathbb{1} + \vec{\varrho} \cdot (\sigma^1, -\sigma^2, \sigma^3) = C\phi(\vec{\varrho})C, \quad \text{with} \quad C\chi := \overline{\chi}, \ \forall \chi \in \mathbb{C}^2. \ (47.3.10)$$

(Recall for the above given Pauli matrices that σ^2 is imaginary and σ^1, σ^3 are real.) The reflection in the state space leads in the observable picture to a sandwiching $\alpha_C(m) := CmC$, $m \in \mathbb{M}_{2,\text{sa}}$, with the antiunitary operator C given by the complex conjugation. This type of a Jordan automorphism has a unique extension to an anti–automorphism in $\mathbb{M}_2$:

$$\alpha_C(m_1 + im_2) := \alpha_C(m_1) - i\alpha_C(m_2) = C(m_1 + im_2)^*C, \quad m_1, m_2 \in \mathbb{M}_{2,\text{sa}}.$$

We confirm from the right-hand side of the preceding equation that α_C transforms the elements in $\mathbb{M}_2$ in a complex-linear, an *-preserving manner, but reverses the factors in the matrix products. Since the multiplicative combination of an automorphism with an anti-automorphism gives an anti-automorphism, we arrive at the following conclusion.

Conclusion 47.3-4 (3-Ball determines C*-Algebra of 2×2-Matrices). The three-dimensional ball $B_{1/2}$ is affine isomorphic to the state space $\mathcal{S}(\mathbb{M}_{2,\text{sa}})$ of the Jordan algebra $\mathbb{M}_{2,\text{sa}}$, and the metric observables, isomorphic to $\text{Aff}_b(B_{1/2})$, are biunivocally realizable by matrices from $\mathbb{M}_{2,\text{sa}}$.

By linear extension of the expectation functionals, $B_{1/2}$ may also be viewed as the state space $\mathcal{S}(\mathbb{M}_2)$ of the C*-algebra $\mathbb{M}_2 = \mathbb{M}_{2,\text{sa}} + i\mathbb{M}_{2,\text{sa}}$.

Each affine bijection ν in $B_{1/2}$ is given by a unique element $R \in O(3)$ and leads to a unique Jordan automorphism α_R in $\mathbb{M}_{2,\text{sa}}$. If $R \in SO(3)$ then α_R extends uniquely to an automorphism in $\mathbb{M}_2$, otherwise α_R extends uniquely to an anti-automorphism in $\mathbb{M}_2$ (both being Jordan automorphisms in $\mathbb{M}_2$).

In this sense, we say that $B_{1/2}$, as a convex and oriented manifold, determines uniquely the non-commutative C*-algebra $\mathbb{M}_2$ by being its state space.

For our model discussions, let us consider special states in $\mathcal{S}(\mathbb{M}_2)$, which come about in thermostatistics and are given by density matrices $\tilde{\varrho} \in \mathcal{T}_1^+(\mathbb{C}^2)$.

Example 47.3-5 (2-Dimensional Equilibrium Matrices). Let again σ^i, $1 \leq i \leq 3$, denote the Pauli matrices.

Those density matrices $\tilde{\varrho}$, which maximize the entropy $S[\tilde{\varrho}] = -k_B \text{tr}[\tilde{\varrho} \ln(\tilde{\varrho})]$, k_B the Boltzmann constant, under the subsidiary conditions $\text{tr}[\tilde{\varrho}\sigma^i] = r^i \in] -1, +1[$, $1 \leq i \leq 3$, are of the form $\tilde{\varrho} = \exp\{-\zeta - \vec{\alpha} \cdot \vec{\sigma}\}$ with $\zeta, \alpha^i \in \mathbb{R}$, where $e^{+\zeta} = \text{tr}[\exp\{-\vec{\alpha} \cdot \vec{\sigma}\}]$ [Gib02], [SR76]. Since the σ^i are linearly independent, the α_i are uniquely determined by the subsidiary conditions.

Since $(\sigma^i)^2 = \mathbb{1}$ we find, by inspecting the exponential series,

$$\exp\{-\vec{\alpha}\cdot\vec{\sigma}\} = \cosh(\|\vec{\alpha}\|)\mathbb{1} - \frac{\sinh(\|\vec{\alpha}\|)}{\|\vec{\alpha}\|}\,\vec{\alpha}\cdot\vec{\sigma}\,,\quad \mathrm{e}^{+\varsigma} = 2\cosh(\|\vec{\alpha}\|)\,. \quad (47.3.11)$$

(By rotating the coordinate system, set $\vec{\alpha}\cdot\vec{\sigma} = \alpha^3\sigma^3$.) Inserting the two exponential expressions into the formula for $\tilde{\varrho}$ we get

$$\tilde{\varrho} = \frac{1}{2}\mathbb{1} - \frac{\tanh(\|\vec{\alpha}\|)}{2\|\vec{\alpha}\|}\,\vec{\alpha}\cdot\vec{\sigma}\,. \quad (47.3.12)$$

Since $\mathrm{tr}[(\sigma^i)^2] = 2$, we obtain for the expectations of the σ^i and the previously introduced $\vec{\varrho}$-parameters

$$\vec{r} = -\frac{\tanh(\|\vec{\alpha}\|)}{\|\vec{\alpha}\|}\,\vec{\alpha}\,,\quad \tilde{\varrho} = \frac{1}{2}\mathbb{1} + \vec{\varrho}\cdot\vec{\sigma} = \phi(\vec{\varrho})\quad \vec{\varrho} = -\vec{r}/2\,. \quad (47.3.13)$$

If the components of $\vec{\alpha}$ are finite then $\|\vec{r}\| < 1$, which narrows the admissible range of the r^i. Especially, for $\vec{\alpha} = 0$, we arrive at $\tilde{\varrho} = \frac{1}{2}\mathbb{1}$, the normalized trace state.

We find that the set of 2×2-equilibrium matrices covers all of the interior of $B_{1/2}$, the mixed states, if we vary the subsidiary conditions in the admitted range. The (extreme) boundary $\partial_e B_{1/2}$ is obtained by a limit $\|\vec{\alpha}\| \to \infty$, corresponding to the physical low temperature limit to pure ground states, or to the high current limit of semiconductor cluster states in Sec. 36.2.3.

Already in this simple case we observe: The complete purification of a quantum state is an idealization, reached only by unphysical limits of the physical parameters.

47.3.3. *Convex Products of Qubit Spaces*

To have a look on more complicated, non-simplicial state spaces, we consider states of the matrical algebras $\mathbb{M}_{2^n}$, $n > 1$, which are isomorphic to the CAR algebras $\mathcal{A}(\mathbb{C}^n)$ (cf. Sec. 33.2). Since $\mathbb{M}_{2^n}$ is an irreducible set of operators in the Hilbert space $\mathbb{C}^{2^n}$, its state space $\mathcal{S}(\mathbb{M}_{2^n})$ is again affine homeomorphic to the density matrices $\mathcal{T}_1^+(\mathbb{C}^{2^n})$ (cf. Sec. 43.2.3).

We choose a basis $\{e^i \mid 0 \le i \le k := 4^n - 1\}$ in $\mathbb{M}_{2^n}$, which is orthonormalized for the Hilbert–Schmidt inner product $(e^i | e^j)_{\mathrm{HS}}/2^n = \mathrm{tr}[e^{i*}e^j]/2^n = \delta^{ij}$ with $e^0 = \mathbb{1}$, the unit of $\mathbb{M}_{2^n}$, and with the remaining $\{e^i \mid 1 \le i \le k\}$ self-adjoint and traceless. Then we write

$$\mathcal{T}_1^+(\mathbb{C}^{2^n}) \ni \tilde{\varrho} = \frac{1}{2^n}\mathbb{1} + \sum_{i=1}^{k} \varrho_i\,e^i\,,\quad \varrho_i := \frac{\mathrm{tr}[\tilde{\varrho}\,e^i]}{2^n} \in \mathbb{R}\,. \quad (47.3.14)$$

The trace state has the coordinates $\varrho_i = 0$. In general we have, by applying the Schwartz inequality to the Hilbert–Schmidt inner product,

$$|\varrho_i|^2 = \frac{|\mathrm{tr}[\tilde{\varrho}\,e^i]|^2}{2^{2n}} \le \frac{\mathrm{tr}[\tilde{\varrho}^2]}{2^n}\frac{\mathrm{tr}[e^{i2}]}{2^n} = \frac{1}{2^n}\mathrm{tr}[\tilde{\varrho}^2] \le \frac{1}{2^n}\,.$$

(The eigenvalues of $\tilde{\varrho}^2$ are not larger than those of $\tilde{\varrho}$.) That is, the one-dimensional diameters of S contract with increasing n. Further restrictions on the real coordinates ϱ_i imposes the positivity of $\tilde{\varrho}$. More details are seen by realizing the e^j, $0 \le j \le k = 4^n - 1$, by all of the possible 4^n tensor products

$$e^j = \otimes_{l=1}^n \sigma^{\kappa_j(l)}, \quad \kappa_j : \{1,\ldots,n\} \to \{0,1,2,3\}, \quad 0 \le j \le k, \qquad (47.3.15)$$

of the Pauli matrices σ^i, $1 \le i \le 3$, and the 2×2-unit matrix $\mathbb{1} = \sigma^0$. Using the parametrization (47.3.4) of the 2-dimensional density matrices, we may write an arbitrary product state in the form

$$\tilde{\varrho} = \otimes_{l=1}^n \phi(\vec{\varrho_l}), \quad \vec{\varrho_l} \in B_{1/2}, \qquad (47.3.16)$$

which each is an obvious linear combination of the above basis. The k parameters ϱ_i in (47.3.14) are now products of the components from the triples $\vec{\varrho_l}$. The product state $\tilde{\varrho}$ is pure, if and only if $\|\vec{\varrho_l}\| = 1/2$ for all $l \in \{1,\ldots,n\}$.

Choose now $m \in \{1,\ldots,n\}$ and fix a selection of triples $\{\vec{\varrho_l} \,|\, l \in \{1,\ldots,n\}, l \ne m\}$, with norm $1/2$ each. The subset of density operators

$$F_m := \{\otimes_{l=1}^n \phi(\vec{\varrho_l}) \,|\, \vec{\varrho_m} \in B_{1/2}\} \qquad (47.3.17)$$

is a face in $S(\mathbb{M}_{2^n})$, since it is convex and convex decompositions of its elements are only possible in the mth factor. By the linearity of the tensor product in each of its factors, F_m is affine isomorphic to $B_{1/2}$. The (extreme) boundary $\partial_e B_{1/2}$ is mapped by the parametrization onto $\partial_e F_m$, which is clearly part of $\partial_e S(\mathbb{M}_{2^n})$. Since a subface of F_m is a singleton from $\partial_e F_m$, F_m is the smallest face containing two of its pure states.

Let us perform the analogous construction for a face $F_{m'}$, $m \ne m' \in \{1,\ldots,n\}$, by choosing a $\vec{\varrho_m} \in \partial_e B_{1/2}$, fixing again the above triples $\vec{\varrho_l}$, $l \ne m, l \ne m'$, and varying $\vec{\varrho_{m'}}$ in $B_{1/2}$. Then the intersection $F_m \cap F_{m'}$ is the pure product state, indexed by the previous $\{\vec{\varrho_l} \,|\, l \ne m\}$ and the chosen $\vec{\varrho_m}$. In this manner, we may cover part of $\partial_e S(\mathbb{M}_{2^n})$ by the surfaces of embedded 3-balls. The latter intersect with each other in at most a pure state, a surface point, since such intersection must be a face again.

To generalize this argument, consider any tuple of different pure states in $\partial_e S(\mathbb{M}_{2^n})$, realized by the 1-dimensional projections onto the vectors $\chi, \chi' \in \mathbb{C}_1^{2^n}$. They determine a 2-dimensional complex subspace $\mathrm{LH}\{\chi,\chi'\} \subset \mathbb{C}^{2^n}$. The set of density operators $F(\chi,\chi')$, which vanish in the complementary space $\mathrm{LH}\{\chi,\chi'\}^\perp$, is affinely isomorphic to $B_{1/2}$. It is obviously the smallest face containing the given two pure states (and its construction does not depend on the Hilbert space under consideration). Thus all of $\partial_e S(\mathbb{M}_{2^n})$ is the union of the surfaces of embedded 3-balls, which intersect with each other in at most a point. It is mathematically and physically most interesting, that this property, combined with the dimension, characterizes uniquely the state spaces of full matrix algebras. These state spaces are more complex than a ball. The only state space $\mathcal{S}(\mathbb{M}_m)$, which is affinely isomorphic to a ball of some dimension, is that obtained for $m = 2$.

If we have e.g., the observable algebra $\mathbb{M}_2 \oplus \mathbb{M}_2 \subsetneq \mathbb{M}_{2^2}$, then $\mathcal{S}(\mathbb{M}_2 \oplus 0)$ and $\mathcal{S}(0 \oplus \mathbb{M}_2)$ are two 3-balls, which split the convex total state space. If the two pure states are taken in each of these 3-balls, the smallest face containing them is the connecting line according to Proposition 47.1-5. Since this situation is a trivial modification of the foregoing it is included into the definition of the n-ball property, discussed in the following section.

47.3.4. *Convex State Spaces with n-Ball Property*

To understand the special structure of a quantum mechanical state space, let us sketch a straightforward generalization.

Definition 47.3-6 (n–Ball respectively Hilbert ball Property). A convex set has the *n-ball property* respectively *Hilbert ball property*, if the smallest face containing two extreme points is detectable and either affinely isomorphic to a real n-ball, especially to a real Hilbert ball, or to a (straight) real line segment.

(Here, an n-ball is defined to be a closed ball with some radius $r > 0$ about the origin in n Euclidean dimensions, namely $B_r^{(n)} := \{x \in \mathbb{R}^n \mid \|x\| \leq r\}$. Analogously, a real Hilbert ball is a closed ball in some real Hilbert space.)

It is illuminating that a modification of the construction in the foregoing section leads to state spaces with an n-ball property, $n \geq 3$. For this, we supplement some general notions on Jordan algebras, already touched upon previously. That class of algebras has been introduced by the theoretical physicist Pascual Jordan, apparently to clarify the basic structure of quantum mechanics ([Jor32]). But in fact, Jordan *generalized* the observable concept of quantum mechanics, as will be revealed by the subsequent elaborations. (The connection between Jordan algebras and the convex state space approach and its spectral theory can be found in [AS78] and [AS79].)

Definition 47.3-7 (Jordan Algebras).

(a) A real distributive algebra is a *Jordan algebra* $\mathcal{J}$, if its product $\circ$ is commutative and satisfies only the following weakened form of associativity

$$a \circ (b \circ a^2) = (a \circ b) \circ a^2, \quad \forall a, b \in \mathcal{J}. \tag{47.3.18}$$

(b) A Jordan algebra $\mathcal{J}$ is called *unital* if it contains a unit element $e \in \mathcal{J}$ with $e \circ a = a$ for all $a \in \mathcal{J}$.

(c) An element a of a Jordan algebra $\mathcal{J}$ is called *positive*, if there is a $b \in \mathcal{J}$ with $a = b \circ b \equiv b^2$. (So e is positive.)

(d) A Jordan algebra $\mathcal{J}$ is called a *JB–algebra* if it is a real Banach space, where the norm satisfies the additional properties

$$\|a \circ b\| \leq \|a\| \, \|b\| \,, \quad \|a^2\| = \|a\|^2 \,, \quad \|a^2\| \leq \|a^2 + b^2\| \qquad (47.3.19)$$

for all $a, b \in \mathcal{J}$.

(e) The *state space* $\mathcal{S}(\mathcal{J})$ of a unital Jordan algebra $\mathcal{J}$ is the convex set of all linear functionals φ, with $\langle \varphi; b^2 \rangle \geq 0$, $\forall b \in \mathcal{J}$ (positivity), and with $\langle \varphi; e \rangle = 1$ (normalization).

A typical example of a JB-algebra $\mathcal{J}$ is the self-adjoint part of a C*-algebra $\mathcal{A}$ with the symmetrized product $a \circ b = \frac{ab+ba}{2}$, $a, b \in \mathcal{A}_{\mathrm{sa}} = \mathcal{J}$, and the C*-norm, but this is only a special case and therefore called *special*. The state space of a unital JB-algebra is weak* compact.

Example 47.3-8 (Spin Factors). In order to compare with the above considerations, we realize the so-called m-dimensional spin factor $\mathcal{J}_m$, $m = 4^n - 1$, by $\mathcal{J}_m := \mathbb{M}_{2^n \mathrm{sa}}$, equipped with the real linear structure and with the Hilbert–Schmidt inner product. We write $\mathcal{J}_m \ni a = \sum_{i=0}^{m} x_i e^i$, where $\{e^i \,|\, 0 \leq i \leq m\}$ denotes again the self–dual Hilbert–Schmidt basis in $\mathbb{M}_{2^n \mathrm{sa}}$. If there is also given an element $b = \sum_{i=0}^{m} y_i e^i$, x_i, y_i being arbitrary real coefficients, we define in $\mathcal{J}_m$ the algebraic product and norm by

$$a \circ b := \left(\sum_{i=0}^{m} x_i y_i \right) e^0 + \sum_{i=1}^{m} (y_0 x_i + x_0 y_i) e^i \,,$$

$$\|a\|_J := \left(\sum_{i=1}^{m} x_i^2 \right)^{1/2} + |x_0| \,. \qquad (47.3.20)$$

By explicit calculations one verifies that $\mathcal{J}_m$ satisfies the postulates of a JB-algebra.

Like the total real dual space, the states are realized by pseudo-density operators $\tilde{\varrho} \in \mathbb{M}_{2^n \mathrm{sa}}$, $\tilde{\varrho} = \sum_{i=0}^{m} \varrho_i e^i$, which act as linear functionals on $\mathcal{J}_m$ again by means of the trace duality,

$$\langle \tilde{\varrho}; a \rangle = \mathrm{tr}_{\mathbb{C}^{2^n}} [\tilde{\varrho} \, a] = \sum_{i=0}^{m} \varrho_i x_i \,, \quad \forall a \in \mathcal{J}_m, \qquad (47.3.21)$$

where we have for shortness, as before, identified the matrix $\tilde{\varrho}$ with the linear functional it generates (what is especially incautious in this context).

Normalization gives $1 = \langle \tilde{\varrho}; e^0 \rangle = \varrho_0 \mathrm{tr}_{\mathbb{C}^{2^n}} [\mathbb{1}]$, requiring $\varrho_0 = 2^{-n}$.

The decisive difference to the relations concerning the usual matrix algebra is the modified positivity postulate for states, adapted to the positivity in $\mathcal{J}_m$. We consider this as essential for understanding generalized "quantum formalisms" and give the calculations. Since $b \circ b = (\sum_{i=0}^{m} y_i^2) e^0 + 2 \sum_{i=1}^{m} y_0 y_i e^i$, we obtain

$$\langle \tilde{\varrho}; b^2 \rangle = \varrho_0 y_0^2 + \varrho_0 \sum_{i=1}^{m} y_i^2 + 2 y_0 \sum_{i=1}^{m} \varrho_i y_i \,. \qquad (47.3.22)$$

For the special $b = -\varrho_0 e^0 + \sum_{i=1}^m \varrho_i e^i$, the right-hand side of (47.3.22) assumes the value $\varrho_0(\varrho_0^2 - \sum_{i=1}^m \varrho_i^2)$ leading to the necessary condition $\sum_{i=1}^m \varrho_i^2 \le \varrho_0^2$. On the other hand, this inequality is sufficient to make (47.3.22) dominating the positive value $\varrho_0(\sqrt{\sum_{i=1}^m y_i^2} - |y_0|)^2$ for all $b \in \mathcal{J}_m$ (with coordinates y_i).

Thus, we see that the state space $\mathcal{S}(\mathcal{J}_m)$, $m = 4^n - 1$, is affinely isomorphic to the closed m-ball $B_{2^{-n}}^{(m)}$ of radius 2^{-n}. This leads to the identification of the pure states with all of the surface of $B_{2^{-n}}^{(m)}$. Quite analogous to the case $n = 1$, the qubit case, the smallest face containing two pure states is all of $B_{2^{-n}}^{(m)}$, also for arbitrary $n > 1$ (leading to an interesting limit $n \to \infty$).

To turn the argument around: If we start from the compact convex set K, given by the m-dimensional ball $B_{2^{-n}}^{(m)}$, $m = 4^n - 1$, then its affine functions (metric observables) $\mathrm{Aff}_b(K)$ may be realized by the real matrices $\mathbb{M}_{2^n,\mathrm{sa}}$ and the trace duality, if K is realized by the pseudo-density operators $\sum_{i=0}^m \varrho_i e^i$, $\varrho_0 = 2^{-n}$, $(\varrho_1, \ldots, \varrho_m) \in B_{2^{-n}}^{(m)}$. But the positivity of $a \in \mathrm{Aff}_b(K)$ (of being a positive function) coincides with the algebraic positivity (of being a square) only, if the product in $\mathbb{M}_{2^n,\mathrm{sa}}$ is the above given Jordan product. In this sense, finite-dimensional balls determine the spin factors as dual objects.

As an exercise one should check, that for $m = 3$ (that is $n = 1$) the symmetric matrix product in $\mathbb{M}_{2\mathrm{sa}}$ coincides with the Jordan product of a spin factor (so that the qubit appears as an especially universal structure).

47.4.   JB-Algebraic and C*-Algebraic State Spaces

47.4.1.   *General Characterization*

Resuming the general structure theory, we start from the stage of a spectral convex set, described in Definition 47.2-27 on page 1747. By means of the spectral representation Eq. (47.2.34), one is able to introduce functions of an $a \in \mathrm{Aff}_b(K)$, especially

$$a^n := \int_{\mathbb{R}} t^n \, dp_t, \quad \forall n \in \mathbb{N}, \tag{47.4.1}$$

where $(p_t)_{\mathbb{R}}$ is the spectral family in terms of projective units, associated with a, which is in one–one correspondence with the spectral family $(F_t)_{\mathbb{R}}$ of F-properties. This enables the notion of a "variance" of an observable a in a state $v \in K$. One is inclined to introduce also a symmetric product for two elements $a, b \in \mathrm{Aff}_b(K)$ by setting

$$a \circ b := ((a+b)^2 - a^2 - b^2)/4. \tag{47.4.2}$$

To gain by that a well shaped Jordan product, one has to supplement further assumptions. Surprisingly simple is the following additional requirement (cf. [AS76]).

Proposition 47.4-1 (Bilinearity Requirement). *Let K be a spectral convex set. Then relation Eq. (47.4.2), taken as a product, makes $\mathrm{Aff}_b(K)$ to a JB-algebra, if and only if this relation is bilinear.*

If one seeks for intrinsic characterizations of K, it turns out that K must exhibit the n-ball property in the more general sense of a Hilbert ball property. More precisely, it holds according to [AS78] the following characterization.

Theorem 47.4-2 (Characterization of JB-Algebraic State Spaces). *A compact convex set K (in some locally convex Hausdorff space) is affinely homeomorphic to the state space of a JB-algebra, if and only if the following three requirements are satisfied:*

(1) *K is a spectral convex set.*
(2) *The σ-convex hull (consisting of countable convex combinations) of $\partial_e K$ is a split face.*
(3) *K owns the Hilbert-ball property.*

Already the "only if"-part is full of interesting results on the state space K of a JB-algebra $\mathcal{J}$, and on $\mathrm{Aff}_b(K)$. Notice that $\mathcal{J}$ is unital since the state space is assumed compact. We learn that $\mathrm{Aff}_b(K)$ is an order-unit space (by means of the algebraic unit), where the elements of $\mathcal{J}$ provide special elements of $\mathrm{Aff}_b(K)$, and we find all further qualities of a spectral convex set in a special realization. Especially, we have here the existence of filtering operations Q as a result of the structure of $\mathcal{J}$, whereas they previously have been introduced only axiomatically.

A further analysis reveals that the bidual $\mathcal{J}^{**}$ is an ordered Banach space, isomorphic to $\mathrm{Aff}_b(K)$, and the Jordan algebraic operations may be continued into $\mathrm{Aff}_b(K)$. That procedure to gain the enveloping JBW–algebra (where "W" signifies the existence of a predual) is completely analogous to constructing the universal von Neumann algebra $\mathcal{M}_u \cong \mathcal{A}^{**}$ for a C*-algebra $\mathcal{A}$. And, as is known for C*-algebras, one finds also for JB-algebras that the complete orthomodular lattice of filtered faces $\mathcal{E}(K)$ is ortho-isomorphic to the set of projections in $\mathcal{J}^{**}$.

Most remarkable is the "if" part of the preceding theorem, which will help us to reach a deeper understanding of non-classical theories.

Following [ASH80], one can now neatly specify those additional attributes, which lead from the state space of a JB-algebra to the state space of a C*-algebra.

Theorem 47.4-3 (Characterization of C*-Algebraic State Spaces). *A compact convex set is K (in some locally convex Hausdorff space) is affinely homeomorphic to the state space of a C*-algebra, if and only if the following four conditions are satisfied:*

(1) *K is a spectral convex set.*
(2) *The σ-convex hull of $\partial_e K$ is a split face.*

(3) *K owns the 3-ball property.*
(4) *K is orientable.*

Again leads the "only if" part of the theorem to a lot of insights into C*-algebraic state spaces. Because we permanently apply these features we elaborate them explicitly in the following Chapters.

The "if" part may be considered as one of the most important results on the foundations of quantum theory.

One should recognize that a Jordan algebraic statistical theory seems already rather similar to usual quantum theory. Thus the implications of orientability and 3-ball property, which specialize Jordan algebraic theory down to C*-algebraic theory, are important to understand. We discuss them by studying in the following two sections (quantum) coherence and transition probabilities.

47.4.2. *General Coherence Relation*

We formulate here the generalization of the quantum mechanical coherent state superposition to rather general convex state spaces.

We assume that the state space K is a projective convex set, so that all its detectable faces are the images of a filtering operation and constitute a complete orthomodular lattice $\mathcal{E}(K)$ according to Theorem 47.2-20. As in Definition 47.2-22, $F_v \in \mathcal{E}(K)$ denotes the supporting face and $\mathcal{F}_v \in \mathcal{E}_c(K)$ the supporting split face of $v \in K$. If for $v \in \partial_e K$ the face $\{v\}$ is in $\mathcal{E}(K)$, then $F_v = \{v\}$. For simplicity, we assume that all pure states are detectable, i.e., $\{v\} \in \mathcal{E}(K)$ for all $v \in \partial_e K$. Of course, all pure states have also minimal classical supports $\mathcal{F}_v$, that are atoms in $\mathcal{E}_c(K)$.

Let now be given two different *pure states* v_1 and v_2 with supports F_1 and F_2. If there is a different third pure state v_3 with support F_3, then all mentioned supports are pair-wise intersection free. If $v_3 \in F_1 \vee F_2$, then we know that v_1 and v_2 cannot be classically different and rather must have the same (minimal) classical support. For, if F_1, F_2 would be classically different, then $F_1 \vee F_2$ would be (according to Proposition 47.1-5) a real line segment and would contain only mixed states, besides v_1 and v_2, and thus could not contain v_3.

If $v_3 \in F_1 \vee F_2$, the state v_3 is in a certain sense "composed" of v_1 and v_2, but being pure, it is not a mixture of the other two. In Hilbert space quantum theory the pure states may expressed as complex unit rays (corresponding to one-dimensional projections) so that, in this formulation, $F_1 \vee F_2$ is the plane spanned by the two unit rays. As $v_3 \in F_1 \vee F_2$ tells us that the unit ray of v_3 lies in that plane, it is obtained by linear combining the vectors of the first two rays. This is the traditional way to describe a coherent superposition.

Since — if $v_3 \in F_1 \vee F_2$ — we have in the described general frame an analogous relation for the supporting faces as for the traditional rays, we want to say also here, that v_3 is a *coherent superposition* of v_1 and v_2, provided all three states are pure. The situation should, however, be symmetric in the participating states, and we want to introduce a ternary symmetric relation, which we then name *coherence relation*.

The fact that the considered three pure states are never alone in the world, and that the remaining macroscopic parts of the surroundings are better described in terms of mixed states, is for itself reason enough to generalize a coherence relation to non-pure states. Moreover, one observes certainly some kind of quantum coherence for non-pure many Boson states, as e.g., for finite temperature Bose–Einstein condensates, as well as for non-pure radiated photon states. It will turn out, that it is useful to employ for the coherence of mixed states the same lattice theoretic relation for their supports as for pure states. We thus make the following ansatz (cf. [RR83] for W*-algebraic theories).

Definition 47.4-4 (General Coherence Relation). Let the statistical state space K be a projective convex set with an orthomodular lattice $\mathcal{E}(K)$ of detectable faces.

We say that three states $v_i \in K$, with supports $F_i \in \mathcal{E}(K)$, $i = 1, 2, 3$, are in *coherence relation*, and write then $K(v_1, v_2, v_3)$, if and only if the following equations are satisfied:

$$F_1 \wedge F_2 = F_2 \wedge F_3 = F_3 \wedge F_1 = \emptyset \,,$$
$$F_1 \vee F_2 = F_2 \vee F_3 = F_3 \vee F_1 \,. \tag{47.4.3}$$

The second line in Eq. (47.4.3) gives the connection of v_3 with v_1 and v_2 in so far as its support F_3 may replace F_1 or F_2 in generating $F_1 \vee F_2$. So, in spite of having a non-overlapping support property with those of v_1 and v_2, the qualities of v_3 are in some sense contained in the combined qualities of v_1 and v_2. That weakens the notion of "distinctness" for states, and the theory acquires a *diffuse character*, if the coherence relation is non-empty.

We have already given above an argument that $K(v_1, v_2, v_3)$ implies the equality $\mathcal{F}_1 = \mathcal{F}_2 = \mathcal{F}_3$ of the classical supports. For illustration, let us prove that fact again for three (different) pure states, where the $\mathcal{F}_i$ are atoms in the distributive $\mathcal{E}_c(K)$. If $\mathcal{F}_3 \neq \mathcal{F}_1$ then $\mathcal{F}_3 \wedge \mathcal{F}_1 = \emptyset$. $v_3 \in F_1 \vee F_2$ implies $\mathcal{F}_3 \leq \mathcal{F}_1 \vee \mathcal{F}_2$, and so $\mathcal{F}_3 = \mathcal{F}_3 \wedge (\mathcal{F}_1 \vee \mathcal{F}_2) = (\mathcal{F}_3 \wedge \mathcal{F}_1) \vee (\mathcal{F}_3 \wedge \mathcal{F}_2) = \mathcal{F}_3 \wedge \mathcal{F}_2 = \mathcal{F}_2$, since not empty. Therefore, $v_1 \in F_2 \vee F_3 = F_3$, and we have a contradiction.

We conclude: *Different classical properties break coherent superposability.*

Whereas this result is out of question for absolute superselection rules like charge, it is still controversially discussed for macroscopic superselection rules (cf. also Sec. 48.2.4 on page 1804). Let us here deal with that fundamental problem only in the form of a remark.

Remark 47.4-5 (Coherence and Schrödinger's Cat). In the well known gedankenexperiment called "Schrödinger's cat" the radioactive nucleus is in a coherent superposition, but not the composite system "nucleus plus cat". For, if the huge assemblage of molecules — those constituents which are described quantum mechanically usually with the unrestricted superposition principle — is recognized as a living or dead cat, then one has necessarily formed classical observables. This is certainly connected with the many degrees of freedom the system "cat" has from the microscopic point of view and is theoretically executed by a kind of thermodynamic limit. But that does not mean at all, that one is allowed to apply that type of classical observables only to infinite systems.

According to the general theory of concept formation one discards always transient cases for introducing a concept. Without that, we would have no knowledge whatsoever from the world. (We refer here merely to [Pri83] and the many examples and references therein.)

It is especially narrow minded to deny this principle of concept formation in the realm of physics. Not a single part of this "exact science" is without crude approximations, be it for macroscopic or be it for microscopic systems. Even the notions of a "nucleus" or of a "molecule", appearing in the so-called "cat paradox" are gained theoretically not without approximating limits, which eliminate transient cases quite analogously as does the thermodynamic limit.

If the lattice $\mathcal{E}(K)$ has a dimension function (see text near Theorem 46.2-36) and if the parallelogram laws is valid (see Eq. (46.2.29) on page 1705) — as is true for JB-algebraic and (thus also for) C*-algebra state spaces — $K(v_1, v_2, v_3)$ implies equal dimension for the F_i, $i = 1, 2, 3$. That means that the support projections must be in some sense of the same size and so the states must have the same degree of mixedness. We give more detailed criteria in the discussion around Proposition 46.2-37 on page 1705. The result mentioned there, that for given states v_1, v_2 the relation $F_1 \sim F_2$ together with $F_1 \wedge F_2 = \emptyset$ implies that there is a coherent superposition state v_3, with valid coherence relation $K(v_1, v_2, v_3)$, let us call "coherence condition". This necessary and sufficient coherence condition has been proved also for JB-algebraic states in [Zan90].

For exercise, let us demonstrate directly that the *coherence relation is empty in a classical theory*. If K is a Bauer simplex, and is thus the state space of the commutative C*-algebra $C(\partial_e K, \mathbb{C})$, then the supports F_i of the arbitrary states $v_i \in K$ coincide with their classical supports $\mathcal{F}_i$. (If the v_i are realized by the probability measures $\mu_i \in M_p(\partial_e K)$, their $\mathcal{F}_i$ are given by the sets of those $\mu \in M_p(\partial_e K)$ the supports of which are contained in $\mathrm{supp}(\mu_i)$.) Since the latter supports must be equal for attempting the relation $K(v_1, v_2, v_3)$, the first line of Eq. (47.4.3) is violated.

We have remarked above that the Hilbert ball property is the essential ingredient to convert a general spectral convex set into the state space of a *JB-algebra*. For the physical interpretation it is interesting that this requirement leads to a kind of homogeneity of the diffuseness of the theory, which may be expressed in terms of the coherence relation.

Proposition 47.4-6 (Homogeneous Diffuseness of Pure States). *Let* v_1, v_2
be two pure states in the state space K *of a JB-algebra with unit, with supporting
faces* $F_1, F_2 \in \mathcal{E}(K)$. *Then the extremal boundary of* $F_1 \vee F_2 \in \mathcal{E}(K)$ *is generated
by the coherent superpositions of* v_1, v_2 *as follows:*

$$\partial_e(F_1 \vee F_2) = \{v_3 \in K \mid K(v_1, v_2, v_3)\} \cup \{v_1, v_2\}. \tag{47.4.4}$$

(For the proof see [Zan90].) Thus, the larger the join $F_1 \vee F_2$ of two given $v_1, v_2 \in$
$\partial_e K$ the more "diffuse" is the statistical theory and this diffuseness may be measured
by the dimension of the Hilbert balls, which are affinely homeomorphic to $F_1 \vee F_2$.

47.4.3. *General Transition Probability*

The notion of a *transition probability* has its deeper origins from the overlap of
weighted observable values in the two states under consideration.

We have introduced a metric observable in terms of a scaled increasing family
$A = (F_t)_{\mathbb{R}} \leftrightarrow (p_t)_{\mathbb{R}}$ of F-properties respectively of projective units. These determine the probabilities for the occurrence of the observable values in a real Borel set
B for a state $v \in K$ (as given in Eq. (47.2.25)):

$$v^A(B) \equiv \mathrm{prob}_v^A(B) := \int_B dp_t(v)) \equiv \int_B dv_t^A, \quad \forall B \in \mathrm{B}(\mathbb{R}), \tag{47.4.5}$$

with $p_t(v) = \tilde{e}(Q_t(v)) =: v_t^A$ and Q_t the filtering projection for F_t.

So we seek a transition probability between two states $v, w \in K$, which measures
the overlap of the probability distributions v^A and w^A for varying observable A.
There is always an observable, which assumes the same value for two given states
v, w. (Take e.g., the one-filter observable A_F for $F = F_v \vee F_w$, which "happens" in
both states with probability 1.) A true measure for the similarity of the two states
v, w tests the minimal overlap between observable values.

Definition 47.4-7 (Cantoni [Can75]). Let K be a spectral convex state space
and v, w two states in K. Since for spectral convex sets the metrical observables
A are, according to Theorem 47.2-28, in bijective correspondence with the affine
functions $a \in \mathrm{Aff}_b(K)$, we use the symbol $\mathrm{Aff}_b(K)$ to indicate the set of observables,
expressed in either way.

The transition probability $T_K(v, w)$ between v and w is by definition

$$T_K(v, w) := \inf \left\{ \left(\int_{\mathbb{R}} \sqrt{\frac{dv^A}{d\mu}} \sqrt{\frac{dw^A}{d\mu}} \, d\mu \right)^2 \mid A \in \mathrm{Aff}_b(K) \right\}, \tag{47.4.6}$$

where μ is any finite (positive) Borel measure on K, with respect to which v^A and
w^A are absolutely continuous, and $\frac{dv^A}{d\mu}$ etc. denote the Radon–Nikodym derivatives.

From the definition, one deduces that $T_K(v, w)$ is well defined, symmetric in the two states, and takes values in $[0, 1]$, since μ appears in the nominator as well as in the denominator and the v^A, w^A are probability measures.

Clearly $T_K(v, v) = 1$ for all $v \in K$. It is also evident that for classically disjoint states, meaning $\mathcal{F}_v \wedge \mathcal{F}_w = \emptyset$, we obtain $T_K(v, w) = 0$, since e.g., the overlap between the observable values for the one-filter observable A_F, with $F = \mathcal{F}_v$, is empty.

Many relations for transition probabilities can be formulated already in the general frame of spectral convex sets, but we pursue this in detail only for C*-algebras in Sec. 48.4.

Let us here merely mention, that in the case of pure states $v, w \in \partial_e K$, we can produce a more explicit expression. We make the plausible assumption that the minimal overlap between the distributed observable values is certainly reached, if the observable is either the one-filter observable A_F, with $F = \{v\}$, or with $F = \{w\}$. In the first case, Eq. (47.2.31) leads to the probability densities $dv_t^F = \delta(t-1)\, dt$ and $dw_t^F = [\tilde{e}(Q_v^\perp(w))\delta(t) + \tilde{e}(Q_v(w))\delta(t-1)]\, dt = [p_v^\perp(w)\delta(t) + p_v(w)\delta(t-1)]\, dt$, where Q_v respectively p_v signify here the filter projection respectively projective unit associated with the face $F = \{v\}$. We can choose for $d\mu$ in Eq. (47.4.6) dw_t^F and arrive at

$$T_K(v, w) = p_v(w) = \tilde{e}(Q_v(w)). \tag{47.4.7}$$

Thus the transition probability is here the size of the normalized ensemble w after having passed the filter Q_v. If the faces F_v and F_w are orthogonal, then so are the corresponding filtering projections and $Q_v(w) = (Q_v \circ Q_w)(w)$ vanishes, so that $T_K(v, w) = 0$.

Because of the symmetry of the transition probability one expects the same result as in Eq. (47.4.7), if one works with the face $F = \{w\}$, what would lead to

$$T_K(v, w) = p_v(w) = p_w(v) = \tilde{e}(Q_v(w)) = \tilde{e}(Q_w(v)). \tag{47.4.8}$$

This equality has in fact been verified, if the Hilbert ball property is valid (cf. [AS78]). It follows then that $\partial_e(F_v \vee F_w)$ is a "transition probability space" in the sense of [BC81]. This space is isomorphic to what is denoted $\mathcal{S}(2, n)$ in the investigation of [Mie68], where n gives the dimension of $F_v \vee F_w$. $T_K(v, w)$ is then proportional to the square of the geometric distance of $v, w \in \mathcal{S}(2, n)$. n is shown to be the maximal number of pure states, which have pair-wise the transition probability $T_K(v, w) = 1/2$.

It be mentioned that in [Lan98a] an axiomatic investigation of transition probability spaces of pure states is undertaken, where beside other things the notion of a *basis* is introduced. These concepts apply to the extreme points $\partial_e(F_v \vee F_w)$ of the Hilbert balls, which certainly must be of the larger dimension, the larger this basis.

All these findings confirm the general tendency, that the variety of pure states, with non-vanishing pair-wise transition probabilities, increases with the dimension of the Hilbert ball $F_v \vee F_w$. The spontaneous transition of one pure state into another pure state, without any dynamical cause, is a typical non-classical feature of the theory, and expresses again its diffuseness. In communication theory, it comes into play as non-classical noise.

47.4.4. *Physical Foundation of C*-Algebraic Quantum Theories*

After having considered the mathematical characterization of various statistical state spaces, for which we already discussed the implications for states and observables, let us try to summarize the basic features, which distinguish C*-algebraic quantum theories. By comparison with more general theories, the empirical meaning of the special features of C*-algebraic state spaces should be elucidated.

If we assume that the compact convex state space K of a statistical theory allows for metric observables in terms of expectation value functionals, then we deal with *spectral convex sets* (according to Proposition 47.2-28). We have there the complete orthomodular lattice of filtered F-properties (projective norm exposed faces), which provide also the constituents of the spectral integrals for observables.

That a theory for a physical system inherits metric observables is certainly a basic requirement and concerns empiric manipulations, and the introduction of a numerical scale is intimately connected with a spectral family.

The important role of a concise (quantum) negation (viz. orthocomplementation) for the filtering of measurable properties and for the spectral representation is clearly brought out in the axioms for spectral convex sets. Already this type of a theory allows for a detailed probability formalism for the rise of observable values. Also a general coherence relation and the notion of a general transition probability may be introduced.

Since there is no algebraic product in $\mathrm{Aff}_b(K)$, one cannot systematically proceed from simpler observables to more complicated ones, what would be desirable for studying models. Furtheron, there seems to be not enough technical machinery to get an overview on how diffuse — in the sense of coherent superposability of states — such a theory may be.

All these aspects are improved by having available a Jordan product for the observables of a JB-*algebra*. The statistical notions are, by that, supplemented by symmetric correlation functions. The fascinating aspect of Theorem 47.4-2 is, that the existence of the Jordan product is derived from requirements on the state space, which must be added to a spectral convex set, and which may so be analyzed on their empirical impact.

The additional requirement (2) of Theorem 47.4-2 refers to those states, which are decomposable into countable convex sums of pure states. These should be separated from the rest of the states by a split face complementation. This appeals to the possible existence of states — in the complementary split face — which represent F-properties, which are not exhibited by pure states. We always mention "temperature" as a typical example. We find that also this technical seeming requirement is not completely free of an empirical meaning.

The additional requirement (3) of Theorem 47.4-2 refers to the structure of the norm closed faces generated by two distinct pure states. We would interpret its requested form of being a Hilbert ball as a kind of homogeneous structure of the diffuseness. The dimension of the Hilbert balls enable now a classification of the diffuseness, respectively of the non-classicality, for statistical theories of JB-type. That is connected with more structure for the coherence relation, which brings it nearer to that of traditional quantum theory.

From the basis of the already well developed JB-theories it is very interesting which further requirements on the statistical state space must be added, to arrive at a *C*-algebraic theory*. (Since only *compact* convex sets are considered, the derived C*-algebras are unital.)

In the assumption of Theorem 47.4-3 (3) the diffuseness of the theory is cut down to the 3-ball property. That enables the coherent superposition of two pure states to be expressed by a linear combination of rays in a *complex* Hilbert space. For a handwaving argument, one should remark that a complex plane, on which the three rays in coherence relation are situated, has four real dimensions, which are reduced by the normalization of the rays to three. In other words, it enables the state formulation in terms of complex wave functions (but does, of course, not distinguish a special Hilbert space representation for a given physical system).

That the observables arise as the self-adjoint elements of a complex C*-algebra is again connected with the possibility of a complex Hilbert space formulation, but also interwoven with postulate (4) of Theorem 47.4-3, concerning the orientability of the convex state space. By means of the orientation, one can discriminate between two kinds of affine homeomorphisms (the structural symmetries of the theory in the Schrödinger picture) acting in the compact convex set: Those which preserve the orientation and those which do not. This corresponds in the Heisenberg picture to the discrimination between automorphisms and anti-automorphisms, possible only for a non-commutative product.

As is illustrated by the anti-automorphism for time inversion, the state space orientation enables, beside other things, two directions of time (what does not introduce irreversibility). Because of that, one has both a forward and backward dynamical development (where irreversibility would exclude the latter). Related with it, is a description of the creation and annihilation of particles by means of non-Hermitian operators. But the aspects of complexification are very involved, occupying us all over the treatise, and we rest content here with these indications.

What we want to emphasize, however, is that certain aspects of the complex formalism of non-commutative C*-algebraic theories have a very deep origin, and are not present in (artificially) complexified classical field theories, describable with commutative C*-algebraic theories. That are those features, which are connected with the 3-ball property of the convex state space (which reduces to a "straight line property" in Bauer simplices for classical theories). And these aspects are neither present in more diffuse, that is, in more non-classical theories. Since also a 2–ball property is ruled out by the requirement of an orientable state space, we may conclude the following.

Conclusion 47.4-8 (Characterization of C*-Algebraic Quantum Theory). C*-algebraic quantum theories may roughly be characterized as follows: Consider the large family of convex state space theories, which allow

(a) for a formulation of metric observables in terms of expectation value functionals by means of spectral representations;
(b) for a "well developed" non-trivial coherence theory, expressing diffuseness;
(c) for introducing the direction of time development.

Then the non-commutative C*-algebraic theories are those among them which exhibit **minimal non-classical diffuseness**.

Concerning the value of these considerations for the theory of light, one needs a fully developed conceptual frame to relate the abundant classical properties and the optical coherence features of radiation with the non-Boolean F-properties and quantum coherence features of the photons; the more as the few photon experiments are of steadily increasing interest. And for a concise theory of noise in optical communication, both stages of description must be related as well as be discriminated.

47.5.   Convex and Spectral Notions in Traditional Quantum Theory

As an illustration of the convex state space approach, we discuss the special convex set of density operators $K \equiv T_1^+(\mathcal{H})$ in the (not necessarily separable) Hilbert space $\mathcal{H}$, which we began to investigate in Sec. 43.2.3. $T_1^+(\mathcal{H})$ is a convex subset of the real Banach space $\mathcal{V} \equiv T(\mathcal{H})_{\text{sa}}$ of all self-adjoint trace class operators, which is closed in the trace norm $\|.\|_{\text{tr}}$. Its bounded affine functions $\text{Aff}_b(T_1^+(\mathcal{H}))$ are shown in Sec. 43.2.3 to be isomorphic to the self-adjoint bounded operators $\mathcal{L}(\mathcal{H})_{\text{sa}}$ in the sense of ordered Banach spaces. That is, for each $a \in \text{Aff}_b(T_1^+(\mathcal{H}))$ there is exactly one $A \in \mathcal{L}(\mathcal{H})_{\text{sa}}$, with $a(T) = \text{tr}[TA]$ for all $T \in T_1^+(\mathcal{H})$, and with $\|a\| \equiv \sup\{|a(T)| \,|\, T \in T_{\text{sa}}(\mathcal{H}), \|T\|_{\text{tr}} \leq 1\} = \|A\|$, so that A is a positive operator, if and only if a is a positive functional (cf. Proposition 43.2-8 on page 1532).

From Proposition 45.3-1, we know that $T_1^+(\mathcal{H})$ is the total state space of the C*-algebra $\mathcal{C}(\mathcal{H})$, given by all compact operators. Since via the trace duality $T_1^+(\mathcal{H})$ and $\mathcal{C}(\mathcal{H})$ mutually separate each other as functionals, we know that those bounded affine functionals on $T_1^+(\mathcal{H})$, which are also weak* continuous, and which we denote by $\mathrm{Aff}_c(\mathcal{T}_1^+(\mathcal{H}))$, are (norm and order preserving) isomorphic to the self-adjoint compact operators $\mathcal{C}(\mathcal{H})_{\mathrm{sa}}$.

Since for infinite-dimensional $\mathcal{H}$ the C*-algebra $\mathcal{C}(\mathcal{H})$ does not contain a unit, $\mathcal{T}_1^+(\mathcal{H})$ is not weak* compact. Nevertheless, we can find most features discussed above for compact convex sets if we presuppose the spectral theory in $\mathcal{L}(\mathcal{H})_{\mathrm{sa}}$. Since we have, as sketched in Sec. 43.3, a spectral theory also for unbounded self-adjoint operators, we may extend the set of metric observables to include unbounded scales, as is practiced in traditional quantum mechanics. But this is possible only by the loss of a universal state space. To avoid this complication, we stick in the following at first to $\mathcal{T}_1^+(\mathcal{H})$, and mention only at the end the peculiarities for unbounded observables.

Proposition 47.5-1. $\mathrm{Aff}_b(\mathcal{T}_1^+(\mathcal{H})) \leftrightarrow \mathcal{L}(\mathcal{H})_{\mathrm{sa}}$ *is an order unit Banach space with order unit* $e = \mathbb{1} \in \mathcal{L}(\mathcal{H})$, *and* $\mathrm{Aff}_c(\mathcal{T}_1^+(\mathcal{H})) \leftrightarrow \mathcal{C}(\mathcal{H})_{\mathrm{sa}}$ *is for infinite-dimensional* $\mathcal{H}$ *an almost order unit Banach space with exterior order unit* $e = \mathbb{1} \in \mathcal{L}(\mathcal{H})$.

The self-adjoint trace class operators $\mathcal{V} = \mathcal{T}(\mathcal{H})_{\mathrm{sa}}$ *are a complete base normed space with respect to the trace norm and base* $\mathcal{T}_1^+(\mathcal{H})$.

Specifically, for each $T \in \mathcal{T}(\mathcal{H})_{\mathrm{sa}}$ *we have two unique numbers* $\lambda_+, \lambda_- \geq 0$ *and two density operators* $T^+, T^- \in \mathcal{T}_1^+(\mathcal{H})$, *with* $T^+T^- = 0$, *unique if the corresponding* λ-*numbers do not vanish, such that there holds the Jordan decomposition*

$$\mathcal{T}(\mathcal{H})_{\mathrm{sa}} \ni T = \lambda_+ T^+ - \lambda_- T^-, \qquad \|T\|_{\mathrm{tr}} = \lambda_+ + \lambda_- . \qquad (47.5.1)$$

Proof. The norm formula $\|A\| = \inf\{\lambda \geq 0 \,|\, A \in [-\lambda\mathbb{1}, \lambda\mathbb{1}]\}$ for $A \in \mathcal{L}(\mathcal{H})_{\mathrm{sa}}$, follows from the spectral radius formula. Also $\mathcal{C}(\mathcal{H})_{\mathrm{sa}}$ is a real Banach space in the usual operator norm.

Equation (47.5.1) derives from (43.2.7). We get from this the relations of Proposition 47.2-9: $\mathcal{V}^+ \equiv \mathcal{T}^+(\mathcal{H}) = \cup_{\lambda \geq 0} \lambda \mathcal{T}_1^+(\mathcal{H})$, and for $T \in \mathcal{T}^+(\mathcal{H})$ by definition holds $\|T\|_{\mathrm{tr}} = \mathrm{tr}[T\mathbb{1}]$.

The self-adjoint unit ball $B = \{T \in \mathcal{T}(\mathcal{H})_{\mathrm{sa}} \,|\, \mathrm{tr}[|T|] \leq 1\}$ equals $B = \mathrm{Conv}(K \cup (-K))$ by rewriting (47.5.1) as $T = (\lambda_+ + \lambda_-)(\lambda T^+ + (1 - \lambda)(-T^-))$ with $\lambda := \lambda_+/(\lambda_+ + \lambda_-)$. From this follows also the base normed formula $\|T\|_{\mathrm{tr}} = \inf\{\lambda \geq 0 \,|\, T \in \lambda B\}$. $\qquad\square$

The set of all norm closed faces of $K = \mathcal{T}_1^+(\mathcal{H})$ is denoted by $\mathcal{E}(\mathcal{T}_1^+(\mathcal{H}))$, and constitutes those *F-properties* which are taken into account in the following.

$\mathcal{E}(K)$ is ordered by inclusion, and the infimum is then $F_1 \wedge F_2 = F_1 \cap F_2$, since the intersection of $F_1, F_2 \in \mathcal{E}(K)$ is again a norm closed face. Since the same is true for arbitrary intersections $\bigwedge_{i \in I} F_i$ and since also $\bigvee_{i \in I} F_i := \bigwedge\{F \in \mathcal{E}(K) \,|\, F \supseteq F_i, \, i \in I\}$ does exist, $\mathcal{E}(K)$ is a complete lattice. (For the general lattice notions cf. Sec. 47.2.2 on page 1731.)

The F-properties are "detected" by the projective units $p \in \mathcal{P}(K)$, that are special affine functions $T \mapsto p(T)$, with values between 0 and 1. More precisely, an $F \in \mathcal{E}(K)$, is detected by an $p \in \mathcal{P}(K)$, if $p(T) = 1$ for $T \in F$ and $p(T) < 1$ otherwise. We shall elaborate the connection between projective units $p \in \mathcal{P}(K)$ and projection operators $P \in \mathcal{P}(\mathcal{H})$.

In an analogous manner as for $\mathcal{E}(K)$, one concludes that $\mathcal{P}(\mathcal{H})$ is a complete lattice under the order relation $P \leq P'$, which is valid if and only if the corresponding closed subspaces are in subset relation, i.e., $P\mathcal{H} \subseteq P'\mathcal{H}$. (Algebraically this is expressed by $PP' = P = P'P$.) Again the arbitrary intersections of closed subspaces are the infima and thus arbitrary suprema exist, too. (Algebraically $P \vee P'$ equals $P + P' - PP'$.) The relation $P \mapsto P^{\perp} = \mathbb{1} - P$ is an orthocomplementation. $\mathcal{P}(\mathcal{H})$ is a complete orthomodular lattice, since $P \leq P'$ implies commutativity and yields thus the orthomodular identity $P' = P' \wedge (P^{\perp} \vee P) = (P' \wedge P^{\perp}) \vee P$, a special distributivity relation.

The following theorem is also basic for characterizing the F-properties of operator algebraic theories.

Theorem 47.5-2. *Let us again denote* $K := T_1^+(\mathcal{H})$. *The map*

$$\mathcal{P}(\mathcal{H}) \ni P \mapsto F_P := \{T \in K \mid \mathrm{tr}[TP] = 1\} \subseteq K \,, \qquad (47.5.2)$$

is a lattice isomorphism between $\mathcal{P}(\mathcal{H})$ *and* $\mathcal{E}(K)$, *where the inverse map is given by*

$$\mathcal{E}(K) \ni F \mapsto P_F := \inf\{P \in \mathcal{P}(\mathcal{H}) \mid \mathrm{tr}[TP] = 1, \ \forall T \in F\} \,. \qquad (47.5.3)$$

(One sets $P_F = 0$ *for the improper face* $F = \emptyset \in \mathcal{E}(K)$.)

Explicitly P_F *is given by the orthogonal projection onto the closed subspace*

$$\mathcal{H}_F := \{\xi \in \mathcal{H} \mid |\hat{\xi})(\hat{\xi}| \in F\} \cup \{0 \in \mathcal{H}\}, \quad where \quad \hat{\xi} := \xi/\|\xi\|. \qquad (47.5.4)$$

By the definition $(F_P)^{\perp} := F_{P^{\perp}}$, $\mathcal{E}(K)$ *becomes a (complete) orthomodular lattice.*

Proof. (a) If $0 < P \in \mathcal{P}(\mathcal{H})$ is given, then there is a unit vector $\xi \in P\mathcal{H}$ and $|\xi)(\xi|$ is in the non-empty F_P. For given $P > 0$, the set F_P clearly is convex. If we have for $T \in F_P$, the non-trivial convex decomposition $T = \lambda T_1 + (1 - \lambda) T_2$ in K, then $1 = \lambda \, \mathrm{tr}[T_1 P] + (1 - \lambda) \, \mathrm{tr}[T_2 P]$ is an equality for positive numbers, where $\mathrm{tr}[T_i P] \leq 1$, what implies $\mathrm{tr}[T_1 P] = \mathrm{tr}[T_2 P] = 1$, so that F_P is a face.

(b) If the net $(T_i)_I \subset F_P$ converges in trace norm to $T \in K$, then surely $\mathrm{tr}[TP] = 1$, and F_P is norm closed. If $0 < P \leq P'$, and $T \in F_P$, then $1 = \mathrm{tr}[TP] \leq \mathrm{tr}[TP'] \leq 1$ and $T \in F_{P'}$, so that $F_P \subseteq F_{P'}$.

(c) For $P \in \mathcal{P}(\mathcal{H})$ we define

$$Q_P : K \to T^+(\mathcal{H}) \quad by \quad Q_P(T) := PTP. \qquad (47.5.5)$$

Then $T \in F_P$, if and only if $\mathrm{tr}[TP^\perp] = 0$. If this is the case, $|\mathrm{tr}[TP^\perp A]|^2 \leq \mathrm{tr}[TAA^*]\mathrm{tr}[TP^\perp] = 0$, for all $A \in \mathcal{L}(\mathcal{H})$, by the Cauchy–Schwartz inequality. We then have $\mathrm{tr}[T(PAP + P^\perp AP + AP^\perp)] = \mathrm{tr}[TA] = \mathrm{tr}[Q_P(T)A]$. But $Q_P(T) = T$, if and only if $T \in Q_P(K) \cap K$. Thus it holds

$$F_P = Q_P(K) \cap K, \quad \text{for } 0 < P \in \mathcal{P}(\mathcal{H}). \tag{47.5.6}$$

(d) If now $F \in \mathcal{E}(K)$ is given, the completeness of $\mathcal{P}(\mathcal{H})$ ensures the existence of P_F in (47.5.3). If, on the other side, ξ_1 and ξ_2 are in $\mathcal{H}_F$, then for any linear combination $\xi = c_1\xi_1 + c_2\xi_2$, we know $|\hat{\xi})(\hat{\xi}| \in F$, since $|\hat{\xi})(\hat{\xi}|$ is in the smallest face in $\mathcal{E}(K)$ which contains $|\hat{\xi}_1)(\hat{\xi}_1|$ and $|\hat{\xi}_2)(\hat{\xi}_2|$ (that is the qubit space generated by ξ_1 and ξ_2, if the vectors are linearly independent). Thus $\mathcal{H}_F$ is a subspace of $\mathcal{H}$.

If the sequence (ξ_n) converges to ξ, then the corresponding norms and unit vectors converge to $\|\xi\|$ respectively $\hat{\xi}$. So it suffices to consider a sequence of unit vectors $(\xi_n) \subset \mathcal{H}_F$ which converges to $\xi \in \mathcal{H}$. Then $(|\xi_n)(\xi_n|) \subset F$ converges in the weak topology, and thus in the σ-weak respectively trace-norm topology, to $|\xi)(\xi| \in F$, due to the norm closedness of F, and we have $\xi \in \mathcal{H}_F$.

Let us denote by P the orthogonal projection onto the closed subspace $\mathcal{H}_F$. Since P is the smallest projection dominating all $|\xi)(\xi| \in F$ and P_F dominates more projections, we have $P \leq P_F$.

If $T = \sum_{k \in \mathbb{N}} \lambda_k |\xi_k)(\xi_k| \in F$, then all $|\xi_k)(\xi_k| \in F$, because of the face property of F, and $Q_P(T) = \sum_{k \in \mathbb{N}} \lambda_k Q_P(|\xi_k)(\xi_k|) = T$. Thus $F \subseteq F_P$, according to (c).

If on the other hand $T = \sum_{k \in \mathbb{N}} \lambda_k |\xi_k)(\xi_k| \in F_P$, then all $|\xi_k)(\xi_k| \in F_P$, because of the face property of F_P. Then $\mathrm{tr}[|\xi_k)(\xi_k|P] = 1$, so $|\xi_k)(\xi_k| \leq P \Leftrightarrow \xi_k \in \mathcal{H}_F$ and we conclude that $|\xi_k)(\xi_k| \in F$ for all $k \in \mathbb{N}$. Because F is convex and trace-norm closed also $T \in F$, so that $F_P \subset F$ and $F = F_P$. Then also $\mathrm{tr}[TP] = 1$, for all $T \in F$. Since P_F is by definition the smallest of such projections, $P_F \leq P$ and we have finally $P = P_F$.

(e) Having demonstrated the lattice isomorphism, the orthomodularity of $\mathcal{E}(\mathcal{H})$ follows now from that of $\mathcal{P}(\mathcal{H})$, if one defines $F \mapsto F^\perp$ as in the assertion. □

We have observed in Proposition 47.2-16, that a (norm continuous) filtering projection acting in K is uniquely defined by its image, which is a norm closed face of K. It is easily verified, that for all $P \in \mathcal{P}(\mathcal{H})$ the map Q_P from Eq. (47.5.5) displays all attributes of a filtering projection as specified in Definition 47.2-15. So each norm closed face is a filtered one (what justifies our symbol $\mathcal{E}(K)$ for them), and all filter projections in $\mathcal{Q}(K)$ are expressible by an orthogonal projection operator $P \in \mathcal{P}(\mathcal{H})$. Therefore, we have ortho-lattice isomorphisms between $\mathcal{E}(K)$, $\mathcal{P}(\mathcal{H})$, and $\mathcal{Q}(K)$.

Finally, all projective units in $p \in \mathcal{P}(K)$ are by definition given by a filtering projection, thus by a Q_P, so that $p(T) := \tilde{e}(Q_P(T)) = \mathrm{tr}[\mathbb{1}PTP] = \mathrm{tr}[PT]$ is the general form. Therefore, also $\mathcal{P}(K)$ is ortho-lattice isomorphic to $\mathcal{P}(\mathcal{H})$. Because each non-vanishing $P \in \mathcal{P}(\mathcal{H})$ dominates a 1-dimensional projection, that is an atom, the lattice $\mathcal{P}(\mathcal{H})$ is atomic.

If $F \in \mathcal{E}(K)$, then the construction of $P_F \in \mathcal{P}(\mathcal{H})$ according to Theorem 47.5-2 shows that F is detected by $p_F(.) := \mathrm{tr}[P_F \,.]$. Since all detectable faces are norm closed they coincide with $\mathcal{E}(K)$, thus with all filtered faces, and thus $K = T_1^+(\mathcal{H})$ is a projective convex set (with the exception of compactness).

Altogether we have

Corollary 47.5-3. *For any Hilbert space $\mathcal{H}$, where we employ again the symbol K for the convex set $T_1^+(\mathcal{H})$ of all density operators, we have ortho-lattice isomorphisms between the complete, orthomodular, atomic lattices of all norm closed faces $\mathcal{E}(K)$, and all projection operators $\mathcal{P}(\mathcal{H})$, and all filtering projections $\mathcal{Q}(K)$, and all projective units $P(K)$,*

$$\mathcal{E}(K) \leftrightarrow \mathcal{P}(\mathcal{H}) \leftrightarrow \mathcal{Q}(K) \leftrightarrow P(K). \tag{47.5.7}$$

The traditional quantum mechanical state space $T_1^+(\mathcal{H})$ is a projective convex set (non-compact in the weak* topology if $\dim(\mathcal{H}) = \infty$).

That the special affine functions $P(T_1^+(\mathcal{H})) \subset \mathrm{Aff}_b(T_1^+(\mathcal{H}))$ constitute a complete lattice contrasts the fact that $\mathrm{Aff}_b(T_1^+(\mathcal{H}))$ is no lattice at all (because $T_1^+(\mathcal{H})$ is not a simplex for $\dim(\mathcal{H}) \geq 2$). Observe in this connection that the weak* continuous projective units $P(T_1^+(\mathcal{H})) \cap \mathrm{Aff}_c(T_1^+(\mathcal{H}))$ form an incomplete, only lower bounded, lattice, which is ortho-lattice isomorphic to the finite projections $FP(\mathcal{H})$. (The C*-algebra $\mathcal{C}(\mathcal{H})$ contains only projections from $FP(\mathcal{H})$, what is not enough for an intrinsic spectral theory, since the eigenvalue 0 may be infinitely degenerated also for compact operators.)

In Sec. 43.3, we have described the construction of a self-adjoint (possibly unbounded) operator B and its measurable functions $f(B)$ in terms of a given *projection–valued measure*, the spectral measure of B. It is useful to consider the spectral measure from the lattice theoretic point of view.

Like every σ-algebra, $\mathsf{B}(\mathbb{R})$ is closed under countable unions and intersections, which expresses nothing else than closedness under countable suprema and infima with respect to the ordering "set inclusion". Thus $\mathsf{B}(\mathbb{R})$ is a σ-complete Boolean lattice (where the lattice orthocomplement is given by the set complement).

Assume now a projection valued measure $P(.) : \mathsf{B}(\mathbb{R}) \to \mathcal{P}(\mathcal{H})$ according to Definition 43.3-2. By the σ-additivity the relation $\Lambda_1 \subseteq \Lambda_2$ implies $P(\Lambda_2) = P(\Lambda_1) + P(\Lambda_2 \backslash \Lambda_1) \geq P(\Lambda_1)$, and one also has $P(\Lambda^c) = P(\Lambda)^\perp$. Therefore, the map $P(.)$ is order and orthocomplement preserving. Since $P(.)$ is usually not injective, one cannot deduce from this alone the preservation of the lattice operations. But we have from Definition 43.3-2 $P(\Lambda_1 \cap \Lambda_2) = P(\Lambda_1)P(\Lambda_2) = P(\Lambda_2)P(\Lambda_1)$, what equals $P(\Lambda_1) \wedge P(\Lambda_2)$ because of the commutativity of the spectral projections. We further conclude $\Lambda_1 \cup \Lambda_2 = \Lambda_1 \cup (\Lambda_2 \backslash (\Lambda_1 \cap \Lambda_2))$, what leads by the additivity to $P(\Lambda_1 \cup \Lambda_2) = P(\Lambda_1) + (P(\Lambda_2) - P(\Lambda_1 \cap \Lambda_2)) = P(\Lambda_1) + P(\Lambda_2) - P(\Lambda_1)P(\Lambda_2) = P(\Lambda_1) \vee P(\Lambda_2)$. Thus $P(.)$ is a lattice homomorphism.

Concerning infinite intersections, $P(\bigcap_{n=1}^{\infty} \Lambda_n)$ is certainly a lower bound for the set $\{P(\Lambda_n) \,|\, 1 \le n \le \infty\}$, but to show its maximality, one needs some convergence property. That one is provided by the σ-additivity of the spectral measure, giving for pair-wise disjoint sets the strong operator limit $\lim_{m \to \infty} \sum_{n=1}^{m} P(\Lambda_n)$ for $P(\bigcup_{n=1}^{\infty} \Lambda_n)$. The converging sum is the smallest projection dominating all summands and equals thus $\bigvee_{n=1}^{\infty} P(\Lambda_n)$. Since a countable union can always be replaced by a pair-wise disjoint countable union, we conclude quite generally $P(\bigcup_{n=1}^{\infty} \Lambda_n) = \bigvee_{n=1}^{\infty} P(\Lambda_n)$.

By the de Morgan formulas, one can replace a countable intersection by complementary countable unions, leading to $P(\bigcap_{n=1}^{\infty} \Lambda_n) = \bigwedge_{n=1}^{\infty} P(\Lambda_n)$.

Observation 47.5-4 (Spectral Lattice Homomorphisms). Each projection–valued measure $P(.) : \mathsf{B}(\mathbb{R}) \to \mathcal{P}(\mathcal{H})$ maps all countable ortho-lattice operations in $\mathsf{B}(\mathbb{R})$ homomorphically onto those in $\mathcal{P}(\mathcal{H})$ and the image $P(\mathsf{B}(\mathbb{R}))$ establishes therefore a σ-complete Boolean sublattice of $\mathcal{P}(\mathcal{H})$. Since $P(.)$ is always a spectral measure of a self-adjoint operator in $\mathcal{H}$, we speak of a spectral lattice homomorphism.

The countable lattice operations in $P(\mathsf{B}(\mathbb{R}))$ are the limits of the finite ones in the strong operator topology. Since $\mathcal{P}(\mathcal{H})$ is contained in the unit ball $\mathcal{L}(\mathcal{H})_1$, the countable lattice operations may also be performed in the σ-strong topology and, of course, in all weaker topologies (cf. Proposition 46.1-2).

We observe also that — as a σ-complete (Boolean) lattice — $P(\mathsf{B}(\mathbb{R}))$ is invariant under homeomorphic mappings in $\mathbb{R}$.

The spectral formalism may be further reduced by defining for a given spectral measure $P(.) : \mathsf{B}(\mathbb{R}) \to \mathcal{P}(\mathcal{H})$ the spectral family

$$\{P_\lambda := P((-\infty, \lambda]) \,|\, \lambda \in \mathbb{R}\} \subset \mathcal{P}(\mathcal{H}), \tag{47.5.8}$$

that is a one-parameter family of increasing and (already by this) mutually commuting orthogonal projections in $\mathcal{H}$.

Definition 47.5-5 (Projection-Valued Spectral Families). A set of orthogonal projections in the Hilbert space $\mathcal{H}$, denoted $\{P_\lambda \in \mathcal{P}(\mathcal{H}) \,|\, \lambda \in \mathbb{R}\} \equiv (P_\lambda)_{\mathbb{R}}$, is called a (projection–valued) spectral family, if it increases monotonously from $P_{-\infty} = 0$ to $P_{\infty} = \mathbb{1}$ and is right continuous in the σ-weak topology of $\mathcal{L}(\mathcal{H})$. (That the family increases is equivalent to $P_\lambda P_\mu = P_\gamma$, with $\gamma = \min\{\lambda, \mu\}$.)

A $\lambda \in \mathbb{R}$ is an increment point of the spectral family $(P_\lambda)_{\mathbb{R}}$, if $P_{\lambda+\varepsilon} - P_{\lambda-\varepsilon} > 0$, for all $\varepsilon > 0$.

The closure of the set of increment points is defined to be the spectrum of the spectral family, and $(P_\lambda)_{\mathbb{R}}$ is termed bounded, if its spectrum is bounded.

A spectral family is also called *partition of the unit*.

Because of $(-\infty, \lambda] = (\bigcup_{n=1}^{\infty} (-\infty, \lambda - \varepsilon_n]) \cup \{\lambda\}$, we obtain $P_\lambda = \bigvee_{n=1}^{\infty} P_{\lambda - \varepsilon_n} + P(\{\lambda\}) = \lim_{m \to \infty} P_{\lambda - \varepsilon_m} + P(\{\lambda\})$, what gives also left continuity for the spectral family at λ, if and only if $P(\{\lambda\}) = 0$.

For *any* density operator $T \in \mathcal{T}_1^+(\mathcal{H})$, the function $\mathbb{R} \ni \lambda \mapsto D_T(\lambda) := \mathrm{tr}[TP_\lambda]$ increases monotonously from $0 = D_T(-\infty)$ to $1 = D_T(+\infty)$. Because of the right σ-weak continuity of the spectral family, $D_T(.)$ is everywhere right continuous (and is also left continuous at λ, if and only if $\mathrm{tr}[TP(\{\lambda\})] = 0$). Thus D_T is a *distribution function* in the sense of probability theory.

The knowledge of the distribution function D_T alone is sufficient to calculate the numerical probability for an arbitrary Borel set by means of the Stieltjes integral

$$\mathrm{prob}_T(\Lambda) = \int_\Lambda d\mathrm{tr}[TP_\lambda] = \int_\Lambda dD_T(\lambda)], \quad \Lambda \in \mathrm{B}(\mathbb{R}). \tag{47.5.9}$$

We may express this equation in terms of operator integrals

$$P(\Lambda) = \sigma\text{-weak} \int_\Lambda dP_\lambda, \quad \Lambda \in \mathrm{B}(\mathbb{R}). \tag{47.5.10}$$

Proposition 47.5-6. *The projection–valued spectral families* $\mathbb{R} \ni \lambda \mapsto P_\lambda \in \mathcal{P}(\mathcal{H})$ *are in one-one correspondence with the projection–valued spectral measures* $\mathrm{B}(\mathbb{R}) \ni \Lambda \mapsto P(\Lambda) \in \mathcal{P}(\mathcal{H})$ *and in one-one correspondence with the σ-weak continuous ortho-lattice homomorphisms of the σ-complete Boolean lattice* $\mathrm{B}(\mathbb{R})$ *into* $\mathcal{P}(\mathcal{H})$ *which map $\emptyset$ onto 0.*

By Theorem 43.2-8 each bounded affine function $a \in \mathrm{Aff}_b(\mathcal{T}_1^+(\mathcal{H}))$ is associated with a bounded self-adjoint operator $A \in \mathcal{L}(\mathcal{H})_{\mathrm{sa}}$ which determines by the spectral Theorem 43.3-3 a bounded spectral family $(P_\lambda)_\mathbb{R}$. (Then the spectrum $\sigma(A)$ coincides with the spectrum of $(P_\lambda)_\mathbb{R}$). If a is σ-weak continuous, i.e., $a \in \mathrm{Aff}_c(\mathcal{T}_1^+(\mathcal{H}))$, then A is compact, and so are its positive and negative parts (according to a general feature of C*-algebras). Thus the positive and negative parts of a are also in $\mathrm{Aff}_c(\mathcal{T}_1^+(\mathcal{H}))$. From this we deduce:

Proposition 47.5-7. *The state space* $\mathcal{T}_1^+(\mathcal{H})$ *of traditional quantum theory is a strongly spectral convex set in the sense of Definition 47.2-27 (being not weak* compact for* $\dim(\mathcal{H}) = \infty$*).*

A bounded spectral family of projective units $(p_\lambda)_\mathbb{R}$ is in one-one correspondence with a bounded spectral family $(F_\lambda)_\mathbb{R}$ of norm closed faces of $\mathcal{T}_1^+(\mathcal{H})$ and has been identified with a metric observable (with a bounded scale). Extending this connection, we can now justify that any self-adjoint (symmetric would not be sufficient) operator $A = \int_\mathbb{R} \lambda dP_\lambda$ in the Hilbert space $\mathcal{H}$ is called an "observable": It is as well associated with a metric observable $(F_\lambda)_\mathbb{R}$, which now, however, may develop unbounded scale values.

Since an increasing family of state faces $(F_\lambda)_\mathbb{R}$ may in principle be constructed by empirical manipulations, the preceding argument resolves in some sense the problem, how a self-adjoint operator may determine a "measurement instrument".

If the self-adjoint A is in fact unbounded, then it defines an affine function a only on a convex subset of $\mathcal{T}_1^+(\mathcal{H})$. That a quantum observable should not so much be associated with a self-adjoint operator in Hilbert space but with a (projection-valued) spectral family has been emphasized e.g., by Mackey [Mac63].

Our foregoing investigation, especially the last remark in Observation 47.5-4, suggests to identify quite generally an empirical observables with a σ-complete Boolean sublattice in the (mostly non-Boolean) complete lattice $\mathcal{E}(K)$ of norm closed filtered faces. A similar point of view has been formulated e.g., in [Pri83] (and in references quoted therein).

In practice the ordering of the faces in the state space is always connected with the construction of a scale, which leads then to a self-adjoint operator, respectively to an affine function on the state space in the bounded case. Note that the type of the operator and the continuity features of the affine function depend on the scale. So may an additive translation of the scale transform a compact operator to a non-compact one (by shifting the spectral accumulation point at 0) and the weak* continuous affine function to an only norm continuous one.

By the way, a single $F \in \mathcal{E}(K)$, which may be viewed as a metric empirical observable with scale $\{0, 1\}$, gives rise to an $a_F \equiv p_F \in \mathrm{Aff}_c(\mathcal{T}_1^+(\mathcal{H}))$, if and only if it is the convex product of finitely many qubits. According to a theorem of Weyl and von Neumann any self-adjoint operator can be written as a sum of a self-adjoint diagonal operator, with real discrete spectrum, and a self-adjoint compact operator. One could use this decomposition for splitting a weak* continuous additive part from an $a \in \mathrm{Aff}_c(\mathcal{T}_1^+(\mathcal{H}))$ in a canonical manner.

Concerning the fourth version $(Q_\lambda)_{\mathbb{R}} \subset \mathcal{Q}(K)$ of a spectral family, given by filtering projections in K, which again is ortho-lattice isomorphic to a metric empirical observable: It has an active touch, since a Q_λ may change the state to which it is applied. Being idempotent, a second application of Q_λ leaves that state now invariant.

In the frame of traditional quantum mechanics, one discussed mostly the case, where λ is a jump point of $(Q_\gamma)_{\mathbb{R}}$, so that $0 < Q(\{\lambda\}) := Q_\lambda - \bigvee_{\gamma < \lambda} Q_\gamma$. The renormalized filtering projection $Q(\{\lambda\})_1 : T \mapsto P(\{\lambda\})TP(\{\lambda\})/\mathrm{tr}[TP(\{\lambda\})]$ has been interpreted by von Neumann [vN32] as to describe an ideal measurement of the value λ, which immediately repeated leads to the same result. In [Pau33], this procedure has been termed *measurement of the first kind*. The change of the state has been phrased *reduction of the wave function* if the initial state T is pure (and then either remains pure, since the filtering does not increase the mixedness, or is totally blocked off). But one can of course also construct a measurement apparatus for the question "is the value smaller than λ" and $Q_{\lambda,1}$ is as well a repeatable (and thus ideal?) measurement.

The change of the measured state to a *reduced* one is not *per se* a typical quantum mechanical feature. The analogous formalism and interpretation holds also for the classical case, characterized by K being a simplex. If the classical initial state is mixed, the filtering may likewise reduce it, blocking off the wrong ensemble members. If the classical initial state is pure it may undergo also a change by being totally blocked off. The typical non-classical feature is the filtering of a pure state into a different pure state. In (traditional and algebraic) quantum mechanics one can state, that for each pure state there are infinitely many filtering projections, which each reduce it to a different pure state. This is a consequence of each pure state sitting on the (extreme) boundary of a 3-ball, with infinitely many neighboring pure states on that surface. This constellation would be violated only by an individual pure state, totally characterized by classical observables, which does not occur in the microscopic regime.

In this connection, let us verbalize formula (47.5.9) as the probability, that the value of the metric empirical observable, associated with $(P_\lambda)_\mathbb{R}$, be in $\Lambda \in \mathsf{B}(\mathbb{R})$, if the system before the measurement is in the state T. Our discussion illustrates that the quantum probabilities are only a special case of a universal probability theory formulated in terms of spectral convex sets, which comprises the classical Bauer simplices as well as the non-simplicial convex set with n-ball property, which are much more non-classical than quantum theory, if $n \gg 3$.

Let us evaluate the transition probabilities between pure states $|\xi_1)(\xi_1|$ and $|\xi_2)(\xi_2|$. It is derived from the general formula (47.4.7) by noting that the projective unit $p_{|\xi_1)(\xi_1|}(.)$ corresponding to the singleton face $\{|\xi_1)(\xi_1|\}$ equals $\mathrm{tr}[|\xi_1)(\xi_1| \cdot |\xi_1)(\xi_1|\mathbb{1}] = \mathrm{tr}[|\xi_1)(\xi_1|.]$, what leads to

$$T_K\big(|\xi_1)(\xi_1|, \ |\xi_2)(\xi_2|\big) = p_{|\xi_1)(\xi_1|}\big(|\xi_2)(\xi_2|\big) = \mathrm{tr}\big[|\xi_1)(\xi_1| \ |\xi_2)(\xi_2|\big] = |(\xi_1|\xi_2)|^2\,.$$
$$(47.5.11)$$

As mentioned for general spectral state spaces, this transition probability measures the size of the one pure ensemble after having been filtered into the other pure state.

The compactification of $\mathcal{T}_1^+(\mathcal{H})$ is investigated in Example 45.3-2 on page 1659. Our foregoing elaborations have shown, that the non-compactness of $\mathcal{T}_1^+(\mathcal{H})$ does not prevent the exposition of traditional quantum mechanical state space notions along the lines of the general theory on compact convex sets. The reason is, that we have here obtained $\mathrm{Aff}_b(K) \cong \mathcal{L}(\mathcal{H})$ directly, and did not need a general existence argument. (By the way, in the general theory one may substitute the requirement of "compactness" for K by "radial compactness" and that K be the base of a base normed space.)

Last not least, let us mention that C*-algebraic quantum theory is a main argument for using *convex state space notions*, since there the spectral families exist in general in the state space, but not in $\mathcal{P}(\mathcal{A})$.

Chapter 48

Orthogonal Decompositions
and Ergodic Averages

48.1.   Orthogonal Measures

48.1.1.   *Basic Notions from Measure Theory*

Let us recall some preliminary notions from measure theory (e.g., [Coh80]). A collection $\mathcal{U}$ of subsets of a set Γ (the elements of which are the basic events in the probability interpretation) is called an *algebra* on Γ, if the following four conditions are valid:

(a) $\Gamma \in \mathcal{U}$.

(b) For each $\Lambda \in \mathcal{U}$, the set complement $\Gamma \backslash \Lambda =: \Lambda^c$ also belongs to $\mathcal{U}$.

(c) For finitely many $\Lambda_1, \ldots, \Lambda_n \in \mathcal{U}$, we have that the union $\bigcup_{j=1}^{n} \Lambda_j$ belongs to $\mathcal{U}$.

(d) For finitely many $\Lambda_1, \ldots, \Lambda_n \in \mathcal{U}$, the intersection $\bigcap_{j=1}^{n} \Lambda_j$ is an element of $\mathcal{U}$.

Clearly, part (d) follows from (b) and (c), since $\bigcap_{j=1}^{n} \Lambda_j = \left(\bigcup_{j=1}^{n} \Lambda_j^c \right)^c$. Especially, the empty set $\emptyset$ is contained in $\mathcal{U}$. The collection $\mathcal{U}$ of subsets of Γ is called a σ-*algebra* on Γ, if in addition in the parts (c) and (d) also countably many subsets are allowed:

(c') For an infinite sequence $\{ \Lambda_j \mid j \in \mathbb{N} \} \subseteq \mathcal{U}$, we have $\bigcup_{j=1}^{\infty} \Lambda_j \in \mathcal{U}$.

(d') For an infinite sequence $\{ \Lambda_j \mid j \in \mathbb{N} \} \subseteq \mathcal{U}$, it follows that $\bigcap_{j=1}^{\infty} \Lambda_j \in \mathcal{U}$.

If $\mathcal{V}$ is a family of subsets of Γ, then there exists a smallest σ-algebra $\mathcal{U}$ on Γ that includes $\mathcal{V}$, that is, we have $\mathcal{V} \subseteq \mathcal{U}$, and every σ-algebra $\tilde{\mathcal{U}}$ containing $\mathcal{V}$ is larger than $\mathcal{U}$, i.e., $\mathcal{U} \subseteq \tilde{\mathcal{U}}$. We say that $\mathcal{V}$ *generates* $\mathcal{U}$.

Especially, if Γ is a topological space, the *Borel* σ-*algebra* $\mathsf{B}(\Gamma)$ on Γ is the smallest σ-algebra that contains all open sets of Γ. If especially $\Gamma = \mathbb{R}^n$, with the usual metric topology, then $\mathsf{B}(\mathbb{R}^n)$ is already generated by the n-dimensional open intervals (parallelepipeds), but also by the closed intervals, and also by the semi-closed intervals. Sets containing only a single point, so-called *singletons*, may be written as countable intersections of intervals and are, together with their countable unions, in $B(\mathbb{R}^n)$.

Let $\mathcal{U}$ be a σ-algebra on Γ. Then the tuple $(\Gamma, \mathcal{U})$ is termed a *measurable space*. A measurable space of the form $(\Gamma, B(\Gamma))$ is called a *Borel space*.

Definition 48.1-1 (Set of Probability Measures $M_p(\Gamma)$). An extended positive function $\mu : \mathcal{U} \to [0, +\infty]$ is called a *measure* on $(\Gamma, \mathcal{U})$, if $\mu(\emptyset) = 0$, and if μ is σ-additive, i.e., if we have

$$\mu(\bigcup_j \Lambda_j) = \sum_j \mu(\Lambda_j)$$

for countably many, pair-wise disjoint sets $\Lambda_j \in \mathcal{U}$. μ is called a *pre-measure*, if it is only finitely additive, in which case $\mathcal{U}$ needs only be an algebra on Γ (and not necessarily a σ-algebra).

Note that in our terminology a (pre-) measure has *always* values in $[0, +\infty]$. If it also assumes negative real values it is called a *signed (pre-) measure*, and if it has complex values it is called a *complex (pre-) measure*.

The (pre-) measure μ on $(\Gamma, \mathcal{U})$ is called *finite*, if $\mu(\Gamma) < \infty$; μ is called normalized or a *probability* (pre-) measure, if $\mu(\Gamma) = 1$. The convex set of all probability measures on the measurable space $(\Gamma, \mathcal{U})$ is denoted by $M_p(\Gamma, \mathcal{U})$, or $M_p(\Gamma)$ if the σ-algebra is understood (what is especially the case for Borel spaces $(\Gamma, B(\Gamma))$).

A measure μ is called σ-*finite* if Γ decomposes into a countable union of subsets, with finite μ-measure each.

The *Lebesgue measure* on $(\mathbb{R}^n, B(\mathbb{R}^n))$ — commonly denoted by λ — is, roughly speaking, obtained by associating the Euclidean volume $|I| := \lambda(I)$ to each finite interval $I \subset \mathbb{R}^n$ and by approximating more general sets by countable unions and intersections of intervals. (One supplements for λ the Borel sets by all subsets of λ-null sets.) Each countable union of singletons has clearly Lebesgue measure 0. λ is a σ-finite measure. The *delta (or point) measure* δ_x on $(\mathbb{R}^n, B(\mathbb{R}^n))$ at $x \in \mathbb{R}^n$ is defined by giving each $\Lambda \in B(\mathbb{R}^n)$ one of the following two values,

$$\delta_x(\Lambda) := \begin{cases} 1, & \text{if } x \in \Lambda, \\ 0, & \text{if } x \notin \Lambda. \end{cases} \tag{48.1.1}$$

We have $\delta_x \in M_p(\mathbb{R}^n, B(\mathbb{R}^n))$. On a general measurable space $(\Gamma, \mathcal{U})$ the point respectively delta measure δ_γ, where $\gamma \in \Gamma$, may be defined analogously, provided the singleton $\{\gamma\}$ is contained in the σ-algebra $\mathcal{U}$. The latter depends on the chosen topology. We shall discuss in Sec. 50 a situation, in which the δ-"measure" is only a pre-measure, a so-called *weak distribution*.

A mapping $f : \Gamma \to \Gamma'$ between the measurable spaces $(\Gamma, \mathcal{U})$ and $(\Gamma', \mathcal{U}')$ is called *measurable*, if $f^{-1}(\Lambda') \in \mathcal{U}$ for all $\Lambda' \in \mathcal{U}'$. Two measurable spaces are said to be *equivalent*, if there is a measurable bijection $f : \Gamma \xrightarrow{\text{onto}} \Gamma'$ with measurable inverse.

Definition 48.1-2 (Polish and Standard Spaces). A topological space Γ is termed *"Polish"* if it is complete, separable, and metrizable. (For metrizable LC-spaces-compare Sec. 49.)

A measurable space $(\Gamma, \mathcal{U})$ is called *standard*, if it is equivalent to a Borel space $(\Gamma', \mathsf{B}(\Gamma'))$, with Γ' a Polish space.

A measure μ on a measurable space $(\Gamma, \mathcal{U})$ is called *standard* if there exists a μ-null set Γ_0 such that $\Gamma_1 := \Gamma \backslash \Gamma_0$, equipped with the relative σ-algebra $\mathcal{U} \cap \Gamma_1$, is a standard measurable space (which is then the interesting part for μ).

The structure of standard measurable spaces is well known. If Γ possesses finitely or countably many elements, with cardinality N, then the standard measurable space $(\Gamma, \mathsf{B}(\Gamma))$ is isomorphic to $(\{1, \ldots, N\}, \mathcal{P}(\{1, \ldots, N\}))$, where $\mathcal{P}(\{1, \ldots, N\})$ denotes the potential set of $\{1, \ldots, N\}$ (consisting of all subsets of $\{1, \ldots, N\}$). If Γ has over-countable cardinality, then the standard measurable space $(\Gamma, \mathsf{B}(\Gamma))$ is isomorphic to $(\mathbb{R}, \mathsf{B}(\mathbb{R}))$ ([Coh80]). That means that isomorphic Borel spaces have the same cardinality, but may topologically be completely different from each other.

For completeness, let us indicate the definition of the *general Lebesgue integral*. If μ is an arbitrary measure on $(\Gamma, \mathcal{U})$ and $f : \Gamma \to [0, +\infty]$ a measurable function, then we form the decomposition $[0, +\infty] = \bigcup_{m=0}^{\infty} [\frac{m}{n}, \frac{m+1}{n}[\cup \{\infty\}$, for each given $n \in \mathbb{N}$. The corresponding *Lebesgue partial sum* is

$$J_n^L(f, \mu) := \sum_{m=0}^{\infty} \frac{m}{n} \mu\big(f^{-1}([\tfrac{m}{n}, \tfrac{m+1}{n}[)\big) + \infty \cdot \mu\big(f^{-1}(\infty)\big), \quad n \in \mathbb{N}, \qquad (48.1.2)$$

which may be finite only if the infinite f-value has zero μ-measure. The functions in our applications always satisfy this condition. The Lebesgue integral is defined by

$$\int_{\Gamma} f(\gamma) \, d\mu(\gamma) := \lim_{n \to \infty} J_n^L(f, \mu), \qquad (48.1.3)$$

including at first diverging limits. If f is $\mathbb{R}$-valued, one Lebesgue integrates its positive and negative parts separately and forms the difference. If f is $\mathbb{C}$-valued, one Lebesgue integrates its real and imaginary parts separately and combines the results. A measurable function on Γ is *Lebesgue integrable*, if all the Lebesgue integrals over its (at most four) positive parts are finite. If μ is a complex measure, we decompose it into its four positive component measures and perform the Lebesgue integration over these separately.

For comparison, we recall roughly the partial sums of the *Riemann integral*, which is tied to $\mathbb{R}^n$. This concept has been developed before the rise of the measure theory. If Λ is a bounded measurable set of $(\mathbb{R}^n, \mathsf{B}(\mathbb{R}^n))$, then we approximate it by a disjoint union $\bigcup_{m=1}^{N} \Lambda_m$ of intervals, the volumina $|\Lambda_m|$ of which are known by elementary Euclidean geometry. Such a decomposition $\mathcal{Z} = (\Lambda_1, \ldots, \Lambda_N)$ is coarser than a decomposition $\mathcal{Z}' = (\Lambda_1', \ldots, \Lambda_{N'}')$, the latter being then finer, if the Λ_i are unions of the Λ'_j. The set $\mathfrak{Z}$, consisting of the decompositions of Λ, is directed under this finer relation.

A general Riemannian partial sum for a measurable function $f : \mathbb{R}^n \to [0, +\infty[$ is then defined as

$$J^R_{\mathcal{Z}}(f) := \sum_{m=1}^N f(x_m) |\Lambda_m| , \quad x_m \in \Lambda_m , \quad \mathcal{Z} = (\Lambda_1, \dots \Lambda_N) \in \mathfrak{Z} . \qquad (48.1.4)$$

The Riemannian integral is the net limit of the Riemannian partial sums

$$\int_\Lambda f(x) \, d^n x := \lim_{\mathcal{Z} \in \mathfrak{Z}} J^R_{\mathcal{Z}}(f) , \qquad (48.1.5)$$

where the disjoint unions $\bigcup_{m=1}^N \Lambda_m$ are to approach Λ. The net limit should not depend on the association of the supporting points x_m with $\mathcal{Z} \in \mathfrak{Z}$. (The latter condition would follow from the result that the net limits of the so-called upper and the lower Riemannian partial sums exist and coincide, which is Riemann's well known, sufficient and necessary integrability criterion.)

A practicable sufficient criterion is: If f is continuous in a compact $\Lambda \subset \mathbb{R}^n$, with the possible exception of a set of (Lebesgue) measure zero, then the *Riemannian integral exists* and equals the corresponding Lebesgue integral for the Lebesgue measure λ,

$$\int_\Lambda f(x) \, d^n x = \int_\Lambda f(x) \, d\lambda(x) .$$

Especially, if $f(x) = 1$ for all $x \in \Lambda$, then

$$\int_\Lambda d^n x = \int_\Lambda d\lambda(x) = |\Lambda| = \lambda(\Lambda)$$

defines the Euclidean volume of Λ.

Example 48.1-3 (Integral Versus Mean Value Over the Brillouin Zone).

We modify Eq. (32.2.2) on page 930 to give the partial closure $\bar{\mathcal{B}}$ of our denumerable first Brillouin Zone $\mathcal{B}$ of a cubic lattice in $\mathbb{R}^d$, with lattice constant $a > 0$, which has the form

$$\bar{\mathcal{B}} = \{ k \in \mathbb{R}^d \mid -\tfrac{\pi}{a} \le k_j < \tfrac{\pi}{a} , \ 1 \le j \le d \} .$$

($\bar{\mathcal{B}}$ is strictly speaking the closure of $\mathcal{B}$, from which a part of the boundary is discarded.) For each $n \in \mathbb{N}$ we consider the crystal lattice in the cubic position space volume Λ_n of size $|\Lambda_n| = V_n = (2^n a)^d$. The associated wave vectors, being elements of the dual lattice, have the form $k = (k_1, \dots, k_d) = 2\pi z/(2^n a)$, where $z \in \mathbb{Z}^d$ with components $-2^{n-1} \le z_j < 2^{n-1}$, $1 \le j \le d$. Thus the number of wave vectors is $N(n) = (2^n)^d$.

We introduce a numbering $m \mapsto k_n(m) = (k_{1,n}(m), \dots, k_{d,n}(m))$, $1 \le m \le N(n)$, of the k's associated with Λ_n. That defines a decomposition $\bar{\mathcal{B}} = \bigcup_{m=1}^{N(n)} \mathcal{B}_n(m)$, with $\mathcal{B}_n(m) = k_n(m) + \{ k \in \mathbb{R}^d \mid 0 \le k_j < 2\pi/(2^n a), 1 \le j \le d \}$, and with the k-space volumina $|\mathcal{B}_n(m)| = (2\pi)^d/(2^n a)^d$.

If n increases, the decompositions of $\bar{\mathcal{B}}$ become finer in the previously mentioned sense. Thus the index n numbers a denumerable subset of decompositions, increasingly ordered by the finer relation, and filling $\bar{\mathcal{B}}$ exactly.

The Riemannian integral of a continuous, bounded function $f : \bar{\mathcal{B}} \to \mathbb{R}$ may therefore be calculated by the limit of the special Riemannian partial sums, built as in (48.1.4),

$$\int_{\bar{\mathcal{B}}} f(k) \, d^d k = \lim_{n \to \infty} \sum_{m=1}^{N(n)} f(k_n(m)) \, |\mathcal{B}_n(m)| = \lim_{n \to \infty} \left(\frac{2\pi}{2^n a} \right)^d \sum_{m=1}^{N(n)} f(k_n(m)) .$$

We know from the general existence theorem on Riemannian integrals that this limit does not depend on the special decompositions of the integration domain $\bar{\mathcal{B}}$ and neither on the supporting points $k_n(m) \in \Lambda_n$.

If we have now any sum of the form $\sum_{m=1}^{N(n)} f(k_n(m))$, taken over the values of an arbitrary continuous function $f : \bar{\mathcal{B}} \to \mathbb{R}$ at the dual lattice points, then we write it as

$$\left(\frac{2\pi}{2^n a} \right)^{-d} \sum_{m=1}^{N(n)} f(k_n(m)) \, |\mathcal{B}_n(m)| \approx \frac{V_n}{(2\pi)^d} \int_{\bar{\mathcal{B}}} f(k) \, d^d k ,$$

for large n. This is, for $n \to \infty$, a diverging expression, if the integral does not vanish, and only the spatial density of the sum has a well defined limit,

$$\lim_{n \to \infty} \frac{1}{V_n} \sum_{m=1}^{N(n)} f(k_n(m)) = \frac{1}{(2\pi)^d} \int_{\bar{\mathcal{B}}} f(k) \, d^d k .$$

But $\sum_{m=1}^{N(n)} f(k_n(m))/(2^n)^d$ seems to have the form of a mean value, at least for a fixed n. To treat also increasing n, we would have to introduce a uniform numbering of the discrete but densely filled Brillouin zone $\mathcal{B}$, so that $\mathcal{B} = \{k(m) \, | \, m \in \mathbb{N}\} = \bigcup_{n \in \mathbb{N}} \{k_n(m) \, | \, 1 \leq m \leq N(n)\}$. For $n \to \infty$ also $N(n) = (2^n)^d \to \infty$. This would lead to the limiting expression $\lim_{N \to \infty} \sum_{m=1}^{N} f(k(m))/N$ having the form of a discrete average.

In general, the criteria of Lemma 33.6-13 on page 1016 would, however, not be fulfilled for non-constant f and the limit would diverge. We recognize that the Riemannian integral is, in terms of the net limit over the Riemannian partial sums, constructed differently from a limiting mean value.

In the coupling of the electron-hole pairs to the photons (see Sec. 37.1), one has originally a Riemannian-type of summation over the wave vectors. Its total operator limit could hardly be defined in weak closures of the CAR algebra to arrive at something like an integral of von Neumann algebras, at least not in usual representations of that C*-algebra. (On the other side, a known strategy to treat the Bloch eigenvalue problem is in fact to work with direct integrals over $\bar{\mathcal{B}}$ of Hilbert spaces, indexed by $k \in \bar{\mathcal{B}}$, as indicated e.g., in [RS78]).

We have chosen in our treatment, a strategy different from a direct Riemannian integral, namely to single out subsequences of wave vectors from $\mathcal{B}$ to obtain limiting mean field operators in a classically extended CAR-algebra.

Also if the corresponding Riemannian integral exists, we interpret it in our applications nevertheless as Lebesgue integral, and we identify $d\lambda(x) \equiv d^n x$. As is common usage, the notation $L^p(\Gamma, \mathbb{C}; \mu)$ for classes of p-integrable $\mathbb{C}$-valued functions $f : \Gamma \to \mathbb{C}$ with respect to the measure μ refers to the Lebesgue integral, with $p > 0$,

$$\|f\|_p = \left(\int_\Gamma |f(x)|^p \, d\mu(x) \right)^{1/p} < \infty, \qquad \forall f \in L^p(\Gamma, \mathbb{C}; \mu) \,.$$

The case $p = \infty$ denotes the μ-a.e. bounded $\mathbb{C}$-valued functions on Γ, that is, $L^\infty(\Gamma, \mathbb{C}; \mu)$. We briefly write $L^p(\Lambda, \mathbb{C})$ if $\mu = \lambda$ is the Lebesgue measure on $\Gamma = \Lambda \subseteq \mathbb{R}^n$. Of special interest in the present work, see especially Chapter 44, is the complex Hilbert space $L^2(\Lambda, \mathbb{C})$ of Lebesgue square integrable functions $\psi : \Lambda \to \mathbb{C}$, equipped with the inner product

$$(\phi|\psi) = \int_\Lambda \overline{\phi(x)} \, \psi(x) \underbrace{\, d\lambda(x)}_{= \, d^n x} \,, \qquad \forall \phi, \psi \in L^2(\Lambda, \mathbb{C}) \,.$$

Definition 48.1-4 (Regular and Baire Measures). A (complex) Borel measure μ on $(\Gamma, \mathsf{B}(\Gamma))$ is *regular* if for $B \in \mathsf{B}(\Gamma)$

$$\mu(B) = \sup\{\mu(C) \,|\, C \subset B, \, C \text{ closed}\} = \inf\{\mu(O) \,|\, B \subset O, \, O \text{ open}\} \,.$$

If Γ is a topological space then the *Baire σ-algebra* $\mathsf{B}_0(\Gamma)$ is defined as the smallest σ-algebra, for which all continuous functions on Γ are measurable.
   A measure μ on the measurable space $(\Gamma, \mathsf{B}_0(\Gamma))$ is called a *Baire measure*.

Proposition 48.1-5 (Borel Versus Baire Measures). *Since all the continuous functions are Borel-measurable, we have* $\mathsf{B}_0(\Gamma) \subset \mathsf{B}(\Gamma)$.
   Given a Borel space $(\Gamma, \mathsf{B}(\Gamma))$, *its Baire measures are in bijective correspondence with its regular Borel measures.*
   If Γ *is second-countable, i.e., each point in* Γ *has a countable neighborhood base, then* $\mathsf{B}_0(\Gamma) = \mathsf{B}(\Gamma)$, *since each Borel measure is regular.*
   (A countable neighborhood base allows for the construction of a metric and vice versa. An LC-space is second-countable, if and only if it is metrizable.)

Let Γ be locally compact (i.e., each point has a compact neighborhood) and $(\Gamma, \mathsf{B}(\Gamma))$ its Borel space, then $C_\infty(\Gamma)$ is the set of complex continuous functions on Γ, which tend to zero, if $\gamma \to \infty$ (which means γ leaving each compact). Then $C_\infty(\Gamma)$ is a commutative C*-algebra with the supremum norm. The dual space consists by definition of the *complex Radon measures* on Γ. These are thus originally no measures but linear functionals $f \mapsto \mu(f)$, which are continuous in the norm of $C_\infty(\Gamma)$. They are, however, closely related with complex measures in virtue of the following constantly used Theorem (which one proves first for the positive, always norm-continuous functionals corresponding to measures, the latter being positive according to our convention).

Theorem 48.1-6 (Riesz–Markov Theorem). *Consider the complex continuous functions* $C_\infty(\Gamma)$ *on the locally compact topological space* Γ, *which vanish at infinity.*

The complex Radon measures $\mu(.)$, *defined as norm-continuous linear functionals on* $C_\infty(\Gamma)$, *are in one-one correspondence with the complex, regular Borel measures* μ *on* $(\Gamma, B(\Gamma))$, *and thus also with the complex Baire measures* μ_0 *on* $(\Gamma, B_0(\Gamma))$, *in such way that*

$$\mu(f) = \int_\Gamma f(\gamma)\, d\mu(\gamma) = \int_\Gamma f(\gamma)\, d\mu_0(\gamma), \quad \forall f \in C_\infty(\Gamma).$$

A decisive characterizing feature of a measure is its support.

Definition 48.1-7 (Support of Measures). A measure μ on the Borel space $(\Gamma, B(\Gamma))$ is *"supported"* by $\Lambda \in B(\Gamma)$, if $\mu(\Lambda^c) = 0$. The *"support"* of μ, denoted by $\text{supp}(\mu)$ is the smallest closed set, on which μ is supported and exists for regular Borel measures.

The measure μ on $(\Gamma, B(\Gamma))$ is called *"pseudo-supported"* by an *arbitrary set* $\Lambda \subset \Gamma$, if $\mu(\Lambda') = 0$ for all Baire sets $\Lambda' \subseteq \Lambda^c$.

If the measurable space is a Borel space $(\Gamma, B(\Gamma))$, we usually employ only regular Borel measures from $M_p(\Gamma)$.

Also in a general (classical or quantum mechanical) statistical theory, the state space is a convex set, since the convex combination of states has the meaning of a statistical mixture and should thus be included in the set of statistical states. Often the convex state space is compact. (If the observables are described by a C*-algebra $\mathcal{A}$, the state space $\mathcal{S}(\mathcal{A})$ is compact in the weak* topology, if and only if $\mathcal{A}$ has a unit. Especially in the classical case $M_p(\Gamma) = \mathcal{S}(C_\infty(\Gamma))$ is compact, if Γ is compact, which implies $C_\infty(\Gamma) = C(\Gamma)$, the condition of vanishing in the infinite region being empty).

The decomposition of a point in a compact convex set into an integral over points nearer to the extreme boundary (less mixed states) is the topic of the Choquet theory.

48.1.2. *Choquet Theory*

Let in this section, K be always a non-empty *compact convex set in a locally convex Hausdorff space* $\mathcal{V}$. We begin with the Krein–Milman Theorem, which ensures the existence of sufficiently many extreme elements of K (e.g., [KR86] Theorem 1.4.3, or [Con85] V.7.4).

Theorem 48.1-8 (Krein–Milman). *The extreme boundary* $\partial_e K$ *of the (non-empty compact convex)* K *is non-empty. Moreover,* K *is the closure of the convex* hull of $\partial_e K$, that is, $K = \overline{\text{Conv}(\partial_e K)}$ (*where* $\text{Conv}(\partial_e K)$ *consists of all finite convex combinations of elements in* $\partial_e K$).

Krein–Milman suggests to go over to infinite, and possibly continuous, "convex combinations", that are integrals by means of probability measures $\mu \in M_p(K)$, to decompose an element $u \in K$ into other elements which are nearer to the extreme boundary. A decomposition of $u \in K$ by means of a $\mu \in M_p(K)$ expresses the fact that u is the barycenter $u = u_\mu$ of μ, that is

$$u_\mu := \int_K v \, d\mu(v), \quad \text{barycenter of } \mu \in M_p(K). \qquad (48.1.6)$$

The integral is understood in the weak sense, i.e., $V(u_\mu) = \int_K V(v) \, d\mu(v)$ for all $V \in \mathcal{V}'$ ($\mathcal{V}'$ is the topological dual of the real, locally convex vector space $\mathcal{V}$).

If a $\mu \in M_p(K)$ is given, we know that it is approximable by convex combinations of point measures, the barycenters of which clearly are in K. Since K is compact, the limiting barycenter u_μ is also in K.

Definition 48.1-9 (Ordering of Measures). Given $\mu, \nu \in M_p(K)$, we define (as e.g., in [BR87]) the binary relation $\nu \trianglelefteq \mu$ by $\nu(f) \leq \mu(f)$ for all convex continuous real functions f on K. (We preserve the sign $\prec$ for *absolute continuity*.)

A measure $\mu \in M_p(K)$ is called *maximal* in $M_p(K)$, if $\mu \trianglelefteq \nu$ implies $\mu = \nu$.

Since convexity of f means $f(\lambda v_1 + (1 - \lambda)v_2) \leq \lambda f(v_1) + (1 - \lambda)f(v_2)$ for all $\lambda \in [0, 1]$ and all $v_1, v_2 \in K$, the larger integral over a convex function f is, the nearer the measure is concentrated at the extreme boundary of K. For example, the point measure at $u \in K$, denoted by $\delta_u \in M_p(K)$, gives $f(u) = \int_K f(v) \, d\delta_u(v)$ for all continuous $\mathbb{R}$-valued functions f on K and satisfies $\delta_u \trianglelefteq \nu$ for all $\nu \in M_p(K)$ with barycenter u.

Proposition 48.1-10 (Maximal Measures). *The relation* $\trianglelefteq$ *is a partial ordering on* $M_p(K)$. (*Thus* $\trianglelefteq$ *is transitive, reflexive, and anti-symmetric, where the latter says that* μ *must be equal to* ν, *if* $\mu \trianglelefteq \nu$ *and* $\nu \trianglelefteq \mu$. "*partial*" *means that not for all pairs the* $\trianglelefteq$ *relation holds in the one or other direction.*)

Each $u \in K$ (*with* K *compact, convex*) *is the barycenter* $u = u_\mu$ *of a maximal measure* $\mu \in M_p(K)$.

If the topology on K is not metrizable, it is a subtle mathematical question in which sense the maximal measures are concentrated on $\partial_e K$. In general, $\partial_e K$ need not even be a Borel set.

If $\Lambda \subseteq \partial_e K$ *is a Borel set and supports the measure* $\mu \in M_p(K)$, the latter fact being expressible by $\mu(\Lambda) = 1$, one knows that μ is maximal in $M_p(K)$. For example, if $u \in \partial_e K$, then δ_u is maximal. If u is not in $\partial_e K$, then u is convex decomposable (by the definition of $\partial_e K$), which gives a discrete decomposing measure, strictly $\trianglelefteq$-dominating δ_u. We conclude that $\mu = \sum_{i=1}^n \lambda_i \delta_{v_i} \in M_p(K)$ is maximal, if and only if all $v_i \in \partial_e K$.

In the general case, one has to work with *pseudo-supports*.

Theorem 48.1-11 (Support of Maximal Measures). *Each maximal* $\mu \in M_p(K)$ *(K compact, convex) is pseudo-supported (in the sense of Definition 48.1-7) by* $\partial_e K$.

Let K be metrizable. Then $\partial_e K$ *is a Borel set. (It is also a Baire set, more precisely, it is the countable intersection of open sets.) Then* $\mu \in M_p(K)$ *is maximal, if and only if* μ *is supported by* $\partial_e K$, *i.e., if* $\mu(\partial_e K) = 1$.

To give an idea how much weaker the first assertion of the preceding Theorem is than the second, we mention that there exist examples in which $\mu(\Lambda) = 0$ for a $\Lambda \in B(K)$, where $\mu \in M_p(K)$, but nevertheless μ is pseudo-supported by Λ.

Combining Proposition 48.1-10 and Theorem 48.1-11, one observes that each point in a metrizable K has a decomposition measure, which is supported by the extreme points. Following [Alf71], we call a probability measure $\mu \in M_p(K)$ a *boundary measure*, if there holds the two equivalent equations

$$\mu(K \backslash \partial_e K) = 0 \;\Leftrightarrow\; \mu(\partial_e K) = 1\,, \quad \text{(boundary measure)}\,. \tag{48.1.7}$$

For a general compact convex set K, there may exist several different boundary measures $\mu \neq \nu$ representing the same point $u \in K$, i.e., u is the barycenter of both measures, $u = u_\mu = u_\nu$. From a statistical point of view, this means that the convex decomposition of $u \in K$ into pure states is non-unique, i.e., different statistical mixtures of pure cases from $\partial_e K$ may lead to the same mixed case $u \in K$, so that the latter cannot be viewed as an ensemble of individual systems.

Let us in this connection recall the notion of a simplex.

Definition 48.1-12 (Choquet Simplex and Bauer Simplex). The compact convex set K is defined to be a simplex, if every $u \in K$ is the barycenter $u = u_\mu$ of a unique boundary measure $\mu \in M_p(\partial_e K) \subset M_p(K)$.

An equivalent definition of a simplex is that its real affine-bounded functions $\text{Aff}_b(K)$ constitute a lattice under point-wise ordering. (See our discussion in connection with Theorem 47.3-3 on page 1750.)

A general compact convex simplex is often also called a *"Choquet simplex"*.

The Choquet simplex K is called a *Bauer simplex*, if its extreme boundary $\partial_e K$ is a closed subset.

Bauer simplices are uniquely characterized as the probability measures on compact Hausdorff spaces (see e.g., [Alf71] § II.4). They are the state spaces of commutative unital C*-algebras, as we state in Example 45.2-24 on page 1651. As the state spaces of classical theories, they are described in detail in Theorem 47.3-2 on page 1749.

48.1.3. Measures on the State Space

We consider now a general unital C*-algebra $\mathcal{A}$ as algebra of observables and know from Proposition 45.2-21 on page 1649 that its convex state space $\mathcal{S} \equiv \mathcal{S}(\mathcal{A})$ is compact in the $\sigma(\mathcal{S}, \mathcal{A})$-topology, also called weak* topology. The Borel sets of $\mathcal{S}$ are the elements of the smallest σ-algebra containing all weak* open sets. A measure μ on $\mathcal{S}$ means here always a positive measure on the Borel sets which is *regular*.

If the unital $\mathcal{A}$ is separable, the weak* topology is metrizable and the Borel space $(\mathcal{S}, B(\mathcal{S}))$ is standard. Then one has the simple form of the support definition: The support $\mathrm{supp}(\mu)$ of such μ is the smallest closed set $\mathcal{S}' \subset \mathcal{S}$ with $\mu(\mathcal{S}') = \mu(\mathcal{S})$. If $\mathcal{A}$ is not separable, as e.g., the C*-Weyl algebra, the measure theory on $(\mathcal{S}, B(\mathcal{S}))$ is quite complicated.

Two positive linear functionals on $\mathcal{A}$ ("scaled states") ω_1, ω_2 are *orthogonal*, written $\omega_1 \perp \omega_2$, if for a positive linear functional ω' with $\omega' \leq \omega_1$, $\omega' \leq \omega_2$ it follows $\omega' = 0$. That is equivalent to the orthogonal decomposition of the GNS Hilbert space $\mathcal{H}_\omega$, associated with $\omega := \omega_1 + \omega_2$, into a direct sum $\mathcal{H}_\omega = \mathcal{H}_{\omega_1} \oplus \mathcal{H}_{\omega_2}$ of the GNS Hilbert spaces, referring to the component states. It is also equivalent to: There is a projection $P \in \Pi_\omega(\mathcal{A})'$ such that

$$\langle \omega; A \rangle = \underbrace{(\Omega_\omega | \Pi_\omega(A) P \Omega_\omega)}_{=\,\langle \omega_1; A \rangle} + \underbrace{(\Omega_\omega | \Pi_\omega(A) P^\perp \Omega_\omega)}_{=\,\langle \omega_2; A \rangle} . \qquad (48.1.8)$$

Starting from ω, this is the first step of an orthogonal decomposition, which by iteration may become more and more refined, ending up into a decomposition by means of a rather arbitrary orthogonal measure. (See also Proposition 45.2-27 and subsequent discussion.)

Definition 48.1-13 (Orthogonal Measures). Let $\mathcal{S}$ be the state space of a unital C*-algebra $\mathcal{A}$.

(a) Let $\mu \in M_p(\mathcal{S})$ be a probability measure (positive, normalized) on $\mathcal{S}$. Then the integral

$$\omega := \text{weak*-} \int_{\mathcal{S}} \omega' \, d\mu(\omega') , \qquad (48.1.9)$$

which is obviously a state, is called the *barycenter* of μ. The set of all probability measures on $\mathcal{S}$ with barycenter ω is denoted by $\mathfrak{M}_\omega$.

(b) A measure μ on $\mathcal{S}$ is called *orthogonal*, if for each Borel set $\mathcal{S}' \subseteq \mathcal{S}$ one has

$$\int_{\mathcal{S}}' \omega' \, d\mu(\omega') \perp \int_{\mathcal{S} \setminus \mathcal{S}'} \omega' \, d\mu(\omega'). \qquad (48.1.10)$$

The set of all orthogonal probability measures on $\mathcal{S}$ with barycenter ω is denoted by $\mathfrak{D}_\omega$.

Decompositions of states by orthogonal measures is most basic for quantum theory, since they constitute a generalization of the diagonalization of density operators, the latter being nothing else than the decomposition of a mixed state into a convex combination of vector states (which are pure states in an irreducible representation). Such a convex combination of vector states may be viewed as an integral by means of a discrete measure.

Quite often, the decomposition of a mixed state into vector states is determined by the simultaneous diagonalization of a set of pair-wise commuting, self-adjoint operators. The general connection between a decomposition measure and an Abelian algebra is provided by the Tomita map, which we introduce in the following Lemma.

Lemma 48.1-14 (Tomita Map). *Let $\mathcal{A}$ be a C*-algebra with unit and $\mathcal{S}$ its state space. For each $A \in \mathcal{A}$ define the affine, weak* continuous function $\hat{A} : \mathcal{S} \to \mathbb{C}$ by $\hat{A}(\omega') := \langle \omega'; A \rangle$ for all $\omega' \in \mathcal{S}$.*

If there is given a $\mu \in \mathfrak{M}_\omega$ for $\omega \in \mathcal{S}$, then there exists a weak* continuous, positive map

$$\theta_\mu : \mathrm{L}^\infty(\mathcal{S}; \mu) \longrightarrow \Pi_\omega(\mathcal{A})',$$

which is uniquely determined by the relation $\theta_\mu(1) = \mathbb{1}_\omega$ (where on the left is the unit function on $\mathcal{S}$ and on the right is the unit operator in $\mathcal{H}_\omega$) and by

$$(\Omega_\omega | \theta_\mu(f) \Pi_\omega(A) \Omega_\omega) = \int_{\mathcal{S}} f(\omega') \hat{A}(\omega') \, d\mu(\omega') , \quad \forall f \in \mathrm{L}^\infty(\mathcal{S}; \mu) , \quad \forall A \in \mathcal{A} . \tag{48.1.11}$$

Uniqueness of θ_μ follows from the fact, that (48.1.11) fixes all scalar products of the form $(\Pi_\omega(B)\Omega_\omega | \theta_\mu(f)\Pi_\omega(A)\Omega_\omega)$ to the values $\int_{\mathcal{S}} f(\omega')(\widehat{B^*A})(\omega') \, d\mu(\omega')$, since $\Pi_\omega(B)^*$ commutes with $\theta_\mu(f)$. Since Ω_ω is cyclic for $(\Pi_\omega, \mathcal{H}_\omega)$, this set of scalar products is sufficient to determine the, obviously bounded, $\theta_\mu(f)$. The right-hand side of (48.1.11) displays already the diagonalized form of the operator $\theta_\mu(f)$.

Note that the positivity of θ_μ implies *-invariance: $\theta_\mu(\bar{f}) = \theta_\mu(f)^*$. The, in general lacking, product homomorphy of θ_μ is related to the orthogonality of μ, as the following Proposition tells us. This and other results on orthogonal measures are elaborated for example in [BR87] and [Tak79].

Proposition 48.1-15 (Basic Facts on Orthogonal Measures). *Let $\mathcal{A}$ be a C*-algebra with unit and $\mathcal{S}$ its state space. In the following, we fix an arbitrary state $\omega \in \mathcal{S}$.*

(a) *A measure $\mu \in \mathfrak{M}_\omega$ is in $\mathcal{D}_\omega$, if and only if its Tomita map θ_μ is a *-isomorphism. Its image is then an Abelian von Neumann algebra $\mathfrak{B}_\mu \subseteq \Pi_\omega(\mathcal{A})'$.*
(b) *If $\mathfrak{B}$ is an Abelian von Neumann algebra in $\Pi_\omega(\mathcal{A})'$ then the orthogonal projection P onto $[\mathfrak{B}\Omega_\omega]$ (the closed subspace containing $\mathfrak{B}\Omega_\omega$) satisfies*

$$P\Omega_\omega = \Omega_\omega , \quad P\Pi_\omega(\mathcal{A})P \subseteq \{P\Pi_\omega(\mathcal{A})P\}' . \tag{48.1.12}$$

(c) *If $P \in \mathcal{L}(\mathcal{H}_\omega)$ is a projection satisfying (48.1.12) then*

$$\mathfrak{B} := \{\Pi_\omega(\mathcal{A}) \cup P\}' \tag{48.1.13}$$

is an Abelian von Neumann algebra in $\Pi_\omega(\mathcal{A})'$ such that

$$P = [\mathfrak{B}\Omega_\omega] . \tag{48.1.14}$$

Thus, the relation between projections P, satisfying (48.1.12), and Abelian von Neumann algebras $\mathfrak{B} \subseteq \Pi_\omega(\mathcal{A})'$ is bijective.

(d) *If P is an orthogonal projection in $\mathcal{H}_\omega$ satisfying (48.1.12), then the prescription*

$$\mu(\hat{A}_1 \hat{A}_2 \dots \hat{A}_m) := (\Omega_\omega | P\Pi_\omega(A_1) P P \Pi_\omega(A_2) P \dots P\Pi_\omega(A_m) P\Omega_\omega) \tag{48.1.15}$$

defines, by continuous extension, a unique $\mu \in \mathfrak{D}_\omega$ (first in the form of a Radon measure, i.e., a linear functional on the continuous functions on $\mathcal{S}$). The commutative von Neumann algebra $\mathfrak{B}_\mu$ in $\Pi_\omega(\mathcal{A})'$, associated with this μ by means of the Tomita map, is equal to $\{\Pi_\omega(\mathcal{A}) \cup P\}'$.

Thus, the relation between projections P, satisfying (48.1.12), and orthogonal measures $\mu \in \mathfrak{D}_\omega$ is bijective.

(e) *If P is an orthogonal projection in $\mathcal{H}_\omega$ satisfying (48.1.12), and if θ_μ is the associated Tomita map, then one has (second "=")*

$$\alpha(\theta_\mu(\hat{A})) := \theta_\mu(\hat{A}) P = P\Pi_\omega(A) P , \quad \forall A \in \mathcal{A} , \tag{48.1.16}$$

and this gives a linear, *-preserving, bijective mapping α between the $\theta_\mu(\hat{A})$ and the $P\Pi_\omega(A)P$, where A varies in $\mathcal{A}$.

The map α has a unique extension to an *-isomorphism

$$\alpha : \mathfrak{B}_\mu \xrightarrow{onto} \overline{P\Pi_\omega(\mathcal{A})P}^{weak} = \{P\Pi_\omega(\mathcal{A})P\}'' . \tag{48.1.17}$$

Perhaps the physical meaning of Proposition 48.1-15 is best understood by starting with the projection P of (48.1.12) (if the state ω is given). This projection may be viewed as a filter for the quantum theory in the GNS representation of ω. The state ω, figured as a ray of systems, passes P unchanged. By sandwiching with P, the observables in $\Pi_\omega(\mathcal{A})$ are reduced to those in a commutative *-algebra, which may be diagonalized simultaneously. The orthogonal measure $\mu \in \mathfrak{D}_\omega$, given by P in virtue of (48.1.15), decomposes ω into the component states $\omega' \in \mathrm{supp}(\mu)$, in which the $P\Pi_\omega(A)P$, $A \in \mathcal{A}$, all have sharp values.

The commutative von Neumann algebra $\mathfrak{B}_\mu$ has no direct interpretation in terms of observables, being in general not in $\mathcal{M}_\omega$; but its use has formal advantages. It is diagonalized by its *-isomorphic realization in terms of functions on $\mathrm{supp}(\mu)$, via the Tomita map θ_μ. Intuitively it is clear that the decomposition of ω becomes finer, if $\mathfrak{B}_\mu$ becomes larger.

On the compact convex state space $\mathcal{S}$ of a unit a C*-algebra, the order relation $\lhd$ of Definition 48.1-9 for probability measures $\mathfrak{M}_\omega$, which decompose the state

$\omega \in \mathcal{S}$, plays an important role. This relation is, by the way, equivalent to

$$\mu_1 \trianglelefteq \mu_2 \quad \Longleftrightarrow \quad \int_{\mathcal{S}} A(\omega')\, d\mu_1(\omega') \le \int_{\mathcal{S}} A(\omega')\, d\mu_2(\omega') , \qquad (48.1.18)$$

for all continuous affine functions A on $\mathcal{S}$ (which are special continuous convex functions). If $\mu_1 \trianglelefteq \mu_2$ we say that μ_1 is coarser than μ_2, or μ_2 is finer than μ_1. As mentioned before, a (decomposition) measure is called *maximal*, if it is maximal for the order $\trianglelefteq$.

The comparison of the integrals in (48.1.18) expresses physically that a decomposition measure becomes finer, if its support is closer to the pure states (the elements of the extremal boundary $\partial_e \mathcal{S}$). A probability measure μ on $\mathcal{S}$ has barycenter ω, if and only if $\delta_\omega \trianglelefteq \mu$, with δ_ω the normalized point measure.

Proposition 48.1-16 (Refined Decompositions). *Let be $\mu_1, \mu_2 \in \mathfrak{M}_\omega$ for fixed $\omega \in \mathcal{S}$, where $\mathcal{S}$ is again the compact convex state space of a unital C*-algebra $\mathcal{A}$.*

(a) *The following equivalent comparison relations are valid for orthogonal measures $\mu \in \mathfrak{O}_\omega$, for which we have associated an Abelian von Neumann algebra $\mathfrak{B}_\mu$ in the commutant of ω's GNS representation and a certain projection P_μ (see Proposition 48.1-15). So, if $\mu_1, \mu_2 \in \mathfrak{O}_\omega$ then*

$$\mu_1 \trianglelefteq \mu_2 \Leftrightarrow \mathfrak{B}_{\mu_1} \subseteq \mathfrak{B}_{\mu_2} \Leftrightarrow P_{\mu_1} \le P_{\mu_2}$$
$$\Leftrightarrow \overline{P_{\mu_1} \Pi_\omega(\mathcal{A}) P_{\mu_1}}^{-weak} \subseteq \overline{P_{\mu_2} \Pi_\omega(\mathcal{A}) P_{\mu_2}}^{-weak} .$$

(b) *For $A \in \mathcal{A}$, let again $\hat{A}$ denote the associated affine function on $\mathcal{S}$. Then we have the following inequality for the variances*

$$\mu_1 \trianglelefteq \mu_2 \quad \Leftrightarrow \quad \mu_1(|\hat{A} - \mu_1(\hat{A})|^2) \le \mu_2(|\hat{A} - \mu_2(\hat{A})|^2) .$$

(c) *If $\mu_1 \trianglelefteq \mu_2$, then there exists a family $\mathcal{S} \ni \varphi \mapsto \mu_\varphi$ of probability measures on $\mathcal{S}$, with the respective barycenters φ, which splits the $d\mu_2$-integration into the iterated integration*

$$\int_{\mathcal{S}} f(\omega')\, d\mu_2(\omega') = \int_{\mathcal{S}} \Big[\int_{\mathcal{S}} f(\omega')\, d\mu_\varphi(\omega') \Big] d\mu_1(\varphi), \quad \forall f \in C(\mathcal{S}, \mathbb{C}). \quad (48.1.19)$$

If $\mathfrak{B}_\mu$ is maximal Abelian (that means, not contained in a strictly larger Abelian von Neumann algebra in $\Pi_\omega(\mathcal{A})'$), μ is maximal, and one anticipates that it decomposes ω into pure states in some sense.

A distinguished role plays also that Abelian von Neumann algebra $\mathcal{Z}_\omega \subseteq \Pi_\omega(\mathcal{A})'$, which is also contained in $\mathcal{M}_\omega$, and maximal in this intersection, that is $\mathcal{Z}_\omega = \mathcal{M}_\omega \cap \Pi_\omega(\mathcal{A})'$. These central observables are compatible with all other observables of the system and signify the *classical observables* (in the Hilbert space quantum theory related to the given state ω).

We have in fact the following assertions.

Proposition 48.1-17 (Various State Decompositions). *Let once more $\mathcal{S}$ be the compact convex state space of a unital C*-algebra $\mathcal{A}$. For a given state $\omega \in \mathcal{S}$*

we identify the following orthogonal decompositions $\mu \in \mathfrak{D}_\omega$ according to the related Abelian von Neumann algebras $\mathfrak{B}_\mu \subset \Pi_\omega(\mathcal{A})'$.

(a) *If $\mathfrak{B}_\mu$ is maximal Abelian in $\Pi_\omega(\mathcal{A})'$, then by definition μ is maximal and decomposes ω into pure states. More precisely: μ is in general only pseudo-supported by $\partial_e \mathcal{S}$.*

(b) *If $\mathfrak{B}_\mu = \mathcal{Z}_\omega$ (the center of $\mathcal{M}_\omega = \Pi_\omega(\mathcal{A})''$) then by definition*

$$\mu =: \mu_\omega \qquad \text{is the central measure} \qquad (48.1.20)$$

and decomposes ω into classically pure (= factorial) states. More precisely: μ is in general only pseudo-supported by the factor states. For any Borel set $\mathcal{S}' \subseteq \mathcal{S}$ one has then

$$\int_{\mathcal{S}}^{'} \omega' \, d\mu(\omega') \, \flat \int_{\mathcal{S} \backslash \mathcal{S}'} \omega' \, d\mu(\omega'), \quad \text{meaning disjointness of scaled states}.$$

$$(48.1.21)$$

(c) *If $\mathfrak{B}_\mu \subset \mathcal{Z}_\omega$, then by definition μ is a subcentral measure. Then Eq. (48.1.21) is valid, but μ is not pseudo-supported by the factorial states.*
   Reversely, if for $\mu \in \mathfrak{M}_\omega$ Eq. (48.1.21) is valid for all Borel sets $\mathcal{S}' \subseteq \mathcal{S}$, then μ is subcentral (and thus in $\mathfrak{D}_\omega$).
   If the C*-algebra $\mathcal{A}$ is separable, then $\mathcal{S}$ is a standard Borel space and the above pseudo-support characterizations go over into genuine support characterizations. Also the following assertion requires some separability conditions for the folium $\mathcal{F}_\omega$, which we do not specify (see e.g., [BR87]).

(d) *If μ is subcentral (i.e., $\mathfrak{B}_\mu \subset \mathcal{Z}_\omega$), then it is dominated (refined) by any maximal measure μ':*

$$\mu \trianglelefteq \mu', \quad \text{for all extremal } \mu' \in \mathfrak{M}_\omega. \qquad (48.1.22)$$

Especially the central measure μ_ω is dominated by all maximal decomposition measures of ω. Reversely, if $\mu \in \mathfrak{D}_\omega$ is dominated by all maximal decomposition measures of ω, then it is subcentral, and the central measure μ_ω is the finest of these.

If $\mathcal{A}$ is non-commutative and ω not pure, then there are many extremal decompositions but much less orthogonal extremal decompositions. Consider $\mathcal{A} = \mathbb{M}_2$, the case of a qubit space. Then $\mathcal{S}$ is affine isomorphic to a 3-ball, and an interior point has many decompositions into a convex sum of (extreme and topological) boundary points. An *orthogonal* extremal decomposition is, however, given by a spectral representation of the associated density matrix, which is only non-unique, if an eigenvalue is degenerate (a case realized here only by the trace state). More generally, in Hilbert space Quantum Theory, a density operator is diagonalized by means of commuting observables. We remark that a maximal Abelian $\mathfrak{B}_\mu$, together with the corresponding $(P_\mu \Pi_\omega(\mathcal{A}) P_\mu)''$, generalizes the notion of a *complete set of commuting observables* of Traditional Quantum Mechanics.

Concerning central decompositions, which diagonalize classical observables, one has to discriminate between absolute superselection rules, as e.g., the electric charge, which pertains also to the microscopic theory, and purely macroscopic classical observables, with no counterpart in the microscopic regime. Prominent examples for the latter case are given by the observables at infinity (of Definition 33.6-2), i.e., $\mathfrak{B}_\mu = \mathcal{Z}_\omega(\infty) \subset \mathcal{Z}_\omega$, and by the limiting mean fields (of Definition 34.1-5), i.e., $\mathfrak{B}_\mu = \mathcal{Z}_\omega^{\mathrm{mf}} \subset \mathcal{Z}_\omega$. For quasilocal algebras, which are built on local algebras of the type $\mathcal{L}(\mathcal{H}_\Lambda)$, we have $\mathcal{Z}_\omega(\infty) = \mathcal{Z}_\omega$, but for the (quasilocal) infinite product algebras, in general $\mathcal{Z}_\omega^{\mathrm{mf}} \nsubseteq \mathcal{Z}_\omega(\infty) = \mathcal{Z}_\omega$.

The characterization in Proposition 48.1-17(d) of the central measure is *basic for a consistent formulation of many body physics, including quantum information theory.* It tells us that there exists a finest measure which decomposes an ensemble into classically distinguishable sub-ensembles, and can thus uniquely be identified (namely, as the central decomposition measure). Also if the system consists of a large number of identical, and thus *indistinguishable, microscopic* particles (Bosons or Fermions), there is a unique decomposition of a mixed state into classically *distinguishable* states, which are classically pure and describe thus *classical individuals.* The classically different subensembles are not coherent superposable (see Sec. 47.4.2 on page 1760), and have vanishing transition probabilities (see Sec. 47.4.3 and especially the end of Sec. 48.4 on page 1841). We have interpreted in Conclusion 46.2-33 on page 1701 the equivalence classes of factor states as constituting the classical configuration space for a given observable algebra.

The problem of indistinguishable microscopic constituents arises only for the observer if he deals with more refined decompositions and state filterings: If he sees the microscopic particles *in full precision*, what is theoretically expressed by an extremal decomposition, he cannot recognize their *averaged* features and loses the affiliation of the microscopic particles with a classical individual.

You cannot recognize your friend, if you see in detail his gigantic array of molecules, the states of which depend even on your way of looking (what tells us the non-uniqueness of the extremal decompositions). So, not any of the single molecules can be associated with him. But if you look — as you always do — coarse grained and form permanently classical observables, then you know for a larger — mesoscopic or macroscopic — amount of molecules, as e.g., a blood droplet, whether it came from him or not. By the way, the classical features of single bio-molecules is a story for its own. To avoid this complication, replace your friend by a buck of water. Or, look at the indistinguishable electrons in metallic pieces! Indeed, only if we acknowledge this kind of reasoning, we can form a microscopic theory of the Josephson junction — as in Chapter 41 —, where we must know whether the electrons drop out from the left- or right-sided electrode.

The application of the decomposition theory to many-electron and many-photon states belongs to the permanent topics of the present treatise. In the realm of thermodynamics, it turns out that the central decomposition describes the disintegration into (equilibrium or non-equilibrium) pure phase states.

A most useful aspect of any $\mu \in \mathfrak{O}_w$ is that it may induce the spatial decomposition of the corresponding GNS triple $(\Pi_w, \mathcal{H}_w, \Omega_w)$. That means especially that $\mathcal{H}_w$ is written as a direct integral over other Hilbert spaces, for which we employ a measurable space to label the component spaces. For performing the mathematical proofs to be valid also for the decomposition of Boson states, we present a detailed exposition of spatial decomposition theory, in spite of the underlying ideas being rather intuitive.

48.2.   Spatial Decomposition Theory

48.2.1.   *Measurable Families of Hilbert Spaces*

Definition 48.2-1 (Construction of Direct Integrals of Hilbert Spaces).
Let be given the σ-finite, standard, measure space (Γ, μ) and relate "measurability" in the following always to (Γ, μ). Let further $\{\mathcal{H}(\gamma) \,|\, \gamma \in \Gamma\}$ be a family of separable complex Hilbert spaces. The Cartesian product $\prod_{\gamma \in \Gamma}^{\times} \mathcal{H}(\gamma)$ is a vector space under the usual point-wise linear operations.

Let us call the elements $\xi \in \prod_{\gamma \in \Gamma}^{\times} \mathcal{H}(\gamma)$ *vector fields*. For each $\gamma \in \Gamma$, the vector field ξ has a component $\xi(\gamma) \in \mathcal{H}(\gamma)$, and $c\xi + \xi'$ has the components $(c\xi + \xi')(\gamma) = c\,\xi(\gamma) + \xi'(\gamma)$, where $c \in \mathbb{C}$.

(a) $\{\mathcal{H}(\gamma) \,|\, \gamma \in \Gamma\}$ is called a *"measurable family of Hilbert spaces"*, if there is a sequence $\{\xi_n \in \prod_{\gamma \in \Gamma}^{\times} \mathcal{H}(\gamma) \,|\, n \in \mathbb{N}\}$ of vector fields with the following properties:

(i) $\gamma \rightarrow (\xi_n(\gamma) | \xi_m(\gamma))_{\mathcal{H}(\gamma)}$ is μ-measurable for every $n, m \in \mathbb{N}$;
(ii) $\{\xi_n(\gamma) \,|\, n \in \mathbb{N}\}$ is dense in $\mathcal{H}(\gamma)$ for each $\gamma \in \Gamma$.

Let us term such a sequence $(\xi_n)_{\mathbb{N}} \subset \prod_{\gamma \in \Gamma}^{\times} \mathcal{H}(\gamma)$ a *"fundamental sequence"* of measurable vector fields.

(b) Given a measurable family of Hilbert spaces with fundamental sequence $(\xi_n)_{\mathbb{N}}$, then $\xi \in \prod_{\gamma \in \Gamma}^{\times} \mathcal{H}(\gamma)$ is called measurable (with respect to $(\xi_n)_{\mathbb{N}}$), if $\gamma \mapsto (\xi(\gamma) | \xi_n(\gamma))_{\mathcal{H}(\gamma)}$ is measurable for all $n \in \mathbb{N}$.
One can show that $\gamma \mapsto \|\xi(\gamma)\|^2_{\mathcal{H}(\gamma)}$ and $\gamma \mapsto (\xi(\gamma) | \xi'(\gamma))_{\mathcal{H}(\gamma)}$ are μ-measurable functions for measurable vector fields ξ and ξ', and that the measurable vector fields constitute a linear subspace $\mathcal{V}$ of $\prod_{\gamma \in \Gamma}^{\times} \mathcal{H}(\gamma)$.
(c) Given a measurable family of Hilbert spaces $\{\mathcal{H}(\gamma) \,|\, \gamma \in \Gamma\}$ (where the fundamental sequence $(\xi_n)_{\mathbb{N}}$ is now tacitly understood), we define the (linear) null space

$$\mathcal{V}_0 := \left\{ \xi \in \prod_{\gamma \in \Gamma}^{\times} \mathcal{H}(\gamma) \,\Big|\, \xi \text{ is measurable, } \|\xi\|^2 := \int_\Gamma \|\xi(\gamma)\|^2_{\mathcal{H}(\gamma)} d\mu(\gamma) = 0 \right\}.$$

We introduce the linear space of equivalence classes $[\xi] = \xi + \mathcal{V}_0$ of measurable, square integrable vector fields ξ and write (using for the first time here a direct integral),

$$\mathcal{H} \equiv \int_{\Gamma}^{\oplus} \mathcal{H}(\gamma) \, d\mu(\gamma) := \Big\{ [\xi] \in \mathcal{V}/\mathcal{V}_0 \,\Big|\, \|\xi\|^2 = \textstyle\int_{\Gamma} \|\xi(\gamma)\|^2_{\mathcal{H}(\gamma)} \, d\mu(\gamma) < \infty \Big\}.$$

We call $\mathcal{H}$ the *"direct integral"* of the family of Hilbert spaces $\{\mathcal{H}(\gamma) \,|\, \gamma \in \Gamma\}$. Equipped with the scalar product

$$(\xi|\eta) := \int_{\Gamma} (\xi(\gamma)|\eta(\gamma))_{\mathcal{H}(\gamma)} \, d\mu(\gamma) , \quad \xi \equiv [\xi], \eta \equiv [\eta] \in \mathcal{H} ,$$

(where we suppress henceforth the bracket for forming the equivalence classes). $\mathcal{H}$ is complete in the norm topology and thus a Hilbert space. A vector field class $\xi \in \mathcal{H}$ will now be written in the form $\xi = \int_{\Gamma}^{\oplus} \xi(\gamma) \, d\mu(\gamma)$, implying that the component vectors are only determined μ-a.e. (almost everywhere).

It follows that the function $\gamma \mapsto n(\gamma) := \dim(\mathcal{H}(\gamma))$ is measurable, and thus the sets $\Gamma_n := \{\gamma \in \Gamma \,|\, n(\gamma) = n\}$ are measurable for all $1 \leq n \leq \infty$. From the fundamental sequence $(\xi_n)_{\mathbb{N}}$ one can always construct by the Gram–Schmidt orthonormalization method an equivalent fundamental sequence $(\xi'_n)_{\mathbb{N}}$ (giving the same space $\mathcal{V}$ of measurable vector fields) which has the following additional properties.

Proposition 48.2-2 (Orthonormalized Vector Fields).   *In an integral of Hilbert spaces, there exists an orthonormalized sequence $(\xi'_n)_{\mathbb{N}}$ of fundamental vector fields which satisfies*

(a) *For each $\gamma \in \Gamma$ the set $\{\xi'_n(\gamma) \,|\, 1 \leq n \leq n(\gamma)\}$ is an orthonormal basis for $\mathcal{H}(\gamma)$.*
(b) $\xi'_n(\gamma) = 0$ *for $n > n(\gamma)$.*

We now describe, how we get from an orthonormalized sequence of vector fields an orthonormalized basis in the Hilbert space $\int_{\Gamma}^{\oplus} \mathcal{H}(\gamma) \, d\mu(\gamma)$.

First we conclude that $\{\xi'_l|_{\Gamma_n} \,|\, 1 \leq l \leq n = n(\gamma)\}$ is a fundamental sequence for the restricted family of Hilbert spaces $\{\mathcal{H}(\gamma) \,|\, \gamma \in \Gamma_n\}$. Thus we may write $\mathcal{H} = \sum_{n=1}^{\infty} \int_{\Gamma_n}^{\oplus} \mathcal{H}(\gamma) \, d\mu(\gamma)$, where a summand is zero, if $\mu(\Gamma_n) = 0$. Special vector fields in $\int_{\Gamma_n}^{\oplus} \mathcal{H}(\gamma) \, d\mu(\gamma)$ have the form $\Gamma_n \ni \gamma \mapsto f(\gamma)\xi'_l(\gamma)$, where $f \in \mathrm{L}^2(\Gamma_n; \mu)$. Take also a $g \in \mathrm{L}^2(\Gamma_n; \mu)$ and calculate with Proposition 48.2-2 that for $1 \leq l, k \leq n$,

$$\left(\int_{\Gamma_n}^{\oplus} f(\gamma)\xi'_l(\gamma) \, d\mu(\gamma) \,\Big|\, \int_{\Gamma_n}^{\oplus} g(\gamma)\xi'_k(\gamma) \, d\mu(\gamma) \right) = \int_{\Gamma_n}^{\oplus} \delta_{l,k} \overline{f(\gamma)} \, g(\gamma) \, d\mu(\gamma) .$$

Now choose for each $n \in \mathbb{N} \cup \{\infty\}$ an orthonormalized basis e_k^n, $1 \leq k \leq n$, in $\mathrm{L}^2(\Gamma_n; \mu)$. We define $f_k|_{\Gamma_n} := e_k^n$ for $k \leq n$ and $f_k|_{\Gamma_n} := 0$ for $k > n$. By means of these restrictions, f_k is defined on all of Γ, for each $k \in \mathbb{N}$. The vector fields $\{f_k \xi'_l \,|\, k, l \in \mathbb{N}\}$ constitute the desired orthonormal basis for $\int_{\Gamma}^{\oplus} \mathcal{H}(\gamma) \, d\mu(\gamma)$.

From the introduced orthonormalized basis, we get a standard form for the integral Hilbert space. Each $\mathcal{H}(\gamma)$, $\gamma \in \Gamma_n$, is unitarily equivalent to any

n-dimensional Hilbert space. Let us choose a fixed infinite-dimensional, separable Hilbert space $\hat{\mathcal{H}}_\infty$, together with an increasing sequence of subspaces $\hat{\mathcal{H}}_n$, $n \in \mathbb{N}$, with $\dim(\hat{\mathcal{H}}_n) = n$ and $\hat{\mathcal{H}}_n \subset \hat{\mathcal{H}}_{n+1} \subset \hat{\mathcal{H}}_\infty$. We denote by $\{\hat{\xi}_l \mid l \in \mathbb{N}\}$ an orthonormal basis of $\hat{\mathcal{H}}_\infty$, which by restriction is assumed to provide an orthonormal basis for each $\hat{\mathcal{H}}_n$. A unitary map is induced by the correspondence

$$\int_{\Gamma_n}^{\oplus} \mathcal{H}(\gamma)\, d\mu(\gamma) \ni \int_{\Gamma_n}^{\oplus} f_k(\gamma)\xi'_l(\gamma)\, d\mu(\gamma) \quad \longleftrightarrow \quad \hat{\xi}_l \otimes f_k \in \hat{\mathcal{H}}_n \otimes \mathrm{L}^2(\Gamma_n; \mu)$$

(48.2.1)

for $1 \le k, l \le n$, where the right-hand side is the tensor product of Hilbert spaces, spanned by the basis of product vectors. We conclude:

Proposition 48.2-3. *Let $\{\mathcal{H}(\gamma) \mid \gamma \in \Gamma\}$ be a measurable family of Hilbert spaces over the standard measure space (Γ, μ) with respect to the fundamental sequence of measurable vector fields $(\xi_n)_\mathbb{N}$ (also with respect to $(\xi'_n)_\mathbb{N}$ of Proposition 48.2-2). Let further $\hat{\mathcal{H}}_n$, $n \in \mathbb{N}$, be the increasing sequence of subspaces of the infinite-dimensional, separable Hilbert space $\hat{\mathcal{H}}_\infty$, as described before. Then there is a unitary isomorphism*

$$\mathcal{H} = \int_\Gamma^{\oplus} \mathcal{H}(\gamma)\, d\mu(\gamma) \ \xrightarrow{\ U\ }\ \bigoplus_{n=1}^{\infty} \left(\hat{\mathcal{H}}_n \otimes \mathrm{L}^2(\Gamma_n; \mu) \right) \oplus \left(\hat{\mathcal{H}}_\infty \otimes \mathrm{L}^2(\Gamma_\infty; \mu) \right),$$

(48.2.2)

which satisfies relation (48.2.1).

Thus the direct integral $\mathcal{H}$ is separable and independent from the fundamental sequence $(\xi_n)_\mathbb{N}$ (since the image of U is so).

In our applications, the component spaces $\mathcal{H}(\gamma)$ have frequently all the same dimension n, so that the right-hand side of Eq. (48.2.2) reduces to a single tensor product.

For an unsymmetrized *Fock space* over the separable one-particle space $\mathcal{H}$, we have $F(\mathcal{H}) = \bigoplus_{n=0}^{\infty} \mathcal{H}(n)$ with $\mathcal{H}(n) = \mathcal{H} \otimes \overset{n}{\ldots} \otimes \mathcal{H}$ for $n > 0$, and $\mathcal{H}(0) = \mathbb{C}$. Written as a direct integral, this reads $F(\mathcal{H}) = \int_{\mathbb{R}}^{\oplus} \mathcal{H}(\gamma)\, d\mu(\gamma)$, where $\mathrm{supp}(\mu) = \mathbb{N}_0$. (The $\mathcal{H}(\gamma)$ for γ not in $\mathrm{supp}(\mu)$ are arbitrary separable Hilbert spaces.) Since for $n > 0$ the component spaces have all the same infinite dimension, they are unitarily equivalent to an infinite-dimensional $\hat{\mathcal{H}}_\infty$, and the right-hand side of Eq. (48.2.2) takes the form $\left(\mathbb{C} \otimes \mathrm{l}^2(\{0\}) \right) \oplus \left(\hat{\mathcal{H}}_\infty \otimes \mathrm{l}^2(\mathbb{N}) \right)$. This is meant as a warning that the above used standard form for a direct integral of Hilbert spaces, in terms of tensor products, is physically not always appropriate.

48.2.2. *Direct Integrals of von Neumann Algebras*

In a direct integral of Hilbert spaces, there is the distinguished class of decomposable operators.

Definition 48.2-4. Let $\mathcal{H} = \int_\Gamma^\oplus \mathcal{H}(\gamma) \, d\mu(\gamma)$ be a direct integral of Hilbert spaces.

(a) A family of bounded operators $\{A(\gamma) \in \mathcal{L}(\mathcal{H}(\gamma)) \,|\, \gamma \in \Gamma\}$ is called *"measurable"*, if $\{A(\gamma)\xi(\gamma) \,|\, \gamma \in \Gamma\}$ is measurable for all measurable vector fields ξ (with respect to a given fundamental sequence of vector fields).

(b) Let the measurable family of bounded operators $\{A(\gamma) \in \mathcal{L}(\mathcal{H}(\gamma)) \,|\, \gamma \in \Gamma\}$ satisfy $\sup_{\gamma \in \Gamma} \|A(\gamma)\| < \infty$. Then $\{A(\gamma)\xi(\gamma) \,|\, \gamma \in \Gamma\}$ is in $\mathcal{H}$ if $\xi \in \mathcal{H}$. We define the linear operator

$$A \equiv \int_\Gamma^\oplus A(\gamma) \, d\mu(\gamma) \quad \text{by} \quad (A\xi)(\gamma) := A(\gamma)\xi(\gamma), \quad \gamma \in \Gamma, \quad \xi \in \mathcal{H}. \quad (48.2.3)$$

Then A is a bounded operator in $\mathcal{H}$ with $\|A\| = \sup_{\gamma \in \Gamma} \|A(\gamma)\|$.

(c) A bounded operator A in $\mathcal{H} = \int_\Gamma^\oplus \mathcal{H}(\gamma) \, d\mu(\gamma)$ is called *"decomposable"* if it has the form as in Eq. (48.2.3).

(d) A bounded operator A in $\mathcal{H} = \int_\Gamma^\oplus \mathcal{H}(\gamma) \, d\mu(\gamma)$ is called *"diagonal"* if it has the form as in Eq. (48.2.3) with $A(\gamma) = f(\gamma) \mathbb{1}_{\mathcal{H}(\gamma)}$, where $f(.) \in L^\infty(\Gamma; \mu)$. Let us then denote this operator by $D_\mu(f)$ and the set of diagonal operators by $\mathcal{D}$.

If $A = \int_\Gamma^\oplus A(\gamma) \, d\mu(\gamma)$ and $B = \int_\Gamma^\oplus B(\gamma) \, d\mu(\gamma)$, then the component-wise linear operations for the vector fields lead us to the component-wise algebraic operations

$$A + B = \int_\Gamma^\oplus \big(A(\gamma) + B(\gamma)\big) \, d\mu(\gamma), \ AB = \int_\Gamma^\oplus A(\gamma)B(\gamma) \, d\mu(\gamma), \ A^* = \int_\Gamma^\oplus A(\gamma)^* d\mu(\gamma).$$

We see that the decomposable and diagonal operators constitute *-algebras each, where in fact $\mathcal{D}$ is obviously *-isomorphic to the Abelian von Neumann algebra $L^\infty(\Gamma; \mu)$.

The proof of the following Proposition is rather technical (cf. [Tak79]).

Proposition 48.2-5. *In a direct integral of Hilbert spaces a bounded operator is decomposable if and only if it commutes with the diagonal algebra $\mathcal{D}$.*

Thus the set of all decomposable operators equals the commutant von Neumann algebra $\mathcal{D}'$, and the further commutant leads back to $\mathcal{D} = \mathcal{D}''$, $\mathcal{D}$ being a von Neumann algebra.

Definition 48.2-6 (Direct Integral of von Neumann Algebras). Let again the symbols $\mathcal{H} = \int_\Gamma^\oplus \mathcal{H}(\gamma) \, d\mu(\gamma)$ denote a direct integral of Hilbert spaces and $\mathcal{D}$ the algebra of diagonal operators. Let further $\{\mathcal{M}(\gamma) \subset \mathcal{L}(\mathcal{H}(\gamma)) \,|\, \gamma \in \Gamma\}$ be a family of von Neumann algebras. The latter is called *"measurable"* if there exists a sequence $M_n = \int_\Gamma^\oplus M_n(\gamma) \, d\mu(\gamma)$, $n \in \mathbb{N}$, of decomposable operators such that $\mathcal{M}(\gamma) = \{M_n(\gamma) \,|\, n \in \mathbb{N}\}''$ for μ–a.e. $\gamma \in \Gamma$. (The measurability property of $\gamma \mapsto \mathcal{M}(\gamma)$ results from the measurability of the $\gamma \mapsto M_n(\gamma)$.)

Given a measurable family $\{\mathcal{M}(\gamma) \,|\, \gamma \in \Gamma\}$ of von Neumann algebras we introduce, as in [BR87], the von Neumann algebra

$$\mathcal{M} := \left[\{M_n \,|\, n \in \mathbb{N}\} \cup \mathcal{D}\right]'' =: \int_\Gamma^\oplus \mathcal{M}(\gamma)\, d\mu(\gamma) \subset \mathcal{L}(\mathcal{H}), \tag{48.2.4}$$

and call it a *"direct integral of von Neumann algebras."*

Remark 48.2-7. If the sequence M_n, $n \in \mathbb{N}$, of decomposable operators in the direct integral $\mathcal{H} = \int_\Gamma^\oplus \mathcal{H}(\gamma)\, d\mu(\gamma)$ satisfies μ–a.e. the relation $\mathcal{M}(\gamma) = \{M_n(\gamma) \,|\, n \in \mathbb{N}\}''$ then it seems that $\mathcal{D} \subset \left[\{M_n \,|\, n \in \mathbb{N}\}\right]''$. But the componentwise commutation is not available at this stage. Thus we adhere to the above definition Eq. (48.2.4) of a direct integral $\mathcal{M}$ of von Neumann algebras, and take it as a derived result, that it is equivalent to: $\mathcal{M} = \int_\Gamma^\oplus \mathcal{M}(\gamma)\, d\mu(\gamma)$ is the set of all decomposable operators with components μ–a.e. in $\mathcal{M}(\gamma)$ (see [Tak79]).

From Eq. (48.2.4), it follows directly that the center of the direct integral $\mathcal{M}$ contains always $\mathcal{D}$ and we have

$$\mathcal{D} \subset \mathcal{M} \subset \mathcal{D}' \subset \mathcal{L}(\mathcal{H}). \tag{48.2.5}$$

If now $\mathcal{M} \subset \mathcal{L}(\mathcal{H}) = \mathcal{L}(\int_\Gamma^\oplus \mathcal{H}(\gamma)\, d\mu(\gamma))$ is any von Neumann algebra, then $\mathcal{M}$ is separable and contains a σ-weakly dense, denumerable set $\{M_n \,|\, n \in \mathbb{N}\}$, since $\mathcal{H}$ is separable. If $\mathcal{M} \subset \mathcal{D}'$ it consists of decomposable operators, and if also $\mathcal{M} \supset \mathcal{D}$, then $\mathcal{M} = \{M_n \,|\, n \in \mathbb{N}\}'' = \left[\{M_n \,|\, n \in \mathbb{N}\} \cup \mathcal{D}\right]''$, so that $\mathcal{M}$ has the form (48.2.4). So we have shown the first part of the following proposition.

Proposition 48.2-8. *A von Neumann algebra $\mathcal{M} \subset \mathcal{L}(\int_\Gamma^\oplus \mathcal{H}(\gamma)\, d\mu(\gamma))$ is a direct integral of von Neumann algebras if and only if relation (48.2.5) is satisfied.*

By forming the commutant of (48.2.5) we obtain $\mathcal{D}' \supset \mathcal{M}' \supset \mathcal{D}$, so that also $\mathcal{M}'$ is a direct integral of von Neumann algebras. But, by the point-wise algebraic operations, decomposable operators commute, if and only if their components commute μ–a.e. Thus

$$\mathcal{M}' = \int_\Gamma^\oplus \mathcal{M}(\gamma)'\, d\mu(\gamma), \tag{48.2.6}$$

and also

$$\mathcal{M} \cap \mathcal{M}' = \int_\Gamma^\oplus \left[\mathcal{M}(\gamma) \cap \mathcal{M}(\gamma)'\right] d\mu(\gamma) \supset \mathcal{D}. \tag{48.2.7}$$

The foregoing Proposition implies the structure of the two extremal cases of integral von Neumann algebras,

$$\mathcal{D} = \int_\Gamma^\oplus \mathbb{C}\mathbb{1}_{\mathcal{H}(\gamma)}\, d\mu(\gamma), \qquad \mathcal{D}' = \int_\Gamma^\oplus \mathcal{L}(\mathcal{H}(\gamma))\, d\mu(\gamma). \tag{48.2.8}$$

If for an integral of von Neumann algebras $\mathcal{M}$, one has $\mathcal{M} \cap \mathcal{M}' = \mathcal{D}$, then (48.2.7) shows that the component von Neumann algebras are factors μ–a.e.

Any (scaled) normal state on an integral von Neumann algebra $\int_\Gamma^\oplus \mathcal{M}(\gamma)\, d\mu(\gamma)$ is the denumerable sum of vector states. Since the vectors in $\int_\Gamma^\oplus \mathcal{H}(\gamma)\, d\mu(\gamma)$ are decomposable, it is not surprising that a (scaled) normal state is so either. In this connection, it is natural to define:

Definition 48.2-9 (Measurable Families of Normal Functionals). Let be given an integral of von Neumann algebras $\mathcal{M} = \int_\Gamma^\oplus \mathcal{M}(\gamma)\, d\mu(\gamma)$ over a σ-finite standard measure space.

A family of normal functionals $\{\omega(\gamma) \in \mathcal{M}_*(\gamma) \,|\, \gamma \in \Gamma\}$ is by definition measurable, if for any $\int_\Gamma^\oplus M(\gamma))\, d\mu(\gamma) \in \mathcal{M}$ the function $\Gamma \ni \gamma \mapsto \langle \omega(\gamma); M(\gamma) \rangle$ is measurable.

Since the norm is the supremum of a denumerable set of expectations (we work in separable Hilbert spaces), we conclude that for a measurable family of normal functionals also the function $\Gamma \ni \gamma \mapsto \|\omega(\gamma)\|$ is measurable. Then one finds (see e.g., [Tak79]):

Proposition 48.2-10 (Disintegration of States). *Let $\int_\Gamma^\oplus \mathcal{M}(\gamma)\, d\mu(\gamma)$ be an integral of von Neumann algebras over a σ-finite standard measure space. Then every scaled state $\omega \in \mathcal{M}_{*+}$ is of the form*

$$\left\langle \omega; \int_\Gamma^\oplus M(\gamma))\, d\mu(\gamma) \right\rangle = \int_\Gamma^\oplus \langle \omega(\gamma); M(\gamma) \rangle\, d\mu(\gamma)\,, \tag{48.2.9}$$

for an μ–a.e. unique measurable family of normal scaled states $\omega(\gamma) \in \mathcal{M}_{*+}(\gamma)$ which satisfies

$$\|\omega\| = \int_\Gamma^\oplus \|\omega(\gamma)\|\, d\mu(\gamma)\,. \tag{48.2.10}$$

Decomposable von Neumann algebras arise in our context mostly by decomposable representations.

48.2.3. Direct Integrals of Representations

As a first step for forming integrals of representations, we set up an assumption, which is basic for the subsequent constructions.

Assumption 48.2-11 (Assumption on Integration Measures). Let $\mathcal{A}$ be a (not necessarily separable) C*-algebra with unit and $\mathcal{S} = \mathcal{S}(\mathcal{A})$ its (weak* compact) state space. Assume a weak* Borel measure μ on $\mathcal{S}$ such that $(\mathcal{S}, \mu)$ is a σ-finite standard measure space. (Then there is a $\mathcal{S}_\mu \subseteq \mathcal{S}$, differing from $\mathcal{S}$ by a μ-null set, which equipped with the weak* topology is homeomorphic to a Polish space, which is not necessarily the case for $\mathcal{S}$ itself.)

We consider the family of GNS representations $\{(\Pi_\varphi, \mathcal{H}_\varphi, \Omega_\varphi) \,|\, \varphi \in \mathcal{S}_\mu\}$ and make the further assumption: There is a *countable family* $\{A_n \in \mathcal{A} \,|\, n \in \mathbf{N}\}$ such that for each $\varphi \in \mathcal{S}_\mu$, the set $\{\Pi_\varphi(A_n) \,|\, n \in \mathbb{N}\}$ is dense in $\Pi_\varphi(\mathcal{A})$, and hence in $\Pi_\varphi(\mathcal{A})'' = \mathcal{M}_\varphi$, with respect to the weak operator topology in $\mathcal{H}_\varphi$.

We draw several conclusions from the Assumption 48.2-11.

Corollary 48.2-12 (Integrals of Representations). *Assume the conditions of the Assumption 48.2-11 satisfied.*

Then $\{\mathcal{H}_\varphi \,|\, \varphi \in \mathcal{S}\}$ is a measurable family of Hilbert spaces with respect to the fundamental sequence of vector fields $(\xi_n)_{\mathbb{N}} := \{(\varphi \to \Pi_\varphi(A_n)\Omega_\varphi) \,|\, n \in \mathbb{N}\}$. In fact, $\varphi \mapsto (\Pi_\varphi(A_m)\Omega_\varphi | \Pi_\varphi(A_n)\Omega_\varphi) = \langle \varphi; A_m^* A_n \rangle$ is weak*-continuous, hence measurable, so that, in combination with the Assumption 48.2-11, the requirements (a) and (b) of Definition 48.2-1 are satisfied.

We can form the vector space $\mathcal{V} \subset \prod_{\mathcal{S}}^\times \mathcal{H}_\varphi$ of measurable vector fields and the direct integral of Hilbert spaces $\mathcal{H}_\mu = \int_{\mathcal{S}}^\oplus \mathcal{H}_\varphi \, d\mu(\varphi)$ as in Definition 48.2-1. We see that for each $A \in \mathcal{A}$, the vector field $\varphi \mapsto \Pi_\varphi(A)\Omega_\varphi$ is in $\mathcal{V}$, and if $f \in L^\infty(\mathcal{S}; \mu)$, then $[\varphi \mapsto f(\varphi)\xi_n(\varphi)] \in \mathcal{V}$. (Form the scalar products with the ξ_n.) We conclude,

$$\hat{\mathcal{V}} := \{f\xi_n \,|\, f \in L^\infty(\mathcal{S}; \mu)\,,\ n \in \mathbb{N}\} \ \text{is dense in } \mathcal{H}_\mu\,. \tag{48.2.11}$$

(This results from the following: $\eta \in \hat{\mathcal{V}}^\perp$ gives

$$(\eta | f\xi_n) = \int_{\mathcal{S}} f(\varphi)(\eta(\varphi)|\xi_n(\varphi)) \, d\mu(\varphi) = 0\,,$$

for all $f \in L^\infty(\mathcal{S}; \mu)$. Thus $(\eta(\varphi)|\xi_n(\varphi)) = 0$ μ-a.e. for all $n \in \mathbb{N}$ and $\eta(\varphi) = 0$ μ-a.e.).

We consider the decomposable operators

$$\Pi_\mu(A) := \int_{\mathcal{S}}^\oplus \Pi_\varphi(A) \, d\mu(\varphi) \ \in \mathcal{D}' \subset \mathcal{L}\Big(\int_{\mathcal{S}}^\oplus \mathcal{H}_\varphi \, d\mu(\varphi)\Big)\,, \quad \forall A \in \mathcal{A}. \tag{48.2.12}$$

In view of the component-wise *-algebraic operations, $\Pi_\mu : \mathcal{A} \to \mathcal{L}(\mathcal{H}_\mu)$ is a representation of $\mathcal{A}$, namely the direct integral of the representations Π_φ, denoted by $\Pi_\mu = \int_{\mathcal{S}}^\oplus \Pi_\varphi \, d\mu(\varphi)$.

If especially $\mu \in \mathfrak{M}_\omega$, that is a probability measure with barycenter $\omega \in \mathcal{S}$, then Π_μ is a representation associated with the decomposition of ω so that for every $A \in \mathcal{A}$,

$$\langle \omega; A \rangle = (\Omega_\mu | \Pi_\mu(A)\Omega_\mu) = \int_{\mathcal{S}} \langle \varphi; A \rangle \, d\mu(\varphi)\,, \quad \Omega_\mu := \int_{\mathcal{S}}^\oplus \Omega_\varphi \, d\mu(\varphi)\,. \tag{48.2.13}$$

Equation (48.2.13) constitutes the first feature of the GNS representation. The condition under which the second feature, that is the cyclicity of Ω_μ, is valid is given in the subsequent Proposition, which generalizes the Effros theorem in a slight sense to non-separable C*-algebras.

Proposition 48.2-13 (Generalized Effros Theorem). *Consider a unital (not necessarily separable) C*-algebra $\mathcal{A}$ with state space $\mathcal{S}$, and fix $\omega \in \mathcal{S}$. Assume in the following that there is given a standard $\mu \in \mathfrak{M}_\omega$ and a denumerable family $\{A_n \in \mathcal{A} \mid n \in \mathbb{N}\}$ such that the Assumption 48.2-11 is satisfied. Then the direct integral representation*

$$\left(\Pi_\mu = \int_{\mathcal{S}}^{\oplus} \Pi_\varphi \, d\mu(\varphi) \,,\, \mathcal{H}_\mu = \int_{\mathcal{S}}^{\oplus} \mathcal{H}_\varphi \, d\mu(\varphi) \right)$$

introduced as above has $\Omega_\mu = \int_{\mathcal{S}}^{\oplus} \Omega_\varphi \, d\mu(\varphi)$ as a cyclic vector, if and only if $\mu \in \mathcal{D}_\omega$, that is, if and only if μ is orthogonal.

Proof. Let Ω_μ be cyclic. Then $(\Pi_\mu, \mathcal{H}_\mu, \Omega_\mu)$ fulfills the two conditions characterizing a GNS representation $(\Pi_\omega, \mathcal{H}_\omega, \Omega_\omega)$ of ω. One concludes that for a given $f \in \mathrm{L}^\infty(\mathcal{S}; \mu)$, the diagonal operator $D_\mu(f) = \int_{\mathcal{S}}^{\oplus} f(\varphi) \mathbb{1}_\varphi \, d\mu(\varphi)$, satisfying $(\Omega_\mu | D_\mu(f) \Pi_\mu(A) \Omega_\mu) = \int_{\mathcal{S}} f(\varphi) \hat{A}(\varphi) \, d\mu(\varphi)$, is a realization of the Tomita map $\theta_\mu : \mathrm{L}^\infty(\mathcal{S}; \mu) \xrightarrow{\text{onto}} \mathcal{D} \subset \Pi_\mu(\mathcal{A})'$. It clearly provides an *-isomorphism, and thus from Proposition 48.1-14, we know that μ is the orthogonal measure in $\mathcal{D}_\omega$ which is associated with the Abelian von Neumann algebra $\mathcal{D}$, the diagonal algebra.

Reversely let $\mu \in \mathcal{D}_\omega$. Then the Tomita map θ_μ maps $\mathrm{L}^\infty(\mathcal{S}; \mu)$ *-isomorphically onto an Abelian von Neumann algebra $\mathcal{B} \subset \Pi_\omega(\mathcal{A})'$. Since Π_ω has the cyclic vector $\Omega_\omega \in \mathcal{H}_\omega$, we know that for each $f \in \mathrm{L}^\infty(\mathcal{S}; \mu)$ and each A_n, $n \in \mathbb{N}$, that there is a $B \in \mathcal{A}$ so that $\|\Pi_\omega(B)\Omega_\omega - \theta_\mu(f)\Pi_\omega(A_n)\Omega_\omega\|$ is small. On the other side we have

$$\|\Pi_\mu(B)\Omega_\mu - D_\mu(f)\Pi_\mu(A_n)\Omega_\mu\|^2 \tag{48.2.14}$$
$$= \left(\Omega_\mu \big| [\Pi_\mu(B^*B) - D_\mu(f)\Pi_\mu(B^*A_n) \right.$$
$$\left. - D_\mu(\overline{f})\Pi_\mu(A_n^*B) + D_\mu(\overline{f})D_\mu(f)\Pi_\mu(A_n^*A_n)]\Omega_\mu \right)$$
$$= \int_{\mathcal{S}} \left[\langle \varphi; B^*B \rangle - f(\varphi)\langle \varphi; B^*A_n \rangle - \overline{f(\varphi)}\langle \varphi; A_n^*B \rangle + \overline{f(\varphi)}f(\varphi)\langle \varphi; A_n^*A_n \rangle \right] d\mu(\varphi)$$
$$= \left(\Omega_\omega \big| [\Pi_\omega(B^*B) - \theta_\mu(f)\Pi_\omega(B^*A_n) - \theta_\mu(\overline{f})\Pi_\omega(A_n^*B) + \theta_\mu(\overline{f}f)\Pi_\omega(A_n^*A_n)]\Omega_\omega \right),$$

where the second equality stems from the definitions of Π_μ and Ω_μ, and the last equality uses $\mu \in \mathcal{D}_\omega$, and refers to Eq. (48.1.11) in the definition of the Tomita map. Taking into account that θ_μ is *-homomorphic we get $\theta_\mu(\overline{f}f) = \theta_\mu(f)^*\theta_\mu(f)$, so that we obtain the equality of (48.2.14) with $\|\Pi_\omega(B)\Omega_\omega - \theta_\mu(f)\Pi_\omega(A)\Omega_\omega\|^2$, which is small.

From Eq. (48.2.11), we know that in the representation space $\mathcal{H}_\mu$ for the integral representation $\Pi_\mu = \int_{\mathcal{S}}^{\oplus} \Pi_\varphi \, d\mu(\varphi)$, the $D_\mu(f)\Pi_\mu(A_n)\Omega_\mu$ for all $f \in \mathrm{L}^\infty(\mathcal{S}; \mu)$ and all $n \in \mathbb{N}$ form a dense set. Thus $\Pi_\mu(B)\Omega_\mu$, for all $B \in \mathcal{A}$, is also a dense set of vectors, so $\Pi_\mu(\mathcal{A})$ has Ω_μ as cyclic vector. $\qquad \square$

In the case $\mathcal{B} \subset \mathcal{Z}_\omega$, the preceding proof of the Effros theorem sheds light on the approximability of classical observables in the center $\mathcal{Z}_\omega = \Pi_\omega(\mathcal{A})' \cap \Pi_\omega(\mathcal{A})''$, in terms of (represented) quasilocal quantum observables from $\Pi_\omega(\mathcal{A})$, by formulating this fact in the language of direct integrals. If we replace in (48.2.14) B by BC and A_n by C, C being an arbitrary element in $\mathcal{A}$, then we obtain that for a given diagonal operator $D_\mu(f)$ there is a $\Pi_\mu(B)$ which comes arbitrarily near to it in the strong operator topology.

If one calls a component of the total representation space a "superselection sector" (what we do in more general terms in Definition 48.2-19 below), then $\Pi_\mu(B)$ has the same component in each superselection sector, but the c-number components of $D_\mu(f)$ may vary from sector to sector, so that the nearness of the two observables is intuitively not quite evident. We consider the approximability of all diagonal observables $\mathcal{D} \cong L^\infty(\mathcal{S}; \mu)$ by quasilocal quantum observables as one of the most basic insights for *deriving a classical theory* as a limiting case from the quantum mechanical *microscopic theory*, so that it deserved also here the detailed treatment.

Corollary 48.2-14 (Decomposition of GNS Representations). *Consider a unital (not necessarily separable) C*-algebra $\mathcal{A}$ with state space $\mathcal{S}$, and fix $\omega \in \mathcal{S}$. Let be given in the GNS representation of ω, an Abelian von Neumann algebra $\mathcal{B} \subset \Pi_\omega(\mathcal{A})'$ which induces the orthogonal measure $\mu \in \mathfrak{D}_\omega$.*

If μ is standard and satisfies together with a countable family $\{A_n \in \mathcal{A} \mid n \in \mathbb{N}\}$ the Assumption 48.2-11, then μ decomposes the GNS triple so that $\mathcal{B}$ corresponds to the diagonal algebra $\mathcal{D}$. That means that there is a unitary mapping U which intertwines the two GNS realizations

$$(\Pi_\omega, \mathcal{H}_\omega, \Omega_\omega) \xrightarrow{U} \int_{\mathcal{S}}^{\oplus} (\Pi_{\omega'}, \mathcal{H}_{\omega'}, \Omega_{\omega'}) \, d\mu(\omega'), \quad U\mathcal{B}U^{-1} = \mathcal{D}. \tag{48.2.15}$$

Explicitly, $\int_{\mathcal{S}}^{\oplus} \mathcal{H}_{\omega'} \, d\mu(\omega') = U\mathcal{H}_\omega$, $\int_{\mathcal{S}}^{\oplus} \Pi_{\omega'} \, d\mu(\omega') = U\Pi_\omega U^{-1}$, $\int_{\mathcal{S}}^{\oplus} \Omega_{\omega'} \, d\mu(\omega') = U\Omega_\omega$.

Then also $\mathcal{S} \ni \omega' \mapsto \Pi_{\omega'}(\mathcal{A})'' \equiv \mathcal{M}_{\omega'}$ is a μ-measurable family of von Neumann algebras and we have

$$U\mathcal{M}_\omega U^{-1} = \mathcal{M}_\mu \left(= \int_{\mathcal{S}}^{\oplus} \mathcal{M}_{\omega'} \, d\mu(\omega') \right) \quad \Longleftrightarrow \quad \mathcal{B} \subseteq \mathcal{Z}_\omega \left(= \mathcal{M}_\omega \cap \mathcal{M}_\omega' \right).$$
$$\tag{48.2.16}$$

In words: Under the Assumption 48.2-11 each orthogonal measure μ decomposes the GNS triple, but only the subcentral and central measures decompose also the GNS von Neumann algebra $\mathcal{M}_\omega$. (Recall from Proposition 48.1-17 that $\mu \in \mathfrak{D}_\omega$ is denoted to be subcentral if $\mathcal{B} \subset \mathcal{Z}_\omega$, and central if $\mathcal{B} = \mathcal{Z}_\omega$.)

Proof. The first part of the Corollary follows directly from the preceding Proposition, where in the first part of its proof we have also shown that $\mathcal{D}$ corresponds to $\mathcal{B}$.

The second part of the Corollary follows firstly from $\mathcal{S} \ni \omega' \mapsto \Pi_{\omega'}(A_n)$, $n \in \mathbb{N}$, generating the measurable family $\omega' \mapsto \mathcal{M}_{\omega'}$, and secondly from the fact that $\mathcal{M}_\mu$ contains always $\mathcal{D}$ by construction (cf. Eq. (48.2.4)). Since the unitary equivalence between the two representation triples associates $\mathcal{D}$ with $\mathfrak{B}$, the left-hand side of (48.2.16) implies the right-hand side.

If reversely the right-hand side of (48.2.16) is valid and if the construction of $\mathcal{M}_\mu$, viz. (48.2.4), is unitarily mapped, via (48.2.15), into the original GNS Hilbert space, then it produces there not a larger von Neumann algebra than the weak closure of $\Pi_\omega(\mathcal{A})$, that is $\mathcal{M}_\omega$, because the pre-image of $\mathcal{D}$, namely $\mathfrak{B}$, is contained in $\mathcal{M}_\omega$.   □

Let us now demonstrate that the Assumption 48.2-11 is satisfied in the two cases, which are of most concern in the discussions of the treatise.

Proposition 48.2-15 (Two Realizations of the Assumption 48.2-11). *The above Assumption 48.2-11 is satisfied in the following two situations*:

(a) *Let $\mathcal{A}$ be a separable unital C*-algebra and μ any σ-finite Borel measure on the state space $\mathcal{S}$ of $\mathcal{A}$ (which is always standard, $\mathcal{S}$ being Polish). This situation covers all denumerable tensor products of matrix algebras and the CAR-algebra over a separable one-Fermion space.*

(b) *Let $\mathcal{A}$ be a (non-separable) Weyl algebra $\mathcal{W}(E, \sigma)$, where in the pre-symplectic test function (E, σ) space one has introduced a topology τ such that σ is jointly continuous and the completion of E, denoted $\check{E}$, is a Fréchet space. Choose a σ-finite Borel measure μ supported by $\mathcal{F}_\tau$, the folium of τ-continuous states on $\mathcal{W}(E, \sigma)$ (cf. the notions of Sec. 18.2), which is then standard.*

Proof.   (a).   Since $\mathcal{A}$ is separable, there is a denumerable, norm-dense family $\{A_n \in \mathcal{A} \,|\, n \in \mathbb{N}\}$. By this one can show that its state space $\mathcal{S}$ is a complete, metrizable, separable topological space (a Polish space) in the weak* topology so that each Borel measure on the measurable space $(\mathcal{S}, \mathsf{B}(\mathcal{S}))$ is standard. Then for each $\varphi \in \mathcal{S}$ the set $\{\Pi_\varphi(A_n) \,|\, n \in \mathbb{N}\}$ is strongly dense in $\Pi_\varphi(\mathcal{A})$.

(b).   Since $\check{E}$ is a separable topological vector space there is a denumerable dense set $\{f_n \in E \,|\, n \in \mathbb{N}\}$. If $\omega \in \mathcal{F}_\tau$ then not only its GNS representation Π_ω is τ-continuous, but also the whole partially universal representation $\Pi_{\mathcal{F}_\tau} \equiv \Pi_\tau$, to which it is also a normal state. That means that $E \ni f \to \Pi_\tau(W(f))$ is τ-strongly continuous. This implies that a denumerable set of elements $\{A_k \in \mathrm{LH}(W(f_n), n \in \mathbb{N}) \,|\, k \in \mathbb{N}\}$ is strongly dense in $\Pi_\tau(\mathcal{W}(E, \sigma))$, and thus in $\Pi_\tau(\mathcal{W}(E, \sigma))''$. (To get a norm dense set in $\mathcal{W}(E, \sigma)$ in terms of Weyl elements, we would need all of the uncountable set $\mathrm{LH}\{W(f), f \in E\}$.)

Because of $\operatorname{supp}(\mu) \subset \mathcal{F}_\tau$ we deal with the weak*-topology on $\mathcal{S}$ restricted to $\mathcal{F}_\tau$. We may use the introduced denumerable set $\{A_k \,|\, k \in \mathbb{N}\}$ to construct a denumerable set of neighborhoods, indexed by the finite sets $\{k_1, \ldots, k_n\} \subset \mathbb{N}$, of the form

$$\mathcal{U}(\omega; A_{k_1}, \ldots, A_{k_n}, \varepsilon) = \{\varphi \in \mathcal{F}_\tau \mid |\langle \omega; A_{k_i} \rangle - \langle \varphi; A_{k_i} \rangle| < \varepsilon, \; i = 1, 2, \ldots, n\}$$
$$= \{\varphi \in \mathcal{F}_\tau \mid |(\Omega_\omega | \Pi_\tau(A_{k_i}) \Omega_\omega) - (\Omega_\varphi | \Pi_\tau(A_{k_i}) \Omega_\varphi)| < \varepsilon, \; i = 1, 2, \ldots, n\}.$$

Since all weak* neighborhoods in $\mathcal{F}_\tau$ are expressible in terms of the $\Pi_\tau(A)$-expectations, the given family is sufficient to constitute a neighborhood base for each $\omega \in \mathcal{F}_\tau$. Thus the weak*-topology restricted to $\mathcal{F}_\tau$ is metrizable and the Borel measures on $\mathcal{F}_\tau$ are standard. Altogether the Assumption 48.2-11 is also fulfilled in this case. □

The Assumption 48.2-11 is almost necessary to reach the conclusions of the Corollary 48.2-14, since the decomposition measure μ employed there must in fact be standard (on its support), and the μ-measurability of $\omega' \mapsto \mathcal{M}_{\omega'}$ requires, according to Definition 48.2-6, a sequence $n \mapsto M_n$ of operator families $M_n = [\omega' \mapsto M_n(\omega') \in \mathcal{M}_{\omega'}]$, which is only specialized in the Assumption 48.2-11 to the form $M_n = [\omega' \mapsto \Pi_{\omega'}(A_n)]$. Just the latter version has been proved constructively useful in both main applications of the Assumption 48.2-11 in Proposition 48.2-15.

Nevertheless, it is advantageous for a general investigation to postulate simply the complete Conclusions of Corollary 48.2-14, including the decomposability of the representation von Neumann algebra, which restricts the setup to a subcentral decomposition measure for the given state ω. Since a subcentral measure is a coarsening of the central measure μ_ω, we need to impose the following conditions only on the central decomposition of a state.

Definition 48.2-16 (Spatially Decomposable States). A state $\omega \in \mathcal{S}(\mathcal{A})$ of a C^*-algebra $\mathcal{A}$ is called *spatially decomposable* if its central measure μ_ω is standard, on its supporting set $\mathcal{T}_\omega \subset \mathcal{S}$, metrizable in the induced weak*-topology, and if in the sense of a unitary equivalence, as in (48.2.15) and (48.2.16), we have

$$(\Pi_\omega, \mathcal{H}_\omega, \Omega_\omega) \overset{U}{=} \int_{\mathcal{T}_\omega}^\oplus (\Pi_\varphi, \mathcal{H}_\varphi, \Omega_\varphi) d\mu_\omega(\varphi) \quad \text{implying} \quad \mathcal{M}_\omega \overset{U}{=} \int_{\mathcal{T}_\omega}^\oplus \mathcal{M}_\varphi \, d\mu_\omega(\varphi).$$
$$(48.2.17)$$

(Recall that the Hilbert spaces appearing in the decomposition are by the definition of the direct integral necessarily separable.) We denote by $\mathcal{F}_s = \mathcal{F}_s(\mathcal{A})$ the set of all spatially decomposable states.

We indicate the concrete meaning of $\omega \in \mathcal{F}_s$ henceforth by writing down the decomposition of the quadruple $(\Pi_\omega, \mathcal{H}_\omega, \Omega_\omega, \mathcal{M}_\omega)$ as in Eq. (48.2.17).

Proposition 48.2-17 (The Folium of Spatially Decomposable States). *Let $\mathcal{A}$ be a unital C^*-algebra. We consider a state $\omega \in \mathcal{F}_s \subset \mathcal{S}(\mathcal{A})$, with standard central measure μ_ω on its support $\mathcal{T}_\omega$, that means we know*

$$(\Pi_\omega, \mathcal{H}_\omega, \Omega_\omega, \mathcal{M}_\omega) \overset{U}{=} \int_{\mathcal{T}_\omega}^\oplus (\Pi_\varphi, \mathcal{H}_\varphi, \Omega_\varphi, \mathcal{M}_\varphi) \, d\mu_\omega(\varphi). \qquad (48.2.18)$$

(a) *Then for all $\psi \in \mathcal{F}_\omega$, we have a decomposition as follows: There are scaled states $\psi(\varphi) \in \mathcal{M}_{\varphi*+}$, $\varphi \in \mathcal{T}_\omega$, so that there exists the common disintegration*

$$\psi = \int_{\mathcal{T}_\omega} \psi(\varphi)\, d\mu_\omega(\varphi) = \int_{\mathcal{T}_\omega} \psi_\varphi\, d\mu_\psi(\varphi) = \int_{\mathcal{T}_\psi} \psi_\varphi\, d\mu_\psi(\varphi) , \qquad (48.2.19)$$

where the last integral coincides with the central decomposition of ψ, expressed in terms of $\psi_\varphi := \psi(\varphi)/\|\psi(\varphi)\|$ and $d\mu_\psi(\varphi) := \|\psi(\varphi)\|\, d\mu_\omega(\varphi)$. μ_ψ is a standard probability measure on $\mathcal{T}_\omega$ and satisfies

$$\frac{d\mu_\psi}{d\mu_\omega}(\varphi) = \|\psi(\varphi)\| , \quad \text{for } \mu_\omega\text{-a.a. } \varphi \in \mathcal{T}_\omega . \qquad (48.2.20)$$

We have also introduced the set

$$\mathcal{T}_\psi := \{\varphi \in \mathcal{T}_\omega \mid \|\psi(\varphi)\| > 0\} , \qquad (48.2.21)$$

which is measurable since the function $\|\psi(.)\|$ is so (see remark preceding Theorem 48.2-10), and which is a supporting set where the normalized ψ_φ are defined.

(b) *We deduce that for arbitrary $\omega \in \mathcal{F}_s$, it holds $\mathcal{F}_\omega \subset \mathcal{F}_s$ and that $\mathcal{F}_s$ is a folium.*

Proof.   The $\psi(\varphi)$ arise from Proposition 48.2-10.

We associate with the factor states ψ_φ the GNS quantities $(\tilde{\Pi}_\varphi, \tilde{\mathcal{H}}_\varphi, \tilde{\Omega}_\varphi, \tilde{\mathcal{M}}_\varphi)$. The sequence $\varphi \mapsto M_n(\varphi)$, $n \in \mathbb{N}$, for defining the measurable family $\varphi \mapsto \mathcal{M}_\varphi$ in the decomposition of $\mathcal{M}_\omega$ is modified to $\varphi \mapsto \tilde{C}_\varphi M_n(\varphi)$, $n \in \mathbb{N}$, where $\tilde{C}_\varphi \in \mathcal{M}_\varphi$ is the central support of ψ_φ. But $\tilde{C}_\varphi \mathcal{M}_\varphi$ is W*-isomorphic to $\tilde{\mathcal{M}}_\varphi$ and this isomorphism transforms $\tilde{C}_\varphi M_n(\varphi)$ into $\tilde{M}_n(\varphi)$, say.

The sequence $\tilde{M}_n(\varphi)$, $n \in \mathbb{N}$, may be applied to the $\tilde{\Omega}_\varphi$ to get the sequence of fundamental vector fields for integrating the $\tilde{\mathcal{H}}_\varphi$ and serves also to integrate the $\tilde{\mathcal{M}}_\varphi$ by the measure μ_ψ. We get then the existence of $\int_{\mathcal{T}_\omega}^{\oplus}(\tilde{\Pi}_\varphi, \tilde{\mathcal{H}}_\varphi, \tilde{\Omega}_\varphi, \tilde{\mathcal{M}}_\varphi)\, d\mu_\psi(\varphi)$. These integrated quantities form a decomposition of ψ via vector states connected with a direct integral of representations. The von Neumann algebra of the representation arises in the form of a central decomposition. This shows that $\mu_\psi \in \mathcal{D}_\psi$. According to the generalized Effros Theorem 48.2-13, this integral representation is cyclic. Thus the quadruple of integrated quantities is unitary equivalent to the GNS quadruple $(\Pi_\psi, \mathcal{H}_\psi, \Omega_\psi, \mathcal{M}_\psi)$, which signifies $\psi \in \mathcal{F}_s$. Thus $\mathcal{F}_\omega \subset \mathcal{F}_s$ for all $\omega \in \mathcal{F}_s$.

Given $\omega_1, \omega_2 \in \mathcal{F}_s$ with $\mathcal{F}_{\omega_1} \cap \mathcal{F}_{\omega_2} = \emptyset$ then any convex combination $\omega = \lambda_1 \omega_1 + \lambda_2 \omega_2$ has the central measure $\lambda_1 \mu_{\omega_1} + \lambda_2 \mu_{\omega_2}$, and (48.2.18) splits accordingly, yielding $\omega \in \mathcal{F}_s$. If reversely $\omega = \lambda_1 \omega_1 + \lambda_2 \omega_2 \in \mathcal{F}_s$, then it is in $\mathcal{F}_\omega \subset \mathcal{F}_s$ and the component states ω_1, ω_2 are so also, $\mathcal{F}_\omega$ being a face.

If finally $\omega_1, \omega_2 \in \mathcal{F}_s$ with $\mathcal{F}_{\omega_1} \cap \mathcal{F}_{\omega_2} \neq \emptyset$, then we form again $\omega = \lambda_1 \omega_1 + \lambda_2 \omega_2$ and have for the central supports $C_\omega = C_1 \vee C_2 = C_1 \oplus (C_2 - C_1 C_2)$. Thus we may write $\omega = \lambda_1 \omega_1 + \lambda_2' \omega_2' + \lambda_2'' \omega_2''$, where for example, $\langle \omega_2'; A \rangle =$

$\langle \omega_2; C_1 C_2 A \rangle / \langle \omega_2; C_1 C_2 \rangle$, if defined, and so on. Therefore ω may be written as a convex combination of two mutually disjoint states in $\mathcal{F}_s$ and is also in $\mathcal{F}_s$. Thus we know that $\mathcal{F}_s$ is a face, which is invariant under perturbations by elements of $\mathcal{A}$.

To demonstrate the norm closedness we need for this metric topology only to choose a sequence (and not a net) $(\omega_i)_\mathbb{N} \subseteq \mathcal{F}_s$ converging in norm to $\omega \in \mathcal{S}$. Let us also choose a sequence $(\lambda_i \in [0,1])_\mathbb{N}$ with $\sum_{i=1}^\infty \lambda_i = 1$ and form $\hat{\omega} := \sum_{i=1}^\infty \lambda_i \omega_i$. If all $\omega_i \in \mathcal{F}_{\omega_1}$, then also $\omega \in \mathcal{F}_{\omega_1}$ and we know $\hat{\omega} \in \mathcal{F}_s$. Otherwise we iterate the procedure of the preceding paragraph and split the sum into partial sums, which all are in different folia. Thus we may assume that all ω_i are mutually disjoint. In this case we know $\mu_{\hat{\omega}} = \sum_{i=1}^\infty \lambda_i \mu_{\omega_i}$ and $\hat{\omega} \in \mathcal{F}_s$. Then $\mathcal{F}_{\hat{\omega}} \subset \mathcal{F}_s$ and thus all $\omega_i \in \mathcal{F}_{\hat{\omega}}$. Since $\mathcal{F}_{\hat{\omega}}$ is norm-closed also $\omega \in \mathcal{F}_{\hat{\omega}} \subset \mathcal{F}_s$.   □

We may now express Proposition 48.2-15(b) in a concise manner.

Corollary 48.2-18. *Assume a Weyl algebra $\mathcal{W}(E,\sigma)$, with E a separable topological vector space in a topology τ, under which the pre-symplectic form σ is jointly continuous (true for our photon setup). Then*

$$\mathcal{F}_\tau \subset \mathcal{F}_s, \qquad\qquad (48.2.22)$$

that is, all τ-continuous states, characterized by a τ-continuous characteristic function, are spatially decomposable.

Let us recall, by the way, that besides the LC-topology, the discrete topology in E is also of importance, namely to exhibit basic algebraic features of the Weyl algebra $\mathcal{W}(E,\sigma)$.

48.2.4. *Superselection Sectors and Rules*

The (spatial) decomposition theory of state folia, which we have shown for Boson states to be connected with some mathematical fine points, is basic for a concise definition of superselection sectors and for the corresponding classical observables. We give only a short account of the basic notions arising in Physics.

Definition 48.2-19 (Superselection Sectors of State Folia). Let $\mathcal{A}$ be a unital (not necessarily separable) C*-algebra with state space $\mathcal{S}$ and with the folium of spatially decomposable states $\mathcal{F}_s$. If $\omega \in \mathcal{F}_s$, with central measure μ_ω (standard on its support T_ω), then we make for all $\psi \in \mathcal{F}_\omega$ visible that their central decompositions (48.2.19) lead to spatial decompositions by writing it as direct integrals

$$\psi = \int_{T_\omega}^\oplus \psi(\varphi)\, d\mu_\omega(\varphi) = \int_{T_\omega}^\oplus \psi_\varphi\, d\mu_\psi(\varphi), \qquad (48.2.23)$$

where in the second version appear as component states the (normalized) normal factor states on the GNS von Neumann algebras $\mathcal{M}_\varphi$ (cf. also [Tak79] for the direct integral notation of state decompositions). But the normal-state spaces of the $\mathcal{M}_\varphi$ are in the norm topology affine homeomorphic to the folia $\mathcal{F}_\varphi$. It is therefore justified to write

$$\mathcal{F}_s \supset \mathcal{F}_\omega = \int_{\mathcal{T}_\omega}^{\oplus} \mathcal{F}_\varphi \, d\mu_\omega(\varphi) \, . \tag{48.2.24}$$

Let us call the $\mathcal{F}_\varphi$, $\varphi \in \mathcal{T}_\omega$, the *superselection sectors* of $\mathcal{F}_\omega$, or the *component folia* of $\mathcal{F}_\omega$. In general, the $\mathcal{F}_\varphi$, $\varphi \in \mathcal{T}_\omega$, are no subfolia of $\mathcal{F}_\omega$, but they are mutually disjoint subfolia of $\mathcal{F}_s$.

The $\psi_\varphi \in \mathcal{F}_\varphi$, which are only defined for μ_ψ–a.a. factor states φ, are termed by us the *sector components* of $\psi \in \mathcal{F}_\omega$.

The fact, that a state (folium) decomposes non-trivially into superselection sectors, is commonly considered as the outflow of *superselection rules*.

The sector components ψ_φ describe the result of the finest filtering of $\psi \in \mathcal{F}_\omega$ which may be achieved by means of classical preparation methods. "Classical" does not mean here, that the preparation uses classical devices (what is always the case), but that the preparation is compatible with all other methods for actualizing the observables in $\Pi_\omega(\mathcal{A})$, even compatible with those in $\Pi_\omega(\mathcal{A})'' = \mathcal{M}_\omega$.

We have already mentioned that there are two classes of *superselection rules*: absolute ones, valid in the microscopic and macroscopic regime, and macroscopic ones, due to macroscopically many degrees of freedom. While the mathematical decomposition theory is the same for both cases, their physical meaning is principally different.

Even the absolute superposition rules have been investigated rather belatedly. The usual reference is [WWW52], where the parity of elementary particles is claimed a superselection rule (in the absolute sense). Only then the general pre-assumption of traditional Hilbert space quantum theory seems to have been fully realized and formulated as the "unrestricted superposition principle", which implicitly Dirac has claimed universal in his foundation of quantum mechanics [Dir30]. Because of the great authority of Dirac, most investigations on the interpretation of quantum mechanics cling still today on unrestricted superposition and run into the known difficulties.

In a theory with different particles, that principle is no longer valid, and one could therefore introduce central observables like parity, electric charge, hyper charge, and so on. In cosmic ray collision processes, the production of particles goes by probability, and mixtures over different superselection sectors are certainly appropriate.

The macroscopic superselection rules are typified by diagonalizing the *observables at infinity* for quasilocal observable algebras. Obviously a living and dead cat is in states, which differ from each other in macroscopically many degrees of freedom, and thus belong to different superselection sectors. We think it unfounded, and even meaningless, to locate them in different "worlds". Rather the discussions in the present treatise illustrate that macroscopic superselection rules are indispensable to recognize and to describe the world in which we live. So we advocate the systematic use also of the macroscopic superselection rules, arising theoretically in the algebraic formulation of quantum theory in a natural manner.

The superselection rules are best understandable in the folium $\mathcal{F}_s$ of spatially decomposable states. If $\omega \in \mathcal{F}_s$, then the corresponding folium $\mathcal{F}_\omega$ is also contained in $\mathcal{F}_s$. Many relations for the mesoscopic states $\psi \in \mathcal{F}_\omega$ are expressed in terms of their sector components ψ_φ, $\varphi \in \mathcal{T}_\psi$. ($\mathcal{T}_\psi$ is the support of the central measure μ_ψ, see (48.2.21).) Thus it is important to construct physically meaningful parametrizations of $\mathcal{T}_\psi$, and of the possibly larger set $\mathcal{T}_\omega$. One important method to achieve this is by means of ergodic decompositions related to symmetry groups (cf. especially the remarks following Proposition 48.3-27 on page 1833 on unbroken symmetries). That is, by the way, equally important for the superselection sectors of microscopic particle states. These parametrizations of the sectors are, of course, basic for introducing numerical scales for the superselection observables. For having a good measurement instrument, the different pointer positions on their scales should correspond to different superselection sectors of the macroscopic measurement system.

48.3.   Ergodic Averages

We deal with group averages in a rather explicit manner, using limits of convex combinations over the group, in order to point out the connections between general algebraic ergodic theory and the equi-distributed summations and integrations on the group, mostly used in physics (also in our main text). Also the direct limits along the group elements, like going to infinity in space or time, are covered by this approach.

48.3.1.   *Invariant Quantities and Automorphism Groups*

We consider in the following a general setup, important for discussing symmetries and dynamics of physical systems.

Definition 48.3-1 (Invariant Quantities of Automorphism Groups). Let $\mathcal{A}$ be a unital C*-algebra and G a group. In the following we assume that G acts *-homomorphically via automorphisms α_g, $g \in G$, in $\mathcal{A}$, what we denote by $(\mathcal{A}, \alpha_G)$. (We set for short $\alpha_G := \{\alpha_g \,|\, g \in G\}$, and similarly for other functions on G).

(a) The set of all G-invariant states $\omega \in \mathcal{S} \equiv \mathcal{S}(\mathcal{A})$ is denoted by $\mathcal{S}^G$. That is, $\omega \in \mathcal{S}^G$ if and only if

$$\omega = \omega \circ \alpha_g \equiv \alpha_g^*(\omega) =: \nu_g^{-1}(\omega), \quad \forall g \in G, \tag{48.3.1}$$

where on the right-hand side the group transformations in the Schrödinger picture are introduced homomorphically in the present chapter.

$\mathcal{S}^G$ is clearly convex and closed under weak* limits, hence weak* compact.

(b) A G-invariant state ω in the extreme boundary $\partial_e \mathcal{S}^G$ of $\mathcal{S}^G$ is called ergodic. ($\partial_e \mathcal{S}^G \neq \emptyset$ by the Krein–Milman Theorem 48.1-8 on page 1783, provided the compact convex $\mathcal{S}^G$ is non-empty.)

(c) For $\omega \in \mathcal{S}^G$ with $(\Pi_\omega, \mathcal{H}_\omega, \Omega_\omega)$ its GNS-triple, we denote the unique unitaries, implementing α_g in $\mathcal{H}_\omega$ and leaving Ω_ω invariant, by $U_\omega(g)$.
(Recall that by definition $U_\omega(g)\Pi_\omega(A)\Omega_\omega = \Pi_\omega(\alpha_g(A))\Omega_\omega$, $A \in \mathcal{A}$, and one has the unitary implementation of the α_g: $\Pi_\omega(\alpha_g(A)) = U_\omega(g)\Pi_\omega(A)U_\omega^*(g)$ for all $g \in G$ and all $A \in \mathcal{A}$.)

(d) For $\omega \in \mathcal{S}^G$, we denote the closed G-invariant subspace $\{\psi \in \mathcal{H}_\omega \mid U_\omega(g)\psi = \psi, \forall g \in G\}$ by $\mathcal{H}_\omega^G$, and the projection onto $\mathcal{H}_\omega^G$ by P_ω^G. (Especially $\Omega_\omega \in \mathcal{H}_\omega^G$.)

(e) We denote the automorphisms, which extend α_g to act on elements $M \in \mathcal{M}_\omega$, $\omega \in \mathcal{S}^G$, via $U_\omega(g)MU_\omega^*(g)$, $g \in G$, by α_g^e, but drop mostly the superscript e, if no confusion may arise.

(f) The set of all α_g^e-invariant elements in $\mathcal{M}_\omega$ is denoted by $\mathcal{M}_\omega^G$ and the invariant part of the center $\mathcal{Z}_\omega$ of $\mathcal{M}_\omega$ is denoted by $\mathcal{Z}_\omega^G$.

(g) Let $G \ni g \mapsto F_g$ be a function on G with values in a linear space. Then we denote the set of convex combinations by

$$\mathrm{Conv}(F_G) := \left\{ \sum_{m=1}^k \lambda_m F_{g_m} \,\Big|\, g_m \in G, \lambda_m \geq 0, \sum_{m=1}^k \lambda_m = 1, k \in \mathbb{N} \right\}. \quad (48.3.2)$$

Some peculiarities of ergodic states will be elucidated by the following considerations.

Proposition 48.3-2 (Ergodicity Conditions). *Let be given the group of automorphisms $(\mathcal{A}, \alpha_G)$, together with an $\omega \in \mathcal{S}^G$, and consider the subsequent four conditions.*

(i) ω *is ergodic.*
(ii) $\{\Pi_\omega(\mathcal{A}) \cup U_\omega(G)\}' = \mathbb{C}\mathbb{1}_\omega$.
(iii) $\dim(\mathcal{H}_\omega^G) = 1$.
(iv) $P_\omega^G = |\Omega_\omega)(\Omega_\omega|$.

Then (i)⇔(ii)⇐(iii)⇔(iv), whereas (ii)⇒(iii) in general is false.

Proof. (i)⇒(ii). Choose $B \in \{\Pi_\omega(\mathcal{A}) \cup U_\omega(G)\}'$, $0 < B < \mathbb{1}_\omega$. Form the positive linear functional $\mathcal{A} \ni A \mapsto (\Omega_\omega|B\Pi_\omega(A)\Omega_\omega)$, which is dominated by ω (i.e., smaller than $\lambda\omega$ for a $\lambda > 0$) and G-invariant. As an extremal invariant state ω dominates only positive G-invariant functionals, which are multiples of itself. Hence $B \in \mathbb{C}\mathbb{1}_\omega$.

(ii)⇒(i). If ω is not ergodic, it dominates a functional $\omega' \in \mathcal{S}^G$, which is not a multiple of itself. By the Riesz representation theorem there is a bounded, positive $B \in \mathcal{L}(\mathcal{H}_\omega)$ such that $\langle \omega'; A \rangle = (\Omega_\omega|B\Pi_\omega(A)\Omega_\omega)$, $A \in \mathcal{A}$. B can be shown to be in $\{\Pi_\omega(\mathcal{A}) \cup U_\omega(G)\}'$ and must then be a scalar by condition (ii). If ω' is normalized, it must then be equal to ω, and we have to conclude that ω is extremal invariant, in contradiction to our assumption.

(iii)$\Rightarrow$(ii). If B is in $\{\Pi_\omega(\mathcal{A}) \cup U_\omega(G)\}'$, then $U_\omega(g)B\Omega_\omega = B\Omega_\omega$. Thus $B\Omega_\omega = \lambda\Omega_\omega$ for some $\lambda \in \mathbb{C}$. This leads to $B\Pi_\omega(A)\Omega_\omega = \Pi_\omega(A)B\Omega_\omega = \lambda\Pi_\omega(A)\Omega_\omega$ for all $A \in \mathcal{A}$, and implies $B = \lambda\mathbb{1}_\omega$ by the cyclicity of Ω_ω.

(iii)$\Leftrightarrow$(iv) is evident.

(ii) does not imply (iii). We give a counterexample in Sec. 31.3 on page 906 treating Bosons in a finite cavity at $\beta = \infty$, for which the one-particle Hamiltonian owns an eigenvector with eigenvalue zero. $\qquad\square$

The connection with the classical theory of ergodic states becomes more transparent if for the automorphism group $(\mathcal{A}, \alpha_G)$ certain conditions for an averaging procedure over G are satisfied, which often are tied to continuity conditions. The most popular continuity condition for automorphism groups is the point-wise norm continuity, which leads to the notion of a C^*-*dynamical system.*

Definition 48.3-3 (C*-Dynamical Systems).   For the unital C*-algebra $\mathcal{A}$, let be given the automorphism group $(\mathcal{A}, \alpha_G)$, where G is a locally compact topological group.

If the function $G \ni g \mapsto \alpha_g(A)$ is norm-continuous for all $A \in \mathcal{A}$, then one says that the triple $(\mathcal{A}, \alpha, G)$ constitutes a C^*-*dynamical system.*

In the following the symbol $(\mathcal{A}, \alpha, G)$ implies local compactness of G and denotes $(\mathcal{A}, \alpha_G)$ plus point-wise norm continuity.

Proposition 48.3-4. *Let $\mathcal{A}$ be a unital C^*-algebra and $\mathcal{S} \equiv \mathcal{S}(\mathcal{A})$ its state space. Let be given the automorphism group $(\mathcal{A}, \alpha_G)$, where G is a locally compact group.*

(a) *If the function $G \ni g \mapsto \alpha_g(A)$ is weakly continuous, i.e., if $G \ni g \mapsto \langle\omega; \alpha_g(A)\rangle$ is continuous for all $\omega \in \mathcal{S}$ and for all $A \in \mathcal{A}$, then this is equivalent to the norm-continuity of $G \ni g \mapsto \alpha_g(A)$ for all $A \in \mathcal{A}$, so that in this case $(\mathcal{A}, \alpha_G)$ constitutes a C^*-dynamical system $(\mathcal{A}, \alpha, G)$.*

(b) *If $(\mathcal{A}, \alpha, G)$ is a C^*-dynamical system, then the transformations in the Schrödinger picture $G \ni g \mapsto \nu_g(\omega) \equiv \alpha_g^{-1*}(\omega)$ are in general not continuous in the norm of $\mathcal{A}^*$.*

The point-wise norm continuity in the notion of a C*-dynamical system is, however, too strong an assumption in many applications. Especially for quasi-free automorphism groups in a C*-Weyl algebra it is never satisfied, because of the norm jump (see Lemma 18.1-6 on page 398). We consider therefore a suitable weakening of the continuity for the automorphic group actions, given in terms of its implementing unitaries.

Lemma 48.3-5 (Continuity of the Unitary Implementation).   *Let be given a group of automorphisms $(\mathcal{A}, \alpha_G)$ for a locally compact group G and let $\omega \in \mathcal{S}^G$.*

Then $G \ni g \mapsto U_\omega(g)$ (*of Definition 48.3-1* (c)) *is strongly continuous* (*in the sense of Hilbert space operators*)*, if* $G \ni g \mapsto \langle \omega; A^* \alpha_g(A) \rangle$ *is continuous for all* A *from a norm-dense subset of* $\mathcal{A}$.

Especially, the preceding assertion implies the continuity of $g \mapsto U_\omega(g)$ *for invariant states* ω *of any* C^*-*dynamical system.*

This implies that $G \ni g \mapsto \alpha_g(A)$ *is* σ-*weakly continuous, if extended* (*by the unitary implementation*) *to transformations in* $\mathcal{M}_\omega$. (*That amounts to* $G \ni g \mapsto \langle \varphi; \alpha_g(A) \rangle$ *being continuous, for all* $\varphi \in \mathcal{F}_\omega$ *and all* $A \in \mathcal{M}_\omega$.) *The triple* $(\mathcal{M}_\omega, \alpha, G)$ *constitutes then a* W*-*dynamical system* (*see Definition 46.2-1*).

Proof. If e denotes the unit of G, we have

$$\lim_{g \to e} \|(U_\omega(g) - U_\omega(e))\Pi_\omega(A)\Omega_\omega\|^2$$
$$= 2\langle \omega; A^* A \rangle - \lim_{g \to e} \langle \omega; \alpha_g(A^*)A \rangle - \lim_{g \to e} \langle \omega; A^* \alpha_g(A) \rangle = 0 \,.$$

This gives strong continuity on a dense domain in the GNS–Hilbert space $\mathcal{H}_\omega$, which may be extended to all of $\mathcal{H}_\omega$ by an $\varepsilon/3$-argument.

For the further implication study for all $\Omega \in \mathcal{H}_\omega$

$$|(\Omega|[U_\omega(g)\Pi_\omega(A)U_\omega^*(g) - \Pi_\omega(A)]\Omega)|$$
$$= |(\Omega|[U_\omega(g)\Pi_\omega(A) - \Pi_\omega(A)]U_\omega^*(g)\Omega) + (\Omega|[\Pi_\omega(A)U_\omega^*(g) - \Pi_\omega(A)]\Omega)|$$
$$\leq 2\|[U_\omega(g^{-1}) - U_\omega(e)]\Omega\| \, \|A\| \, \|\Omega\| \,,$$

which tends to 0 for $g \to e$. The (finite) convex sums of the $|\Omega)(\Omega|$, $\Omega \in \mathcal{H}_\omega$, provide a norm-dense set of states in the folium $\mathcal{F}_\omega$. Thus we get the assertion by an $\varepsilon/3$-argument. $\qquad\square$

48.3.2. *Group Averages*

Let now be given $(\mathcal{A}, \alpha_G)$ together with an $\omega \in \mathcal{S}^G$. A group *average* $m_G(A)$ of an $A \in \mathcal{A}$ (or $A \in \mathcal{M}_\omega$) is a certain average over the α_G-transforms of A. The simplest form would be a net limit of sums of the type

$$\frac{1}{k} \sum_{m=1}^{k} \alpha_{g_m}(A) \in \mathrm{Conv}(\alpha_G(A)), \quad \text{for some } k \in \mathbb{N} \text{ and } g_1, \ldots, g_k \in G. \quad (48.3.3)$$

That is, we ask for the existence of limits of the following shape

$$m_G(A) = \lim_{i \in I} \frac{1}{k_i} \sum_{m=1}^{k_i} \alpha_{g_m^i}(A), \quad g_m^i \in G, \quad k_i \in \mathbb{N}, \quad (48.3.4)$$

converging with respect to some suitable operator topology. Of course, the choice of $I \ni i \mapsto k_i \in \mathbb{N}$ and of the $g_m^i \in G$ determines the specific net under consideration. (Especially, (48.3.4) includes the case $k_i = 1$ for all $i \in I$.)

If now some of the g_m^i are equal to each other, we obtain a weighted average. In fact, the set of the special convex combinations in (48.3.3) is norm-dense in

$\mathrm{Conv}(\alpha_G(A))$. To see this, approximate the $\lambda_n > 0$ with $\sum_n \lambda_n = 1$ in a convex combination

$$C(\alpha)(A) := \sum_{n=1}^{l} \lambda_n \, \alpha_{g_n}(A) = \lim_{k \to \infty} \sum_{n=1}^{l} r_n^k \, \alpha_{g_n}(A) \qquad (48.3.5)$$

$$\underbrace{\qquad\qquad\qquad}_{\text{of type (48.3.3)}}$$

by rationals r_n^k, $k \in \mathbb{N}$, form the main denominator of the r_n^k, and replace the nominators by iterated sums of the same summands. We abbreviate occasionally α_G by α. Hence, any G-average, defined by some limit

$$m_G(A) := \lim_{i \in I} C_i(\alpha)(A) = \lim_{i \in I} \sum_{n=1}^{l_i} \lambda_n^i \, \alpha_{g_n^i}(A), \qquad A \in \mathcal{A}, \qquad (48.3.6)$$

may be obtained by limits of equi-distributed sums Eq. (48.3.4).

If, for example, G denotes the group of finite permutations $\mathbb{P}$ of $\mathbb{N}$ and acts via automorphisms in a product algebra $\mathcal{A}$, constituting $(\mathcal{A}, \alpha_{\mathbb{P}})$, then we have introduced the limiting mean fields by certain weak limits of equi-distributional averages over $\mathbb{P}$, and we remark now that weighted averages in these limits would provide us with no surplus of averages. (A surplus of averages would have provided us with a surplus of classical observables, in view of the asymptotic Abelianess of $(\mathcal{A}, \alpha_{\mathbb{P}})$, according to Sec. 48.3.4.)

A special G-average would be the *direct limit* $\lim_{i \in I} \alpha_{g^i}(A)$, with only one element in the convex combinations (producing e.g., "observables at infinity," as they occur via the space translation group in quasilocal algebras).

In any case, we have $m_G(A) \geq 0$ for $A \geq 0$, and $m_G(\mathbb{1}) = \mathbb{1}$, where we assume that $\mathcal{A}$ is unital. From this and from linearity, we deduce that by defining $\langle m_G^*(\omega); A \rangle := \langle \omega; m_G(A) \rangle$ we obtain a G-averaged state $m_G^*(\omega) \in \mathcal{S}(\mathcal{A}) \equiv \mathcal{S}$.

This setup may be generalized on the side of the states, by choosing a G-invariant folium $\mathcal{F} \subset \mathcal{S}$, i.e., $\alpha_g^*(\mathcal{F}) = \mathcal{F}$, $\forall g \in G$. The dual $\mathrm{LH}(\mathcal{F})^*$ may be identified with the von Neumann algebra $\mathcal{M}_\mathcal{F}$, and is the natural set of observables for the restricted state space $\mathcal{F}$. Then α_g is $\sigma(\mathcal{M}_\mathcal{F}, \mathcal{F})$-continuously extensible to $\alpha_g^\mathcal{F} \in {}^*\text{-aut}(\mathcal{M}_\mathcal{F})$ by means of sandwiching with the unitaries $U_\mathcal{F}(g)$, acting in the partially universal representation space $\mathcal{H}_\mathcal{F}$.

We have then two cases of interest. First assume that we can show the existence of

$$m_G(A) = \sigma(\mathcal{A}, \mathcal{F})\text{-}\lim_{i \in I} C_i(\alpha)(A), \qquad \forall A \in \mathcal{A}. \qquad (48.3.7)$$

(This amounts to $\lim_{i \in I} \langle \omega; C_i(\alpha)(A) \rangle$ converging for all $\omega \in \mathcal{F}$ and all $A \in \mathcal{A}$.)

For two states $\omega, \varphi \in \mathcal{F}$ we have $|\langle \omega - \varphi; m_G(A) \rangle| = |\lim_{i \in I} \langle \omega - \varphi; C_i(\alpha)(A) \rangle| \leq \|\omega - \varphi\| \|A\|$. Thus $m_G(A)$ acts norm-continuously on $\mathcal{F}$ and is in $\mathcal{M}_\mathcal{F}$. (Only if $\langle \omega; m_G(A) \rangle$ is defined for all $\omega \in \mathcal{S}$ and depends weak*-continuously on ω, then $m_G(A) \in \mathcal{A}$.) For $\omega \in \mathcal{F}$ the state average $m_G^*(\omega) \in \mathcal{S}$ is, however, in general not in $\mathcal{F}$.

Second, assume that we can show the existence of the limit

$$m_G(M) = \sigma(\mathcal{M}_{\mathcal{F}}, \mathcal{F})-\lim_{i \in I} C_i(\alpha)(M), \quad \forall M \in \mathcal{M}_{\mathcal{F}}, \qquad (48.3.8)$$

(also called "weak*" or "σ-weak limit"). Then again $m_G(M)$ is in $\mathcal{M}_{\mathcal{F}}$. But Eq. (48.3.8) is equivalent to the dual limit $\lim_{i \in I} C_i(\alpha^*)(\omega)$ converging in norm for all $\omega \in \mathcal{F}$. Since $\mathcal{F}$ is closed under convex combinations and norm limits, we know then that $m_G^*(\omega) \in \mathcal{F}$, for $\omega \in \mathcal{F}$.

A hint for the existence of certain σ-weak converging G-averages is the following: Since $\{C_i(\alpha)(M) \,|\, i \in I\}$ is bounded by $\|M\|$, and since the unit ball in $\mathcal{M}_{\mathcal{F}}$ is σ-weak compact, the given net has a σ-weak converging subnet. The subnet depends in general on M, but we shall find cases, where its limit may be translated into a linear map (preserving positivity and the unit anyway).

The most frequent examples for invariant folia are $\mathcal{F} = \mathcal{S}$ the whole state space, and $\mathcal{F} = \mathcal{F}_\omega$ for $\omega \in \mathcal{S}^G$. Recall that in the first example $\mathcal{M}_{\mathcal{F}}$ is Banach space-isomorphic to $\mathcal{A}^{**}$ and in the second example $\mathcal{M}_{\mathcal{F}}$ is W*-isomorphic to the GNS von Neumann algebra $\mathcal{M}_\omega$.

We concentrate on the second example, substituting the symbol "$\mathcal{F}_\omega$" by "ω" when using it as index. Modifications therefrom to other invariant folia are mostly obvious and are discussed at the pertinent places.

Definition 48.3-6 (Invariant G-Averages). Let $(\mathcal{A}, \alpha_G)$ be an automorphism group, and $\omega \in \mathcal{S}^G$ a G-invariant state. The extension of α_G to $\mathcal{M}_\omega$ is denoted by α_G^ω.

Under a G-ω average for $(\mathcal{A}, \alpha_G)$ we understand the following construction for a map $m_G : \mathcal{A} \to \mathcal{M}_\omega$, which depends on a fixed net $(C_i(\alpha))_I$ of convex combinations

$$\sum_{m=1}^{k_i} \lambda_m^i \, \alpha_{g_m^i}^\omega (M) = \sum_{m=1}^{k_i} \lambda_m^i \, U_\omega(g_m^i) M U_\omega(g_m^i)^* =: C_i(\alpha)(M), \quad M \in \mathcal{M}_\omega,$$
$$(48.3.9)$$

where we write $C_i(\alpha)(\Pi_\omega(A)) \equiv C_i(\alpha)(A)$ for $A \in \mathcal{A}$. And we postulate that the limits

$$\lim_{i \in I}\langle \varphi; C_i(\alpha)(A)\rangle =: \langle \varphi; m_G(A)\rangle, \qquad (48.3.10)$$

exist for all $A \in \mathcal{A}$ and all $\varphi \in \mathcal{F}_\omega$.

m_G is called *right-invariant* if $m_G \circ \alpha_h = m_G$, and *left-invariant* if $\alpha_h^\omega \circ m_G = m_G$ for all $h \in G$ ($\alpha_h^\omega \equiv \alpha_h^{\mathcal{F}_\omega}$). A right- and left-invariant G-average is called *bi-invariant* or simply *invariant*.

The dual of m_G, restricted to $\mathcal{F}_\omega$, is denoted by $m_G^* : \mathcal{F}_\omega \to \mathcal{S}$, so that $\langle m_G^*(\varphi); A\rangle := \langle \varphi; m_G(A)\rangle$ for all $\varphi \in \mathcal{F}_\omega$ and all $A \in \mathcal{A}$.

If m_G is right-invariant, then clearly $m_G^* : \mathcal{F}_\omega \to \mathcal{S}^G$.

Assume now that we have a C*-dynamical system $(\mathcal{A}, \alpha_G)$ (with G locally compact). Then for each $\omega \in \mathcal{S}$ and each $A \in \mathcal{A}$, the function

$$f \equiv \langle \omega; \alpha_\bullet(A) \rangle : G \to \mathbb{C}, \quad g \mapsto \langle \omega; \alpha_g(A) \rangle,$$

(where at $\bullet$ the variable g has to be inserted) is continuous (by Proposition 48.3-4), and bounded with bound $\|A\|$, that is $f \in C_b(G, \mathbb{C})$. If we fix ω and vary $A \in \mathcal{A}$, then we collect f's from a linear, complex conjugation-invariant subset $C^\omega \subset C_b(G, \mathbb{C})$ which contains positive functions (for $A \geq 0$) and the identity (for $A = \mathbb{1}$).

If the given net of convex combination $\{C_i(\alpha)(A) \,|\, i \in I\}$ from (48.3.9) converges weakly for all $A \in \mathcal{A}$, it defines now a *mean* $m_G[.]$ on C^ω (with . replacing a function) by the prescription

$$m_G[f] \equiv m_G[\langle \omega; \alpha_\bullet(A) \rangle] := \lim_{i \in I} \langle \omega; C_i(\alpha)(A) \rangle, \qquad (48.3.11)$$

which is linear, positive and normalized. If $\omega \in \mathcal{S}^G$, then the net limit gets trivial and we have

$$m_G[f] = m_G[\langle \omega; \alpha_\bullet(A) \rangle] = \lim_{i \in I} \langle \omega; \sum_{m=1}^{k_i} \lambda_m^i \alpha_{g_m^i}(A) \rangle = \langle \omega; A \rangle$$
$$= \langle \omega; \alpha_h(A) \rangle = m_G[f_h], \quad \forall h \in G, \quad \text{where } f_h(g) := f(gh). \qquad (48.3.12)$$

If $m_G[.]$ may, in fact, be extended to a positive linear functional on $C_b(G, \mathbb{C})$, it is a state on this commutative unital C*-algebra, which for G-invariant ω is invariant under right translations. Those states do not exist for all locally compact groups.

Definition 48.3-7 (Invariant Means on Amenable Groups). A locally compact group G, for which there exists a right-invariant state $m_G[.]$ on $C_b(G, \mathbb{C})$ is called *amenable*.

Each such $m_G[.]$ is called a *right-invariant mean* on G.

From standard textbooks (e.g., [Gre69]) one knows the following: If G has a right invariant mean it has also a left and bi-invariant (= invariant) mean. Each Abelian locally compact group and each compact group is amenable, and also semi-direct compositions of such groups (as e.g., the Euclidean group) are amenable. A connected semi-simple Lie group is amenable, if and only if it is compact. (Thus the Lorentz group is not amenable.) In general, an amenable group has more than a single right-invariant mean.

In our applications occur the time and space translations and the internal symmetries of clustered Fermion algebras as examples for amenable groups. On the other side, the above-mentioned cluster permutation group $\mathbb{P}$ is an important example of a locally compact, non-compact, and non-amenable group.

Assume now G amenable with right-invariant mean $m_G[.]$. If in Eq. (48.3.11) ω means any state, for which the functions $\langle \omega; \alpha_\bullet(A) \rangle$ on G are continuous for all $A \in \mathcal{A}$ (those functions constituting C^ω), then the application of $m_G[.]$ to C^ω

provides a linear, positive, normalized functional on $\mathcal{A}$, that is a state $m_G^*(\omega) \in \mathcal{S}$. Moreover, we get for all $h \in G$

$$\langle \alpha_h^*(m_G^*(\omega)); A \rangle = m_G[\langle \omega; \alpha_{\bullet h}(A) \rangle] = \langle m_G^*(\omega); A \rangle, \ \forall A \in \mathcal{A},$$

demonstrating the G-invariance of the state $m_G^*(\omega)$.

The open question is, in how far that $m_G^*(\omega)$ depends on the special right invariant mean $m_G[.]$ of the amenable group G. Since that is not decidable in the general frame (see e.g., Example 48.3-11 below), and since we need only the mean of functions on G formed by G-shifted expectation values (like the elements in $\mathbb{C}^\omega$), we renounce on the condition of amenability and work directly with nets of the form (48.3.9) (including especially our treatment of the non-amenable permutation group $\mathbb{P}$). Notice again that our notion of a G average does not require any continuity of $g \mapsto \alpha_g$ and is applicable to arbitrary (not even topological) groups.

If, however, $(\mathcal{A}, \alpha, G)$ is in fact a C*-dynamical system for an amenable group G, then an invariant mean $m_G[.]$ (as a state on $C_b(G, \mathbb{C})$), applied to g-shifted expectations, can be approximated by a net of convex combinations, of the type we used to define a G-average. This is clear for compact groups, which are unimodular and possess a normalized Haar measure. For locally compact, non-compact, unimodular groups, the infinite Haar measures may be approximated by finite integrals, which for themselves are approximated by finite sums. By normalization, one arrives at an approximation by finite convex combinations. (We have that expounded in Eq. (31.3.1) on page 907 for the non-compact time translation group $G = \mathbb{R}$. The rigorous constructions for general amenable groups use the so-called "M-nets" of [Gre69].)

Thus many results on G-averages apply automatically to C*-dynamical systems with amenable groups, where the invariant group means lead to invariant G-averages.

If we have an invariant $G-\omega$ average m_G, any $C \in \mathcal{A}^G$ may be pulled out from $m_G(CA)$ to the left, and from $m_G(AC)$ to the right, since this holds for any finite convex combination $C_i(\alpha)(A)$, due to the automorphism property of α_g, $g \in G$.

Proposition 48.3-8 (Invariant G-Averages as Conditional Expectations).

Assume that $(\mathcal{A}, \alpha_G)$ possesses an $\omega \in \mathcal{S}^G$ and an invariant G-ω-average $m_G : \mathcal{A} \to \mathcal{M}_\omega$. That is, for each $A \in \mathcal{A}$, there exists the averaged observable $m_G(A) \in \mathcal{M}_\omega$, defined by $\langle \varphi; m_G(A) \rangle := \lim_{i \in I} \langle \varphi; C_i(\alpha)(A) \rangle$ for all $\varphi \in \mathcal{F}_\omega$, where $(C_i(\alpha))_I$ is a given net of convex combinations (48.3.9). Furtheron $m_G(A)$ is then invariant under the extended α_G^ω-transformations, i.e., $m_G(A) \in \mathcal{M}_\omega^G$, what is equivalent to $m_G(A) \in \mathcal{M}_\omega \cap U_\omega(G)'$.

The linear map $m_G : \mathcal{A} \to \mathcal{M}_\omega^G$ preserves positivity and the unit, and satisfies the so-called "right- and left-module property"

$$m_G(BAC) = \Pi_\omega(B)m_G(A)\Pi_\omega(C), \ \forall A \in \mathcal{A} \ and \ for \ all \ B, C \in \mathcal{A}^G. \quad (48.3.13)$$

Those properties characterize m_G as a "conditional expectation", if $\mathcal{A}$ is a W*-algebra, or if m_G is extended to a map $m_G : \mathcal{M}_\omega \to \mathcal{M}_\omega^G$ (cf. Definition 31.3-3 on page 914).

Often a group average in W*-algebras is just defined *as such a conditional expectation onto the G-invariant elements.*

Taking into account the considerations preceding Definition 48.3-7, we are led immediately to the following assertions.

Proposition 48.3-9 (Existence of Invariant States). *Let $(\mathcal{A}, \alpha_G)$ be an automorphic representation of a group G in the C*-algebra $\mathcal{A}$.*

(a) *Assume there is a non-empty α_G^*-invariant folium $\mathcal{F} \subset \mathcal{S}$ (especially $\mathcal{F} = \mathcal{S}$ is of interest) and a right-invariant G-average m_G, given by the prescription*

$$\langle \varphi; m_G(A) \rangle := \lim_{i \in I} \langle \varphi; C_i(\alpha)(A) \rangle, \quad \forall \varphi \in \mathcal{F}, \quad \forall A \in \mathcal{A}. \tag{48.3.14}$$

Then there exist the G-invariant states $\omega = m_G^*(\varphi) \in \mathcal{S}^G$ (which may coincide) for all $\varphi \in \mathcal{F}$. Thus $\mathcal{S}^G$, and also $\partial_e \mathcal{S}^G$ (the ergodic states), are non-empty sets under this condition.

Each G-average m_G leads therefore to an affine state averaging map

$$m_G^* : \mathcal{F} \xrightarrow{onto} \mathcal{S}^G .$$

Notice that $\mathcal{F} \cap \mathcal{S}^G$ may be empty, if $\mathcal{F} \neq \mathcal{S}$.

(b) *If $(\mathcal{A}, \alpha, G)$ is a C*-dynamical system, with G amenable, then each of the existing right-invariant means $m_G[.]$ (as a state on $C_b(G, \mathbb{C})$) provides invariant states $\omega \in \mathcal{S}^G$ and an observable average $m_G : \mathcal{A} \to \mathcal{A}^{**G}$ by the prescription*

$$\langle \omega; A \rangle := m_G[\langle \varphi; \alpha_\bullet(A) \rangle] =: \langle \varphi; m_G(A) \rangle, \quad \forall \varphi \in \mathcal{S}, \forall A \in \mathcal{A}. \tag{48.3.15}$$

(c) *If G is amenable and $\mathcal{F}$ is again an α_G^*-invariant folium so that $(\mathcal{A}, \alpha_G)$ may be extended to a W*-dynamical system $(\mathcal{M}_\mathcal{F}, \alpha^\mathcal{F}, G)$ (only point-wise σ-weak continuity has to be shown) then the prescription*

$$\langle \omega; M \rangle := m_G[\langle \varphi; \alpha_\bullet^\mathcal{F}(M) \rangle] =: \langle \varphi; m_G(M) \rangle, \quad \forall \varphi \in \mathcal{F}, \forall M \in \mathcal{M}_\mathcal{F} \tag{48.3.16}$$

provides G-invariant states $\omega \in \mathcal{F} \cap \mathcal{S}^G$ and an observable average $m_G : \mathcal{M}_\mathcal{F} \to \mathcal{M}_\mathcal{F}^G$.

Comment 48.3-10. In the first assertion (a) of the foregoing Proposition, genuine subfolia $\mathcal{F} \subsetneq \mathcal{S}$ may make the existence proof for the invariant G-average easier. It suffices in fact to find a non-empty $\mathcal{F}$, in which the invariant G-average does exist, to obtain an invariant ω.

So we have for the permutation group $G = \mathbb{P}$ of a clustered CAR-algebra $\mathcal{A}$ introduced the folia of "mean field separating states", in which only the convergence of $\mathbb{P}$-averages are investigated. This is performed, however, only for the (embedded) one-cluster subalgebra and for products of averages, so that these considerations do not quite fit into the present setup.

The setup of assertion (a) allows for the evasion of the invariant equilibrium state from the original G-invariant folium $\mathcal{F}$. This is especially important for scattering systems, with $G = \mathbb{R}$, if the G-average is realized by the direct limit $t \to \infty$ (see also the subsequent Example). True photonic radiation states must leave, for e.g., the Fock folium in the infinite time limit.

The last assertion (c) is e.g., of relevance, if one has already determined an $\omega \in \mathcal{S}^G$, giving rise to the G-invariant folium $\mathcal{F}_\omega$. If one "perturbs" now $\alpha_G^\omega \subset$ *-aut$(\mathcal{M}_\omega)$ to $\alpha'_G \subset$ *-aut$(\mathcal{M}_\omega)$, then the question for the existence of a perturbed invariant equilibrium state ω' within $\mathcal{F}_\omega$ is answered by assertion (c) in the affirmative, if G is amenable.

The preceding Proposition involves the *existence* of invariant G-averages as a consequence of the amenability of the group G and of certain continuity properties of the group actions. In physical applications, these continuity conditions are not always fulfilled. We indicate a more general reasoning in the following Example, demonstrating that for the mere existence of G-averages, continuity is not necessary.

Example 48.3-11 (General Time Averages). Let be given a dynamical automorphism group $(\mathcal{A}, \alpha_\mathbb{R})$. The functions $[t \mapsto \langle \varphi; \alpha_t(A) \rangle]$, with $\varphi \in \mathcal{S}$ and $A \in \mathcal{A}$, are in general not in $C_b(\mathbb{R}, \mathbb{C})$ but in $F_b(\mathbb{R}, \mathbb{C})$, the bounded functions on $\mathbb{R}$.

According to [HR70], nr. (17.20), there exist invariant means $m_\mathbb{R}[.]$ on $\mathcal{F}_b(\mathbb{R})$, which — like those on $C_b(\mathbb{R})$ — are defined as linear, positive, normalized functionals, invariant under left and right translations (which here coincide). In spite of $F_b(\mathbb{R}, \mathbb{C})$ being no C*-algebra, the three mentioned conditions, which characterize a state, also imply here that the mean is a bounded functional, i.e.,

$$|m_G[f]| \leq \sup\{|f(t)| \,|\, t \in \mathbb{R}\}, \quad f \in F_b(\mathbb{R}, \mathbb{C}). \tag{48.3.17}$$

One knows that here exists more than one invariant mean on $F_b(\mathbb{R}, \mathbb{C})$.

Assuming an $\mathbb{R}$-invariant folium $\mathcal{F} \subset \mathcal{S}$ and applying $m_\mathbb{R}[\langle \varphi; \alpha_\bullet^\mathcal{F}(M) \rangle] =: \langle \varphi; m_\mathbb{R}(M) \rangle$ as in Eq. (48.3.15), for all $\varphi \in \mathrm{LH}(\mathcal{F})$ and an $M \in \mathcal{M}_\mathcal{F}$, leads to a linear functional $m_\mathbb{R}(M)$ acting on $\mathrm{LH}(\mathcal{F})$, with $|\langle \varphi - \omega; m_G(M) \rangle| \leq \sup\{|\langle \varphi - \omega; \alpha_t^\mathcal{F}(M) \rangle| \,|\, t \in \mathbb{R}\} \leq \|\varphi - \omega\| \|M\|$, that is, $m_\mathbb{R}(M) \in \mathcal{M}_\mathcal{F}$.

The invariance of $m_\mathbb{R}[.]$ implies the left and right module properties so that we obtain again an observable average $m_\mathbb{R} : \mathcal{M}_\mathcal{F} \to \mathcal{M}_\mathcal{F}^\mathbb{R}$ in terms of a conditional expectation.

If the direct limits $\lim_{t \to \pm\infty} \langle \varphi; \alpha_t(M) \rangle$ exist (what does not pre-suppose any continuity of $\alpha_\mathbb{R}$), then these constitute special $\mathbb{R}$-averages, concretely given by limits of that most simple convex combinations. Any $m_\mathbb{R}(M)$ lies between those direct limits.

There is especially an invariant mean $m_\mathbb{R}[.]$ for which $m_\mathbb{R}[\langle \varphi; \alpha_\bullet(A) \rangle]$ equals the direct limit $\lim_{t \to \infty} \langle \varphi; \alpha_t(A) \rangle$, whenever that limit exists.

The G-averages are mainly of interest, when their result does not depend on the chosen special net of convex-combinations. For this purpose, we investigate more closely covariant representations of the given automorphism group.

Proposition 48.3-12 (Projections on Invariant Vectors). *Let $(\mathcal{A}, \alpha_G)$ possess an invariant G-ω-average m_G (where $\omega \in \mathcal{S}^G$), constructed with the net $I \ni i \mapsto C_i(\alpha) = \sum_{m=1}^{k_i} \lambda_m^i \, \alpha_{g_m^i}$, and recall the implementation $\Pi_\omega(\alpha_g(A)) = U_\omega(g)\Pi_\omega(A)U_\omega^*(g)$, $U_\omega(g)\Omega_\omega = \Omega_\omega$, $\forall g \in G$, $\forall A \in \mathcal{A}$. Then we have for the projection P_ω^G on the $U_\omega(G)$-invariant vectors in $\mathcal{H}_\omega$ the limiting relation in the weak operator topology*

$$P_\omega^G = \text{weak--}\lim_{i \in I} \sum_{m=1}^{k_i} \lambda_m^i U_\omega(g_m^i) =: \text{weak--}\lim_{i \in I} C_i(U_\omega), \qquad (48.3.18)$$

(independently of the special G-ω-average).
   In fact, for this relation, the left-invariance of m_G is already sufficient.

Proof. By assumption, the limit $\lim_{i \in I} \sum_{m=1}^{k_i} \lambda_m^i (\phi | U_\omega(g_m^i)\Pi_\omega(A)U_\omega^*(g_m^i)\phi)$ exists, since a normalized vector $\phi \in \mathcal{H}_\omega$ represents a state $\varphi \in \mathcal{F}_\omega$. By the polarization identity (see Lemma 43.5-1), we may replace the right-hand vector ϕ by Ω_ω, which eats the $U_\omega^*(g_m^i)$. We obtain then the existence of

$$\lim_{i \in I} \sum_{m=1}^{k_i} \lambda_m^i (\phi | U_\omega(g_m^i)\Pi_\omega(A)\Omega_\omega) =: (\phi | B\Pi_\omega(A)\Omega_\omega), \ \forall \phi \in \mathcal{H}_\omega \text{ and } \forall A \in \mathcal{A},$$

$$(48.3.19)$$

where $B \in \mathcal{L}(\mathcal{H}_\omega)$ arises from the Riesz representation theorem, since the limit is a bounded sesquilinear form. (Observe the cyclicity of Ω_ω.)
   Notice now the frequently used formula

$$U_\omega(g)P_\omega^G = P_\omega^G = P_\omega^G U_\omega(g), \ \forall g \in G, \qquad (48.3.20)$$

which arises from the fact that for $\Omega \in \mathcal{H}_\omega^G$ we have also $U_\omega(g)\Omega \in \mathcal{H}_\omega^G$, since $U_\omega(g')U_\omega(g)\Omega = \Omega = U_\omega(g)\Omega$, $\forall g' \in G$. This gives $U_\omega(g)P_\omega^G = P_\omega^G$, for all $g \in G$, and the commuted version results from that by Hermitian adjointing.
   Denoting $P_\omega^G \equiv P$ we find by substituting $\Pi_\omega(A)\Omega_\omega$ in (48.3.19) by $P\psi$, in account of (48.3.20), that $(\phi | BP\psi) = (\phi | P\psi)$, for all $\phi, \psi \in \mathcal{H}_\omega$, which means $BP = P$.
   On the other side, the left-invariance of the G-average leads to

$$(\phi | U_\omega(h)B\psi) = \lim_{i \in I} \sum_{m=1}^{k_i} \lambda_m^i (\phi | U_\omega(h)U_\omega(g_m^i)\psi) = (\phi | B\psi).$$

Thus $U_\omega(h)B\psi = B\psi$ for all $h \in G$, and thus $B\psi \in \mathcal{H}_\omega^G$ for all $\psi \in \mathcal{H}_\omega$, giving $PB = B$.

But we may execute the same procedure with replacing in (48.3.19) the $U_\omega(g_m^i)$ by their Hermitian adjoints, which leads in the limit to the operator B^*, with the same properties concerning P as B. We conclude:

$$P\frac{B + B^*}{2} = \frac{B + B^*}{2} = \frac{B + B^*}{2}P = P$$
$$P\frac{B - B^*}{2i} = \frac{B - B^*}{2i} = \frac{B - B^*}{2i}P = 0\,,$$

where the second equalities in each line follow by Hermitian adjointing. Thus $B = P$. $\qquad\square$

From (48.3.18) follows obviously that $P_\omega^G \in \overline{\mathrm{Conv}(U_G)}^w$. If one does not know about the existence of an invariant G-average, this relation is, however, a non-trivial, well known theorem.

Theorem 48.3-13 (Alaoglu–Birkhoff Mean Ergodic Theorem). *Let us consider a family* $U_G := \{U_g \,|\, g \in G\}$ *of bounded operators in the Hilbert space $\mathcal{H}$ which satisfies the following conditions:*

(i) $\|U_g\| \leq 1$ *for all* $g \in G$;
(ii) $U_{g_1} U_{g_2} \in U_G$ *for all* $g_1, g_2 \in G$.

Then one knows for the projection P^G onto the subspace $\mathcal{H}^G \subset \mathcal{H}$ of U_G-invariant vectors the relation

$$P^G \in \overline{\mathrm{Conv}(U_G)}^w\,. \tag{48.3.21}$$

(The closure in the weak operator topology of a convex set is the same as that in any weaker-than-norm topology.)

The power of the preceding Theorem is e.g., demonstrated by a reverse conclusion to Proposition 48.3-12.

Proposition 48.3-14 (Ergodic Implications of Invariant States). *Let the automorphism group $(\mathcal{A}, \alpha_G)$ possess an $\omega \in \mathcal{S}^G$.*

(a) *Then there exists a left-invariant net* $C_j(U_\omega) = \sum_{m=1}^{k_j} \lambda_m^j U_\omega(g_m^j)$, $j \in J$, *which converges weakly to P_ω^G.*
(b) *For each $M \in \mathcal{M}_\omega$ there exists a subnet of (a) such that*

$$\lim_{i \in I} \sum_{m=1}^{k_i} \lambda_m^i U_\omega(g_m^i) M U_\omega^*(g_m^i) =: \lim_{i \in I} C_i(\alpha)(M) =: \tilde{m}_G(M)$$

converges weakly.
(c) *For each $M \in \mathcal{M}_\omega$, with net $(C_i(\alpha))_I$ of the form (b), one has*

$$\lim_{i \in I} C_i(\alpha)(M) P_\omega^G = P_\omega^G \tilde{m}_G(M) P_\omega^G = P_\omega^G M P_\omega^G\,. \tag{48.3.22}$$

Proof.   (a) By the G-invariance of ω, we have the unitaries $U_\omega(g)$ and their weakly closed, convex hull $\overline{\text{Conv}(U_\omega(G))}^w$, from which we may choose a net $(C_j(U_\omega))_J$, weakly converging to P_ω^G, according to Alaoglu–Birkhoff. But $P_\omega^G = U_\omega(h)P_\omega^G = \lim_{j \in J} C_j(U_\omega(h)U_\omega)$, since one-sided multiplication is weakly continuous.

(b) Since $(C_j(\alpha)(M))_J$ is contained in the weakly compact ball of radius $\|M\|$ within the von Neumann algebra $\mathcal{M}_\omega$, there is a weakly convergent subnet $(C_j(\alpha)(M))_J$ with limit $\tilde{m}_G(M) \in \mathcal{M}_\omega$, say.

(c) The relations (48.3.22) follow from (48.3.20), telling us that P_ω^G eats the $U_\omega^*(g_m^i)$.   □

We have now the existence of a kind of average $\tilde{m}_G(M)$, but it has still several shortcomings: 1. Its construction depends on the observable M to be averaged. 2. The left and right-invariant relations in Eq. (48.3.22) are valid only in front of the projection P_ω^G, so that we cannot deduce the invariance properties for $\lim_{i \in I} C_i(\alpha)(M)$ for itself.

To get more structure on $\tilde{m}_G(M)$, one often assumes in mean-ergodic theory that P_ω^G be separating. This is the essential assumption in the following well known Theorem of Kovacs–Szücs, dealing with a general von Neumann algebra $\mathcal{M}$ in a Hilbert space $\mathcal{H}$ (cf. [BR87]). The additional condition expresses a certain largeness of $\mathcal{M}'P^G$, namely that the closed subspace $[\mathcal{M}'P^G\mathcal{H}]$ be equal to $\mathcal{H}$, which means P^G is cyclic for $\mathcal{M}'$. Then for $M \in \mathcal{M}$, the relation $MP^G = 0$ implies $MM'P^G = 0$, and, by cyclicity, $M = 0$, which means that P^G is separating for $\mathcal{M}$.

Theorem 48.3-15 (Theorem of Kovacs–Szücs).   *Let U_G be a group of unitaries in the Hilbert space $\mathcal{H}$ which implements *-automorphisms $\alpha_g = U_g \cdot U_g^*, g \in G$, in a von Neumann algebra $\mathcal{M} \subset \mathcal{L}(\mathcal{H})$, and let P^G project onto the subspace of U_G-invariant vectors.*

If P^G is cyclic for $\mathcal{M}'$, then there exists a unique positive (= positivity preserving), idempotent, α_G-invariant, linear map

$$m_G : \mathcal{M} \xrightarrow{onto} \mathcal{M}^G, \text{ with } m_G(B_1AB_2) = B_1m_G(A)B_2, \ A \in \mathcal{M}, \ B_{1/2} \in \mathcal{M}^G.$$
$$(48.3.23)$$

Let us call m_G also G-average. It is a special case of a so-called conditional expectation, (which we have also described in Definition 31.3-3 on page 914) and has the following further properties:

(a) *m_G is normal in the sense that for a norm-bounded subset $\mathcal{M}_0$ of self-adjoint elements in $\mathcal{M}$,*

$$\sup\{m_G(M) \,|\, M \in \mathcal{M}_0\} = m_G\,(\sup\{M \in \mathcal{M}_0\});\qquad(48.3.24)$$

(b) *m_G is faithful in the sense that $0 \leq M \in \mathcal{M}$ and $m_G(M) = 0$ implies $M = 0$;*
(c) *for $M \in \mathcal{M}$, $m_G(M)$ is the unique element in $\overline{\text{Conv}(\alpha_G(M))}^w \cap \mathcal{M}^G$;*
(d) *for $M \in \mathcal{M}$, $m_G(M)$ is the unique element in $\mathcal{M}$ with*

$$m_G(M)P^G = P^GMP^G.\qquad(48.3.25)$$

Proof. According to Alaoglu–Birkhoff, we may write P^G as a limit of a net in $\mathrm{Conv}(U_G)$ and conclude as in Proposition 48.3-14 that there exists for each $M \in \mathcal{M}$ an element $m_G(M) \in \mathcal{M}$, which satisfies (48.3.25) and which is now unique by the separability of P^G.

Positivity is obvious, and $m_G(\alpha_g(M))P^G = m_G(M)P^G$ is valid by (48.3.25) and (48.3.20), giving α_g-invariance. With $m_G(M)$ also $U_g m_G(M)U_g^*$ is in $\mathcal{M}$ and $m_G(M)P^G$ is equal to $U_g m_G(M)U_g^* P^G$ by (48.3.25). Thus $m_G(M) \in \mathcal{M}^G$, $\forall M \in \mathcal{M}$.

If $B \in \mathcal{M}^G$, it commutes with P^G by Alaoglu–Birkhoff and $m_G(BM)P^G = P^G BM P^G = BP^G M P^G = Bm_G(M)P^G$ so that the equality in (48.3.23) is derived.

Calculate $m_G(\mathbb{1})P^G = P^G$, leading to $m_G(\mathbb{1}) = \mathbb{1}$. The equality in (48.3.23) then gives for $B \in \mathcal{M}^G$ that $B = m_G(B)$. Hence the first part of (48.3.23) is now proved and also the idempotence of m_G.

By the strong continuity of multiplication, we obtain (a). If $0 \leq M \in \mathcal{M}$ and $m_G(M) = 0$, then from $P^G \sqrt{M} \sqrt{M} P^G = 0 = \sqrt{M} P^G$ the separability of P^G gives $\sqrt{M} = 0 = M$, and we have (b).

If $B \in \mathcal{M}^G$ and if $B = \text{strong–}\lim_I C_i(\alpha)(M)$ then

$$BP^G = P^G BP^G = \text{strong–}\lim_{i \in I} P^G C_i(\alpha)(M)P^G = P^G M P^G.$$

This identifies it with the present $m_G(M)$, because of (d), demonstrating (c). □

If the automorphism group $(\mathcal{A}, \alpha_G)$ possesses an invariant state $\omega \in \mathcal{S}^G$, then the averages $\tilde{m}_G$ of Proposition 48.3-14, which satisfy (48.3.25), coincide with the m_G of Kovacs–Szücs, if P_ω^G is separating. If P_ω^G is not separating then the following modification of the Kovacs–Szücs theorem may be applied, which we prove for algebraic exercise.

Corollary 48.3-16 (Modified Kovacs–Szücs Theorem). *Let U_G be a group of unitaries in the Hilbert space $\mathcal{H}$ which implements *-automorphisms α_g in a von Neumann algebra $\mathcal{M} \subset \mathcal{L}(\mathcal{H})$, and let $P^G = [\mathcal{H}^G]$. Introduce $Q := [\mathcal{M}' P^G \mathcal{H}]$, which in general is smaller than $\mathbb{1}$.*

Then $Q \in \mathcal{M}^G \cap (\mathcal{M}^G)'$, and Kovacs–Szücs holds for the map

$$m_G|_{Q\mathcal{M}Q} : Q\mathcal{M}Q \xrightarrow{onto} Q\mathcal{M}^G Q = (Q\mathcal{M}Q)^G. \tag{48.3.26}$$

That means that for $M \in Q\mathcal{M}Q$, there exists a unique element $m_G(M)$ in $Q\mathcal{M}^G Q$ with $m_G(M)P^G = P^G M P^G$.

Proof. We begin with the operator algebraic exercise to show $Q \in \mathcal{M}$: $B \in \mathcal{M}' \Rightarrow BQ\mathcal{H} \subset Q\mathcal{H} \Rightarrow BQ\Omega = QBQ\Omega$, $\forall \Omega \in \mathcal{H}$. $QBQ = BQ$ implies $QB^*Q = QB^*$. Therefore, $QB = (B^*Q)^* = (QB^*Q)^* = QBQ = BQ$, which gives $Q \in \mathcal{M}'' = \mathcal{M}$.

Since α_G leaves $\mathcal{M}$-invariant, it leaves also its commutant $\mathcal{M}'$-invariant. Thus we obtain $U(g)Q = [U(g)\mathcal{M}'U(g)^* P^G \mathcal{H}] = Q$. On the other side $QU(g) = QP^G U(g) = Q$ and $Q \in \mathcal{M}^G$.

If $A \in \mathcal{M}^G \subset \mathcal{M}$, it commutes (with all $U(g)$ and) with P^G and $A[\mathcal{M}'P^G\mathcal{H}] = [\mathcal{M}'AP^G\mathcal{H}] = [\mathcal{M}'P^G\mathcal{H}]A$. Thus A commutes also with Q and $Q \in (\mathcal{M}^G)'$.

Thus, U_G implements the group of automorphisms also in $Q\mathcal{M}Q$, and we may apply Kovacs–Szücs for $Q\mathcal{M}Q$ as a von Neumann subalgebra of $\mathcal{L}(Q\mathcal{H})$. In principle P^G must then be replaced by $P^G Q$, but Q drops out beside an $M \in Q\mathcal{M}Q$. □

48.3.3. *Ergodic Decompositions*

We shall learn more about the possible $m_G(M)$'s if we impose some kind of asymptotic commutativity for $(\mathcal{A}, \alpha_G)$. Those features are especially of interest for the construction of classical observables.

The asymptotic commutativity may be valid in the expectations of special states only. There are many variants of the notion of "asymptotic Abelianess" in the literature. We concentrate ourselves on the following versions.

Definition 48.3-17 (G-Abelianess and Asymptotic Abelianess).   Let be given the group of automorphisms $(\mathcal{A}, \alpha_G)$.

(a) For $\omega \in \mathcal{S}^G$, we say that the triple $(\mathcal{A}, \alpha_G, \omega)$ is *G-Abelian* if

$$\inf_{A' \in \mathrm{Conv}(\alpha_G(A))} |\langle \varphi; [A', B] \rangle| = 0, \tag{48.3.27}$$

for all $A, B \in \mathcal{A}$ and for all G-invariant vector states φ of $(\Pi_\omega, \mathcal{H}_\omega)$.
(b) If $(\mathcal{A}, \alpha_G, \omega)$ is *G-Abelian* for all $\omega \in \mathcal{S}^G$, we say that $(\mathcal{A}, \alpha_G)$ is *G-Abelian*.
(c) If for each $A \in \mathcal{A}$, the group G contains a sequence $(g_n)_\mathbb{N}$ with

$$\lim_{n \to \infty} \|[\alpha_{g_n}(A), B]\| = 0, \quad \forall B \in \mathcal{A}, \tag{48.3.28}$$

we call $(\mathcal{A}, \alpha_G)$ *asymptotic Abelian*.

The notions of G-Abelianess (a) and (b) seem well established in the literature, while the asymptotic Abelianess (c), due to [Sto67], is a much weaker form than is usually introduced. In the literature, it is mostly applied to C*-algebraic systems $(\mathcal{A}, \alpha, G)$, where $(g_n)_\mathbb{N}$ means then *any* sequence going to infinity in the sense of locally compact groups (that is, leaving any compact set).

We observe that $(\mathcal{A}, \alpha_G, \omega)$ is G-Abelian, if and only if there is, for all G-invariant vector states φ of $(\Pi_\omega, \mathcal{H}_\omega)$ and for all $A, B \in \mathcal{A}$, a net $(C_i)_I \subset \mathrm{Conv}(\alpha_G(A))$ such that

$$0 = \lim_{i \in I} |\langle \varphi; [C_i, B] \rangle| \quad \left(\leq \lim_{i \in I} \|[C_i, B]\| \right). \tag{48.3.29}$$

(From a set with an accumulation point, one may select a net, converging to this accumulation point). The inequality in the bracket of (48.3.29) may be applied, in the case of asymptotic Abelianess, to the special sequence of (c) and that demonstrates that asymptotic Abelianess for $(\mathcal{A}, \alpha_G)$ *implies* G-Abelianess for $(\mathcal{A}, \alpha_G)$.

If there is given a group of automorphisms $(\mathcal{A}, \alpha_G)$, together with an $\omega \in \mathcal{S}^G$, then according to Alaoglu–Birkhoff, there is a convex combination $C(U_\omega) = \sum_{m=1}^{k} \lambda_m U_\omega(g_m)$ which is near P_ω^G. We shall denote again the convex combinations involving α_g, which correspond to

$$C(U_\omega) = \sum_{m=1}^{k} \lambda_m U_\omega(g_m), \quad \text{by} \quad C(\alpha) := \sum_{m=1}^{k} \lambda_m U_\omega(g_m) \cdot U_\omega^*(g_m), \quad (48.3.30)$$

where $C(\alpha)(M)$ means, as before, its application to operators M in $\mathcal{L}(\mathcal{H}_\omega)$.

Thus we obtain for all elements $A, B \in \mathcal{A}$ and for every vector $\psi \in \mathcal{H}_\omega^G$ that $(\psi | P_\omega^G \Pi_\omega(A) P_\omega^G \ P_\omega^G \Pi_\omega(B) P_\omega^G \psi) = (\psi | \Pi_\omega(A) \ P_\omega^G \ \Pi_\omega(B) \psi)$ is near $(\psi | \Pi_\omega(A) \ C(U_\omega) \ \Pi_\omega(B) \psi) = (\psi | \Pi_\omega(A) \ C(\alpha)(\Pi_\omega(B)) \psi)$.

If now $(\mathcal{A}, \alpha_G, \omega)$ is G-Abelian, then the last term is near $(\psi | C(\alpha)(\Pi_\omega(B)) \Pi_\omega(A) \psi)$, and this is near $(\psi | \ \Pi_\omega(B) P_\omega^G \Pi_\omega(A) \psi)$, which equals $(\psi | P_\omega^G \Pi_\omega(B) P_\omega^G \ P_\omega^G \Pi_\omega(A) P_\omega^G \psi)$ (because also $\sum_{m=1}^{k} \lambda_m U_\omega(g_m)^*$ is near P_ω^G, by the self-adjointness of P_ω^G).

Since this is true for all $\psi \in \mathcal{H}_\omega^G$, we have shown the following.

Proposition 48.3-18. $(\mathcal{A}, \alpha_G, \omega)$ *is G-Abelian, if and only if the family* $\{P_\omega^G \Pi_\omega(A) P_\omega^G \mid A \in \mathcal{A}\}$ *consists of mutually commuting operators.*

The property of G-Abelianess provides now a direct connection to the theory of orthogonal measures, since under this assumption P_ω^G satisfies the conditions of the P in Proposition 48.1-15(b). Thus, if $(\mathcal{A}, \alpha_G, \omega)$ is G-Abelian, there exists a $\mu_\omega^G \in \mathfrak{O}_\omega$, which is uniquely associated with the Abelian von Neumann algebra $\mathfrak{B}_\omega^G = \{\Pi_\omega(\mathcal{A}) \cup P_\omega^G\}' \subset \Pi_\omega(\mathcal{A})'$.

By Alaoglu–Birkhoff we may also in the foregoing relation replace P_ω^G by $U_\omega(G)$ which is the content of the following Lemma.

Lemma 48.3-19. *If there is given a group of automorphisms $(\mathcal{A}, \alpha_G)$, together with an $\omega \in \mathcal{S}^G$, then*

$$\{\Pi_\omega(\mathcal{A}) \cup P_\omega^G\}' = \{\Pi_\omega(\mathcal{A}) \cup U_\omega(G)\}' \quad (48.3.31)$$

Proof. If $B \in \{\Pi_\omega(\mathcal{A}) \cup P_\omega^G\}'$ then $B U_\omega(g) \Pi_\omega(\mathcal{A}) \Omega_\omega = B \Pi_\omega(\alpha_g(\mathcal{A})) \Omega_\omega = \Pi_\omega(\alpha_g(\mathcal{A})) B \Omega_\omega = U_\omega(g) \Pi_\omega(\mathcal{A}) B \Omega_\omega = U_\omega(g) B \Pi_\omega(\mathcal{A}) \Omega_\omega$ for all $A \in \mathcal{A}$. Thus B commutes with all $U_\omega(g)$.

If, on the other side, the latter relation is true, we observe that B commutes with all elements of $\mathrm{Con}(U_\omega(G))$ and thus with its limit point P_ω^G. $\square$

In this connection, we find a distinguished class of G-invariant measures.

Proposition 48.3-20 (G-Invariant Measures). *Let be given $(\mathcal{A}, \alpha_G)$, together with an $\omega \in \mathcal{S}^G$, and let the orthogonal decomposition measure $\mu \in \mathfrak{O}_\omega$ be associated with the Abelian von Neumann algebra $\mathfrak{B}_\mu \subset \Pi_\omega(\mathcal{A})'$ and with the projection P_μ*

according to Proposition 48.1-15 on page 1787. Denote as before by $\nu_g^{-1} := \alpha_g^*$ the action of G in the state space $\mathcal{S}$ and by $\nu_g^\times$ the pullback $\nu_g^\times(f) := f \circ \nu_g^{-1}$ for functions f on $\mathcal{S}$.

(a) *Then $\mathfrak{B}_\mu$ commutes with $U_\omega(G)$, if and only if*
(b) *the relation*

$$\mu(f_0 \nu_g^\times(f)) = \mu(f_0 f), \quad \text{is valid for } \forall g \in G, \text{ and } f_0, f \in C(\mathcal{S}). \quad (48.3.32)$$

(c) *Equation (48.3.32), in turn, is equivalent to*

$$\operatorname{supp}(\mu) \subset \mathcal{S}^G. \quad (48.3.33)$$

(d) *Furtheron, $\mathfrak{B}_\mu$ commuting with $U_\omega(G)$ is equivalent to*

$$U_\omega(g)P_\mu = P_\mu, \quad \forall g \in G, \quad (48.3.34)$$

(besides the relations $P_\mu \Omega_\omega = \Omega_\omega$ and $P_\mu \Pi_\omega(\mathcal{A})P_\mu \subset (P_\mu \Pi_\omega(\mathcal{A})P_\mu)'$, implied directly by the definition of P_μ).

Proof. We take the special continuous product function $f = \hat{A}_0 \ldots \hat{A}_n$, $A_i \in \mathcal{A}$, and evaluate by means of Lemma 48.1-14 and Eq. (48.1.15)

$$\mu(f_0 \hat{A}_0 \ldots \hat{A}_n) = (\Omega_\omega | \Pi_\omega(A_0) \, \theta_\mu(f_0) \, \Pi_\omega(A_1) \ldots \Pi_\omega(A_n) \Omega_\omega); \quad (48.3.35)$$

$$\mu(f_0 \nu_g^*(\hat{A}_0 \ldots \hat{A}_n)) = (\Omega_\omega | \Pi_\omega(\alpha_g(A_0)) \, \theta_\mu(f_0) \, \Pi_\omega(\alpha_g(A_1)) \ldots \Pi_\omega(\alpha_g(A_n)) \Omega_\omega)$$
$$= (\Omega_\omega | \Pi_\omega(A_0) \, U_\omega(g)^* \theta_\mu(f_0) U_\omega(g) \, \Pi_\omega(A_1) \ldots \Pi_\omega(A_n) \Omega_\omega). \quad (48.3.36)$$

Thus $\theta_\mu(f_0)$ commutes with $U_\omega(g)$, if and only if the left-hand sides of (48.3.35) and (48.3.36) are equal. But the arbitrary f may be approximated by linear combinations of the products $\hat{A}_0 \ldots \hat{A}_n$, in virtue of the Stone–Weierstrass theorem.

The implication (48.3.33) $\Rightarrow$ (48.3.32) is clear. For the reverse implication, we use the first part in the proof of Lemma 48.3-19 and consider an n-dimensional subalgebra $\mathfrak{N}_n$ of $\mathfrak{B}_\mu$, which commutes with $U_\omega(G)$. The corresponding orthogonal measure μ_n is supported on the G-invariant states ω_{P_i}, $1 \leq i \leq n$, where the P_i are the atomic projections in $\mathfrak{N}_n$. If the sequence $\mathfrak{N}_n$ approaches $\mathfrak{B}_\mu$, the corresponding $\operatorname{supp}(\mu_n)$ approach $\operatorname{supp}(\mu)$, being still contained in $\mathcal{S}^G$, because of the weak*-closedness of this convex set.

We know from Proposition 48.1-15 that $P_\mu = [\mathfrak{B}_\mu \Omega_\omega]$. If $\mathfrak{B}_\mu$ commutes with $U_\omega(g)$, then $U_\omega(g)$ is eaten by Ω_ω. If reversely relation (48.3.34) is valid, then the general relation $\mathfrak{B}_\mu = \{\Pi_\omega(\mathcal{A}) \cup P_\mu\}'$ implies $\mathfrak{B}_\mu = \{\Pi_\omega(\mathcal{A}) \cup U_\omega(G)\}'$, as in the first part of the proof of Lemma 48.3-19. □

If $(\mathcal{A}, \alpha_G, \omega)$ is G-Abelian, then $\mathfrak{B}_\omega^G = \{\Pi_\omega(\mathcal{A}) \cup U_\omega(G)\}'$ is Abelian according to Propositions 48.3-18 and 48.3-20, and is the largest Abelian von Neumann algebra in $\Pi_\omega(\mathcal{A})'$, which commutes with $U_\omega(G)$, whereas $\mathbb{C}\mathbb{1}_\omega$ is the smallest of those Abelian von Neumann algebras.

In the case of G-Abelianess, Eq. (48.1.17) provides a *-isomorphism between $\mathfrak{B}_\omega^G$ and $P_\omega^G \mathcal{M}_\omega P_\omega^G$, which extends $\theta_\omega^G(\hat{A})P_\omega^G \mapsto P_\omega^G \Pi_\omega(A)P_\omega^G$, $A \in \mathcal{A}$ (where θ_ω^G denotes the Tomita map of μ_ω^G). Thus the orthogonal measure μ_ω^G diagonalizes in some sense the commutative von Neumann algebra $P_\omega^G \mathcal{M}_\omega P_\omega^G$.

Proposition 48.3-21 (Implications of G-Abelianess). *Let* $(\mathcal{A}, \alpha_G, \omega)$, *with* $\omega \in \mathcal{S}^G$, *be G-Abelian.*

(a) *Then the orthogonal measure μ_ω^G, induced by the projection P_ω^G onto the space of invariant vectors $\mathcal{H}_\omega^G \subset \mathcal{H}_\omega$, $\trianglelefteq$-dominates all $\mu \in \mathfrak{D}_\omega$, which are supported by $\mathcal{S}^G$. It is the only measure in $\mathfrak{D}_\omega$ which is (pseudo-) supported by the ergodic states $\partial_e \mathcal{S}^G$.*

(b) *The following conditions are then mutually equivalent:*

    (i) *ω is ergodic;*

    (ii) *$\{\Pi_\omega(\mathcal{A}) \cup U_\omega(G)\}' = \mathbb{C}\mathbb{1}$;*

    (iii) *$\dim(\mathcal{H}_\omega^G) = 1$;*

    (iv) *$P_\omega^G = |\Omega_\omega)(\Omega_\omega|$;*

    (v) *For any G-average m_G, which satisfies the relation (48.3.22), we have G-clustering for the 2-point function of ω (extended to $\mathcal{M}_\omega$):*

$$\langle \omega; m_G(A)B \rangle = \langle \omega; A \rangle \langle \omega; B \rangle, \quad A, B \in \mathcal{M}_\omega. \tag{48.3.37}$$

(c) *If $(\mathcal{A}, \alpha_G)$ is G-Abelian, then all G-invariant states have a unique decomposition into extremal invariant (ergodic) states and $\mathcal{S}^G$ is a Choquet simplex.*

Proof. (a) By construction and by Proposition 48.3-20, μ_ω^G is the $\trianglelefteq$-largest measure in $\mathfrak{D}_\omega$ supported by $\mathcal{S}^G$, since it is uniquely determined by the largest Abelian von Neumann algebra in $\{\Pi_\omega(\mathcal{A}) \cup U_\omega(G)\}'$. Any measure $\mu \in \mathfrak{D}_\omega$, with $\mathfrak{B}_\mu \subset \{\Pi_\omega(\mathcal{A}) \cup U_\omega(G)\}'$, leads to an iterated form of μ_ω^G, as given in (48.1.19), so that the states in $\mathrm{supp}(\mu)$ are further decomposed. This implies that $\mathrm{supp}(\mu) \subset \partial_e \mathcal{S}^G$ is only possible for $\mu = \mu_\omega^G$.

(b). For the equivalence of the first four conditions, we only have, in view of Proposition 48.3-2, to show (b)(ii)$\Rightarrow$(b)(iv). If ω is ergodic, then Proposition 48.3-2 gives $\mathfrak{B}_\omega^G = \mathbb{C}\mathbb{1}_\omega$, and G-Abelianess makes this isomorphic to $P_\omega^G \mathcal{M}_\omega P_\omega^G$. Thus P_ω^G is an Abelian projection for $\mathcal{M}_\omega$ which dominates $|\Omega_\omega)(\Omega_\omega|$; hence $P_\omega^G = |\Omega_\omega)(\Omega_\omega|$.

(b)(i)$\Rightarrow$(b)(v). If ω is ergodic then, by (48.3.22) and the preceding paragraph, we have

$$\langle \omega; m_G(A)B \rangle = \langle \omega; P_\omega^G \, m_G(A) \, B \rangle \tag{48.3.38}$$
$$= \langle \omega; \, |\Omega_\omega)(\Omega_\omega| \, A \, |\Omega_\omega)(\Omega_\omega| \, B \rangle = (\Omega_\omega|A\,\Omega_\omega)(\Omega_\omega|B\,\Omega_\omega),$$

that is G-clustering.

(b)(v)$\Rightarrow$(b)(i). If reversely the last relation is valid then

$$(A\Omega_\omega|P_\omega^G \, B\Omega_\omega) = (\Omega_\omega|m_G(A^*)B\Omega_\omega) = \langle \omega; A^* \rangle \langle \omega; B \rangle = (A\Omega_\omega|\,[\,|\Omega_\omega)(\Omega_\omega|B\,]\,\Omega_\omega)$$

for all $A, B \in \mathcal{M}_\omega$. Thus $P_\omega^G = |\Omega_\omega)(\Omega_\omega|$.

(c) From (a) it follows that all $\omega \in \mathcal{S}^G$ have a unique extremal ($=$ ergodic) decomposition, which is (pseudo-) supported by $\partial_e \mathcal{S}^G$. This is equivalent with the simplex property according to Choquet theory.   □

Thus $(\mathcal{A}, \alpha_G, \omega)$ is G-Abelian if and only if $\{\Pi_\omega(\mathcal{A}) \cup U_\omega(G)\}'$ is Abelian. Since, by Proposition 48.3-2, $\omega \in \mathcal{S}^G$ is ergodic if and only if $\{\Pi_\omega(\mathcal{A}) \cup U_\omega(G)\}'$ is trivial, $(\mathcal{A}, \alpha_G, \omega)$ is always G-Abelian for an ergodic state. Especially each pure state $\omega \in \mathcal{S}^G$ is ergodic and G-Abelian ($\Pi_\omega(\mathcal{A})$ having a trivial commutant).

That means that a G-Abelian automorphism group $(\mathcal{A}, \alpha_G)$ provides a classical state space $\mathcal{S}^G$, compact since here $\mathcal{A}$ is always supposed unital. $\mathcal{S}^G$ is the state space of a commutative C*-algebra $\mathcal{C}^G$, which in some sense contains all of the $P_\omega^G \Pi_\omega(A) P_\omega^G$, $\omega \in \mathcal{S}^G$. $\mathcal{C}^G$ may be realized by the continuous functions $C(\partial_e \mathcal{S}^G)$, where $\partial_e \mathcal{S}^G$ is compact in a certain topology, weaker than the $\sigma(\mathcal{S}, \mathcal{A})$-topology. The $\omega \in \mathcal{S}^G$ give then, by means of their extremal decomposition, (Radon) measures on $C(\partial_e \mathcal{S}^G)$. The $P_\omega^G \Pi_\omega(A) P_\omega^G$ are then realized by functions in $C(\text{supp}(\mu_\omega^G)) \subset C(\partial_e \mathcal{S}^G)$.

A coarse measurement method, which produces only time averages over the group $\mathbb{R}$, leads for an $\mathbb{R}$-Abelian Heisenberg dynamics $(\mathcal{A}, \alpha_{\mathbb{R}})$ to a classical sub-theory, in the sense that all time averages commute with each other. In general, however, they do not commute with all other operators for measurement methods.

48.3.4. *Asymptotic Abelian Systems*

The asymptotic Abelianess has been formulated in terms of a special sequence $(g_n)_\mathbb{N}$ of group elements of an arbitrary group, in order to make the discussion rather general (see Definition 49.1-1 on page 1879). It is easily seen that for all $h \in G$, the sequences $(hg_n)_\mathbb{N}$ and $(g_n h)_\mathbb{N}$ do the same job. We shall often write such a sequence also in the notation $(g_i)_I$ of a net.

For the conception of classical collective observables by using invariant group averages, it is necessary that the averaging of operators reaches the center of the representation von Neumann algebra. This situation is typified by $(\mathcal{A}, \alpha_G)$ being a *large group of automorphisms* in the sense of [Sto67], which means

$$\overline{\text{Conv}\left(\Pi_\omega(\alpha_G(A))\right)}^w \cap \mathcal{Z}_\omega^G \neq \emptyset, \quad \forall A \in \mathcal{A} \text{ and } \forall \omega \in \mathcal{S}^G . \qquad (48.3.39)$$

We subsequently demonstrate in a rather direct manner that asymptotic Abelian automorphism groups $(\mathcal{A}, \alpha_G)$ satisfy this condition. The basic idea is that for given $\omega \in \mathcal{S}^G$ and $A \in \mathcal{A}$, we have in the Hilbert space $\mathcal{H}_\omega$ the existence of the direct limit

$$\text{weak--}\lim_{j \in J} \Pi_\omega\left(\alpha_{g_j}(A)\right) =: Z_\omega(A) \in \mathcal{Z}_\omega , \qquad (48.3.40)$$

where $\left(\Pi_\omega(\alpha_{g_j}(A))\right)_J$ is a weakly convergent subnet (for "subnet" see Definition 49.1-1 on page 1879) of the bounded sequence $\left(\Pi_\omega(\alpha_{g_n}(A))\right)_\mathbb{N}$, where $(g_n)_\mathbb{N}$ means a distinguished sequence leading for A to asymptotic commutativity.

(The weak compactness of the ball with radius $\|\Pi_\omega(A)\|$ in $\mathcal{M}_\omega$ guarantees the convergent subnet.)

The limiting element $Z_\omega(A) \in \mathcal{M}_\omega$ commutes in fact by asymptotic Abelianess with all $\Pi_\omega(B) \in \Pi_\omega(\mathcal{A})$ (since $n \in \mathbb{N}$ goes with $j \in J$ to infinity by the subnet definition).

For some groups G, $Z_\omega(A)$ is automatically α_G-invariant, especially for $G = \mathbb{R}$ (see Example 48.3-11 on page 1815). If that is not the case, we may employ Proposition 48.3-14, since we assume a G-invariant state $\omega \in \mathcal{S}^G$. Thus we know (see Eq. (48.3.22)) that there is a net of convex combinations for which weak-$\lim_{i \in I} C_i'(\alpha)(Z_\omega(A))$ exists, which is an element of Z_ω (since the automorphisms leave Z_ω invariant and Z_ω is weakly closed). This limit satisfies

$$\text{weak--}\lim_{i \in I} C_i'(\alpha)(Z_\omega(A))P_\omega^G = P_\omega^G \tilde{m}_G(Z_\omega(A))P_\omega^G = P_\omega^G Z_\omega(A)P_\omega^G , \qquad (48.3.41)$$

where $\tilde{m}_G$ is the preliminary average, introduced in Proposition 48.3-14.

Combining the two limits provides us for each $A \in \mathcal{A}$ with a weakly converging net of convex combinations

$$\text{weak--}\lim_{i \in I} C_i(\alpha)(\Pi_\omega(A)) = \tilde{m}_G(Z_\omega(A)) =: m_G^0(A) \in Z_\omega . \qquad (48.3.42)$$

We must immediately observe that $m_G^0(A)$ is defined by means of $\Pi_\omega(A)$, so that we also have defined $m_G^0(\Pi_\omega(A))$.

At first, we do not know whether this newly introduced average depends sensitively on the chosen net of convex combinations. This question is solved by introducing the projection

$$0 < R_\omega := [\mathcal{Z}_\omega^G \Omega_\omega] \leq [\mathcal{H}_\omega^G] = P_\omega^G . \qquad (48.3.43)$$

(We denote by $[\mathcal{V}]$ the orthogonal projection on the smallest closed subspace containing the set of Hilbert space vectors $\mathcal{V}$.)

We find that $[(\mathcal{Z}_\omega)'R_\omega\mathcal{H}_\omega] = \mathbb{1}_\omega$ (since $(\mathcal{Z}_\omega)' \supset \mathcal{M}_\omega$), so that R_ω is separating for $\mathcal{Z}_\omega$. What makes R_ω especially attractive is that it fulfills the conditions of Proposition 48.3-20, being the projection associated with $\mathcal{Z}_\omega^G \subset \mathcal{B}_\omega^G = (\Pi_\omega(\mathcal{A}) \cup P_\omega^G)'$ in the sense of orthogonal measures, as formulated in Proposition 48.1-15. ($\mathcal{B}_\omega^G$ is Abelian since asymptotic Abelianess implies G-Abelianess.) Thus we know immediately that R_ω, or equivalently $\mathcal{Z}_\omega^G$, defines an orthogonal measure, which is subcentral, and which is supported by $\mathcal{S}^G$ and is $\triangleleft$-dominated by the ergodic decomposition measure μ_ω^G (cf. Proposition 48.3-21).

We conclude for each $A \in \mathcal{A}$ that

$$\begin{aligned}
m_G^0(A)R_\omega &= m_G^0(A)P_\omega^G R_\omega = P_\omega^G m_G^0(A)P_\omega^G R_\omega \\
&= U_\omega(h)P_\omega^G m_G^0(A)R_\omega = U_\omega(h)m_G^0(A)U_\omega^*(h)R_\omega , \quad \forall h \in G ,
\end{aligned} \qquad (48.3.44)$$

which gives by the separating property of R_ω for $\mathcal{Z}_\omega$

$$m_G^0(A) = U_\omega(h)m_G^0(A)U_\omega^*(h) \in \mathcal{Z}_\omega^G, \quad \forall h \in G. \tag{48.3.45}$$

But then we have also $m_G^0(A)R_\omega \mathcal{H}_\omega \subset R_\omega \mathcal{H}_\omega$, and thus

$$
\begin{aligned}
m_G^0(A)R_\omega &= R_\omega m_G^0(A)R_\omega = R_\omega \Pi_\omega(A)R_\omega \\
&= R_\omega U_\omega(h)\Pi_\omega(A)U_\omega^*(h)R_\omega = m_G^0\big(U_\omega(h)\Pi_\omega(A)U_\omega^*(h)\big)R_\omega,
\end{aligned}
\tag{48.3.46}
$$

where in the second step, R_ω has eaten all $U_\omega(g_i)$ of the convex combinations and in the third step spit out the $U_\omega(h)$ for any $h \in G$. Thus we have demonstrated that $m_G^0(A)$ is left- and right-invariant and independent of the net $(C_i(\alpha))_I$ in Eq. (48.3.42).

Theorem 48.3-22 (Center-Valued Averages). *Let the automorphism group* $(\mathcal{A}, \alpha_G)$ *be asymptotic Abelian and assume an arbitrary* $\omega \in \mathcal{S}^G$.

(a) $(\mathcal{A}, \alpha_G)$ *constitutes a large group of automorphisms. More specifically, for each* $A \in \mathcal{A}$, *the average* $m_G^0(\Pi_\omega(A))$ *is equal to the unique element in*

$$\overline{\mathrm{Conv}\left(\Pi_\omega(\alpha_G(A))\right)}^w \cap \mathcal{Z}_\omega^G. \tag{48.3.47}$$

(b) *For each* $\omega \in \mathcal{S}^G$, *the first relation in (48.3.46) may be continuously extended to a map* $m_G^0 : \mathcal{M}_\omega \xrightarrow{onto} \mathcal{Z}_\omega^G$, *which is uniquely characterized by the relation*

$$m_G^0(M)R_\omega = R_\omega M R_\omega, \quad \forall M \in \mathcal{M}_\omega. \tag{48.3.48}$$

The extended m_G^0 *is a normal, linear, positive, G-invariant map with*

$$m_G^0(B_1 M B_2) = B_1 m_G^0(M)B_2, \tag{48.3.49}$$

for all $M \in \mathcal{M}_\omega$ *and all* $B_1, B_2 \in \mathcal{Z}_\omega^G$.

Thus m_G^0 *is a conditional expectation, but in general is not point-wise* $\mathcal{M}_\omega^G$ *preserving and not faithful.*

Proof. (a) The existence of a $m_G^0(A) \in \mathcal{Z}_\omega^G$ has been demonstrated in the text preceding the Theorem.

If now $B \in \overline{\mathrm{Conv}\left(\Pi_\omega(\alpha_G(A))\right)}^w \cap \mathcal{Z}_\omega^G$, then it can be directly approximated by a net $(C_i(\Pi_\omega(\alpha_G(A))))_I$. That leads by unitary implementations (which may be eaten by R_ω), to $BR_\omega = R_\omega BR_\omega = R_\omega \lim_I C_i(\Pi_\omega(\alpha_G(A))R_\omega = R_\omega \Pi_\omega(A)R_\omega = m_G^0(\Pi_\omega(A))R_\omega$, demonstrating $B = m_G^0(\Pi_\omega(A))$.

(b) If $M \in \mathcal{M}_\omega$ is weakly approximated by the net $(\Pi_\omega(A_\kappa))_K$, then $\lim_K R_\omega \Pi_\omega(A_\kappa)R_\omega =: m_G^0(M)$ exists and constitutes an element in $\mathcal{Z}_\omega^G$, since the latter is weakly closed. It trivially satisfies (48.3.48). By Kaplansky's density theorem, each $Z \in \mathcal{Z}_\omega^G$ may be approximated by a net in $\Pi_\omega(\mathcal{A}) \cap \mathcal{Z}_\omega^G$, which leads to $m_G^0(Z) = Z$. Thus the image of the extended m_G^0 is the whole of $\mathcal{Z}_\omega^G$.

If there is another map $m : \mathcal{M}_\omega \xrightarrow{onto} \mathcal{Z}_\omega^G$ satisfying (48.3.48), then $m(M)R_\omega = R_\omega M R_\omega = m_G^0(M)R_\omega$ and thus $m(M) = m_G^0(M)$, for all $M \in \mathcal{M}_\omega$.

The properties of a conditional expectation follow as in the proof of Kovacs–Szücs.

If there is an $M \in \mathcal{M}_\omega^G$ which is not in $\mathcal{Z}_\omega^G$, then $m_G^0(M) \in \mathcal{Z}_\omega^G$ must be different from M. Then $M - m_G^0(M) \neq 0$ (no point-wise invariance), but $m_G^0\big([M - m_G^0(M)]^*[M - m_G^0(M)]\big) = 0$ may happen, as in Eq. (48.3.60) below (no faithfulness). □

Up to now, we do not know whether P_ω^G might not be strictly larger than R_ω. This question is solved by studying systematically the G-invariant states.

Proposition 48.3-23 (Invariant States of Asymptotic Abelian Systems).
Let be $(\mathcal{A}, \alpha_G)$ asymptotic Abelian and employ the notation of the preceding Proposition.

(a) $\mathcal{S}^G$ *constitutes a Choquet simplex.*
(b) *Let $\omega \in \mathcal{S}^G$. A normal state ω' on $\mathcal{M}_\omega$ is G-invariant, if and only if it is equal to $\omega' \circ m_G^0$ and is thus uniquely given by its restriction to $\mathcal{Z}_\omega^G$ (in spite of m_G^0 being not faithful).*
(c) *If ω, ω' are in $\mathcal{S}^G$, and if there is a $\lambda > 0$ such that $\omega' \leq \lambda \omega$, then there is a unique positive $Z \in \mathcal{Z}_\omega^G$ so that $\omega' = \omega_Z$.*
(d) *If $\omega \in \mathcal{S}^G$, then*

$$\mathcal{B}_\omega^G \equiv \big(\Pi_\omega(\mathcal{A}) \cup U_\omega(G)\big)' = \mathcal{Z}_\omega^G, \qquad (48.3.50)$$

implying

$$P_\omega^G = R_\omega \text{ and, therefore, } \mathcal{H}_\omega^G = \overline{\mathcal{Z}_\omega^G \Omega_\omega}. \qquad (48.3.51)$$

(e) *For $\omega \in \mathcal{S}^G$ the projection $P_\omega^G = R_\omega$ is in general not separating for $\mathcal{M}_\omega$ (and Kovacs–Szücs is not applicable).*
(f) *For each $\omega \in \mathcal{S}^G$, the subcentral measure corresponding to $\mathcal{Z}_\omega^G$ is equal to μ_ω^G (and provides the unique ergodic decomposition of ω into extremal invariant states).*
Thus, the central measure μ_ω equals μ_ω^G, if and only if it is (pseudo-) supported by $\mathcal{S}^G$.
(g) *For $\omega \in \mathcal{S}^G$, the following conditions are equivalent:*

(i) *ω is in the extreme boundary $\partial_e \mathcal{S}$ of $\mathcal{S}^G$ (ergodic state);*
(ii) *$\mathcal{Z}_\omega^G = \mathbb{C}\mathbb{1}_\omega$;*
(iii) *$R_\omega = |\Omega_\omega)(\Omega_\omega|$;*
(iv) *The extension of ω to $\mathcal{M}_\omega$ satisfies the central G-clustering condition*

$$\langle \omega; B m_G^0(M) C \rangle = \langle \omega; M \rangle \langle \omega; CB \rangle, \quad \forall M, B, C \in \mathcal{M}_\omega, \qquad (48.3.52)$$

for the 3-point functions.

By rewriting this clustering in terms of scalar products, one observes that it is equivalent to the operator equality

$$m_G^0(M) = \langle \omega; M \rangle \mathbb{1}_\omega, \quad \forall M \in \mathcal{M}_\omega. \tag{48.3.53}$$

(v) ω is the only state in $\mathcal{S}^G \cap \mathcal{F}_\omega$.

(h) Two states in $\partial_e \mathcal{S}^G$ are equal to each other or disjoint.

Proof. (a). Follows from G-Abelianess (cf. remark after Equation (48.3.29) and Proposition 48.3-21).

(b). Since m_G^0 is G-invariant also $\omega' \circ m_G^0$ is G-invariant for any normal state ω' on $\mathcal{M}_\omega$.

On the other side, we know from Proposition 48.3-22(a) that $m_G^0(\Pi_\omega(A))$ is contained in $\overline{\text{Conv}\left(\Pi_\omega(\alpha_G(A))\right)}^w$. But the expectation of an element in $\text{Conv}\left(\Pi_\omega(\alpha_G(A))\right)$ in a normal invariant ω' is equal to $\langle \omega'; \Pi_\omega(A) \rangle$ and thus also $\langle \omega'; m_G^0(\Pi_\omega(A)) \rangle = \langle \omega'; \Pi_\omega(A) \rangle$ for all $A \in \mathcal{A}$. Since $\Pi_\omega(\mathcal{A})$ is weakly dense in $\mathcal{M}_\omega$, we have by the normality of ω' and m_G^0, the desired relation $\langle \omega'; M \rangle = \langle \omega'; m_G^0(M) \rangle$, $M \in \mathcal{M}_\omega$.

(c). There is a unique positive element $B \in \Pi_\omega(\mathcal{A})'$ such that $\langle \omega'; \Pi_\omega(\mathcal{A}) \rangle = (B\Omega_\omega | \Pi_\omega(\mathcal{A})\Omega_\omega)$, $A \in \mathcal{A}$, which is equal to $(B\Omega_\omega | U_\omega(g)\Pi_\omega(\mathcal{A})U_\omega^*(g)\Omega_\omega)$, because of G-invariance of ω'. Thus $U_\omega^*(g)BU_\omega(g)$ may be substituted for B in the ω'-expression. Because the $U_\omega(g)$ implement automorphisms in $\mathcal{M}_\omega$ they do this also in $\Pi_\omega(\mathcal{A})'$ and $U_\omega^*(g)BU_\omega(g) \in \Pi_\omega(\mathcal{A})'$. Uniqueness implies then $B = U_\omega^*(g)BU_\omega(g) \in \left(\Pi_\omega(\mathcal{A}) \cup U_\omega(G)\right)'$.

Because of (b), ω and ω' are in bijective correspondence to states on $\mathcal{Z}_\omega^G$. In the function representation of $\mathcal{Z}_\omega^G$ the state ω' is realized by a probability measure which is absolutely continuous to that of ω. The corresponding Radon–Nykodym derivative is back-transformed to a positive element Z^2 in $\mathcal{Z}_\omega^G$, which equals B by uniqueness. Then $\omega' = \omega_Z$, with $Z^2 = B$, where Z is unique by positivity.

(d). If $B \in \mathcal{B}_\omega^G$, then it may define an invariant state ω', which is dominated by ω as in the preceding paragraph. Thus $B \in \mathcal{Z}_\omega^G$. Since also $\mathcal{Z}_\omega^G \subset \mathcal{B}_\omega^G$ we have $\mathcal{Z}_\omega^G = \mathcal{B}_\omega^G$. By the theory of orthogonal measures the associated projections must also be equal and project on the same sub-Hilbert spaces.

(e). We have examples for asymptotic Abelian systems $(\mathcal{A}, \alpha_G)$ on a Fermion algebra, which have a pure symmetric state ω. (Take e.g., the permutation group $\mathbb{P}$ for G and the Fock vacuum for ω.) Then $P_\omega^G = |\Omega_\omega)(\Omega_\omega|$, which is (not cyclic for the algebra $\mathbb{C}\mathbb{1}_\omega$ and thus) not separating for $\mathcal{M}_\omega = \mathcal{L}(\mathcal{H}_\omega)$.

(f). According to Proposition 48.3-21, the ergodic decomposition measure is associated with $\mathcal{B}_\omega^G$, hence with $\mathcal{Z}_\omega^G \subset \mathcal{Z}_\omega$.

(g). In Proposition 48.3-21 the corresponding assertions (g)(i) ... (g)(iv) for $\omega \in \partial_e \mathcal{S}$ have been proved using $P_\omega^G = |\Omega_\omega)(\Omega_\omega|$ which here equals R_ω. The G-clustering of the 2-point function is here equal to that of the 3-point function, since $m_G^0(M)$, as a central element, commutes with the B in (48.3.52).

(g)(v) Let be $\omega \in \partial_e \mathcal{S}^G$ and assume that $\omega' \in \mathcal{S}^G \cap \mathcal{F}_\omega$, which implies $\lambda\omega + (1-\lambda)\omega' =: \omega_0 \in \mathcal{S}^G \cap \mathcal{F}_\omega$ for $\lambda \in (0,1)$. ω_0 dominates $\lambda\omega$ as well as $(1-\lambda)\omega'$ and has the same central support in the universal $\mathcal{M}_u$ as ω. By (c) we conclude $\omega = \omega_{0,Z}$, $\omega' = \omega_{0,Z'}$ for some $Z, Z' \in \mathcal{Z}_{\omega'}^G$. But $\mathcal{M}_{\omega'}$ is W*-isomorphic to $\mathcal{M}_\omega$ and thus $\mathcal{Z}_{\omega'}^G = \mathbb{C}\mathbb{1}_\omega$. By normalization $\omega' = \omega$.

If, on the other side, $\omega \in \mathcal{S}^G$ is the only element in $\mathcal{S}^G \cap \mathcal{F}_\omega$, then $\mathcal{Z}_\omega^G$ must be equal to $\mathbb{C}\mathbb{1}_\omega$, since otherwise there would be a ω_Z, $Z \in \mathcal{Z}_\omega^G$, in $\mathcal{S}^G \cap \mathcal{F}_\omega$, which would be different from ω.

(h). It follows from the foregoing considerations that two different ergodic states are in disjoint folia. $\qquad\square$

Observe that Eq. (48.3.53) is an interesting operator version of the *original ergodic idea*: The center-valued operator G-average $m_G^0(M)$ equals the ensemble expectation $\langle \omega; M \rangle \mathbb{1}_\omega$, a c-number.

Proposition 48.3-24 (Invariant Observables). *Let be $(\mathcal{A}, \alpha_G)$ asymptotic Abelian and $\omega \in \mathcal{S}^G \cap \mathcal{F}_s$, that is, invariant and spatially decomposable (see Proposition 48.2-17 on page 1802). Take into account the preceding two Propositions.*

(a) *Let μ_ω^G be the ergodic decomposition measure of ω. Then we know from its being a subcentral (orthogonal) measure, the spatial decomposition relation for the GNS-triples*

$$(\Pi_\omega, \mathcal{H}_\omega, \Omega_\omega) \cong \int_{\partial_e \mathcal{S}^G}^{\oplus} (\Pi_{\omega'}, \mathcal{H}_{\omega'}, \Omega_{\omega'}) \, d\mu_\omega^G(\omega'), \qquad (48.3.54)$$

and for its GNS von Neumann algebra

$$\mathcal{M}_\omega \cong \int_{\partial_e \mathcal{S}^G}^{\oplus} \Pi_{\omega'}(\mathcal{A})'' \, d\mu_\omega^G(\omega') \equiv \int_{\partial_e \mathcal{S}^G}^{\oplus} \mathcal{M}_{\omega'} \, d\mu_\omega^G(\omega'). \qquad (48.3.55)$$

We then find for α_g, extended to $\mathcal{M}_\omega$, the decomposition

$$\alpha_g^\omega = \int_{\partial_e \mathcal{S}^G}^{\oplus} \alpha_g^{\omega'} \, d\mu_\omega^G(\omega'), \quad \forall g \in G, \qquad (48.3.56)$$

where $\alpha_g^{\omega'}$ denotes the extension of α_g to $\mathcal{M}_{\omega'}$, $\omega' \in \partial_e \mathcal{S}^G$.

(b) *The projection R_ω is a decomposable operator, more precisely:*

$$R_\omega = \int_{\partial_e \mathcal{S}^G}^{\oplus} |\Omega_{\omega'}\rangle\langle\Omega_{\omega'}| \, d\mu_\omega^G(\omega'). \qquad (48.3.57)$$

For each $M = \int_{\partial_e \mathcal{S}^G}^{\oplus} M_{\omega'} \, d\mu_\omega^G(\omega') \in \mathcal{M}_\omega$, we have therefore

$$m_G^0(M) = \int_{\partial_e \mathcal{S}^G}^{\oplus} (\Omega_{\omega'}|M_{\omega'}\Omega_{\omega'}) \, \mathbb{1}_{\omega'} \, d\mu_\omega^G(\omega'), \qquad (48.3.58)$$

demonstrating how the m_G^0-average leads into the diagonal algebra.

(c) *Not all of the invariant observables are classical, that is in the image of m_G^0; that means we have in general:*

$$\mathcal{M}_\omega^G \not\supseteq \mathcal{Z}_\omega^G = m_G^0(\mathcal{M}_\omega). \tag{48.3.59}$$

Proof. (a) The decomposition formula Eq. (48.3.56) follows directly from $\alpha_g(\Pi_\omega(A)) = \Pi_\omega(\alpha_g(A)) = \int_{\partial_e \mathcal{S}^G}^\oplus \Pi_{\omega'}(\alpha_g(A)) \, d\mu_\omega^G(\omega')$, showing that the *-isomorphic transformation α_g is transferred μ_ω^G-a.e. to each component representation, preserving the group homomorphism property. Since the ω' are μ_ω^G-a.e. G-invariant, they allow for a weakly continuous extension of the $\Pi_{\omega'} \circ \alpha_g$ to the $\mathcal{M}_{\omega'}$.

(b) $R_\omega = [\mathcal{Z}_\omega^G \Omega_\omega] = [\int_{\partial_e \mathcal{S}^G}^\oplus \mathbb{C}\Omega_{\omega'} \, d\mu_\omega^G(\omega')] = \int_{\partial_e \mathcal{S}^G}^\oplus |\Omega_{\omega'})(\Omega_{\omega'}| \, d\mu_\omega^G(\omega')$ by definition. Apply this to $R_\omega M R_\omega = m_G^0(M) R_\omega$.

(c) As a counter example we may take the Fermion field algebra $\mathcal{A}(\mathfrak{h})$ in a product realization $\otimes_\mathbb{S} \mathcal{A}(\mathfrak{k}_\sigma)$, where the $\mathfrak{k}_\sigma$ are equally-sized cluster subspaces, and consider the automorphism group $(\mathcal{A}(\mathfrak{h}), \alpha_\mathbb{P})$ of the cluster permutations, cf. Example 34.1-9 on page 1030. In the irreducible Fock representation, we have the particle Number operator N_ω and the operator $\exp\{iN_\omega\}$ is in $\mathcal{M}_\omega^\mathbb{P} \neq \mathbb{C}\mathbb{1}_\omega$. Since $\exp\{iN_\omega\}\Omega_\omega = \Omega_\omega$, this does not contradict $P_\omega^\mathbb{P} = R_\omega$. Furthermore $m_\mathbb{P}^0(\exp\{iN_\omega\}) = (\Omega_\omega| \exp\{iN_\omega\}\Omega_\omega)\mathbb{1}_\omega = \mathbb{1}_\omega$. Thus

$$\exp\{iN_\omega\} - \mathbb{1}_\omega \neq 0, \quad m_\mathbb{P}^0([\exp\{iN_\omega\} - \mathbb{1}_\omega]^*[\exp\{iN_\omega\} - \mathbb{1}_\omega]) = 0. \tag{48.3.60}$$

The first relation proves (48.3.59), the second demonstrates the non-faithfulness of $m_\mathbb{P}^0$, mapping a strictly positive operator onto 0. □

For asymptotic Abelian automorphism groups, direct G-limits lead to classical observables without any further averaging. In the following Proposition, we formulate relations which involve direct G-limits.

Proposition 48.3-25 (Ergodicity and Direct Asymptotic Relations). *Consider the asymptotic Abelian automorphism group $(\mathcal{A}, \alpha_G)$ and assume an $\omega \in \mathcal{S}^G$. Again $U_\omega(g)$, $g \in G$, denote the unique implementing unitaries in the GNS representation $(\Pi_\omega, \mathcal{H}_\omega)$ with $U_\omega(g)\Omega_\omega = \Omega_\omega$, $\forall g \in G$.*

For a net $(g_i)_I \subset G$, leading to asymptotic commutativity, the following conditions are equivalent:

(i) *For each $A \in \mathcal{A}$, there exists the direct G limit for the transformed observables:*
weak-$\lim_I \Pi_\omega(\alpha_{g_i}(A)) = \langle \omega; A \rangle \mathbb{1}_\omega$ *(which implies* weak-$\lim_I \Pi_\omega(\alpha_{g_i}(A)) = m_G^0(A)$).

(ii) *For the implementing unitaries, we have the direct G-limit*

$$\underset{i \in I}{\text{weak-lim }} U_\omega(g_i) = |\Omega_\omega)(\Omega_\omega|. \tag{48.3.61}$$

(iii) *For all $A, B, C \in \mathcal{A}$, we have the clustering of the 3-point function under a direct G-limit*

$$\lim_{i \in I} \langle \omega; B\alpha_{g_i}(A)C \rangle = \langle \omega; A \rangle \langle \omega; BC \rangle. \tag{48.3.62}$$

(iv) *For all $A, C \in \mathcal{A}$, we have the clustering of the 2-point function under a direct G-limit*

$$\lim_{i \in I} \langle w; \alpha_{g_i}(A)C \rangle = \langle w; A \rangle \langle w; C \rangle , \qquad (48.3.63)$$

what we also call asymptotic product property *for $w \in \mathcal{S}^G$ (especially for the photon states).*

If one of the foregoing equivalent conditions is satisfied, then necessarily $w \in \partial_e \mathcal{S}^G$ (and $\mathcal{Z}_w^G = \mathbb{C}\mathbb{1}_w$).

If reversely, $w \in \partial_e \mathcal{S}^G$ and is factorial (implying $\mathcal{Z}_w = \mathbb{C}\mathbb{1}_w = \mathcal{Z}_w^G$), then there exists a net $(g_i)_I$ leading to asymptotic commutativity, which satisfies the above equivalent conditions (i)–(iv). Then also the nets $(hg_i g)_I$ do the same job for all $h, g \in G$.

Proof. First we notice, according to the assumption, weak-$\lim_I \Pi_w(\alpha_{g_i}(A)) =: Z \in \mathcal{Z}_w^G$ and satisfies as a scalar trivially $Z R_w = R_w Z R_w$. Thus $Z = m_G^0(A)$.

(i)$\Rightarrow$(ii): We have for all $A \in \mathcal{A}$

$$\text{weak-}\lim_{i \in I} U_w(g_i) \Pi_w(A) U_w^*(g_i) |\Omega_w)(\Omega_w| = \text{weak-}\lim_{i \in I} U_w(g_i) \Pi_w(A) |\Omega_w)(\Omega_w|$$

$$= \langle w; A \rangle |\Omega_w)(\Omega_w| = |\Omega_w)(\Omega_w| \; \Pi_w(A) |\Omega_w)(\Omega_w| .$$

Compare now the second with the last term. Then the assertion (ii) follows by the cyclicity of $|\Omega_w)(\Omega_w|$ for $\Pi_w(\mathcal{A})$.

(ii)$\Rightarrow$(i). We have for all $A, B \in \mathcal{A}$

$$\text{weak-}\lim_{i \in I} U_w(g_i) \Pi_w(A) U_w^*(g_i) \Pi_w(B) |\Omega_w)(\Omega_w|$$

$$= \Pi_w(B) \, \text{weak-}\lim_{i \in I} U_w(g_i) \Pi_w(A) |\Omega_w)(\Omega_w|$$

$$= \Pi_w(B) |\Omega_w)(\Omega_w| \Pi_w(A) |\Omega_w)(\Omega_w| = \langle w; A \rangle \mathbb{1}_w \Pi_w(B) |\Omega_w)(\Omega_w| .$$

(i)$\Leftrightarrow$(iii) is immediate.

(iii)$\Leftrightarrow$(iv). By setting $B = \mathbb{1}$, we get (iv) from (iii).

If we have (iv), we replace C by BC and use asymptotic Abelianess to get (iii).

Having proved all equivalence conditions, we see $w \in \partial_e \mathcal{S}^G$ e.g., from (iii), since that implies the condition (g)(iv) of Theorem 48.3-23 by extension.

If now the ergodic w is also factorial, then $\mathcal{Z}_w = \mathbb{C}\mathbb{1}_w = \mathcal{Z}_w^G$. Then for a given net $\big(\Pi_w(\alpha_{g_i}(A)) \big)_I$, which provides asymptotic Abelianess, there is a weakly converging subnet $\big(\Pi_w(\alpha_{g_j}(A)) \big)_J$ with limit in $\overline{\text{Conv} \big(\Pi_w(\alpha_G(A)) \big)}^w \cap \mathcal{Z}_w = \overline{\text{Conv} \big(\Pi_w(\alpha_G(A)) \big)}^w \cap \mathcal{Z}_w^G$, which equals according to (48.3.47) $m_G^0(A) = c\mathbb{1}_w = \langle w; A \rangle \mathbb{1}_w$, where the last step follows from the sandwiching with Ω_w.

The last assertion follows from the invariance of w and from $\big(\Pi_w(\alpha_{hg_j g}(A)) \big)_J = U_w(h) \big(\Pi_w(\alpha_{g_j}(\alpha_g(A))) \big)_J U_w^*(h)$. $\qquad \square$

Example 48.3-26 (Ergodic Properties in Abelian Algebras). Let be given the automorphism group $(\mathcal{A}, \alpha_G)$ for an Abelian C*-algebra $\mathcal{A}$.

Our most important application is $(\mathcal{W}(E,0), \alpha_{\mathbb{R}})$ with $\mathcal{A} = \mathcal{W}(E,0)$ a commutative Weyl algebra and $\alpha_{\mathbb{R}}$ an automorphic dynamics, especially the free Maxwell dynamics. Notice that the norm jump occurs also in classical Weyl algebras, so that we have neither here a C*-dynamical system.

Then $(\mathcal{A}, \alpha_G)$ is asymptotic Abelian for each net $(g_i)_I$, and we have to conclude that it constitutes a large group of automorphisms, that is $\overline{\text{Conv}\left(\Pi_\omega(\alpha_G(A))\right)}^w \cap \mathcal{Z}_\omega^G \neq \emptyset$ for $A \in \mathcal{A}$, $\omega \in \mathcal{S}^G$. This condition is empty, if there is no $\omega \in \mathcal{S}^G$. If $\mathcal{S}^G \neq \emptyset$, then this condition is in fact satisfied since already $\text{Conv}\left(\Pi_\omega(\alpha_G(A))\right) \subset \mathcal{Z}_\omega$, and averaging goes into $\mathcal{Z}_\omega^G$.

That demonstrates that "largeness" alone has nothing to do with ergodic theory. The first step into ergodic-like notions originates form the existence of an $\omega \in \mathcal{S}^G$, from which the construction of m_G is possible by virtue of (48.3.22). That provides then a special generalized invariant mean, acting initially on all of $\mathcal{A}$ in terms of special convex combinations. Now Abelianess tells that a generalized invariant mean m_G maps here always into the center $\mathcal{Z}_\omega^G = \mathcal{M}_\omega^G$, so that it always constitutes a center-valued mean $m_G = m_G^0$. Abelianess tells us also that R_ω is separating for $\mathcal{Z}_\omega = \mathcal{M}_\omega$. So $m_G^0(A)R_\omega = R_\omega A R_\omega$ (equivalent to $m_G(A)P_\omega^G = P_\omega^G A P_\omega^G$) determines $m_G(A)$ uniquely. (We have the situation of Kovacs–Scücs.)

True ergodic features arise if ω is ergodic, that is according to Proposition 48.3-2 on page 1807, if $(\Pi_\omega(\mathcal{A}) \cup U_\omega(G))' = \mathbb{C}\mathbb{1}_\omega$. That algebra is $\mathcal{Z}_\omega^G$, since $\Pi_\omega(\mathcal{A})''$ has a cyclic vector and hence is maximal Abelian, giving $\Pi_\omega(\mathcal{A})' = \mathcal{M}_\omega$ with invariant part $\mathcal{Z}_\omega^G$. (The result follows also from Proposition 48.3-23, (g)(ii).) Especially we have — since asymptotic Abelianess implies G-Abelianess (or also have from (48.3.52)) — the clustering $\langle \omega; Bm_G^0(M)C \rangle = \langle \omega; M \rangle \langle \omega; CB \rangle$, $\forall M, B, C \in \mathcal{M}_\omega$.

But direct limits and clustering do not follow from ergodicity alone in asymptotic Abelian systems. We have set up in Proposition 48.3-25 as additional condition that ω be factorial, in order to give direct limits. This is in the Abelian case the hard condition $\mathcal{M}_\omega = \mathcal{Z}_\omega = \mathbb{C}\mathbb{1}_\omega$, implying ω to be pure.

If we realize $\mathcal{A}$ as $C(\Gamma)$, with Γ compact, then states are measures and an invariant pure state is given by a point measure δ_γ, stable under the flow $\kappa_g \gamma = \gamma$, and clustering is satisfied in the trivial form $\langle \delta_\gamma; \alpha_g(A)B \rangle = A(\kappa_g \gamma)B(\gamma) = A(\gamma)B(\gamma)$.

Interesting are only non-factorial invariant states ω, given by "equi-partitioned" measures μ on Γ, which are ergodic, i.e., $\mathcal{Z}_\omega^G = \mathbb{C}\mathbb{1}_\omega$. In that case, $\mathcal{Z}_\omega$ is "much larger" than $\mathcal{Z}_\omega^G$, if Γ has "many" points. The triviality of $\mathcal{Z}_\omega^G$ implies metric transitivity of μ, which means that each invariant subset of Γ has measure 0 or 1.

For an ergodic state one has, as mentioned above, by Eq. (48.3.52) clustering in the mean: $\langle \omega; m_G(A)C \rangle = \langle \omega; A \rangle \langle \omega; C \rangle$. The direct clustering of Eq. (48.3.63), namely weak-$\lim_I \langle \omega; \alpha_{g_i}(A)C \rangle = \langle \omega; A \rangle \langle \omega; C \rangle$ is stronger a condition (if Γ has more than a single point and ω is a mixed state) and is called "strong clustering" or "strong mixing."

The non-pure strongly mixing states, which equivalently exhibit the "asymptotic product property", are those we consider in Sec. 14.1.2 for classical radiation theory. As we know, they are special ergodic states. There the group is $G = \mathbb{R}$ and a function realization may be achieved over $\widehat{E^\top}$, in which the transversal free Maxwell dynamics acts as a flow. In general, we prefer, however, the algebraic formulation, which has there much advantages. Especially, by the use of characteristic functions for the states and by the concept of state folia, we gain a close similarity to the theory of asymptotic Abelian systems for the quantized Weyl algebra, in spite of the triviality of asymptotic Abelianess in the commutative case.

Let us mention also in this connection, that in statistical mechanics "mixing" is usually viewed as a disorder condition, whereas in (classical and quantized) field theory it may express "order".

In field theory and statistical mechanics one speaks of *unbroken symmetries* if the component states of the central decomposition (the pure phases or pure vacua) have the same symmetry as the integrated (mixed phase or mixed vacuum) state. In this case, one has nice direct G-limits for the macroscopically mixed states, since the direct G-limits for the factor states work with one and the same net $(g_i)_I$, stemming from the integrated state. Applying the Lebesgue-dominated convergence theorem leads immediately to the following relations.

Proposition 48.3-27 (Asymptotic Relations for Unbroken Symmetries).
Let be $(\mathcal{A}, \alpha_G)$ asymptotic Abelian with $(g_i)_I$ a net providing asymptotic commutativity (as in Eq. (48.3.40)), and let $\omega \in \mathcal{S}^G \cap \mathcal{F}_s$. We denote by μ_ω^G again the unique ergodic decomposition measure and take into account the spatial decomposition integrals of Proposition 48.3-24.

We make the additional assumption that the central measure μ_ω be supported by $\mathcal{S}^G$ (unbroken symmetries).

(a) *The ergodic decomposition coincides now with the central decomposition, i.e., $\mu_\omega^G = \mu_\omega$.*

(b) *For $g \in G$, the unique unitary $U_\omega(g)$ in $\mathcal{H}_\omega$, which implements α_g and leaves Ω_ω invariant, has the spatial decomposition*

$$U_\omega(g) = \int_{\partial_e \mathcal{S}^G}^{\oplus} U_{\omega'}(g) \, d\mu_\omega^G(\omega') , \qquad (48.3.64)$$

where $U_{\omega'}(g)$ is μ_ω^G-a.e. equal to the unique unitary in $\mathcal{H}_{\omega'}$ which implements α_g and leaves $\Omega_{\omega'}$ invariant. We have the direct G-limit

$$\text{weak-lim}_{i \in I} U_\omega(g_i) = \int_{\partial_e \mathcal{S}^G}^{\oplus} |\Omega_{\omega'})(\Omega_{\omega'}| \, d\mu_\omega^G(\omega') . \qquad (48.3.65)$$

(c) *We also obtain the direct G-limits for all $A \in \mathcal{A}$*

$$\text{weak-lim}_{i \in I}\, \Pi_\omega(\alpha_{g_i}(A)) = \int_{\partial_e \mathcal{S}^G}^{\oplus} \langle \omega'; A \rangle \mathbb{1}_{\omega'}\, d\mu_\omega^G(\omega') = m_G^0(\Pi_\omega(A))\,. \quad (48.3.66)$$

(d) *We have for all Π_ω-normal states φ (constituting the folium $\mathcal{F}_\omega$) and for all $A \in \mathcal{A}$ the asymptotic (stability) relation in terms of a direct G-limit*

$$\lim_{i \in I} \langle \nu_{g_i}^{-1}(\varphi); A \rangle := \lim_{i \in I} \langle \varphi; \alpha_{g_i}(A) \rangle = \int_{\text{supp}(\mu_\omega^G)}^{\oplus} \langle \varphi_{\omega'}; \langle \omega; A \rangle \mathbb{1}_{\omega'} \rangle\, d\mu_\varphi^G(\omega') = \langle \omega; A \rangle\,,$$
$$(48.3.67)$$

having set again $\nu_g \equiv \alpha_{g^{-1}}^*$.
Notice that ω is here in general non-factorial (as are the photonic product states $\varphi \in \mathcal{S}_{ph}^{asym}$ used for stable radiation).

(e) *We see from (d), that direct clustering implies the shrinking of the ergodic measure to a point measure, which equals here the central measure: Direct clustering implies factorialness.*

In the second step of Eq. (48.3.67), we refer to the Definition 48.2-19 of *sector components*. Let us be explicit on this point: By the ergodic (and here subcentral) decomposition of the von Neumann algebra $\mathcal{M}_\omega$, $\omega \in \mathcal{S}^G$, we obtain for $\varphi \in \mathcal{F}_\omega$ the decomposition $\varphi = \int_{\partial_e \mathcal{S}^G}^{\oplus} \varphi(\omega')\, d\mu_\omega^G(\omega')$ into scaled states, as is possible for normal functionals on $\mathcal{M}_\omega$ (see Eq. (48.2.23)). Introduce via $n_\varphi(\omega') := \langle \varphi(\omega'); \mathbb{1} \rangle$ the (normalized) states $\varphi_{\omega'} := \frac{\varphi(\omega')}{n_\varphi(\omega')}$ (where they are defined). Then

$$\varphi = \int_{\partial_e \mathcal{S}^G}^{\oplus} \varphi_{\omega'}\, n_\varphi(\omega')\, d\mu_\omega^G(\omega') = \int_{\text{supp}(\mu_\omega^G)}^{\oplus} \varphi_{\omega'}\, d\mu_\varphi(\omega') \quad (48.3.68)$$

is the central decomposition of the (not necessarily invariant) φ, where the $\varphi_{\omega'}$ are undefined on a μ_φ-null set. If we insist on the integration domain $\text{supp}(\mu_\omega^G)$, then we gain a *uniform parametrization* of the central decompositions for the $\varphi \in \mathcal{F}_\omega$, provided by the ergodic decomposition of ω. This is advantageous for calculating transition probabilities.

The fact that for time translations $G = \mathbb{R}$, one has often the unbroken symmetry relation $\mu_\omega = \mu_\omega^G$ for stationary states ω, has led some authors to identify the *time ergodic decomposition* with the decomposition into *pure–phase states*. But it is the central decomposition, which provides in any case the decomposition into pure phases, defined as factorial — i.e., classically pure — states, the more it is applicable also to non-equilibrium states and to not asymptotic Abelian systems.

In Proposition 48.3-25, we have shown for asymptotic Abelian automorphism groups that a factorial ergodic state gives direct clustering, and reversely, the latter implies always ergodicity. If one knows $\mu_\omega = \mu_\omega^G$, then direct clustering for ω implies ergodicity plus factorialness, since a non-trivial central disintegration is no longer possible.

In case of the quasi-free time translations for Bosons, there arises, in fact, the phenomenon of "broken time invariance", meaning $\mu_\omega \neq \mu_\omega^{\mathbb{R}}$, as we are going to discuss in the next subsection.

48.3.5. *Quasi-Free Ergodic Boson States*

We consider a one-parametric, quasi-free automorphism group $(\mathcal{W}(E, \hbar\sigma), \alpha_{\mathbb{R}})$, where we suppose $\hbar > 0$, with non-degenerate symplectic form $\sigma = \text{Im}(.|.)$. The quasi-free dynamics $\alpha_{\mathbb{R}}$ is given in terms of a self-adjoint operator S in a Hilbert space $\mathcal{H}$, so that $\exp\{itS\}$ leaves the test function space $E \subset \mathcal{H}$ invariant, and $\alpha_t(W(f)) := W(v_t f)$ with $v_t f := \exp\{itS\}f$ for $f \in E$. The special symplectic form, with explicit Planck parameter, conforms with our notation in photon theory.

From the Weyl relations, we deduce for $\varphi \in \mathcal{S}$ that

$$\langle \varphi; W(f)W(v_t g)\rangle = \exp\{-\tfrac{i}{2}\hbar\,\text{Im}(f|v_t g)\}C_\varphi(f + v_t g)\,,$$

where $E \ni f \mapsto C_\varphi(f) = \langle \varphi; W(f)\rangle$ denotes the characteristic function for φ.

Let us now assume that, for $\varphi \in \mathcal{S}^{\mathbb{R}}$, $E \ni f \mapsto C_\varphi(f)$ is continuous in a locally convex topology τ on E, stronger than the norm of $\mathcal{H}$ (we have these φ called "τ-continuous" in Sec. 18.2.3 on page 412), and that $t \mapsto v_t g$ is τ-continuous for $g \in E$ (as we have arranged it for the free Maxwell dynamics). Then $t \mapsto \langle \varphi; \sum_i W(f_i) \sum_j W(v_t g_j)\rangle$ is continuous and we may apply Proposition 48.3-5 to obtain that $t \mapsto U_\varphi(t)$ is weakly and strongly continuous, where $U_\varphi(t)$ are the standard implementing unitaries in the GNS representation over φ, which lead to the extended $\alpha_t^\varphi \in {}^*\text{-aut}(\mathcal{M}_\varphi)$. $(\mathcal{M}_\varphi, \alpha^\varphi, \mathbb{R})$ is then a W*-dynamical system.

We know then from the amenability of the Abelian group $\mathbb{R}$ that we *have* invariant time averages $m_{\mathbb{R}}(M)$ for all operators $M \in \mathcal{M}_\varphi$, which in general, however, are not unique. If, however, $\varphi = \varphi^\beta$ is the previously described quasi-free thermal state (cf. Chapter 30),

$$C_\beta(f) := \langle \varphi^\beta; W(f)\rangle = \exp\{-\tfrac{\hbar}{4}\|f\|^2 - \tfrac{\hbar}{2}\|(e^{\beta S} - \mathbb{1})^{-1/2}f\|^2\}\,, \quad \forall f \in E\,,$$

we can demonstrate that $f \mapsto C_\beta(f)$ is indeed τ-continuous (which is due to the special construction of τ for this special E, where $S > 0$). So we have for $(\mathcal{M}_\beta, \alpha^\beta, \mathbb{R})$ invariant time averages $m_{\mathbb{R}} : \mathcal{M}_\beta \to \mathcal{M}_\beta^{\mathbb{R}}$.

Then, because of $P_\beta^{\mathbb{R}}$ being separating, each existing invariant time average $m_{\mathbb{R}}(M)$ equals the unique operator in $\mathcal{M}_\beta$, which is identified by the relation $m_{\mathbb{R}}(M)P_\beta^{\mathbb{R}} = P_\beta^{\mathbb{R}}MP_\beta^{\mathbb{R}}$. We know, therefore, that in thermal equilibrium, there exists a unique time average $m_{\mathbb{R}}(M)$ for the Boson observables, expressible by the usual averaged time integrals over the time-dependent observable, if their infinite-time limits exist. Notice again that this holds in any bounded or infinite cavity. Some more details are given in Sec. 31.3.1 on page 906.

In the present discussion, we want to look more closely on the case, where S owns an *absolutely continuous spectrum*, which ensures by the Riemann–Lebesgue lemma that $\lim_{t\to\pm\infty}(f|v_t g) = 0$ for all f and g in $\mathcal{H}$ (see Eq. (38.5.25) on page

1311). The quasi-free Heisenberg dynamics satisfying the latter condition will be called *relaxing*.

Proposition 48.3-28 (From Relaxing to Asymptotic Abelianess). *If a one-particle Hamiltonian S possesses an absolutely continuous spectrum, then the (relaxing) quasi-free automorphism group $(\mathcal{W}(E, \hbar\sigma), \alpha_\mathbb{R})$ is asymptotic Abelian, where all sequences $(t_i)_\mathbb{N}$, with $t_i \to \pm\infty$, realize asymptotic commutativity.*

Proof. By the Weyl relations we get for the commutator of two Weyl elements $[W(v_t f), W(g)] = [\exp\{-\frac{i}{2}\hbar\,\mathrm{Im}(v_t f|g)\} - \exp\{+\frac{i}{2}\hbar\,\mathrm{Im}(v_t f|g)\}]\, W(v_t f + g)$. Since $\|W(v_t f + g)\| = 1$, we find $\|[W(v_t f), W(g)]\| \leq |\exp\{-\frac{i}{2}\hbar\,\mathrm{Im}(v_t f|g)\} - \exp\{+\frac{i}{2}\hbar\,\mathrm{Im}(v_t f|g)\}| \overset{t\to\infty}{\longrightarrow} 0$. The analogue is valid for $t \to -\infty$, where $t \to \pm\infty$ just means sequences which approach finally $\pm\infty$.

This asymptotic commutativity holds also for linear combinations of Weyl operators which are norm-dense in the non-separable Weyl algebra. With an $\varepsilon/3$-argument, one proves that $(\mathcal{W}(E, \hbar\sigma), \alpha_\mathbb{R})$ is asymptotic Abelian, where the sequences with $t \to \pm\infty$ are cases of the $(g_i)_\mathbb{N}$, which provide asymptotic commutativity (as in Eq. (48.3.40)). $\qquad\qquad\qquad\qquad\qquad\qquad$ □

If $\varphi \in \mathcal{S}^\mathbb{R}$, then there exists according to the considerations in the foregoing subsection a special $\mathbb{R}$-average $m_\mathbb{R}^0 : \mathcal{M}_\varphi \to \mathcal{Z}_\varphi^\mathbb{R}$, which produces *time invariant central elements*.

In consequence of asymptotic Abelianess, $(\mathcal{W}(E, \hbar\sigma), \alpha_\mathbb{R})$ is also $\mathbb{R}$-*Abelian* (by (48.3.29)). Thus we know from Proposition 48.3-21 that the compact convex set $\mathcal{S}^\mathbb{R}$ of invariant states is a *Choquet simplex* and its extremal states (the ergodic states) are characterized by the $(G = \mathbb{R})$-clustering of their 2-point functions.

For asymptotic Abelian systems, there may be ergodic states, in which one realizes the center-valued m_G^0-average of the observables by a direct limit. The direct 3-point cluster property (48.3.62) is then equivalent to the direct 2-point cluster property. In the special case of Weyl elements, the latter clustering condition reads for an invariant state $\varphi \in \mathcal{S}^\mathbb{R}$ (using in the second step the relaxing condition)

$$
\begin{aligned}
\lim_{t\to\pm\infty} \langle\varphi; W(v_t f)W(g)\rangle &= \lim_{t\to\pm\infty} \langle\varphi; W(v_t f + g)\rangle \exp\{-\tfrac{i}{2}\hbar\,\mathrm{Im}(v_t f|g)\} \\
&= \lim_{t\to\pm\infty} \langle\varphi; W(v_t f + g)\rangle = \langle\varphi; W(f)\rangle\langle\varphi; W(g)\rangle, \quad \forall f, g \in E.
\end{aligned}
\tag{48.3.69}
$$

The last part of Eq. (48.3.69) can be expressed entirely in terms of characteristic functions $E \ni f \mapsto C_\varphi(f) = \langle\varphi; W(f)\rangle$ as the *asymptotic product property*,

$$
\lim_{t\to\pm\infty} C_\varphi(v_t f + g) = C_\varphi(f)\, C_\varphi(g), \quad \forall f, g \in E.
\tag{48.3.70}
$$

That relation may be shown, by an $\varepsilon/3$-argument, to be equivalent to the general 2-point clustering, if one uses again the norm-denseness of the linear hull of the Weyl operators.

Definition 48.3-29 (Asymptotic Product States). We denote the set of states, satisfying Eq. (48.3.70), by means of some net $(t_i)_I \subset \mathbb{R}$, by $\mathcal{S}^{asym}$, and call them asymptotic product states.

We obtain an illustration of Proposition 48.3-25 in terms of explicit arguments (where in the following always $\hbar > 0$.)

Proposition 48.3-30 (Properties of Asymptotic Product States). *Let the one-parametric, quasi-free automorphism group $(\mathcal{W}(E, \hbar\sigma), \alpha_{\mathbb{R}})$ be relaxing, implying asymptotic Abelianess. (No continuity property for the automorphism group is assumed.)*

(a) *A state φ on the Weyl algebra $\mathcal{W}(E, \hbar\sigma)$, which satisfies the asymptotic product property Eq. (48.3.70) for its characteristic function, constitutes an ergodic state in $\partial_e \mathcal{S}^{\mathbb{R}}$. (It is invariant, since $\lim_{t \to \infty} C_\varphi(v_{t+t'} f) = C_\varphi(v_{t'} f) = C_\varphi(f)$ for all $t' \in \mathbb{R}$.) Thus $\mathcal{S}^{asym} \subset \partial_e \mathcal{S}^{\mathbb{R}}$.*

(b) *An ergodic state $\varphi \in \partial_e \mathcal{S}^{\mathbb{R}}$, which is also factorial, satisfies the asymptotic product property Eq. (48.3.70) for some time net, so that $\varphi \in \mathcal{S}^{asym}$. If that φ is in addition quasi-free, it satisfies Eq. (48.3.70) for all sequences $t \to \pm\infty$.*

(c) *$\varphi \in \mathcal{S}^{asym}$ is equivalent to*

$$\underset{t \to \pm\infty}{\text{weak--lim}} \; W_\varphi(v_t f) = m_{\mathbb{R}}^0(W(f)) = C_\varphi(f)\mathbb{1}_\varphi, \quad \forall f \in E, \qquad (48.3.71)$$

where $W_\varphi(f) := \Pi_\varphi(W(f))$ denotes the represented $W(f)$, and the time limits may be along special nets in the general case, but along arbitrary sequences $t \to \pm\infty$ for quasi-free states.

Notice the equivalence to the strong resolvent convergence

$$\underset{t \to \pm\infty}{\text{srs--lim}} \; \Phi_\varphi(v_t f) = -i\frac{dC_\varphi(sf)}{ds}\Big|_{s=0} \mathbb{1}_\varphi = \langle\varphi; \Phi_\varphi(f)\rangle\mathbb{1}_\varphi, \quad \forall f \in E, \qquad (48.3.72)$$

if C_φ is differentiable (as it is in the quasi-free case).

(d) *If $\varphi \in \mathcal{S}^{asym}$, then we know from (c) the existence and equality of the two direct time limits. This implies by Example 48.3-11 on page 1815 the equality of all existing invariant operator means.*

Especially, suppose the net of weighted integrals

$$\left\{ \frac{1}{T_2 - T_1} \int_{T_1}^{T_2} W_\varphi(v_t f) \, dt \; \Big| \; (T_1, T_2) \in \mathbb{R}^2, \; T_1 < T_2 \right\}$$

to exist in the GNS representation of a state $\varphi \in \mathcal{S}$ in terms of weak integration, where the net-ordering $(T_1, T_2) \preceq (T_1', T_2')$ is defined by the inclusion $[T_1, T_2] \subset [T_1', T_2']$. Then $\varphi \in \mathcal{S}^{asym}$ implies

$$\underset{(T_1, T_2) \to \infty}{\text{weak--lim}} \; \frac{1}{T_2 - T_1} \int_{T_1}^{T_2} W_\varphi(v_t f) \, dt = \langle\varphi; W(f)\rangle\mathbb{1}_\varphi, \quad \forall f \in E, \qquad (48.3.73)$$

for a subnet of weighted integrals. (This pertains to the case, where φ is τ-continuous, as discussed at the beginning of this subsection.)

That expresses historic "ergodicity" in operator form, namely the coincidence of the time and the ensemble averages, *since, because of linearity and norm limits, we may replace $W_\varphi(v_t f)$ by $\alpha_t(A)$ for all $A \in \mathcal{W}(E, \hbar\sigma)$. On a dense domain in $\mathcal{H}_\varphi$, we may read this as*

$$
\begin{aligned}
\text{weak–lim}_{(T_1,T_2)\to\infty} \frac{1}{T_2 - T_1} \int_{T_1}^{T_2} \Phi_\varphi(v_t f)\, dt &= \langle\varphi; \Phi_\varphi(f)\rangle \mathbb{1}_\varphi \\
&= \text{weak–lim}_{(T_1,T_2)\to\infty} \Phi_\varphi\left(\int_{T_1}^{T_2} v_t f/(T_2 - T_1)\, dt\right), \quad \forall f \in E,
\end{aligned}
\tag{48.3.74}
$$

where the last formulation would enable a strong resolvent limit.

(e) *There are quasi-free ergodic states $\varphi \in \partial_e \mathcal{S}^{\mathbb{R}}$ which neither are factor states nor are in $\mathcal{S}^{asym}$.*

Proof.   (a) follows in the same way as in Proposition 48.3-25.

(b). First part follows from Proposition 48.3-25.

Illustrative is the quasi-free case, in which φ has in general the characteristic function of the form

$$
C_\varphi(f) = \exp\{iF(f)\} \exp\{-\tfrac{1}{4}s(f, f)\}, \tag{48.3.75}
$$

with F an $\mathbb{R}$-linear form and s a positive quadratic form.

Then φ is in $\mathcal{S}^{\mathbb{R}}$ and is factorial, if and only $F(v_t f) = F(f)$ and there is a positive operator T such that

$$
s(f, f) = \|T^{1/2} f\|^2, \quad \text{and} \quad Tv_t = v_t T. \tag{48.3.76}
$$

Then the relaxation property implies $\lim_{t\to\pm\infty} (T^{1/2}g|T^{1/2}v_t f) = 0$ and we see directly $\varphi \in \mathcal{S}^{asym}$.

(c).   We have in Eq. (48.3.74) the direct limit form for $m_{\mathbb{R}}^0(A)$ for a special $A \in \mathcal{W}(E, \hbar\sigma)$, which we know from Proposition 48.3-25 (i) and which is shown there to be equivalent with the clustering condition (iv).

(d). The net of averaged finite time integrals can be written as a special net of convex combinations, which owns a convergent subnet. This constitutes a special operator time average. It induces an operator time average for all $A \in \mathcal{W}(E, \hbar\sigma)$ by linear extension and norm closure.

For (e) see Example 48.3-32 below.   □

So we have confirmed by Eq. (48.3.74) the usual "ergodicity" assumption of quantum optics in macroscopic (infinite) cavities in terms of operator averages. For more interpretational remarks see Sec. 31.3.1 on page 906.

Remark 48.3-31 (From Asymptotic Product Property to Factorialness?).
To treat the reverse of Proposition 48.3-27 (b) for a quasi-free state seems not easy. We assume that the generator S of v_t has absolutely continuous spectrum. A state with characteristic function Eq. (48.3.75) displays the asymptotic product property if and only if $\lim_{t\to\pm\infty} s_t := \lim_{t\to\pm\infty} s(v_t f, g) = 0$, $\forall f, g \in E$. If we also assume continuity, then $s_t \in C_\infty(\mathbb{R})$, the space which contains the Fourier transforms of L^1-functions according to Riemann–Lebesgue. Necessary for the special form $s(v_t f, g) = (v_t f | Tg)$, with T a positive operator, would be that there exists an $\hat{s}_E \in L^1(\mathbb{R}, \mathbb{C}, \lambda)$ with $\int_\mathbb{R} \exp\{-itE\}\hat{s}_E \, dE = s_t$.

But such kind of a reverse of the Riemann–Lebesgue Lemma seems not to be known.

Example 48.3-32 (Non-factorial Ergodic States). We write the characteristic function of a general time-invariant quasi-free state φ in the form

$$C_\varphi(f) = \exp\{iF(f) - \tfrac{1}{4}s(f,f)\} = \exp\{iF(f)\}\exp\{-\tfrac{1}{4}\|T^{1/2}f\|^2\}\exp\{-\tfrac{1}{4}s_s(f,f)\},$$
$$(48.3.77)$$

where the real $\mathbb{R}$-linear functional $F : E \to \mathbb{R}$ satisfies $F(v_t f) = F(f)$ and also $s(v_t f, v_t f) = s(f, f)$ must hold for the quadratic form for all $t \in \mathbb{R}$ and all $f \in E$. The closable part $s_c(f, f) = \|T^{1/2}f\|^2$ is given by a positive, self-adjoint operator T, which commutes with v_t, and also the singular part s_s of s must be time-invariant by the uniqueness of the decomposition of s into s_c and s_s (see Definition 43.5-14 on page 1547).

Let us now assume the special shape of the invariant singular quadratic form

$$s_s(f, f) = c \overline{L(f)}L(f), \qquad (48.3.78)$$

with some $c > 0$, where $f \mapsto L(f)$ be an unbounded $\mathbb{C}$-linear form on E.

We know from Theorem 25.1-17 on page 662, that the quasi-free state φ is not factorial and see directly that the asymptotic product property is not valid. We refer now to Eq. (25.1.51) and write it in the form, which appears after having performed the integration over the macroscopic phase angle θ:

$$\exp\{-\tfrac{c}{4}\overline{L(f)}L(f)\} = \int_0^\infty e^{-\varrho} J_0(|c^{1/2}L(f)|\varrho^{1/2}) \, d\varrho, \qquad (48.3.79)$$

in which the 0th Bessel function J_0 is decomposed by formula (25.1.52)

$$J_0(|c^{1/2}L(f)|\varrho^{1/2}) = \int_0^{2\pi} \exp\{i\operatorname{Re}\big((c\varrho)^{1/2}e^{i\theta}L(f)\big)\} \frac{d\theta}{2\pi} \qquad (48.3.80)$$

into an integral over positive-definite functions on E, and is thus an element of $\mathcal{P}(E)$ for itself.

Since $|c^{1/2}L(f)|$ is time-invariant (by assumption on the quasi-free state φ with invariant (48.3.78)), the decomposition

$$C_\varphi(f) = \int_0^\infty e^{-\varrho} \underbrace{\exp\{iF(f)\}\exp\{-\tfrac{1}{4}\|T^{1/2}f\|^2\} J_0(|c^{1/2}L(f)|\varrho^{1/2})}_{=:\, C_\varrho(f)} \, d\varrho, \quad (48.3.81)$$

signifies a subcentral decomposition $\varphi = \int_0^\infty \varphi_\varrho\, e^{-\varrho} d\varrho$ into the time-invariant states φ_ϱ given by the characteristic functions $C_\varrho(f)$, $\varrho \in [0,\infty[$.

The central decomposition of φ_ϱ into the factor states is gotten by inserting into the integrand of (48.3.81) the decomposition (48.3.80). That gives

$$C_\varrho(f) = \int_0^{2\pi} \underbrace{\exp\{iF(f)\}\exp\{-\tfrac{1}{4}\|T^{1/2}f\|^2\} \exp\{i\,\mathrm{Re}\big((c\varrho)^{1/2}e^{i\theta}L(f)\big)\}}_{=:\, C_{\varrho,\theta}(f)} \, \frac{d\theta}{2\pi},$$

$$(48.3.82)$$

which conforms to the general quasi-free central decomposition of Theorem 25.1-17 on page 662,

$$\varphi = \int_0^{2\pi}\int_0^\infty \varphi_{\varrho,\theta}\; e^{-\varrho}\, d\varrho\; \frac{d\theta}{2\pi},$$

since the $C_{\varrho,\theta}(f)$ define mutually disjoint factorial states $\varphi_{\varrho,\theta}$.

But the $C_{\varrho,\theta}(f)$ depend on $e^{i\theta}L(f)$ and thus may not be time-invariant, as in the following physically relevant example (cf. Sec. 31.3.2 on page 914): If the spin-0 Bosons condense into the mode k we have with $E \subset L^2(\mathbb{R}^3, \mathbb{C}, d^3x)$ that $L(f) := \widehat{f}(k)$ is the point evaluation at the fixed momentum $k \in \mathbb{R}^3$. Moreover one has $L(v_t f) = \exp\{it|k|^n\}\widehat{f}(k)$, where the value $n = 2$ is typical for material Bosons and $n = 1$ for photons (where f then is the polarization component). For $k \neq 0$ the unbounded linear form L is not time-invariant (meaning an oscillating macroscopic plane wave), but $\overline{cL(v_t f)}L(v_t f) = c\overline{\widehat{f}(k)}\widehat{f}(k)$ is time-independent.

Because of asymptotic Abelianess, the ergodic decomposition of φ_ϱ is subcentral, and must thus be obtained by such a coarsening of the finest subcentral decomposition Eq. (48.3.82), which leads to an invariant expression. This succeeds only by integrating over the total phase angle interval, what produces just φ_ϱ. We conclude therefrom that the φ_ϱ are extremal time-invariant and that (48.3.81) gives the ergodic decomposition of the invariant quasi-free state φ.

We see that the ergodic states φ_ϱ are not factorial and do not satisfy the asymptotic product property. So the φ_ϱ especially do not satisfy the direct 3-point clustering, but do of course satisfy the $\mathbb{R}$-cluster condition. The latter is directly verified by observing that the scalars are the time-invariant part of the center of the GNS representation over φ_ϱ, and $m_{\mathbb{R}}^0$ maps therefore $\mathcal{M}_\varrho$ onto $\mathbb{C}\mathbb{1}_\varrho$, giving $m_{\mathbb{R}}^0(M) = \langle \varphi_\varrho; M\rangle\mathbb{1}_\varrho$. In accordance with Eq. (48.3.37) on page 1823 and with

Proposition 48.3-23 (g)(iv) on page 1827, we obtain

$$\langle \varphi_\varrho; m^0_{\mathbb{R}}(M)C \rangle = \langle \varphi_\varrho; M \rangle \langle \varphi_\varrho; C \rangle, \quad \forall M, C \in \mathcal{M}_\varrho. \tag{48.3.83}$$

We have here "broken time invariance" in the central decomposition of φ_ϱ, and remark by the way, that $m^0_{\mathbb{R}}$ is not decomposed by that decomposition, in contrast to "unbroken time invariance".

48.4. Algebraic Transition Probabilities

48.4.1. *Generalities*

Transition probabilities are formulated in traditional Hilbert space quantum mechanics for vector states only. This notion has been generalized by several authors to general states in a much wider framework. We have discussed it in the convex state space approach for spectral convex sets in Sec. 47.4.3 according to Cantoni's ansatz [Can75]. This general setting discloses very clearly the basic features and statistical meaning of transition probabilities. Since the state spaces of C*-algebras are special spectral convex sets, the general notions and results can be taken over immediately. The Hilbert space representations of C*-algebras and their states provide of course more powerful analytical tools and more detailed expressions.

For C*-algebras, the convex state space approach, following [Can75], [Gud78], [Had82] on the one side, and the direct definition via density operators in representations, employed in [Bur69], [Uhl76], [Rag82], [AR82], [Alb83], [AU83], [Uhl85], [Alb92] on the other side, have been proved equivalent. For our applications in the C*-algebraic framework, we need additional results, which we extract from our unpublished works [Zan95], [GRZ03]. The derived formulas seem of use in many-body physics and quantum optics. Among other things, the subcentral decompositions of the transition probabilities would provide a clear distinction between classical fluctuations and quantum noise.

As mentioned in Sec. 47.4.3, Gudder [Gud78] gave a direct axiomatic characterization of Cantoni's transition probability in the rather general frame of a Mackey system (which covers also the classical case). This shows, that Cantoni's definition is based, in fact, on the fundamental aspects of a transition probability. We give again Cantoni's definition, now adapted to von Neumann and C*-algebras.

A positive linear functional on a C*-algebra differs from a state by a positive scaling factor and thus is denoted a *scaled state*.

Definition 48.4-1 (Cantoni [Can75]). Let $\mathcal{M}$ be a W*-algebra and $\omega, \varphi \in \mathcal{M}_{*,+}$ normal scaled states. For an observable $A = \int_{\mathbb{R}} t \, dP_A(t) \in \mathcal{M}_{\mathrm{sa}}$ let ω^A, and φ^A be the corresponding measures over the reals obtained by using the spectral measure ($\omega^A(\mathsf{B}) = \langle \omega; P_A(\mathsf{B}) \rangle$, B a real Borel set, and similar for φ^A). The transition probability between ω and φ is then defined as

$$T_{\mathcal{M}}(\omega,\varphi) := \inf_{A \in \mathcal{M}_{\mathrm{sa}}} \left\{ \left(\int_{\mathbb{R}} \sqrt{\frac{d\omega^A}{d\sigma}} \sqrt{\frac{d\varphi^A}{d\sigma}} \, d\sigma \right)^2 \right\}, \qquad (48.4.1)$$

where σ is any finite measure, with respect to which ω^A and φ^A are absolutely continuous.

For scaled states $\omega, \varphi \in \mathcal{A}_+^*$ of a C^*-algebra $\mathcal{A}$, the transition probability is defined using the bidual von Neumann algebra $\mathcal{A}^{**} \equiv \mathcal{M}_u$ (where we do not in this context distinguish notationally between the states on $\mathcal{A}$ and their normal extensions to $\mathcal{A}^{**}$):

$$T_{\mathcal{A}}(\omega,\varphi) := T_{\mathcal{A}^{**}}(\omega,\varphi). \qquad (48.4.2)$$

The transition probability is thus determined by the infimum of a kind of "spectral overlap", taken over all observables. There are *always* observables for which the integral in (48.4.1) gives unity, and thus only an infimum definition introduces a non-trivial structure. The integral in (48.4.1) compares for fixed observable A two statistical distributions on its spectrum. It is a special case of an *informational divergence*

$$f(\mu,\nu) := \int_{\mathbb{R}} f\left(\frac{d\mu}{d\sigma}, \frac{d\nu}{d\sigma}\right) d\sigma, \qquad (48.4.3)$$

or *f-divergence*, where f is some convex function. The other most popular f-divergence is the *relative entropy*

$$S(\mu,\nu) := -\int_{\mathbb{R}} \ln\left(\frac{d\mu}{d\nu}\right) d\nu, \quad \mu \prec \nu. \qquad (48.4.4)$$

($\mu \prec \nu$ means that μ is absolutely continuous with respect to ν.)

From the general theory of f–divergences follow some properties of the transition probability.

Proposition 48.4-2. *Let $\mathcal{A}$ be a C^*-algebra with state space $\mathcal{S}(\mathcal{A})$. Then the transition probability mapping*

$$T_{\mathcal{A}} : \mathcal{S}(\mathcal{A}) \times \mathcal{S}(\mathcal{A}) \longrightarrow [0,1], \quad (\omega,\varphi) \longmapsto T_{\mathcal{A}}(\omega,\varphi)$$

is separately convex and jointly continuous with respect to the norm topology. It is jointly lower semi-continuous with respect to the weak* topology [Zan95].

Furtheron we have [Uhl76] the inequalities:

$$0 \leq T_{\mathcal{A}}^{\frac{1}{2}}(\omega,\varphi) \leq 1 - \frac{1}{2}\|\omega - \varphi\| \leq 1, \qquad (48.4.5)$$

where for two pure states, the equality is valid in the second comparison, so that in this case norm difference and transition probability are in a bijective decreasing relation with each other:

$$\|\omega - \varphi\| = 2\left(1 - T_{\mathcal{A}}^{\frac{1}{2}}(\omega,\varphi)\right). \qquad (48.4.6)$$

We conclude that the transition probability vanishes between any two states with the norm difference 2, the maximal norm difference.

In this connection let us prove that maximal norm difference holds for disjoint states (cf. Definition 46.2-17 for disjoint states).

Lemma 48.4-3 (Norm Difference between Disjoint States). *The norm difference between any two disjoint states ω and φ on a C*-algebra $\mathcal{A}$ is equal to 2 (so that they have vanishing transition probability by Eq. (48.4.5)).*

Proof. Let C_ω and C_φ be the central, mutually orthogonal supports (in $\mathcal{A}^{**}$) of the two states and note that $\mathcal{A}^{**} = C_\omega \mathcal{A}^{**} C_\omega \oplus C_\varphi \mathcal{A}^{**} C_\varphi \oplus (\mathbb{1} - C_\omega - C_\varphi)\mathcal{A}^{**}(\mathbb{1} - C_\omega - C_\varphi)$. By this direct sum decomposition, the norm of an element $A \in \mathcal{A}^{**}$ is the supremum over the norms of its reductions to the direct summands, and we obtain $\|C_\omega - C_\varphi\| \leq \sup\{\|C_\omega\|, \|C_\varphi\|\} \leq 1$. So,

$$2 \geq \|\omega - \varphi\| = \sup_{\|A\| \leq 1} |\langle \omega - \varphi; A\rangle| \geq |\langle \omega - \varphi; C_\omega - C_\varphi\rangle| = \langle \omega; C_\omega\rangle + \langle \varphi; C_\varphi\rangle = 2$$

(48.4.7)

gives the result. $\square$

Conversely, vanishing transition amplitude, or norm difference 2, is of course not sufficient for the disjointness of two states.

Without the reference to a representation, there holds the surprising, useful relation [Alb83]:

Proposition 48.4-4 (Variation over Invertible Operators). *Let ω and φ be states on a C*-algebra $\mathcal{A}$, then*

$$T_A(\omega, \varphi) = \inf\{\langle \omega; A\rangle\langle \varphi; A^{-1}\rangle \mid A \in \mathcal{A}^+, \ A \text{ invertible}\}.$$

A first connection to expressions with the Hilbert space *transition amplitudes*, which arise here as secondary notions, provides the following result (cf. [Uhl76], [AR82]).

Theorem 48.4-5 (Connection with Transition Amplitudes). *Let ω and φ be scaled states of a C*-algebra $\mathcal{A}$. Then*

$$T_A(\omega, \varphi) = \sup\left\{|(\Omega \mid \Phi)|^2\right\},$$

(48.4.8)

where the supremum is taken over all vector representatives Ω and Φ of ω and φ within all non-degenerate representations of $\mathcal{A}$ in Hilbert spaces.

Observe that in (48.4.8) the modulus of the transition amplitudes is maximized, while varying the Hilbert space representations, what conforms more to the traditional point of view. For two given states, there are *always* two mutually orthogonal vector representatives, and thus one has to seek the maximal modulus of the transition amplitudes. The equivalence to Cantoni's expression, fitting to general spectral convex state spaces, demonstrates that the complex transition amplitudes in Hilbert space formalism are not indispensable for expressing *a–priori* transition probabilities between (pure) states.

In Eq. (48.4.8), it suffices to work in a fixed representation of $\mathcal{A}$ in which both of the states are represented by vectors. As prominent examples for such a representation we mention the universal, and for W*-algebras the standard, representation where *all* states, respectively *all normal* states, are represented by some vectors. The supremum is then taken over all vector representatives of ω and φ in the chosen representation. If one analyzes the set of representing vectors further, the following result arises:

Proposition 48.4-6 (Alberti [Alb83]). *Let ω, φ be states of a C*-algebra $\mathcal{A}$, and Π a non-degenerate representation of $\mathcal{A}$ on some Hilbert space $\mathcal{H}$, such that ω and φ are represented by $\Omega, \Phi \in \mathcal{H}$. Then*

$$T_{\mathcal{A}}(\omega, \varphi) = \sup_{K \in \Pi(\mathcal{A})'_1} \left\{ \left| (\Omega | K\Phi) \right|^2 \right\} = \sup_{U \in U(\Pi(\mathcal{A})')} \left\{ \left| (\Omega | U\Phi) \right|^2 \right\}, \qquad (48.4.9)$$

with $\Pi(\mathcal{A})'_1$ the unit sphere of the commutant $\Pi(\mathcal{A})'$ of $\Pi(\mathcal{A})$ and $U(\Pi(\mathcal{A})')$ the unitary elements therein.

As an exercise, we prove the following.

Lemma 48.4-7 (Transitions to a Perturbed State). *Let ω be a state of the unital C*-algebra $\mathcal{A}$, which we extend to a normal state on $\mathcal{A}^{**}$, and let $C > 0$ be an element in $\mathcal{A}^{**}$, such that $\langle \omega; C^*C \rangle > 0$. Then (with ω_C as introduced in Definition 46.2-12) it holds*

$$T_{\mathcal{A}}(\omega, \omega_C) = \frac{|(\Omega|C\Omega)|^2}{\|C\Omega\|^2} \overset{\text{if } C \text{ equals a projection } P}{=} \langle \omega; P \rangle.$$

Note that also for $C \in \mathcal{A}^{**}$ we have still $\omega_C \in \mathcal{F}_\omega$, and that ω feels effectively only $C_\omega C$ as a perturbation, where again $C_\omega \in \mathcal{A}^{**}$ is the central support of ω.

Proof. Let ω be represented by the vector Ω in the Hilbert space of the universal representation of $\mathcal{A}$. Then $\frac{C\Omega}{\|C\Omega\|}$ represents ω_C and by the preceding Proposition we have

$$T_{\mathcal{A}}^{\frac{1}{2}}(\omega, \omega_C) = \sup \left\{ \frac{|(\Omega|UC\Omega)|}{\|C\Omega\|} \,\middle|\, U \text{ is a unitary in } (\mathcal{A}^{**})' \right\}$$

$$= \sup \left\{ \frac{|(C^{1/2}\Omega|UC^{1/2}\Omega)|}{\|C\Omega\|} \,\middle|\, U \text{ is a unitary in } (\mathcal{A}^{**})' \right\}$$

$$= \frac{|(C^{1/2}\Omega|C^{1/2}\Omega)|}{\|C\Omega\|},$$

where in the last step the Cauchy–Schwartz inequality has been used. □

Without proof we communicate further consequences of Proposition 48.4-6.

Corollary 48.4-8. *Let* ω, φ *be normal scaled states on a W*-algebra* $\mathcal{M}$. *Then we have:*

(a) $T_{\mathcal{M}}(\omega, \varphi) = T_{\mathcal{M}}(\omega, \varphi_{P_\omega})$, *where* P_ω *is the support of* ω *in* $\mathcal{P}(\mathcal{M})$, *the lattice of orthogonal projections in* $\mathcal{M}$, *and* $\langle \varphi_{P_\omega} ; \cdot \rangle := \langle \varphi; P_\omega \cdot P_\omega \rangle$.

(b) $T_{\mathcal{M}}(\omega, \varphi) = 0$, *if and only if* $P_\omega \perp P_\varphi$. *Especially if* $\mathcal{M}$ *is* $\mathcal{A}^{**}$ *for a C*-algebra* $\mathcal{A}$, *one has (for all* $\omega, \varphi \in \mathcal{S}(\mathcal{A})$)

$$T_{\mathcal{A}}(\omega, \varphi) = 0, \text{ if and only if } S_\omega \perp S_\varphi,$$

where S_ω *is the support of* ω *in* $\mathcal{A}^{**}$ *etc.*

(c) *If* $P_\omega, P_\varphi \leq P \in \mathcal{P}(\mathcal{M})$, *then*

$$T_{\mathcal{M}}(\omega, \varphi) = T_{P\mathcal{M}P}(\omega, \varphi).$$

(d) *If the C*-algebra* $\mathcal{A}$ *is also a W*-algebra then both versions of Definition 48.4-1 coincide for normal states.*

If we combine the previous (b) with (48.4.6) we obtain another result on the norm difference of states, what is of general interest for continuity questions concerning the Schrödinger dynamics.

Corollary 48.4-9 (Maximal Norm Difference between Pure States). *The norm difference between any two pure (normal) states on a C*-algebra* $\mathcal{A}$ *(W*-algebra* $\mathcal{M}$) *attains the maximal value 2, if and only if the states have mutually orthogonal support projections in* $\mathcal{A}^{**}$ *(* $\mathcal{M}$ *); and this is valid if and only if the states have vanishing transition probability.*

For a direct verification in the case of two vector states on $\mathcal{L}(\mathcal{H})$, represented by $\Omega, \Phi \in \mathcal{H}$, take (48.4.7) with $A = |\Omega)(\Omega| - |\Phi)(\Phi|$ and show $\||\Omega)(\Omega| - |\Phi)(\Phi|\|| = 1$, for orthogonal vectors.

Combining this with a result of [GK60], we may announce.

Proposition 48.4-10 (Unitary Equivalence of Pure States). *If the transition probability between two pure states* ω, φ *on a C*-algebra* $\mathcal{A}$ *is non-vanishing, then there is a unitary* $U \in \mathcal{A}$ *such that* $\omega = \varphi_U$ *(the latter relation being equivalent to the unitary equivalence of the two irreducible GNS representations over the two pure states).*

If this strengthened form $\omega = \varphi_U$ *of quasi-equivalence, called* unitary *or* spatial equivalence, *is not valid, then the two pure states are disjoint, denoted* $\omega \,\flat\, \varphi$ *(and have norm difference 2 and vanishing transition probability).*

Of course, also for pure states, vanishing transition probability, being equivalent to norm difference 2, does not imply disjointness.

After having exhibited the usefulness of Proposition 48.4-6, we sharpen it.

Proposition 48.4-11 (Special Vector Representatives). *Let* ω, φ *be scaled states on a C*-algebra* $\mathcal{A}$, *and* Π *a non-degenerate representation of* $\mathcal{A}$ *in some*

Hilbert space $\mathcal{H}$, such that ω, φ are represented by $\Omega, \Phi \in \mathcal{H}$. Then:

(a) *There is a $K \in \Pi(\mathcal{A})'_1$ such that:*

$$T_{\mathcal{A}}(\omega, \varphi) = \left(\Omega \mid K\Phi\right)^2.$$

(b) *For each $\Omega' \in \mathcal{H}$ which represents ω there is a $\Phi' \in \mathcal{H}$ such that:*

$$T_{\mathcal{A}}(\omega, \varphi) = \left(\Omega' \mid \Phi'\right)^2.$$

We have the following measure theoretic results due to Hadjisavvas [Had82] and Kosaki [Kos83] which allow to take the infimum in Definition 48.4-1 over a smaller class of observables.

Proposition 48.4-12 (Infimum Over Fewer Observables). *Let ω, φ be normal states on a von Neumann algebra $\mathcal{M}$.*

(a) *Denote by $\mathcal{O}_f$ the set of those observables in $\mathcal{M}_{sa}$, whose spectrum consists of a finite number of points and by*

$$\mathcal{Z}_f = \left\{ (P_i)_{i \le n} \,\middle|\, n \in \mathbb{N}, \ P_i \in \mathcal{P}(\mathcal{M}), \ \sum_{i \le n} P_i = \mathbb{1} \right\}$$

the set of finite decompositions of the identity in pair-wise orthogonal projections. Then we have:

$$T_{\mathcal{M}}^{\frac{1}{2}}(\omega, \varphi) = \inf_{A \in \mathcal{O}_f} \left\{ \int_{\mathbb{R}} \sqrt{\frac{d\omega_A}{d\sigma}} \sqrt{\frac{d\varphi_A}{d\sigma}} \, d\sigma \right\} = \inf_{(P_i)_{i \le n} \in \mathcal{Z}_f} \left\{ \sum_{i \le n} \left(\langle \omega \, ; P_i \rangle \langle \varphi \, ; P_i \rangle\right)^{\frac{1}{2}} \right\}.$$

(b) *Let $(\mathcal{M}_i)_{i \in I}$ be an increasing net of von Neumann subalgebras of $\mathcal{M}$ satisfying $\mathcal{M} = \left(\bigcup_{i \in I} \mathcal{M}_i\right)''$ then one may work with the state restrictions $\omega_{|\mathcal{M}_i}, \varphi_{|\mathcal{M}_i}$,*

$$T_{\mathcal{M}}(\omega, \varphi) = \inf_{i \in I} T_{\mathcal{M}_i}(\omega_{|\mathcal{M}_i}, \varphi_{|\mathcal{M}_i}) = \lim_{i \in I} T_{\mathcal{M}_i}(\omega_{|\mathcal{M}_i}, \varphi_{|\mathcal{M}_i}).$$

Now we show, how the concept of a transition probability can be further employed to exhibit and illustrate the disjointness of states.

Proposition 48.4-13 (Perturbed Vanishing Transition Probabilities). *Let $\mathcal{A}$ be a C*-algebra, with a norm-dense subset $\mathcal{B} \subset \mathcal{A}$, and ω and φ be (normalized) states on $\mathcal{A}$. Then*

$$T_{\mathcal{A}}(\omega_B, \varphi) = 0 \text{ for all } B \in \mathcal{B}, \text{ if and only if } \omega \, \delta \, \varphi, \qquad (48.4.10)$$

(where, in the context of normalized states, we repeat that

$$\langle \omega_A ; \cdot \rangle := \begin{cases} \langle \omega; A^* \cdot A \rangle / \langle \omega; A^* A \rangle & \text{if } \langle \omega; A^* A \rangle \neq 0, \\ \langle \omega; \cdot \rangle & \text{otherwise;} \end{cases}$$

and that $\omega \, \delta \, \varphi$ denotes the disjointness of ω and φ, cf. Definition 46.2-17).

Especially that demonstrates that $T_{\mathcal{A}}(\psi, \varphi) = 0 \ \forall \psi \in \mathcal{F}_\omega$ is equivalent to the disjointness relation $\omega \, \delta \, \varphi$.

Proof. If ω and φ are disjoint states on $\mathcal{A}$, then also ω_B and φ are disjoint, and we can apply Lemma 48.4-3 to get the left-hand side of (48.4.10).

For the reverse part note that (48.4.10) implies that $T_\mathcal{A}(\omega', \varphi) = 0$ for all ω' from the folium $\mathcal{F}_\omega$. For this, use the convexity and norm continuity of $T_\mathcal{A}(\omega, \varphi)$ in ω, according to Proposition 48.4-2. This implies $S_\varphi \wedge C_\omega = 0$ and thus $S_\varphi \wedge [C_\varphi - C_\varphi \wedge C_\omega] = S_\varphi \wedge C_\varphi = S_\varphi$. Since C_φ is the smallest central projection dominating S_φ, $C_\varphi \wedge C_\omega$ must be zero and the two states are disjoint. $\qquad\square$

In words: The states ω and φ are disjoint, if and only if sufficiently many perturbations of the one state have vanishing transition probability to the other state; a neat expression for a global distinctness of states.

The preceding "sufficiently many perturbations", formed with a norm-dense subset of observables, may be modified as follows.

Proposition 48.4-14. *Let be* $\mathcal{A} = \overline{\bigcup_{\Lambda \in \mathcal{L}} \mathcal{A}_\Lambda}^{\|\cdot\|}$ *a quasilocal algebra in the sense of Chapter 2.6 of [BR87] (see also our Proposition 33.3-7 on page 989), where the index set* $\mathcal{L}$ *is equipped with a partial ordering* $\leq$ *and an orthogonality relation* $\perp$. *For every* $\Lambda \in \mathcal{L}$, *one introduces the outside algebra*

$$\mathcal{A}_\Lambda^\perp := \bigcup_{\Lambda' \perp \Lambda} \mathcal{A}_{\Lambda'}^{ev} \subset \mathcal{A}_\Lambda^{ev\,\prime}, \quad \text{(where the dash designates the commutant within}\,\mathcal{A}).$$

Here $\mathcal{A}_\Lambda^{ev} := \mathcal{A}_\Lambda + \sigma(\mathcal{A}_\Lambda)$ *are the so-called even elements with respect to the involutive automorphism* σ, *which become relevant in the presence of Fermions.*

Now, two states ω *and* φ *are disjoint, if and only if* $T_{\mathcal{A}_\Lambda^\perp}(\omega, \varphi) = 0$ *for all* $\Lambda \in \mathcal{L}$. *This is the case if and only if there is an absorbing subnet* $\mathcal{L}' \subset \mathcal{L}$ *with* $\lim_{\Lambda' \in \mathcal{L}} T_{\mathcal{A}_{\Lambda'}^\perp}(\omega, \varphi) = 0$.

In words: The vanishing of the "spectral overlap" of all observables at infinity (including especially the mean field averages) is already sufficient for disjointness. This plays a role for a subcentral decomposition of states, especially for the canonical decomposition of mean field supporting into mean field-fixing states.

It is not trivial to express the transition probability for mixed states in traditional quantum mechanics in terms of their density operators.

Proposition 48.4-15 (Uhlmann [Uhl76]). *Let* ω, φ *be normal states on* $\mathcal{L}(\mathcal{H})$, *which are given in terms of the density operators* $\rho_\omega, \rho_\varphi$, *respectively. Then it holds:*

$$T_{\mathcal{L}(\mathcal{H})}^{\frac{1}{2}}(\omega, \varphi) = \mathrm{tr}_\mathcal{H}\left\{ \left(\rho_\omega^{\frac{1}{2}} \rho_\varphi \rho_\omega^{\frac{1}{2}} \right)^{\frac{1}{2}} \right\}. \qquad (48.4.11)$$

48.4.2.   *Transition Probabilities between Finite Products of States*

Given two C*-algebras $\mathcal{A}_1, \mathcal{A}_2$ for the observables of separated systems, and a C*-cross norm $\|.\|_\beta$, we introduce as in the text before Definition 45.3-17 on page 1669 the C*-tensor product

$$\mathcal{A}_\beta = \mathcal{A}_1 \otimes_\beta \mathcal{A}_2 \tag{48.4.12}$$

in order to describe the composite system.

A product state $\varphi = \varphi_1 \otimes \varphi_2$ of the composite system is characterized by

$$\langle \varphi \,;\, A_1 \otimes A_2 \rangle = \langle \varphi_1 \,;\, A_1 \rangle \langle \varphi_2 \,;\, A_2 \rangle \,, \tag{48.4.13}$$

for all $A_1 \in \mathcal{A}_1, A_2 \in \mathcal{A}_2$, where φ_i are states on $\mathcal{A}_i$, $i \in \{1, 2\}$. The factorization in Eq. (48.4.13) describes the statistical independence of the subsystems in the state φ (but does not exclude an "ordered situation").

The following plausible result is technically not quite trivial.

Proposition 48.4-16 (C*-Tensor Product Factorization). *Let $\mathcal{A}_1, \mathcal{A}_2$ be C*-algebras and $\omega_1, \varphi_1 \in \mathcal{S}(\mathcal{A}_1)$, $\omega_2, \varphi_2 \in \mathcal{S}(\mathcal{A}_2)$. For the product states $\omega = \omega_1 \otimes \omega_2$ and $\varphi = \varphi_1 \otimes \varphi_2$ on $\mathcal{A} = \mathcal{A}_1 \otimes_\beta \mathcal{A}_2$, where β is any cross norm on the algebraic tensor product $\mathcal{A}_1 \odot \mathcal{A}_2$, we have*

$$T_\mathcal{A}(\omega, \varphi) = T_{\mathcal{A}_1}(\omega_1, \varphi_1) \cdot T_{\mathcal{A}_2}(\omega_2, \varphi_2) \,. \tag{48.4.14}$$

Proof. We first obtain an upper bound for the product of transition probabilities by means of transition amplitudes in Hilbert space representations.

Let Π_i $(i \in \{1, 2\})$ be representations of $\mathcal{A}_i$ in $\mathcal{H}_i$ such that ω_i, φ_i are represented by $\Omega_i \in \mathcal{H}_i$ and $\Phi_i \in \mathcal{H}_i$. Then $\Pi_1 \odot \Pi_2$ extends to a representation of $\mathcal{A}$ and ω, φ are realized by $\Omega_1 \otimes \Omega_2$ and $\Phi_1 \otimes \Phi_2$. By Theorem 48.4-5 we have:

$$\sup \left| (\Omega_1 | \Phi_1) \right|^2 \left| (\Omega_2 | \Phi_2) \right|^2 = T_{\mathcal{A}_1}(\omega_1, \varphi_1) \cdot T_{\mathcal{A}_2}(\omega_2, \varphi_2) \le T_\mathcal{A}(\omega, \varphi). \tag{48.4.15}$$

On the other hand, by an algebraic formula, we obtain the lower bound: If $A_i \in \mathcal{A}_i$ are positive and invertible, then $A_1 \otimes A_2$ is positive and invertible, too. We now apply Proposition 48.4-4 and get:

$$\begin{aligned}
T_\mathcal{A}(\omega, \varphi) &= \inf \left\{ \langle \omega \,;\, A \rangle \langle \varphi \,;\, A^{-1} \rangle \mid A \in \mathcal{A}^+, \, A \text{ invertible} \right\} \\
&\le \inf \left\{ \langle \omega \,;\, A_1 \otimes A_2 \rangle \langle \varphi \,;\, A_1^{-1} \otimes A_2^{-1} \rangle \mid A_i \in \mathcal{A}_i^+, \, A_i \text{ invertible} \right\} \\
&= \inf \left\{ \langle \omega_1 \,;\, A_1 \rangle \langle \varphi_1 \,;\, A_1^{-1} \rangle \mid A_1 \in \mathcal{A}_1^+, \, A_1 \text{ invertible} \right\} \cdot \\
&\qquad\qquad \cdot \inf \left\{ \langle \omega_2 \,;\, A_2 \rangle \langle \varphi_2 \,;\, A_2^{-1} \rangle \mid A_2 \in \mathcal{A}_2^+, \, A_2 \text{ invertible} \right\} \\
&= T_{\mathcal{A}_1}(\omega_1, \varphi_1) \cdot T_{\mathcal{A}_2}(\omega_2, \varphi_2).
\end{aligned}$$

$\square$

For the study of transition probabilities always von Neumann algebras come into play, for which we define spatial tensor products. (The here pre-supposed tensor product of Hilbert spaces is supplemented in Definition 48.4-23 below.)

Definition 48.4-17 (Abstract and Spatial W*-Tensor Products). Let be given two W*-algebras $\mathcal{M}_1$ and $\mathcal{M}_2$.

(a) For defining the abstract (= Hilbert space independent) W*-tensor product one forms first the injective C^*-tensor product $\mathcal{A} = \mathcal{M}_1 \otimes \mathcal{M}_2$. Denoting by $\mathcal{M}_{1*} \otimes \mathcal{M}_{2*}$ the algebraic tensor product of the preduals $\mathcal{M}_{i*}$ completed by the dual cross norm in $\mathcal{A}^*$ of the injective C^*-cross norm in $\mathcal{A}$, we write

$$\mathcal{M}_1 \overline{\otimes} \mathcal{M}_2 := (\mathcal{M}_{1*} \otimes \mathcal{M}_{2*})^* = \mathcal{A}^{**} Z \qquad (48.4.16)$$

for the abstract W*-tensor product, where Z is the central projection in the universal enveloping von Neumann algebra $\mathcal{A}^{**}$ of $\mathcal{A}$, which is associated with $\mathcal{M}_{1*} \otimes \mathcal{M}_{2*}$.

(Concerning the central projection $Z \subset \mathcal{A}^{**}$, observe that $\mathcal{M}_{1*} \otimes \mathcal{M}_{2*}$ is by definition a subspace of $\mathcal{A}^*$, the predual of $\mathcal{A}^{**}$, which is norm-closed and bi-invariant under perturbations by elements of the C^*-algebra $\mathcal{A}$, and apply the theorems on such bi-invariant spaces in [Sak71, Tak79]; or note that the intersection of that bi-invariant subspace with $\mathcal{S}(\mathcal{A})$ is a folium and apply Theorem 46.2-21.)

(b) For the spatial W*-tensor product consider two Neumann algebras $\widetilde{\mathcal{M}}_i$ in the Hilbert spaces $\mathcal{H}_i$, and form $\widetilde{\mathcal{M}}_1 \overline{\otimes}_{\mathcal{H}} \widetilde{\mathcal{M}}_2$ as the smallest von Neumann algebra in $\mathcal{H} := \mathcal{H}_1 \otimes \mathcal{H}_2$, which contains the canonically embedded algebras $(i = 1, 2)$

$$\alpha_i : \widetilde{\mathcal{M}}_i \longrightarrow \mathcal{L}(\mathcal{H}_1 \otimes \mathcal{H}_2) \,, \; \alpha_1(M_1) = M_1 \otimes \mathbb{1}, \alpha_2(M_2) = \mathbb{1} \otimes M_2 \,. \quad (48.4.17)$$

That means,

$$\widetilde{\mathcal{M}}_1 \overline{\otimes}_{\mathcal{H}} \widetilde{\mathcal{M}}_2 := \left(\alpha_1(\widetilde{\mathcal{M}}_1) \cup \alpha_2(\widetilde{\mathcal{M}}_2) \right)'' \,. \qquad (48.4.18)$$

From the abstract construction (a) follows that two normal states φ_i on $\mathcal{M}_i$ lead to an unique normal product state φ on $\mathcal{M}_1 \overline{\otimes} \mathcal{M}_2$, what is even more evident for the spatial construction (b).

Proposition 48.4-18 ("Spatial" versus "Represented" Tensor Products).
Let be given two W-algebras $\mathcal{M}_{1/2}$ and two faithful normal representations*

$$\Pi_i : \mathcal{M}_i \xrightarrow{onto} \widetilde{\mathcal{M}}_i \subset \mathcal{L}(\mathcal{H}_i) \,, \quad i = 1, 2 \,.$$

Then the product representation of the injective C^*-tensor product

$$\Pi_1 \otimes \Pi_2 : \mathcal{M}_1 \otimes \mathcal{M}_2 \longrightarrow \mathcal{L}(\mathcal{H}_1 \otimes \mathcal{H}_2)$$

extends uniquely to the faithful normal representation of the abstract tensor product

$$\Pi_1 \otimes \Pi_2 : \mathcal{M}_1 \overline{\otimes} \mathcal{M}_2 \xrightarrow{onto} \widetilde{\mathcal{M}}_1 \overline{\otimes} \widetilde{\mathcal{M}}_2 \,.$$

This demonstrates the isomorphic structure of the W-algebraic and spatial tensor products, irrespective of the employed Hilbert spaces, and we henceforth shall mostly drop the index $\mathcal{H}$ for the spatial tensor product.*

The preceding Proposition is relevant for the observable algebra of two *combined physical systems*, which in traditional Hilbert space quantum theory have each an observable algebra of the type $\mathcal{A}_i = \mathcal{M}_i = \mathcal{L}(\mathcal{H}_i)$. The C*-tensor product $\mathcal{M}_1 \otimes \mathcal{M}_2$, as completion of the algebraic tensor product by the injective cross norm, is as such not related to the Hilbert space $\mathcal{H} = \mathcal{H}_1 \otimes \mathcal{H}_2$, but has a faithful representation in it. The extension of the representation to a representation of the abstract W*-tensor product $\mathcal{M}_1 \overline{\otimes} \mathcal{M}_2$ gives by the preceding Proposition the image algebra $\mathcal{L}(\mathcal{H}_1) \overline{\otimes}_{\mathcal{H}} \mathcal{L}(\mathcal{H}_2) = \mathcal{L}(\mathcal{H})$, so that the succession of the steps in that construction is irrelevant.

The abstract and spatial W*-tensor products can be associatively extended to finitely many members.

We are now able to generalize the product formulas for transition probabilities of [Bur69], given there for semi-finite W*-algebras only.

Proposition 48.4-19. *Let be given a finite family of arbitrary W*-algebras $\mathcal{M}_i$ with pairs of normal states $\omega_i,\, \varphi_i \in \mathcal{M}_{i*,1}^+$, $1 \leq i \leq n$. For each i fix a normal, faithful representation $\Pi_i : \mathcal{M}_i \xrightarrow{onto} \widetilde{\mathcal{M}}_i \subseteq \mathcal{L}(\mathcal{H}_i)$, in which $\Omega_i, \Phi_i \in \mathcal{H}_i$ realize ω_i and φ_i. In the following we consider the Ω_i arbitrary but fixed. For the normal product states $\omega = \omega_1 \otimes \cdots \otimes \omega_n$, $\varphi = \varphi_1 \otimes \cdots \otimes \varphi_n$ on $\mathcal{M} = \mathcal{M}_1 \overline{\otimes} \cdots \overline{\otimes} \mathcal{M}_n \supseteq \mathcal{A} = \mathcal{M}_1 \otimes \cdots \otimes \mathcal{M}_n$ (where $\mathcal{A}$ is given by the injective C*-tensor product) it holds:*

$$T_{\mathcal{M}}(\omega, \varphi) = T_{\mathcal{A}}(\omega, \varphi) = \prod_{i=1}^{n} (\Omega_i \,|\, \Phi_i')^2 = \prod_{i=1}^{n} T_{\mathcal{M}_i}(\omega_i, \varphi_i),$$

where the special vector representatives Φ_i' are characterized by

$$(\Omega_i \,|\, \Phi_i')^2 = \sup_{\Phi_i} |(\Omega_i \,|\, \Phi_i)|^2,$$

which exist according to Proposition 48.4-11.

Proof. By Proposition 48.4-16, we get inductively

$$T_{\mathcal{A}}(\omega, \varphi) = \prod_{i=1}^{n} T_{\mathcal{M}_i}(\omega_i, \varphi_i) = \prod_{i=1}^{n} (\Omega_i \,|\, \Phi_i')^2,$$

since $\mathcal{A}$ is a C*-tensor product of the $\mathcal{M}_i$.

Since $\mathcal{M} \subset \mathcal{A}^{**}$ and since the supports of ω, φ (namely $S_\omega = S_{\omega_i} \otimes \cdots \otimes S_{\omega_n}$ and $S_\varphi = S_{\varphi_i} \otimes \cdots \otimes S_{\varphi_n}$) as states on $\mathcal{A}$ are contained in $\mathcal{M}$, we have with Corollary 48.4-8 (d) that $T_{\mathcal{M}}(\omega, \varphi) = T_{\mathcal{A}}(\omega, \varphi)$. $\square$

48.4.3. *Infinite Tensor Product Spaces and their Operators*

We now generalize the setup to an infinite family $\{\mathcal{A}_i; i \in I\}$ of C*-algebras (which often are W*-algebras), where I is an index set of arbitrary infinite cardinality. For this, we expound the notions of an infinite numerical product and of an infinite tensor product of Hilbert spaces, introduced by von Neumann in [vN38].

The motivation for doing that more detailed than usual is the physical practice to go to quantum systems with infinitely many degrees of freedom by extending finite tensor products to infinite ones in a somewhat light-hearted manner. We demonstrate that physical concepts may then be lost and illustrate the advantage of algebraic concepts over more explicit constructions.

48.4.3.1. *Infinite Products of c-Numbers*

For the net convergence of an infinite product $\prod_I c_i$ of complex numbers

$$c_i = |c_i| \exp\{i \operatorname{Arg} c_i\} \in \mathbb{C},$$

there arise complications from the infinite number of complex phases $\operatorname{Arg} c_i \in [-\pi, \pi[$, which are to be summed up in the product. The net convergence of $\sum_I \operatorname{Arg} c_i$ means the convergence of the net of all finite partial sums, $\sum_J \operatorname{Arg} c_i, J \in F(I)$, where $F(I)$ denotes again the set of all finite subsets of I, directed by inclusion. Net convergence of the sum is valid, if and only if at most denumerably many summands are non-vanishing and the sum converges as limit of the sequence of partial sums, in any ordering of the summands, that is, in the absolute sense. If $\sum_I \operatorname{Arg} c_i$ is net-convergent, we say that $\sum_I^n \operatorname{Arg} c_i$ converges. Thus $\sum_I^n \operatorname{Arg} c_i$ converges if and only if $\sum_I^n |\operatorname{Arg} c_i|$ converges.

Similarly the net convergence of $\prod_I c_i$, which we denote by the symbol $\prod_I^n c_i$, means the convergence of the net of all finite partial products $\prod_J^n c_i, J \in F(I)$, and neither depends on a possible ordering of I. But now $\prod_I^n c_i$ converges if and only if both $\prod_I^n |c_i|$ and $\sum_I^n \operatorname{Arg} c_i$ converge. The omission of the latter condition has led von Neumann to a weakened product convergence, which he termed "quasi convergence". Another problem is the convergence of the product (to zero), if only finitely many (may be only one) factors vanish, however wild the other factors may change their values. The ruling out of such kind of a net convergence leads to a stronger concept, the "proper convergence".

Let us list these three types of product convergence in an overview ([vN38, Bur69]):

- *Net convergence:* $\prod_I^n c_i = c$, if and only if $\lim_{J \in F(I)} \prod_J c_i = c$. This holds, if and only if $\prod_I^n |c_i| = |c|$ and $\sum_I^n \operatorname{Arg} c_i = \operatorname{Arg} c$.
- *Quasi convergence:* By definition $\prod_I^q c_i$ converges, if and only if $\prod_I^q |c_i|$ converges. The value of $\prod_I^q c_i$ equals that of $\prod_I^n c_i$ if the latter converges, and the value of $\prod_I^q c_i$ is set to 0, if $\prod_I^n c_i$ does not converge (that is, if $\sum_I^n \operatorname{Arg} c_i$ does not converge).
- *Proper convergence:* $\prod_I^p c_i = c$, if and only if $\prod_I^n c_i = c$ and $\prod_{I \setminus J}^n c_i \neq 0$ for some $J \in F(I)$.

If $c_i \geq 0, \forall i \in I$, then the phases trivially converge and $\prod_I^q c_i = \prod_I^n c_i$ in any case, that is, quasi convergence is the same as net convergence.

Proper convergence implies always net convergence, and this in the way that a non-zero product value is obtained after eliminating a finite set of factors (which may have the value zero). If, the other way round, $\prod_I^p c_i$ is not convergent, thus being "divergent", this means the following: Either there is no net convergence (i.e., the moduli product and/or the sum of phases are not net-convergent), or there is net-convergence, but for all $J \in F(I)$ one has $\prod_{I\backslash J}^n c_i = 0$. Thus

$$\prod_I^n c_i = \begin{cases} \prod_I^p c_i \text{ or} \\ \prod_{I\backslash J}^n c_i = 0, \forall J \in F(I). \end{cases}$$

Concerning the moduli product, it vanishes if one modulus is 0, and thus we consider first the case $c_i > 0$ for all $i \in I$. We then note that $\prod_I^n c_i = \prod_I \exp\{\ln(c_i)\}$ is convergent, if and only if $\sum_I^n \ln(c_i) = \sum_I^n \ln(1 + r_i)$, $r_i := c_i - 1$, converges. This holds if and only if there is a denumerable subset $I_0 \cong \mathbb{N}$ with $r_i = 0$ for all $i \in I\backslash I_0$, and $\sum_{\mathbb{N}} \ln(1 + r_i)$ converges absolute.

Necessary is $\lim_{\mathbb{N}} r_i = 0$. Thus eventually (after a finite number of steps), the r_i wander into the interval $]-\frac{1}{2}, \frac{1}{2}[$, and the c_i into $]\frac{1}{2}, \frac{3}{2}[$. If we moreover know that the c_i always are in $[0, 1]$ (as in the case of transition probabilities), the r_i wander eventually into $]-\frac{1}{2}, 0]$. Using the Taylor power series expansion for $\ln(1 + r_i)$, we obtain

$$\frac{\ln(1 + r_i)}{r_i} = 1 - \frac{r_i}{2} + \frac{r_i^2}{3} - \frac{r_i^3}{4} \pm \dots .$$

If we define

$$R := \frac{|r_i|}{2} + \frac{|r_i|^2}{3} + \frac{|r_i|^3}{4} + \dots \leq \frac{|r_i|}{2} \sum_{m=0}^{\infty} |r_i|^m = \frac{|r_i|}{2(1 - |r_i|)} < \frac{1}{2}, \quad |r_i| < \frac{1}{2},$$

then $\frac{1}{2} \leq 1 - R \leq \frac{\ln(1+r_i)}{r_i} \leq 1 + R \leq \frac{3}{2}$ for $r_i \in]-\frac{1}{2}, \frac{1}{2}[$, which gives the two-sided estimate

$$\frac{1}{2}|r_i| \leq |\ln(1 + r_i)| < \frac{3}{2}|r_i|, \quad \text{for all } r_i \in]-\frac{1}{2}, \frac{1}{2}[. \tag{48.4.19}$$

Thus, $\sum_I^n |r_i|$ converges, if and only if $\sum_I^n |\ln(1 + r_i)|$ converges.

The above inequalities have been derived for $c_i > 0$. If a single c_i equals 0, then $\prod_I^n c_i$ is convergent with value 0, but, because of $|\ln(1 + r_i)| = \infty$, $\sum_I^n |\ln(1 + r_i)|$ cannot converge and cannot be dominated by $\sum_I^n |c_i - 1|$. If, on the other side, we know that $\sum_I^n |c_i - 1|$ converges, then only finitely many c_i can vanish (since the latter give summands of modulus 1).

For a converging product, we obtain for $c_i > 0$ the lower estimate

$$\prod_{\mathbb{N}} c_i \geq \prod_{\mathbb{N}} \exp\{-|\ln(c_i)|\} \geq \exp\left\{-\frac{3}{2}\sum_{\mathbb{N}}^n |c_i - 1|\right\} > 0. \tag{48.4.20}$$

We arrive at the following Lemma.

Lemma 48.4-20 (Positive Convergence). *Assume first that $c_i > 0$ for all $i \in I$. Then $\prod_I^n c_i$ converges, if and only if $\sum_I^n |c_i - 1|$ converges. Its value satisfies then the lower estimate $\prod_I^n c_i \geq \exp\{-\frac{3}{2} \sum_{\mathbb{N}} |c_i - 1|\}$, which is strictly larger than 0.*

Consider now the slightly more general case with all $c_i \geq 0$. If at least one c_i is in fact equal to 0, then $\prod_I^n c_i$ converges with value 0, irrespectively of the values of the non-vanishing c_i. So, the convergence of $\sum_I^n |c_i - 1|$ is sufficient for the convergence of $\prod_I^n c_i$, but is sufficient and necessary for the convergence of $\prod_I^p c_i$. (We know that after elimination of the finitely many vanishing c_i the rest product converges to a value greater than 0, which is also necessary.)

Generally, for $c_i \geq 0$ and $\prod_I^n c_i$ convergent, this is different from $\prod_I^p c_i$, if and only if some c_i vanish, and where for the non-vanishing c_i, convergence is not satisfied.

Let us consider now $\prod_I c_i$ where the c_i are complex. By means of the estimations

$$||c_i| - 1|, \quad \frac{1}{\pi}|\operatorname{Arg} c_i| \leq |c_i - 1| \leq ||c_i| - 1| + |\operatorname{Arg} c_i|, \qquad (48.4.21)$$

one sees that the convergence of $\sum_{i \in I}^n |c_i - 1|$ dominates also the sum of phases, and one derives with the help of the preceding Lemma:

Lemma 48.4-21 (Complex Convergence). *Let $0 \neq c_i \in \mathbb{C}$ for all $i \in I$. Then the infinite product $\prod_I^n c_i$ is convergent, if and only if $\sum_I^n |c_i - 1|$ converges. Its value is then different from 0.*

The infinite product $\prod_I^q c_i$, with arbitrary $c_i \in \mathbb{C}$, converges to a value different from 0, if and only if $\prod_I^n c_i$ converges to the same value. This holds if and only if all c_i are different from 0 and $\sum_I^n |c_i - 1|$ converges. (If only $\sum_I^n ||c_i| - 1|$ converges and $\sum_I^n |\operatorname{Arg} c_i|$ or equivalently $\sum_I^n |c_i - 1|$ does not converge, then $\prod_I^q c_i$ converges by definition to 0.)

Quite generally, the convergence of $\sum_I^n |c_i - 1|$ is sufficient and necessary for the convergence of $\prod_I^p c_i$ (and not necessary for the convergence of $\prod_I^n c_i$).

Altogether, the convergence of $\prod_I^n c_i$ to a value different from 0 implies that at most, denumerably many c_i are different from 1, and that the latter have moduli converging to 1 and phases converging to 0 (quickly enough that the sums of the $c_i - 1$ and of the $\operatorname{Arg} c_i$ converge absolutely). Since, in case of $\sum_I^n |\operatorname{Arg} c_i|$ being not convergent, the product $\prod_I^q c_i$ is set 0, no "oscillation of the phases" is required for that. Especially, $|\operatorname{Arg} c_i|$ being constant and different from 0, makes the product quasi-convergent to 0, rather than to build up a "macroscopic phase". (The latter is realized in our frame by a central observable, arising from the gauge behavior of macroscopic *states*, and not of macroscopic *vectors* as infinite product vectors.)

48.4.3.2. *(Infinite) Tensor Products of Hilbert Spaces*

Assume for each i from the arbitrary index set I a complex Hilbert space $\mathcal{H}_i$ of arbitrary dimension. A family of vectors $(\Omega_i) \equiv (\Omega_i)_I \equiv \{\Omega_i \in \mathcal{H}_i \mid i \in I\}$ is called a *C-net*, if and only if $\prod_I^n \|\Omega_i\|$ converges. Let us denote the set of all *C-nets* by $(\mathcal{H}_i) \equiv (\mathcal{H}_i)_I$.

The *product vectors* are not directly defined via the *C-nets* but in terms of the *complex multilinear functionals* (i.e., linear in each component) Φ on $(\mathcal{H}_i)$, where we denote the set of these functionals by $\mathcal{H}_\odot$. This allows to introduce in $\mathcal{H}_\odot$ the point-wise complex linear structure without a representation of the Φ's:
$$(c\Phi_1 + \Phi_2)[(\Omega_i)] := c\Phi_1[(\Omega_i)] + \Phi_2[(\Omega_i)].$$

Most basic are, of course, the multilinear functionals $\otimes\Omega_i' \equiv \otimes_I\Omega_i'$, which are formed by a *C-net* (Ω_i') and defined by $(\otimes\Omega_i')[(\Omega_i)] := \prod_I^q(\Omega_i'|\Omega_i)$, which means (only) that $\prod_I^n |(\Omega_i'|\Omega_i)|$ has to converge. Since $|(\Omega_i'|\Omega_i)| \leq \|\Omega_i'\|\|\Omega_i\|$ the convergence seems plausible and is confirmed by the subsequent Proposition of [vN38].

Proposition 48.4-22 (Scalar Product of Product Vectors). *A complex multilinear functional* $\Omega = \otimes\Omega_i \in \mathcal{H}_\odot$, *which is given by a C-net* $(\Omega_i) \in (\mathcal{H}_i)$, *is called a* product vector.

If (Ω_i') *and* (Ω_i) *are in* $(\mathcal{H}_i)$, *then*

$$\prod_I^q(\Omega_i'|\Omega_i) =: (\otimes\Omega_i' | \otimes \Omega_i) \tag{48.4.22}$$

is (quasi) convergent (and constitutes by definition the scalar product for the product vectors).

We introduce now the *linear subspace* $\mathcal{H}_\otimes' \subset \mathcal{H}_\odot$ of all complex linear combinations $\Phi = \sum_k \otimes \Omega_i^k$ of all $\otimes\Omega_i$, where (Ω_i) runs through all *C-nets*. The inner product

$$(\Phi|\Phi') \equiv \left(\sum_k \otimes \Omega_i^k \Big| \sum_l \otimes \Omega_i^{l'}\right) := \sum_{k,l} \prod_I^q(\Omega_i^k|\Omega_i^{l'}) \tag{48.4.23}$$

is well defined, i.e., does not depend on the special forms of the linear combinations for the functionals Φ and Φ' on $(\mathcal{H}_i)$. It is, in fact, a positive-definite sesquilinear form on $\mathcal{H}_\otimes'$ and makes, as a scalar product, $\mathcal{H}_\otimes'$ to a pre-Hilbert space. Especially $\|\Phi\| := \sqrt{(\Phi|\Phi)} = 0$ implies that Φ is the null functional. (This is seen by the following: If $\|\Phi\| = 0$, then $|(\Phi|\Psi)| \leq \|\Phi\|\|\Psi\| = 0$ for all $\Psi = \otimes\Omega_i$, which leads to $\Phi[(\Omega_i)] = 0$ for all $(\Omega_i) \in (\mathcal{H}_i)$. This shows, without any representation by sums of product vectors, that Φ must be the null functional.)

Definition 48.4-23 (Von Neumann's Complete Tensor Product Space). Let be given, as before, a family of complex Hilbert spaces $\{\mathcal{H}_i \,|\, i \in I\}$ for an arbitrary (finite or infinite) index set I, and introduce the preceding notions. The completion of $\mathcal{H}_\otimes'$ in the norm topology (consisting of all norm-Cauchy nets in $\mathcal{H}_\otimes'$) is called the *complete tensor product* and denoted by

$$\mathcal{H}_\otimes \equiv \bigotimes_I \mathcal{H}_i \quad (\text{for the Hilbert space family } \{\mathcal{H}_i \,|\, i \in I\}). \tag{48.4.24}$$

The adjective "complete" is omitted for this product Hilbert space, if I is a finite set, but its introduction in terms of functionals is always the adequate one.

We assume from now on that the index set I *has infinite cardinality.* Recall that (Ω_i) being a C-net (and $\otimes\Omega_i \in \mathcal{H}'_\otimes$) is equivalent to the convergence of $\sum_I^n |\|\Omega_i\| - 1|$, *provided no* Ω_i *vanishes.* If some Ω_i vanish, then (Ω_i) is in any case a C-net, and $\otimes\Omega_i$ represents $0 \in \mathcal{H}_\otimes$.

Definition 48.4-24 (C_0-Nets). The requirement of the convergence of $\sum_I^n |\|\Omega_i\| - 1|$ restricts the set $(\mathcal{H}_i)$ of C-nets to the set $(\mathcal{H}_i)^0$ of C_0-nets.

Since convergence of $\sum_I^n |\|\Omega_i\| - 1|$ allows for the vanishing of finitely many Ω_i only, we can also say: (Ω_i) is a C_0-net, if and only if $\prod_I^p \|\Omega_i\|$ is (proper) convergent.

The subscript 0 for a C_0-net (Ω_i) indicates thus the allowance of finitely many 0-vectors Ω_i, and the remaining vectors may be tensorized to a well behaved (infinite) product.

A C-net $(\Omega_i) \in (\mathcal{H}_i)$ is automatically a C_0-net, $(\Omega_i) \in (\mathcal{H}_i)^0$, if the existing value $\prod_I^n \|\Omega_i\|$ is different from 0. Especially all nets (Ω_i), $\Omega_i \in \mathcal{H}_i$, with normalized Ω_i, i.e., $\|\Omega_i\| = 1$, constitute C_0-nets.

Lemma 48.4-25 (Equivalence and Weak Equivalence of C_0-Nets). *Consider the set $(\mathcal{H}_i)^0$ of C_0-nets. At first we give two important definitions.*

(a) *Two C_0-nets (Ω_i) and (Ω'_i) are called* equivalent, *written $(\Omega_i) \approx (\Omega'_i)$, if and only if $\sum_I^n |(\Omega_i|\Omega'_i) - 1|$ converges.*

(b) *Two C_0-nets (Ω_i) and (Ω'_i) are called* weakly equivalent, *written $(\Omega_i) \sim (\Omega'_i)$, if and only if $\sum_I^n ||(\Omega_i|\Omega'_i)| - 1|$ converges.*
   One finds: For two C_0-nets $(\Omega_i), (\Omega'_i) \in (\mathcal{H}_i)^0$ the relation $(\Omega_i) \sim (\Omega'_i)$ is valid, if and only if there are $c_i \in \mathbb{C}$, such that $(c_i\Omega_i) \in (\mathcal{H}_i)^0$ and $(c_i\Omega_i) \approx (\Omega'_i)$; and without restriction in generality the c_i may be assumed to satisfy $|c_i| = 1$.

The two binary relations $\approx$ and $\sim$ are reflexive, symmetric and transitive, and are thus, in fact, equivalence relations in $(\mathcal{H}_i)^0$. By these, $(\mathcal{H}_i)^0$ is decomposed into pair-wise non-intersecting classes $\mathfrak{C}_w$ of weakly equivalent C_0-nets and is also finer decomposed into pair-wise non-intersecting classes $\mathfrak{C}$ of equivalent C_0-nets. Clearly $\approx$ implies $\sim$.

If $(\Omega_i) \in \mathfrak{C}$, then we write also $\mathfrak{C} = \mathfrak{C}[(\Omega_i)]$ and if $\mathfrak{C}[(\Omega_i)] \subset \mathfrak{C}_w$ we may write $\mathfrak{C}_w = \mathfrak{C}_w[(\Omega_i)]$. Of course $\mathfrak{C}_w[(\Omega_i)] \supset \mathfrak{C}[(\Omega_i)]$.

Two C_0-nets are easily seen to be equivalent, if they differ in a finite number of members only. Since all the following relations are concerned with the explicit form of product vectors, we give them a special naming if they are built on a C_0-net.

Definition 48.4-26 (C_0-Vectors and Incomplete Tensor Products). Let us call a product vector $\Omega = \otimes\Omega_i$, built on a C_0-net, a C_0-*vector.* (Each C_0-vector is then by definition a product vector, and any product vector in $\mathcal{H}_\otimes$, different from 0, is automatically a C_0-vector).

We take over both equivalence relations from above: Two C_0-vectors Ω and Ω' are called (*weakly*) *equivalent*, if the associated C_0-nets are (weakly) equivalent, written $\Omega \approx \Omega'$ (respectively $\Omega \sim \Omega'$).

The closed linear hull $\mathcal{H}_\otimes^\mathfrak{C}$ of all C_0-vectors from the equivalence class $\mathfrak{C}$ is called the $\mathfrak{C}$-*adic incomplete tensor product* (over the complex Hilbert spaces $\{\mathcal{H}_i \mid i \in I\}$). If $\mathfrak{C} = \mathfrak{C}[\Omega]$, with Ω a C_0-vector, then we write $\mathcal{H}_\otimes^\mathfrak{C} = \mathcal{H}_\otimes^\Omega$ and call $\mathcal{H}_\otimes^\Omega$ the *incomplete tensor product along* Ω.

Analogously we denote by $\mathcal{H}_\otimes^{\mathfrak{C}w}$ the closed linear hull of all C_0-vectors from the weak equivalence class $\mathfrak{C}_w$.

The following Proposition from [vN38] illustrates again that infinite products are technically delicate.

Proposition 48.4-27 (Non-associativity of Complete Tensor Product). *The formation of the complete tensor product is restrictively associative: It is invariant under the insertion of finitely many brackets (.) about a group of factors, where the complete sub-tensor product within a bracket (.) may have infinitely many factors.*

In general the complete tensor product is not associative.

The incomplete tensor product is (unrestricted) associative.

We recognize further implications of the diverse definitions of product convergence.

Proposition 48.4-28 (Orthogonality of Product Vectors). *We consider C_0-vectors as introduced in the preceding Definition 48.4-26.*

(a) *Two C_0-vectors $\otimes\Omega_i \in \mathcal{H}_\otimes^\mathfrak{C}$ and $\otimes\Omega'_i \in \mathcal{H}_\otimes^{\mathfrak{C}'}$ are orthogonal, if $\mathfrak{C} \neq \mathfrak{C}'$ (i.e., if $\mathfrak{C}[(\Omega_i)] \cap \mathfrak{C}[(\Omega'_i)] = \emptyset$).*
For: $\prod_I^q(\Omega'_i|\Omega_i) = (\otimes\Omega'_i| \otimes \Omega_i)$ vanishes if $\sum_I^n |(\Omega_i|\Omega'_i) - 1|$ is not convergent, which just means that the C_0-nets are not equivalent. (They may be of course weakly equivalent.)

(b) *If the C_0-vectors $\otimes\Omega_i$ and $\otimes\Omega'_i$ are from one and the same equivalence class, they are orthogonal, if and only if $(\Omega_i|\Omega'_i) = 0$ for some $i \in I$.*
For: Convergence of $\sum_I^n |(\Omega_i|\Omega'_i) - 1|$ implies the non-vanishing of $\prod_I^q(\Omega'_i|\Omega_i)$, if not at least one $(\Omega_i|\Omega'_i)$ vanishes.

(c) *Let the complex product $\prod_I^q c_i$ be (quasi) convergent (implying $|c_i| \to 1$) and $\otimes\Omega_i \neq 0$ be a C_0-vector. Then the relation*

$$\left(\prod_I^q c_i\right) \otimes \Omega_i = \otimes c_i\Omega_i \tag{48.4.25}$$

is valid, with a C_0-vector on the right-hand side, if $\sum_I^n |c_i - 1|$ converges. In this case $\otimes\Omega_i \approx \otimes c_i\Omega_i$.

(d) *If $\sum_I^n |c_i - 1|$ does not converge (due to a not converging phase sum), then the equality sign may fail to hold in (48.4.25), that is, the left-hand side is 0 but the right-hand side may be different from 0.*

Whenever the equality in (48.4.25) is invalid (i.e., if $\prod_I^q c_i$ is convergent but $\prod_I^n c_i$ is not convergent and $\otimes\Omega_i \neq 0$), we have $\otimes c_i\Omega_i$ is orthogonal to $\otimes\Omega_i$. For: $\prod_I^q(\Omega_i|c_i\Omega_i)$ has then a non-converging phase sum (that of the c_i) and vanishes.

Lemma 48.4-29 (Form of an Incomplete Tensor Product). *In each $\mathcal{H}_\otimes^\mathfrak{C}$ is a C_0-vector $\otimes\Omega_i$ with $\|\Omega_i\| = 1, \forall i \in I$.*

$\mathcal{H}_\otimes^\mathfrak{C} = \mathcal{H}_\otimes^\Omega$ is then obtained as the closed linear hull of all C_0-vectors, which differ from $\otimes\Omega_i$ with respect to finitely many factors only.

In view of Proposition 48.4-28, it is clear that there are overcountably many mutually non-equivalent, and hence mutually orthogonal, product vectors (the cardinality of our I is infinite). One concludes:

Proposition 48.4-30 (Decomposition of the Complete Tensor Product). *Consider the complete tensor product $\mathcal{H}_\otimes = \otimes_I \mathcal{H}_i$. Let us denote the set of all $\mathfrak{C}$ by Γ and the set of all $\mathfrak{C}_w$ by Γ_w.*

(a) *The complete tensor product $\mathcal{H}_\otimes$ decomposes into the direct sum of incomplete tensor product spaces as follows,*

$$\mathcal{H}_\otimes = \bigoplus_{\mathfrak{C}_w \in \Gamma_w} \mathcal{H}_\otimes^{\mathfrak{C}_w} = \bigoplus_{\mathfrak{C}\in\Gamma} \mathcal{H}_\otimes^\mathfrak{C}, \quad \mathcal{H}_\otimes^{\mathfrak{C}_w} = \bigoplus_{\mathfrak{C}\subset\mathfrak{C}_w} \mathcal{H}_\otimes^\mathfrak{C}.$$

(b) *If all $\mathcal{H}_i$, $i \in I$, are separable and I is denumerable, then an incomplete tensor product $\mathcal{H}_\otimes^\mathfrak{C}$ is a separable Hilbert space.*
Hint: Choose a $0 \neq \Omega = \otimes\Omega_i \in \mathcal{H}_\otimes^\mathfrak{C}$ and choose for each $i \in I$ a (denumerable) orthonormal basis $\{\Omega_i^{(n)} \mid n \in \mathbf{N}\}$ in $\mathcal{H}_i$ with first vector equal to the normalized Ω_i. According to Lemma 48.4-29, one obtains a denumerable basis for $\mathcal{H}_\otimes^\mathfrak{C} = \mathcal{H}_\otimes^\Omega$ by replacing in $\otimes\Omega_i$ finitely many Ω_i by basis elements from $\mathcal{H}_i$ in all possible manner.
(c) *An $\mathcal{H}_\otimes^{\mathfrak{C}_w}$, and thus $\mathcal{H}_\otimes$, is always a non-separable Hilbert space (assuming always $\mathcal{H}_i \neq \{0\}, \forall i \in I$).*
Hint: Choose a $0 \neq \Omega = \otimes\Omega_i \in \mathcal{H}_\otimes^{\mathfrak{C}_w}$ and form the C_0-vectors $\otimes c_i\Omega_i$ for all nets $(c_i) \subset \mathbb{C}$ for which $\prod_I^q c_i$, but not $\prod_I^n c_i$, converges. (Choose for example $c_i = e^{i\theta} \neq 1, \forall i \in I$.) By virtue of Proposition 48.4-28 (c), (d), one obtains overcountably many C_0-vectors, which are orthogonal and weakly equivalent to $\otimes\Omega_i$.
(d) *If infinitely many of the $\mathcal{H}_i$, $i \in I$, have dimension strictly greater than 1, then $\mathcal{H}_\otimes$ has overcountably many $\mathcal{H}_\otimes^{\mathfrak{C}_w}$ subspaces.*
Hint: Construct vectors analogously to (b), but replace now infinitely many Ω_i by the orthonormal basis vectors $\{\Omega_i^{(n(i))} \mid n(i) \in \mathcal{N}(i) \subset \mathbf{N}\}$ in $\mathcal{H}_i$. (If the $\mathcal{H}_i$ are not separable, then one obtains even more orthogonal vectors in $\mathcal{H}_\otimes$.) Then $\sum_I(|(\Omega_i^{(n(i))}|\Omega_i^{(m(i))})| - 1)$ does not converge, if the nets $(n(i))_I$ and $(m(i))_I$

have infinitely many distinct members, indicating invalid weak equivalence. This may happen if the cardinality of $\mathcal{N}(i)$ is strictly larger than 1, for infinitely many $i \in I$.

For illustration, let us consider the case $\mathcal{H}_i = \mathbb{C}_{(i)} \equiv \mathbb{C}$, for all $i \in I$, so that $\mathcal{H}_\otimes = \bigotimes_I \mathbb{C}_{(i)}$. Let $\Omega = \otimes c_i$ and $\Omega' = \otimes c_i'$ be C_0-vectors with $|c_i| = |c_i'| = 1$, for all $i \in I$. If $\Omega \approx \Omega'$, then $\sum_I |\overline{c_i} c_i' - 1| < \infty$ and thus $\prod_I^n \overline{c_i} c_i'$ converges. We have then $\Omega' = \otimes(\overline{c_i} c_i') c_i = (\prod_I^n \overline{c_i} c_i') \Omega$, and thus $\Omega' \in \mathbb{C}\Omega$, and all $\mathcal{H}_\otimes^{\mathfrak{C}}$, $\mathfrak{C} \in \Gamma$, are 1-dimensional. If $\sum_I |\overline{c_i} c_i' - 1|$ diverges, then nevertheless $\sum_I ||\overline{c_i} c_i'| - 1| = 0$ converges and $\Omega \sim \Omega'$. Then $(\Omega|\Omega') = \prod_I^q \overline{c_i} c_i' = 0$.

If we choose e.g., $c_i := 1$ and $c_i' \equiv c_i^\theta := e^{i\theta}$ for all $i \in I$, then $\Omega \sim \Omega^\theta$ but $(\Omega|\Omega^\theta) = \prod_I^q \overline{c_i} c_i^\theta = 0$ for $\Omega = \otimes c_i$ and $\Omega^\theta = \otimes c_i^\theta$ with θ from the overcountable set $]0, 2\pi[$, implying that there are overcountably many C_0-vectors Ω^θ orthogonal to Ω.

Thus the complete tensor product $\mathcal{H}_\otimes = \bigoplus_\Gamma \mathcal{H}_\otimes^{\mathfrak{C}} \cong l^2(\Gamma)$ is a non-separable Hilbert space, which is identical with $\mathcal{H}_\otimes^{\mathfrak{C}w}$ built with the only weak equivalence class.

Let us indicate, for the case of Bosons, certain difficulties which one encounters if one works solely in terms of state vectors (instead of states in application to observables).

Example 48.4-31 (Boson Tensor Product Spaces). Let $I \cong \mathbb{N}$ be the denumerable index set of Boson modes and $\Omega_i^{(0)}$ signify, for all $i \in I$, a special state vector for the 0-Boson state (vacuum) with respect to the i-th mode. With $\mathcal{N}(i) \subset \mathbb{N}_0$, $\mathcal{N}(i) \ni 0$, we denote the allowed occupation numbers for the i-th mode and we form the orthonormal basis $\{\Omega_i^{(n(i))} \mid n(i) \in \mathcal{N}(i)\}$ for $\mathcal{H}_i$. $\Omega_i^{(n(i))}$ is to describe $n(i)$ Bosons in the mode i. We investigate $\mathcal{H}_\otimes = \bigotimes_I \mathcal{H}_i$.

If no Boson occupation is allowed, i.e., $\mathcal{N}(i) = \{0\}, \forall i \in I$, then $\mathcal{H}_\otimes$ is the space described just before this example. It contains overcountably many C_0-vectors $\otimes c_i \Omega_i^{(0)}$, where the $(c_i)_I$ run through all complex nets with $|c_i| = 1$, and uncountably many of them are orthogonal to each other and to $\otimes \Omega_i^{(0)}$. But all of them are weakly equivalent to each other. A single equivalence class degenerates here to a unit ray.

If $\mathcal{N}(i) = \{0, 1\}, \forall i \in I$, (a case relevant also for Fermions) then a sequence $n(.) : I \to \{0, 1\}$ indexes the product vectors $\otimes \Omega_i^{(n(i))}$. If the sequence $n'(.)$ differs from $n(.)$ in at most a finite number of entries, then the corresponding product vectors Ω' and Ω (C_0-vectors) may be orthogonal, but are equivalent, and the set of such Ω' constitutes an orthonormal basis for $\mathcal{H}_\otimes^\Omega$. Each $\mathcal{H}_\otimes^\Omega$ is infinite-dimensional and separable. For fixed $n(.)$, $\mathcal{H}_\otimes$ contains overcountably many mutually inequivalent but weakly equivalent $\otimes c_i \Omega_i^{n((i))}$, with $|c_i| = 1$. If the sequence $n'(.)$ differs from $n(.)$ in an infinite number of entries, then the corresponding C_0-vectors are not weakly equivalent.

Even in the maximal case, $\mathcal{N}(i) = \mathbb{N}_0, \forall i \in I$, each $\mathcal{H}_\otimes^{\mathfrak{C}}$ is a separable Hilbert space.

The question how to interpret the structure of $\mathcal{H}_\otimes$, especially the non-equivalent but weakly equivalent product vectors, depends on the chosen algebra of observables. In any case, the $\otimes c_i \Omega_i^{n((i))}$, with $\prod_I^n c_i$ convergent and different from 0, belong to the unit ray of $\otimes \Omega_i^{n((i))}$ and denote the same state.

If the observable algebra would be all of $\mathcal{L}(\mathcal{H}_\otimes)$, then $\otimes c_i \Omega_i^{n((i))}$ with $\prod_I^n |c_i| \neq 0$ convergent, but $\prod_I^q c_i = 0$, would describe different states (e.g., overcountably many different vacua!).

More interesting is the case of an observable algebra with product structure like the C*-tensor products $\bigotimes_I \mathcal{L}(\mathcal{H}_i)$ or $\bigotimes_I \mathcal{W}(\mathbb{C}\Omega_i) \cong \mathcal{W}(E)$, with $E = \mathrm{LH}\{\Omega_i \mid i \in \mathbb{N}\}$ and the Ω_i forming an orthonormal family. Or certain W*-tensor products. For these product algebras, we need further investigations.

Definition 48.4-32 (Basic Operators on the Complete Tensor Product).
We consider the complete tensor product space $\mathcal{H}_\otimes = \bigotimes_I \mathcal{H}_i$.

(a) For any index $j \in I$ and any component operator $A_j \in \mathcal{L}(\mathcal{H}_j)$, we define its *extension* $\overline{A_j}$ by acting on C_0-vectors $\Omega = \otimes_I \Omega_i \in \mathcal{H}_\otimes$ as

$$\overline{A_j} \otimes_I \Omega_i := (A_j \Omega_j) \otimes (\otimes_{I \setminus j} \Omega_i) = (A_j \otimes \mathbb{1}_{I \setminus j})(\Omega_j \otimes (\otimes_{I \setminus j} \Omega_i)) \,,$$

where the splitting of the tensor product is not necessary but allowed by the associativity under finite bracketing according to Proposition 48.4-27.
After having checked that this is well defined (independent of the special realization of Ω) and that its linear extension is bounded, we denote the continuously extended operator to all of $\mathcal{H}_\otimes$ still by $\overline{A_j}$.
(Since $\mathbb{1}_{I \setminus j}$ is not compact, neither is $\overline{A_j}$.)

(b) The smallest von Neumann algebra containing all $\overline{A_j}$, $A_j \in \mathcal{L}(\mathcal{H}_j)$, $j \in I$, is denoted by $\mathcal{B}^\#$.
(It is the bi-commutant of the set of the $\overline{A_j}$ and contains, in fact, the unit operator $\mathbb{1} \in \mathcal{L}(\mathcal{H}_\otimes)$ and various compact operators. In the sense of Definition 48.4-17 (b), $\mathcal{B}^\#$ may be described as the infinite spatial tensor product of the $\overline{\mathcal{L}(\mathcal{H}_j)}$ in $\mathcal{H}_\otimes$.)

(c) For any $\mathfrak{C} \in \Gamma$, we introduce the orthogonal projection $P_{\mathfrak{C}}$ of $\mathcal{H}_\otimes$ onto $\mathcal{H}_\otimes^{\mathfrak{C}}$.

(d) For every net (c_i) of complex numbers with modulus 1, we define an operator $U[(c_i)] \equiv U$ by its action on C_0-vectors

$$U[(c_i)] \otimes \Omega_i := \otimes c_i \Omega_i$$

and by linear extension and closure, what leads to a well defined *unitary* U in $\mathcal{L}(\mathcal{H}_\otimes)$.

Observe that $U[(c_i)] \otimes \Omega_i$ is at least weakly equivalent to the given C_0-vector $\otimes \Omega_i$, and that for $\otimes \Omega_i \approx \otimes \Omega_i'$ also $U \otimes \Omega_i \approx U \otimes \Omega_i'$. Thus, for $\mathfrak{C} \subset \mathfrak{C}_w$, U transforms $\mathcal{H}_\otimes^{\mathfrak{C}}$ onto an $\mathcal{H}_\otimes^{\mathfrak{C}'}$, with $\mathfrak{C}' \subset \mathfrak{C}_w$.

Theorem 48.4-33 (Characterization of Operators in $\mathcal{B}^{\#}$). *Let be given the complete tensor product* $\mathcal{H}_{\otimes} = \bigotimes_I \mathcal{H}_i$.

(a) *An operator* $A \in \mathcal{L}(\mathcal{H}_{\otimes})$ *is contained in* $\mathcal{B}^{\#}$, *if and only if it commutes with all* $P_{\mathfrak{C}}$, $\mathfrak{C} \in \Gamma$, *and with all* $U[(c_i)]$, *where the* $(c_i) \subset \mathbb{C}$ *run through all complex nets with* $|c_i| = 1$.

(b) *Especially all* $P_{\mathfrak{C}}$, $\mathfrak{C} \in \Gamma$, *are in* $\mathcal{B}^{\#}$ *(commuting with the* $U[(c_i)]$*).*

(c) *If all* $\mathcal{H}_i$ *are equal (or unitary equivalent) to* $\mathcal{H}$ *then all (mean field and) limiting mean field operators*

$$m(A) := \text{weak–}\lim_{K \in F(I)} \frac{1}{|K|} \sum_{i \in K} \overline{A_i}, \quad \forall A \in \mathcal{L}(\mathcal{H}),$$

are in $\mathcal{B}^{\#}$.

As a consequence of the above (a), each $A \in \mathcal{B}^{\#}$ leaves every subspace $\mathcal{H}_{\otimes}^{\mathfrak{C}}$ for all $\mathfrak{C} \in \Gamma$ invariant.

For systems with infinitely many degrees of freedom, let us now find the connection between the Hilbert space approach via the complete tensor product and the algebraic approach by means of an abstract quasilocal algebra. Many quasilocal algebras, as the Weyl algebra and the CAR-algebra, can be written as a C*-tensor product. So, let for each $i \in I$ now $\mathcal{A}_i$ denote an arbitrary unital C*-algebra and form the (injective) C*-tensor product $\bigotimes \mathcal{A}_i = \mathcal{A}$ (using the C*-inductive limit according to Definition 45.3-18 on page 1669).

Consider a product state $\omega = \otimes \omega_i \in \mathcal{S}(\mathcal{A})$, where $\omega_i \in \mathcal{S}(\mathcal{A}_i)$ for all $i \in I$, with GNS triplets $(\Pi_{\omega_i}, \mathcal{H}_{\omega_i}, \Omega_i)$ and von Neumann Algebras $\mathcal{M}_{\omega_i} = \Pi_{\omega_i}(\mathcal{A}_i)''$. So, also in the abstract C*-algebraic approach, the selection of states leads to spatial structures, which we here combine into the complete tensor product $\mathcal{H}_{\otimes} = \bigotimes_I \mathcal{H}_{\omega_i}$ and the von Neumann algebra $\mathcal{B}^{\#}$.

In many cases, especially if $\mathcal{A}$ is simple, the embedded C*-tensor product $\overline{\mathcal{A}} = \bigotimes \overline{\Pi_{\omega_i}(\mathcal{A})}_i \subset \mathcal{B}^{\#}$ is *-isomorphic to $\mathcal{A}$. If the $\mathcal{A}_i$ are separable and I is denumerable, then $\overline{\mathcal{A}}$ is a separable C*-algebra in the huge non-separable Hilbert space $\mathcal{H}_{\otimes}$. In any case, $\overline{\mathcal{A}}$ leaves each incomplete tensor product $\mathcal{H}_{\otimes}^{\mathfrak{C}}$ invariant, and may be restricted to it. In this manner we obtain for any $\bigotimes \mathcal{A}_i = \mathcal{A}$ a representation

$$\Pi_{\mathfrak{C}} : \bigotimes \mathcal{A}_i \longrightarrow \bigotimes \overline{\Pi_{\omega_i}(\mathcal{A})}_i \big|_{\mathcal{H}_{\otimes}^{\mathfrak{C}}} \subset \mathcal{L}(\mathcal{H}_{\otimes}^{\mathfrak{C}}), \quad \forall \mathfrak{C} \in \Gamma. \tag{48.4.26}$$

If $\overline{\mathcal{A}}$ is, in fact, *-isomorphic to $\mathcal{A}$, then the representation $\Pi_{\mathfrak{C}}$ consists essentially only of the restriction map from $\mathcal{H}_{\otimes}$ to $\mathcal{H}_{\otimes}^{\mathfrak{C}}$. This is a nice illustration for the point of view that a representation of the abstract quasilocal C*-algebra (the latter describing the microscopic observables), reflects physically global subsidiary conditions under which the microscopic constituents are prepared and measured. The global subsidiary conditions would here be represented by the choice of $\mathcal{H}_{\otimes}^{\mathfrak{C}}$, to which $\mathcal{A}$ is to be restricted.

For studying transition probabilities, we need weak completions, that is von Neumann algebras, or — by the abstraction process — W*-algebras.

48.4.4. *Transition Probabilities between Infinite Product States*

Let us consider the family $\{\mathcal{M}_i; i \in I\}$ of W*-algebras, where I is an index set of arbitrary infinite cardinality. (If one starts with C*-algebras $\mathcal{A}_i$, as in the discussion at the end of the preceding subsection, the $\mathcal{M}_i$ may be viewed as the $\Pi_{\omega_i}(\mathcal{A}_i)''$.)

For each $i \in I$, we choose a normal, faithful representation $\Pi_i \colon \mathcal{M}_i \xrightarrow{\text{onto}} \widetilde{\mathcal{M}}_i \subset \mathcal{L}(\mathcal{H}_i)$, in which *all* normal states ω_i on $\mathcal{M}_i$ (also the mixed ones) are realized each by a vector $\Omega_i \in \mathcal{H}_i$.

Having now the representation spaces $\mathcal{H}_i$, we form the complete tensor product $\mathcal{H}_\otimes = \bigotimes_I \mathcal{H}_i$ and observe that every $\widetilde{\mathcal{M}}_i$ is *-isomorphic to the von Neumann algebra $\overline{\mathcal{M}}_i \subset \mathcal{B}^\# \subset \mathcal{L}(\mathcal{H}_\otimes)$, generated by the extensions (see Definition 48.4-32) of the $\widetilde{\mathcal{M}}_i$-operators.

To define directly an abstract infinite W*-tensor product would require non-trivial modifications of the infinite C*-tensor product of Definition 45.3-18, and we prefer a spatial construction within the complete tensor product Hilbert space. We introduce for that the von Neumann algebra

$$\overline{\mathcal{M}} := \left(\cup_{i \in I} \overline{\mathcal{M}}_i \right)'' =: \bigotimes_{\mathcal{H}_\otimes} \overline{\mathcal{M}}_i \subset \mathcal{B}^\# \subset \mathcal{L}(\mathcal{H}_\otimes) \quad \text{(complete W*-tensor product)},$$
$$(48.4.27)$$

which is the smallest von Neumann algebra containing all $\overline{\mathcal{M}}_i$. It is constructed like a finite spatial W*-tensor product in Definition 48.4-17(b). Let us call it the *complete W*-tensor product* since it is acting on the whole of the complete tensor product space $\mathcal{H}_\otimes$. Clearly we have for every $i \in I$ the embedding *-isomorphism

$$\overline{\alpha}_i : \mathcal{M}_i \xrightarrow{\text{onto}} \overline{\mathcal{M}}_i \subset \overline{\mathcal{M}}. \quad (48.4.28)$$

Remark 48.4-34 (Quasilocal Structure of Complete W*-Tensor Product).

The complete W*-tensor product is perhaps further elucidated by considering the family of "local" von Neumann algebras $\{\overline{\mathcal{M}}_J := \bigotimes_J \overline{\alpha}_i(\mathcal{M}_i) \,|\, J \in F(I)\}$, given by the finite spatial W*-tensor products in $\mathcal{H}_\otimes$ according to Definition 48.4-17 (b). The $\overline{\mathcal{M}}_J$ are W*-isomorphic to the abstract W*-tensor products $\bigotimes_J \mathcal{M}_i$, introduced in Definition 48.4-17(a), and are thus, as W*-algebras, insensitive to the representation space.

The decisive, representation-sensitive step is the weak closure of their union

$$\left(\cup_{J \in F(I)} \overline{\mathcal{M}}_J \right)'' = \bigotimes_{\mathcal{H}_\otimes} \overline{\mathcal{M}}_i \subset \mathcal{L}(\mathcal{H}_\otimes). \quad (48.4.29)$$

It is e.g., no longer W*-isomorphic to the weak closures in incomplete tensor products. The classification of the latter had been at the heart of the classification theory for von Neumann algebras.

In any case, $\bigcup_{J \in F(I)} \overline{\mathcal{M}}_J$ is weakly dense in the respective closures.

A normal state $\bar{\omega}$ on $\overline{\mathcal{M}}$ is called a *product state*, if for every finite set $J \subset I$ and every selection $\{A_i \in \mathcal{M}_i; \, i \in J\}$, it factorizes as

$$\langle \bar{\omega}; \prod_{i \in J} \bar{\alpha}_i(A_i) \rangle = \prod_{i \in J} \langle \bar{\omega}; \bar{\alpha}_i(A_i) \rangle = \prod_{i \in J} \langle \omega_i; A_i \rangle,$$

where the last step associates with $\bar{\omega}$ a normal state ω_i on $\mathcal{M}_i$ for every $i \in I$. Reversely, for each family $(\omega_i)_{i \in I}$ of normal states on $\mathcal{M}_i$, we associate a product vector $\Omega = \otimes \Omega_i \in \mathcal{H}_\otimes$ that induces a normal state $\bar{\omega}$ on $\overline{\mathcal{M}}$, which is as such independent of the special vector realizations Ω_i.

As a subalgebra of $\mathcal{B}^\#$, the von Neumann algebra $\overline{\mathcal{M}}$ leaves $\mathcal{H}_\otimes^\Omega$ invariant for every C_0-vector $\Omega = \otimes \Omega_i \in \mathcal{H}_\otimes$. The restriction of $\overline{\mathcal{M}}$ to $\mathcal{H}_\otimes^\Omega$ defines the von Neumann algebra $\mathcal{M}^\Omega \subset \mathcal{L}(\mathcal{H}_\otimes^\Omega)$. Since $\mathcal{M}^\Omega$ is by definition generated by the embeddings $\alpha_i^\Omega : \mathcal{M}_i \to \mathcal{L}(\mathcal{H}_\otimes^\Omega)$, $\alpha_i^\Omega = \bar{\alpha}_i|_{\mathcal{H}_\otimes^\Omega}$, it is identical with Bures' algebra $\otimes(\widetilde{\mathcal{M}}_i, \Omega_i)$.

The W*-algebraic abstraction from $(\widetilde{\mathcal{M}}_i, \Omega_i)$ by varying over all faithful normal representations of $\mathcal{M}_i$, with vector realizations Ω_i of ω_i, is denoted in [Bur69] by $\otimes(\mathcal{M}_i, \omega_i)$. We have obtained it in a little roundabout manner, but by using easy steps only. The embedding *-isomorphisms, which depend on the family $\omega = (\omega_i)_{i \in I}$, will be denoted by

$$\alpha_j^\omega : \mathcal{M}_j \longrightarrow \otimes(\mathcal{M}_i, \omega_i).$$

If a family $\varphi = (\varphi_i)_{i \in I}$ of normal states φ_i on $\mathcal{M}_i$ with vector realizations $\Phi_i \in \mathcal{H}_i$ gives rise to a product vector $\Phi = \otimes \Phi_i$ in $\mathcal{H}_\otimes^\Omega$, then it defines a normal product state on $\otimes(\widetilde{\mathcal{M}}_i, \Omega_i)$ and thus on $\otimes(\mathcal{M}_i, \omega_i)$. The latter will be denoted also by φ. Obviously, this construction is possible only for special families φ, which depend on ω.

For discussing infinite products of transition probabilities, we have to formulate a supplementary Lemma.

Lemma 48.4-35. *For a net $(c_i)_I \subset \mathbb{C}$ with $|c_i| \leq 1$, we have*

$$\prod_I^{n,p} |c_i|^2 \quad converges \quad \Longleftrightarrow \quad \prod_I^{n,p} |c_i| \quad converges, \tag{48.4.30}$$

where the equivalence is valid with both sides fulfilling net convergence and also with both sides fulfilling proper convergence. (Quasi convergence is here the same as net convergence.)

Proof. If one $|c_i| = 0$, the assertion is evident. In the other case, we have to investigate the convergences of $\sum_I^n ||c_i|^{(2)} - 1|$. But $1 - |c_i|^2 = (1 - |c_i|)(1 + |c_i|)$, so $(1 - |c_i|) \leq (1 - |c_i|^2) \leq 2(1 - |c_i|)$. □

After these preparations, we arrive at the following generalization of Theorems 4.1 and 4.2 of [Bur69].

Theorem 48.4-36 (Isomorphisms between W*-Tensor Products). *For each $i \in I$ let be given two arbitrary W*-algebras $\mathcal{M}_i$ and $\mathcal{N}_i$, and a *-isomorphism*

$$\alpha_i : \mathcal{M}_i \xrightarrow{\text{onto}} \mathcal{N}_i.$$

For two families $\left(\omega_i \in \mathcal{M}_{i*,1}^{+}\right)_{i \in I}$ and $\left(\varphi_i \in \mathcal{N}_{i*,1}^{+}\right)_{i \in I}$ of normal states the following conditions are equivalent:

(i) *There exists an *-isomorphism*

$$\alpha : \bigotimes(\mathcal{M}_i, \omega_i) \xrightarrow{\text{onto}} \bigotimes(\mathcal{N}_i, \varphi_i)$$

   with $\alpha \circ \alpha_i^{\omega} = \alpha_i^{\varphi} \circ \alpha_i$ for all $i \in I$.

(ii) *The family $(\varphi_i \circ \alpha_i)_{i \in I}$ defines a normal product state on $\bigotimes(\mathcal{M}_i, \omega_i)$.*

(iii) $\prod_I^p T_{\mathcal{M}_i}(\omega_i, \varphi_i \circ \alpha_i)$ *converges.*

(iv) *For every family of representations $\Pi_i : \mathcal{M}_i \to \mathcal{L}(\mathcal{H}_i)$ and vector realizations $\Omega_i, \Phi_i \in \mathcal{H}_i$ of $\omega_i, \varphi_i \circ \alpha_i$ there exists a family of vector representatives $\Phi_i' \in \mathcal{H}_i$ for $\varphi_i \circ \alpha_i$ with*

$$\sum_I \left| (\Omega_i \,|\, \Phi_i') - 1 \right| < +\infty, \tag{48.4.31}$$

   signifying equivalent product vectors in $\bigotimes_I \mathcal{H}_i$.

If we do not employ the very special vector representatives Φ_i', which make the transition amplitudes positive, we have to take the moduli of the transition amplitudes in (48.4.31) and the product vectors are then only weakly equivalent.

Proof. The proof for (i)$\Leftrightarrow$(ii)$\Leftrightarrow$(iii) is taken over from [Bur69] by observing that the restriction to semi-finite W*-algebras $\mathcal{M}_i$ and $\mathcal{N}_i$ there is due to the product formula for the transition probabilities for product states. This restriction is overcome by our Proposition 48.4-19. We proof (iii)$\Rightarrow$(iv).

$$\prod_I^p T_{\mathcal{M}_i}(\omega, \varphi) \text{ converges} \iff \sum_I \left| \sup_{\Phi_i} \left| (\Omega_i \,|\, \Phi_i) \right|^2 - 1 \right| < \infty \text{ for fixed } \Omega_i \text{ and } \Pi_i,$$

$$\iff \sum_I \left| \sup_{\Phi_i} \left| (\Omega_i \,|\, \Phi_i) \right| - 1 \right| < \infty \text{ for fixed } \Omega_i \text{ and } \Pi_i,$$

$$\iff \sum_I \left| (\Omega_i \,|\, \Phi_i') - 1 \right| < \infty \text{ for some choice } \Phi_i' \text{ of the } \Phi_i.$$

In the second step, we have referred to the foregoing Lemma, and in the third step to the second part of Proposition 48.4-11. For (iv)$\Rightarrow$(iii), observe that

$$\sum_I \left| \sup_{\Phi_i} \left| (\Omega_i \,|\, \Phi_i) \right|^2 - 1 \right| \leq \sum_I \left| \left| (\Omega_i \,|\, \Phi_i') \right|^2 - 1 \right|$$

for an arbitrary choice Φ_i' of the Φ_i, due to the normalization of the Ω_i and Φ_i'.

□

One important case is $\mathcal{M}_i = \mathcal{N}_i$ (and the α_i are the identity mappings), for which we deduce the following assertions.

Proposition 48.4-37 (Transition Probabilities in W*-Tensor Products).
For a given family of arbitrary W*-algebras $\mathcal{M}_i$, we consider normal faithful representations $\overline{\alpha}_i : \mathcal{M}_i \longmapsto \widetilde{\mathcal{M}}_i \subset \mathcal{L}(\mathcal{H}_i)$, in which all normal states ω_i on $\mathcal{M}_i$ are realized by vectors $\Omega_i \in \mathcal{H}_i$, and we form the complete tensor product algebra $\overline{\mathcal{M}}$ in $\mathcal{L}(\mathcal{H}_\otimes)$, $\mathcal{H}_\otimes = \bigotimes_I \mathcal{H}_i$.

(a) *For two normal product states $\overline{\omega} = \otimes \omega_i$ and $\overline{\varphi} = \otimes \varphi_i$ on $\overline{\mathcal{M}}$, one has*

$$T_{\overline{\mathcal{M}}}(\overline{\omega}, \overline{\varphi}) = \prod_I^n T_{\mathcal{M}_i}(\omega_i, \varphi_i).$$

There is a pair of vector realizations $\Omega = \otimes \Omega_i$ and $\Phi' = \otimes \Phi'_i$ in $\mathcal{H}_\otimes$ of $\overline{\omega}, \overline{\varphi}$ respectively, such that

$$T_{\overline{\mathcal{M}}}(\overline{\omega}, \overline{\varphi}) = \left(\Omega \,|\, \Phi'\right)^2 = \prod_I^n \left(\Omega_i \,|\, \Phi'_i\right)^2.$$

(b) *In the situation of (a), there are exactly two, mutually exclusive, possibilities:*

(1) $T_{\overline{\mathcal{M}}}(\overline{\omega}, \overline{\varphi}) = \prod_I^p T_{\mathcal{M}_i}(\omega_i, \varphi_i)$, *if and only if for each product vector realization Ω of $\overline{\omega}$, there is a Φ of $\overline{\varphi}$, such that $\Omega \sim \Phi$.*

(2) $T_{\overline{\mathcal{M}}}(\overline{\omega}, \overline{\varphi}) = 0 = \prod_{I\backslash J}^n T_{\mathcal{M}_i}(\omega_i, \varphi_i), \forall J \in F(I)$, *and this holds if and only if for every pair of product vectors Ω and Φ realizing $\overline{\omega}$ and $\overline{\varphi}$, Ω is not weakly equivalent to Φ.*

Note again that for the convergence of $\prod_I^n (\Omega_i|\Phi'_i)^2 = \prod_I^n |(\Omega_i|\Phi_i)|^2$, the phases of the single transition amplitudes are irrelevant and this convergence can thus imply only weak equivalence for the general product vectors Φ, but even equivalence for the special product vector Φ'.

Proof. According to the assumption, there is a pair of vector realizations $\Omega = \otimes \Omega_i$ and $\Phi = \otimes \Phi_i$ for the given states $\overline{\omega}$ and $\overline{\varphi}$, which define the incomplete tensor products $\mathcal{H}_\otimes^\Omega$ and $\mathcal{H}_\otimes^\Phi$. Part (a). Since the family $\{\overline{\mathcal{M}}_J = \overline{\otimes}_J \overline{\alpha}_i(\mathcal{M}_i) \,|\, J \in F(I)\}$ generates $\overline{\mathcal{M}}$, we conclude from Proposition 48.4-12(b) and Proposition 48.4-19

$$T_{\overline{\mathcal{M}}}(\overline{\omega}, \overline{\varphi}) = \lim_{J \in F(I)} T_{\overline{\mathcal{M}}}(\overline{\omega}_{|\overline{\mathcal{M}}_J}, \overline{\varphi}_{|\overline{\mathcal{M}}_J}) = \prod_I^n T_{\mathcal{M}_i}(\omega_i, \varphi_i).$$

Choose for all $i \in I$ vectors Ω_i, Φ_i (or Φ'_i) such that $T_{\mathcal{M}_i}(\omega_i, \varphi_i) = |(\Omega_i|\Phi_i)|^2$ (or $\ldots = (\Omega_i|\Phi'_i)^2$), which gives the appropriate product vectors.

Part (b). Apply Theorem 37.2-14 for $\mathcal{M}_i = \mathcal{N}_i$ and α_i the identity map in $\mathcal{M}_i, \forall i \in I$. Then the equivalence (iii)$\Leftrightarrow$(iv) in Theorem 37.2-14 gives the present case (b)(1) according to the weak equivalence of Ω and Φ. Case (b)(2) follows as logical complement for the infinite product and from observing that $\Omega \sim \Phi$ would lead to (b)(1). $\qquad\square$

Let for each $i \in I$ now $\mathcal{A}_i$ denote an arbitrary unital C^*-algebra and form the (injective) C^*-tensor product $\bigotimes \mathcal{A}_i = \mathcal{A}$. Consider a product state $\omega = \otimes \omega_i \in S(\mathcal{A})$, where $\omega_i \in S(\mathcal{A}_i)$, with GNS triplets $(\Pi_{\omega_i}, \mathcal{H}_{\omega_i}, \Omega_i)$ and von Neumann Algebras $\mathcal{M}_{\omega_i}$.

Then $\bigotimes \Pi_{\omega_i} : \mathcal{A} \longmapsto \mathcal{L}(\mathcal{H}_{\otimes}^{\Omega})$ is cyclic for $\Omega = \otimes \Omega_i$, so $\left(\otimes \Pi_{\omega_i}, \mathcal{H}_{\otimes}^{\Omega}, \Omega \right)$ is the GNS triplet for ω.

In the following, the relations $\omega \approx \varphi$ and $\omega \,\flat\, \varphi$ denote again quasiequivalence and disjointness for algebraic states on $\mathcal{A}$.

Theorem 48.4-38 (Transition Probabilities in C*-Tensor Products). *Let* $\omega = \otimes \omega_i$ *and* $\varphi = \otimes \varphi_i$ *be product states on* $\bigotimes \mathcal{A}_i = \mathcal{A}$. *Then we have the net convergent product for the transition probability*

$$T_{\mathcal{A}}(\omega, \varphi) = \Pi_I^n T_{\mathcal{A}_i}(\omega_i, \varphi_i).$$

More specifically, the following is valid:

(a) *If* $\omega \approx \varphi$ *then* $\Pi_I^p T_{\mathcal{A}_i}(\omega_i, \varphi_i)$ *converges* (*in the proper sense*).
(b) *If* $\omega_i \approx \varphi_i$, $\forall i \in I$, *and* $\Pi_I^p T_{\mathcal{A}_i}(\omega_i, \varphi_i)$ *converges, then* $\omega \approx \varphi$.
(c) *If* $\omega_i \approx \varphi_i$, $\forall i \in I$, *and* $\omega \,\flat\, \varphi$, *then* $\Pi_I^p T_{\mathcal{A}_i}(\omega_i, \varphi_i)$ *diverges to zero.*
(d) *If* $\Pi_I^p T_{\mathcal{A}_i}(\omega_i, \varphi_i)$ *diverges to zero, then* $\omega \,\flat\, \varphi$.

Proof. Part (a). From the definition of $\omega \approx \varphi$, we conclude that there is a *-isomorphism

$$\alpha : \bigotimes (\mathcal{M}_{\omega_i}, \Omega_i) \xrightarrow{\text{onto}} \bigotimes (\mathcal{M}_{\varphi_i}, \Phi_i)$$

such that

$$\alpha(\otimes_{i \in J} \Pi_{\omega_i}(A_i)) = \otimes_{i \in J} \Pi_{\varphi_i}(A_i)$$

for all $J \in F(I)$ and all $A_i \in \mathcal{A}_i$, $i \in J$. This gives mappings

$$\alpha_i : \mathcal{M}_{\omega_i} \xrightarrow{\text{onto}} \mathcal{M}_{\varphi_i}$$

hence $\omega_i \approx \varphi_i$, $\forall i \in I$ and $\alpha \circ \alpha_i^\omega = \alpha_i^\varphi \circ \alpha_i$. By Theorem 37.2-14, $\Pi_I^p T_{\mathcal{A}_i}(\omega_i, \varphi_i)$ converges since $T_{\mathcal{M}_{\omega_i}}(\omega_i, \varphi_i \circ \alpha_i) = T_{\mathcal{A}_i}(\omega_i, \varphi_i)$.

Part (b). If $\omega_i \approx \varphi_i$, then there are $\alpha_i : \mathcal{M}_{\omega_i} \xrightarrow{\text{onto}} \mathcal{M}_{\varphi_i}$ with $\alpha(\Pi_{\omega_i}(A_i)) = \Pi_{\varphi_i}(A_i)$ for all $i \in I$ and all $A_i \in \mathcal{A}_i$. Since $\Pi_I^p T_{\mathcal{A}_i}(\omega_i, \varphi_i)$ is assumed to converge, there is by Proposition 48.4-37 a *-isomorphism

$$\alpha : \bigotimes (\mathcal{M}_{\omega_i}, \Omega_i) \xrightarrow{\text{onto}} \bigotimes (\mathcal{M}_{\varphi_i}, \Phi_i)$$

with $\alpha \circ \alpha_i^\omega = \alpha_i^\varphi \circ \alpha_i$. Therefore

$$\alpha(\otimes_{i \in J} \Pi_{\omega_i}(A_i)) = \otimes_{i \in J} \Pi_{\varphi_i}(A_i), \qquad \forall A_i \in \mathcal{A}_i,$$

i.e., $\alpha(\Pi_\omega(A)) = \Pi_\varphi(A)$, $\forall A \in \mathcal{A}$, hence $\omega \approx \varphi$.

Part (c). $\omega_i \approx \varphi_i$ for all $i \in I$ and $\omega \,\flat\, \varphi$ implies $\Pi_I^p T_{\mathcal{A}_i}(\omega_i, \varphi_i)$ diverges, since otherwise $\omega \approx \varphi$ would follow by from (b).

Part (d). If $\prod_I^p T_{\mathcal{A}_i}(\omega_i, \varphi_i)$ diverges to zero, then $\prod_I^n T_{\mathcal{A}_i}(\omega_i, (\varphi_i)_{C_i}) = 0$ for every finite selection $\{C_i \in \mathcal{A}_i \mid i \in J \in F(I)\}$. Therefore $\omega \perp \varphi_C$ for all $C \in \mathcal{A}_0 := \bigcup \mathcal{A}_i$. This implies, that ω is *not* Π_φ-normal. Since this argument is symmetric, the disjointness of ω and φ follows. □

Observe that by means of Proposition 48.4-14, the results of the preceding Theorem may be derived without the use of von Neumann algebras. Especially (d) follows directly if one uses $\mathcal{A}_J^\perp = \bigotimes_{I \setminus J} \mathcal{A}_i$.

Corollary 48.4-39.

(a) *Two product states $\omega = \otimes \omega_i$ and $\varphi = \otimes \varphi_i$ on $\bigotimes \mathcal{A}_i = \mathcal{A}$ with $\omega_i \approx \varphi_i$ for all $i \in I$ are quasi-equivalent if and only if there are vector representatives Ω_i, Φ_i such that $\sum_{i \in I}(1 - |(\Omega_i | \Phi_i)|)$ converges, that is the equivalence $\otimes \Omega_i \approx \otimes \Phi_i$ in von Neumann's sense. Otherwise they are disjoint.*
(b) *Every $\bigotimes \mathcal{A}_i$, with $\dim \mathcal{A}_i \geq 2$ for an infinite number of $i \in I$, has uncountably many pair-wise disjoint (irreducible, factorial) representations.*

So we find, that even the smallest infinite product algebra, depicting a macroscopic (mesoscopic) number of spins-1/2 systems, develops a rich, continuous classical structure, either exhibited by its many disjoint representations or by the many disjoint state folia. That is, the purely classical world has the atomic folia as its pure states.

Example 48.4-40 (Quasi-Free Fermion States). We introduce the CAR-algebra by means of the Jordan–Wigner representation as a quasilocal product algebra $\mathcal{A} := \bigotimes_{k \in \mathbb{N}} \mathcal{A}_k$, $\mathcal{A}_k \cong \mathbb{M}_2(\mathbb{C})$, $\forall k \in \mathbb{N}$, where k is the index of an orthonormal basis in the one-Fermion Hilbert space. For each finite $\mathsf{K} \in F(\mathbb{N})$, the *local algebras* are given by $\mathcal{A}_\mathsf{K} = \bigotimes_{k \in \mathsf{K}} \mathcal{A}_k$ and are considered in the following as subalgebras of $\mathcal{A}$.

A quasi-free Fermion system be characterized by a net of local Hamiltonians H_K, $\mathsf{K} \in F(\mathbb{N})$, which have — after some diagonalization procedure — the form

$$H_\mathsf{K} = \sum_{k \in \mathsf{K}} E_k c_k^* c_k = \sum_{k \in \mathsf{K}} E_k n_k, \qquad n_k = c_k^* c_k,$$

where $E_k > 0$ for $k > 0$, and $c_k^\#$ are the annihilation and creation operators (# meaning both, a star or not), whereas the projections $n_k = c_k^* c_k$ are occupation number operators. For $\beta > 0$, the unique thermodynamic equilibrium state is the quasi-free product state ω^β given by

$$\omega^\beta = \otimes_{k \in \mathbb{N}} \omega_k^\beta, \qquad \omega_k^\beta \in \mathcal{S}(\mathcal{A}_k),$$

where the density operator ϱ_k^β for the states ω_k^β on $\mathcal{A}_k$ may be written as

$$\varrho_k^\beta = n_k(1 + e^{\beta E_k})^{-1} + n_k^\perp(1 + e^{-\beta E_k})^{-1} \in \mathcal{A}_k.$$

Notice that there are no restrictions on the E_k to give a well defined state.

According to Theorem 48.4-38, (a) plus (b), a product state $\varphi = \otimes_{k \in \mathbb{N}} \varphi_k$ is in the folium $\mathcal{F}_\beta$ (the smallest folium containing ω^β), if and only if

$$T_\mathcal{A}(\omega^\beta, \varphi) = \prod_{k \in \mathbb{N}}^p T_{\mathcal{A}_k}(\omega_k^\beta, \varphi_k)$$

converges (properly).

Since the ω_k^β are faithful on $\mathcal{A}_k$, this holds, if and only if $\prod_{k \in \mathbb{N}}^n T_{\mathcal{A}_k}(\omega_k^\beta, \varphi_k)$ converges to a strictly positive value. Now, $\mathcal{F}_{\omega^\beta}$ represents the classical property, that a state has the temperature β [Rie91,Pri83]. Thus, the product state φ has the temperature β, if and only if there is a finite transition probability to the equilibrium state ω^β. In a certain sense, φ is then a *fluctuation* of ω^β. Consider, for example, $\varphi = \otimes_{k \in \mathbb{N}} \omega_k^{\beta_k}$ where the $\beta_k \neq \beta$ is a fluctuation, if and only if the β_k approach β so quickly that $\sum_{k \in \mathbb{N}} (1 - T_{\mathcal{A}_k}^{1/2}(\omega_k^\beta, \omega_k^{\beta_k}))$ converges (see Corollary 48.4-39).

A spontaneous finite temperature splitting over macroscopic regimes, forbidden by the second law of thermodynamics, is not a statistical fluctuation, because we use the thermodynamic limit. That speaks once more for using the thermodynamic limit.

In order to discuss particle fluctuations, let us now consider specific (de-) excitations, where $\#$ assumes the values "empty" and "$*$",

$$\langle \omega_{c_k^\#}^\beta; \cdot \rangle = \frac{\langle \omega^\beta; c_k^{\#*} \cdot c_k^\# \rangle}{\langle \omega^\beta; c_k^{\#*} c_k^\# \rangle} \in \mathcal{F}_{\omega^\beta}$$

of the equilibrium state and observe that these are equal to $\omega_{n_k^{(\perp)}}^\beta$, $k \in \mathbb{N}$. Thus, we set for a more global perturbation $P = \prod_{I_1} n_i \prod_{I_2} n_i^\perp$, $I_{1,2} \subset \mathbb{N}$, $I_1 \cap I_2 = \emptyset$. Lemma 48.4-7 gives

$$T_\mathcal{A}(\omega^\beta, \omega_P^\beta) = \prod_{I_1} \langle \omega^\beta; n_i \rangle \prod_{I_2} \langle \omega^\beta; n_i^\perp \rangle = \prod_{I_1} \left(1 + e^{\beta E_i}\right)^{-1} \prod_{I_2} \left(1 + e^{-\beta E_i}\right)^{-1},$$

(48.4.32)

which is greater than zero, if and only if both of the $I_{1,2}$ are finite sets.

Here the Fermi occupation probabilities arise as transition probabilities (between mixed states), which seems to speak against the absolute character of those quantum mechanical thermal occupation probabilities.

48.4.5. *Integral Decompositions*

Lemma 48.4-41. *Let* $\omega, \varphi \in \mathcal{M}_*^+$ *be two normal scaled states on a von Neumann algebra* $\mathcal{M}$ *and let* $C \in \mathcal{M}$ *be a central projection with orthocomplement* $C^\perp$. *Denote by* $\omega_{C^{(\perp)}}$ *the two filtered scaled states* $\langle \omega_{C^{(\perp)}}; \cdot \rangle = \langle \omega; C^{(\perp)} \cdot \rangle$, *and similar for* φ. *We have then the additive decompositions*

$$T_\mathcal{M}^{\frac{1}{2}}(\omega, \varphi) = T_\mathcal{M}^{\frac{1}{2}}(\omega_C, \varphi_C) + T_\mathcal{M}^{\frac{1}{2}}(\omega_{C^\perp}, \varphi_{C^\perp}) = T_{C\mathcal{M}}^{\frac{1}{2}}(\omega_C, \varphi_C) + T_{C^\perp \mathcal{M}}^{\frac{1}{2}}(\omega_{C^\perp}, \varphi_{C^\perp}),$$

where in the last expressions the restricted von Neumann algebras $C^{(\perp)}\mathcal{M} = C^{(\perp)}\mathcal{M}C^{(\perp)}$ are used.

Proof.   Let $(p_i)_{i\le k} \in \mathcal{Z}_f$ and $(r_i)_{i\le n} \in \mathcal{Z}_f$ orthogonal decompositions according to Proposition 48.4-12 on page 1846, then $(q_i)_{i\le n+k}$ defined by $q_i := p_i C$, $i \le k$, $q_{i+k} := r_i C^\perp$, $i \le n$, is in $\mathcal{Z}_f$ and

$$\sum_{i\le n+k} \left(\langle\omega\,;\,q_i\rangle\langle\varphi\,;\,q_i\rangle\right)^{\frac{1}{2}} = \sum_{i\le k}\left(\langle\omega\,;\,Cp_i\rangle\langle\varphi\,;\,Cp_i\rangle\right)^{\frac{1}{2}} + \sum_{i\le n}\left(\langle\omega\,;\,C^\perp r_i\rangle\langle\varphi\,;\,C^\perp r_i\rangle\right)^{\frac{1}{2}}$$

$$= \sum_{i\le k}\left(\langle\omega_C\,;\,p_i\rangle\langle\varphi_C\,;\,p_i\rangle\right)^{\frac{1}{2}} + \sum_{i\le n}\left(\langle\omega_{C^\perp}\,;\,r_i\rangle\langle\varphi_{C^\perp}\,;\,r_i\rangle\right)^{\frac{1}{2}}.$$

Therefore, taking the infima over the (p_i) and (r_i),

$$T_{\mathcal{M}}^{\frac{1}{2}}(\omega,\varphi) \le T_{\mathcal{M}}^{\frac{1}{2}}(\omega_C,\varphi_C) + T_{\mathcal{M}}^{\frac{1}{2}}(\omega_{C^\perp},\varphi_{C^\perp}),$$

and the reverse inequality follows from the concavity of T in both arguments.   □

We generalize this decomposition property of $T_{\mathcal{M}}^{\frac{1}{2}}(\omega,\varphi)$ to general subcentral decompositions. Since there seems no proof to be published for this suggestive and physically most important formula, we present a demonstration.

Theorem 48.4-42 (Transition between States on Integral Algebras). *Let*

$$\mathcal{M} = \int_X^\oplus \mathcal{M}(x)d\mu(x)$$

be a direct integral of von Neumann algebras in terms of a σ-finite measure μ on a standard Borel space (X,Σ) (cf. Chapter IV of [Tak79], and our Sec. 48.1.1 on page 1777). Then for $\omega = \int_X^\oplus \omega(x)d\mu(x)$, $\varphi = \int_X^\oplus \varphi(x)d\mu(x) \in \mathcal{M}_*^+$

$$T_{\mathcal{M}}^{\frac{1}{2}}(\omega,\varphi) = T_{\mathcal{M}}^{\frac{1}{2}}\left(\int_X^\oplus \omega(x)d\mu(x), \int_X^\oplus \varphi(x)d\mu(x)\right) = \int_X T_{\mathcal{M}(x)}^{\frac{1}{2}}\left(\omega(x),\varphi(x)\right)d\mu(x).$$

Since the diagonal algebra is a subalgebra of the center of $\mathcal{M}$, $d\mu(x)$ is a subcentral measure in a certain parametrization.

Proof.   We may assume that ω and φ are represented by Hilbert space vectors of the underlying Hilbert space $\mathcal{H} = \int^\oplus \mathcal{H}(x)d\mu(x)$, i.e., $\langle\omega\,;.\rangle = (\Omega|.\,\Omega)$ and $\langle\varphi\,;.\rangle = (\Phi|.\,\Phi)$ with $\Omega = \int^\oplus \Omega(x)d\mu(x)$ and $\Phi = \int^\oplus \Phi(x)d\mu(x)$ from $\mathcal{H}$. (Take for instance the standard representation for $\mathcal{M}$, which is the direct integral of the standard representations of the $\mathcal{M}(x)$ [Bös76].) Then by the uniqueness, we have μ-almost everywhere the vector representations $\omega(x) = \omega_{\Omega(x)}$ and $\varphi(x) = \omega_{\Phi(x)}$.

In order to apply Proposition 48.4-6 we note that $\mathcal{M}' = \int^\oplus \mathcal{M}'(x)d\mu(x)$, and by the definition of the direct integral of von Neumann algebras, there is a countable family

$$\left\{ A_n = \int_X^{\oplus} A_n(x) d\mu(x) \in \mathcal{M}'_1 \,\middle|\, n \in \mathbb{N} \right\}$$

such that $\{A_n(x), n \in \mathbb{N}\}$ is for almost all values of $x \in X$ weakly dense in $\mathcal{M}(x)'_1$ (the subscript 1 means operators B with norm $\|B\| = 1$). It follows that the function

$$T^{\frac{1}{2}}_{\mathcal{M}(x)}(\omega(x), \varphi(x)) = \sup_{n \in \mathbb{N}} \left\{ |(\Omega(x)|A_n(x)\Phi(x))| \right\}$$

is measurable, since it is a supremum of countably many measurable functions. Furtheron, we have by (48.4.5) that $T^{\frac{1}{2}}_{\mathcal{M}(x)}(\omega(x), \varphi(x))$ is integrable and

$$T^{\frac{1}{2}}_{\mathcal{M}}(\omega, \varphi) = \sup \left\{ \int |(\Omega(x)|K(x)\Phi(x))| \, d\mu(x) \,\middle|\, K(x) \in \mathcal{M}'_1(x) \text{ is measurable} \right\}$$

$$\leq \int \sup \left\{ |(\Omega(x)|K(x)\Phi(x))| \,\middle|\, K(x) \in \mathcal{M}'_1(x) \right\} d\mu(x)$$

$$= \int T^{\frac{1}{2}}_{\mathcal{M}(x)}(\omega(x), \varphi(x)) \, d\mu(x).$$

On the other hand, by Corollary 48.4-11, there is an $A = \int^{\oplus} A(x) d\mu(x) \in \mathcal{M}'_1$ such that

$$T^{\frac{1}{2}}_{\mathcal{M}}(\omega, \varphi) = (\Omega|A\Phi) = \int (\Omega(x)|A(x)\Phi(x)) \, d\mu(x).$$

Define the function $v : X \to \mathbb{C}$ by

$$v(x) := \begin{cases} 1 & \text{for } (\Omega(x)|A(x)\Phi(x)) = 0, \\ |(\Omega(x)|A(x)\Phi(x))|/(\Omega(x)|A(x)\Phi(x)) & \text{otherwise.} \end{cases}$$

Then v is measurable and $V := \int^{\oplus} v(x) \mathbb{1}_x d\mu(x)$ is an element in $\mathcal{M}'_1$ (in fact in $\mathcal{M}' \cap \mathcal{M}$) such that $VA \in \mathcal{M}'_1$. We then have

$$(\Omega|A\Phi) \geq |(\Omega|VA\Phi)| = \left| \int (\Omega(x)|v(x)A(x)\Phi(x)) \, d\mu(x) \right|$$

$$= \int (\Omega(x)|v(x)A(x)\Phi(x)) \, d\mu(x) = \int |(\Omega(x)|A(x)\Phi(x))| \, d\mu(x)$$

$$\geq \left| \int (\Omega(x)|A(x)\Phi(x)) \, d\mu(x) \right| = |(\Omega|A\Phi)| = (\Omega|A\Phi),$$

hence $(\Omega|A\Phi) = \int |(\Omega(x)|A(x)\Phi(x))| \, d\mu(x)$.

Now we show that for all $n, k \in \mathbb{N}$,

$$X_{n,k} := \{x \mid |(\Omega(x)|A_n(x)\Phi(x))| - |(\Omega(x)|A(x)\Phi(x))| \geq 1/k\}$$

is a null set. Assume the contrary. If we define

$$\tilde{A}(x) := \begin{cases} A_n(x) & \text{for } x \in X_{n,k}, \\ A(x) & \text{otherwise,} \end{cases}$$

then $\tilde{A} = \int^{\oplus} \tilde{A}(x) d\mu(x) \in \mathcal{M}_1'$ and

$$T_{\mathcal{M}}^{\frac{1}{2}}(\omega, \varphi) = \int |(\Omega(x)|A(x)\Phi(x))| \, d\mu(x)$$

$$= \int_{X_{n,k}} |(\Omega(x)|A(x)\Phi(x))| \, d\mu(x) + \int_{X \setminus X_{n,k}} |(\Omega(x)|A(x)\Phi(x))| \, d\mu(x)$$

$$< \int_{X_{n,k}} |(\Omega(x)|A_n(x)\Phi(x))| \, d\mu(x) + \int_{X \setminus X_{n,k}} |(\Omega(x)|A(x)\Phi(x))| \, d\mu(x)$$

$$= \int |(\Omega(x)|\tilde{A}(x)\Phi(x))| \, d\mu(x) = (\Omega|\tilde{A}\Phi) \leq T_{\mathcal{M}}^{\frac{1}{2}}(\omega, \varphi),$$

which is a contradiction.

Using this result we conclude that

$$\left\{x \,\middle|\, T_{\mathcal{M}(x)}^{\frac{1}{2}}(\omega(x), \varphi(x)) - (\Omega(x)|A(x)\Phi(x)) > 0\right\} = \bigcup_{(n,k) \in \mathbb{N} \times \mathbb{N}} X_{n,k}$$

is a null set. Therefore,

$$T_{\mathcal{M}}^{\frac{1}{2}}(\omega, \varphi) = \int |(\Omega(x)|A(x)\Phi(x))| \, d\mu(x) = \int T_{\mathcal{M}(x)}^{\frac{1}{2}}(\omega(x), \varphi(x)) d\mu(x).$$

$\qquad\qquad\qquad\qquad\qquad\qquad\qquad\qquad\qquad\qquad\qquad\qquad\qquad\quad \square$

If one wants to deal only with states, then one has to normalize the vector representatives of the normal functionals. According to our assumption, there exists for a given normal functional φ a vector $\Phi = \int_X^{\oplus} \Phi(x) \, d\mu(x)$, where the family $X \ni x \mapsto \Phi(x) \in \mathcal{H}_x$ is μ–a.e. unique. The set $X_\varphi := \{x \in X \mid \Phi(x) \neq 0\}$ is measurable and depends on φ in a μ–a.e. unique manner. Define $\Phi_x := \Phi(x)/\|\Phi(x)\|$ for $x \in X_\varphi$, where also $X \ni x \mapsto \|\Phi(x)\|$ is μ-measurable. The Φ_x represent the component states φ_x, for $x \in X_\varphi$.

We also introduce the probability measure (see also Eq. (48.2.20)) μ^φ on X via

$$d\mu^\varphi(x) := \|\Phi(x)\|^2 \, d\mu(x), \qquad \left[\frac{d\mu^\varphi}{d\mu}\right](x) = \|\Phi(x)\|^2, \quad x \in X. \qquad (48.4.33)$$

Observe that the introduced Radon–Nikodym derivative is different from 0 only for $x \in X_\varphi$, the set on which the φ_x are defined.

We have now only to observe that $T_{\mathcal{M}}^{\frac{1}{2}}$ scales like a scalar product to deduce the following result.

Corollary 48.4-43. *In the situation of Theorem 48.4-42 we have for the transition between the two normal states ω, φ on $\mathcal{M}$, where $\omega = \int_X^\oplus \omega(x) d\mu(x)$, and $\varphi = \int_X^\oplus \varphi(x) d\mu(x)$, the decomposition formula*

$$T_{\mathcal{M}}^{\frac{1}{2}}(\omega, \varphi) = \int_X T_{\mathcal{M}(x)}^{\frac{1}{2}}(\omega_x, \varphi_x) \left[\frac{d\mu^\varphi}{d\mu} \frac{d\mu^\psi}{d\mu} \right]^{\frac{1}{2}}(x) \, d\mu(x),$$

where we used the notation preceding the Corollary. Especially, the (normalized) states ω_x, φ_x on $\mathcal{M}$, are both defined on $X_\omega \cap X_\varphi$, just the set on which $[.]^{1/2}$ is non-vanishing.

In order to apply Theorem 48.4-42 and Corollary 48.4-43 to disintegrated states on a not necessarily separable C*-algebra $\mathcal{A}$, we have to make a special assumption, since an orthogonal decomposition does in general not decompose the GNS triples associated with the states. We therefore suppose that the states are elements of $\mathcal{F}_s$, so that they are *spatially decomposable* in the sense of Definition 48.2-16. Then we know, in case of a subcentral decomposition, that they not only decompose the GNS triples, but also the associated von Neumann algebras.

We then must find a centrally decomposable von Neumann algebra to which the two given $\omega, \omega' \in \mathcal{F}_s$ are normal. The essential use of the von Neumann algebra is to provide a common parametrization of the (sub-) central decompositions of ω, ω'. Since the subcentral decompositions are coarsenings of the central decomposition, we look mainly for disintegrations into factor states, where the latter are either disjoint or quasi-equivalent. Since a non-vanishing transition probability may occur only within a quasi-equivalence class, it is natural to decompose the states in the argument of $T_{\mathcal{A}}^{\frac{1}{2}}(.,.)$ first into their components sitting in the smallest quasi-equivalence classes, that are those of factorial states, and calculate in the second step $T_{\mathcal{A}}^{\frac{1}{2}}(.,.)$ between these components.

Recall that φ and φ' are quasi-equivalent, if and only if the corresponding folia $\mathcal{F}_\varphi$ and $\mathcal{F}'_\varphi$ coincide. The quasi-equivalence classes $x = [\varphi]$ of the factor states φ constitute mathematically the *factor spectrum* of the C*-algebra $\mathcal{A}$ (e.g., [Ped79]). If $\mathcal{A}$ has the physical meaning of an observable algebra, we say that they constitute the *classical configurations space* $X = X(\mathcal{A})$ (see Proposition 46.2-31). For a non-vanishing transition probability, we need an overlap of the central measures on the factor spectrum.

If $\omega = \int_{\mathcal{T}_\omega}^\oplus \varphi \, d\mu_\omega(\varphi)$ is the central decomposition of $\omega \in \mathcal{F}_s$, with $\mathcal{T}_\omega \subset \mathcal{F}_s$ the support of the central measure μ_ω, then $\mathcal{T}_\omega \cap x$ contains at most one element $\varphi_x \in x$, for each equivalence class $x \in X$. Thus the reverse connection $\mathcal{T}_\omega \ni \varphi \mapsto x_\varphi \in X$ is an injection, with the image denoted X_ω. We define the transferred central measure by $\mu^\omega(Y) := \mu_\omega(\{\varphi_x \mid x \in Y \cap X_\omega\})$ for $Y \in \mathsf{B}(X)$ (where the σ-algebra $\mathsf{B}(X)$ has been defined in Proposition 46.2-31 on page 1700). That allows to rewrite the central decomposition in the form $\omega = \int_{X_\omega}^\oplus \varphi_x \, d\mu^\omega(x)$, in which one obviously integrates over the same states with the same statistical weight as in the original disintegration. Analogously $\omega' = \int_{X_{\omega'}}^\oplus \varphi'_x \, d\mu^{\omega'}(x)$. In this manner, we employ the classical configuration space X as the universal parameter space for the central state decompositions into sector components. (For sector components, see Definition 48.2-19 on page 1804, where we proposed also the direct integral notation, in certain applications.)

Our many-body and photonic observable algebras exhibit, as we know especially from their infinite tensor product realizations, a rich factor spectrum. Disintegrations on the factor spectrum have e.g., been investigated in [Ped79], but only for separable algebras. We do not try here a mathematically fully developed presentation of a generalized disintegration theory on the factor spectrum, since we are only interested in special applications. (For a rigorous introduction of $x \mapsto \varphi_x$ in the case of separable C*-algebras, we refer to [Ped79], Theorem 4.8.7.) Under that mathematical proviso, we arrive at the following decomposition formula.

Theorem 48.4-44 (Transition between States on C*-Algebras). *Let $\mathcal{A}$ be an arbitrary unital C*-algebra with state space $\mathcal{S}$, and ω, ω' two spatially decomposable states from $\mathcal{F}_s \subset \mathcal{S}$, with central measures μ_ω and $\mu_{\omega'}$. (Recall that the factor states of $\mathcal{S}$ all are in $\mathcal{F}_s$.)*

Then there exists a measure μ on $\mathsf{B}(X)$, to which the transferred measures μ^ω and $\mu^{\omega'}$ are absolutely continuous, so that we have

$$T_{\mathcal{A}}^{\frac{1}{2}}(\omega, \omega') = T_{\mathcal{A}}^{\frac{1}{2}}\left(\int_X^\oplus \varphi_x \, d\mu^\omega(x), \int_X^\oplus \varphi'_x \, d\mu^{\omega'}(x)\right)$$

$$= \int_X T_{\mathcal{A}}^{\frac{1}{2}}(\varphi_x, \varphi'_x) \left[\frac{d\mu^\omega}{d\mu} \frac{d\mu^{\omega'}}{d\mu}\right]^{\frac{1}{2}}(x) \, d\mu(x). \qquad (48.4.34)$$

If the central measures of ω and ω' lead to functions φ_x, φ'_x for the sector components, with $\varphi_x = \varphi'_x$, $\forall x \in X_\omega \cap X_{\omega'}$, then we obtain for some μ, to which $\mu^\omega, \mu^{\omega'}$ are absolutely continuous,

$$T_{\mathcal{A}}^{\frac{1}{2}}(\omega, \omega') = \int_X \left[\frac{d\mu^\omega}{d\mu} \frac{d\mu^{\omega'}}{d\mu}\right]^{\frac{1}{2}}(x) \, d\mu(x). \qquad (48.4.35)$$

That is, we obtain a purely classical transition probability, which is non-vanishing, if the central measures overlap (in an evident sense).

Proof.   We form the mixture $\psi := \lambda\omega + (1-\lambda)\omega'$, $\lambda \in]0,1[$, which is also in $\mathcal{F}_s$. We take for μ in the assertion the central measure μ_ψ transferred to X. We employ μ to decompose the von Neumann algebra $\mathcal{M}_\psi$ associated with the GNS representation $(\Pi_\psi, \mathcal{H}_\psi)$. Since ω, ω' are normal to $\mathcal{M}_\psi$ they are decomposed into scaled states via μ and into states via μ^ω and $\mu^{\omega'}$ as described in the text preceding Corollary 48.4-43. We can now proceed as in the proofs for Theorem 48.4-42 and Corollary 48.4-43.

The purely classical expression follows as a special case. $\qquad\square$

The classical transition probability seems hitherto not having been used in common theoretical physics. It is remarkable that it results automatically from a universal quantum theory, if that is reduced to its classical contents (see Conclusion 46.2-33 on page 1701). In Mathematics, the same formula as for the square root of the classical transition probability has been introduced to quantify the likeness between probability measures without, apparently, giving it a special name (e.g., [Hid80]).

In physical model discussions, one looks especially for (commutative) sub-C*-algebras of the universal center $\mathcal{Z}_u$, for finding labels for the $x \in X$, or for coarsenings of the x, so that the larger classes contain also non-factorial states.

We illustrate that first in terms of the *mean field algebra* for infinite tensor products $\mathcal{A} = \otimes_\mathbb{N} \mathcal{A}_k$ (with minimal C*-cross norm). The $\mathcal{A}_k$ are assumed *-isomorphic to the unital C*-algebra $\mathcal{A}_1$ for all $k \in \mathbb{N}$. Especially the clustered Fermion algebras are of this form, where $\mathcal{A}_{k=1}$ is taken finite-dimensional, and we stick also here to this assumption for simplicity and set $\mathcal{A}_{k=1} \cong \mathbb{M}_{2^n}$. Then $\mathcal{A}$ is separable and its state space $\mathcal{S} = \mathcal{S}(\mathcal{A})$ is a standard Borel space with respect to the weak* topology. As in the beginning of Sec. 34.1 on page 1021, we introduce in $\mathbb{M}_{2^n}$ the basis $\{e^i \,|\, 0 \leq i \leq r\}$, $r = 4^n - 1$, and form the local mean fields $m_S(e^i) = \sum_{k \in S} e^i_{(k)}/|S|$, $S \in F(\mathbb{N})$.

In the representations over mean field supporting states $\varphi \in \mathcal{F}_{\mathrm{ms}}$, the polynomials Q in the $m_S(e^i)$ converge for $S \to \mathbb{N}$. To the folium $\mathcal{F}_{\mathrm{ms}}$ corresponds a central projection $C_{\mathrm{ms}} \in \mathcal{P}_c \subset \mathcal{M}_u$ and a partially universal representation $(\Pi_{\mathrm{ms}}, \mathcal{H}_{\mathrm{ms}})$. We know that we have in the von Neumann algebra $\mathcal{M}_{\mathrm{ms}} \cong C_{\mathrm{ms}} \mathcal{M}_u$ the convergent limits

$$\sigma-\mathrm{strong-lim}_{S \in F(\mathbb{N})} \Pi_{\mathrm{ms}}\big(Q(m_S(e^1), \ldots, m_S(e^r))\big) = Q(m(e^1), \ldots, m(e^r))), \quad (48.4.36)$$

where

$$m(e^i) := \sigma-\mathrm{strong-lim}_{S \in F(\mathbb{N})} \Pi_{\mathrm{ms}}(m_S(e^i)), \quad \forall i \in \{1, \ldots, r\}.$$

The smallest C*-algebra $\mathcal{C}_{\mathrm{ms}}$ containing all $Q(m(e^1) \ldots, m(e^r)))$ is *-isomorphic to $C(\mathsf{P}, \mathbb{C})$, where $\mathsf{P} := \mathcal{S}(\mathbb{M}_{2^n})$. (Set $Q(m(e^1), \ldots, m(e^r)) \leftrightarrow Q(\langle\varrho; e^1\rangle, \ldots, \langle\varrho; e^1\rangle)$, $\varrho \in \mathsf{P}$, and form norm limits to reach all continuous functions by the Stone–Weierstrass theorem.)

In any GNS representation $(\Pi_\varphi, \mathcal{H}_\varphi)$, $\varphi \in \mathcal{F}_{\mathrm{ms}}$, the associated von Neumann algebra $\mathcal{M}_\varphi \cong C_\varphi \mathcal{M}_{\mathrm{ms}}$, with C_φ the central support of φ, contains $C_\varphi \mathcal{C}_{\mathrm{ms}}$, as well as its weak closure $\mathcal{Z}_\varphi^{\mathrm{ms}}$, in its center $\mathcal{Z}_\varphi$. $\mathcal{Z}_\varphi^{\mathrm{ms}}$ defines a (possibly trivial) subcentral decomposition, which always may be brought into the form

$$\varphi = \int_{\mathsf{P}} \varphi_\varrho \, d\bar{\mu}_\varphi(\varrho) \equiv \int_{\mathsf{P}}^{\oplus} \varphi_\varrho \, d\bar{\mu}_\varphi(\varrho), \quad \bar{\mu}_\varphi \in M_p(\mathsf{P}).$$

(48.4.37)

($M_p(\mathsf{P})$ are the probability measures on P). In Sec. 34.1, we have derived this result directly in $(\Pi_\varphi, \mathcal{H}_\varphi)$. Here it is integrated into a global point of view. The support of $\bar{\mu}_\varphi$ depends on what C_φ cuts out from the global $\mathcal{C}_{ms}$. The smallest support of a $\bar{\mu}_\varphi$ is a point $\varrho \in \mathsf{P}$, which characterizes the φ_ϱ.

In any case, using the previous argumentation, we can always write for two mean field-supporting states φ, φ'

$$\begin{aligned} T_{\mathcal{A}}^{\frac{1}{2}}(\varphi, \varphi') &= T_{\mathcal{A}}^{\frac{1}{2}}\Big(\int_{\mathsf{P}}^{\oplus} \varphi_\varrho \, d\bar{\mu}_\varphi(\varrho), \int_{\mathsf{P}}^{\oplus} \varphi'_\varrho \, d\bar{\mu}_{\varphi'}(\varrho) \Big) \\ &= \int_{\mathsf{P}} T_{\mathcal{A}}^{\frac{1}{2}}(\varphi_\varrho, \varphi'_\varrho) \left[\frac{d\bar{\mu}_\varphi}{d\bar{\mu}} \frac{d\bar{\mu}_{\varphi'}}{d\bar{\mu}} \right]^{\frac{1}{2}} (\varrho) \, d\bar{\mu}(\varrho), \end{aligned}$$

(48.4.38)

where $\bar{\mu}$ is a measure on P to which $\bar{\mu}_\varphi$ and $\bar{\mu}_{\varphi'}$ are absolutely continuous.

Recall that the group $\mathbb{P}$ of finite permutations of $\mathbb{N}$ acts in $\mathcal{A}$ by permuting the factors in the tensor product. We get the asymptotic Abelian C*-dynamical system $(\mathcal{A}, \alpha, \mathbb{P})$, with invariant states $\mathcal{S}^{\mathbb{P}}$.

If φ, φ' are from $\mathcal{S}^{\mathbb{P}}$, then the previous decomposition, to reach sharp mean field values, coincides always with the central decomposition and with the ergodic decomposition pertaining to $(\mathcal{A}, \alpha, \mathbb{P})$ (see Proposition 33.6-8 on page 1010). We have the case of "unbroken symmetries" (cf. Proposition 48.3-27 on page 1833). So the $\varphi_\varrho, \varphi'_\varrho$ are extremal permutation-invariant (ergodic) states, and both equal the product state $\otimes_{\mathbb{N}} \varrho = \varphi_\varrho = \varphi'_\varrho$. We have the case of Eq. (48.4.35) and obtain the purely classical expression

$$T_{\mathcal{A}}^{\frac{1}{2}}(\varphi, \varphi') = \int_{\mathsf{P}} \left[\frac{d\bar{\mu}_\varphi}{d\bar{\mu}} \frac{d\bar{\mu}_{\varphi'}}{d\bar{\mu}} \right]^{\frac{1}{2}} (\varrho) \, d\bar{\mu}(\varrho).$$

(48.4.39)

This confirms that the Bauer simplex $\mathcal{S}^{\mathbb{P}}$ for itself represents a purely classical state space. Quantum features come into play only if the permutation-invariant states are perturbed.

Weak perturbations of symmetric states are represented by elements of $\mathcal{F}_{\mathbb{P}}$, the smallest folium containing $\mathcal{S}^{\mathbb{P}}$. According to Observation 34.1-10 on page 1030, we have for each $\varphi \in \mathcal{F}_{\mathbb{P}}$ a unique $\omega \in \mathcal{S}^{\mathbb{P}}$ so that $\mathcal{F}_\varphi = \mathcal{F}_\omega$. In other words: In the quasi-equivalence class $[\varphi]$ of φ is always a distinguished symmetric representative ω, say. (Since $(\mathcal{A}, \alpha, \mathbb{P})$ is asymptotic Abelian we have the center-valued average $m_{\mathbb{P}}^0 : \mathcal{M}_\omega \to \mathcal{Z}_\omega$, and we may write $\omega = m_{\mathbb{P}}^{0\,*}(\varphi)$ (see Theorem 48.3-22).

We can therefore use the central decomposition of ω to parameterize the central decomposition of φ, which is of course of the form Eq. (48.4.37). The additional insight is, that also in this case the mean field center $\mathcal{Z}_\varphi^{\mathrm{ms}}$ equals the center $\mathcal{Z}_\varphi$: The filtering to make the mean fields sharp in a perturbed symmetric state φ, is sufficient to reduce φ to a factorial state.

The states in $\mathcal{F}_{\mathrm{ms}}$ represent even stronger deviations from permutation-invariant states, which we do not term "weak perturbations". Let us repeat, that we consider the existence of limiting mean fields — as in mean field supporting states — as a rather weak form of ordering in microscopic states.

Following the preceding argumentation in the reverse, we remark that the theory for the $\mathcal{F}_{\mathbb{P}}$-states, and then for the $\mathcal{F}_{\mathrm{ms}}$-states, generalizes in some sense the ergodic decomposition theory over the invariant states $\mathcal{S}^{\mathbb{P}}$ of $(\mathcal{A}, \alpha, \mathbb{P})$.

As a second application for the (sub-) central decompositions of $T_{\mathcal{A}}^{\frac{1}{2}}$, let us sketch a fluctuation theory over *macroscopic coherent Boson states*. We denote by E a separable complex LC-space, which is also a pre-Hilbert space owning a (right linear) scalar product $(f|g)$, $f, g \in E$, the norm closure of which is denoted by $\overline{E}$. The associated Weyl algebra is denoted by $\mathcal{W}(E) \equiv \mathcal{W}(E, \hbar \operatorname{Im}(.|.))$. Given a $\mathbb{C}$-linear form $L : E \to \mathbb{C}$, which is LC-continuous, but *unbounded* in the norm topology (describing a complex macroscopic classical field), we have discussed in Sec. 26.4 the set of first-order coherent states

$$\mathcal{S}_L^{(1)} = \left\{\omega = \int_{\mathbb{C}} \omega_z \, d\mu(z) \,\middle|\, \mu \in M_p(\mathbb{C}), \quad \mu \text{ analytic}\right\}, \tag{48.4.40}$$

where the states ω_z, $z \in \mathbb{C}$, on $\mathcal{W}(E)$ are identified by the characteristic functions

$$C_z(f) = \langle \omega_z; W(f) \rangle := \exp\{-\tfrac{\hbar}{4}\|f\|^2\} \exp\{i\sqrt{2}\operatorname{Re}(zL(f))\}, \tag{48.4.41}$$

and where μ is analytic if and only if $\int_{\mathbb{C}} e^{\delta|z|} d\mu(z) < \infty$ for some $\delta > 0$.

Thus, for given $\omega \in \mathcal{S}_L^{(1)}$, which is spatially decomposable, there exists a unique analytic measure $\mu = \mu^\omega \in M_p(\mathbb{C})$. If $b\mathbb{C}$ denotes the Bohr compactification of $\mathbb{C}$ (cf. [HR70]), then the regular Borel probability measures $M_p(\mathbb{C})$ are contained in $M_p(b\mathbb{C})$, since the canonical embedding of $\mathbb{C}$ into $b\mathbb{C}$ is an open map. For $z \in b\mathbb{C}\backslash\mathbb{C}$, the function $C_z(f)$ — which has the general shape $\exp\{-\tfrac{\hbar}{4}\|f\|^2\}N_z(f)$ — is a limit of the characteristic functions of the form Eq. (48.4.41), which has no longer an exponential form for $N_z(f)$. N_z is nevertheless a character on the additive group E and defines a pure state. Thus the Bauer simplex of so-called *L-distributed states* (see Proposition 26.4-14 on page 739)

$$\mathcal{S}_L := \left\{\omega = \int_{b\mathbb{C}} \omega_z \, d\mu(z) \,\middle|\, \mu \in M_p(b\mathbb{C})\right\} \tag{48.4.42}$$

contains $\mathcal{S}_L^{(1)}$ as subset. $\mathcal{S}_L$ consists of classical states, which are regular, if and only if $\operatorname{supp}(\mu) \subset \mathbb{C}$. The compact extreme boundary $\partial_e \mathcal{S}_L$ of $\mathcal{S}_L$ consists of the pure states ω_z, $z \in b\mathbb{C}$. Since the extremal decomposition (48.4.42) of $\omega \in \mathcal{S}_L$ along $\partial_e \omega \in \mathcal{S}_L$ is also its central decomposition (and also maximal, see

Theorem 26.4-18 on page 745), we have the GNS representation (Sec. 26.4.6)

$$\Pi_\omega(W(f)) = W_{\Pi_F}(f) \otimes \exp\{i\sqrt{2}\operatorname{Re}(zL(f))\}, \quad \forall f \in E, \quad \omega \in \mathcal{S}_L, \quad (48.4.43)$$

where $W_{\Pi_F}(f) = W_F(\sqrt{\hbar}f)$ are the Weyl operators in the Fock representation $(\Pi_F, F_+(\overline{E}))$, and the exponential is a multiplication operator in $L^2(b\mathbb{C}, \mathbb{C}; \mu^\omega)$. That is

$$\mathcal{H}_\omega = F_+(\overline{E}) \otimes L^2(b\mathbb{C}, \mathbb{C}; \mu^\omega), \quad \Omega_\omega = \Omega_{\text{vac}} \otimes 1, \quad (48.4.44)$$

with Ω_{vac} the Fock vacuum vector and $1(z) = 1$ the unit function on $b\mathbb{C}$. By the weak closure of $\Pi_\omega(\mathcal{W}(E))$, we obtain the representation von Neumann algebra $\mathcal{M}_\omega$ with its center $\mathcal{Z}_\omega$ as

$$\mathcal{M}_\omega = \mathcal{L}(F_+(\overline{E})) \otimes L^\infty(b\mathbb{C}, \mathbb{C}; \mu^\omega), \quad \mathcal{Z}_\omega = \mathbb{1} \otimes L^\infty(b\mathbb{C}, \mathbb{C}; \mu^\omega). \quad (48.4.45)$$

We remark that we have found in the present case a classical subtheory, signified by the Bauer simplex $\mathcal{S}_L$, without a symmetry group. The central decompositions of the states $\omega \in \mathcal{S}_L$ is already expressed in terms of the even continuous parametrization $b\mathbb{C} \ni z \mapsto \omega_z$. (Recall that state convergence in the weak* topology results from the point-wise convergence of the characteristic functions.) The ω_z are distinguished representatives of the (quasi-) equivalence classes $[\omega_z]$ of pure (thus factorial) states.

By the way, we could increase the analogy of $\mathcal{S}_L$ to the permutation-invariant states $\mathcal{S}^\mathbb{P}$ by introducing the group of automorphisms

$$G_L := \{\alpha \in \text{*-aut}(\mathcal{W}(E)) \,|\, \omega \circ \alpha = \omega, \forall \omega \in \mathcal{S}_L\}. \quad (48.4.46)$$

Then $\mathcal{S}_L$ is the set of invariant states of the automorphism group $(\mathcal{W}(E), G_L)$, which is simplicial (as defined in [Gui74]). The latter fact allows to introduce a kind of group average, as described by the following construction.

We may extend the parametrization of the central state decompositions from $\mathcal{S}_L$ to the smallest folium $\mathcal{F}_L$ which contains $\mathcal{S}_L$ in quite the same manner as for $\mathcal{F}_\mathbb{P}$. That is, we construct a special realization of the W*-algebra $\mathcal{M}_L$, characterized by its folium of normal states $\mathcal{F}_L$, so that for each $\varphi \in \mathcal{F}_L$ there is associated a unique $\omega \in \mathcal{S}_L$ with $\omega \in [\varphi]$. For this, we select a family $\{\omega_i \,|\, i \in I\} \subset \mathcal{S}_L$ of mutually disjoint states, so that the direct sum of their central supports $\oplus_I C_i$ equals C_L, the central support of $\mathcal{F}_L$. Then a $\varphi \in \mathcal{F}_L$ is a countable convex combination $\varphi = \sum_J \lambda_i \varphi_i$ of states φ_i, with central supports each not larger than C_i, so that $\varphi_i \in \mathcal{F}_{\omega_i}$ (cf. Eq. (46.2.20)). Since $\mathcal{S}_L$ is convex and weak* closed, $\omega := \sum_J \lambda_i \omega_i \in \mathcal{S}_L$. This can be arranged so that $C_\varphi = C_\omega$. If $\mathcal{Z}_L$ denotes the center of $\mathcal{M}_L$, ω is also characterized by the condition $\varphi|_{\mathcal{Z}_L} = \omega|_{\mathcal{Z}_L}$. Since $\varphi \in \mathcal{F}_\omega$, we may consider φ a weak perturbation of the macroscopic coherent state ω (strictly speaking, only if μ^ω is supported by $\mathbb{C}$).

For $[\varphi] \ni \omega$, we can — via the central decomposition of $\mathcal{M}_\omega$, arising from the decomposition of ω as shown in Eq. (48.4.40) — now parameterize the central decomposition of φ, getting

$$\varphi = \int_{b\mathbb{C}} \varphi_z \, d\mu^\omega(z), \quad \varphi_z \in \mathcal{F}_{\omega_z}. \tag{48.4.47}$$

(In this normalization $d\mu^\omega(z) = d\mu^\varphi(z)$, but we keep to the ω-index.)

Altogether, we arrive at the following decomposition formula: Let $\varphi, \varphi' \in \mathcal{F}_L$, then there is a measure μ on $b\mathbb{C}$, so that μ^ω and $\mu^{\omega'}$ are absolutely continuous to it, and we have

$$T^{\frac{1}{2}}_{\mathcal{W}(E)}(\varphi, \varphi') = \int_{b\mathbb{C}} T^{\frac{1}{2}}_{\mathcal{W}(E)}(\varphi_z, \varphi'_z) \left[\frac{d\mu^\omega}{d\mu} \frac{d\mu^{\omega'}}{d\mu} \right]^{\frac{1}{2}}(z) \, d\mu(z). \tag{48.4.48}$$

As an example choose two bounded measurable functions $g, g' : \mathbb{C} \to E$. For $z \in \mathbb{C}$ let be φ_z the state on $\mathcal{W}(E)$ with characteristic function

$$\langle \varphi_z; W(f) \rangle = \exp\{-\tfrac{\hbar}{4}\|f\|^2\} \exp\{i\sqrt{2}\,\mathrm{Re}[zL(f) + (g_z|f)]\}, \quad \forall f \in E.$$

and define φ'_z analogously via g'. We use Eq. (48.4.47) to form the states φ and φ' in terms of measures $\mu^\omega, \mu^{\omega'} \in M_p(\mathbb{C})$. We see that φ and φ' describe weak coherent deformations of the first order coherent states ω, ω', associated with the measures $\mu^\omega, \mu^{\omega'}$.

If e.g., L means a macroscopic plane wave, then ω and ω' depict situations, in which the macroscopic phases and amplitudes of zL vary according to the measures μ^ω and $\mu^{\omega'}$, besides the already included vacuum fluctuations. The states φ and φ' signify deformations of zL by z-dependent small ($=$ square integrable in position space representation) wave packets.

For an arbitrary measure μ on $\mathbb{C}$, dominating μ^ω and $\mu^{\omega'}$, we may employ now Eq. (48.4.48) for decomposing the square root of the transition probability $T^{\frac{1}{2}}_{\mathcal{W}(E)}(\varphi, \varphi')$. In the GNS representation (given by Eq. (48.4.44)) for ω_z, with the characteristic function $\exp\{-\tfrac{\hbar}{4}\|f\|^2\}\exp\{i\sqrt{2}\,\mathrm{Re}(zL(f))\}$, we may realize φ_z in terms of the vector $G(g_z) \otimes 1$, where we use the ($\hbar$-modified) Glauber vector in Fock space $G(g_z) = W_F(-i(2/\hbar)^{\frac{1}{2}}g_z)\Omega_{\mathrm{vac}}$. This is verified by calculating in terms of the Weyl relations

$$(G(g_z)|W_{\Pi_F}(f)G(g_z)) = \exp\{-\tfrac{\hbar}{4}\|f\|^2\} \exp\{i\sqrt{2}\,\mathrm{Re}[(g_z|f)]\}.$$

Since the Fock representation, as well as the GNS representation over the pure ω_z, are irreducible, we deduce from the first part of Proposition 48.4-11 on page 1845 (there the K must now be a scalar) that the algebraic transition amplitude is expressible by the almost unique vector representatives (without any extremal procedure)

$$T^{\frac{1}{2}}_{\mathcal{W}(E)}(\varphi_z, \varphi'_z) = |(G(g_z) \otimes 1 | G(g'_z) \otimes 1)| = \exp\left\{ \tfrac{1}{2\hbar} \left[2(g_z | g'_z) - \|g_z\|^2 - \|g'_z\|^2 \right] \right\},$$

where we employed Proposition 18.5-7 (i) on page 443.

If we imagine that a piece of information should be communicated by sending the first-order coherent state $\varphi = \omega$, $g_z \equiv 0$, then we can calculate the probability that the receiver gets the above modified wrong state φ', $g'_z \neq 0$, connected with ω'. Namely, that is the transition probability which arises from the absolute transition amplitude

$$T^{\frac{1}{2}}_{\mathcal{W}(E)}(\omega, \varphi') = \int_{\mathbb{C}} \exp\left\{ -\tfrac{1}{2\hbar} \|g'_z\|^2 \right\} \left[\frac{d\mu^\omega}{d\mu} \frac{d\mu^{\omega'}}{d\mu} \right]^{\frac{1}{2}} (z) \, d\mu(z). \tag{48.4.49}$$

That tells us that the probability for the error φ' vanishes, if the error state is disjoint to the signal state ω, so that there is no overlap between the central measures μ^ω and $\mu^{\omega'}$: Macroscopic errors, which would change the sectors, do not arise spontaneously. The microscopic quantum errors within a sector may happen, but are less probable, the larger the norms of the spontaneously arising wave packets g'_z, and that with exponential decrease. The additive decomposition of the transition amplitude induces, of course, cross terms in the total transition probability for simultaneous transitions in different sectors.

Chapter 49

Locally Convex (LC) Spaces

49.1. Systems of Semi-Norms

We supplement here some basic notions and properties of locally convex (LC) topological vector spaces, called "LC-spaces" for short (e.g., [Con85], [RS73b], and [Sch66]). We construct special LC-spaces for our formulation of (Q)ED.

Quite generally, a *topological vector space* is a vector space V equipped with a topology such that the linear vector space operations (addition, multiplication by a scalar) are continuous (that is a linear space, with a *vector space topology*).

Recall that a *topological space* M is a set equipped with a family τ of subsets, — called *open sets* —, which is invariant under arbitrary unions and finite intersections. The complement of an open set is called a *closed set*. The *interior* $\dot{X}$ of a subset $X \subseteq M$ is the union of all open sets contained in X. A *neighborhood* of a point $f \in M$ is a set $N \subset M$ such that $f \in \dot{N}$. A family $\mathcal{B} \subset \tau$ is a *base of* τ, if each element of τ is the union of sets in $\mathcal{B}$. A family $\mathcal{N} \subset \tau$ is a *neighborhood base at* $f \in M$, if each neighborhood of f contains an element of $\mathcal{N}$. If $\mathcal{B}$ is a base of τ, then $\{X \in \mathcal{B} \,|\, X \ni f\}$ is a neighborhood base at f.

For two given topological spaces M and N a map $T : M \to N$ is *continuous*, if $T^{-1}(B)$ is open in M provided that B is open in N, equivalently, $T^{-1}(B)$ is a neighborhood of any $f \in M$ for a neighborhood B of $T(f) \in N$.

If certain quantities p_α are indexed by $\alpha \in I$, with index set I, we briefly write $(p_\alpha)_I$ for this family or collection (meaning $(p_\alpha)_{\alpha \in I}$). If $I \subseteq \mathbb{Z}$ we employ the common notation k, l, m, n for the indices and write e.g., $(p_k)_I$.

Definition 49.1-1 (Convergence of Nets).

(a) A set I is by definition *directed*, if it is partially ordered, with two elements always dominated by a third one.

(b) A *net* is any set $(f_\alpha)_I$ indexed by a directed set I.

(c) A net $(g_\beta)_J$ is called a *subnet* of the net $(f_\alpha)_I$ if there is a monotone and cofinal map $r : J \to I$, with $g_\beta = f_{r(\beta)}$. (*cofinal:* for each $\alpha \in I$ there is $\beta \in J$ with $r(\beta) \geq \alpha$.)

(d) A net $(f_\alpha)_I \subset M$ of a topological space M converges to an $f \in M$, if for any neighborhood $N(f)$ of f there is an α_0 with $f_\alpha \in N(f)$ for all $\alpha \geq \alpha_0$.

We frequently appeal to the fact that a net $(f_\alpha)_I$ converges to f, if and only if all of its subnets converge to f.

In an LC-space there are open sets of a special geometric quality. This leads to the possibility to define the topology in terms of semi-norms.

Definition 49.1-2 (LC-Spaces). Let E be a real or complex vector space.

(a) A *semi-norm* on E is a map $p : E \to [0, \infty[$ with

$$p(f + g) \le p(f) + p(g), \quad \forall f, g \in E,$$
$$p(zf) = |z| p(f), \quad \forall z \in \mathbb{R}, \text{ or } \forall z \in \mathbb{C}.$$

A family of semi-norms $(p_\alpha)_I$ on E, where I is an arbitrary index set, is said to be *separating*, if

$$\left(p_\alpha(f) = 0 \quad \forall \alpha \in I \right) \quad \Longrightarrow \quad f = 0.$$

A family of semi-norms $(p_\alpha)_I$ on E is called *directed*, if for each finite subset $\Gamma \subset I$ there exists a constant $c > 0$ and a $\beta \in I$ such that

$$\sum_{\alpha \in \Gamma} p_\alpha(f) \le c\, p_\beta(f), \quad \forall f \in E.$$

(b) E is called an LC-space, if E is equipped with a separating family $(p_\alpha)_I$ of semi-norms, and if E carries the weakest vector space topology in which all p_α are continuous. We write sometimes $E[(p_\alpha)_I]$ for an LC-space, when the LC-topology on E is induced by the family $(p_\alpha)_I$ of semi-norms (the latter being, of course, not unique).

A net $(f_\beta)_J$, with J a directed index set, in an LC-space $E = E[(p_\alpha)_I]$ is called *Cauchy*, if it is Cauchy in each p_α. (For each $\epsilon > 0$ and each $\alpha \in I$ there is a $\beta_0 \in J$ so that $p_\alpha(f_\beta - f_{\beta'}) < \epsilon$ for all $\beta, \beta' \ge \beta_0$.) $(f_\beta)_J$ is said convergent to $f \in E$ if it converges in each p_α. (For each $\epsilon > 0$ and each $\alpha \in I$ there is a $\beta_0 \in J$ such that $p_\alpha(f_\beta - f) < \epsilon$ for all $\beta \ge \beta_0$.)

An LC-space E is called *complete* (denoted CLC-space), if each Cauchy net converges to an element of E. So, in general, an LC-space E is not *a priori* complete!

The separating property of the family of semi-norms defining the LC-topology τ (of the LC-space $E = E[(p_\alpha)_I]$) ensures τ to be Hausdorff. In the literature the LC-topology is defined sometimes without the separating property, but must be added as an extra condition in the pertinent cases.

A neighborhood base at $0 \in E[(p_\alpha)_I]$ is given by the sets

$$\mathcal{N}_{\alpha_1 \ldots \alpha_n, \epsilon} := \{ f \in E \mid p_\alpha(f) < \epsilon, \ \alpha \in \{\alpha_1, \ldots, \alpha_n\} \},$$

where $\alpha_1, \ldots, \alpha_n \in I$ and $\epsilon > 0$, and $n \in \mathbb{N}$. A neighborhood base at $f \in E$ is provided by the sets $f + \mathcal{N}_{\alpha_1 \ldots \alpha_n, \epsilon}$, and each open set in $E[(p_\alpha)_I]$ is the union of these neighborhood base sets, the latter constituting a base of the LC-topology.

A special case of an CLC-space $E[(p_\alpha)_I]$ is a *Banach space* (denoted a "B-space"), where by definition the index set I contains only one element and the corresponding semi-norm $\|.\| \equiv p_\alpha$ is in fact a norm (i.e., $p_\alpha(f) = \|f\| = 0 \Longrightarrow f = 0$). The earlier mentioned neighborhood base is for a B-space the family of all open balls, and each open set is the union of open balls. A special B-space is a *Hilbert space* (sometimes called "H-space"), if its norm arises from its scalar product $(.|.)$ by $\|f\| = \sqrt{(f|f)}$ (the latter being called a *Hilbert norm*).

If for an LC-space $E[(p_k)_I]$ the index set I is denumerable, so that I may be considered a subset of $\mathbb{N}$, then the topology may introduced by means of the metric

$$\rho(f,g) := \sum_{k \in I} \frac{2^{-k} p_k(f-g)}{1 + p_k(f-g)}.$$

In this case $E[(p_k)_I]$ is called *metrizable*. A metrizable CLC-space is called a *Fréchet space* (briefly *F-space*), and its LC-topology an *F-topology*.

For a given LC-space $E[(p_\alpha)_I]$, it is frequently useful to change the family of semi-norms $(p_\alpha)_I$ to an *equivalent family* $(q_\beta)_J$, giving by definition the same LC-topology.

Proposition 49.1-3. *In a given LC-space $E = E[(p_\alpha)_I]$ another family of semi-norms $(q_\beta)_J$ induces the same topology, if and only if the following is valid: For each $\alpha \in I$ there are $\beta_1, \ldots, \beta_n \in J$ (with $n \in \mathbb{N}$) and a $c > 0$ such that*

$$p_\alpha(f) \leq c\,[q_{\beta_1}(f) + \ldots + q_{\beta_n}(f)], \quad \forall f \in E,$$

and also for each $\beta \in J$ there are $\alpha_1, \ldots, \alpha_m \in I$ (with $m \in \mathbb{N}$) and a $c' > 0$ such that

$$q_\beta(f) \leq c'\,[p_{\alpha_1}(f) + \ldots + p_{\alpha_m}(f)], \quad \forall f \in E.$$

As a consequence, we obtain that each LC-space $E = E[(p_\alpha)_I]$ possesses an equivalent family of semi-norms $(q_\beta)_J$, which is increasingly directed. The simple proof goes as follows: Let $J = F(I)$ consist of the finite subsets of I, and define $q_\beta(f) := \sum_{\alpha \in \beta} p_\alpha(f)$ for each $\beta \in J$. Here J is partially ordered by the set inclusion which induces the natural partial ordering of the semi-norms: $\beta \subseteq \beta'$ implies $q_\beta \leq q_{\beta'}$, which means $q_\beta(f) \leq q_{\beta'}(f)$ for all $f \in E$.

Corollary 49.1-4 (Directed Family of all Continuous Semi-Norms). *Consider the LC-space $E = E[(p_\alpha)_I]$. Sometimes it is useful to work with the family of all continuous semi-norms on E, which is automatically directed, and which is automatically equivalent to the initial semi-norm system $(p_\alpha)_I$.*

Each LC-space $E[(p_\alpha)_I]$ gives rise to the family $(E_\alpha)_I$ of B-spaces, where E_α is the separated completion of E with respect to p_α. (That means that E_α is the completion of the quotient $E/p_\alpha^{-1}(0)$ with respect to the norm $\|\hat{f}\|_\alpha := p_\alpha(f)$ for the equivalence class $\hat{f} \in E/p_\alpha^{-1}(0)$ corresponding to the representative $f \in E$.) If

$p_\alpha \leq p_\beta$, then each p_β-Cauchy net is also a p_α-Cauchy net, and hence there exists a canonical inclusion mapping

$$\Upsilon_{\alpha,\beta} : E_\beta \to E_\alpha, \quad \hat{f} \mapsto \hat{f}, \tag{49.1.1}$$

which maps, for each representative $f \in E$, the p_β-equivalence class $\hat{f} \in E_\beta$ onto the associated p_α-equivalence class $\hat{f} \in E_\alpha$. In case of an injective $\Upsilon_{\alpha,\beta}$ one may consider E_β as a subspace of E_α.

Let us turn to some specific LC-spaces, the so–called *chains*. For a given LC-space E it is often possible to find an equivalent family of semi-norms $(p_\alpha)_I$, which is *linearly ordered* (also termed *totally ordered*). That will say that the index set I as well as the family of semi-norms are linearly ordered and $\alpha \leq \beta$ implies $p_\alpha \leq p_\beta$ (where often $I = \mathbb{R}$, or $I = \mathbb{N}$). Suppose in addition to the chain property that the canonical inclusion maps $\Upsilon_{\alpha,\beta}$ from (49.1.1) all are injective, which ensures that the p_α are true norms (and not only semi-norms). Then $E_\alpha \supseteq E_\beta$ for $\alpha \leq \beta$, and the completion $\overline{E}$ of E has the form

$$\overline{E} = \bigcap_{\alpha \in I} E_\alpha .$$

Such an LC-space $E = E[(p_\alpha)_I]$ is called briefly a *chain*, and in case of completeness a *B-I-chain*. Obviously, every B-I-chain with countable index set I constitutes an F-space.

Definition 49.1-5 (H- and Sobolev Chains). A B-I-chain $E[(p_\alpha)_I]$, for which the p_α are Hilbert norms, is called an *H-I-chain*.

An H-I-chain with a countable index set I (e.g., $I = \mathbb{Z}$, or $I = \mathbb{N}$, or $I = \{k \in \mathbb{Z} \mid k \geq d\} =: N_d$ for some $d \in \mathbb{Z}$) is called a *Sobolev chain*.

A B-I-chain with $I \equiv N_d$ for some $d \in \mathbb{Z}$ (denoted B-N_d-chain), is called an *inverse limit Banach chain (ILB-chain)* in [Omo97] (and denoted there by the symbol $\{\mathbf{E}, E^k; k \in N_d\}$). An H-$I$-chain with $I \equiv N_d$ (here denoted H-N_d-chain), is called an *inverse limit Hilbert chain (ILH-chain)* in [Omo97].

Further LC-spaces of interest are the *nuclear spaces*. Here we make use of the following facts (compare Sec. 43.2.1 on page 1525): Let $\Upsilon : \mathcal{U} \to \mathcal{V}$ be a bounded linear operator from the infinite-dimensional Hilbert space $\mathcal{U}$ into the infinite-dimensional Hilbert space $\mathcal{V}$ with $\mathrm{dom}(\Upsilon) = \mathcal{U}$. The operator Υ is defined to be *compact*, if it maps bounded sets of $\mathcal{U}$ onto pre-compact sets of $\mathcal{V}$, the latter having compact closures by definition. As a result, one obtains that Υ is compact, if and only if there exist two orthonormal systems $\{e_j^\mathcal{U} \mid j \in \mathbb{N}\} \subset \mathcal{U}$ and $\{e_j^\mathcal{V} \mid j \in \mathbb{N}\} \subset \mathcal{V}$ and a sequence of positive numbers $v_j \geq 0$, $j \in \mathbb{N}$, with $\lim_{j \to \infty} v_j = 0$ such that

$$\Upsilon f = \sum_{j \in \mathbb{N}} v_j (e_j^{\mathcal{U}} | f) e_j^{\mathcal{V}}, \quad \forall f \in \mathcal{U}. \tag{49.1.2}$$

Υ is defined to be a *Hilbert–Schmidt operator*, if

$$\sum_{j \in J} (e_j | \Upsilon^* \Upsilon e_j) < \infty, \tag{49.1.3}$$

whenever the e_j, $j \in J$, constitute an orthonormal basis of $\mathcal{U}$. A Hilbert–Schmidt operator is a special compact operator, for which the v_j, $j \in \mathbb{N}$, in Eq. (49.1.2) are square summable, i.e., $\sum_{j \in \mathbb{N}} v_j^2 < \infty$. Furthermore, the compact operator Υ is called *nuclear*, if the $v_j \geq 0$, $j \in \mathbb{N}$, in Eq. (49.1.2) are summable, i.e., $\sum_{j \in \mathbb{N}} v_j < \infty$. (If $\mathcal{U} = \mathcal{V}$ one speaks of a trace class operator.)

Definition 49.1-6 (Nuclear Space). Let $E = E[(p_\alpha)_I]$ be an LC-space with partially ordered Hilbert semi-norms p_α. Then E is called a *nuclear space*, if the canonical inclusion maps $\Upsilon_{\alpha,\beta}$, $p_\alpha \leq p_\beta$ (with $p_\alpha \neq p_\beta$), all are nuclear.

This definition of nuclearity is equivalent to that in [Sch66] Sec. III-§7 and in [Ume65]. (This is seen from [Sch66] III-7.2(c) and III-7.3). In general a nuclear space E may be incomplete, but its completion is nuclear, too.

If for the nuclear space E its family of Hilbert semi-norms $(p_k)_I$ is countable and if in addition E is complete, then E is a special kind of an F-space.

In [Hid80], Appendix A.3, one finds a restricted definition of a nuclear space. There a (countably Hilbert) nuclear space is defined to be an H-$\mathbb{N}$-chain $E = E[(p_k)_\mathbb{N}]$ with nuclear canonical inclusion maps $\Upsilon_{l,m}$ for $l < m$.

Without proof we state some properties of nuclear spaces, referring to [Sch66] and [Ume65].

Proposition 49.1-7. *The following assertions are valid:*

(a) *Every bounded subset of a nuclear space is pre-compact.*
(b) *If the nuclear topology of E arises from a norm, then E is of finite dimension.*
(c) *Every separated completion E_α is a separable Hilbert space.*
(d) *Every subspace of a nuclear space is nuclear in the relative topology.*
(e) *Inductive and projective limits of nuclear spaces are nuclear, too.*
(f) *Countably locally convex direct sums and projective tensor products of nuclear spaces are also nuclear.*

In our applications of LC-spaces we consider exclusively linear operators, which are defined on the entire spaces, in contrast to the Hilbert space theory of operators in Chapter 43. The general definition of a *continuous map*, as formulated previously, appeals to arbitrary open sets (or neighborhoods). There is a much simpler criterion in the case of LC-spaces and linear maps. A linear operator T from the LC-space

$E = E[(p_\alpha)_I]$ into the LC-space $F = F[(q_\beta)_J]$ is continuous, if and only if for each $\beta \in J$ there are $\alpha_1, \ldots, \alpha_n \in I$ (with $n \in \mathbb{N}$) and a constant $c > 0$ with

$$q_\beta(Tf) \leq c[p_{\alpha_1}(f) + \ldots + p_{\alpha_n}(f)], \quad \forall f \in E.$$

If the system of semi-norms $(p_\alpha)_I$ is increasingly directed, then continuity of T is equivalent to: For each $\beta \in J$ there is an $\alpha \in I$ and a $c > 0$ such that

$$q_\beta(Tf) \leq c\, p_\alpha(f), \quad \forall f \in E.$$

When taking the (equivalent) directed families of all continuous semi-norms for the LC-spaces E and F, then the operator $T : E \to F$ is continuous, if and only if for each continuous semi-norm q on F there exists a continuous semi-norm p on E such that

$$q(Tf) \leq p(f), \quad \forall f \in E.$$

Definition 49.1-8 (Strongly Continuous One-Parameter Groups). Let T_t, $t \in \mathbb{R}$, be a one-parameter group of linear operators on the LC-space E, such that $T_{t=0} = \mathbb{1}$. The operator group $t \mapsto T_t$ is called *strongly continuous*, if $t \mapsto T_t f$ is continuous for every $f \in E$, and if for each continuous semi-norm q on E there exists a continuous semi-norm p on E and a continuous numerical map $t \mapsto a_t \geq 0$ such that

$$q(T_t f) \leq a_t p(f), \quad \forall f \in E, \quad \forall t \in \mathbb{R}.$$

It follows that T_t is a homeomorphism of E with $T_t^{-1} = T_{-t}$ for each $t \in \mathbb{R}$.

Since $\mathbb{R}$ and $\mathbb{C}$ are special CLC-spaces with a single norm $|.|$ (each other norm is equivalent to the absolute value), the linear functional $L : E \to \mathbb{R}$ respectively $L : E \to \mathbb{C}$ on the LC-space $E = E[(p_\alpha)_I]$, with increasingly directed semi-norm system, is continuous, if and only if there is an $\alpha \in I$ and a $c > 0$ such that L fulfills the inequality

$$|L(f)| \leq c\, p_\alpha(f), \quad \forall f \in E. \tag{49.1.4}$$

This leads to a characterization of the topological dual space

$$E' := \{L : E \to \mathbb{R} \text{ respectively } \mathbb{C} \mid L \text{ linear and continuous}\} \tag{49.1.5}$$

as follows: If $L \in E'$ then we have according to Eq. (49.1.4) $L(g) = 0$ for all $g \in p_\alpha^{-1}(0)$, and consequently, the definition $L(\hat{f}) := L(f + g)$ implies that L is a continuous linear form on the separated completion E_α. (Recall that $\hat{f} \in E/p_\alpha^{-1}(0)$ is the equivalence class of the representative $f \in E$.) Conversely, if L is an element of the B-space dual E'_α, then there is a constant $c > 0$ with $|L(\hat{f})| \leq c\|\hat{f}\|_\alpha = c\, p_\alpha(f)$ for all $f \in E$, and hence $L(f + g) := L(\hat{f})$, with $g \in p_\alpha^{-1}(0)$, defines an element of E'. So for each $\alpha \in I$ we may consider E'_α as a subspace of E', and we have proved the following proposition.

Proposition 49.1-9. *The topological dual space E' of the increasingly directed LC-space $E = E[(p_\alpha)_I]$ has the form $E' = \bigcup\limits_{\alpha \in I} E'_\alpha$.*

49.2. Sobolev Chains for (Q)ED

In the smeared field formalism we are confronted with the problem of how to make a unbounded Hilbert space operator continuous by acting on appropriate LC-test function spaces. Certain solutions are investigated in the present section. In a first subsection we outline the problem in some detail and motivate our strategy followed in the subsequent subsections.

49.2.1. *Motivation for Test Function Topologies*

Let us consider a *real or complex* Hilbert space $\mathcal{H}$ with inner product $(.|.)$ and associated norm $\|.\|$. We choose an unbounded operator D with dense domain $\mathrm{dom}(D) \subset \mathcal{H}$.

Unboundedness is equivalent to discontinuity (by Sec. 43.1 on page 1522). In order to make D continuous we introduce in $\mathrm{dom}(D)$ the scalar product

$$(f|g)_D := (f|g) + (Df|Dg), \quad \forall f, g \in \mathrm{dom}(D), \tag{49.2.1}$$

and the corresponding norm $\|.\|_D$. This makes $\mathrm{dom}(D)$ an inner product space. By construction one has automatically

$$\|Df\| \leq \|f\|_D, \quad \forall f \in \mathrm{dom}(D),$$

ensuring that D is a bounded operator from the inner product space $\mathrm{dom}(D)$ (with inner product $(.|.)_D$) into the Hilbert space $\mathcal{H}$ (with inner product $(.|.)$).

We recognize that $\|.\|_D$ is just the graph norm of D (defined in Eq. (43.1.4) on page 1524). If our operator D is closed, then $\mathrm{dom}(D)$, equipped with the inner product $(.|.)_D$, is complete and thus also a Hilbert space.

Let us assume that $\ker(D) = 0$. Then we obtain by means of the definition

$$(f|g)'_D := (Df|Dg), \quad \forall f, g \in \mathrm{dom}(D), \tag{49.2.2}$$

(with associated norm $\|.\|'_D$) an inner product on $\mathrm{dom}(D)$, which is simpler than $(.|.)_D$ from Eq. (49.2.1). In fact, $\mathrm{dom}(D)$ equipped with $(.|.)'_D$ is an inner product space, and D is an isometry, thus again continuous with $\|Df\| = \|f\|'_D, \forall f \in \mathrm{dom}(D)$.

The question arises, under which circumstances is $\mathrm{dom}(D)$ complete with respect to the new norm $\|.\|'_D$? To approach an answer, we assume for simplicity that D is a strictly positive, self-adjoint operator. (Recall from Sec. 43.1, that strict positivity of D means $(f|Df) > 0$ for all $0 \neq f \in \mathrm{dom}(D)$, or equivalently, D is positive with vanishing kernel, and is especially injective.)

Let us denote by $\Lambda \mapsto P(\Lambda)$, Λ running through the Borel subsets of $\mathbb{R}$, the projection-valued measure of D (according to Theorem 43.3-3 on page 1536), considered as given by operators on $\mathcal{H}$. Because D is strictly positive (especially 0 is not an eigenvalue of D), it follows that $P(]-\infty, 0]) = 0$, and thus $P(]0, \infty[) = \mathbb{1}$, meaning that the projection valued measure P lives on $]0, \infty[$, only.

The self-adjointness implies the closedness of D, and so $\mathrm{dom}(D)$ is complete with respect to the first (graph) norm $\|.\|_D$, but in general not with respect to the second norm $\|.\|'_D$.

First we suppose that the spectrum of D is contained in $[d, \infty[$, $d > 0$. Then we obtain from Theorem 43.3-3 on page 1536 that

$$\|Df\|^2 = \int_d^\infty \lambda^2\, d(f|P(\lambda)f) \geq d^2 \int_d^\infty d(f|P(\lambda)f) = d^2\|f\|^2\,.$$

Consequently, $d^2\|f\|^2 + d^2\|Df\|^2 \leq (1+d^2)\|Df\|^2 \leq (1+d^2)(\|Df\|^2 + \|f\|^2)$, from which we finally arrive at the estimation

$$d\|f\|_D \leq \sqrt{1+d^2}\,\|f\|'_D \leq \sqrt{1+d^2}\,\|f\|_D\,, \quad \forall f \in \mathrm{dom}(D)\,.$$

This ensures that the norms $\|.\|_D$ and $\|.\|'_D$ are equivalent on $\mathrm{dom}(D)$. So $\mathrm{dom}(D)$ is also $\|.\|'_D$-complete, and thus is a Hilbert space with respect to the second inner product $(.|.)'_D$.

Secondly we treat the case, when zero is contained in the spectrum of our positive D. For each $a > 0$ the spectral projection $P([0,a])$ is then non-vanishing, and there exists a vector $f_a \in P([0,a])\mathcal{H} \subset \mathrm{dom}(D)$ with $\|f_a\| = 1$. On the other side, we have

$$\|f_a\|'_D{}^2 = \|Df_a\|^2 = \int_0^a \lambda^2\, d(f|P(\lambda)f) \leq a^2 \int_0^a d(f|P(\lambda)f) = a^2\|f_a\|^2 = a^2\,.$$

From this we conclude that $\lim_{a\to 0} \|f_a\|'_D = 0$, but $\|f_a\|_D \geq 1$ for all $a > 0$. So now the norms $\|.\|_D$ and $\|.\|'_D$ on $\mathrm{dom}(D)$ no longer are equivalent, and we cannot derive completeness of $\mathrm{dom}(D)$ with respect to $\|.\|'_D$ from that with $\|.\|_D$. Also we see that there exist $\|.\|'_D$-Cauchy sequences in $\mathrm{dom}(D)$ which are not $\|.\|$-Cauchy sequences, and then their limits do not exist in general within $\mathcal{H}$. That means that $\mathrm{dom}(D)$ is not complete with respect to $\|.\|'_D$, and its $\|.\|'_D$-completion would escape the Hilbert space $\mathcal{H}$.

Similar arguments are valid for D^{-1}. If we want to treat both operators D and D^{-1} simultaneously, then we take the inner product

$$(f|g)_{1,1} := (Df|Dg) + (D^{-1}f|D^{-1}g) \tag{49.2.3}$$

for all $f, g \in \mathrm{dom}(D) \cap \mathrm{dom}(D^{-1}) =: \mathcal{H}^{1,1}$. The corresponding norm is denoted by $\|.\|_{1,1}$. For each $f \in \mathcal{H}^{1,1}$ we obtain the estimation

$$\|f\|_{1,1}^2 = \int_0^\infty (\lambda^{-2} + \lambda^2)\, d(f|P(\lambda)f) \geq \int_0^\infty d(f|P(\lambda)f) = \|f\|^2\,,$$

which implies that every $\|.\|_{1,1}$-Cauchy sequence is also a $\|.\|$-Cauchy sequence. We conclude that, in this case, it is not necessary to add the original inner product $(.|.)$, as in our previous argumentation for zero in the spectrum of D, forming

$(.|.)_D = (.|.)'_D + (.|.)$. In Proposition 49.2-1, we show that $\mathcal{H}^{1,1}$ is indeed $\|.\|_{1,1}$-complete and thus a Hilbert space with respect to $(.|.)_{1,1}$, which finally arises from the fact that every operator function $u(D)$ is closed (with $u : \mathbb{R} \to \mathbb{C}$ an arbitrary Borel measurable function).

As a last remark let us mention that the estimation $\|D^{\pm 1}f\| \leq \|f\|_{1,1}, \forall f \in \mathcal{H}^{1,1}$, yields that D and D^{-1} are continuous operators from $\mathcal{H}^{1,1}$ into $\mathcal{H}$ (with $\|.\|_{1,1}$ in $\mathcal{H}^{1,1}$ and $\|.\|$ in $\mathcal{H}$).

In the next two subsections we generalize the previous situation.

49.2.2. Polynormed F-Spaces

In the present and following subsection let us fix again a *real or complex* Hilbert space $\mathcal{H}$ with inner product $(.|.)$, and an, in general, unbounded, *strictly positive*, self-adjoint operator D on $\mathcal{H}$.

Again we denote by $P = [\Lambda \mapsto P(\Lambda)]$ the projection-valued measure of D on $\mathcal{H}$. Recall that functions $u(D)$ of the operator D, acting on $\mathcal{H}$, are constructed by the spectral integrals

$$u(D) = \int_{]0,\infty[} u(\lambda)\, dP(\lambda),$$

$$\mathrm{dom}(u(D)) = \left\{ f \in \mathcal{H} \mid \|u(D)f\|^2 = \int_{]0,\infty[} |u(\lambda)|^2 d(f|P(\lambda)f) < \infty \right\},$$

where $u :\,]0,\infty[\to \mathbb{C}$ is any Borel function. Let us emphasize that the functions $u(D)$ are always operators on $\mathcal{H}$, and not on further introduced Hilbert spaces, constructed from subspaces of $\mathcal{H}$ (in terms of stronger norms).

The subsequent construction is performed for $m, n \in [0, \infty[$, but nothing is lost if one assumes $m, n \in \mathbb{N}_0$. For every $m, n \in [0, \infty[$ we introduce the vector space

$$\mathcal{H}^{m,n} := \mathrm{dom}(D^m) \cap \mathrm{dom}(D^{-n}), \tag{49.2.4}$$

which we equip with the inner product

$$(f|g)_{m,n} := (D^m f|D^m g) + (D^{-n} f|D^{-n} g), \quad \forall f, g \in \mathcal{H}^{m,n}. \tag{49.2.5}$$

The associated norm is denoted by $\|.\|_{m,n}$. As a special case we re-obtain the original Hilbert space $\mathcal{H}$ by $\mathcal{H}^{0,0} = \mathcal{H}$ for $m = n = 0$, and have especially $(.|.)_{0,0} = 2(.|.)$.

Proposition 49.2-1. *For every $m, n \in [0, \infty[$ the space $\mathcal{H}^{m,n}$ is a Hilbert space with respect to its inner product $(.|.)_{m,n}$. From $\lim\limits_{k \to \infty} \|g_k - g\|_{m,n} = 0$ it follows that $\lim\limits_{k \to \infty} \|D^p g_k - D^p g\| = 0$ for all $p \in \mathbb{R}$ with $-n \leq p \leq m$.*

Furthermore, for given $\|.\|_{m,n}$, there exists an equivalent Hilbert norm $\|.\|^o_{m,n}$ in $\mathcal{H}^{m,n}$, satisfying

$$\|f\| \leq \|f\|^o_{m,n} \leq \|f\|_{m,n} \leq \left({\|f\|^o_{m,n}}^2 + \|f\|^2 \right)^{1/2}, \quad \forall f \in \mathcal{H}^{m,n}.$$

The family $\{\|.\|_{m,n}^{o} \mid m, n \in [0, \infty[\}$ is partially ordered (this being indicated by the superscript "o") according to the partial ordering in $[0, \infty[^2$. That means

$$\mathcal{H}^{p,q} \supseteq \mathcal{H}^{m,n},$$

$$\|f\|_{p,q}^{o} \leq \|f\|_{m,n}^{o}, \quad \forall f \in \mathcal{H}^{m,n}, \qquad \text{for } p \leq m \text{ and } q \leq n. \qquad (49.2.6)$$

Proof.   For $f \in \mathcal{H}$ we introduce the positive measure $d\rho_f(\lambda) := (f|dP(\lambda)f)$ on $\mathbb{R}$. For the self-adjoint operator $\Gamma_{m,n} := P(]0,1])D^{-n} + P(]1,\infty[)D^m$ in $\mathcal{H}$ we obtain then the following estimations

$$\|f\|_{m,n}^{o}{}^2 := \|\Gamma_{m,n}f\|^2 = \left\|P(]0,1])D^{-n}f\right\|^2 + \left\|P(]1,\infty[)D^m f\right\|^2$$

$$= \int_{]0,1]} \lambda^{-2n}\, d\rho_f(\lambda) + \int_{]1,\infty[} \lambda^{2m}\, d\rho_f(\lambda)$$

$$\leq \int_{]0,\infty[} (\lambda^{-2n} + \lambda^{2m})\, d\rho_f(\lambda) = \left\|D^m f\right\|^2 + \left\|D^{-n}f\right\|^2$$

$$= \|\Gamma_{m,n}f\|^2 + \int_{]1,\infty[} \lambda^{-2n}\, d\rho_f(\lambda) + \int_{]0,1]} \lambda^{2m}\, d\rho_f(\lambda) \leq \|f\|_{m,n}^{o}{}^2 + \|f\|^2,$$

where we used $\lambda^{-2n} \leq 1$ for $\lambda \in]1,\infty[$ and $\lambda^{2m} \leq 1$ for $\lambda \in]0,1]$. On the other hand, one shows analogously that $\|f\|_{m,n}^{o}{}^2 \geq \|f\|^2$. Putting all facts together one obtains

$$\tfrac{1}{2}\left(\|f\|_{m,n}^{o}{}^2 + \|f\|^2\right) \leq \|f\|_{m,n}^{o}{}^2 \leq \|f\|_{m,n}^2 \leq \|f\|_{m,n}^{o}{}^2 + \|f\|^2,$$

which implies that $\mathrm{dom}(\Gamma_{m,n}) = \mathcal{H}^{m,n}$, but also that the norm $\|.\|_{m,n}^{o}$, the graph norm $\|.\|_{\Gamma_{m,n}}$ (defined by $\|f\|_{\Gamma_{m,n}}^2 := \|\Gamma_{m,n}f\|^2 + \|f\|^2$, see Eq. (43.1.4) on page 1524), as well as the norm $\|.\|_{m,n}$ are equivalent on $\mathcal{H}^{m,n}$. But $\Gamma_{m,n}$ being self-adjoint on $\mathcal{H}$ yields $\Gamma_{m,n}$ to be closed, and the latter is equivalent to $\mathcal{H}^{m,n}$ being complete with respect to $\|.\|_{\Gamma_{m,n}}$, and thus with respect to $\|.\|_{m,n}$.

With the foregoing techniques it is immediate to show that $\|D^p f\| \leq \|\Gamma_{m,n}f\| \leq \|f\|_{\Gamma_{m,n}}$ for every $-n \leq p \leq m$, providing the convergence assertions. The rest is obvious. $\square$

Let $1 < q = n$, but $p < m$. Then with the techniques used in the previous proof it is immediately checked that $\|f\|_{p,q} > \|f\|_{m,n}$ for $0 \neq f \in P(]0,1[)\mathcal{H}$ (provided $P(]0,1[) \neq 0$). This contrasts $\|f\|_{p,q} < \|f\|_{m,n}$ for $0 \neq f \in P(]1,\infty[)\mathcal{H}$ (provided $P(]1,\infty[) \neq 0$). Thus the norms $\|.\|_{m,n}$ are in general not partially ordered according to the partial ordering of $(m,n) \in [0,\infty[^2$ as in formula (49.2.6). Only subsystems of these norms may be ordered increasingly as is seen in Theorem 49.2-2(b).

Let us define the vector space

$$E := \bigcap_{m,n\in[0,\infty[} \mathcal{H}^{m,n} = \bigcap_{m,n\in\mathbb{N}_0} \mathcal{H}^{m,n} = \bigcap_{k\in\mathbb{Z}} \mathrm{dom}(D^k), \qquad (49.2.7)$$

which we equip with the LC-topology τ arising from the system of norms $\|.\|_{m,n}$ with $m, n \in [0, \infty[$, or equivalently, from the system of norms $\|.\|^o_{m,n}$ with $m, n \in [0, \infty[$. With the earlier Proposition we conclude that for each $p \in \mathbb{R}$ the mapping

$$E \ni f \longmapsto \|D^p f\| =: \|f\|_p \tag{49.2.8}$$

is a τ-continuous Hilbert norm on E. Clearly, the norms $\|.\|_p$, $p \in \mathbb{R}$, generate the topology τ on E, too. But τ is also generated, if one takes the norms $\|.\|_{rk+l} = \|D^{rk+l}.\|$, $k \in \mathbb{Z}$, for a fixed $r \in \mathbb{N}$ and $l \in \mathbb{Z}$. It suffices, however, to take the system of norms $\|.\|_{a(n)} = \|D^{a(n)}.\|$ and $\|.\|_{b(n)} = \|D^{b(n)}.\|$ with any two real sequences $a(n)$ and $b(n)$, $n \in \mathbb{N}$ satisfying $\lim_{n \to \infty} a(n) = +\infty$ and $\lim_{n \to \infty} b(n) = -\infty$.

Theorem 49.2-2 (F-Space, Equivalent Norm Systems, Sobolev Chains).

Let all be as given earlier. Then E is an F-space (with respect to its just described topology τ). Moreover, the following assertions are valid:

(a) *E is $\|.\|_{m,n}$-dense in $\mathcal{H}^{m,n}$ for every $m, n \in [0, \infty[$ (or $m, n \in \mathbb{N}_0$).*
(b) *Let $a(n) \geq 0$ and $b(n) \leq 0$, $n \in \mathbb{N}$, be two sequences satisfying $\lim_{n \to \infty} a(n) = +\infty$ and $\lim_{n \to \infty} b(n) = -\infty$. Then the norms $\|.\|_{a(n),b(n)}$, $n \in \mathbb{N}$, constitute an equivalent norm system for the F-topology τ on E.*
(c) *E rewrites in several kinds as a Sobolev chain (H-N-chain): With the two sequences of part (b) we have that $E = E[(\|.\|_{a(n),b(n)})_{n \in \mathbb{N}}]$ with $\mathcal{H}^{a(n),b(n)}$ as separated completions.*

The parts (a) to (c) remain valid, when taking the norms $\|.\|^o_{m,n}$ instead of $\|.\|_{m,n}$.

Proof. Since each $\mathcal{H}^{m,n}$ is $\|.\|_{m,n}$-complete, E is complete (with respect to τ) according to its construction. Because of the ordering (49.2.6), also the countable number of norms $\|.\|^o_{a(n),b(n)}$ (or $\|.\|_{a(n),b(n)}$), where $n \in \mathbb{N}$, leads to the topology τ, ensuring that E is an F-space. Now only prove that E is $\|.\|_{m,n}$-dense in $\mathcal{H}^{m,n}$. The rest is easily checked with the techniques known from the proof of Proposition 49.2-1, especially that the norms $\|.\|_{r(m+l),r(m+l')}$, $m \in \mathbb{N}_0$, increase. We obtain for $0 < a < b < \infty$ that $P([a,b])f \in E$ for every $f \in \mathcal{H}$. Since 0 is not an eigenvalue of D we have that $\lim_{a \to 0, b \to \infty} \|P([a,b])g - g\| = 0$ for every $g \in \mathcal{H}$. Consequently for every $f \in \mathcal{H}^{m,n}$ we obtain

$$\|P([a,b])f - f\|^2_{m,n} = \|P([a,b])D^m f - D^m f\|^2 + \|P([a,b])D^{-n}f - D^{-n}f\|^2 \longrightarrow 0,$$

as $a \to 0$ and $b \to \infty$. Hence the subspace $\{P([a,b])f \mid 0 < a < b < \infty, f \in \mathcal{H}\} \subset E$ is $\|.\|_{m,n}$-dense in $\mathcal{H}^{m,n}$, and thus τ-dense in E. $\qquad\square$

Further equivalent norm systems, and further Sobolev chains, may be constructed in a similar way.

Let us now consider the situation, where the operator D is lower bounded with lower bound $d > 0$, i.e., $(f|Df) \geq d\|f\|^2$ for all $f \in \text{dom}(D)$. Then the previous construction becomes simpler. Since now D^{-n} are bounded operators on $\mathcal{H}$, the part for the index $n \in \mathbb{N}$ (or $n \in [0, \infty[$) is not needed: For every $m \in \mathbb{N}_0$ it holds that

$$E_m := \mathcal{H}^{m,n} = \mathcal{H}^{m,0}, \quad \forall n \in \mathbb{N},$$

and that both norms $\|.\|_{m,n}$ and $\|.\|_{m,0}$ are equivalent to the Hilbert norm $\|.\|'_m$ arising from the inner product

$$(f|g)'_m := d^{-2m}(D^m f | D^m g), \quad \forall f, g \in E_m, \tag{49.2.9}$$

(this may be shown immediately with the techniques used in the proof of Proposition 49.2-1). Notice that $\|.\|'_m$ coincides with $\|.\|_m$ from (49.2.8) up to the factor d^m. By construction, $\|.\|'_m \le \|.\|'_{m+1}$, thus we have the Sobolev chain $E = E[(\|.\|'_m)_{\mathbb{N}_0}]$ with separated completions E_m.

We go now a step further and suppose that $\mathcal{H}$ is separable and that D has a purely discrete spectrum such that every eigenspace is finite-dimensional. Thus there exists an orthonormal basis $\{e_j \mid j \in \mathbb{N}\}$ of $\mathcal{H}$ such that $D e_j = \lambda_j e_j$ for all $j \in \mathbb{N}$, where the eigenvalues λ_j of D are strictly positive numbers, which may be ordered increasingly (repeated according to their multiplicity)

$$0 < \lambda_1 \le \lambda_2 \le \lambda_3 \le \lambda_4 \le \dots ;$$

especially the lowest eigenvalue $d := \lambda_1$ is a strictly positive lower bound for D. Conversely, if an orthonormal basis of $\mathcal{H}$ and increasing values λ_j are given, then the strictly positive, self-adjoint operator D on $\mathcal{H}$ may be defined in the previous way. Consequently,

$$E_m = \left\{ f = \sum_{j \in \mathbb{N}} x_j e_j \ \Big| \ \sum_{j \in \mathbb{N}} \lambda_j^{2m} |x_j|^2 < \infty \right\}, \quad m \in \mathbb{N}, \tag{49.2.10}$$

and the scalar product from Eq. (49.2.9) rewrites as

$$(f|g)'_m = d^{-2m} \sum_{j \in \mathbb{N}} \lambda_j^{2m} \overline{x_j} y_j, \quad f = \sum_{j \in \mathbb{N}} x_j e_j, \quad g = \sum_{j \in \mathbb{N}} y_j e_j. \tag{49.2.11}$$

We may extend the Sobolev chain $E = E[(\|.\|_m)_{\mathbb{N}_0}]$ from the index set $\mathbb{N}_0$ to all of $\mathbb{Z}$ by defining E_m and $(.|.)'_m$ — as in the Eqs. (49.2.10) and (49.2.11) — for negative $m \in \mathbb{Z}$ in terms of sequence spaces $f = (x_j)_{j \in \mathbb{N}} =: \sum_{j \in \mathbb{N}} x_j e_j$. Then the Sobolev chain E is given by $E = E[(\|.\|_m)_{\mathbb{Z}}]$, and the family $\{e_j^m := (d/\lambda_j)^m e_j \mid j \in \mathbb{N}\}$ is an orthonormal basis of the Hilbert space E_m for each $m \in \mathbb{Z}$.

For $l < m$ the canonical identical embedding map $\Upsilon_{l,m} : E_m \to E_l$, $f \mapsto f$ from Eq. (49.1.1) writes in terms of the two orthonormal basis systems as

$$\Upsilon_{l,m} f = d^{(m-l)} \sum_{j \in \mathbb{N}} \lambda_j^{(l-m)} (e_j^m | f)'_m e_j^l, \quad \forall f \in E_m. \tag{49.2.12}$$

If $\lim_{j \to \infty} \lambda_j = \infty$, the embedding operators $\Upsilon_{l,m}$, $l < m$, all are compact (for the notion of a compact, Hilbert–Schmidt, and nuclear operator, see page 1883). $\Upsilon_{l,m}$

with $l < m$ is Hilbert–Schmidt, if the $\lambda_j^{(l-m)}$, $j \in \mathbb{N}$, are square summable, and it is a nuclear operator, if the $\lambda_j^{(l-m)}$, $j \in \mathbb{N}$, are summable. Clearly the condition to be Hilbert–Schmidt is weaker a condition than to be nuclear.

Observation 49.2-3. *E is a nuclear space, if $\sum_{j \in \mathbb{N}} \lambda_j^{-r} < \infty$ for a single $r \in \mathbb{N}$.*

Proof. $\sum_j \lambda_j^{-r} < \infty$ gives $\sum_j \lambda_j^{-nr} < \infty$ for all $n \in \mathbb{N}$. Thus $\Upsilon_{k+mr,k+m'r}$ is nuclear for all $k \in \mathbb{Z}$ and all $m, m' \in \mathbb{Z}$ with $m' > m$. But for fixed $k \in \mathbb{Z}$ the system of norms $\|.\|_{k+mr}$, $m \in \mathbb{Z}$, also constructs the F-topology τ on E. That is, $E = E[(\|.\|_{k+mr})_{m \in \mathbb{Z}}]$ is a Sobolev chain, for which the canonical embedding maps all are nuclear. $\qquad\square$

From this observation we conclude, that the increasing values $\lambda_j = (a+j)^b$ with some constants $a > 0$ and $b > 0$ always lead to nuclear Sobolev chains, but not for $\lambda_j = [\ln(a+j)]^b$. In [Hid80] it is shown that the Schwartz test function space $S(\mathbb{R}^n, \mathbb{C})$ (also called functions of rapid decrease) may be topologized in terms of Hilbert norms with $\lambda_j = 1 + j$ and hence is nuclear.

49.2.3. *Operator Restrictions, Part 1*

We continue the investigation of the previous subsection, based on a *strictly positive*, self-adjoint operator D on $\mathcal{H}$. We consider restrictions of the operators $D^{\pm p}$ and of the unitary one-parameter group $\exp\{itu(D)\}$ (for an arbitrary measurable function $u : \mathbb{R} \to \mathbb{R}$) to the subspaces $\mathcal{H}^{m,n} \subset \mathcal{H}$ to $E = \bigcap_{m,n \in [0,\infty[} \mathcal{H}^{m,n} \subset \mathcal{H}$. In order that those unitaries be well defined, we have to suppose that $\mathcal{H}$ be a *complex* Hilbert space, but in fact, only in those statements in which unitary groups do occur.

Theorem 49.2-4. *Let all be as introduced previously, and $m, n \in [0, \infty[$ be arbitrary. Then the following assertions are valid:*

(a) *For each $p \in [0, \infty[$ it holds $\mathcal{H}^{m+p,n} \subset \mathrm{dom}(D^p)$ and $D^p(\mathcal{H}^{m+p,n}) = \mathcal{H}^{m,n+p}$. Furthermore, D^p is an isometric bijection from $\mathcal{H}^{m+p,n}$ onto $\mathcal{H}^{m,n+p}$ (thus D^{-p} from $\mathcal{H}^{m,n+p}$ onto $\mathcal{H}^{m+p,n}$). Consequently, $D^p(E) = E$, and $D^{\pm p}|_E$ are τ-homeomorphisms on E which are inverse to each other.*

(b) *Let $\mathbb{R} \ni t \mapsto U_t$ be a strongly continuous unitary one-parameter group on $\mathcal{H}$ commuting with D, i.e., U_t commutes with the spectral projections of D. Then this unitary group leaves $\mathcal{H}^{m,n}$ and E invariant: $U_t(\mathcal{H}^{m,n}) = \mathcal{H}^{m,n}$ and $U_t(E) = E$. Moreover, the restrictions of $\mathbb{R} \ni t \mapsto U_t$ constitute a strongly continuous unitary one-parameter group on the Hilbert space $\mathcal{H}^{m,n}$ (with respect to $(.|.)_{m,n}$), and a strongly τ-continuous one-parameter group on the F-space E in the sense of Definition 49.1-8.*

Proof. Part (a). Whenever either k and l both are positive or both are negative, then the spectral calculus yields $D^{k+l} = D^k D^l$. Thus $\mathrm{dom}(D^{k+l}) = \{g \in \mathrm{dom}(D^l) \mid$

$D^l g \in \text{dom}(D^k)\}$. This is, however, not valid for $k < 0$ and $l > 0$ and neither for $k > 0$ and $l < 0$; so $D^{-k} D^k g = g$ only for $g \in \text{dom}(D^k)$ (since the domain of the operator product $D^{-k} D^k$ is given by $\text{dom}(D^{-k} D^k) = \text{dom}(D^k)$). Hence, $f \in \mathcal{H}^{m+p,n}$ implies, on the one side, that $f \in \text{dom}(D^p)$ and $D^p f \in \text{dom}(D^m)$, and, on the other side, that $D^p f \in \text{dom}(D^{-n-p})$, i.e., $D^p f \in \mathcal{H}^{m,n+p}$. That is, $D^p(\mathcal{H}^{m+p,n}) \subset \mathcal{H}^{m,n+p}$, and analogously one shows $D^{-p}(\mathcal{H}^{m,n+p}) \subset \mathcal{H}^{m+p,n}$. Thus we arrive at the equalities, $D^p(\mathcal{H}^{m+p,n}) = \mathcal{H}^{m,n+p}$ and $D^{-p}(\mathcal{H}^{m,n+p}) = \mathcal{H}^{m+p,n}$. The proposed isometric properties of $D^{\pm p}$ are now immediate.

Part (b). It follows that $U_t D^k = D^k U_t$ for all $k \in \mathbb{R}$. Thus $U_t(\mathcal{H}^{m,n}) = \mathcal{H}^{m,n}$. $t \mapsto U_t$ being a strongly continuous unitary group on the original Hilbert space $\mathcal{H}$ yields

$$\|(U_t - \mathbb{1})f\|^2_{m,n} = \|(U_t - \mathbb{1})D^m f\|^2 + \|(U_t - \mathbb{1})D^{-n} f\|^2 \xrightarrow{t \to 0} 0, \quad \forall f \in \mathcal{H}^{m,n}.$$

The assertions concerning E are immediate, taking into account the construction of E. $\qquad\qquad\qquad\qquad\qquad\qquad\qquad\qquad\qquad\qquad\qquad\qquad\qquad\qquad\qquad$ □

Examples of such unitary groups U_t, $t \in \mathbb{R}$, are found as follows: Let $u: \mathbb{R} \to \mathbb{R}$ be any Borel measurable function, then $u(D)$ is self-adjoint, and constitutes the strongly continuous unitary one-parameter group $\mathbb{R} \ni t \mapsto \exp\{itu(D)\} \equiv U_t$ on $\mathcal{H}$ commuting with D by the spectral calculus (cf. Theorem 43.3-3), especially, $\exp\{itu(D)\}v(D) = v(D)\exp\{itu(D)\}$ for each Borel measurable function $v : \mathbb{R} \to \mathbb{C}$. We want to deduce the generators of the restricted group on $\mathcal{H}^{m,n}$ on E for the special case $u(D) = D^q$ for $q \in \mathbb{R}$.

But before proceeding, let us take a detailed look on operator restrictions. As described in the Secs. 43.1 and 43.7, an operator B on the Hilbert space $\mathcal{H}$ is restricted, if its domain $\text{dom}(B)$ is a subspace $\mathcal{D} \subset \text{dom}(B)$, e.g., the subspace $\mathcal{D} = \text{dom}(B) \cap \mathcal{H}^{m,n}$ (the restriction is denoted by $B|_{\mathcal{D}}$). In general, however, one has $Bf \notin \mathcal{H}^{m,n}$ for some $f \in \text{dom}(B) \cap \mathcal{H}^{m,n}$, and so the restriction of B to the domain $\text{dom}(B) \cap \mathcal{H}^{m,n}$ does not lead to an operator acting on the Hilbert space $\mathcal{H}^{m,n}$. Thus, in order to obtain an operator restriction, denoted by $B\lceil_{m,n}$ and acting on $\mathcal{H}^{m,n}$, we have to demand

$$\begin{aligned} \text{dom}(B\lceil_{m,n}) &:= \{f \in \text{dom}(B) \cap \mathcal{H}^{m,n} \mid Bf \in \mathcal{H}^{m,n}\}, \\ B\lceil_{m,n} f &:= Bf, \quad \forall f \in \text{dom}(B\lceil_{m,n}). \end{aligned} \qquad (49.2.13)$$

For the operator $B\lceil_{m,n}$ on $\mathcal{H}^{m,n}$ one may investigate continuity, closedness, self-adjointness, positivity, as well as its adjoint (with respect to the inner product $(.|.)_{m,n}$).

Example 49.2-5. Let $q \in \mathbb{R}$ with $q/2 \le m + n$. Then the restriction $D^q\lceil_{m,n}$ is a strictly positive, self-adjoint operator on the Hilbert space $\mathcal{H}^{m,n}$ with the domain and the image

for $q > 0$: $\mathrm{dom}(D^q\lceil_{m,n}) = \mathcal{H}^{m+q,n} \subset \mathcal{H}^{m,n}$, $\mathrm{ran}(D^q\lceil_{m,n}) = \mathcal{H}^{m,n+q} \subset \mathcal{H}^{m,n}$,

for $q < 0$: $\mathrm{dom}(D^q\lceil_{m,n}) = \mathcal{H}^{m,n-q} \subset \mathcal{H}^{m,n}$, $\mathrm{ran}(D^q\lceil_{m,n}) = \mathcal{H}^{m-q,n} \subset \mathcal{H}^{m,n}$.

Furthermore, $D^q\lceil_{m,n}$ is the generator of the strongly $\|.\|_{m,n}$-continuous unitary group $t \mapsto \exp\{itD^q\}$ restricted to $\mathcal{H}^{m,n}$, i.e., $\exp\{itD^q\lceil_{m,n}\} = \exp\{itD^q\}|_{\mathcal{H}^{m,n}}$ for all $t \in \mathbb{R}$.

Proof.   Without restriction in generality we assume $q > 0$. $\mathrm{dom}(D\lceil_{m,n}) = \mathcal{H}^{m+q,n}$ is immediately checked with the definition (49.2.13). The image $\mathrm{ran}(D^q\lceil_{m,n}) = D^q(\mathcal{H}^{m+q,n}) = \mathcal{H}^{m,n+q}$ follows from Theorem 49.2-4(a). By Theorem 49.2-2 $E \subset \mathcal{H}^{m+q,n}$ is $\|.\|_{m,n}$-dense in $\mathcal{H}^{m,n}$, yielding $D^q\lceil_{m,n}$ to be densely defined.

Clearly $D^q\lceil_{m,n}$ is symmetric. To prove its self-adjointness, we show that

$$\mathrm{dom}(D^q\lceil^*_{m,n}) = \{f \in \mathcal{H}^{m,n} \mid \mathrm{dom}(D^q\lceil_{m,n}) \ni g \mapsto (f|D^q g)_{m,n} \text{ is } \|.\|_{m,n}\text{-continuous}\}$$

coincides with $\mathrm{dom}(D^q\lceil_{m,n}) = \mathcal{H}^{m+q,n}$. Since $|(D^{-n+q/2}f|D^{-n+q/2}g)| \le \|f\|_{m,n}\|g\|_{m,n}$ (where $-n + q/2 \le m$ by assumption) and $(f|D^q g)_{m,n} = (D^m f|D^q D^m g) + (D^{-n+q/2}f|D^{-n+q/2}g)$, and E is a core for D^q on $\mathcal{H}$ (which may be shown with the techniques in the proof of Theorem 49.2-2), we conclude that $f \in \mathrm{dom}(D^q\lceil^*_{m,n})$, if and only if $E \ni h \mapsto (D^m f|D^q h)$ is $\|.\|$-continuous. The latter implies $D^m f \in \mathrm{dom}(D^q)$, or equivalently, $f \in \mathcal{H}^{m+q,n}$.

The strict positivity of $D^q\lceil_{m,n}$ in $\mathcal{H}^{m,n}$ follows immediately from that of D^q in $\mathcal{H}$.

Finally we mention that the expression

$$\left\|\frac{\exp\{itD^q\}f - f}{t} - iD^q f\right\|^2_{m,n} = \left\|\frac{(\exp\{itD^q\} - \mathbb{1})D^m f}{t} - iD^q D^m f\right\|^2$$
$$+ \left\|\frac{(\exp\{itD^q\} - \mathbb{1})D^{-n}f}{t} - iD^q D^{-n}f\right\|^2$$

vanishes as $t \to 0$, if and only if $D^m f, D^{-n}f \in \mathrm{dom}(D^q)$, or equivalently, if and only if $f \in \mathcal{H}^{m+q,n}$. $\square$

Analogously as in this example one may conclude that the τ-homeomorphism $iD^q|_E$ is the generator of the strongly τ-continuous one-parameter group $t \mapsto \exp\{itD^q\}|_E$ on E, that is,

$$\frac{d\exp\{itD^q\}f}{dt}\bigg|_{t=0} = iD^q f, \quad \forall f \in E,$$

with respect to the F-topology τ.

Let us finally supplement details for the *complex case*. We suppose the existence of a conjugation C on the complex Hilbert space $\mathcal{H}$ so that our strictly positive, self-adjoint operator D is C-real. For these notions, see Definition 43.7-3 on page 1555. By Sec. 43.7, especially the Eqs. (43.7.3) and (43.7.4), the conjugation C decomposes uniquely the complex Hilbert space $\mathcal{H}$ into the real Hilbert space $\mathcal{H}_r = \{f \in \mathcal{H} \mid Cf = f\}$, that is $\mathcal{H} = \mathcal{H}_r + i\mathcal{H}_r$, where the inner product on $\mathcal{H}_r$ arises from that on $\mathcal{H}$ by restriction. From Proposition 43.7-4 on page 1556 it follows that C decomposes each complex Hilbert space $\mathcal{H}^{m,n}$ as

$$\mathcal{H}^{m,n} = \mathcal{H}_r^{m,n} + i\mathcal{H}_r^{m,n}$$

with the real part Hilbert space

$$\mathcal{H}_r^{m,n} = \mathcal{H}^{m,n} \cap \mathcal{H}_r = \{f \in \mathcal{H}^{m,n} \mid Cf = f\}, \quad \forall m, n \in \mathbb{N}_0 .$$

Analogously we obtain the decomposition of the complex F-space from Eq. (49.2.7),

$$E = E_r + iE_r$$

into the real F-space

$$E_r = \bigcap_{m,n \in \mathbb{N}_0} \mathcal{H}_r^{m,n} = E \cap \mathcal{H}_r = \{f \in E \mid Cf = f\},$$

where its F-topology is obtained by restricting τ from E to E_r.

Observation 49.2-6. Since D is C-real, it follows that $u(D)$ on $\mathcal{H}$ restricts to a well defined self-adjoint operator $u(D)_r$ on $\mathcal{H}_r$ for all Borel measurable functions $u :]0, \infty[\rightarrow \mathbb{R}$ (by Proposition 43.7-4 on page 1556). Clearly, the assertions in part (a) of Theorem 49.2-4 remain valid for the C-real restrictions $D_r^{\pm p}$.

49.2.4. *Operator Restrictions, Part 2*

Generalizing the previous situation, let now $\mathcal{H}_1$ and $\mathcal{H}_2$ be *two real or two complex* Hilbert spaces, where for convenience both inner products are denoted by $(.|.)$ and also both corresponding norms by $\|.\|$. Let A be a densely defined, closed operator from $\mathcal{H}_1$ into $\mathcal{H}_2$ with adjoint A^* (acting from $\mathcal{H}_2$ into $\mathcal{H}_1$), from which we construct the two operators

$$D_1 := A^*A \quad \text{on } \mathcal{H}_1, \qquad D_2 := AA^* \quad \text{on } \mathcal{H}_2 . \tag{49.2.14}$$

These operator products are automatically self-adjoint and positive (see the considerations preceding Eq. (43.3.8) on page 1537).

Observation 49.2-7. D_1 is strictly positive, if and only if $\ker(A) = 0$, or equivalently, if and only if $\operatorname{ran}(A^*)$ is dense in $\mathcal{H}_1$, whereas D_2 is strictly positive, if and only if $\ker(A^*) = 0$, or equivalently $\operatorname{ran}(A)$ is dense in $\mathcal{H}_2$.

Proof. [Sketch] Recall from Sec. 43.1 that for a closed, densely defined operator from one Hilbert space into another it holds that $B = B^{**}$, and $\ker(B^*B) = \ker(B) = \operatorname{ran}(B^*)^\perp$. $\square$

From now on we suppose that both D_1 and D_2 are *strictly* positive on $\mathcal{H}_1$ and on $\mathcal{H}_2$ respectively (and thus invertible). Then, doubling the situation from Eq. (49.2.7) on page 1888, we introduce the two F-spaces

$$E_1 := \bigcap_{k \in \mathbb{Z}} \operatorname{dom}(D_1^k) \subset \mathcal{H}_1, \qquad E_2 := \bigcap_{k \in \mathbb{Z}} \operatorname{dom}(D_2^k) \subset \mathcal{H}_2, \tag{49.2.15}$$

equipped with the associated F-topologies τ_1 and τ_2, respectively. Recall that each τ_j arises from the system of norms $E_j \ni f \mapsto \|D_j^k f\| =: \|f\|_k^{(j)}$ with $k \in \mathbb{Z}$ and $j = 1, 2$.

Theorem 49.2-8. *Let D_1 and D_2 be strictly positive, arising from the closed $A : \mathcal{H}_1 \to \mathcal{H}_2$ as in Eq. (49.2.14), and introduce the preceding F-spaces E_1 and E_2. Then A and A^* must be injective operators, and it holds $E_1 \subset \operatorname{dom}(A)$ and $E_2 \subset \operatorname{dom}(A^*)$, as well as $A(E_1) = E_2$ and $A^*(E_2) = E_1$. Furthermore, A is a τ_1-τ_2-homeomorphism from E_1 onto E_2, whereas A^* is a τ_2-τ_1-homeomorphism from E_2 onto E_1.*

Regarded as the original operators between Hilbert spaces, it follows that E_1 is a core for A and D_1, and that E_2 is a core for A^* and D_2.

Proof. We have $\|D_1^{1/2} f\| = \|Af\|$ for all $f \in \operatorname{dom}(A) = \operatorname{dom}(D_1^{1/2})$ and $\|D_2^{1/2} g\| = \|A^* g\|$ for all $g \in \operatorname{dom}(A^*) = \operatorname{dom}(D_2^{1/2})$ by Eq. (43.3.8) on page 1537. Thus the injectivity of A and A^* follows from that of $D_j^{1/2}$, $j = 1, 2$.

Recall that $D_j^p(E_j) = E_j$ for each $p \in \mathbb{R}$ by Theorem 49.2-4(a). Then the defining relations $D_1 = A^*A$ and $D_2 = AA^*$ (from Eq. (49.2.14)) yield

$$E_1 \subset \operatorname{dom}(A), \quad E_1 \subset \operatorname{ran}(A^*) = \operatorname{dom}(A^{*-1}),$$
$$E_2 \subset \operatorname{dom}(A^*), \quad E_2 \subset \operatorname{ran}(A) = \operatorname{dom}(A^{-1}).$$

Equation (49.2.14) ensures that $AD_1^m = A(A^*A)^m = (AA^*)^m A = D_2^m A$ for all $m \in \mathbb{N}_0$. Taking carefully into account the domains of definition, we multiply by the inverse operators D_j^{-m}, $j = 1, 2$, from the left and from the right respectively. Then we arrive at the operator identities (product of operators acting between Hilbert spaces)

$$AD_1^k = D_2^k A, \quad \forall k \in \mathbb{Z}. \tag{49.2.16}$$

Now $E_1 \subset \operatorname{dom}(A)$ and $D_1^k(E_1) = E_1$ ensure $A(E_1) \subset \operatorname{dom}(D_2^k) \,\forall k \in \mathbb{Z}$ respectively $A(E_1) \subseteq E_2$. Consequently, for $f \in E_1$ we have

$$\|Af\|_k^{(2)} = \|D_2^k Af\| = \|AD_1^k f\| = \|D_1^{k+1/2} f\| = \|f\|_{k+1/2}^{(1)}, \tag{49.2.17}$$

(identifying here the norms by a superscript for clarity). Since the norms $\|\cdot\|_{k+1/2}^{(1)}$, $k \in \mathbb{Z}$, are τ_1-continuous, this implies that A is τ_1-τ_2-continuous from E_1 into E_2.

Applying in (49.2.16), with care on the domains, the inverse of A from the left and from the right, we get the operator identities

$$D_1^k A^{-1} = A^{-1} D_2^k, \quad \forall k \in \mathbb{Z}. \tag{49.2.18}$$

From these we conclude in the same way as previously that $A^{-1}(E_2) \subseteq E_1$, and that A^{-1} is τ_2-τ_1-continuous from E_2 into E_1. A similar argumentation concerning A^* finally gives the result.

Let us prove that E_1 is a core for D_1 and A, where E_2 being a core for D_2 and A^* is demonstrated analogously. Using the spectral calculus it is immediately checked that an analytic vector for D_1 is also an analytic vector for its square root $D_1^{1/2}$. Since the analytic vectors of D_1 are contained in E_1 by its construction in Eq. (49.2.15), it follows from Proposition 43.6-3 (c) on page 1552 that E_1 is a core for D_1 and for $D_1^{1/2}$. Using the polar decomposition $A = UD^{1/2}$ (cf. Proposition 43.3-5 on page 1537) we conclude that E_1 is also a core for A. □

Let us finally consider the following operator $\mathbb{A}$ acting on the direct sum Hilbert space $\mathcal{H} := \mathcal{H}_1 \boxplus \mathcal{H}_2$,

$$\mathbb{A} := \begin{pmatrix} 0 & A^* \\ -A & 0 \end{pmatrix}, \tag{49.2.19}$$

where we use the *notations* of our treatment *of the Maxwell dynamics*, especially the $\boxplus$-symbol for the direct sum of different field spaces.

$\mathbb{A}$ is anti-selfadjoint, i.e., $\mathbb{A}^* = -\mathbb{A}$ (so that $i\mathbb{A}$ is self-adjoint in the complex case), and possesses by the previous Theorem the core $E := E_1 \boxplus E_2$. The operator

$$\mathbb{A}^* \mathbb{A} = -\mathbb{A}^2 = \begin{pmatrix} D_1 & 0 \\ 0 & D_2 \end{pmatrix} =: D \tag{49.2.20}$$

is strictly positive and self-adjoint.

Our preceding argumentation demonstrates that $\mathbb{A}$ acts homeomorphic on the Cartesian product LC-space E, satisfying especially $\mathbb{A}(E) = E$. The product LC-topology $\tau = \tau_1 \boxplus \tau_2$ on

$$E = E_1 \boxplus E_2 = \bigcap_{k \in \mathbb{Z}} \mathrm{dom}((\mathbb{A})^{2k}) = \bigcap_{k \in \mathbb{Z}} \mathrm{dom}(D^k)$$

arises from the equivalent system of Hilbert norms

$$f \equiv (f_1, f_2) \longmapsto \|f\|_k := \|\mathbb{A}^{2k} f\| = \|D^k f\| = \sqrt{\|D_1^k f_1\|^2 + \|D_2^k f_2\|^2}, \quad k \in \mathbb{Z}. \tag{49.2.21}$$

Thus we are in the situation of the Secs. 49.2.2 and 49.2.3 with the strictly positive, self-adjoint operator $D = -\mathbb{A}^2$ on the Hilbert space $\mathcal{H}$.

The anti-selfadjointness of $\mathbb{A}$ ensures that $\exp\{t\mathbb{A}\}$, $t \in \mathbb{R}$, constitutes a strongly continuous orthogonal respectively unitary group on the Hilbert space $\mathcal{H}$, with $\exp\{t\mathbb{A}\}(E) = E$ for all $t \in \mathbb{R}$. It fulfills for each $k \in \mathbb{Z}$

$$\|\exp\{t\mathbb{A}\}f\|_k = \|f\|_k, \quad \forall f \in E, \quad \forall t \in \mathbb{R},$$

for the equivalent norm system (49.2.21). The unitary group $t \mapsto \exp\{t\mathbb{A}\}$ commutes with D, and thus Theorem 49.2-4(b) ensures (also in the case of real Hilbert spaces $\mathcal{H}_1$ and $\mathcal{H}_2$):

Lemma 49.2-9. $t \mapsto \exp\{t\mathbb{A}\}|_E$ *is a strongly τ-continuous one-parameter group on E in the sense of Definition 49.1-8.*

49.3. Twofold Gelfand Triples

In the present section we present some notions and results, which are necessary for the extended electromagnetic field formalism, comprising via dual spaces non-integrable fields. We denote by E, E_1, and E_2 real LC-spaces, the topological duals of which are denoted by E', E_1', and E_2'.

49.3.1. *LC-Continuous Operators in LC-Gelfand Triples*

Let the LC-space E be a $\|.\|$-dense subspace of a real Hilbert space $\mathcal{R}$ (with inner product $(.|.)$ and associated norm $\|.\|$). Then each element $\xi \in \mathcal{R}$ gives rise to the following $\mathbb{R}$-linear form on E, where we identify notationally the Hilbert space element with the linear form,

$$\xi : E \to \mathbb{R}, \quad f \mapsto (\xi|f) \equiv \xi(f).$$

Provided the LC-topology is finer than the $\|.\|$-topology on E, the Hilbert space norm restricted to E is LC-continuous. Thus the Cauchy–Schwartz inequality $|(\xi|f)| \le \|\xi\| \, \|f\|$ for all $f \in E$ yields that the linear form ξ is LC-continuous, or equivalently, $\xi \in E'$. Since E is a $\|.\|$-dense subspace in $\mathcal{R}$, we obtain an injective mapping

$$\mathcal{R} \to E' : \quad \xi \mapsto \xi(.) = (\xi|.), \qquad \text{(injective embedding)}.$$

This embedding is just the smearing procedure of the electromagnetic L^2-fields and L^2-potentials and leads naturally to the following notion.

Definition 49.3-1 (Gelfand Triple). A triple of spaces

$$E \subset \mathcal{R} \subset E', \qquad \text{(Gelfand triple)}$$

is called a *Gelfand triple* if the following is true: E is a real LC-space which is a $\|.\|$-dense subspace of a real Hilbert space $\mathcal{R}$, such that the LC-topology is finer than the $\|.\|$-topology on E, or equivalently, the Hilbert space norm $\|.\|$ is continuous with respect to the LC-topology on E. $\mathcal{R}$ is embedded into the LC-topological dual E'.

Lemma 49.3-2. *Let be given a Gelfand triple $E \subset \mathcal{R} \subset E'$. Then each $\|.\|$-dense subspace Γ of $\mathcal{R}$ is weak* dense in E'. This is especially valid for $\Gamma = E$ and $\Gamma = \mathcal{R}$.*

Proof. The annihilator $\Gamma^\perp \subset E$ of $\Gamma \subset E'$, given by

$$\Gamma^\perp := \{g \in E \mid \xi(g) = (\xi|g) = 0 \text{ for all } \xi \in \Gamma\},$$

vanishes since Γ is $\|.\|$-dense in $\mathcal{R}$. But as a consequence of the Hahn–Banach Theorem, a subspace $\Gamma \subset E'$ is weak* dense in E', if and only if its annihilator $\Gamma^\perp$ is trivial (see, e.g., [Con85] Corollary IV.3.14). $\qquad\square$

For each LC-continuous $\mathbb{R}$-linear operator $A\colon E_1 \to E_2$ we obtain by duality theory the weak* continuous $\mathbb{R}$-linear operator $A'\colon E_2' \to E_1'$ defined by

$$(A'\eta)(f) = \eta(Af), \quad \forall \eta \in E_2', \quad \forall f \in E_1. \tag{49.3.1}$$

If A is a homeomorphism of E_1 onto E_2 (i.e., LC-continuously invertible), then A' is a homeomorphism from E_2' onto E_1' with respect to the weak* topologies, and it holds

$$(A^{-1})' = (A')^{-1}. \tag{49.3.2}$$

Suppose in this situation that each E_j is part of the Gelfand triple $E_j \subset \mathcal{R}_j \subset E_j'$ for $j = 1, 2$. Then we may regard A as an operator from the Hilbert space $\mathcal{R}_1$ into the Hilbert space $\mathcal{R}_2$ with the $\|.\|$-dense domain of definition $\mathrm{dom}(A) = E_1$. The dual operator A' has the following connection to the Hilbert space adjoint operator A^*: The Hilbert space domain of definition of A^* and its action are given by

$$\mathrm{dom}(A^*) = \{\eta \in E_2' \mid \eta \in \mathcal{R}_2 \subset E_2', A'\eta \in \mathcal{R}_1 \subset E_1'\},$$
$$(A^*\eta|f) = (\eta|Af), \quad \forall \eta \in \mathrm{dom}(A^*), \quad \forall f \in \mathrm{dom}(A) = E_1,$$

(which immediately follows from the definition of the Hilbert space adjoint in Sec. 43.1 on page 1522). So we have

$$A'\eta = A^*\eta, \quad \forall \eta \in \mathrm{dom}(A^*) \subset \mathcal{R}_2 \subset E_2'.$$

If $\mathrm{dom}(A^*)$ is $\|.\|$-dense in $\mathcal{R}_2$, then by the previous Lemma $\mathrm{dom}(A^*)$ is weak* dense in E_2', which leads to the following fact.

Lemma 49.3-3 (Weak* Continuous Operator Extension). *Suppose that the previous treated A be a closable Hilbert space operator from $\mathcal{R}_1$ into $\mathcal{R}_2$ (with domain $\mathrm{dom}(A) = E_1 \|.\|$-dense in $\mathcal{R}_1$), or equivalently, let $\mathrm{dom}(A^*)$ be $\|.\|$-dense in $\mathcal{R}_2$. Then it follows that the dual operator $A'\colon E_2' \to E_1'$ is the unique weak* continuous extension of the Hilbert space adjoint operator A^* (from $\mathcal{R}_2$ into $\mathcal{R}_1$ with domain $\mathrm{dom}(A^*)$).*

In the earlier sense we determined in Lemma 44.4-2 on page 1585 the Hilbert space adjoints for our six vector differential operators $\mathrm{grad}_0, \ldots, \mathrm{curl}$ with E being the usual test function space of infinitely differentiable functions with compact support and thus E' the familiar space of distributions. Unfortunately, this test function space is incompatible with the Helmholtz–Hodge decomposition. However, in Chapter 8 we introduced test function spaces, which fit perfectly to ED and its Helmholtz–Hodge decomposition.

49.3.2.   *The Structure of Twofold Gelfand Triples*

If we combine the considerations of Sec. 49.2.4 with the notions of a Gelfand triple in Sec. 49.3.1 we arrive at the structure of a twofold Gelfand triple, which provides us with a standard procedure to extend a field dynamics to larger (dual) spaces. Let us compile the essential facts.

Suppose $\mathcal{R}_1$ and $\mathcal{R}_2$ to be two real Hilbert spaces, and A a densely defined, closed operator from $\mathcal{R}_1$ into $\mathcal{R}_2$ with adjoint A^* (from $\mathcal{H}_2$ into $\mathcal{H}_1$), such that both A and A^* are injective. Then the two operators

$$A^*A \quad \text{on} \quad \mathcal{R}_1, \qquad AA^* \quad \text{on} \quad \mathcal{R}_2,$$

are automatically self-adjoint and strictly positive, thus invertible. With the Hilbert space spectral calculus we may perform the operators $(A^*A)^{m/n}$ and $(AA^*)^{m/n}$ for $m \in \mathbb{Z}$ and $n \in \mathbb{N}$.

Theorem 49.3-4 (Existence of Twofold Gelfand Triples). *There exist two Gelfand triples $E_j \subset \mathcal{R}_j \subset E'_j$, $j = 1, 2$, with*

$$E_1 \subseteq E_1^A := \bigcap_{k \in \mathbb{Z}} \mathrm{dom}((A^*A)^k), \qquad E_2 \subseteq E_2^A := \bigcap_{k \in \mathbb{Z}} \mathrm{dom}((AA^*)^k),$$

such that (for each $m \in \mathbb{Z}$ and $n \in \mathbb{N}$):

(GT1) *E_1 is a Hilbert space core for A and $(A^*A)^{m/n}$, as well as E_2 for A^* and $(AA^*)^{m/n}$.*

(GT2) *$A(E_1) = E_2$ and $A^*(E_2) = E_1$. Furthermore, A is an LC-homeomorphism from E_1 onto E_2, and A^* is an LC-homeomorphism from E_2 onto E_1.*

(GT3) *$(A^*A)^{m/n}(E_1) = E_1$ and $(AA^*)^{m/n}(E_2) = E_2$, where $(A^*A)^{m/n}$ is an LC-homeomorphism on E_1, and $(AA^*)^{m/n}$ is an LC-homeomorphism on E_2.*

(GT4) *By (GT3) we have that $f \mapsto \|(A^*A)^{m/n}f\|$ is an LC-continuous norm on E_1, and $g \mapsto \|(AA^*)^{m/n}g\|$ on E_2 (recall, $\|.\|$ denotes the Hilbert space norm on $\mathcal{R}_1$ and $\mathcal{R}_2$).*

(GT5) *By (GT1) and (GT2) the operator $\mathbb{A} = \begin{pmatrix} 0 & A^* \\ -A & 0 \end{pmatrix}$, which acts anti-selfadjointly on the direct sum Hilbert space $\mathcal{R} := \mathcal{R}_1 \boxplus \mathcal{R}_2$, possesses the core $E := E_1 \boxplus E_2$. The associated strongly continuous orthogonal (unitary) group on $\mathcal{R}$ leaves E invariant, so that $\exp\{t\mathbb{A}\}(E) = E$ for all $t \in \mathbb{R}$.*

(GT6) *$t \mapsto \exp\{t\mathbb{A}\}|_E$ is a strongly LC-continuous one-parameter group on E (with product LC-topology on the Cartesian product LC-space $E = E_1 \boxplus E_2$). That means, each $\exp\{t\mathbb{A}\}$ is an LC-homeomorphism on E, and $t \mapsto \exp\{t\mathbb{A}\}f$ is LC-continuous for every $f \in E$, and for each continuous semi-norm q on E there exists a continuous semi-norm p on E together with a continuous numerical function $t \mapsto a_t \geq 0$ such that (cf. Definition 49.1-8 on page 1884)*

$$q(\exp\{t\mathbb{A}\}f) \leq a_t p(f), \quad \forall f \in E, \quad \forall t \in \mathbb{R}. \qquad (49.3.3)$$

(GT7) *Extend the self-adjoint operator* $(A^*A)^{1/2}$ $\mathbb{C}$*-linearly to the complex Hilbert space* $\mathcal{R}_1 + i\mathcal{R}_1$. *Then the strongly continuous unitary group* $\exp\{it(A^*A)^{1/2}\}$, $t \in \mathbb{R}$, *on* $\mathcal{R}_1 + i\mathcal{R}_1$ *leaves* $E_1 + iE_1$ *invariant, giving* $\exp\{it(A^*A)^{1/2}\}(E_1 + iE_1) = E_1 + iE_1$ *for all* $t \in \mathbb{R}$. *By* (GT1) $E_1 + iE_1$ *is a Hilbert space core for* $(A^*A)^{1/2}$.

The dual operators A' *and* $A^{*\prime}$ *of* A *and* A^* *constitute weak* homeomorphisms from* E_2' *onto* E_1' *and from* E_1' *onto* E_2'. *In the product Gelfand triple* $E \subset \mathcal{R} \subset E'$ *the dual operator* $\mathbb{A}'$ *of* $\mathbb{A}$ *is a homeomorphism on* E', *which gives rise to the one-parameter group* $\exp\{t\mathbb{A}'\}$ *on* E', *being the dual to* $\exp\{t\mathbb{A}\}$.

Proof.   In Sec. 49.2 on page 1885 the existence of such two Gelfand triples constructed via the operators A and A^*, such that $E_j \subset \mathcal{R} \subset E_j'$, $j = 1, 2$, satisfy the earlier seven items (GT1) to (GT7), is shown for $E_1 = E_1^A$ and $E_2 = E_2^A$. This leads to the F-spaces with F-topologies arising just from the norm systems of item (GT4) with varying $m \in \mathbb{Z}$ and $n \in \mathbb{N}$.

("F-"means Fréchet. Equivalent norm systems are obtained, e.g., with fixed $n \in \mathbb{N}$ and with m varying over $k\mathbb{Z} = \{0, \pm k, \pm 2k, \pm 3k, \ldots\}$ for fixed $k \in \mathbb{N}$.)

This demonstrates the existence of such a pair of Gelfand triples, where the properties of the dual operators follow directly from duality theory. $\square$

Definition 49.3-5 (Twofold Gelfand Triple). Suppose $\mathcal{R}_1$ and $\mathcal{R}_2$ to be two real Hilbert spaces, and A a densely defined, closed operator from $\mathcal{R}_1$ into $\mathcal{R}_2$ with adjoint A^* (from $\mathcal{H}_2$ into $\mathcal{H}_1$), such that both A and A^* are injective.

Then any two triples $E_j \subset \mathcal{R}_j \subset E_j'$, $j = 1, 2$, with

$$E_1 \subseteq E_1^A := \bigcap_{k \in \mathbb{Z}} \mathrm{dom}((A^*A)^k), \qquad E_2 \subseteq E_2^A := \bigcap_{k \in \mathbb{Z}} \mathrm{dom}((AA^*)^k), \qquad (49.3.4)$$

such that all properties (GT1)–(GT7) of Theorem 49.3-4 are satisfied, constitute by definition a *twofold Gelfand triple induced by* A.

The case arising from $E_j = E_j^A$ for $j = 1, 2$ is called the *minimal twofold Gelfand triple* (induced by A).

As a first alternative to the minimal twofold Gelfand triple one may take suitable proper subspaces $E_1 \subset E_1^A$ and $E_2 \subset E_2^A$ with the restricted F-topologies, being F-dense in E_1^A and E_2^A respectively, such that all the seven items are valid. Here we have the same dual spaces $E_1{}' = E_1^{A'}$ and $E_2{}' = E_2^{A'}$.

A different twofold Gelfand triple may arise from finer LC-topologies, and so from proper inclusions in Eq. (49.3.4), leading to larger dual spaces than the $E_j^{A'}$. So, in general it is not appropriate to introduce the notion of twofold Gelfand triples only in a unique (say minimal) version.

Concerning our applications, we remark: In Sec. 8.1.2 for the transversal electromagnetic fields we employ a *twofold Gelfand triple* induced by the transversally restricted curl operator, which satisfies all of the seven requirements of Theorem 49.3-4. However, for the longitudinal electromagnetic fields it suffices a weaker version of the twofold Gelfand triple, which is induced by the restricted divergence (and its adjoint gradient operator), satisfying only the first four requirements (GT1) to (GT4).

Chapter 50

Measures on Duals of LC-Spaces

Besides for our own applications to classical and quantum mechanical states in field theory, the integration theory over function spaces has far reaching importance for several fields of mathematical physics. It arose in the theory of random processes, especially for the Brownian motion. In this connection one has to mention the Wiener integrals, which were generalized by A. N. Kolmogorov.

Most basic for quantum theory are the path integrals of R. Feynman. For a Feynman integral there exists no σ-additive measure, in contradistinction to the Wiener integrals, and the existence problem seems up to now not completely clarified. Certain mathematical aspects for this are treated in the survey of Gelfand and Yaglom [GY56].

We expound in the present chapter integration theory over pre-measures, as far as it is required for the expectation functionals in the well developed formalism of commutative Weyl algebras.

50.1. Cylinder Sets and σ-Algebras

For the more general notions of measure theory we refer to Sec. 48.1.1 on page 1777.

In the present chapter, we collect and generalize basic facts on (pre-) measure theory over dual linear spaces, mostly without giving proofs. There is some relationship to [Ume65], [Sko74], and [Hid80].

We start from a real vector space E equipped with an LC-topology τ. We assume that E is *infinite-dimensional*, since otherwise the presented results are well known from usual measure theory. The τ-topological dual E'_τ be equipped with the $\sigma(E'_\tau, E)$-topology, which turns out to be also an LC-topology.

We denote by $\mathsf{B}(\mathbb{R}^m)$ the Borel σ-algebra on the m-dimensional Euclidean space $\mathbb{R}^m$, where $m \in \mathbb{N}$ is finite.

Definition 50.1-1 (Cylinder Sets). Let $m \in \mathbb{N}$. Then for $\Lambda \in \mathsf{B}(\mathbb{R}^m)$, and $f_1, \ldots, f_m \in E$ the set

$$U(f_1, \ldots, f_m; \Lambda) := \{ F \in E'_\tau \mid (F(f_1), \ldots, F(f_m)) \in \Lambda \}$$

1903

is called a *cylinder set* of E'_τ. (Like for an infinite cylinder only the cross-section is specified by the "coordinates" $F(f_i)$.)

If D is a (real) subspace of E, then we denote by $\Sigma(E'_\tau, D)$ the smallest σ-algebra on E'_τ, which contains all the cylinder sets $U(f_1, \ldots, f_m; \Lambda)$, with any $f_1, \ldots, f_m \in D$ for arbitrary $m \in \mathbb{N}$ and all $\Lambda \in \mathsf{B}(\mathbb{R}^m)$.

We state some properties of the σ-algebra $\Sigma(E'_\tau, D)$. Let us recall from Eq. (12.3.1) on page 250 the classical smeared field functions $\Phi^0(f)$, $f \in E$, given by

$$\Phi^0(f) : E'_\tau \to \mathbb{R}, \quad F \mapsto F(f) = \Phi^0(f)(F), \qquad (50.1.1)$$

with their exponentials

$$W^0(f) := \exp\{i\Phi^0(f)\} : E'_\tau \to \mathbb{C}, \quad F \mapsto \exp\{iF(f)\} = W^0(f)(F), \qquad (50.1.2)$$

named "classical Weyl elements". They generate the commutative C*-Weyl algebra $\mathcal{W}(E, 0)$ of the continuous almost periodic functions $A : E'_\tau \to \mathbb{C}$ with respect to the sup-norm $\|.\|_{\sup}$.

Lemma 50.1-2. *Let D be an arbitrary subspace of E. The following assertions are valid:*

(a) $\Sigma(E'_\tau, D)$ *is the smallest σ-algebra on E'_τ, that includes all cylinder sets $U(f;]a, \infty[)$, where $f \in D$ and $a \in \mathbb{R}$.*

(b) $\Sigma(E'_\tau, D)$ *is the smallest σ-algebra on E'_τ such that all field functions $\Phi^0(f)$ with $f \in D$ are measurable. Hence each polynomial of the $\Phi^0(f)$ with $f \in D$ and every $W^0(f)$ with $f \in D$ are measurable with respect to $\Sigma(E'_\tau, D)$. Consequently, the elements of $\mathcal{W}(E, 0)$ are $\Sigma(E'_\tau, E)$-measurable.*

(c) $\Sigma(E'_\tau, D)$ *is stable under the vector space structure of E'_τ, that is, if $\mathcal{V} \in \Sigma(E'_\tau, D)$, $F \in E'_\tau$, and $a \in \mathbb{R}\backslash\{0\}$, then $a\mathcal{V} + F \in \Sigma(E'_\tau, D)$.*

(d) *Let $n \in \mathbb{N}$ and suppose D n-dimensional with an arbitrary basis $\{g_1, \ldots, g_n\}$. Then*

$$\Sigma(E'_\tau, D) = \{U(g_1, \ldots, g_n; \Lambda) \mid \Lambda \in \mathsf{B}(\mathbb{R}^n)\}. \qquad (50.1.3)$$

Moreover, $\Sigma(E'_\tau, D)$ is the smallest σ-algebra on E'_τ which includes all cylinder sets $U(g_k;]a, \infty[)$, where $k = 1, \ldots, n$ and $a \in \mathbb{R}$.

From part (d) it follows that for each finite-dimensional subspace $D \subset E$ the σ-algebra $\Sigma(E'_\tau, D)$ is just given by the cylinder sets $U(f_1, \ldots, f_m; \Lambda)$, where $f_k \in D$, $m \in \mathbb{N}$, and $\Lambda \in \mathsf{B}(\mathbb{R}^m)$ are chosen arbitrarily. (This is in general not true for infinite-dimensional D.) Hence, the union

$$\mathcal{U}_{cs}(E'_\tau) := \cup\{\Sigma(E'_\tau, D) \mid D \subset E, \ \dim_{\mathbb{R}}(D) < \infty\}, \qquad (50.1.4)$$

which ranges over all finite-dimensional subspaces D of E, constitutes the *family of all cylinder sets* of E'_τ, what be indicated by the subscript "cs".

The cylinder sets $\mathcal{U}_{cs}(E'_\tau)$ do not constitute a σ-algebra but only a set algebra on E'_τ. By Definition 50.1-1, $\Sigma(E'_\tau, E)$ is the smallest σ-algebra comprising $\mathcal{U}_{cs}(E'_\tau)$.

Proposition 50.1-3. *Assume a countable set $C \subset E$, which is total in E (i.e., E is separable) with respect to the $\sigma(E, E'_\tau)$-topology. Then the following assertions are valid:*

(a) *For every $F \in E'_\tau$ and each $\Lambda \in B(\mathbb{R})$ the set $\Lambda F := \{aF \mid a \in \Lambda\}$ is an element of the σ-algebra $\Sigma(E'_\tau, E)$; especially $\{F\} \in \Sigma(E'_\tau, E)$.*

(b) *If in addition the $\sigma(E, E'_\tau)$-topology on E is metrizable (i.e., the $\sigma(E, E'_\tau)$-topology arises from a countable set of semi-norms), then $\Sigma(E'_\tau, E)$ is the smallest σ-algebra on E'_τ including all the cylinder sets $U(g;]a, \infty[)$, where $g \in C$ and $a \in \mathbb{Q}$. That is, $\Sigma(E'_\tau, E)$ is countably generated.*

Since the original LC-topology τ is finer than the $\sigma(E, E'_\tau)$-topology on E, it follows that the separability with respect to τ implies the separability with respect to the $\sigma(E, E'_\tau)$-topology. Similarly, the metrizability of τ yields the metrizability of the $\sigma(E, E'_\tau)$-topology.

For a topology with its open sets there are allowed only finite intersections but arbitrary, possibly uncountable, unions. So, the topological structure is sometimes not compatible with the countability in measure theory. In general one has

$$\Sigma(E'_\tau, E) \subseteq B(E'_\tau) \tag{50.1.5}$$

for the Borel σ-algebra $B(E'_\tau)$ on E'_τ (the smallest σ-algebra including the open sets of E'_τ with respect to the $\sigma(E'_\tau, E)$-topology), which is a consequence of Lemma 50.1-2(b). In order to obtain equality in Eq. (50.1.5) it is sufficient that the topological structure on E'_τ arises countably.

Lemma 50.1-4 (Separable Hilbert Space). *Let E be a separable real Hilbert space so that the LC-topology τ coincides with the norm topology arising from the real inner product $(.|.)$. The dual E'_τ may be identified with E itself, according to the Riesz Theorem 43.1-1 on page 1522. Then the Borel σ-algebra on $E'_\tau \equiv E$ for the $\sigma(E'_\tau, E)$-topology (weak topology on E) coincides with the Borel σ-algebra $B(E)$ for the norm topology, and we have $\Sigma(E'_\tau, E) = B(E)$.*

50.2. Weak Distributions and Measures

Suppose $\{g_1, \ldots, g_n\}$ to be a basis for the finite-dimensional subspace D of E. Then Eq. (50.1.3) yields that each measure ν on the measurable space $(E'_\tau, \Sigma(E'_\tau, D))$

defines a unique measure $\tilde{\nu}$ on the Borel sets $\mathsf{B}(\mathbb{R}^n)$ by setting

$$\nu(U(g_1, \ldots, g_n; \Lambda)) =: \tilde{\nu}(\Lambda), \quad \forall \Lambda \in \mathsf{B}(\mathbb{R}^n). \tag{50.2.1}$$

Conversely, taken (50.2.1) as the definition for the left-hand side, it constitutes a definition of a measure ν on $(E'_\tau, \Sigma(E'_\tau, D))$ from a Borel measure on $\mathsf{B}(\mathbb{R}^n)$. Clearly, this construction depends on the chosen basis of D.

A normalized measure μ on the measurable space $(E'_\tau, \Sigma(E'_\tau, E))$ may be restricted to the sub-σ-algebras $\Sigma(E'_\tau, D)$ for the finite-dimensional subspaces D of E, and the restrictions are then denoted by μ_D. (Besides σ-additivity and positivity, μ_D satisfies also the normalization condition, since $U(g_1, \ldots, g_n; \mathbb{R}^n) = E'_\tau$ is in the restricted σ-algebra.) For given measure μ on $(E'_\tau, \Sigma(E'_\tau, E))$ and for a fixed basis in each finite-dimensional subspace D, we obtain in this manner the collection of normalized measures

$$\{\mu_D \mid D \subseteq E, \dim_{\mathbb{R}}(D) < \infty\} \equiv \{\mu_D\}.$$

The restricted measures $\{\mu_D\}$, and the associated Borel measures $\{\tilde{\mu}_D\}$ on $\mathbb{R}^n$ have to fulfill some compatibility conditions: If $U(f_1, \ldots, f_m; \Lambda) = U(g_1, \ldots, g_n; \Lambda')$ for some basis $\{f_1, \ldots, f_m\}$ for the subspace C and a $\Lambda \in \mathsf{B}(\mathbb{R}^m)$, as well as for some basis $\{g_1, \ldots, g_n\}$ for D and a $\Lambda' \in \mathsf{B}(\mathbb{R}^n)$, then it must hold the equality of the associated measures

$$\tilde{\mu}_C(\Lambda) = \mu_C(U(f_1, \ldots, f_m; \Lambda)) = \mu_D(U(g_1, \ldots, g_n; \Lambda')) = \tilde{\mu}_D(\Lambda'). \tag{50.2.2}$$

But, in the reverse direction, this set of compatibility conditions for measures on cylinder sets does in general not lead to a measure μ on $(E'_\tau, \Sigma(E'_\tau, E))$. This is the origin of the following Definition.

Definition 50.2-1 (Weak Distributions). Suppose for every finite-dimensional subspace D of E to be given a probability measure $\mu_D \in M_p(E'_\tau, \Sigma(E'_\tau, D))$. Then the family of normalized measures $\mu_* := \{\mu_D\}$ is called a weak distribution on E'_τ, if it fulfills the compatibility conditions (50.2.2).

We denote by $M_{\mathrm{wd}}(E'_\tau)$ the convex set of weak distributions on E'_τ.

Clearly every weak distribution $\mu_* = \{\mu_D\}$ defines a unique normalized pre-measure μ_* on the algebra of cylinder sets $\mathcal{U}_{\mathrm{cs}}(E'_\tau)$ of E'_τ from Eq. (50.1.4) by setting

$$\mu_*(\mathcal{V}) := \mu_D(\mathcal{V})$$

for the cylinder sets $\mathcal{V} \in \Sigma(E'_\tau, D)$ arising for some finite-dimensional $D \subset E$. This leads to an alternative definition of a weak distribution.

Observation 50.2-2 (Weak Distribution). A weak distribution μ_* is a probability pre-measure on the algebra of cylinder sets $\mathcal{U}_{\mathrm{cs}}(E'_\tau)$ such that the finite-dimensional restrictions μ_D are genuine probability measures on the σ-algebras $\Sigma(E'_\tau, D)$, with $\dim_{\mathbb{R}}(D) < \infty$.

In the sequel we do not distinguish between the pre-measure μ_* and the family $\{\mu_D\}$, and call both a "weak distribution".

It is evident that we may associate to each probability measure μ on the measurable space $(E'_\tau, \Sigma(E'_\tau, E))$ a unique weak distribution μ_* on E'_τ, which is given by the restriction to the algebra of cylinder sets $\mathcal{U}_{\mathrm{cs}}(E'_\tau)$. According to the previous remarks this mapping

$$M_p(E'_\tau, \Sigma(E'_\tau, E)) \to M_{\mathrm{wd}}(E'_\tau), \quad \mu \mapsto \mu_*, \qquad (50.2.3)$$

is affine and injective, but in general not surjective.

If $\mu \mapsto \mu_*$ is not surjective, then not every weak distribution μ_* on E'_τ can be extended to a probability measure μ on $\Sigma(E'_\tau, E)$. Let us communicate the most known conditions under which a weak distribution μ_* extends uniquely to a probability measure on $(E'_\tau, \Sigma(E'_\tau, E))$. In the literature such results are known as *Minlos–Sazonov theorems*. The first result concerns separable Hilbert spaces.

Theorem 50.2-3 (Measure Extensions on Separable Hilbert Spaces). *Suppose the situation of Lemma 50.1-4, where $E \equiv E'_\tau$ is a separable real Hilbert space and the τ-topology coincides with the norm topology. Then the weak distribution $\mu_* \in M_{\mathrm{wd}}(E)$ extends uniquely to a probability measure μ on the Borel σ-algebra $\mathsf{B}(E)$, if and only if μ_* satisfies the following condition: For every $\varepsilon > 0$ there exists an $r_\varepsilon > 0$ such that for all finite-dimensional $D \subset E$*

$$\mu_D(\{f \in E \mid \|P_D f\| \leq r_\varepsilon\}) \geq 1 - \varepsilon, \qquad (50.2.4)$$

where P_D is the orthogonal projection of E onto D. (Note: If $\{e_1, \ldots, e_m\}$ is an orthonormal basis for D, then we have $\{f \in E \mid \|P_D f\| \leq r_\varepsilon\} = U(e_1, \ldots, e_m; B^D_{r_\varepsilon})$, which indeed is a cylinder set in E'_τ, where $B^D_{r_\varepsilon} = \{g \in D \mid \|g\| \leq r_\varepsilon\}$ denotes the ball with radius r_ε in D.)

That means that the affine injection $\mu \mapsto \mu_*$ in Eq. (50.2.3) is non-surjective, and its convex image is given by those elements $\mu_* \in M_{\mathrm{wd}}(E)$ which satisfy condition (50.2.4).

The second result concerns nuclear spaces (introduced in Definition 49.1-6 on page 1883).

Theorem 50.2-4 (Measure Extensions on Nuclear Spaces). *Let E be a nuclear real vector space, with our LC-topology τ given by the nuclear topology. Then a weak distribution $\mu_* \in M_{\mathrm{wd}}(E'_\tau)$ extends uniquely to a probability measure μ on the σ-algebra $\Sigma(E'_\tau, E)$, if μ_* satisfies the following condition: For every $\varepsilon > 0$ there exists a neighborhood $\mathcal{N}_\varepsilon$ of the origin in E (with respect to the nuclear topology*

τ) *such that*

$$\mu_*(U(f;] - 1, 1[)) \geq 1 - \varepsilon, \quad \forall f \in \mathcal{N}_\varepsilon . \qquad (50.2.5)$$

Let us denote by $N_p(E'_\tau, \Sigma(E'_\tau, E))$ *the convex subset of those probability mea-sures* μ *on* $(E'_\tau, \Sigma(E'_\tau, E))$ *for which the associated weak distribution* μ_* *satisfies that condition* (50.2.5). *Then we have the inclusion*

$$N_p(E'_\tau, \Sigma(E'_\tau, E)) \subseteq M_p(E'_\tau, \Sigma(E'_\tau, E)) , \qquad (50.2.6)$$

and the mapping $\mu \mapsto \mu_*$ *from Eq.* (50.2.3) *ensures an affine one-to-one correspon-dence between* $N_p(E'_\tau, \Sigma(E'_\tau, E))$ *and those elements* $\mu_* \in M_{wd}(E'_\tau)$, *which fulfill condition* (50.2.5).

We have equality in Eq. (50.2.6), if and only if τ is metrizable.

50.3. Integration with Respect to Weak Distributions

It is interesting to note that some classes of functions lead to a sensible integration theory with respect to weak distributions $\mu_* \in M_{wd}(E'_\tau)$. To these functions belong the cylinder functions.

Definition 50.3-1 (Cylinder Functions). The mapping $A : E'_\tau \to \mathbb{C}$ is called a *cylinder function*, if there exists a finite-dimensional subspace $D \subset E$, such that it is measurable with respect to the σ-algebra $\Sigma(E'_\tau, D)$; or equivalently, such that it has the representation

$$A(F) = \tilde{A}_D(F(g_1), \dots, F(g_n)), \quad \forall F \in E'_\tau , \qquad (50.3.1)$$

for some Borel measurable function $\tilde{A}_D : \mathbb{R}^n \to \mathbb{C}$ and some basis $\{g_1, \dots, g_n\}$ of the finite-dimensional D.

We term a finite-dimensional subspace $D \subset E$ which allows the representation (50.3.1) for a cylinder function A a *pre-support* of A.

Choose a pre-support $D \subset E$ of the cylinder function A, then $A(F) = 0$ for all $F \in E'_\tau$, which vanish on D (that are the F's from the polar of D).

Clearly, for a cylinder function $A : E'_\tau \to \mathbb{C}$ a pre-support $D \subset E$ is non-unique: If C and D are two pre-supports (finite-dimensional subspaces with basis systems $\{f_1, \dots, f_m\}$ and $\{g_1, \dots, g_n\}$ so that (50.3.1) is valid) then one has the following compatibility condition for the representing Borel functions

$$A(F) = \tilde{A}_C(F(f_1), \dots, F(f_m)) = \tilde{A}_D(F(g_1), \dots, F(g_n)), \quad \forall F \in E'_\tau . \quad (50.3.2)$$

Definition 50.3-2 (Weak Integrals for Cylinder Functions). For each posi-tive cylinder function $A : E'_\tau \to [0, \infty[$ one defines the "integral" with respect to a weak distribution $\mu_* \in M_{\mathrm{wd}}(E'_\tau)$ by

$$\int_{E'_\tau} A \, d\mu_* \equiv \int_{E'_\tau} A(F) \, d\mu_*(F) := \int_{E'_\tau} A(F) \, d\mu_D(F) = \int_{\mathbb{R}^n} \tilde{A}_D(x) \, d\tilde{\mu}_D(x),$$

(50.3.3)

where D is a pre-support for A.

That is, one takes the coordinates of the $F \in E'_\tau$ with respect to an arbitrary pre-support $D \cong \mathbb{R}^n$ of A and forms the usual general Lebesgue integral (cf. (48.1.3)) over the representing Borel function with respect to the Borel measure $\tilde{\mu}_D$, obtained by restriction. (One may show that this expression is independent from the chosen subspace D if one uses the compatibility conditions for the measures $\tilde{\mu}_D$ in Eq. (50.2.2) and for the representing Borel functions in Eq. (50.3.2).)

The μ_*-integral of a general, $\mathbb{C}$-valued cylinder function A is defined by decomposing its real and imaginary part into positive functions $A = A_1 - A_2 + i(A_3 - A_4)$, where one knows that each A_k is a cylinder function. Then the μ_*-integral of A is by definition

$$\int_{E'_\tau} A \, d\mu_* := \int_{E'_\tau} A_1 \, d\mu_* - \int_{E'_\tau} A_2 \, d\mu_* + i \int_{E'_\tau} A_3 \, d\mu_* - i \int_{E'_\tau} A_4 \, d\mu_*.$$

The μ_*-integral of A *exists*, provided each μ_*-integral $\int_{E'_\tau} A_k \, d\mu_* < \infty$, for $k = 1, 2, 3, 4$. Obviously, the μ_*-integral of a cylinder function $A : E'_\tau \to \mathbb{C}$ exists, if and only if its absolute value $|A|$ (which is also a cylinder function) satisfies $\int_{E'_\tau} |A| \, d\mu_* < \infty$.

Since the family of integrals in Eq. (50.3.3), with varying pre-supports D, leads in general not to a proper general Lebesgue integral over E'_τ we call it "μ_*-integral" or "weak integral".

Remark 50.3-3. There are the following facts:

(a) Since $\Sigma(E'_\tau, E)$ is the smallest σ-algebra on E'_τ containing the cylinder sets $\mathcal{U}_{\mathrm{cs}}(E'_\tau)$ it follows that every cylinder function $A : E'_\tau \to \mathbb{C}$ is not only measurable on $\mathcal{U}_{\mathrm{cs}}(E'_\tau)$, the algebra of cylinder sets, but also on $\Sigma(E'_\tau, E)$.

(b) Suppose that the weak distribution μ_* arises from a probability measure μ on $\Sigma(E'_\tau, E)$. Then the weak integral for μ_* agrees with the Lebesgue integral over the genuine measure μ, that is

$$\int_{E'_\tau} A(F) \, d\mu(F) = \int_{E'_\tau} A(F) \, d\mu_*(F),$$

for every cylinder function $A : E'_\tau \to \mathbb{C}$.

50.4. Characteristic Functions, Moments

50.4.1. *Characteristic Functions, Weak Fourier Transformation*

Let $\mathcal{P}(E)$ be the convex set of normalized, positive-definite functions $P : E \to \mathbb{C}$ (as in Definition 12.6-1 on page 255), which we call *characteristic functions*.

For every $f \in E$, the classical Weyl function $W^0(f) : E'_\tau \to \mathbb{C}$, $F \mapsto \exp\{iF(f)\}$ is a cylinder function (and thus measurable on $\Sigma(E'_\tau, D)$ for every subspace $D \subseteq E$ containing f; see Lemma 50.1-2 (b) on page 1904). The smallest pre-support D for $W^0(f)$ is evidently the one-dimensional subspace $\mathbb{R}f \subset E$.

For each weak distribution $\mu_* \in M_{\mathrm{wd}}(E'_\tau)$ the μ_*-integral of $W^0(f)$ exists, and may given by an evaluation on $\mathbb{R}$ as follows

$$P(f) := \int_{E'_\tau} W^0(f)\, d\mu_* = \int_{E'_\tau} \exp\{iF(f)\}\, d\mu_*(F) = \int_{\mathbb{R}} \exp\{ix\}\, d\tilde{\mu}_D(x)\,, \quad \forall f \in E\,.$$

$$(50.4.1)$$

The function $P : E \to \mathbb{C}$ is called the (*weak*) *Fourier transform* of μ_*. By construction, P is continuous and positive-definite on each finite-dimensional subspace D of E.

Definition 50.4-1 (Regular Characteristic Functions). The characteristic function $P \in \mathcal{P}(E)$ is called *regular*, if it fulfills one of the following equivalent conditions:

  (i)   For each $f \in E$ the mapping $\mathbb{R} \ni t \mapsto P(tf)$ is continuous at the origin.
 (ii)   For each $f \in E$ the mapping $\mathbb{R} \ni t \mapsto P(tf)$ is continuous.
(iii) P is continuous on each finite-dimensional subspace D of E.

We denote by $\mathcal{P}_{\mathrm{reg}}(E)$ the convex subset of $\mathcal{P}(E)$ consisting of regular elements.

Proof.   [sketch] P is the characteristic function of a unique state ω on the commutative Weyl algebra $\mathcal{W}(E, 0)$ by Theorem 18.1-23 on page 408 (choose there $\hbar = 0$ or $\sigma = 0$). Now the result follows from Proposition 18.3-7 (a) on page 419.   □

Using Bochner's theorem for finite dimensions [RS73b] Theorem IX.9, [HR70] Sec. 33, one may show the following result.

Theorem 50.4-2 (Affine Bijection). *There exists an affine one-to-one correspondence between the two convex sets $\mathcal{P}_{reg}(E)$ and $M_{wd}(E'_\tau)$, given by the weak Fourier transformation from Eq. (50.4.1).*

Let us add a remark on weak integration. Since every element $A : E'_\tau \to \mathbb{C}$ of $\Delta(E, 0) = \mathrm{LH}\{W^0(f) \mid f \in E\}$ is a cylinder function, the μ_*-integrals $\int_{E'_\tau} W^0(f)\, d\mu_*$, $f \in E$, in Eq. (50.4.1) may be extended by linearity to $\Delta(E, 0)$. Unfortunately, $\mathcal{W}(E, 0)$ contains also non-cylinder functions. Hence the extension of the μ_*-integral to all of the sup-norm closure $\mathcal{W}(E, 0)$ of $\Delta(E, 0)$ does not work for a proper weak distribution μ_*. Such an extension to all of $\mathcal{W}(E, 0)$ is possible for genuine probability measures μ on $\Sigma(E'_\tau, E)$, only.

Example 50.4-3 (Weak Delta Distributions). For $F \in E'_\tau$ the point measure δ^F is defined by $\delta^F(\mathcal{V}) = 1$ if $F \in \mathcal{V}$, and $\delta^F(\mathcal{V}) = 0$ otherwise, $\mathcal{V} \in \Sigma(E'_\tau, E)$. Besides positivity and normalization also σ-additivity is quickly seen for δ^F, since in a disjoint union $\cup_{i \in \mathbb{N}} \mathcal{V}_i$ the element F can only be in one $\mathcal{V}_i$. The associated weak distribution δ^F_* is only defined on cylinder sets $U(f_1, \ldots, f_m; \Lambda)$. Recall that we have $F \in U(f_1, \ldots, f_m; \Lambda)$, if and only if $(F(f_1), \ldots, F(f_m)) \in \Lambda$.

We take the latter relation to generalize the notion of a point measure to a weak distribution: Let $L : E \to \mathbb{R}$ be a non-τ-continuous linear form, thus not contained in E'_τ. We define the weak distribution $\delta^L_* \in M_{\mathrm{wd}}(E'_\tau)$ by the prescription

$$\delta^L_*(U(f_1, \ldots, f_m; \Lambda)) := \begin{cases} 1, & \text{if } (L(f_1), \ldots, L(f_m)) \in \Lambda \in \mathsf{B}(\mathbb{R}^n), \\ 0, & \text{if } (L(f_1), \ldots, L(f_m)) \notin \Lambda, \end{cases} \quad (50.4.2)$$

on the cylinder sets. Thus, δ^L_* is some kind of weak point measure at L, but it cannot be a genuine point measure, since $L \notin E'_\tau$. It is checked that the Fourier transform of δ^L_* is given by

$$\exp\{iL(f)\} = \int_{E'_\tau} \exp\{iF(f)\} \, d\delta^L_*(F) = \int_{\mathbb{R}} \exp\{ix\} \, d\tilde{\delta}^L_D(x), \quad \forall f \in E, \quad (50.4.3)$$

where $D = \mathbb{R}f$ and the one-dimensional delta distribution $\tilde{\delta}^L_D$ is localized on $x = L(f)$. Obviously $\exp\{iL(.)\} \in \mathcal{P}_{\mathrm{reg}}(E)$.

The given argument for σ-additivity is not applicable to δ^L_*, whenever it holds $L \notin E'_\tau$.

The preceding example demonstrates that every linear form $L : E \to \mathbb{R}$, also the non-τ-continuous ones, leads to a weak δ-distribution. Indeed, the construction of weak distributions may be executed also with the algebraic dual space E' of E, instead of E'_τ as performed here.

This kind of independence from the LC-topology τ is already expressed in Theorem 50.4-2 in terms of the τ-independence of $\mathcal{P}_{\mathrm{reg}}(E)$.

However, an eventual extension of the weak distribution μ_* to a genuine probability measure μ needs detailed topological aspects, as we have seen in the two Minlos–Sazonov Theorems 50.2-3 and 50.2-4. The LC-topology τ comes also into play, if τ-continuous characteristic functions $P \in \mathcal{P}(E)$ are treated instead of only regular ones, as we will see in the Bochner–Minlos–Sazonov Theorems 50.5-2 and 50.5-3 below, or in the case of Gaussian measures in Sec. 50.6.

Using again Bochner's theorem for finite dimensions, and the fact that each continuous character on a finite-dimensional real vector space D is of type $f \mapsto \exp\{iL(f)\}$ with some linear form $L : D \to \mathbb{R}$ (e.g., [Sch66] IV-1.2 and [HR70] 23.32(a)) one may show the following result.

Corollary 50.4-4 (Extreme Boundaries). *The affine one-to-one correspondence of Theorem 50.4-2 maps the extreme boundary*

$$\partial_e \mathcal{P}_{reg}(E) = \{\exp\{iL(.)\} \mid L : E \to \mathbb{R} \text{ is a linear form}\}$$

of $\mathcal{P}_{reg}(E)$ onto the extreme boundary

$$\partial_e M_{wd}(E'_\tau) = \{\delta_*^L \mid L : E \to \mathbb{R} \text{ is a linear form}\}$$

of the weak distributions $M_{wd}(E'_\tau)$, via $\exp\{iL(.)\} \mapsto \delta_*^L$.

50.4.2. *Moment Functionals*

We now turn to the *moments* of a weak distribution μ_* on E'_τ. For every $f \in E$ the mapping $\Phi^0(f) : E'_\tau \to \mathbb{C}$, $F \mapsto F(f)$ from Eq. (50.1.1) is a cylinder function (with pre-support e.g., $D = \mathbb{R}f$), and hence every monomial $\Phi^0(f_1) \cdots \Phi^0(f_m)$ is a cylinder function, too, which is measurable with respect to the σ-algebra $\Sigma(E'_\tau, D)$ for every subspace $D \subseteq E$ satisfying $f_1, \ldots, f_m \in D$ (by Lemma 50.1-2 (b) on page 1904).

Definition 50.4-5 (Weak Moments). For a weak distribution $\mu_* \in M_{wd}(E'_\tau)$ we call the expression

$$s_m^{\mu_*}(f_1, \ldots, f_m) := \int_{E'_\tau} F(f_1) \cdots F(f_m) \, d\mu_*(F) = \int_{E'_\tau} \Phi^0(f_1) \cdots \Phi^0(f_m) \, d\mu_*$$

$$(50.4.4)$$

the m-th weak moment at $f_1, \ldots, f_m \in E$, where $m \in \mathbb{N}$ is finite. If the μ_*-integral in Eq. (50.4.4) exists — that means $\int_{E'_\tau} |\Phi^0(f_1) \cdots \Phi^0(f_m)| \, d\mu_* < \infty$ by construction of the μ_*-integral — then we say that the m-th moment of μ_* exists for $f_1, \ldots, f_m \in E$.

If for fixed $m \in \mathbb{N}$ all the associated m-th moments exist — i.e., $s_m^{\mu_*}(f_1, \ldots, f_m)$ exists for every $f_1, \ldots, f_m \in E$ —, then the mapping $s_m^{\mu_*} : E \times \ldots \times E \to \mathbb{R}$ is called the m-th moment functional of μ_*; it is a symmetric, $\mathbb{R}$-multilinear form on E.

Moments can be expressed in terms of the characteristic function via differentiation. By construction, the μ_*-integral of a cylinder function reduces to integration on a finite-dimensional subspace of E. So we may apply the results in [Ric66], Sec. V.6, to obtain the following statements concerning the moments of a weak distribution.

Theorem 50.4-6. *Let be given the weak distribution $\mu_* \in M_{wd}(E'_\tau)$ with associated characteristic function $P(f) = \int_{E'_\tau} W^0(f) \, d\mu_*$ for all $f \in E$, where $P \in \mathcal{P}_{reg}(E)$.*

(a) *Let D be a finite-dimensional subspace of E with basis B_D, and assume $n \in \mathbb{N}$. Suppose that for every $m \in \{1, \ldots, n\}$ the m-th moments $s_m^{\mu_*}(g_1, \ldots, g_m)$ for the basis elements $g_1, \ldots, g_m \in B_D$ exist.*

For each $m \leq n$, all test functions $f_1, \ldots, f_m \in D$, and arbitrary $f \in E$, we have then the continuous mapping

$$\mathbb{R}^m \ni (t_1 \ldots, t_m) \mapsto \frac{\partial^m}{\partial t_1 \cdots \partial t_m} P\left(f + \sum_{k=1}^m t_k f_k\right)$$

$$= i^m \int_{E'_\tau} \exp\{iF(f)\} \left(\prod_{k=1}^m F(f_k) \exp\{it_k F(f_k)\}\right) d\mu_*(F),$$

where the differential quotients and the μ_*-integrals exist. Note: If $f_j = f_l$ for $j \neq l$, then $\frac{\partial^2}{\partial t_j \partial t_l} P(f + \sum_k t_k f_k) = \frac{\partial^2}{\partial t_j^2} P(f + \sum_k t_k f_k)$. Consequently, all m-th moments $s_m^{\mu_*}(f_1, \ldots, f_m)$, with test functions in D, exist and are given by

$$s_m^{\mu_*}(f_1, \ldots, f_m) = (-i)^m \frac{\partial^m}{\partial t_1 \cdots \partial t_m} P\left(\sum_{k=1}^m t_k f_k\right)\Bigg|_{t_1 = \ldots = t_m = 0}.$$

(b) *Suppose that, now for arbitrary $f_1, \ldots, f_m \in E$, the differential quotient*

$$U_0 \ni (t_1, \ldots, t_m) \mapsto \frac{\partial^{2m}}{\partial t_1^2 \cdots \partial t_m^2} P\left(\sum_{k=1}^m t_k f_k\right)$$

exists and is continuous in a neighborhood of the origin $U_0 \subseteq \mathbb{R}^m$. Then the $2m$-th moment $s_{2m}^{\mu_*}(f_1, f_1, f_2, f_2, \ldots, f_m, f_m)$ exists and is given by

$$s_{2m}^{\mu_*}(f_1, f_1, f_2, f_2, \ldots, f_m, f_m) = (-1)^m \frac{\partial^{2m}}{\partial t_1^2 \cdots \partial t_m^2} P\left(\sum_{k=1}^m t_k f_k\right)\Bigg|_{t_1 = \ldots = t_m = 0}.$$

Let us refer a result from [Ric66], V.(4.47), which ensures the existence of moments arising from the existence of certain "higher" moments. For $p \in \mathbb{N}$ we denote by $(g)^p$ the p-tuple $(g, g, \ldots, g)$, where $g \in E$ is indicated p-times.

Lemma 50.4-7. *For $n \in \mathbb{N}$, let $f_1, \ldots, f_n \in E$ and $m_1, \ldots, m_n \in \mathbb{N}$ be fixed. Suppose for all possibilities $p_k \in \{0, m_k\}$, $k = 1, \ldots, n$, the existence of the moments $s_p^{\mu_*}((f_1)^{p_1}, (f_2)^{p_2}, \ldots, (f_n)^{p_n})$, where $p = \sum_{k=1}^n p_k$. Then also all moments*

$$s_q^{\mu_*}((f_1)^{q_1}, (f_2)^{q_2}, \ldots, (f_n)^{q_n}), \quad \text{with } 0 \leq q_k \leq m_k \text{ for } k = 1, \ldots, n,$$

exist, where $q = \sum_{k=1}^n q_k$.

The preceding Lemma and Theorem 50.4-6 lead to the following result.

Corollary 50.4-8. *Let $P \in \mathcal{P}_{reg}(E)$ be the Fourier transform of the weak distribution $\mu_* \in M_{wd}(E'_\tau)$ according to Eq. (50.4.1), i.e., $P(f) = \int_{E'_\tau} W^0(f) d\mu_*$ for all $f \in E$. Suppose D to be a subspace of E, and let $n \in \mathbb{N}$. Then we have the following equivalent statements:*

(i) *For each $f \in D$ the mapping $\mathbb{R} \ni t \mapsto P(tf)$ is $2n$-times continuously differentiable in a neighborhood of the origin.*

(ii) *For each $f \in D$ the $2n$-th moment $s_{2n}^{\mu_*}((f)^{2n})$ exists.*

(iii) *For each $1 \leq m \leq 2n$ and every $f_1, \ldots, f_m \in D$ the moment $s_m^{\mu_*}(f_1, \ldots, f_m)$ exists.*

Proof. (i)$\Rightarrow$(ii) follows from Theorem 50.4-6(b). (ii)$\Rightarrow$(iii): Applying Lemma 50.4-7 to the moment $s_{2n}^{\mu_*}((f)^{2n})$ yields the existence of the moments $s_m^{\mu_*}((f)^m)$ with $m \leq 2n$ for every $f \in D$. Now the estimation $|F(f_1) \cdots F(f_m)| \leq |F(\sum_k \pm f_k)^m|$ — take $+f_k$ if $F(f_k) \geq 0$, and take $-f_k$ if $F(f_k) < 0$ — and $\int_{E'_\tau} |F(\sum_k \pm f_k)^m| d\mu_*(F) < \infty$ implies the existence of the moments $s_m^{\mu_*}(f_1, \ldots, f_m)$. (iii)$\Rightarrow$(i) is a consequence of Theorem 50.4-6(a). $\qquad\square$

If the weak distribution μ_* arises from a measure $\mu \in M_p(E'_\tau, \Sigma(E'_\tau, E))$, then the μ_*-integral agrees with the integral for the measure μ by Remark 50.3-3(b), and for the m-th moments (50.4.4) we have

$$s_m^\mu(f_1, \ldots, f_m) := \int_{E'_\tau} F(f_1) \cdots F(f_m) \, d\mu(F) = \int_{E'_\tau} F(f_1) \cdots F(f_m) \, d\mu_*(F) \, .$$

$$(50.4.5)$$

Lemma 50.4-9 (Separable Hilbert Spaces). *Suppose the situation as with Lemma 50.1-4, where $E \equiv E'_\tau$ is a separable real Hilbert space and the τ-topology coincides with the norm. If the m-th moment functional s_m^μ exists for the probability measure $\mu \in M_p(E, \mathcal{B}(E))$, then it is a bounded (jointly norm continuous) m-linear form on E. Furthermore, the following assertions are valid:*

(a) *Provided its existence, the first moment functional s_1^μ is given with a unique vector $h_\mu \in E$ by*

$$s_1^\mu(f) = (h_\mu | f), \quad \forall f \in E \, . \tag{50.4.6}$$

   h_μ *is called the mean value for the probability measure μ.*
(b) *Provided its existence, the second moment functional s_2^μ is given with a unique self-adjoint, bounded operator A_μ on E by*

$$s_2^\mu(f, g) = (f | A_\mu g), \quad \forall f, g \in E \, . \tag{50.4.7}$$

   A_μ *is called the covariance operator for the probability measure μ. If in addition $\int_E \|f\|^2 d\mu(f) < \infty$, then A_μ is a positive trace class operator satisfying*

$$\mathrm{tr}(A_\mu) = \int_E \|f\|^2 \, d\mu(f) \, . \tag{50.4.8}$$

50.5. Bochner–Minlos–Sazonov Theorems

In Theorem 50.4-2 we have ensured an affine one-to-one correspondence between characteristic functions $P \in \mathcal{P}_{\mathrm{reg}}(E)$ and weak distributions $\mu_* \in M_{\mathrm{wd}}(E'_\tau)$ given via Fourier transformation. If the weak distribution μ_* arises from the probability measure μ on the σ-algebra $\Sigma(E'_\tau, E)$, then for its Fourier transform $P \in \mathcal{P}_{\mathrm{reg}}(E)$

$$P(f) = \int_{E'_\tau} \exp\{iF(f)\}\, d\mu(F) = \int_{E'_\tau} \exp\{iF(f)\}\, d\mu_*(F), \quad f \in E, \qquad (50.5.1)$$

there follows via the Lebesgue dominated convergence theorem (e.g., [Coh80] Theorem 2.4.4) a more stringent continuity than only the continuity on the finite-dimensional subspaces of E. Note that Lebesgue's dominated convergence theorem is valid only for *sequences* of functions but not for nets. Also recall that continuity of a function always implies sequential continuity, but the converse is in general not true. For a metrizable topological space, however, sequential continuity is equivalent to continuity.

Observation 50.5-1 (τ-Continuity). For $\mu \in M_p(E'_\tau, \Sigma(E'_\tau, E))$ define $P \in \mathcal{P}(E)$ as in Eq. (50.5.1). Then P is sequentially continuous with respect to the τ-topology on E (and also with respect to the $\sigma(E, E'_\tau)$-topology). If the LC-topology τ on E is metrizable, then P is τ-continuous.

Let us denote by $\mathcal{P}_\tau(E)$ the convex subset of $\mathcal{P}_{\mathrm{reg}}(E)$ consisting of those $P \in \mathcal{P}(E)$ which are τ-continuous.

In general, not every τ-continuous characteristic function P arises as the Fourier transform of a probability measure $\mu \in M_p(E'_\tau, \Sigma(E'_\tau, E))$. Additional conditions must be imposed on P, in order that this be true. Such results are connected with the names of the mathematicians Bochner, Minlos, and Sazonov.

As in Sec. 50.2 concerning the extension of a weak distribution to a measure, we also here treat only the two cases, where E is a separable real Hilbert space, or a real nuclear space. In virtue of the one-to-one correspondence between $\mathcal{P}_{\mathrm{reg}}(E)$ and $M_{\mathrm{wd}}(E'_\tau)$ via Fourier transformation, the following two results may be considered as a reformulation of the Minlos–Sazonov Theorems 50.2-3 and 50.2-4 in terms of characteristic functions.

Theorem 50.5-2 (Characteristic Functions on Separable Hilbert Spaces).
Consider the situation of Lemma 50.1-4 and of Theorem 50.2-3, where $E \equiv E'_\tau$ is a separable real Hilbert space and the τ-topology coincides with the norm. Suppose the characteristic function $P \in \mathcal{P}(E)$ to be norm continuous.

Then there exists a probability measure μ on the Borel σ-algebra $\mathsf{B}(E)$ such that Eq. (50.5.1) is valid, if and only if for every $\varepsilon > 0$ there exists a positive trace class operator S_ε on E so that $\mathrm{Re}(P(0) - P(f)) < \varepsilon$ for all $f \in E$ satisfying $(f|S_\varepsilon f) < 1$.

In contrast to the preceding restricted result, there exists for nuclear spaces a one-to-one correspondence between nuclear continuous characteristic functions and probability measures on E'_τ. This fact distinguishes nuclear spaces among other LC-spaces.

Theorem 50.5-3 (Characteristic Functions on Nuclear Spaces). *Let E be a nuclear real vector space as in Theorem 50.2-4, i.e., the locally convex topology τ coincides with the nuclear topology.*

Then the Fourier transformation (50.5.1) *provides an affine one-to-one correspondence between $N_p(E'_\tau, \Sigma(E'_\tau, E))$ and $\mathcal{P}_\tau(E)$. (Recall from Theorem 50.2-4 on page 1907 that $N_p(E'_\tau, \Sigma(E'_\tau, E)) \subseteq M_p(E'_\tau, \Sigma(E'_\tau, E))$, where we have equality exactly in case of metrizability of the nuclear topology τ.)*

50.6.   Gaussian Measures

Let us first give a concise definition of what we understand under a "Gaussian function" and under a "Gaussian measure".

Definition 50.6-1 (Gaussian Functions and (Pre-) Measures). Let be given a real vector space E, and let $s : E \times E \to \mathbb{R}$, $(f,g) \mapsto s(f,g)$, be any positive symmetric $\mathbb{R}$-bilinear form and $F : E \to \mathbb{R}$ any $\mathbb{R}$-linear form. (Observe that no boundedness or continuity assumptions have been imposed.)

Then the mapping

$$P : E \to \mathbb{C}, \quad f \mapsto P(f) := \exp\left\{iF(f) - \tfrac{1}{4}s(f,f)\right\} \qquad (50.6.1)$$

is called a *Gaussian function* on E. We denote by $\mathcal{P}_{\text{Gauss}}(E)$ the set of all Gaussian functions on E. Obviously, $\mathcal{P}_{\text{Gauss}}(E) \subset \mathcal{P}_{\text{reg}}(E)$.

We assume now an LC-topology τ on E. Theorem 50.4-2 on page 1910 implies for every Gaussian function $P \in \mathcal{P}_{\text{Gauss}}(E)$ a unique weak distribution $\mu_* = \{\mu_D\} \in M_{\text{wd}}(E'_\tau)$, such that P arises as the Fourier transform (50.4.1) of μ_*. Each finite-dimensional probability measure $\mu_D \cong \tilde{\mu}_D$ of that weak distribution is obviously a finite-dimensional Gaussian measure on some $\mathbb{R}^n$, well known from usual probability theory.

Let us term the weak distribution $\mu_* = \{\mu_D\}$ a *Gaussian pre-measure* on E'_τ. If the Gaussian pre-measure μ_* may be extended to a $\mu \in M_p(E'_\tau, \Sigma(E'_\tau, E))$, then μ is called a *Gaussian measure* on E'_τ.

A Gaussian function P is τ-continuous, and thus an element of $\mathcal{P}_{\text{Gauss}}(E) \cap \mathcal{P}_\tau(E)$, if $F \in E'_\tau$ and if s is jointly τ-continuous. In order to ensure the existence of Gaussian measures one uses the Bochner–Minlos–Sazonov Theorems, leading to the following results.

Proposition 50.6-2 (Gaussians on Separable Hilbert Spaces). *Suppose the situation of Lemma 50.1-4, where $E \equiv E'_\tau$ is a separable real Hilbert space and the τ-topology coincides with the norm. Then a norm continuous Gaussian function $P : E \to \mathbb{C}$ arises from a (Gaussian) measure μ on E, if and only if P is of the* *form*

$$P(f) := \exp\left\{i(h|f) - \tfrac{1}{4}(f|Af)\right\}, \quad \forall f \in E,$$

with some $h \in E$ and some positive trace class operator A on E. In this case we have $h = h_\mu$ and $A = A_\mu + |h_\mu)(h_\mu|$ with the mean value h_μ and the covariance operator A_μ for μ from Lemma 50.4-9 on page 1914.

As an immediate consequence of Theorem 50.5-3, we obtain the existence of Gaussian measures in case of a nuclear E.

Corollary 50.6-3 (Gaussians on Nuclear Spaces). *Let E be a nuclear real vector space so that the LC topology τ coincides with the nuclear topology. Then for each τ-continuous Gaussian function $P : E \to \mathbb{C}$ there exists a unique Gaussian measure $\mu \in N_p(E'_\tau, \Sigma(E'_\tau, E))$ such that P is its Fourier transform (50.5.1).*

Let us finally treat a norm continuous Gaussian on a real separable Hilbert space E.

Example 50.6-4 (Difficulty with a Simple Gaussian on Hilbert Space). A most simple Gaussian on the real separable Hilbert space E, with scalar product $(.|.)$ and associated $\|.\|$, is given by

$$E \ni f \mapsto \exp\{-c\|f\|^2\}, \quad \text{for some } c > 0. \tag{50.6.2}$$

Suppose that there exists a probability measure μ on $\mathsf{B}(E)$ such that

$$\exp\{-c\|f\|^2\} = \int_E \exp\{i(f|g)\}\, d\mu(g), \quad \forall f \in E.$$

Then for every orthonormal basis $\{e_n \mid n \in \mathbb{N}\}$ of E we obtain, by inserting $f = \lambda e_n$, that

$$\exp\{-c\lambda^2\} = \int_E \exp\{i\lambda(e_n|g)\}\, d\mu(g), \quad \forall \lambda \in \mathbb{R}, \quad \forall n \in \mathbb{N}. \tag{50.6.3}$$

Now we observe that for each $f \in E$ the weak limit $\lim\limits_{n\to\infty} (e_n|g) = 0$ and get by Lebesgue's dominated convergence theorem that for $n \to \infty$ the right-hand side of Eq. (50.6.3) approaches unity (since $1 = \mu(E)$). That leads to the contradiction $\exp\{-c\lambda^2\} = 1$ for all $\lambda \in \mathbb{R}$. Consequently, the norm continuous Gaussian function from Eq. (50.6.2) does not arise from a genuine probability measure on E.

Now assume E to be a nuclear (= topology τ) space and that the Hilbert norm $\|.\|$ appearing in Eq. (50.6.2) is τ-continuous. E equipped with the inner product $(.|.)$ is incomplete here, only its norm completion $\overline{E}$ is a proper Hilbert space. There exists a Gaussian measure μ on E'_τ so that the simple Gaussian function (50.6.2) arises as the Fourier transform of μ. In the Fourier transformation $(f|g)$ has then to be replaced by the duality relation $F(f)$, and the integration has to be extended over E'_τ. Since τ is stronger than the norm, the dual E'_τ is larger than $\overline{E}$, and the support of μ is larger than $\overline{E} \subset E'_\tau$. Thus the limits $\lim\limits_{n\to\infty} F(e_n) = 0$ are not valid for all $F \in E'_\tau$ and cannot cause a contradiction.

We see that the Hilbert space is too "small" for functional integration. The example of classical black body radiation demonstrates that even duals of nuclear spaces are not sufficient, if the frequencies of the eigenmodes increase too slowly with the mode number. This and other reasons (regular states) have led us to the weak distributions.

Remark 50.6-5 (Difficulty with Interpreting Characteristic Functionals).
We consider the simple Gaussian $\exp\{-c\|f\|^2\}$, with $c > 0$, of the preceding Example on the nuclear space $E = E_\tau$. It is a τ-continuous positive-definite function and the corresponding probability measure μ on E'_τ is a typical (statistical) state for a classical field theory with phase space E'_τ.

The same setup may, however, be also interpreted in terms of a quantum field theory, achieved by deformation quantization. Assume a polarization $E = E_a \boxplus E_y$ and the symplectic form $\sigma(f,g) := (f_a|g_y) - (f_y|g_a)$. Provided $c \geq \frac{\hbar}{4}$, then $\exp\{-c\|f\|^2\}$ is also σ-positive-definite. That means that it determines also a state φ on the non-commutative Weyl algebra $\mathcal{W}(E,\hbar\sigma)$ (e.g., the bare quantum vacuum in case of $c = \frac{\hbar}{4}$). In the sense of deformation quantization, $\mathcal{W}(E,\hbar\sigma)$ may be realized by a function algebra on E'_τ equipped with an $\hbar$-dependent star product. The expectations of φ appear then as functional integrals $\langle\varphi; A\rangle = \int_{E'_\tau} A[F]\,d\mu(F)$, with the same Gaussian measure μ as before. Thus one and the same Gaussian measure may determine either a mixed classical state or a possibly pure quantum state.

The lesson to be learned is this: Expectations in terms of functional integrals (or in terms of derivatives of characteristic functionals) alone do not determine the theory. They do not even tell us whether we are in the classical or quantized regime. Only the combination with a specified observable algebra discloses the physical contents.

(On the other side, the — deformed or not — C*-observable algebra alone determines the theory, if the states are defined as positive, linear, normalized functionals, where positivity $\langle\varphi; A\rangle \geq 0$ refers to positive observables $A \geq 0$ in the sense of the algebra, which is different a notion for one and the same phase space functions $F \mapsto A[F]$, depending on whether they mean classical or quantum observables.)

50.7.   Pseudo-Support of Measures

Let $\widehat{E}$ denote again the commutative group of characters on the vector group E. If E is discrete topologized, then $\widehat{E}$ is compact with respect to the associated Δ-topology. According to [HR70] (23.13) and (23.15), that is just the topology of point-wise convergence (in which the net of characters $(\chi_\alpha)_{\alpha \in I}$ converges to $\chi \in \widehat{E}$, if and only if $\lim_\alpha \chi_\alpha(f) = \chi(f)$ for all $f \in E$). As stated already in Sec. 12.6.1 on page 254, Bochner's theorem ensures an affine one-to-one correspondence between the characteristic functions $P \in \mathcal{P}(E)$ (all being continuous in the discrete topology) and the regular Borel probability measures $\hat{\mu} \in M_p(\widehat{E})$ via Fourier transformation

$$P(f) = \int_{\widehat{E}} \chi(f) \, d\hat{\mu}(\chi), \quad \forall f \in E. \tag{50.7.1}$$

If we suppose that a $P \in \mathcal{P}_{\mathrm{reg}}(E)$ is given by a measure $\mu \in M_p(E'_\tau, \Sigma(E'_\tau, E))$ according to Eq. (50.5.1), then together with (50.7.1) we have the two representations of $P(f)$ by probability measures

$$P(f) = \int_{\widehat{E}} \chi(f) \, d\hat{\mu}(\chi) = \int_{E'_\tau} \exp\{iF(f)\} \, d\mu(F), \quad \forall f \in E. \tag{50.7.2}$$

The question arises, how the two measures, $\hat{\mu} \in M_p(\widehat{E})$ and $\mu \in M_p(E'_\tau, \Sigma(E'_\tau, E))$, are related to each other? For an analysis, the measure μ is better accessible than $\hat{\mu}$, since μ is given uniquely by its finite-dimensional restrictions $\mu_* = \{\mu_D\}$. And the compatible probability measures μ_D may be constructed directly from the finite-dimensional restrictions of P, cf., e.g., P. Levy's formula in [Hid80] Theorems 1.2. Moreover, in the literature there exist statements concerning the support of μ, e.g., [Hid80] Theorems 3.1.

From Lemma 12.3-2 on page 251 we know that

(a) The mapping $F \mapsto \exp\{iF(.)\}$ is a bijection from E'_τ onto $\widehat{E}_\tau$, where $\widehat{E}_\tau$ denotes the subgroup of the τ-continuous characters on E.

(b) $\widehat{E}_\tau$ is dense in $\widehat{E}$ with respect to the topology of point-wise convergence.

The conjection would be that $\hat{\mu}$ should be the image measure of μ under the continuous embedding $E'_\tau \to \widehat{E}$, $F \mapsto \exp\{iF(.)\}$. Clearly, this embedding is measurable for the respective Borel-σ-algebras on E'_τ and $\widehat{E}$. Unfortunately, in general the σ-algebra $\Sigma(E'_\tau, E)$ is smaller than the Borel σ-algebra $\mathsf{B}(E'_\tau)$ (see Eq. (50.1.5)), so that the measurability of $F \mapsto \exp\{iF(.)\}$ with respect to $\Sigma(E'_\tau, E)$ is not clear.

However, one obtains measurability with respect to the Baire σ-algebra $\mathsf{B}_0(\widehat{E})$ on $\widehat{E}$, where $\mathsf{B}_0(\widehat{E})$ is defined to be the smallest σ-algebra on $\widehat{E}$ such that all continuous functions $A : \widehat{E} \to \mathbb{C}$ are measurable. Clearly $\mathsf{B}_0(\widehat{E}) \subset \mathsf{B}(\widehat{E})$.

Let $\widehat{W}^0(f) : \widehat{E} \to \mathbb{C}$, $\chi \mapsto \chi(f)$, be the extended Weyl functions from Eq. (12.3.7) on page 252. The $\widehat{W}^0(f)$, $f \in E$, separate the points of $\widehat{E}$ and generate the C*-algebra $C(\widehat{E})$ of the continuous functions on $\widehat{E}$ by the Stone–Weierstrass theorem with respect to the sup-norm. Consequently, $\mathsf{B}_0(\widehat{E})$ is the smallest σ-algebra on $\widehat{E}$ such that all functions $\widehat{W}^0(f)$, $f \in E$, are measurable. In addition one may show that $\mathsf{B}_0(\widehat{E})$ is the smallest σ-algebra on $\widehat{E}$ containing all the sets $\{\chi \in \widehat{E} \mid |\chi(f) - z| < a\}$, where $f \in E$, $z \in \mathbb{C}$, and $a \in \mathbb{R}$.

Theorem 50.7-1. *Let all be as introduced before. The following assertions are valid:*

(a) *The embedding $E'_\tau \to \widehat{E}$, $F \mapsto \exp\{iF(.)\}$ is measurable with respect to the σ-algebra $\Sigma(E'_\tau, E)$ on E'_τ and the Baire sets $\mathsf{B}_0(\widehat{E})$ on $\widehat{E}$.*

(b) *Let* $\hat{\mu} \in M_p(\widehat{E})$ *and* $\mu \in M_p(E'_\tau, \Sigma(E'_\tau, E))$ *define the same* $P_{reg} \in \mathcal{P}(E)$ *as in Eq. (50.7.2). If for* $\mathcal{V} \in \Sigma(E'_\tau, E)$ *we have* $\mu(\mathcal{V}) = 1$, *then for* $\exp\{i\mathcal{V}\} := \{\exp\{iF(.)\} \mid F \in \mathcal{V}\}$ *we have*

$$\hat{\mu}(\mathcal{K}) = 0 \quad \text{for all} \quad \mathcal{K} \in \mathsf{B}_0(\widehat{E}) \quad \text{with} \quad \mathcal{K} \cap \exp\{i\mathcal{V}\} = \emptyset. \tag{50.7.3}$$

That means nothing else than $\hat{\mu}$ *is pseudo-supported by* $\exp\{i\mathcal{V}\}$, *in the sense of Definition 48.1-7 on page 1783.*

Dynamics and Perturbation Theory

Chapter 51

Perturbation Series
on Fréchet State Vector Spaces

In the present and next two chapters we supplement *mathematical details* of the electron–photon perturbation theory in a somewhat generalized version.

51.1.   Generalities

As we have described in Secs. 21.6, 37.1, and 38.1, the material coupling operators are sums over bounded (de-) excitation operators taken from the CAR-algebra (possibly reduced to a tensor product of finite dimensional cluster algebras), which now are replaced by a finite number of unspecified bounded operators B_j. The coupling operators for the photons are substituted by general Boson creation and annihilation operators in Fock space. Thus we are treating interactions of the form

$$\Upsilon := \sum_{j=1}^{M} \left[B_j \otimes a_F(\phi_j) + B_j^* \otimes a_F^*(\phi_j) \right], \qquad (51.1.1)$$

(where we use now the Greek I-like letter Υ for this general interaction Hamiltonian). Let us emphasize again, that — like for the electron–photon interaction — the considered type of interaction comprises finitely many material transitions combined with the full spectrum of Boson transitions in the linear coupling approximation.

In quantum field theory for elementary particles, the basic matter fields are Fermion fields, whereas the interactions between them arise by Boson exchanges. Our material coupling operators may be viewed as belonging to a (clustered) Fermion algebra, so that we are discussing a kind of Fermion–Boson interaction. In that quantum field theoretic interaction in non-relativistic form, not only the material operators dress the Boson operators (as they do also in our weak coupling limit) but also the Boson operators dress the matter expressions (and may induce material term shifts). Locality in the Boson field is ensured by the inherent summation over all one-Boson modes. Our later expounded estimation methods work also, if the Fock representation for the Bosons is generalized to a GNS representation over quasifree states, which includes especially thermal field theory.

We are going to demonstrate in an *ab-initio* elaboration, that for that interaction a perturbation series for the unitary time translations in the interaction picture is possible, which is finite in all orders and converges by summing up over all orders. Since these implement, in faithful representations of the combined observable algebra, an automorphism group, we gain also a perturbation theory for the Heisenberg dynamics. The latter corresponds to the previous

$$\alpha^{\text{tot}} = \{\alpha_t^{\text{tot}} \mid t \in \mathbb{R}\} \quad \text{on the composite C*-algebra } \mathcal{A}_e \otimes \mathcal{W}(E^\top, \hbar \operatorname{Im}(.|.))$$

in Chapter 38, where the electronic CAR algebra is classically extended to $\mathcal{A}_e$, which we also imitate in the present more general frame by including "partially commutative couplings".

The pre-requisites for such well behaved field dynamics are concisely displayed by our detailed investigation. The finite norms of the B_j and of the "coupling functions" ϕ_j occur permanently in the mathematical estimations: Without smearing the fields, there is no convergence.

Because the smeared Bosonic annihilation and creation operators occurring in interaction operators of type (51.1.1) are always unbounded, for general Bosonic representations Π it is not possible to control the growth of the expansion series uniformly in the Hilbert space norm or in the operator norm. However, for the Boson annihilation and creation operators there exist estimates on the finite particle vectors in Fock space. This suggests that the necessary growth control of the Dyson expansion series can be done for Fock-like representations Π of the Boson part. This is the reason why in the present and next Chapter we directly deal with the Fock representations, but we treat in Chapter 53 some further Fock-like representation.

Since the Boson operators are unbounded, the operator terms of the perturbation series require a special domain of definition. The damping for increasing Boson numbers is achieved by a special system of norms, which make the domain of definition to a Fréchet space. The topological features of that LC-space are fully exploited and described in an introductory style. All operator expressions, including operator integrals over parameter spaces, are handled in terms of continuous operators on Fréchet spaces. Altogether, the present and next two chapters may also be considered as an example for applied functional analysis.

The possibility for a limit $M \to \infty$ is also investigated, so that all material transitions may — in principle — be taken into account, but we combine the increase of matter modes with a scaling down of the coupling constants. That procedure restricts the Bosonic coupling to the collective matter modes. The justification for that model assumption for mesoscopic matter has been analyzed in the elaboration of our radiation models. Here we pursue a more classificatory strategy to get an overview on the class of possible models in that weak coupling limit. In fact, the models in that limit may essentially be characterized by two functions on the collective matter modes, which satisfy certain cocycle equations and which for themselves are derivable from the coupling function.

51.2. Setup of the Interacting Matter-Boson System

To treat the interactions between an unspecified material system and a general Bosonic system in Hilbert space formalism, we assume for the composite system the tensor product Hilbert space

$$\mathcal{H} \otimes F_+(\mathcal{V}) \quad \text{(Hilbert space of composite matter-Boson system)},$$

where the complex Hilbert space $\mathcal{H}$ describes the material system, and the Bosonic system is given in terms of the Fock space $F_+(\mathcal{V})$ over an arbitrary complex one-Boson Hilbert space $\mathcal{V}$, whereby the complex unit i of $\mathcal{V}$ determines the one-particle structure. For convenience we set $\hbar = 1$ throughout this chapter.

With an arbitrary self-adjoint material Hamiltonian A on $\mathcal{H}$ (think of one or several or even infinite atoms), an arbitrary self-adjoint one-Boson Hamiltonian S on $\mathcal{V}$, bounded operators B_j on $\mathcal{H}$, and "test functions" $\phi_j \in \mathcal{V}$ for $j \in \{1, 2, \ldots, M\}$, we formulate the total Hamiltonian

$$H := \underbrace{A \otimes \mathbb{1} + \mathbb{1} \otimes d\Gamma(S)}_{=:\, K,\text{ free Hamiltonian}} + \underbrace{\sum_{j=1}^{M} \left[B_j \otimes a_F(\phi_j) + B_j^* \otimes a_F^*(\phi_j) \right]}_{=:\, \Upsilon,\text{ interaction}}, \quad (51.2.1)$$

acting on $\mathcal{H} \otimes F_+(\mathcal{V})$. Here $d\Gamma(S)$ means the second quantization of the one-Boson Hamiltonian S. The $a_F(\phi_j)$ and $a_F^*(\phi_j)$ are the common annihilation and creation operators on Fock space (cf. Sec. 18.5).

51.2.1. *Self-adjointness of the Interacting Hamiltonian*

For treating the Boson operators, we first have to introduce a norm dense subspace D of our composite Hilbert space $\mathcal{H} \otimes F_+(\mathcal{V})$. With the number operator $N_F = d\Gamma(\mathbb{1})$ on $F_+(\mathcal{V})$ ($\mathbb{1}$ indicating the identity operator on the space under discussion, which here is $\mathcal{V}$ and in the next formula is $\mathcal{H}$) we define

$$D := \bigcap_{a \geq 1} \mathrm{dom}(\mathbb{1} \otimes a^{N_F}) \subset \mathcal{H} \otimes F_+(\mathcal{V}). \quad (51.2.2)$$

By the spectral calculus, each a^{N_F} is a well defined positive self-adjoint operator on $F_+(\mathcal{V})$. Remark, that $D \subset \mathrm{dom}(\Upsilon)$, and that $D \cap \mathrm{dom}(K)$ is dense in $\mathcal{H} \otimes F_+(\mathcal{V})$.

The self-adjointness of the free Hamiltonian K is standard according to its tensor product construction. The (essential) self-adjointness of the total Hamiltonian H is treated in the next result.

Proposition 51.2-1 ((Essential) Self-adjointness). *For the total Hamiltonian H from (51.2.1) the following two statements are valid:*

(a) *H is essentially self-adjoint on $\mathrm{dom}(K) \cap \mathrm{dom}(\Upsilon)$, its unique self-adjoint extension is denoted by H, too. Moreover, $D \cap \mathrm{dom}(K) = D \cap \mathrm{dom}(H)$ is a core for the self-adjoint H.*

(b) *Suppose that A is semi-bounded from below, and $S > 0$ (i.e., S is strictly posi-*
    tive, or equivalently, S is injective and positive), and $\phi_1, \ldots, \phi_M \in \mathrm{dom}(S^{-\frac{1}{2}})$.
    Then $\mathrm{dom}(K) \subseteq \mathrm{dom}(\Upsilon)$ and Υ is relatively bounded with respect to K with
    relative bound 0.
    Thus, by the Kato–Rellich Theorem, H is self-adjoint with domain $\mathrm{dom}(H) =$
    $\mathrm{dom}(K)$, and H is bounded from below, and moreover, each core of K is a core
    of H. (The notion of relative boundedness and the Kato–Rellich Theorem are
    found in Sec. 43.4 on page 1538.)

Proof.   Let us agree on the following simplification: We set $M = 1$ in the interaction operator Υ of Eq. (51.2.1) when elaborating the proofs. That is, in the proofs
we use exclusively the interaction operator

$$\Upsilon := B \otimes a_F(\phi) + B^* \otimes a_F^*(\phi), \qquad (51.2.3)$$

with a bounded operator B on $\mathcal{H}$ and a $\phi \in \mathcal{V}$. The generalization to an arbitrary
$M \in \mathbb{N}$ is then immediate.

Part (a) is shown at the end of part (b) in the proof of Theorem 51.3-5.

Part (b). The given proof follows [Hon91c] Lemma 4.1 and was inspired by a
similar argument in [Dav81].

Recall that $\odot$ denotes the algebraic tensor product. By construction of the
second quantization the subspace

$$\mathcal{D} := \bigcup_{m=1}^{\infty} \bigoplus_{n=0}^{m} P_+(\odot_n \mathrm{dom}(S)),$$

is a core of $d\Gamma(S)$. So, $\mathcal{D}$ consists of the linear combinations of the symmetrized
finite particle vector $P_+(f_1 \otimes \cdots \otimes f_n)$ with $f_k \in \mathrm{dom}(S)$ and arbitrary $n \in \mathbb{N}$,
including the Fock vacuum Ω_{vac} for $n = 0$. Let $\alpha := \|S^{-\frac{1}{2}}\phi\|$ and put $p := |\phi\rangle\langle\phi|$.
We obtain

$$(g|pg) = |(\phi|g)|^2 = |(S^{-\frac{1}{2}}\phi|S^{\frac{1}{2}}g)|^2 \le \alpha^2 \|S^{\frac{1}{2}}g\|^2 = \alpha^2(g|Sg), \quad \forall g \in \mathrm{dom}(S),$$

that is $p \le \alpha^2 S$. Consequently we arrive at $a_F^*(\phi)\,a_F(\phi) = d\Gamma(p) \le \alpha^2 d\Gamma(S)$ on $\mathcal{D}$,
which finally leads to the operator inequality

$$\mathbb{1} \otimes a_F^*(\phi)a_F(\phi) \le \alpha^2 \mathbb{1} \otimes d\Gamma(S) \quad \text{on } \mathcal{H} \odot \mathcal{D}.$$

Now let $\psi \in \mathrm{dom}(A) \odot \mathcal{D}$, and express the semi-boundedness from $A \ge -\gamma\mathbb{1}$ for
some $\gamma \ge 0$. With help of the CCR

$$a_F(\phi)\,a_F^*(\phi) = a_F^*(\phi)\,a_F(\phi) + \|\phi\|^2 \mathbb{1}$$

we estimate that

$$\|\Upsilon\psi\|^2 = \|[B \otimes a_F(\phi) + B^* \otimes a_F^*(\phi)]\psi\|^2$$

$$\leq \|B\|^2 \big(\|[1 \otimes a_F(\phi)]\psi\| + \|[1 \otimes a_F^*(\phi)]\psi\|\big)^2$$

$$\leq 2\|B\|^2 \big(\|[1 \otimes a_F(\phi)]\psi\|^2 + \|[1 \otimes a_F^*(\phi)]\psi\|^2\big)$$

$$= 2\|B\|^2 \big((\psi|[1 \otimes a_F^*(\phi)\, a_F(\phi)]\psi) + (\psi|[1 \otimes a_F(\phi)\, a_F^*(\phi)]\psi)\big)$$

$$\overset{\text{CCR}}{\leq} 4\|B\|^2 \underbrace{(\psi|[1 \otimes a_F^*(\phi)\, a_F(\phi)]\psi)}_{\leq\, \alpha^2 (\psi|[1 \otimes d\Gamma(S)]\psi)} + 2\|B\|^2\|\phi\|^2\|\psi\|^2$$

$$\leq 4\|B\|^2\alpha^2(\psi|[1 \otimes d\Gamma(S)]\psi) + 2\|B\|^2\|\phi\|^2\|\psi\|^2$$

$$= 4\|B\|^2\alpha^2(\psi|[A \otimes 1 + 1 \otimes d\Gamma(S)]\psi) \underbrace{-4\|B\|^2\alpha^2(\psi|[A \otimes 1]\psi)}_{\leq\, 4\|B\|^2\alpha^2\gamma\|\psi\|^2} + 2\|B\|^2\|\phi\|^2\|\psi\|^2$$

$$\leq \Big(\frac{a}{\varepsilon}\|\psi\|\Big)\varepsilon\|[A \otimes 1 + 1 \otimes d\Gamma(S)]\psi\| + b\|\psi\|^2$$

$$\leq \varepsilon^2\|[A \otimes 1 + 1 \otimes d\Gamma(S)]\psi\|^2 + \Big(\frac{a^2}{\varepsilon^2} + b\Big)\|\psi\|^2$$

$$\leq \Big(\varepsilon\|K\psi\| + \Big(\frac{a^2}{\varepsilon^2} + b\Big)^{\frac{1}{2}}\|\psi\|\Big)^2, \qquad \forall \varepsilon > 0\,,$$

where $a := 4\|B\|^2\alpha^2$ and $b := 2\|B\|^2(2\alpha^2\gamma + \|\phi\|^2)$. (At the second inequality sign we applied $(x + y)^2 = x^2 + 2xy + y^2 \leq 2(x^2 + y^2)$; at the last but one inequality sign we used $xy \leq 2xy \leq x^2 + y^2$ arising from $0 \leq (x - y)^2 = x^2 - 2xy + y^2$; and at the last inequality sign we took $x^2 + y^2 \leq x^2 + 2xy + y^2 = (x + y)^2$; for $x, y \geq 0$.)

Consequently, for each $\varepsilon > 0$ there exist some $a_\varepsilon := \big(\frac{a^2}{\varepsilon^2} + b\big)^{\frac{1}{2}} > 0$ such that

$$\|\Upsilon\psi\| \leq \varepsilon\|K\psi\| + a_\varepsilon\|\psi\|\,.$$

This inequality may be extended from $\psi \in \text{dom}(A) \odot \mathcal{D}$ to all $\psi \in \text{dom}(K)$, since $\text{dom}(A) \odot \mathcal{D}$ is a core for K. $\qquad\square$

51.3. Dyson Perturbation Expansions

Let us equip the in $\mathcal{H} \otimes F_+(\mathcal{V})$ dense subspace

$$D = \bigcap_{a \geq 1} \text{dom}(1 \otimes a^{N_F}), \tag{51.3.1}$$

(from Eq. (51.2.2)) with the directed system of norms

$$D \ni \psi \mapsto \|(1 \otimes a^{N_F})\psi\|, \quad a \geq 1,$$

each of which being stronger than the norm $\|.\|$ of the composite Hilbert space $\mathcal{H} \otimes F_+(\mathcal{V})$. Since $1^{N_F} = 1$ on $F_+(\mathcal{V})$, the Hilbert space norm $\|.\|$ is re-obtained for

$a = 1$. That is,

$$\|\psi\| \leq \|(\mathbb{1} \otimes a^{N_F})\psi\| \leq \|(\mathbb{1} \otimes b^{N_F})\psi\|, \quad \forall \psi \in D, \quad 1 \leq a \leq b. \quad (51.3.2)$$

D equipped with that directed system of norms constitutes an F-space ("F" means Fréchet, cf. Sec. 49.1).

The mathematical strategy is, to formulate many occurring operators — such as Υ, e^{itK}, e^{itH}, $a_F(f)$, $a_F^*(f)$, and $\Phi_F(f) = 2^{-\frac{1}{2}}(a_F(f) + a_F^*(f))$, but not K and H for themselves, — as F-continuous operators acting on D, instead of regarding them as possibly unbounded (= discontinuous) operators on $\mathcal{H} \otimes F_+(\mathcal{V})$. Finally, after having done all work on D, we only have to extend the bounded ones from D to all of $\mathcal{H} \otimes F_+(\mathcal{V})$ by continuity in the operator norm.

51.3.1. F-Norm Estimates on the Fréchet space D

In order to show that a possibly unbounded operator Z on $\mathcal{H} \otimes F_+(\mathcal{V})$ fits in our scheme to constitute an F-continuous operator on D, the first necessary step is $D \subseteq \mathrm{dom}(Z)$. Remember that this is true for Υ. Secondly, in order to show that Z leaves D invariant, we use the argument

$$Z\psi \in D \quad\quad \Longleftrightarrow \quad\quad \|(\mathbb{1} \otimes a^{N_F})Z\psi\| < \infty, \quad \forall a \geq 1,$$

for each $\psi \in D$. Since the norm system for the F-topology is directed, Z acts F-continuously on D, if and only if for each $a \geq 1$ there exists an $b(a) \geq 0$ and a $c(a) \geq 0$ such that

$$\|(\mathbb{1} \otimes a^{N_F})Z\psi\| \leq c(a)\|(\mathbb{1} \otimes b(a)^{N_F})\psi\| < \infty, \quad \forall \psi \in D. \quad (51.3.3)$$

Of course, when proving the F-continuity, the argument for D-invariance is automatically included. For notational convenience we mostly omit writing $Z|_D$ for the restriction of Z from $\mathrm{dom}(Z)$ to the smaller domain D. If Eq. (51.3.3) is satisfied, we call Z an "F-continuous operator on D".

Let us translate the notion of a strongly LC-continuous one-parameter group from Definition 49.1-8 to our special F-case here.

Definition 51.3-1 (Strongly F-Continuous One-Parameter Group on D).
Let V_t, $t \in \mathbb{R}$, with $V_0 = \mathbb{1}$, be a one-parameter group of operators on D. Then $t \mapsto V_t$ is called "strongly F-continuous", if the following three requirements are fulfilled:

- Each V_t acts F-continuously on D.
- The mapping $t \mapsto V_t$ is F-continuous on D, i.e., for each $t \in \mathbb{R}$ we have

$$\lim_{s \to t} \|(\mathbb{1} \otimes a^{N_F})[V_s - V_t]\psi\| = 0, \quad \forall \psi \in D, \quad \forall a \geq 1.$$

- For each $a \geq 1$ there is a $b(a) \geq 1$ and a map $t \mapsto c(a, t) \geq 0$ (in general depending on a) such that

$$\|(\mathbb{1} \otimes a^{N_F})V_t\psi\| \leq c(a, t)\|(\mathbb{1} \otimes b(a)^{N_F})\psi\|, \quad \forall \psi \in D, \quad \forall t \in \mathbb{R}.$$

Note that the group property ensures that actually each V_t is an F-homeomorphism on D.

As a first example let us demonstrate in the subsequent proof the previous conditions for the unitary group $t \mapsto e^{itK}$ of the free dynamics. Later we demonstrate that also the interacting one-parameter group $t \mapsto e^{itH}$ is strongly F-continuous.

Lemma 51.3-2 (Strong F-Continuity of the Free Evolution Group). $t \mapsto e^{itK}$ *is a strongly F-continuous one-parameter group on D, which moreover conserves the single norms of the directed system of norms. That means,*

$$\lim_{s \to t} \|(\mathbb{1} \otimes a^{N_F})[e^{isK} - e^{itK}]\psi\| = 0, \qquad \|(\mathbb{1} \otimes a^{N_F})e^{itK}\psi\| = \|(\mathbb{1} \otimes a^{N_F})\psi\|,$$

for all $\psi \in D$ and every $a \geq 1$, for each $t \in \mathbb{R}$.

Proof. By construction of the second quantization, $e^{itd\Gamma(S)}$ leaves each ℓ-particle subspace $P_+(\otimes_\ell \mathcal{V})$ of $F_+(\mathcal{V})$ invariant. But each ℓ-particle space is an eigenspace of the number operator N_F with eigenvalue ℓ. Thus $e^{itd\Gamma(S)}$ commutes with a^{N_F}, and consequently e^{itK} commutes with $\mathbb{1} \otimes a^{N_F}$. Since $e^{itK} = e^{itA} \otimes e^{itd\Gamma(S)}$ is unitary, we have $\|e^{itK}\xi\| = \|\xi\|$ for all $\xi \in \mathcal{H} \otimes F_+(\mathcal{V})$, and thus especially for $\xi = (\mathbb{1} \otimes a^{N_F})\psi$ it holds

$$\|(\mathbb{1} \otimes a^{N_F})e^{itK}\psi\| = \|e^{itK}(\mathbb{1} \otimes a^{N_F})\psi\| = \|(\mathbb{1} \otimes a^{N_F})\psi\|, \quad \forall \psi \in D,$$

for all $a \geq 1$. As a strongly continuous unitary group, e^{itK} satisfies $\lim_{s \to t} \|[e^{isK} - e^{itK}]\xi\|$ for all $\xi \in \mathcal{H} \otimes F_+(\mathcal{V})$, and it follows that

$$\lim_{s \to t} \|(\mathbb{1} \otimes a^{N_F})[e^{isK} - e^{itK}]\psi\| = \lim_{s \to t} \|[e^{isK} - e^{itK}](\mathbb{1} \otimes a^{N_F})\psi\| = 0,$$

for all $a \geq 1$ and every $\psi \in D$, which demonstrates F-continuity in $t \in \mathbb{R}$. $\qquad \square$

Let us agree to write the **shorthand symbol**

$$A_k(g_k) \in \{a_F(g_k), a_F^*(g_k), \Phi_F(g_k)\}, \qquad g_k \in \mathcal{V}. \tag{51.3.4}$$

Lemma 51.3-3 (F-Continuity and Approximation Results). *In terms of the previously introduced notation, the following two assertions are valid:*

(a) *For $C \in \mathcal{L}(\mathcal{H})$ and $g_1, \ldots g_n \in \mathcal{V}$ (with $n \in \mathbb{N}$) the operator $C \otimes \prod_{k=1}^{n} A_k(g_k)$ acts F-continuously on D. More precisely, we have the estimations*

$$\left\|(\mathbb{1} \otimes a^{N_F})\left[C \otimes \prod_{k=1}^{n} A_k(g_k)\right]\psi\right\| \leq (2a)^n \sqrt{n!} \, \|g_1\| \cdots \|g_n\| \underbrace{\|(C \otimes (2^{\frac{1}{2}}a)^{N_F})\psi\|}_{\leq \|C\| \, \|(\mathbb{1} \otimes (2^{\frac{1}{2}}a)^{N_F})\psi\|}$$

for all $\psi \in D$ and every $a \geq 1$.

(b) *Let $m, n \in \mathbb{N}$. The mapping*

$$(C_1, \ldots, C_m, g_1, \ldots, g_n) \longmapsto \prod_{j=1}^{m} C_j \otimes \prod_{k=1}^{n} \mathsf{A}_k(g_k),$$

is jointly F-continuous on D, with respect to the strong operator topology on (norm) bounded subsets of $\mathcal{L}(\mathcal{H})$ for the C_j, and with respect to the norm on $\mathcal{V}$ for the g_k.
Let us reformulate this as follows: If for each $j \in \{1, \ldots, m\}$ we have a sequence $\lim_{\nu \to \infty} C_{j,\nu} = C_j$ in the strong operator topology with $\|C_{j,\nu}\| \leq c_j$ for all $\nu \in \mathbb{N}$ for some $c_j > 0$ in $\mathcal{L}(\mathcal{H})$ (then also $\|C_j\| \leq c_j$), and if for each $k \in \{1, \ldots, n\}$ we have a sequence $\lim_{\nu \to \infty} \|g_{k,\nu} - g_k\| = 0$ in $\mathcal{V}$, then it follows

$$\lim_{\nu \to \infty} \left\| (\mathbb{1} \otimes a^{N_F}) \left[\prod_{j=1}^{m} C_{j,\nu} \otimes \prod_{k=1}^{n} \mathsf{A}_k(g_{k,\nu}) - \prod_{j=1}^{m} C_j \otimes \prod_{k=1}^{n} \mathsf{A}_k(g_k) \right] \psi \right\| = 0,$$

for each $a \geq 1$ and every $\psi \in D$.

Especially, by part (a) the interaction operator Υ acts F-continuously on D.

Proof.   Part (a). Starting point is the estimation for the Fock annihilation and creation operators from Eq. (18.5.9) on page 438, which leads for each $f \in \mathcal{V}$ to

$$\|\mathsf{A}(f)\eta\| \leq 2^{\frac{1}{2}} (\ell + 1)^{\frac{1}{2}} \|f\| \|\eta\|, \quad \forall \eta \in P_+(\otimes_\ell \mathcal{V}), \tag{51.3.5}$$

for the ℓ-particle vectors η, where $\ell \in \{0, 1, 2, 3, \ldots\}$. The factor $2^{\frac{1}{2}}$ arises from the fact that possibly $\mathsf{A}(f) = \Phi_F(f) = 2^{-\frac{1}{2}}(a_F(f) + a_F^*(f))$, and with the triangle inequality.

In combination with the material system, we also denote $\psi \in \mathcal{H} \otimes P_+(\otimes_\ell \mathcal{V})$ an "ℓ-particle vector". Of course $(C \otimes \mathbb{1})\psi$ is also an ℓ-particle vector, and $(C \otimes \mathsf{A}(f))\psi$ is at best an $\ell + 1$-particle vector, and thus we arrive at

$$\|(C \otimes \mathsf{A}(f))\psi\| = \|(\mathbb{1} \otimes \mathsf{A}(f))(C \otimes \mathbb{1})\psi\| \leq 2^{\frac{1}{2}}(\ell + 1)^{\frac{1}{2}} \|f\| \|(C \otimes \mathbb{1})\psi\|, \tag{51.3.6}$$

for all ℓ-particle vectors $\psi \in \mathcal{H} \otimes P_+(\otimes_\ell \mathcal{V})$.

Note that the ℓ-particle spaces $\mathcal{H} \otimes P_+(\otimes_\ell \mathcal{V})$ are just the eigenspaces of $\mathbb{1} \otimes a^{N_F}$ with eigenvalues a^ℓ, respectively. Thus for $\psi \in \mathcal{H} \otimes P_+(\otimes_\ell \mathcal{V})$, at best $(C \otimes \prod_{k=1}^{n} \mathsf{A}(g_k))\eta$ is an $\ell + n$-particle vector. Consequently, for $\psi \in \mathcal{H} \otimes P_+(\otimes_\ell \mathcal{V})$ we obtain for every $a \geq 1$ the estimations, by applying (51.3.6) n times,

$$\left\| (\mathbb{1} \otimes a^{N_F}) \left[C \otimes \prod_{k=1}^{n} \mathsf{A}_k(g_k) \right] \psi \right\| \leq a^{\ell+n} \left\| \left[C \otimes \prod_{k=1}^{n} \mathsf{A}_k(g_k) \right] \psi \right\|$$

$$\leq a^{\ell+n} 2^{\frac{n}{2}} \underbrace{\left((\ell+n)(\ell+n-1) \cdots (\ell+1) \right)^{\frac{1}{2}}}_{\leq 2^{\ell+n} n!} \|g_1\| \cdots \|g_n\| \|(C \otimes \mathbb{1})\psi\|$$

$$\leq (2a)^n \sqrt{n!} \, \|g_1\| \cdots \|g_n\| \|(C \otimes (2^{\frac{1}{2}}a)^{N_F})\psi\|,$$

where we used

$$(\ell + n)(\ell + n - 1)\cdots(\ell + 1) = \frac{(\ell + n)!}{\ell!\, n!}\, n! = \binom{\ell + n}{n} n! \le 2^{\ell + n} n!.$$

In the final step we have to sum over all ℓ-particle spaces to arrive at the stated estimations for arbitrary $\psi \in D$.

Part (b). Let $\gamma_k > 0$, such that $\|g_{k,\nu}\| \le \gamma_k$ for all $\nu \in \mathbb{N}$. With the $\mathbb{R}$-linearity of $f \mapsto A_k(f)$ let us separate,

$$\prod_{j=1}^{m} C_{j,\nu} \otimes \prod_{k=1}^{n} A_k(g_{k,\nu}) - \prod_{j=1}^{m} C_j \otimes \prod_{k=1}^{n} A_k(g_k)$$

$$= \sum_{k=1}^{n} \prod_{j=1}^{m} C_{j,\nu} \otimes A_1(g_{1,\nu})\cdots A_{k-1}(g_{k-1,\nu}) A_k(g_{k,\nu} - g_k) A_{k+1}(g_{k+1})\cdots A_n(g_n)$$

$$+ \sum_{j=1}^{m} C_{1,\nu}\cdots C_{j-1,\nu}(C_{j,\nu} - C_j) C_{j+1}\cdots C_m \otimes \prod_{k=1}^{n} A_k(g_k).$$

Now we apply the triangle inequality and then part (a) to arrive at

$$\left\| (\mathbb{1} \otimes a^{N_F}) \left[\prod_{j=1}^{m} C_{j,\nu} \otimes \prod_{k=1}^{n} A_k(g_{k,\nu}) - \prod_{j=1}^{m} C_j \otimes \prod_{k=1}^{n} A_k(g_k) \right] \psi \right\|$$

$$\le \sum_{k=1}^{n} (2a)^n \sqrt{n!}\, \|g_{1,\nu}\|\cdots\|g_{k-1,\nu}\|\, \|g_{k,\nu} - g_k\|\, \|g_{k+1}\|\cdots\|g_n\| \cdot \cdots$$

$$\cdots \cdot \left\| \prod_{j=1}^{m} C_{j,\nu} \right\| \|(\mathbb{1} \otimes (2^{\frac{1}{2}} a)^{N_F})\psi\|$$

$$+ \sum_{j=1}^{m} (2a)^n \sqrt{n!}\, \|g_1\|\cdots\|g_n\| \cdot \cdots$$

$$\cdots \cdot \left\| [C_{1,\nu}\cdots C_{j-1,\nu} \otimes \mathbb{1}] [(C_{j,\nu} - C_j) \otimes \mathbb{1}] [C_{j+1}\cdots C_m \otimes (2^{\frac{1}{2}} a)^{N_F}] \psi \right\|$$

$$\le \sum_{k=1}^{n} (2a)^n \sqrt{n!}\, \gamma_1 \cdots \gamma_{k-1} \|g_{k,\nu} - g_k\|\, \gamma_{k+1}\cdots\gamma_n\, c_1 \cdots c_m \, \|(\mathbb{1} \otimes (2^{\frac{1}{2}} a)^{N_F})\psi\|$$

$$+ \sum_{j=1}^{m} (2a)^n \sqrt{n!}\, \gamma_1 \cdots \gamma_n\, c_1 \cdots c_{j-1} \underbrace{\left\| [(C_{j,\nu} - C_j) \otimes \mathbb{1}] [C_{j+1}\cdots C_m \otimes (2^{\frac{1}{2}} a)^{N_F}] \psi \right\|}_{\text{fixed vector in } \mathcal{H} \otimes F_+(\mathcal{V})}.$$

But $\lim\limits_{\nu \to \infty} C_{j,\nu} = C_j$ implies $\lim\limits_{\nu \to \infty} C_{j,\nu} \otimes \mathbb{1} = C_j \otimes \mathbb{1}$, with respect to the strong operator topologies. Consequently the result follows for $\nu \to \infty$. $\qquad\square$

51.3.2. *Dyson Expansion for the Unitary One-Parameter Group*

The Dyson expansion of the total unitary group — with bounded material coupling operators — is basic for the entire construction of the interacting dynamics. In order to be able to carry through that in rigorous terms, we have first to develop a suitable definition of integrals over unbounded operator-valued functions.

Observation 51.3-4 (Integrals over Operator-Valued Functions). For our application there fits best the situation of a bounded Borel measurable $\mathsf{K} \subseteq \mathbb{R}^\kappa$ (for a $\kappa \in \mathbb{N}$) equipped with the Lebesgue measure $d^\kappa \mathsf{k} \equiv d\mathsf{k}$, the boundedness yields $|\mathsf{K}| := \int_\mathsf{K} d\mathsf{k} < \infty$. Let $\mathcal{K}$ be any Hilbert space which the occurring operators act on.

An operator-valued function $\mathsf{K} \ni \mathsf{k} \mapsto O(\mathsf{k})$ is simply called "integrable (over K)", if the three conditions are fulfilled:

- The operators $O(\mathsf{k})$, $\mathsf{k} \in \mathsf{K}$, possess a common dense domain of definition D.
- $\mathsf{k} \mapsto (\psi | O(\mathsf{k}) \xi)$ is measurable for all $\psi \in \mathcal{K}$ and all $\xi \in D$, which is called "weak measurability on D".
- $\sup\{\|O(\mathsf{k})\xi\| \mid \mathsf{k} \in \mathsf{K}\} =: c_\xi < \infty$, that is the uniform boundedness in the variable $\mathsf{k} \in \mathsf{K}$ for each $\xi \in D$.

The integral is introduced weakly in the following way: Because of $|\int (\psi | O(\mathsf{k}) \xi) d\mathsf{k}| \leq \int |(\psi | O(\mathsf{k}) \xi)| d\mathsf{k} \leq \|\psi\| c_\xi |\mathsf{K}|$, the linear form $\psi \mapsto \int (\psi | O(\mathsf{k}) \xi) d\mathsf{k}$ is bounded, and thus via the Riesz Theorem 43.1-1 it is given by a unique Hilbert space vector, which we suggestively denote by "$\int O(\mathsf{k}) \xi d\mathsf{k}$". By construction $D \ni \xi \mapsto \int O(\mathsf{k}) \xi d\mathsf{k}$ is a linear operator, denoted briefly as

$$\int O \equiv \int_\mathsf{K} O(\mathsf{k}) d\mathsf{k}, \quad \mathrm{dom}(\textstyle\int O) = D.$$

Note that $O \mapsto \int O$ is linear. By construction $\int O$ is given weakly by

$$(\psi | \textstyle\int O\, \xi) = \int_\mathsf{K} (\psi | O(\mathsf{k}) \xi) d\mathsf{k}, \quad \forall \psi \in \mathcal{K}, \quad \forall \xi \in D.$$

Such integral operators possess the following four useful properties:

(1) If $\mathsf{k} \mapsto \|O(\mathsf{k})\xi\|$ is measurable for each $\xi \in D$ (following automatically for separable Hilbert space $\mathcal{K}$), then

$$\|\textstyle\int O\, \xi\| \leq \int_\mathsf{K} \|O(\mathsf{k})\xi\| d\mathsf{k}, \quad \forall \xi \in D. \tag{51.3.7}$$

(2) If the $O(\mathsf{k})$ are bounded operators and $\mathsf{k} \mapsto \|O(\mathsf{k})\|$ is measurable (following automatically for separable $\mathcal{K}$), then $\int O$ is bounded with the operator norm estimation

$$\|\textstyle\int O\| \leq \int_\mathsf{K} \|O(\mathsf{k})\| d\mathsf{k}. \tag{51.3.8}$$

(3) Suppose C to be an operator on $\mathcal{K}$, such that $\mathsf{k} \mapsto CO(\mathsf{k})$ is integrable on the domain D, too, and that $\mathrm{dom}(C^*)$ is dense in $\mathcal{K}$, then

$$C \int_\mathsf{K} O(\mathsf{k}) d\mathsf{k} \subseteq \int_\mathsf{K} CO(\mathsf{k}) d\mathsf{k}, \quad \text{briefly,} \quad C \textstyle\int O \subseteq \int CO. \tag{51.3.9}$$

(4) Provided $k \mapsto O(k)\xi$ is norm continuous for each $\xi \in D$, or F-continuous with uniform F-estimations in $k \in K$ as in our previous Lemma 51.3-3, then the integral $\int O$ converges in this topology point-wise.

Proof. (1) and (2). For $\psi \in \mathcal{K}$ and $\xi \in D$, as well as $\xi \in \mathcal{K}$ in case (2), we obtain

$$\left| \int_K (\psi|O(k)\xi)dk \right| \leq \int_K |(\psi|O(k)\xi)|dk$$

$$\text{only for (1):}\quad \leq \|\psi\| \int_K \|O(k)\xi\|dk,$$

$$\text{only for (2):}\quad \leq \|\psi\|\,\|\xi\| \int_K \|O(k)\|dk.$$

Taking for (1) the supremum over $\|\psi\| = 1$, estimation (51.3.7) follows, whereas for (2) the supremum over $\|\psi\| = 1 = \|\xi\|$ implies (51.3.8).

If $\mathcal{K}$ is separable, then there exists a sequence of vectors ψ_n with $\|\psi_n\| \leq 1$, $n \in \mathbb{N}$, which is dense in the unit ball $\{\psi \in \mathcal{K} \mid \|\psi\| \leq 1\}$. For $\xi \in D$ we thus have

$$\|O(k)\xi\| = \sup\{|(\psi_n|O(k)\xi)| \mid n \in \mathbb{N}\}, \quad \forall k \in K.$$

But the supremum over a sequence of measurable functions $k \mapsto |(\psi_n|O(k)\xi)|$ is also measurable. Analogously for (2) the operator norms are given by

$$\|O(k)\| = \sup\{|(\psi_m|O(k)\psi_n)| \mid m, n \in \mathbb{N}\}, \quad \forall k \in K,$$

where the supremum over the (double) sequence of measurable functions $k \mapsto |(\psi_m|O(k)\psi_n)|$ is measurable, too.

(3). Let $\xi \in D$ with $\int O\,\xi \in \operatorname{dom}(C)$. Then for $\psi \in \operatorname{dom}(C^*)$, according to the weak definition,

$$(\psi|C\int O\,\xi) = (C^*\psi|\int O\,\xi) = \int_K (C^*\psi|O(k)\xi)dk = \int_K (\psi|CO(k)\xi)dk = (\psi|\int CO\,\xi).$$

Since $\operatorname{dom}(C^*)$ is supposed to be dense in $\mathcal{K}$, Eq. (51.3.9) follows.

In (4) approximate $k \mapsto O(k)\xi$ by elementary step functions. $\square$

The unboundedness of the annihilation and creation operators in the interaction operator Υ, does not allow a Dyson expansion converging simply with respect to the strong operator topology as for bounded interaction operators. Here, our F-space D comes into play, which allows an F-continuous and "F-bounded" Dyson perturbation expansion on D, instead on the whole Hilbert space $\mathcal{H} \otimes F_+(\mathcal{V})$.

Theorem 51.3-5 (Dyson Expansion for the Total Unitary Time Shifts).

Let the total Hamiltonian H and the F-space D be as introduced before. The following assertions are valid:

(a) *The total dynamics $t \mapsto e^{itH}$ is a strongly F-continuous one-parameter group on D in the sense of Definition 51.3-1 on page 1928. (Recall from Lemma 51.3-2, that the free evolution group $t \mapsto U_t := e^{itK}$ is already shown strongly F-continuous.)*

(b) *For the total unitaries e^{itH} the Dyson expansion (see Eq. (37.1.60) on page 1162)*

$$e^{itH} = \sum_{n=0}^{\infty} i^n \int_{t_1=0}^{t} dt_1 \int_{t_2=0}^{t_1} dt_2 \cdots \int_{t_n=0}^{t_{n-1}} dt_n \, U_{t-t_1} \Upsilon U_{t_1-t_2} \Upsilon U_{t_2-t_3} \Upsilon \cdots U_{t_{n-1}-t_n} \Upsilon U_{t_n}$$

is valid for each $t \in \mathbb{R}$ in point-wise application to vectors from the F-space D, where the series and integrals converge with respect to the F-topology on D.

(c) *Suppose the existence of a von Neumann algebra $\mathcal{M}$ on $\mathcal{H}$, such that the material *-automorphism group*

$$\alpha_t^{mat}(.) = e^{itA} \cdot e^{-itA}, \quad \forall t \in \mathbb{R},$$

leaves $\mathcal{M}$ invariant, and furthermore, that $B_j \in \mathcal{M}$ for all $j \in \{1, \ldots, M\}$. Then both types of propagators, $e^{itH} e^{-itK}$ and $e^{-itK} e^{itH}$, are elements of the von Neumann algebra $\mathcal{M} \overline{\otimes} \mathcal{L}(F_+(\mathcal{V}))$ (here $\overline{\otimes}$ denotes the W*-tensor product, see Definition 48.4-17 on page 1848), on $\mathcal{H} \otimes F_+(\mathcal{V})$ for every $t \in \mathbb{R}$.

Proof. We give the proof for $M = 1$, that is, for $\Upsilon = B \otimes a_F(\phi) + B^* \otimes a_F^*(\phi)$ (see Eq. (51.2.3); recall in the following that U_t denotes the free evolution).

Parts (a) and (b). For short, let us define the series expression $V_t := \sum_{n=0}^{\infty} U_t^{[n]}$ with $U_t^{[0]} = U_t$ and

$$U_t^{[n]} := i^n \int_{t_1=0}^{t} dt_1 \int_{t_2=0}^{t_1} dt_2 \cdots \int_{t_n=0}^{t_{n-1}} dt_n \, \underbrace{U_{t-t_1} \Upsilon U_{t_1-t_2} \Upsilon U_{t_2-t_3} \Upsilon \cdots U_{t_{n-1}-t_n} \Upsilon U_{t_n}}_{:= F(t, t_1, \ldots, t_n)}.$$

$$(51.3.10)$$

The proof is divided in two steps. In the first step we prove that V_t is a strongly continuous unitary one-parameter group on $\mathcal{H} \otimes F_+(\mathcal{V})$, which restricted to D is F-continuous. In the second part we show that $V_t = e^{itH}$.

(1) According to Sec. 18.5 concerning Fock space, we have

$$e^{itd\Gamma(S)} a_F^{\#}(f) e^{-itd\Gamma(S)} = a_F^{\#}(e^{itS} f)$$

for the annihilation and creation operators. Consequently,

$$\Upsilon(-t_k) := U_{-t_k} \Upsilon U_{t_k} = e^{-it_k A} B e^{it_k A} \otimes a_F(e^{-it_k S} \phi) + e^{-it_k A} B^* e^{it_k A} \otimes a_F^*(e^{-it_k S} \phi).$$

Thus we arrive at

$$F(t, t_1, \ldots, t_n) = U_t \Upsilon(-t_1) \Upsilon(-t_2) \cdots \Upsilon(-t_n)$$

$$= U_t \sum_{2^n \text{ terms}} \left[\prod_{k=1}^{n} e^{-it_k A} B^{\#} e^{it_k A} \right] \otimes \left[\prod_{k=1}^{n} a_F^{\#} (e^{-it_k S} \phi) \right] \qquad (51.3.11)$$

with a sum over 2^n terms of that type, where at some positions there is a star for adjointing. With Lemma 51.3-2 applied to the operator U_t as the first multiplicative term, and with the triangle inequality we obtain from Lemma 51.3-3(a) the F-estimations

$$\|(\mathbb{1} \otimes a^{N_F}) F(t, t_1, \ldots, t_n) \psi\| \leq (4a \, \|B\| \, \|\phi\|)^n \sqrt{n!} \, \|(\mathbb{1} \otimes (2^{\frac{1}{2}} a)^{N_F}) \psi\| \qquad (51.3.12)$$

for all $\psi \in D$ and every $a \geq 1$. With Lemma 51.3-3(b) we finally conclude that

$$\mathbb{R}^{n+1} \ni (t, t_1, \ldots, t_n) \longmapsto F(t, t_1, \ldots, t_n)$$

is jointly F-continuous, with F-norm bounds (51.3.12) which are uniform in $(t, t_1, \ldots, t_n)$.

Since $\int_0^t dt_1 \int_0^{t_1} dt_2 \ldots \int_0^{t_{n-1}} dt_n = \frac{t^n}{n!}$, the F-estimations (51.3.12) and Observation 51.3-4 (parts (3) and (1)) yield

$$\|(\mathbb{1} \otimes a^{N_F}) U_t^{[n]} \psi\| \leq \underbrace{\frac{(4a \, \|B\| \, \|\phi\| \, |t|)^n}{\sqrt{n!}}}_{\xrightarrow{t \to 0} 0 \text{ for } n \geq 1} \|(\mathbb{1} \otimes (2^{\frac{1}{2}} a)^{N_F}) \psi\|, \qquad (51.3.13)$$

where summation over n leads to

$$\|(\mathbb{1} \otimes a^{N_F}) V_t \psi\| \leq \underbrace{\left[\sum_{n=0}^{\infty} \frac{(4a \, \|B\| \, \|\phi\| \, |t|)^n}{\sqrt{n!}} \right]}_{=: \, c(a,t)} \|(\mathbb{1} \otimes (2^{\frac{1}{2}} a)^{N_F}) \psi\|. \qquad (51.3.14)$$

Thus, $U_t^{[n]}$ and V_t act F-continuously, and $\sum_n$ converges F-continuously. Moreover, $c(a, t)$ is defined in virtue of the third topic of Definition 51.3-1, where $b(a) = 2^{\frac{1}{2}} a$.

Up to now, the Dyson expansion is well defined and F-continuous on D in all terms. Now we extend V_t to a strongly continuous unitary one-parameter group on $\mathcal{H} \otimes F_+(\mathcal{V})$ as follows: Calculating with convergent power series, one checks that by differentiation

$$(U_t^{[n]} \psi | \xi) = (\psi | U_{-t}^{[n]} \xi), \quad \sum_{k=0}^{n} U_s^{[n-k]} U_t^{[k]} = U_{s+t}^{[n]},$$

giving for all $\psi, \xi \in D$ and every $s, t \in \mathbb{R}$

$$(V_s \psi | V_t \xi) = (\psi | V_{t-s} \xi).$$

Especially, for $s = t$ we arrive with $V_0 = \mathbb{1}$ at $(V_t \psi | V_t \xi) = (\psi | \xi)$. So, each V_t extends to a unique unitary on $\mathcal{H} \otimes F_+(\mathcal{V})$ with $V_t^* = V_{-t}$. Furthermore, the group property $V_s V_t = V_{s+t}$ follows.

We show F-continuity of $t \mapsto V_t$. Let us fix $t \in \mathbb{R}$, and take $s \in \mathbb{R}$ variable. Then Eqs. (51.3.14) and (51.3.13) lead to

$$\|(\mathbb{1} \otimes a^{N_F})[V_s - V_t]\psi\| = \|(\mathbb{1} \otimes a^{N_F})V_t[V_{s-t} - \mathbb{1}]\psi\|$$

$$\leq \underbrace{\left[\sum_{n=0}^{\infty} \frac{(4a\,\|B\|\,\|\phi\|\,|t|)^n}{\sqrt{n!}}\right]}_{=:\,c} \|(\mathbb{1} \otimes (2^{\frac{1}{2}}a)^{N_F})[V_{s-t} - \mathbb{1}]\psi\|$$

$$\leq c\|(\mathbb{1} \otimes (2^{\frac{1}{2}}a)^{N_F})[V_{s-t} - U_{s-t}]\psi\| + c\|(\mathbb{1} \otimes (2^{\frac{1}{2}}a)^{N_F})[U_{s-t} - \mathbb{1}]\psi\|$$

$$= c\left\|(\mathbb{1} \otimes (2^{\frac{1}{2}}a)^{N_F}) \sum_{n=1}^{\infty} U_{s-t}^{[n]}\psi\right\| + c\|(\mathbb{1} \otimes (2^{\frac{1}{2}}a)^{N_F})[U_{s-t} - \mathbb{1}]\psi\|$$

$$\leq c\underbrace{\left[\sum_{n=1}^{\infty} \frac{(4a\,\|B\|\,\|\phi\|\,|s-t|)^n}{\sqrt{n!}}\right]}_{\overset{s \to t}{\longrightarrow}\,0} \|(\mathbb{1} \otimes (2^{\frac{1}{2}}a)^{N_F})\psi\| + c\underbrace{\|[U_{s-t} - \mathbb{1}](\mathbb{1} \otimes (2^{\frac{1}{2}}a)^{N_F})\psi\|}_{\overset{s \to t}{\longrightarrow}\,0},$$

where in the second approximation we used the fact that $U_t = e^{itK}$ commutes with $\mathbb{1} \otimes a^{N_F}$ (cf. the proof of Lemma 51.3-2). Since the F-topology is stronger than the Hilbert space norm, it also follows that $t \mapsto V_t$ is a strongly continuous unitary one-parameter group on $\mathcal{H} \otimes F_+(\mathcal{V})$.

(2) On D, we find

$$\frac{1}{t}(V_t - \mathbb{1}) - \frac{1}{t}(U_t - \mathbb{1}) - i\Upsilon = \frac{1}{t}(V_t - U_t) - i\Upsilon = \left[\frac{1}{t}U_t^{[1]} - i\Upsilon\right] + \sum_{n=2}^{\infty} U_t^{[n]}.$$

That $\lim_{t \to 0} \sum_{n=2}^{\infty} U_t^{[n]} = 0$, with respect to the F-topology, is a consequence of (51.3.13). Using our previous Observation 51.3-4(3), and the fact that U_t and $\mathbb{1} \otimes a^{N_F}$ commute, we decompose

$$(\mathbb{1} \otimes a^{N_F})\left[\frac{1}{t}U_t^{[1]} - i\Upsilon\right] = \frac{i}{t}\int_0^t dt_1\, U_{t-t_1}(\mathbb{1} \otimes a^{N_F})\Upsilon[U_{t_1} - \mathbb{1}]$$

$$+ \frac{i}{t}U_t \int_0^t dt_1\, [U_{-t_1} - \mathbb{1}](\mathbb{1} \otimes a^{N_F})\Upsilon$$

$$+ i[U_t - \mathbb{1}](\mathbb{1} \otimes a^{N_F})\Upsilon.$$

Let $\psi \in D$. Without restriction in generality we suppose $t > 0$ (for $t < 0$ substitute $t_1 \to -t_1$). Hence, with Observation 51.3-4(1) and the estimation (51.3.12) for $n = 1$,

$$\left\|\frac{i}{t}\int_0^t dt_1\, U_{t-t_1}(\mathbb{1} \otimes a^{N_F})\Upsilon[U_{t_1} - \mathbb{1}]\psi\right\| \leq \frac{1}{t}\int_0^t dt_1 \|(\mathbb{1} \otimes a^{N_F})\Upsilon[U_{t_1} - \mathbb{1}]\psi\|$$

$$\leq 4a\,\|B\|\,\|\phi\|\,\frac{1}{t}\int_0^t dt_1 \|[U_{t_1} - \mathbb{1}](\mathbb{1} \otimes (2^{\frac{1}{2}}a)^{N_F})\psi\| \overset{t \to 0}{\longrightarrow} 0,$$

where the latter limit follows from the mean value theorem (that is, $\int_0^t f(x)dx = tf(\varepsilon t)$ with some $0 \le \varepsilon \le 1$ depending on t, for any ordinary continuous function $\mathbb{R} \ni x \mapsto f(x) \in \mathbb{R}$). Analogously,

$$\left\| \frac{i}{t} U_t \int_0^t dt_1 [U_{-t_1} - \mathbb{1}](\mathbb{1} \otimes a^{N_F}) \Upsilon \psi \right\| \le \frac{1}{t} \int_0^t dt_1 \| [U_{t_1} - \mathbb{1}](\mathbb{1} \otimes a^{N_F}) \Upsilon \psi \| \xrightarrow{t \to 0} 0.$$

Finally, $\lim_{t \to 0} \| [U_t - \mathbb{1}](\mathbb{1} \otimes a^{N_F}) \Upsilon \psi \| = 0$ is immediate.

Altogether, for every $a \ge 1$ we arrive at

$$\lim_{t \to 0} \left\| (\mathbb{1} \otimes a^{N_F}) \left[\frac{1}{t}(V_t - \mathbb{1}) - \frac{1}{t}(U_t - \mathbb{1}) - i\Upsilon \right] \psi \right\| = 0, \quad \forall \psi \in D.$$

Since U_t is the free evolution, the first part in $[.]$ is the *dynamical generator in the interaction picture* (times i), gained by differentiation in the F-topology, which is now shown to equal $i\Upsilon$. Since we know that K is the generator for U_t, we obtain information on the self-adjoint generator H for V_t, the generator in the *Heisenberg picture*.

With $a = 1$ we conclude $\mathrm{dom}(H) \cap D = \mathrm{dom}(K) \cap D$, and that H coincides with (51.2.1) on $\mathrm{dom}(H) \cap D$. Now, since both $\mathrm{dom}(H)$ and D are invariant under $V_t = e^{itH}$, it follows that H is essentially self-adjoint on $\mathrm{dom}(H) \cap D$ (*the latter argument being a very useful standard result, formulated e.g., in* [RS73b] Theorem VIII.10 and in our Theorem 43.6-1 on page 1550). Now recall $D \subset \mathrm{dom}(\Upsilon)$, which finally proves part (a) of Proposition 51.2-1.

Part (c). Let $C \in \mathcal{M}'$ (commutant of $\mathcal{M}$). Then $C \otimes \mathbb{1}$ commutes with $\Upsilon(s)$ for all $s \in \mathbb{R}$, and thus with $U_{-t}F(t, t_1, \ldots, t_n)$. Since we also have

$$F(t, t_1, \ldots, t_n) = \Upsilon(t - t_1)\Upsilon(t - t_2) \cdots \Upsilon(t - t_n)U_t,$$

$C \otimes \mathbb{1}$ commutes also with $F(t, t_1, \ldots, t_n)U_{-t}$. Consequently, the expansion implies $C \otimes \mathbb{1}$ to commute with both, $U_{-t}e^{itH}$ and $e^{itH}U_{-t}$, ensuring that these are elements of the commutant $(\mathcal{M}' \otimes \mathbb{1})' = \mathcal{M} \otimes \mathcal{L}(F_+(\mathcal{V}))$. □

With the Dyson expansion theory on D we are able to answer the question: If the different parts in H are approximated, does this take over to the total interacting Hamiltonians in a suitable mathematical sense?

Corollary 51.3-6 (Limits of Unitary One-Parameter Groups). *Let A_ν, $\nu \in \mathbb{N}$, be a sequence of self-adjoint operators on $\mathcal{H}$, and S_ν, $\nu \in \mathbb{N}$, a sequence of self-adjoint operators on $\mathcal{V}$, such that $\lim_{\nu \to \infty} A_\nu = A$ and $\lim_{\nu \to \infty} S_\nu = S$ in the strong resolvent sense.*

In addition, for each $j \in \{1, \ldots, M\}$ suppose a sequence $\lim_{\nu \to \infty} B_{j,\nu} = B_j$ of operators $B_{j,\nu}$ on $\mathcal{H}$ converging with respect to the strong operator topology, such *that there exists a $b_j > 0$ with $\|B_j\| \leq b_j$ and $\|B_{j,\nu}\| \leq b_j$ for all $\nu \in \mathbb{N}$ (uniform boundedness in ν); moreover, there be a sequence $\lim_{\nu \to \infty} \phi_{j,\nu} = \phi_j$ of vectors $\phi_{j,\nu} \in \mathcal{V}$ converging in norm.*

Analogously to H in Eq. (51.2.1) let us define for each $\nu \in \mathbb{N}$ the self-adjoint

$$H_\nu := \underbrace{A_\nu \otimes \mathbb{1} + \mathbb{1} \otimes d\Gamma(S_\nu)}_{=:\, K_\nu,\ \text{free Hamiltonian}} + \underbrace{\sum_{j=1}^{M} \left[B_{j,\nu} \otimes a_F(\phi_{j,\nu}) + B_{j,\nu}^* \otimes a_F^*(\phi_{j,\nu}) \right]}_{=:\, \Upsilon_\nu,\ \text{interaction}}$$

$$(51.3.15)$$

acting on $\mathcal{H} \otimes F_+(\mathcal{V})$. Then it holds

$$\lim_{\nu \to \infty} H_\nu = H \qquad \text{in the strong resolvent sense on } \mathcal{H} \otimes F_+(\mathcal{V}),$$

or equivalently (due to Proposition 43.6-6 on page 1553) for each $t \in \mathbb{R}$,

$$\lim_{\nu \to \infty} e^{itH_\nu} = e^{itH} \qquad \text{in the strong operator topology of } \mathcal{L}(\mathcal{H} \otimes F_+(\mathcal{V})). \quad (51.3.16)$$

In addition, the limits (51.3.16) are valid (point-wise) on D in the F-topology. Moreover, for the Heisenberg dynamics we have the strong limit

$$\lim_{\nu \to \infty} e^{itH_\nu} Z e^{-itH_\nu} = e^{itH} Z e^{-itH}, \quad \forall Z \in \mathcal{L}(\mathcal{H} \otimes F_+(\mathcal{V})), \quad \forall t \in \mathbb{R}.$$

Proof.   Let us continue the proof of the previous Theorem 51.3-5 for $M = 1$. For the expansion of e^{itH_ν} all occurring operators get an index ν. The limits $\lim_{\nu \to \infty} \phi_\nu = \phi$ and $\lim_{\nu \to \infty} S_\nu = S$ imply $\lim_{\nu \to \infty} e^{itS_\nu} \phi_\nu = e^{itS} \phi$ in norm, since

$$\|e^{itS_\nu} \phi_\nu - e^{itS} \phi\| = \|e^{itS_\nu}(\phi_\nu - \phi) + (e^{itS_\nu} - e^{itS})\phi\|$$

$$\leq \|\phi_\nu - \phi\| + \|(e^{itS_\nu} - e^{itS})\phi\| \xrightarrow{t \to 0} 0.$$

In addition, $\lim_{\nu \to \infty} B_\nu = B$ and $\lim_{\nu \to \infty} A_\nu = A$ imply $\lim_{\nu \to \infty} e^{itA_\nu} B_\nu e^{-itA_\nu} = e^{itA} B e^{-itA}$ strongly (since the operator product is strongly continuous in bounded domains).

Consequently, Lemma 51.3-3(b) ensures the convergence

$$\lim_{\nu \to \infty} F_\nu(t, t_1, \dots, t_n) = F(t, t_1, \dots, t_n)$$

with respect to the F-topology on D. Because $F_\nu(t, t_1, \dots, t_n)$ and $F(t, t_1, \dots, t_n)$ possess (uniformly in ν) the same F-norm bounds (51.3.12), we may exchange $\sum_n$ and the serial integrals with the limit $\nu \to \infty$, which yields

$$\|(\mathbb{1} \otimes a^{N_F})(e^{itH_\nu} - e^{itH})\psi\| = 0, \quad \forall \psi \in D, \quad a \geq 1.$$

Choose $a = 1$ and extend from $\psi \in D$ to $\psi \in \mathcal{H} \otimes F_+(\mathcal{V})$.

Let us finally show the approximation of the Heisenberg dynamics. With $Z \in \mathcal{L}(\mathcal{H} \otimes F_+(\mathcal{V}))$ and $t \in \mathbb{R}$ we obtain for each $\psi \in \mathcal{H} \otimes F_+(\mathcal{V})$ that

$$\| (e^{itH_\nu} Z e^{-itH_\nu} - e^{itH} Z e^{-itH}) \psi \|$$

$$= \| e^{itH_\nu} Z (e^{-itH_\nu} - e^{itH}) \psi + (e^{itH_\nu} - e^{itH}) Z e^{-itH} \psi \|$$

$$\leq \| Z \| \, \| (e^{-itH_\nu} - e^{itH}) \psi \| + \| (e^{itH_\nu} - e^{itH}) Z e^{-itH} \psi \| \xrightarrow{t \to 0} 0. \qquad \square$$

51.3.3. Dyson Expansion for the Total *-Automorphism Group

With our self-adjoint Hamiltonians K and H from Eq. (51.2.1) we may define the associated *-automorphism groups on the von Neumann algebra $\mathcal{L}(\mathcal{H} \otimes F_+(\mathcal{V}))$ of bounded operators on $\mathcal{H} \otimes F_+(\mathcal{V})$ for every $t \in \mathbb{R}$ by

$$\alpha_t^{\text{free}}(.) = e^{itK} \cdot e^{-itK},$$
$$\alpha_t^{\text{tot}}(.) = e^{itH} \cdot e^{-itH}. \qquad (51.3.17)$$

As a direct consequence of Theorem 51.3-5(c), we come to the following conclusion.

Observation 51.3-7 (Restriction of Dynamics to von Neumann Algebra).
Suppose that there is a von Neumann algebra $\mathcal{M}$ on the material Hilbert space $\mathcal{H}$, which is invariant under the *-automorphism group

$$\alpha_t^{\text{mat}}(.) = e^{itA} \cdot e^{-itA}, \qquad \forall t \in \mathbb{R},$$

and that the material coupling operators satisfy $B_j \in \mathcal{M}$ for all $j \in \{1, \ldots, M\}$.

Then both *-automorphism groups $\alpha^{\text{free}} := \{\alpha_t^{\text{free}} \mid t \in \mathbb{R}\}$ and $\alpha^{\text{tot}} := \{\alpha_t^{\text{tot}} \mid t \in \mathbb{R}\}$ leave the von Neumann algebra $\mathcal{M} \otimes \mathcal{L}(F_+(\mathcal{V}))$ (W*-tensor product) invariant.

Definition 51.3-8 (F-Continuous Operators on D). Let us denote by $\mathcal{O}_F(D)$ the algebra of all F-continuous operators on D, which we also regard as acting on $\mathcal{H} \otimes F_+(\mathcal{V})$ with a domain of definition including D.

Especially, e^{itK} and e^{itH} are elements of $\mathcal{O}_F(D)$, and so α^{free} and α^{tot} constitute well defined one-parameter automorphism groups acting on $\mathcal{O}_F(D)$.

Example 51.3-9 (F-Continuous Operators on D). We find:

(a) Operators of type $C \otimes \prod_k A_k(g_k)$, with $C \in \mathcal{L}(\mathcal{H})$, (finite product) are elements of $\mathcal{O}_F(D)$.
(b) $\sum_k X_k \otimes W_F(f_k) \in \mathcal{O}_F(D)$ (finite sum), where $X_k \in \mathcal{L}(\mathcal{H})$ and $f_k \in \mathcal{V}$. Here $W_F(f)$, $f \in \mathcal{V}$, are the Weyl operators acting on the Fock space $F_+(\mathcal{V})$.
(c) For $\nu \in \mathbb{N}$ let Q_ν be the orthogonal projection from $\mathcal{H} \otimes F_+(\mathcal{V})$ onto the direct sum of finite particle subspaces

$$\bigoplus_{m=0}^{\nu} \mathcal{H} \otimes P_+(\otimes_m \mathcal{V}) = \mathcal{H} \otimes \bigoplus_{m=0}^{\nu} P_+(\otimes_m \mathcal{V}).$$

Then for each $Z \in \mathcal{L}(\mathcal{H} \otimes F_+(\mathcal{V}))$ it holds that

$$Q_\nu Z \in \mathcal{O}_F(D) \cap \mathcal{L}(\mathcal{H} \otimes F_+(\mathcal{V})), \quad \forall \nu \in \mathbb{N}.$$

Proof.   Part (b).   For $X \otimes W_F(f) = \sum\limits_{n=0}^{\infty} \frac{i^n}{n!} X \otimes \Phi_F(f)^n$ we obtain from Lemma 51.3-3 the F-estimations

$$\|(\mathbb{1} \otimes a^{N_F})[X \otimes W_F(f)]\psi\| \leq \sum_{n=0}^{\infty} \frac{(2a\|f\|)^n}{\sqrt{n!}} \|X\| \, \|(\mathbb{1} \otimes (2^{\frac{1}{2}}a)^{N_F})\psi\|,$$

which especially means that D consists of analytic vectors for $\mathbb{1} \otimes \Phi_F(f)$. Part (c) is very simple. Since ν is the highest finite particle space occurring in the direct sum, we conclude that

$$\|(\mathbb{1} \otimes a^{N_F})Q_\nu Z\psi\| \leq a^\nu \|Z\psi\| \leq a^\nu \|Z\| \, \|\psi\| = a^\nu \|Z\| \, \|(\mathbb{1} \otimes \mathbb{1}^{N_F})\psi\|$$

(with $b(a) = 1$ and $c(a) = a^\nu$ in (51.3.3)), for each $a \geq 1$ and all $\psi \in D$. $\square$

The perturbation expansion for $\alpha_t^{tot}(Z)$ may be executed only on D and only for F-continuous operators $Z \in \mathcal{O}_F(D)$.

Theorem 51.3-10 (Dyson Expansion for Total Heisenberg Dynamics).
Let all be as described before. For each $Z \in \mathcal{O}_F(D)$ the Dyson perturbation expansion of the interacting Heisenberg dynamics $\alpha^{tot} = \{\alpha_t^{tot} \mid t \in \mathbb{R}\}$ is given in application on vectors of D by

$$\alpha_t^{tot}(Z) = \sum_{n=0}^{\infty} i^n \int_{t_1=0}^{t} dt_1 \cdots \int_{t_n=0}^{t_{n-1}} dt_n \, [\alpha_{t_n}^{free}(\Upsilon), [\cdots [\alpha_{t_1}^{free}(\Upsilon), \alpha_t^{free}(Z)] \cdots]].$$

The series and integrals converge with respect to the F-topology on D.

Proof.   Recall that for $Z \in \mathcal{O}_F(D)$ there exists a $b(a) \geq 0$ and a $c(a) \geq 0$ such that

$$\|(\mathbb{1} \otimes a^{N_F})Z\psi\| \leq c(a)\|(\mathbb{1} \otimes b(a)^{N_F})\psi\| < \infty, \quad \forall \psi \in D.$$

By Lemma 51.3-2 and its proof, e^{itK} commutes with $\mathbb{1} \otimes a^{N_F}$. Hence

$$\|(\mathbb{1} \otimes a^{N_F})\alpha_t^{free}(Z)\psi\| = \|e^{itK}(\mathbb{1} \otimes a^{N_F})Ze^{-itK}\psi\|$$
$$\leq c(a)\|(\mathbb{1} \otimes b(a)^{N_F})e^{-itK}\psi\| = c(a)\|(\mathbb{1} \otimes b(a)^{N_F})\psi\|.$$

So, with our F-estimations for $\Upsilon(s) \equiv U_s \Upsilon U_{-s} = \alpha_s^{free}(\Upsilon)$ in the proof of Theorem 51.3-5, the stated expansion converges F-continuously on D. By induction over n one now may show that

$$\sum_{k=0}^{n} U_t^{[n-k]} Z U_{-t}^{[k]} = i^n \int_{t_1=0}^{t} dt_1 \cdots \int_{t_n=0}^{t_{n-1}} dt_n \, [\alpha_{t_n}^{free}(\Upsilon), [\cdots [\alpha_{t_1}^{free}(\Upsilon), \alpha_t^{free}(Z)] \cdots]].$$

Finally, employing the expansion series for $e^{\pm itH}$ one checks that

$$\alpha_t^{\text{tot}}(Z) = e^{itH} Z e^{-itH} = \sum_{n=0}^{\infty} \sum_{k=0}^{n} U_t^{[n-k]} Z U_{-t}^{[k]}.$$

□

51.3.4. The "*Limiting Renormalization*" Concept

The Dyson expansion for the interacting dynamics α^{tot} is also useful, if a sequence A_ν, $\nu \in \mathbb{N}$, of self-adjoint material Hamiltonians A_ν on $\mathcal{H}$ generate a material limiting Heisenberg dynamics, which is implemented by a "limiting" self-adjoint Hamiltonian A on $\mathcal{H}$, without satisfying the strong resolvent convergence of the A_ν to A. More precisely, we mean the following scenario: There is a von Neumann algebra $\mathcal{M}$ on $\mathcal{H}$, which is invariant under all the mentioned (material) one-parameter *-automorphism groups

$$\alpha_{t,\nu}^{\text{mat}}(.) = e^{itA_\nu} \cdot e^{-itA_\nu}, \quad \nu \in \mathbb{N}, \qquad \alpha_t^{\text{mat}}(.) = e^{itA} \cdot e^{-itA}, \tag{51.3.18}$$

where in addition we have the limiting relation

$$\lim_{\nu \to \infty} \underbrace{e^{itA_\nu} X e^{-itA_\nu}}_{= \alpha_{t,\nu}^{\text{mat}}(X)} = \underbrace{e^{itA} X e^{-itA}}_{= \alpha_t^{\text{mat}}(X)}, \quad \forall X \in \mathcal{M}, \tag{51.3.19}$$

in the strong operator topology for each $t \in \mathbb{R}$.

Definition 51.3-11 (Renormalized Limiting Hamiltonian). Let us generalize the foregoing scenario to an arbitrary von Neumann algebra $\mathcal{M}$ on some Hilbert space $\mathcal{H}$, where Eq. (51.3.19) is valid for certain self-adjoint operators A_ν and A.

We call then A a *renormalized limiting Hamiltonian* (of the sequence (A_ν) with respect to $\mathcal{M}$).

Since — as for the material A_ν — the direct approximation of the total interacting Hamiltonian H from (51.2.1) by the sequence of the H_ν in the strong resolvent sense (like in Corollary 51.3-6) is neither ensured, we must content us with a renormalized limiting Hamiltonian. That is, with an approximation in terms of the related total local Heisenberg dynamics

$$\lim_{\nu \to \infty} \underbrace{e^{itH_\nu} Z e^{-itH_\nu}}_{= \alpha_{t,\nu}^{\text{tot}}(Z)} = \underbrace{e^{itH} Z e^{-itH}}_{= \alpha_t^{\text{tot}}(Z)}, \quad \forall Z \in \mathcal{M} \overline{\otimes} \mathcal{L}(F_+(\mathcal{F})), \tag{51.3.20}$$

where in addition the $B_{j,\nu}$ (occurring in H_ν) and the B_j (occurring in H) are elements of $\mathcal{M}$, knowing then that the interacting *-automorphism groups α_ν^{tot} and α^{tot} leave the von Neumann algebra $\mathcal{M} \overline{\otimes} \mathcal{L}(F_+(\mathcal{V}))$ invariant.

Theorem 51.3-12 (Existence of Total Hamiltonian Limiting Dynamics).
Consider the Hilbert space $\mathcal{H} \otimes F_+(\mathcal{V})$ for the total system and assume a von Neumann algebra $\mathcal{M}$ on the material Hilbert space $\mathcal{H}$.

Let — on the material side — A_ν, $\nu \in \mathbb{N}$, be a sequence of self-adjoint operators on $\mathcal{H}$, such that the self-adjoint A on $\mathcal{H}$ is a limiting renormalization with respect to $\mathcal{M}$ in the sense of Eq. (51.3.19), and suppose for each $j \in \{1, \dots, M\}$ a sequence $B_{j,\nu} \in \mathcal{M}$ converging with respect to the strong operator topology to $B_j \in \mathcal{M}$, such that there exists a $b_j > 0$ with $\|B_j\| \leq b_j$ and $\|B_{j,\nu}\| \leq b_j$ for all $\nu \in \mathbb{N}$ (uniform boundedness in ν). Stipulate moreover that

$$\lim_{\nu \to \infty} e^{itA_\nu} B_{j,\nu}\, e^{-itA_\nu} = e^{itA} B_j\, e^{-itA}, \quad \forall t \in \mathbb{R}, \quad \forall j \in \{1, \dots, M\}, \qquad (51.3.21)$$

be valid with respect to the strong operator topology in $\mathcal{L}(\mathcal{H})$.

Furtheron, let — on the Boson side — be given a sequence S_ν, $\nu \in \mathbb{N}$ of self-adjoint operators on $\mathcal{V}$, such that $\lim_{\nu \to \infty} S_\nu = S$ in the strong resolvent sense, as well as a sequence $\lim_{\nu \to \infty} \phi_{j,\nu} = \phi_j$ of vectors $\phi_{j,\nu} \in \mathcal{V}$ converging in norm.

Analogously to our basic H (from Eq. (51.2.1))

$$H = A \otimes \mathbb{1} + \mathbb{1} \otimes d\Gamma(S) + \sum_{j=1}^{M} \left[B_j \otimes a_F(\phi_j) + B_j^* \otimes a_F^*(\phi_j) \right],$$

let us define as in Corollary 51.3-6, for each $\nu \in \mathbb{N}$, the self-adjoint

$$H_\nu = \underbrace{A_\nu \otimes \mathbb{1} + \mathbb{1} \otimes d\Gamma(S_\nu)}_{=:\, K_\nu,\ \text{free Hamiltonian}} + \underbrace{\sum_{j=1}^{M} \left[B_{j,\nu} \otimes a_F(\phi_{j,\nu}) + B_{j,\nu}^* \otimes a_F^*(\phi_{j,\nu}) \right]}_{=:\, \Upsilon_\nu,\ \text{interaction}} \quad (51.3.22)$$

acting also on $\mathcal{H} \otimes F_+(\mathcal{V})$.

Then the limits (51.3.20) are valid, for all $Z \in \mathcal{M} \otimes \mathcal{L}(F_+(\mathcal{V}))$ and for each $t \in \mathbb{R}$, in the strong operator topology. In other words, H is the limiting renormalization for the sequence H_ν, $\nu \in \mathbb{N}$, with respect to the von Neumann algebra $\mathcal{M} \overline{\otimes} \mathcal{L}(F_+(\mathcal{V}))$.

Observe that neither A nor H are uniquely determined by the H_ν.

Before giving the proof, let us state a side result.

Corollary 51.3-13 (Limit in F-Topology). *Let all be as in the earlier stated Theorem. If $Z \in \mathcal{O}_F(D) \cap (\mathcal{M} \otimes \mathcal{L}(F_+(\mathcal{V})))$, then the limits (51.3.20) are valid in application on vectors in D in the F-topology.*

Provided $\mathcal{M} = \mathcal{L}(\mathcal{H})$, then (51.3.20) holds in the F-topology on D for all $Z \in \mathcal{O}_F(D)$.

Proof. For proving the Theorem, let first — as in the Corollary — $Z \in \mathcal{O}_F(D) \cap (\mathcal{M} \otimes \mathcal{L}(F_+(\mathcal{V})))$. The limit $\nu \to \infty$ in (51.3.20) may be done term by term in the related expansions. Convergence in the F-topology on D arises, since by the in ν uniform F-norm bounds on D one may exchange power series and integrals with the limit $\nu \to \infty$ in the associated expansion parts, similarly to those for the limiting Dyson expansion of $\lim_{\nu \to \infty} e^{itH_\nu} = e^{itH}$ from the proofs of Theorem 51.3-5 and Corollary 51.3-6. In this manner, one also proves the second part of our Corollary 51.3-13.

Taking $a = 1$, the limits (51.3.20) turn out to be valid in the strong operator topology. Since $\|e^{itH_\nu}\| = \|e^{itH}\| = 1$, one may extend to Z contained in the operator norm closure of $\mathcal{O}_F(D) \cap (\mathcal{M} \otimes \mathcal{L}(F_+(\mathcal{V})))$, which in general may not be all of $\mathcal{M} \otimes \mathcal{L}(F_+(\mathcal{V}))$. So we need more refined techniques to obtain the result.

For $Z \in \mathcal{M} \otimes \mathcal{L}(F_+(\mathcal{V}))$ we know from example 51.3-9(c), that $Q_\mu Z \in \mathcal{O}_F(D) \cap (\mathcal{M} \otimes \mathcal{L}(F_+(\mathcal{V})))$ for all $\mu \in \mathbb{N}$, since $Q_\mu \in \mathcal{M} \otimes \mathcal{L}(F_+(\mathcal{V}))$. We now show that (51.3.20) remains true in the strong operator limit $\lim_{\mu \to \infty} Q_\mu Z = Z$. The demonstration is divided into several steps.

(1) Here we demonstrate that in the operator norm it holds

$$\lim_{\mu \to \infty} \|(\mathbb{1} - Q_\mu) Z (\mathbb{1} \otimes a^{-N_F})\| = 0, \quad \forall a > 1.$$

Since $a > 1$, the operator a^{-N_F} is bounded. In order to elaborate the essential point, we simplify the situation:

Let $\mathcal{K}$ be a separable Hilbert space with orthonormal basis $\{e_n \mid n \in \mathbb{N}_0\}$, and define $Q_\mu := \sum_{n=0}^{\mu} |e_n)(e_n|$. Then, $\lim_{\mu \to \infty} Q_\mu = \mathbb{1}$ in the strong, and weak operator topology. N be the number operator, $Ne_n = ne_n$ for each $n \in \mathbb{N}_0$, for which $a^{-N}e_n = \frac{1}{a^n}e_n$. Thus for $Z \in \mathcal{L}(\mathcal{K})$ and $a > 1$ we have

$$\|Za^{-N}\|_{\mathrm{HS}}^2 = \mathrm{tr}(a^{-N}Z^*Za^{-N}) = \sum_{n=0}^{\infty}(e_n|a^{-N}Z^*Za^{-N}e_n)$$

$$= \sum_{n=0}^{\infty}(a^{-N}e_n|Z^*Za^{-N}e_n) = \sum_{n=0}^{\infty}\frac{1}{a^{2n}}(e_n|Z^*Ze_n) \leq \left(\sum_{n=0}^{\infty}\frac{1}{a^{2n}}\right)\|Z\|^2 < \infty,$$

implying Za^{-N} to be a Hilbert–Schmidt operator on $\mathcal{K}$. Since $\mathbb{1} - Q_\mu$ is a projection, it follows that

$$\|(\mathbb{1} - Q_\mu)Za^{-N}\|_{\mathrm{HS}} \leq \|\mathbb{1} - Q_\mu\| \, \|Za^{-N}\|_{\mathrm{HS}} = \|Za^{-N}\|_{\mathrm{HS}}, \quad \forall \mu \in \mathbb{N},$$

according to Sec. 43.2.1. Because that bound is uniform in μ, we may exchange $\sum_n$ with the limit $\mu \to \infty$ in

$$\lim_{\mu \to \infty}\|(\mathbb{1} - Q_\mu)Za^{-N}\|^2 \leq \lim_{\mu \to \infty}\|(\mathbb{1} - Q_\mu)Za^{-N}\|_{\mathrm{HS}}^2$$

$$= \lim_{\mu \to \infty}\mathrm{tr}(a^{-N}Z^*(\mathbb{1} - Q_\mu)Za^{-N}) = \lim_{\mu \to \infty}\sum_{n=0}^{\infty}(Za^{-N}e_n|(\mathbb{1} - Q_\mu)Za^{-N}e_n)$$

$$= \sum_{n=0}^{\infty}\lim_{\mu \to \infty}(Za^{-N}e_n|(\mathbb{1} - Q_\mu)Za^{-N}e_n) = 0.$$

The generalization to our "real world" is obvious: $\mathbb{C}e_n$ stands for the n-particle space $\mathcal{H} \otimes P_+(\otimes_n \mathcal{V})$, and $\mathcal{K}$ for $\mathcal{H} \otimes F_+(\mathcal{V}) = \bigoplus_{n=0}^{\infty} \mathcal{H} \otimes P_+(\otimes_n \mathcal{V})$. But we have to use the partial Hilbert–Schmidt property over the index n, not within the finite particle spaces.

(2) We write $H_{(\nu)}$, if we mean both H as well as the H_ν, $\nu \in \mathbb{N}$. As previously, we take $M = 1$ in the interaction Υ. Since $\lim_{\nu \to \infty} \|\phi_\nu - \phi\| = 0$, there exists a constant $\gamma \geq 0$ with $\|\phi_{(\nu)}\| \leq \gamma$ for all ν. Together with the assumption $\|B_{(\nu)}\| \leq b$, we conclude from the F-estimation (51.3.14) that we have F-bounds uniform in ν,

$$\|(\mathbb{1} \otimes a^{N_F})\mathrm{e}^{-itH_{(\nu)}}\psi\| \leq \left[\sum_{n=0}^{\infty} \frac{(4ab\gamma|t|)^n}{\sqrt{n!}} \right] \|(\mathbb{1} \otimes (2^{\frac{1}{2}}a)^{N_F})\psi\| =: c(a,\psi), \quad \forall \nu \in \mathbb{N}.$$

Consequently, for $\psi \in D$ and $a > 1$ we obtain,

$$\begin{aligned}
\|(Z - Q_\mu Z)\mathrm{e}^{-itH_{(\nu)}}\psi\| &= \|(Z - Q_\mu Z)(\mathbb{1} \otimes a^{-N_F})(\mathbb{1} \otimes a^{N_F})\mathrm{e}^{-itH_{(\nu)}}\psi\| \\
&\leq \|(\mathbb{1} - Q_\mu)Z(\mathbb{1} \otimes a^{-N_F})\| \, \|(\mathbb{1} \otimes a^{N_F})\mathrm{e}^{-itH_{(\nu)}}\psi\| \\
&\leq c(a,\psi)\|(\mathbb{1} - Q_\mu)Z(\mathbb{1} \otimes a^{-N_F})\| \xrightarrow{\mu \to \infty} 0, \quad \forall \nu \in \mathbb{N}.
\end{aligned}$$

(3) For our $Z \in \mathcal{M} \otimes \mathcal{L}(F_+(\mathcal{V}))$ and $\psi \in D$ we estimate for fixed $t \in \mathbb{R}$ that

$$\begin{aligned}
&\left\| \left[\mathrm{e}^{itH_\nu} Z \mathrm{e}^{-itH_\nu} - \mathrm{e}^{itH} Z \mathrm{e}^{-itH} \right]\psi \right\| \\
&= \left\| \left[\mathrm{e}^{itH_\nu}(Z - Q_\mu Z)\mathrm{e}^{-itH_\nu} + \mathrm{e}^{itH_\nu}Q_\mu Z \mathrm{e}^{-itH_\nu} \right.\right. \\
&\qquad\quad \left.\left. - \mathrm{e}^{itH}Q_\mu Z \mathrm{e}^{-itH} + \mathrm{e}^{itH}(Q_\mu Z - Z)\mathrm{e}^{-itH} \right]\psi \right\| \\
&\leq \|(Z - Q_\mu Z)\mathrm{e}^{-itH_\nu}\psi\| + \|(Q_\mu Z - Z)\mathrm{e}^{-itH}\psi\| \\
&\quad + \left\| \left[\mathrm{e}^{itH_\nu}Q_\mu Z \mathrm{e}^{-itH_\nu} - \mathrm{e}^{itH}Q_\mu Z \mathrm{e}^{-itH} \right]\psi \right\| \\
&\leq 2c(a,\psi)\|(\mathbb{1} - Q_\mu)Z(\mathbb{1} \otimes a^{-N_F})\| + \left\| \left[\mathrm{e}^{itH_\nu}Q_\mu Z \mathrm{e}^{-itH_\nu} - \mathrm{e}^{itH}Q_\mu Z \mathrm{e}^{-itH} \right]\psi \right\|.
\end{aligned}$$

For $\varepsilon > 0$ choose a fixed $\mu \in \mathbb{N}$ with $c(a,\psi)\|(\mathbb{1} - Q_\mu)Z(\mathbb{1} \otimes (1/a)^{N_F})\| < \varepsilon/3$. Since $Q_\mu Z \in \mathcal{O}_F(D) \cap (\mathcal{M} \otimes \mathcal{L}(F_+(\mathcal{V})))$, there exists according to the earlier established F-convergence a $\nu_\varepsilon \in \mathbb{N}$ with (for $a = 1$)

$$\left\| \left[\mathrm{e}^{itH_\nu}Q_\mu Z \mathrm{e}^{-itH_\nu} - \mathrm{e}^{itH}Q_\mu Z \mathrm{e}^{-itH} \right]\psi \right\| < \varepsilon, \quad \forall \nu \geq \nu_\varepsilon.$$

Altogether, $\left\| \left[\mathrm{e}^{itH_\nu}Z\mathrm{e}^{-itH_\nu} - \mathrm{e}^{itH}Z\mathrm{e}^{-itH} \right]\psi \right\| < \varepsilon$ for all $\nu \geq \nu_\varepsilon$, implying (51.3.20) point-wise in norm on D. The extension from D to $\mathcal{H} \otimes F_+(\mathcal{V})$ is immediate. $\square$

For our applications we specialize the foregoing results.

Conclusion 51.3-14 (Limiting Dynamics with Material Mean Fields). In case of a mean field description of radiating matter, the A_ν of Theorem 51.3-12 would correspond at first sight to the local mean field Hamiltonians $H_\mathsf{K}^{\mathrm{mat}}$, $\mathsf{K} \in F(\mathbb{N})$, of Sec. 36.1 on page 1113. Then, however, Eq. (51.3.19) should be replaced by the so-called "combined limit", in which the material observables, acted upon by the local dynamics, perform simultaneously the thermodynamic limit, in order to get the collective flow.

So, instead, one takes the stationary sequence $(A_\nu \equiv H_\theta^{\mathrm{mat}})$, where H_θ^{mat} is a generating Hamiltonian of the material limiting dynamics — in the combined sense —, where θ indicates an invariant state. In the total Hamiltonians $H_\nu \equiv \hat{H}_\mathsf{K}$

$$\hat{H}_\mathsf{K} := H_\theta^{\mathrm{mat}} \otimes \mathbb{1}_{\mathrm{ph}} + \mathbb{1}_{\mathrm{mat}} \otimes d\Gamma(S) + \frac{1}{\sqrt{2}} \sum_{j=1}^{M} \{ R_j^{\mathsf{K}*} \otimes a_F(\phi_j) + R_j^{\mathsf{K}} \otimes a_F^*(\phi_j) \}, \quad (51.3.23)$$

only the material coupling operators $B_{j,\nu} \equiv R_j^{\mathsf{K}}$ take then part in the thermodynamic limit, where the limiting operators R_j^θ are reached under uniform boundedness.

Since Eq. (51.3.21) is valid and all Boson operators are independent of K, also in this case the requirements of Theorem 51.3-12 are satisfied, and a renormalized total limiting Hamiltonian, on the Hilbert space $\mathcal{H}_{\mathrm{tot}} = \mathcal{H}_\theta \otimes F_+(\mathcal{H}^\top)$, is e.g., given by

$$H_\theta := H_\theta^{\mathrm{mat}} \otimes \mathbb{1}_{\mathrm{ph}} + \mathbb{1}_{\mathrm{mat}} \otimes d\Gamma(S) + \frac{1}{\sqrt{2}} \sum_{j=1}^{M} \{ R_j^{\theta*} \otimes a_F(\phi_j) + R_j^\theta \otimes a_F^*(\phi_j) \}. \quad (51.3.24)$$

The R_j^θ being central operators, does not play a role for the present existence results for the total limiting dynamics and Hamiltonians, but will further be investigated in the next Sec. 52.1. Because of the combined limit Eq. (51.3.21) for the material coupling operators, their central limiting operators "feel" the collective material dynamics.

That would not be so, if we would have followed the first idea $A_\nu \equiv H_\mathsf{K}^{\mathrm{mat}}$. If, however, in the latter ansatz, we would perform a combined limit for the total dynamics (letting Z depend on K on the left-hand side in Eq. (51.3.20) with limit Z on the right-hand side of that relation) then an even more complicated classical flow would enter the radiation theory (with a feed back of the radiation to the classical material flow?).

Remark that the existence of the limiting total Heisenberg dynamics, with its renormalized limiting Hamiltonians, rests on the existence of the corresponding limiting unitaries (as is e.g., seen in part (3) of the proof for Theorem 51.3-12). These are treated in Sec. 51.3.2 in terms of Dyson expansions, which even are required for the self-adjointness of Hamiltonians like $\hat{H}_\mathsf{K}$ and H_θ.

Chapter 52

Algebraic Perturbation Theory

We continue our elaboration on perturbation theory from the previous chapter. Here, however, the special situation of commuting matter interaction parts is treated.

52.1. Partially Commutative Coupling Operators

In the preceding Sec. 51.3.4 we have considered a von Neumann algebra $\mathcal{M} \subset \mathcal{L}(\mathcal{H})$ of operators on the material Hilbert space $\mathcal{H}$. We now assume that there exists a commutative sub-C*-algebra $\mathcal{A}_{\text{com}}$ of $\mathcal{M}$. (In our models, the coupling operators $B_{j,\nu}$ of Theorem 51.3-12 converge in the so-called "weak coupling limit" strongly to some $B_j \in \mathcal{A}_{\text{com}}$.)

One knows (from Theorem 46.1-10 on page 1675) that the elements of $\mathcal{A}_{\text{com}}$ possess a joint spectral calculus over a Borel set P, which we assume to be a measurable subset of $\mathbb{R}^d$, $d \in \mathbb{N}$. (In our applications — but not here — P is compact.) We denote the elements of P by ϱ. So, $\mathcal{A}_{\text{com}}$ consists just of all operators of the type

$$\int_{\mathsf{P}} \gamma(\varrho) \, dP(\varrho) =: \int_{\mathsf{P}} \gamma \, dP \ \in \mathcal{A}_{\text{com}}, \tag{52.1.1}$$

with a unique bounded continuous function $\gamma : \mathsf{P} \to \mathbb{C}$. Here $dP(\varrho)$ indicates the common measure on P with values in the projections of $\mathcal{M} \subset \mathcal{L}(\mathcal{H})$.

We assume in addition that the free material Heisenberg dynamics $\alpha^{\text{mat}} = \{\alpha_t^{\text{mat}}(.) = e^{itA} \cdot e^{-itA} \mid t \in \mathbb{R}\}$, given in terms of the self-adjoint Hamiltonian A on $\mathcal{H}$, satisfies $\alpha_t^{\text{mat}}(\mathcal{A}_{\text{com}}) = \mathcal{A}_{\text{com}}$, and acts on P by a continuous flow $\kappa \equiv \{\kappa_t \mid t \in \mathbb{R}\}$ according to

$$\alpha_t^{\text{mat}}\left(\int_{\mathsf{P}} \gamma \, dP\right) = e^{itA}\left(\int_{\mathsf{P}} \gamma(\varrho) \, dP(\varrho)\right)e^{-itA}$$

$$= \int_{\mathsf{P}} \gamma \circ \kappa_t \, dP = \int_{\mathsf{P}} \gamma(\kappa_t \varrho) \, dP(\varrho) \quad \in \quad \mathcal{A}_{\text{com}}, \tag{52.1.2}$$

for each element (52.1.1). Observe the group property $\kappa_s \circ \kappa_t = \kappa_{s+t}$.

That is, the spectral measure $dP(\varrho)$ indicates an *-isomorphism from $\mathcal{A}_{\mathrm{com}}$ onto the C*-algebra $C_b(\mathsf{P}, \mathbb{C})$ of the bounded continuous, $\mathbb{C}$-valued functions on P, and via that *-isomorphism the Heisenberg dynamics α^{mat} restricted to $\mathcal{A}_{\mathrm{com}}$ coincides with the flow κ on P, and with the pullback to $C_b(\mathsf{P}, \mathbb{C})$. Physically one may interpret P as a *classical collective configuration space* upon which the dynamical collective flow κ is acting.

With each $B_j \in \mathcal{A}_{\mathrm{com}}$, occurring in the interaction operator Υ from Eq. (51.2.1), we associate the complex conjugate of a function $\xi_j \in C_b(\mathsf{P}, \mathbb{C})$ by

$$B_j = \int_{\mathsf{P}} \overline{\xi_j(\varrho)} \, dP(\varrho) \in \mathcal{A}_{\mathrm{com}}, \quad \forall j \in \{1, \dots, M\}. \tag{52.1.3}$$

Assumption 52.1-1 (Partially Commutative Situation). In the "partially commutative situation" the self-adjoint Hamiltonian H on $\mathcal{H} \otimes F_+(V)$ is assumed to be of the form

$$H = \underbrace{A \otimes \mathbb{1} + \mathbb{1} \otimes d\Gamma(S)}_{= K, \text{ free Hamiltonian}} + \underbrace{\sum_{j=1}^{M} \left[\overbrace{\int_{\mathsf{P}} \overline{\xi_j(\varrho)} \, dP(\varrho)}^{= B_j} \otimes a_F(\phi_j) + \overbrace{\int_{\mathsf{P}} \xi_j(\varrho) \, dP(\varrho)}^{= B_j^*} \otimes a_F^*(\phi_j) \right]}_{= \Upsilon, \text{ interaction operator}}$$

with $\xi_j \in C_b(\mathsf{P}, \mathbb{C})$ and $\phi_j \in V$, and with a self-adjoint one-Boson Hamiltonian S on V. The free (self-adjoint) material Hamiltonian A is assumed to generate the flow κ on P via Eq. (52.1.2).

Let us apply the theory of von Neumann algebras (for which we refer to Sec. 46.1, especially to Sec. 46.1.2 on page 1673) and define

$$\mathcal{M}_{\mathrm{com}} := \mathcal{A}_{\mathrm{com}}'', \quad \text{(bicommutant of } \mathcal{A}_{\mathrm{com}} \text{ within } \mathcal{L}(\mathcal{H})\text{)},$$

a commutative von Neumann algebra on $\mathcal{H}$. Since $\mathcal{M}_{\mathrm{com}}$ agrees with the closure of $\mathcal{A}_{\mathrm{com}}$ in any of the weak operator topologies, it follows in fact that the spectral projections of our spectral measure $dP(\varrho)$ are contained in $\mathcal{M}_{\mathrm{com}} \subset \mathcal{M}$, and that the Heisenberg dynamics α^{mat}, which leaves $\mathcal{A}_{\mathrm{com}}$ invariant by assumption, leaves $\mathcal{M}_{\mathrm{com}}$ invariant (by its unitary implementation). As a consequence, α^{mat} leaves also the in general non-commutative von Neumann algebra

$$\mathcal{M}_{\mathrm{com}}' = \mathcal{A}_{\mathrm{com}}', \quad \text{(commutant of } \mathcal{M}_{\mathrm{com}} \text{ and of } \mathcal{A}_{\mathrm{com}} \text{ in } \mathcal{L}(\mathcal{H})\text{)},$$

invariant. Since $\mathcal{M}_{\mathrm{com}}$ is commutative, $\mathcal{M}_{\mathrm{com}} \subseteq \mathcal{M}_{\mathrm{com}}'$.

The great advantage of the partially commutative situation is, that we are able to deduce explicit expressions for the interacting dynamical unitary group $\{e^{itH} \mid t \in \mathbb{R}\}$. For that, we use two different mathematical methods, namely,

- Dyson perturbation expansions on our F-space D;
- Trotter's product formula $\exp\{itH\} = \lim_{n \to \infty} \left(\exp\{i\frac{t}{n}K\} \exp\{i\frac{t}{n}\Upsilon\} \right)^n$.

The two different mathematical techniques, which lead to different intuitive pictures for the virtual individual interaction events, are expounded in Secs. 52.1.4 and 52.1.5, respectively.

In any case, we need integrals over operator-valued functions with respect to our spectral measure $dP(\varrho)$ on P. The next two subsections are devoted to their mathematical elaboration.

52.1.1.   *Spectral Integrals over Operator-Valued Functions*

For integrating general operator-valued functions with respect to a projection-valued measure there are very strong conditions [AGJ71] (cf. also [AJS77] Chapter 6). In our cases the conditions for existence are, however, weaker.

Let our spectral measure $dP(\varrho)$ act on the (material) Hilbert space $\mathcal{H}$, and consider the projection-valued measure $dP(\varrho) \otimes \mathbb{1}$ on the tensor product $\mathcal{H} \otimes \mathcal{K}$, formed with an additional complex Hilbert space $\mathcal{K}$. $\mathcal{K}$ is in principle arbitrary, but we take mostly $\mathcal{K} = F_+(\mathcal{V})$. For weakly measurable operator-valued functions

$$X : \mathsf{P} \to \mathcal{L}(\mathcal{K}), \quad \varrho \mapsto X(\varrho),$$

we are going to introduce the spectral integrals

$$\int_{\mathsf{P}} [\mathbb{1} \otimes X(\varrho)]\,(dP(\varrho) \otimes \mathbb{1}). \tag{52.1.4}$$

The mentioned weak measurability of $\varrho \mapsto X(\varrho)$ refers to the weak operator topology, where the additional condition $\sup\{\|X(\varrho)\| \mid \varrho \in \mathsf{P}\} < \infty$ is also required for the following expressions and one uses countable basis systems (see also the proof for Observation 51.3-4.)

By means of the inner products

$$\left(\mu_1 \otimes \eta_1 \,\Big|\, \int_{\mathsf{P}} [\mathbb{1} \otimes X(\varrho)]\,(dP(\varrho) \otimes \mathbb{1})\, \mu_2 \otimes \eta_2 \right) := \int_{\mathsf{P}} (\eta_1 | X(\varrho)\eta_2)(\mu_1 | dP(\varrho)\mu_2),$$

for all $\mu_1, \mu_2 \in \mathcal{H}$ and all $\eta_1, \eta_2 \in \mathcal{K}$, and by (bi-) linear and continuous extension, a unique bounded operator is defined on all of $\mathcal{H} \otimes \mathcal{K}$, denoted by (52.1.4). By construction, the integral is $\mathbb{C}$-linear in the functions X.

Proposition 52.1-2. *The spectral integral operators of type (52.1.4) are elements of the von Neumann algebra $\mathcal{M}_{com}\overline{\otimes}\mathcal{L}(F_+(\mathcal{V}))$. Or equivalently, for all $C \in \mathcal{M}'_{com}$ we have*

$$[C \otimes \mathbb{1}]\Big[\int_{\mathsf{P}} [\mathbb{1} \otimes X(\varrho)]\,(dP(\varrho) \otimes \mathbb{1})\Big] = \Big[\int_{\mathsf{P}} [\mathbb{1} \otimes X(\varrho)]\,(dP(\varrho) \otimes \mathbb{1})\Big][C \otimes \mathbb{1}].$$

Proof.   The spectral projections are contained in $\mathcal{M}_{com}$, thus C commutes with them, indicated by $CdP(\varrho) = dP(\varrho)C$. By construction we obtain for vectors of type $\psi_i = \mu_i \otimes \eta_i \in \mathcal{H} \otimes \mathcal{K}$ with $i = 1, 2$,

$$\left(\psi_1 \Big| [C \otimes \mathbb{1}] \int_P [\mathbb{1} \otimes X(\varrho)] \, (dP(\varrho) \otimes \mathbb{1}) \, \psi_2 \right)$$

$$= \left([C^* \otimes \mathbb{1}]\psi_1 \Big| \int_P [\mathbb{1} \otimes X(\varrho)] \, (dP(\varrho) \otimes \mathbb{1}) \, \psi_2 \right)$$

$$= \int_P (\eta_1 | X(\varrho)\eta_2)(C^*\mu_1 | dP(\varrho)\mu_2) = \int_P (\eta_1 | X(\varrho)\eta_2)(\mu_1 | dP(\varrho)C\mu_2)$$

$$= \left(\psi_1 \Big| \int_P [\mathbb{1} \otimes X(\varrho)] \, (dP(\varrho) \otimes \mathbb{1}) \, [C \otimes \mathbb{1}]\psi_2 \right).$$

The first and the last term extend linearly and continuously to all $\psi_i \in \mathcal{H} \otimes \mathcal{K}$. $\square$

In general, however, $\int (\mathbb{1} \otimes X(\varrho))(dP(\varrho) \otimes \mathbb{1})$ is not an element in the C*-tensor product algebra $\mathcal{A}_{\mathrm{com}} \otimes \mathcal{L}(F_+(\mathcal{V}))$, even if $\varrho \mapsto X(\varrho)$ is continuous in some of the weak operator topologies.

Operators of type (52.1.4) possess the following expected properties:

$$\left\| \int_P [\mathbb{1} \otimes X(\varrho)] \, (dP(\varrho) \otimes \mathbb{1}) \right\| \leq \sup\{\|X(\varrho)\| \mid \varrho \in P\}. \qquad (52.1.5)$$

$$\left(\int_P [\mathbb{1} \otimes X(\varrho)] \, (dP(\varrho) \otimes \mathbb{1}) \right)^* = \int_P [\mathbb{1} \otimes X(\varrho)^*] \, (dP(\varrho) \otimes \mathbb{1}). \qquad (52.1.6)$$

If for two such operator-valued functions X and Y the product $\varrho \mapsto X(\varrho)Y(\varrho)$ is weakly measurable, then

$$\int_P [\mathbb{1} \otimes X(\varrho)Y(\varrho)] \, (dP(\varrho) \otimes \mathbb{1})$$
$$= \left[\int_P [\mathbb{1} \otimes X(\varrho)] \, (dP(\varrho) \otimes \mathbb{1}) \right] \left[\int_P [\mathbb{1} \otimes Y(\varrho)] \, (dP(\varrho) \otimes \mathbb{1}) \right]. \qquad (52.1.7)$$

Provided $\mathcal{K}$ is separable, then the weak measurability of $\varrho \mapsto X(\varrho)Y(\varrho)$ results automatically from the weak measurability of $\varrho \mapsto X(\varrho)$ and $\varrho \mapsto Y(\varrho)$.

If $\varrho \mapsto \|X(\varrho)\|$ is measurable, then it follows for all $\psi \in \mathcal{H} \otimes \mathcal{K}$

$$\left\| \int_P [\mathbb{1} \otimes X(\varrho)](dP(\varrho) \otimes \mathbb{1})\psi \right\|^2 \leq \int_P \|X(\varrho)\|^2 (\psi|(dP(\varrho) \otimes \mathbb{1})\psi). \qquad (52.1.8)$$

Provided $\mathcal{K}$ is separable, the measurability of $\varrho \mapsto \|X(\varrho)\|$ is implied. If $\|\psi\| = 1$, then $(\psi|(dP(\varrho) \otimes \mathbb{1})\psi)$ is an ordinary probability measure on P.

Moreover, if $\varrho \mapsto X(\varrho)^*X(\varrho)$ is weakly measurable (following automatically in the case of a separable $\mathcal{K}$), then for all $\mu \in \mathcal{H}$ and $\eta \in \mathcal{K}$ we have

$$\left\| \int_P [\mathbb{1} \otimes X(\varrho)] \, (dP(\varrho) \otimes \mathbb{1})\mu \otimes \eta \right\|^2 = \int_P \|X(\varrho)\eta\|^2 (\mu|dP(\varrho)\mu). \qquad (52.1.9)$$

For $\|\mu\| = 1$, $(\mu|dP(\varrho)\mu)$ is again an ordinary probability measure on P.

Lemma 52.1-3 (Strong Continuity). *Suppose a uniformly bounded sequence converging point-wise in the strong operator topology, that is*

$$\lim_{\nu \to \infty} X_\nu(\varrho) = X(\varrho), \ \forall \varrho \in \mathsf{P}, \qquad \sup\{\|X_\nu(\varrho)\|, \|X(\varrho)\| \mid \varrho \in \mathsf{P}, \ \nu \in \mathbb{N}\} < \infty,$$

and assume in addition that all products $X^*_{(\nu)} X_{(\nu')}$ are weakly measurable. Then we have

$$\lim_{\nu \to \infty} \int_\mathsf{P} [\mathbb{1} \otimes X_\nu(\varrho)] \, (dP(\varrho) \otimes \mathbb{1}) = \int_\mathsf{P} [\mathbb{1} \otimes X(\varrho)] \, (dP(\varrho) \otimes \mathbb{1})$$

with respect to the strong operator topology in $\mathcal{L}(\mathcal{H} \otimes \mathcal{K})$.

Proof. Let us first take product vectors $\psi = \mu \otimes \eta$. With (52.1.9) we obtain

$$\left\| \left[\int_\mathsf{P} [\mathbb{1} \otimes X_\nu(\varrho)] \, (dP(\varrho) \otimes \mathbb{1}) - \int_\mathsf{P} [\mathbb{1} \otimes X(\varrho)] \, (dP(\varrho) \otimes \mathbb{1}) \right] \psi \right\|^2$$

$$= \left\| \left[\int_\mathsf{P} \{\mathbb{1} \otimes [X_\nu(\varrho) - X(\varrho)]\} \, (dP(\varrho) \otimes \mathbb{1}) \right] \mu \otimes \eta \right\|^2$$

$$= \int_\mathsf{P} \|[X_\nu(\varrho) - X(\varrho)]\eta\|^2 (\mu|dP(\varrho)\mu) \overset{\nu \to \infty}{\longrightarrow} 0$$

according to Lebesgue's dominated convergence theorem. Now we use the standard argument for the extension: Taking linear combinations and the triangle inequality, the convergence remains valid for all ψ in the algebraic tensor product $\mathcal{H} \odot \mathcal{K}$. Uniform boundedness ensures the continuous extension to all $\psi \in \mathcal{H} \otimes \mathcal{K}$. $\qquad \square$

52.1.2. *Spectral Integrals over Products of Field Operators*

In contrast to the bounded spectral integrals of the previous subsection, we deal here with spectral integrals over a special type of unbounded operator-valued functions, namely

$$\int_\mathsf{P} \zeta(\varrho) \left[\mathbb{1} \otimes \prod_{k=1}^n \mathsf{A}_k(g_k(\varrho)) \right] (dP(\varrho) \otimes \mathbb{1}), \qquad (52.1.10)$$

and $\mathbb{C}$-linear combinations thereof. Here $[\varrho \mapsto \zeta(\varrho)] \in C_b(\mathsf{P}, \mathbb{C})$ and $[\varrho \mapsto g_k(\varrho)] \in C_b(\mathsf{P}, \mathcal{V})$, where $C_b(\mathsf{P}, \mathcal{V})$ denotes the norm continuous bounded functions $\mathsf{P} \ni \varrho \mapsto g(\varrho) \in \mathcal{V}$.

Similarly to D in Eq. (51.3.1), we define the F-space

$$D_F := \bigcap_{a \geq 1} \mathrm{dom}(a^{N_F}) \qquad (52.1.11)$$

(the index F in D_F stands for "Fock"), which be equipped with the directed system of norms

$$D_F \ni \psi \mapsto \|a^{N_F}\psi\|, \quad a \geq 1.$$

Clearly, D_F is norm dense in $F_+(\mathcal{V})$, and the algebraic tensor product $\mathcal{H} \odot D_F$ is F-dense in D. For D_F we obtain analogous results to those in Lemma 51.3-3, namely

$$\left\| a^{N_F} \prod_{k=1}^{n} A_k(g_k)\eta \right\| \le (2a)^n \sqrt{n!} \, \|g_1\| \cdots \|g_n\| \, \|(2^{\frac{1}{2}}a)^{N_F}\eta\|$$

for all $\eta \in D_F$ and every $a \ge 1$, where

$$\mathcal{V}^n \ni (g_1, \ldots, g_n) \longmapsto \prod_{k=1}^{n} A_k(g_k)$$

is jointly F-continuous, point-wise on D_F with respect to the norm on $\mathcal{V}$ for the $g_k \in \mathcal{V}$.

So, for $\zeta \in C_b(\mathsf{P}, \mathbb{C})$ and $g_k \in C_b(\mathsf{P}, \mathcal{V})$ it follows that

$$\mathsf{P} \ni \varrho \longmapsto \zeta(\varrho) \prod_{k=1}^{n} A_k(g_k(\varrho))$$

is an F-continuous operator-valued function, acting on D_F, where

$$\left\| a^{N_F} \zeta(\varrho) \prod_{k=1}^{n} A_k(g_k(\varrho))\eta \right\|$$

$$\le (2a)^n \sqrt{n!} \, |\zeta(\varrho)| \, \|g_1(\varrho)\| \cdots \|g_n(\varrho)\| \, \|(2^{\frac{1}{2}}a)^{N_F}\eta\| \qquad (52.1.12)$$

$$\le (2a)^n \sqrt{n!} \, \|\zeta\|_\infty \|g_1\|_\infty \cdots \|g_n\|_\infty \|(2^{\frac{1}{2}}a)^{N_F}\eta\|$$

for all $\eta \in D_F$ and every $a \ge 1$. Note that $\|a^{N_F}\zeta(\varrho)\mathbb{1}\eta\| = |\zeta(\varrho)| \, \|a^{N_F}\eta\|$. Consequently, we may perform the *-algebraic span as follows.

Definition 52.1-4 (*-Algebra $\mathcal{F}(\mathsf{P}, D_F)$ of Operator-Valued Functions).

The basic operator-valued functions, acting on D_F, are given by

$$\varrho \mapsto \zeta(\varrho)\mathbb{1}, \ \forall \zeta \in C_b(\mathsf{P}, \mathbb{C}), \qquad \varrho \mapsto a_F(g(\varrho)), \ \forall g \in C_b(\mathsf{P}, \mathcal{V}).$$

The *-algebraic span, denoted by $\mathcal{F}(\mathsf{P}, D_F)$, is defined to consist of all products, adjoints, and linear combinations of the basic operator-valued functions.

Since $[\varrho \mapsto X(\varrho)] \in \mathcal{F}(\mathsf{P}, D_F)$ is F-continuous, it is immediate that $\varrho \mapsto (\eta_1|X(\varrho)\eta_2)$ is Borel measurable for all $\eta_1, \eta_2 \in D_F$. Thus we may define

$$\left(\mu_1 \otimes \eta_1 \,\middle|\, \int_\mathsf{P} [\mathbb{1} \otimes X(\varrho)] \, (dP(\varrho) \otimes \mathbb{1}) \, \mu_2 \otimes \eta_2 \right) := \int_\mathsf{P} (\eta_1|X(\varrho)\eta_2)(\mu_1|dP(\varrho)\mu_2),$$

for all $\mu_1, \mu_2 \in \mathcal{H}$ and all $\eta_1, \eta_2 \in D_F$, which by (bi-) linear extension leads to a well defined operator $\int [\mathbb{1} \otimes X(\varrho)](dP(\varrho) \otimes \mathbb{1})$ on the algebraic tensor product $\mathcal{H} \odot D_F$. (Uniqueness is shown by using the Gram–Schmidt orthogonalization techniques.) In order to extend F-continuously from $\mathcal{H} \odot D_F$ to all of D, we decompose $\varrho \mapsto X(\varrho)$ into a (finite) sum over terms $\varrho \mapsto \zeta(\varrho)\left[\mathbb{1} \otimes \prod_{k=1}^{n} A_k(g_k(\varrho))\right]$.

Theorem 52.1-5 (F-Extension and F-Estimation for Operator Integrals).
Let $\zeta \in C_b(\mathsf{P}, \mathbb{C})$ and $g_k \in C_b(\mathsf{P}, \mathcal{V})$. Then the earlier defined operators

$$\int_{\mathsf{P}} \zeta(\varrho) \big[\mathbb{1} \otimes \prod_{k=1}^{n} \mathsf{A}_k(g_k(\varrho)) \big] (dP(\varrho) \otimes \mathbb{1})$$

extend F-continuously from $\mathcal{H} \odot D_F$ to a unique F-continuous operator on D, denoted by the same symbol.
The following F-estimations,

$$\left\| (\mathbb{1} \otimes a^{N_F}) \int_{\mathsf{P}} \zeta(\varrho) \big[\mathbb{1} \otimes \prod_{k=1}^{n} \mathsf{A}_k(g_k(\varrho)) \big] (dP(\varrho) \otimes \mathbb{1}) \psi \right\|^2$$

$$\leq (2a)^{2n} n! \int_{\mathsf{P}} |\zeta(\varrho)|^2 \prod_{k=1}^{n} \|g_k(\varrho)\|^2 \underbrace{((\mathbb{1} \otimes (2^{\frac{1}{2}}a)^{N_F}) \psi | (dP(\varrho) \otimes \mathbb{1})(\mathbb{1} \otimes (2^{\frac{1}{2}}a)^{N_F}) \psi)}_{=: \, d\mu_\psi^a(\varrho), \text{ positive bounded measure on } \mathsf{P}}$$

$$\leq (2a)^{2n} n! \, \|\zeta\|_\infty^2 \prod_{k=1}^{n} \|g_k\|_\infty^2 \|(\mathbb{1} \otimes (2^{\frac{1}{2}}a)^{N_F}) \psi\|^2$$

are valid for all $\psi \in D$ and every $a \geq 1$.
For $\varrho \mapsto X(\varrho)$ and $\varrho \mapsto Y(\varrho)$ contained in $\mathcal{F}(\mathsf{P}, D_F)$, it holds on D

$$\left(\int_{\mathsf{P}} [\mathbb{1} \otimes X(\varrho)] \, (dP(\varrho) \otimes \mathbb{1}) \right)^* \Big|_D = \int_{\mathsf{P}} [\mathbb{1} \otimes X(\varrho)^*] \, (dP(\varrho) \otimes \mathbb{1}) \, .$$

$$\int_{\mathsf{P}} [\mathbb{1} \otimes X(\varrho)Y(\varrho)] \, (dP(\varrho) \otimes \mathbb{1})$$

$$= \left[\int_{\mathsf{P}} [\mathbb{1} \otimes X(\varrho)] \, (dP(\varrho) \otimes \mathbb{1}) \right] \left[\int_{\mathsf{P}} [\mathbb{1} \otimes Y(\varrho)] \, (dP(\varrho) \otimes \mathbb{1}) \right],$$

where the adjoint $\left(\int [\mathbb{1} \otimes X(\varrho)](dP(\varrho) \otimes \mathbb{1}) \right)^*$ is taken with respect to the inner product of our underlying Hilbert space $\mathcal{H} \otimes F_+(\mathcal{V})$.

Proof. The spectral integral theory for uniformly bounded $\varrho \mapsto X(\varrho)$ of the previous Subsection may be also carried through, if the $X(\varrho)$ are bounded operators from the Hilbert space $\mathcal{K}_1$ into a different Hilbert space $\mathcal{K}_2$. Then

$$\int_{\mathsf{P}} [\mathbb{1} \otimes X(\varrho)] \, (dP(\varrho) \otimes \mathbb{1})$$

turns out to be a bounded operator from $\mathcal{H} \otimes \mathcal{K}_1$ into $\mathcal{H} \otimes \mathcal{K}_2$, and all stated results remain valid in an analogous manner.
If we restrict the operator $\zeta(\varrho) \prod_{k=1}^{n} \mathsf{A}_k(g_k(\varrho))$ to an ℓ-particle space $P_+(\otimes_\ell \mathcal{V})$, then we obtain a bounded operator into a (finite) direct sum of finite particle spaces with

the estimations in the operator norm,

$$\left\| a^{N_F} \zeta(\varrho) \prod_{k=1}^{n} A_k(g_k(\varrho)) \right\|_{\ell} \leq (2^{\frac{1}{2}} a)^{\ell} (2a)^n \sqrt{n!} \, |\zeta(\varrho)| \, \|g_1(\varrho)\| \cdots \|g_n(\varrho)\|, \quad (52.1.13)$$

arising from Eq. (52.1.12) with $\eta \in P_+(\otimes_{\ell} \mathcal{V})$ for each $a \geq 1$, by noting that $(2^{\frac{1}{2}} a)^{N_F} \eta = (2^{\frac{1}{2}} a)^{\ell} \eta$. The lower index ℓ at the norm indicates the ℓ-particle space.

For $a = 1$, we now may employ the stated results of the previous subsection to check that

$$\int_P \zeta(\varrho) \left[\mathbb{1} \otimes \prod_{k=1}^{n} A_k(g_k(\varrho)) \right] (dP(\varrho) \otimes \mathbb{1})$$

constitutes a bounded operator from all of $\mathcal{H} \otimes P_+(\otimes_{\ell} \mathcal{V})$ into a finite direct sum of suitable finite particle spaces. That provides the norm estimation of Eq. (52.1.8). Since its image consists at best of $\ell + n$-particle vectors, we estimate, for all $\psi \in \mathcal{H} \otimes P_+(\otimes_{\ell} \mathcal{V})$ and every $a \geq 1$,

$$\left\| (\mathbb{1} \otimes a^{N_F}) \left[\int_P \zeta(\varrho) [\mathbb{1} \otimes \prod_{k=1}^{n} A_k(g_k(\varrho))] (dP(\varrho) \otimes \mathbb{1}) \right] \psi \right\|_{\ell}^2$$

$$\leq a^{2(\ell+n)} \left\| \int_P \zeta(\varrho) [\mathbb{1} \otimes \prod_{k=1}^{n} A_k(g_k(\varrho))] (dP(\varrho) \otimes \mathbb{1}) \psi \right\|_{\ell}^2$$

$$\overset{\dagger}{\leq} a^{2(\ell+n)} \int_P |\zeta(\varrho)|^2 \| \prod_{k=1}^{n} A_k(g_k(\varrho)) \|_{\ell}^2 (\psi|(dP(\varrho) \otimes \mathbb{1})\psi)$$

$$\overset{\star}{\leq} a^{2(\ell+n)} 2^{\ell} 2^{2n} n! \int_P |\zeta(\varrho)|^2 \|g_1(\varrho)\|^2 \cdots \|g_n(\varrho)\|^2 (\psi|(dP(\varrho) \otimes \mathbb{1})\psi)$$

$$= (2a)^{2n} n! \int_P |\zeta(\varrho)|^2 \prod_{k=1}^{n} \|g_k(\varrho)\|^2 ((\mathbb{1} \otimes (2^{\frac{1}{2}} a)^{N_F})\psi|(dP(\varrho) \otimes \mathbb{1})(\mathbb{1} \otimes (2^{\frac{1}{2}} a)^{N_F})\psi)$$

$$\leq (2a)^{2n} n! \, \|\zeta\|_{\infty}^2 \prod_{k=1}^{n} \|g_k\|_{\infty}^2 \|(\mathbb{1} \otimes (2^{\frac{1}{2}} a)^{N_F})\psi\|^2.$$

At $\dagger$, we used the norm estimation from Eq. (52.1.8), and at $\star$, we took into account the estimation (52.1.13) for $a = 1$.

The latter estimations may be extended to all of D, since the finite-particle spaces $\mathcal{H} \otimes P_+(\otimes_{\ell} \mathcal{V})$ are mutually orthogonal.

For the further stated results we use the same trick and apply Eqs. (52.1.6) and (52.1.7) to show the result for the bounded spectral integral operators on the finite particle spaces, and then extend F-continuously to all of D by summing up directly the finite-particle terms.   □

Corollary 52.1-6 (Coupling Functions in Spectral Interaction Integrals).
The partially commutative interaction operator Υ, from Assumption 52.1-1, acts F-continuously on D (in spite of the unbounded Boson operators), where it is given

by the spectral integral

$$\Upsilon = \int_{\mathsf{P}} \left[\mathbb{1} \otimes \Phi_F(\phi(\varrho)) \right] (dP(\varrho) \otimes \mathbb{1}), \qquad (52.1.14)$$

(integration over material collective modes in which the smearing of the Boson field replaces the formal integration over point-localized field operators).

The spectrally disintegrated interaction displays the uniquely associated coupling function

$$\phi : \mathsf{P} \to \mathcal{V}, \quad \varrho \mapsto \phi(\varrho) := 2^{\frac{1}{2}} \sum_{j=1}^{M} \xi_j(\varrho) \phi_j. \qquad (52.1.15)$$

Because of $\xi_j \in C_b(\mathsf{P}, \mathbb{C})$, the coupling function is bounded, that is

$$\|\phi\|_\infty := \sup\{\|\phi(\varrho)\| \mid \varrho \in \mathsf{P}\} < \infty.$$

So, instead by the operator Υ, the interaction may be expressed biunivocally by the coupling function $\varrho \mapsto \phi(\varrho) \in \mathcal{V}$, which couples the material collective modes ϱ with the Bosonic (de-) excitations, by appearing in the argument of the Boson field operator.

Furtheron, the spectral integral transforms under the free dynamics of the total system as

$$e^{itK} \Upsilon e^{-itK} = \int_{\mathsf{P}} \left[\mathbb{1} \otimes \Phi_F(e^{itS} \phi(\kappa_t \varrho)) \right] (dP(\varrho) \otimes \mathbb{1}), \qquad (52.1.16)$$

exhibiting the twofold time dependence of the coupling function in reference to the collective material dynamics κ_t and the free Boson dynamics e^{itS}.

Proof. We calculate directly the dynamically transformed Υ. The linearity of $f \mapsto a_F^*(f)$, and the antilinearity of $f \mapsto a_F(f)$, and $\Phi_F(f) = 2^{-\frac{1}{2}}(a_F(f) + a_F^*(f))$ lead for each $t \in \mathbb{R}$ to

$$e^{itK} \Upsilon e^{-itK} \qquad (52.1.17)$$

$$= \sum_{j=1}^{M} \left\{ \underbrace{\int_{\mathsf{P}} \overline{\xi_j(\kappa_t \varrho)} \, dP(\varrho)}_{= \, e^{itA} B_j \, e^{-itA}} \otimes a_F(e^{itS} \phi_j) + \underbrace{\int_{\mathsf{P}} \xi_j(\kappa_t \varrho) \, dP(\varrho)}_{= \, e^{itA} B_j^* \, e^{-itA}} \otimes a_F^*(e^{itS} \phi_j) \right\}$$

$$= \sum_{j=1}^{M} \left\{ \int_{\mathsf{P}} \left[\mathbb{1} \otimes a_F(\xi_j(\kappa_t \varrho) e^{itS} \phi_j) \right] (dP(\varrho) \otimes \mathbb{1}) \right.$$

$$+ \left. \int_{\mathsf{P}} \left[\mathbb{1} \otimes a_F^*(\xi_j(\kappa_t \varrho) e^{itS} \phi_j) \right] (dP(\varrho) \otimes \mathbb{1}) \right\}$$

$$= 2^{\frac{1}{2}} \int_{\mathsf{P}} \Big[\mathbb{1} \otimes \Phi_F \big(\sum_{j=1}^{M} \xi_j(\kappa_t \varrho) e^{itS} \phi_j \big) \Big] (dP(\varrho) \otimes \mathbb{1})$$

$$= \int_{\mathsf{P}} \big[\mathbb{1} \otimes \Phi_F (e^{itS} \phi(\kappa_t \varrho)) \big] (dP(\varrho) \otimes \mathbb{1}).$$

$\square$

52.1.3. *Spectral Integral Operators of the Type* $Q(\zeta, \psi)$

Let us introduce a family of spectral integrals, indexed by two functions.

Definition 52.1-7 (Spectrally Represented Unitaries). For each pair of continuous $\varrho \mapsto \zeta(\varrho) \in \mathbb{R}$ and norm continuous $\varrho \mapsto \psi(\varrho) \in \mathcal{V}$, let us define the operator

$$Q(\zeta, \psi) := \int_{\mathsf{P}} e^{i\zeta(\varrho)} \big[\mathbb{1} \otimes W_F(\psi(\varrho)) \big] (dP(\varrho) \otimes \mathbb{1}), \qquad (52.1.18)$$

which is norm-bounded on $\mathcal{H} \otimes F_+(\mathcal{V})$ (where the spectral integration performs according to Sec. 52.1.1).

Notice that $f \mapsto W_F(f)$ is strongly continuous on Fock space (in dependence of the norm on $\mathcal{V}$), and that each $W_F(f)$ is unitary. Thus $\varrho \mapsto e^{i\zeta(\varrho)} W_F(\psi(\varrho))$ is weakly measurable and uniformly bounded in ϱ with respect to the operator norm of $\mathcal{L}(F_+(\mathcal{V}))$.

The $Q(\zeta, \psi)$-integrals play an *essential role* since, in their time-dependent form, they constitute our most general unitary propagators — in the interaction picture — for mesoscopic matter–Boson interactions. Let us call them "propagator routines".

Proposition 52.1-8 (Further Properties of Propagator Routines). *Operators of the type* $Q(\zeta, \psi)$, *the propagator routines, exhibit several remarkable features.*

(a) *Each* $Q(\zeta, \psi)$ *is a unitary operator on* $\mathcal{H} \otimes F_+(\mathcal{V})$, *satisfying*

$$Q(\zeta, \psi)^* = Q(-\zeta, -\psi), \qquad (\text{unitarity relation}).$$

Moreover, $Q(\zeta, \psi) \in \mathcal{M}_{com} \otimes \mathcal{L}(F_+(\mathcal{V}))$, *and for the special case of a vanishing* ψ *we have* $Q(\zeta, 0) = \big[\int_{\mathsf{P}} e^{i\zeta(\varrho)} dP(\varrho) \big] \otimes \mathbb{1} \in \mathcal{A}_{com} \otimes \mathbb{1}$.

(b) *With* $\zeta \diamond \tilde{\zeta} : \mathsf{P} \to \mathbb{R}$, $\varrho \mapsto (\zeta \diamond \tilde{\zeta})(\varrho) := \zeta(\varrho) + \tilde{\zeta}(\varrho) - \frac{1}{2} \operatorname{Im}(\psi(\varrho) | \tilde{\psi}(\varrho))$, *it follows*

$$Q(\zeta, \psi) \, Q(\tilde{\zeta}, \tilde{\psi}) = Q(\zeta \diamond \tilde{\zeta}, \psi + \tilde{\psi}).$$

Especially, for $\zeta = 0$ *and* $\psi = 0$, *we get* $Q(0, 0) = \mathbb{1} \otimes \mathbb{1} = \mathbb{1}$, *the identity on* $\mathcal{H} \otimes F_+(\mathcal{V})$.

(c) *Let there be sequences of continuous functions converging point-wise for each* ϱ,

$$\lim_{\nu \to \infty} |\zeta_\nu(\varrho) - \zeta(\varrho)| = 0, \qquad \lim_{\nu \to \infty} \|\psi_\nu(\varrho) - \psi(\varrho)\| = 0,$$

with $\mathbb{R}$-*valued functions* $\varrho \mapsto \zeta_\nu(\varrho) \in \mathbb{R}$. *Then it follows*

$$\lim_{\nu \to \infty} Q(\zeta_\nu, \psi_\nu) = Q(\zeta, \psi) \qquad \text{in the strong operator topology.}$$

(d) *For each* $t \in \mathbb{R}$, *we have the dynamical evolution*

$$e^{itK} Q(\zeta, \psi)\, e^{-itK} = Q(\zeta \circ \kappa_t, e^{itS}\psi \circ \kappa_t),$$

where $\zeta \circ \kappa_t$ *means* $\varrho \mapsto \zeta(\kappa_t \varrho)$, *and* $e^{itS}\psi \circ \kappa_t$ *means* $\varrho \mapsto e^{itS}\psi(\kappa_t \varrho)$.

(e) *It holds for all* $f \in V$ *and all* $C \in M_{com}$ *that*

$$Q(\zeta, \psi)[C \otimes W_F(f)]\, Q(\zeta, \psi)^*$$

$$\in \mathcal{A}_{com}$$

$$= \overbrace{\left\{ \left[\int_P \exp\{-i\,\mathrm{Im}(\psi(\varrho)|f)\}\, dP(\varrho) \right] \otimes \mathbb{1} \right\} [C \otimes W_F(f)]}.$$

$$= Q(-\,\mathrm{Im}(\psi(.)|f), 0)$$

Parts (a) and (b) may be considered as a strongly continuous group representation: With the group action $\circ$ defined by

$$(\zeta, \psi) \circ (\tilde{\zeta}, \tilde{\psi}) := (\zeta \diamond \tilde{\zeta}, \psi + \tilde{\psi}), \quad \text{where } \zeta \diamond \tilde{\zeta}(\varrho) = \zeta(\varrho) + \tilde{\zeta}(\varrho) - \frac{1}{2}\,\mathrm{Im}(\psi(\varrho)|\tilde{\psi}(\varrho)),$$

the neutral element $(0,0)$, and $(-\zeta, -\psi)$ as inverse to (ζ, ψ), we make the Cartesian product $C(P, \mathbb{R}) \times C(P, V)$ to a group, denoted by $(G, \circ)$. Now

$$Q : (G, \circ) \to \mathcal{U}, \quad (\zeta, \psi) \mapsto Q(\zeta, \psi),$$

is a group representation within the unitaries $\mathcal{U}$ of $M_{com} \otimes \mathcal{L}(F_+(V))$. Especially, we decompose commutatively,

$$(\zeta, \psi) = (0, \psi) \circ (\zeta, 0) = (\zeta, 0) \circ (0, \psi) \;\Rightarrow\; Q(\zeta, \psi) = Q(0, \psi) Q(\zeta, 0) = Q(\zeta, 0) Q(0, \psi).$$

Proof. (a) and (b) follow from (52.1.6) and (52.1.7) with the Weyl relations $W_F(f) W_F(g) = \exp\{-\frac{i}{2}\,\mathrm{Im}(f|g)\} W_F(f + g) = \exp\{-i\,\mathrm{Im}(f|g)\} W_F(g) W_F(f)$ and $W_F(f)^* = W_F(-f)$. Especially, $Q(\zeta, \psi)^* Q(\zeta, \psi) = \mathbb{1} \otimes \mathbb{1}$, proving that $Q(\zeta, \psi)$ is unitary. (c) follows from Lemma 52.1-3, since $f \mapsto W_F(f)$ is strongly continuous (in the norm on V), and $\|W_F(f)\| = 1$.

By Proposition 52.1-2, $C \otimes \mathbb{1}$ commutes with $Q(\zeta, \psi)$. Thus we conclude

$$Q(\zeta, \psi)[C \otimes W_F(f)] Q(\zeta, \psi)^* = [C \otimes \mathbb{1}] Q(\zeta, \psi)[\mathbb{1} \otimes W_F(f)] Q(\zeta, \psi)^*$$

$$= [C \otimes \mathbb{1}] \int_P \left[\mathbb{1} \otimes W_F(\psi(\varrho)) W_F(f) W_F(\psi(\varrho))^* \right] (dP(\varrho) \otimes \mathbb{1}),$$

that is (e). Finally we turn to (d). Recall $e^{itK} = e^{itA} \otimes e^{itd\Gamma(S)}$. By assumption, A generates the flow κ on P, $e^{itA}\left(\int_P \gamma\, dP\right) e^{-itA} = \int_P \gamma \circ \kappa_t\, dP$, which tells that the material free dynamics acts via the flow κ on the functions, only, i.e., $[\varrho \mapsto \gamma(\varrho)]$ evolves to $[\varrho \mapsto \gamma(\kappa_t \varrho)] = \gamma \circ \kappa_t$, according to Eq. (52.1.2). On the Boson side, it holds $e^{itd\Gamma(S)} W_F(f) e^{-itd\Gamma(S)} = W_F(e^{itS} f)$. Combining both leads to the following time evolution, where the integral is written as a function,

$$e^{itK}\left[\varrho \mapsto e^{i\zeta(\varrho)}\{\mathbb{1} \otimes W_F(\psi(\varrho))\}\right]e^{-itK} = \varrho \mapsto e^{i\zeta(\kappa_t \varrho)}\{\mathbb{1} \otimes W_F(e^{itS}\psi(\kappa_t \varrho))\}. \qquad \square$$

In the foregoing Proposition, we supposed the functions $\varrho \mapsto \zeta(\varrho) \in \mathbb{R}$ and $\varrho \mapsto \psi(\varrho) \in \mathcal{V}$ to be continuous, only. For our next result they — in addition — have to be bounded, in order that we may apply our theory of the spectral integrals over operator-valued functions from the previous subsection.

Corollary 52.1-9 (F-Expansion and -Continuity of Propagator Routine).
Provided $[\varrho \mapsto \zeta(\varrho)] \in C_b(\mathsf{P}, \mathbb{R})$ and $[\varrho \mapsto \psi(\varrho)] \in C_b(\mathsf{P}, \mathcal{V})$, we know that the propagator routine $Q(\zeta, \psi)$ is an F-continuous operator on D. On D it possesses the F-continuous decomposition

$$Q(\zeta, \psi)\big|_D = \sum_{n=0}^{\infty} \frac{i^n}{n!} \int_\mathsf{P} \{\mathbb{1} \otimes [\Phi_F(\psi(\varrho)) + \zeta(\varrho)\mathbb{1}]^n\}(dP(\varrho) \otimes \mathbb{1}).$$

Moreover, if there are uniformly bounded sequences

$$\lim_{\nu \to \infty} |\zeta_\nu(\varrho) - \zeta(\varrho)| = 0, \quad \sup\{|\zeta_\nu(\varrho)| \mid \varrho \in \mathsf{P}, \, \nu \in \mathbb{N}\} < \infty,$$

$$\lim_{\nu \to \infty} \|\psi_\nu(\varrho) - \psi(\varrho)\| = 0, \quad \sup\{\|\psi_\nu(\varrho)\| \mid \varrho \in \mathsf{P}, \, \nu \in \mathbb{N}\} < \infty,$$

in $C_b(\mathsf{P}, \mathbb{R})$ and in $C_b(\mathsf{P}, \mathcal{V})$ (converging point-wise in ϱ), then we have

$$\lim_{\nu \to \infty} Q(\zeta_\nu, \psi_\nu)\big|_D = Q(\zeta, \psi)\big|_D \quad \text{with respect to the F-topology on } D. \qquad (52.1.19)$$

Proof. For each n, we decompose the elements of $\mathcal{F}(\mathsf{P}, D_F)$ as

$$[\Phi_F(\psi(\varrho)) + \zeta(\varrho)\mathbb{1}]^n = \sum_{m=0}^{n} \binom{n}{m} \zeta(\varrho)^{n-m} \Phi_F(\psi(\varrho))^m,$$

on D_F possessing according to (52.1.12) the following estimations for $\eta \in D_F$ and $a \geq 1$,

$$\left\| a^{N_F} [\Phi_F(\psi(\varrho)) + \zeta(\varrho)\mathbb{1}]^n \eta \right\|$$

$$\leq \sum_{m=0}^{n} \binom{n}{m} (2a)^m \sqrt{m!} \, |\zeta(\varrho)|^{n-m} \|\psi(\varrho)\|^m \|(2^{\frac{1}{2}}a)^{N_F}\eta\| \qquad (52.1.20)$$

$$\leq (2a)^n \sqrt{n!} \, [|\zeta(\varrho)| + \|\psi(\varrho)\|]^n \|(2^{\frac{1}{2}}a)^{N_F}\eta\|$$

$$\leq (2a)^n \sqrt{n!} \, [\|\zeta\|_\infty + \|\psi\|_\infty]^n \|(2^{\frac{1}{2}}a)^{N_F}\eta\|.$$

Like in previous proofs, for each $\psi \in D$, we finally arrive at the F-estimations

$$\left\| (\mathbb{1} \otimes a^{N_F}) \left[\int_\mathsf{P} (\mathbb{1} \otimes [\Phi_F(\psi(\varrho)) + \zeta(\varrho)\mathbb{1}]^n)(dP(\varrho) \otimes \mathbb{1}) \right] \psi \right\|$$

$$\leq (2a)^n \sqrt{n!} \, [\|\zeta\|_\infty + \|\psi\|_\infty]^n \|(\mathbb{1} \otimes (2^{\frac{1}{2}}a)^{N_F})\psi\|.$$

Consequently, the limiting operator in the series

$$\sum_{n=0}^{\infty} \frac{i^n}{n!} \int_{\mathrm{P}} \left(\mathbb{1} \otimes \left[\Phi_F(\psi(\varrho)) + \zeta(\varrho)\mathbb{1}\right]^n\right)(dP(\varrho) \otimes \mathbb{1}) \qquad (52.1.21)$$

is an F-continuous operator on D, where $\sum_n \ldots$ converges with respect to the F-topology.

In a last step we have to show that this operator coincides with $Q(\zeta, \psi)$ restricted to D. Taking $a = 1$ in Formula (52.1.20), it follows that D_F consists of analytic vectors for the self-adjoint operators $\Phi_F(\psi(\varrho)) + \zeta(\varrho)\mathbb{1}$ on Fock space. Thus we may sum up the series on D_F

$$\sum_{n=0}^{\infty} \frac{(it)^n}{n!} \left[\Phi_F(\psi(\varrho)) + \zeta(\varrho)\mathbb{1}\right]^n = \exp\{it[\Phi_F(\psi(\varrho)) + \zeta(\varrho)\mathbb{1}]\} = \exp\{it\zeta(\varrho)\}W_F(t\psi(\varrho))$$

for each $t \in \mathbb{R}$, especially for $t = 1$. The F-estimations (52.1.20), for every $a \geq 1$, imply that these series converge on D_F in the F-topology (and so D_F consists of analytic vectors for the self-adjoint $\Phi_F(\psi(\varrho)) + \zeta(\varrho)\mathbb{1}$). Now let $\mu_i \otimes \eta_i \in \mathcal{H} \odot D_F$ for $i = 1, 2$, then we obtain within the inner product

$$\left(\mu_1 \otimes \eta_1 \,\middle|\, \left[\sum_{n=0}^{\infty} \frac{i^n}{n!} \int_{\mathrm{P}} \left(\mathbb{1} \otimes \left[\Phi_F(\psi(\varrho)) + \zeta(\varrho)\mathbb{1}\right]^n\right)(dP(\varrho) \otimes \mathbb{1})\right] \mu_2 \otimes \eta_2\right)$$

$$= \sum_{n=0}^{\infty} \frac{i^n}{n!} \int_{\mathrm{P}} \left(\eta_1 \,\middle|\, \left[\Phi_F(\psi(\varrho)) + \zeta(\varrho)\mathbb{1}\right]^n \eta_2\right)(\mu_1 | dP(\varrho)\mu_2)$$

$$\overset{\star}{=} \int_{\mathrm{P}} \left(\eta_1 \,\middle|\, \underbrace{\sum_{n=0}^{\infty} \tfrac{i^n}{n!} \left[\Phi_F(\psi(\varrho)) + \zeta(\varrho)\mathbb{1}\right]^n}_{= \, e^{i\zeta(\varrho)} W_F(\psi(\varrho))} \eta_2\right)(\mu_1 | dP(\varrho)\mu_2)$$

$$= (\mu_1 \otimes \eta_1 | Q(\zeta, \psi)\mu_2 \otimes \eta_2).$$

At $\star$, we used the fact that our F-estimations allow the interchange of $\sum_n$ with $\int \ldots$ by Lebesgue's dominated convergence theorem. Since the linear combinations of vectors of type $\mu \otimes \eta$ with $\eta \in D_F$ just give $\mathcal{H} \odot D_F$ we conclude for all $\psi_1, \psi_2 \in \mathcal{H} \odot D_F$ that

$$\left(\psi_1 \,\middle|\, \left[\sum_{n=0}^{\infty} \frac{i^n}{n!} \int_{\mathrm{P}} \left(\mathbb{1} \otimes \left[\Phi_F(\psi(\varrho)) + \zeta(\varrho)\mathbb{1}\right]^n\right)(dP(\varrho) \otimes \mathbb{1})\right] \psi_2\right) = (\psi_1 | Q(\zeta, \psi)\psi_2).$$

But $Q(\zeta, \psi)$ is unitary on $\mathcal{H} \otimes F_+(V)$ and the limiting operator (52.1.21) is F-continuous on D. We obtain that the last equality remains valid for all $\psi_1 \in \mathcal{H} \otimes F_+(V)$ and all $\psi_2 \in D$. (Recall that the F-topology is stronger than the norm by (51.3.2)).

Eq. (52.1.19) finally follows from a suitable application of our elaborated F-estimates and limits.   □

The continuity of the propagator routines $Q(\zeta, \psi)$ in dependence on the two index functions leads later to a continuity on the coupling function and enables to approximate models.

52.1.4. *Direct Expression for e^{itH} via Dyson Expansion*

Let us first investigate some pre-requisites, concerning a combinatorial result, which works whenever well-definiteness and convergence of the associated expressions — like integrals, partial integration, or power series — are ensured. Since possibly unbounded self-adjoint operators are involved, well-definiteness and convergence are given only point-wise on some suitable subspace of analytic vectors; moreover, the result may be valid not for all $z \in \mathbb{C}$, but only for $z = is$ with $s \in \mathbb{R}$. In the formulation of the combinatorial result, these complications are, however, not taken into account.

Lemma 52.1-10 (Combinatorics). *Let $o : \mathbb{R} \ni t \mapsto o(t)$ be an operator-valued mapping on some Hilbert space, such that the commutators $[o(t_2), o(t_1)]$ commute with $o(t)$ for arbitrary $t_1, t_2, t \in \mathbb{R}$. We define the following basic integrals*

$$O(t) := \int_{t_1=0}^{t} dt_1\, o(t_1),$$

$$c(t) := [O(t), o(t)] = \int_{t_1=0}^{t} dt_1\, [o(t_1), o(t)],$$

$$C(t) := \int_{t_1=0}^{t} dt_1\, c(t_1) = \int_{t_1=0}^{t} dt_1\, [O(t_1), o(t_1)] = \int_{t_1=0}^{t} dt_1 \int_{t_2=0}^{t_1} dt_2\, [o(t_2), o(t_1)].$$

In addition, we set for each $n \in \mathbb{N}$ and all $t \in \mathbb{R}$,

$$A_0(t) := \mathbb{1}, \qquad A_n(t) := \int_{t_1=0}^{t} dt_1 \int_{t_2=0}^{t_1} dt_2 \ldots \int_{t_n=0}^{t_{n-1}} dt_n\, o(t_1)\, o(t_2) \cdots o(t_n).$$

Then for each $t \in \mathbb{R}$ the following combinatorial formula is valid

$$\sum_{n=0}^{\infty} z^n A_n(t) = \exp\{zO(t) - \tfrac{z^2}{2}C(t)\} = \exp\{zO(t)\} \exp\{-\tfrac{z^2}{2}C(t)\}, \qquad (52.1.22)$$

for all allowed $z \in \mathbb{C}$. Note that the last equality sign holds, because $O(t)$ commutes with $C(t)$.

Proof. We use the short notations: $O(t) = \int_0^t o$ for an integral, and a prime for differentiation to t; we briefly write O instead of $O(t)$, etc. Define

$$F(z) := \exp\left\{ zO - \tfrac{z^2}{2}C \right\} = \sum_{n=0}^{\infty} \frac{1}{n!} \left[zO - \frac{z^2}{2}C \right]^n$$

$$= \sum_{n=0}^{\infty} \frac{1}{n!} \left[\sum_{k=0}^{n} \binom{n}{k} (zO)^{n-k} \left(-\frac{z^2}{2}C \right)^k \right]$$

$$= \sum_{n=0}^{\infty} \frac{1}{n!} \left[\underbrace{\sum_{k=0}^{n} \binom{n}{k} \left(-\frac{1}{2} \right)^k O^{n-k} C^k z^{n+k}}_{=: \; T_n(z)} \right].$$

For every $m \in \mathbb{N}$, we find

$$\frac{d^m T_n(z)}{dz^m}\bigg|_{z=0} = \begin{cases} m! \binom{n}{m-n} \left(-\frac{1}{2} \right)^{m-n} O^{2n-m} C^{m-n}, & \text{for } 2n \geq m \geq n, \\ 0, & \text{otherwise.} \end{cases}$$

So we arrive at,

$$\frac{d^m F(z)}{dz^m}\bigg|_{z=0} = \sum_{n=0}^{\infty} \frac{1}{n!} \frac{d^m T_n(z)}{dz^m}\bigg|_{z=0} = \sum_{n=[m/2]}^{m} \frac{m! \, (-1/2)^{m-n}}{(m-n)! \, (2n-m)!} O^{2n-m} C^{m-n},$$

where the summation $\sum_n$ begins at

$$[m/2] := \begin{cases} \frac{m}{2}, & \text{for even } m \in \mathbb{N}, \\ \frac{m+1}{2}, & \text{for odd } m \in \mathbb{N}. \end{cases}$$

On the other side,

$$\frac{d^m}{dz^m} \sum_{n=0}^{\infty} z^n A_n \bigg|_{z=0} = m! A_m.$$

Taking $\frac{d^m}{dz^m}\big|_{z=0}$ on both sides in (52.1.22), it follows that we have to prove

$$A_m = \sum_{n=[m/2]}^{m} \frac{(-1/2)^{m-n}}{(m-n)! \, (2n-m)!} O^{2n-m} C^{m-n}, \qquad \forall m \in \mathbb{N}. \qquad (52.1.23)$$

We will demonstrate this by induction over $m \in \mathbb{N}$.

For $m = 1$, we get $[m/2] = [1/2] = 1$; thus the sum on the right-hand side of (52.1.23) has only a single term with result O. This agrees with $A_1(t) = \int_0^t o = O(t)$, and the begin of the induction is verified. For the induction step $(m-1) \to m$, $m \geq 2$, we need three arguments.

(1) Let $j \in \mathbb{N}$, then with $Oo = oO + c$, where our commutator $c = [O, o]$ commutes with O, we have that $O^j o = O^{j-1} oO + cO^{j-1}$. Doing so several times we finally arrive at $O^j o = oO^j + jcO^{j-1}$. Consequently, applying this to $(O^k)' =$

$oO^{k-1} + OoO^{k-2} + O^2oO^{k-3} + \ldots + O^{k-1}o$, we obtain — with $\sum_{j=0}^{k-1} j = \frac{k(k-1)}{2}$ —

that

$$(O^k)' = koO^{k-1} + \frac{k(k-1)}{2}\, cO^{k-2}, \quad \forall k \in \mathbb{N},$$

where for convenience we set $O^{-j} := 0$ for $j \in \mathbb{N}$. Noting that c, C, and O commute with each other, we conclude, with $(C^l)' = lcC^{l-1}$ and $(O^kC^l)' = (O^k)'C^l + O^k(C^l)'$, that

$$(O^kC^l)' = koO^{k-1}C^l + c\left[lO^kC^{l-1} + \frac{k(k-1)}{2}O^{k-2}C^l\right], \quad \forall k, l \in \mathbb{N}_0. \quad (52.1.24)$$

(2) For $m \geq 2$ let us differentiate the right side of (52.1.23), which, with (52.1.24), gives

$$\frac{d}{dt} \sum_{n=[m/2]}^{m} \frac{(-1/2)^{m-n}}{(m-n)!\,(2n-m)!} O^{2n-m}C^{m-n}$$

$$= \sum_{n=[m/2]}^{m} \frac{(-1/2)^{m-n}}{(m-n)!\,(2n-m)!} (O^{2n-m}C^{m-n})'$$

$$= \sum_{n=[m/2]}^{m} \frac{(-1/2)^{m-n}}{(m-n)!\,(2n-m)!} \Big\{ (2n-m)oO^{2n-m-1}C^{m-n} + \ldots$$

$$\ldots + c\Big[(m-n)O^{2n-m}C^{m-n-1} + \frac{(2n-m)(2n-m-1)}{2}O^{2n-m-2}C^{m-n}\Big]\Big\}$$

$$= o \underbrace{\sum_{n=[(m+1)/2]}^{m} \frac{(-1/2)^{m-n}}{(m-n)!\,(2n-m-1)!} O^{2n-m-1}C^{m-n}}_{=:\,\alpha}$$

$$+ c \underbrace{\sum_{n=[m/2]}^{m-1} \frac{(-1/2)^{m-n}}{(m-n-1)!\,(2n-m)!} O^{2n-m}C^{m-n-1}}_{=:\,\beta}$$

$$+ c \underbrace{\sum_{n=[m/2]+1}^{m} \frac{(-1/2)^{m-n}}{(m-n)!\,(2n-m-2)!}\frac{1}{2} O^{2n-m-2}C^{m-n}}_{=:\,\gamma}.$$

We substitute $k := n+1$ in β, hence $2n - m = 2k - m - 2$, to get

$$\beta = \sum_{k=[m/2]+1}^{m} \frac{(-1/2)^{m-k}(-1/2)}{(m-k)!\,(2k-m-2)!} O^{2k-m-2}C^{m-k} = -\gamma.$$

For calculating α we substitute $\nu := n - 1$,

$$\alpha = \sum_{\nu=[(m-1)/2]}^{m-1} \frac{(-1/2)^{(m-1)-\nu}}{((m-1)-\nu)!\,(2\nu-(m-1))!} O^{2\nu-(m-1)} C^{(m-1)-\nu} = A_{m-1}.$$

The last equality sign holds, because (52.1.23) is assumed to be true for $m - 1$, according to the induction step $(m - 1) \to m$.

(3) Altogether we have shown in (2) that

$$\frac{d}{dt} \sum_{n=[m/2]}^{m} \frac{(-1/2)^{m-n}}{(m-n)!\,(2n-m)!} O^{2n-m} C^{m-n} = oA_{m-1}, \quad \forall m \geq 2. \qquad (52.1.25)$$

Since $A_m(t) = \int_0^t oA_{m-1}$, by definition of the A_n and by $O(0) = C(0) = 0$, it follows — via integration $\int_0^t (52.1.25)$ — that (52.1.23) is valid also for m. Thus the induction step has been proved.

In a final step we have to show that (52.1.23) indeed yields (52.1.22). This simply may be done in terms of a Taylor series expansion for $F(z) = \exp\{zO(t) - \frac{z^2}{2} C(t)\}$ (sandwiched by two vectors in a scalar product). □

Using the foregoing combinatorial result, we are able to treat the total dynamics.

Theorem 52.1-11 (Total Dynamics via Summed-Up Dyson Expansion).
Suppose the partially commutative situation introduced in Assumption 52.1-1. With the help of the uniquely associated coupling function $\phi(\varrho) = 2^{\frac{1}{2}} \sum_{j=1}^{M} \xi_j(\varrho)\phi_j$ from Corollary 52.1-6, we define two mappings $\psi_t : P \to V$ and $\zeta_t : P \to \mathbb{R}$, for each $t \in \mathbb{R}$, by

$$\psi_t(\varrho) \equiv \psi(t, \varrho) := \int_{t_1=0}^{t} dt_1\, e^{it_1 S} \phi(\kappa_{t_1} \varrho) \quad \in V, \qquad (52.1.26)$$

$$\zeta_t(\varrho) \equiv \zeta(t, \varrho) := -\frac{1}{2} \int_{t_1=0}^{t} dt_1 \int_{t_2=0}^{t_1} dt_2\, \mathrm{Im}(e^{it_2 S} \phi(\kappa_{t_2} \varrho)|e^{it_1 S} \phi(\kappa_{t_1} \varrho)) \in \mathbb{R}, \quad (52.1.27)$$

involving the flow κ on P which results from the free material dynamics generated by the Hamiltonian A.

Then on the total Hilbert space $\mathcal{H} \otimes F_+(V)$, the following closed expression for the dynamical propagator in the interaction picture is valid

$$e^{itH} e^{-itK} = e^{it(K+\Upsilon)} e^{-itK} = Q(\zeta_t, \psi_t), \quad \forall t \in \mathbb{R}, \qquad (52.1.28)$$

where by Eq. (52.1.18) — using spectral integration —

$$Q(\zeta_t, \psi_t) = \int_P e^{i\zeta_t(\varrho)} \big[\mathbb{1} \otimes W_F(\psi_t(\varrho))\big] (dP(\varrho) \otimes \mathbb{1}).$$

That means that the unitary propagator $Q(\zeta_t, \psi_t)$ arises from the propagator routine $Q(\zeta, \psi)$ by inserting the special functions (52.1.26) and (52.1.27), which in turn depend uniquely on the time dependent coupling function $e^{itS}\phi(\kappa_t \varrho)$.

Proof. Let us take over the notions from the proof of Theorem 51.3-5. Our subsequent calculations with F-continuous operators are valid on D according to Sec. 52.1.2. The final result may be extended continuously from D to $\mathcal{H} \otimes F_+(\mathcal{V})$, since only unitaries are involved.

Inserting (52.1.17) into the Dyson expansion for e^{itH} we arrive — with the free dynamics U_t — at

$$
e^{itH} = \sum_{n=0}^{\infty} U_t^{[n]} = U_t \sum_{n=0}^{\infty} i^n \int_{t_1=0}^{t} dt_1 \int_{t_2=0}^{t_1} dt_2 \ldots \int_{t_n=0}^{t_{n-1}} dt_n \, F(t, t_1, \ldots, t_n)
$$

$$
= U_t \int_{\mathsf{P}} \Big[\mathbb{1} \otimes \Big\{ \ldots
$$

$$
\ldots \sum_{n=0}^{\infty} i^n \underbrace{\int_{t_1=0}^{t} dt_1 \int_{t_2=0}^{t_1} dt_2 \ldots \int_{t_n=0}^{t_{n-1}} dt_n \prod_{k=1}^{n} \overbrace{\Phi_F(e^{-it_k S} \phi(\kappa_{-t_k} \varrho))}^{=: \, o(t_k)}}_{=: \, A_n(t)} \Big\} \Big] (dP(\varrho) \otimes \mathbb{1})
$$

$$
= U_t \int_{\mathsf{P}} \big[\mathbb{1} \otimes \exp\{iO(t) + C(t)/2\} \big] (dP(\varrho) \otimes \mathbb{1}) \tag{52.1.29}
$$

$$
= U_t \int_{\mathsf{P}} \exp\{-i\zeta_{-t}(\varrho)\} \big[\mathbb{1} \otimes W_F(-\psi_{-t}(\varrho)) \big] (dP(\varrho) \otimes \mathbb{1})
$$

$$
= U_t Q(-\zeta_{-t}, -\psi_{-t}),
$$

where we applied the combinatoric Lemma 52.1-10 for $z = i$ with

$$
O(t) = \int_{t_1=0}^{t} dt_1 \, o(t_1) = \Phi_F\Big(\int_{t_1=0}^{t} dt_1 e^{-it_1 S} \phi(\kappa_{-t_1} \varrho) \Big)
$$

$$
= \Phi_F(-\psi_{-t}(\varrho)),
$$

$$
C(t) = \int_{t_1=0}^{t} dt_1 \int_{t_2=0}^{t_1} dt_2 \, [o(t_2), o(t_1)]
$$

$$
= i \int_{t_1=0}^{t} dt_1 \int_{t_2=0}^{t_1} dt_2 \, \mathrm{Im}(e^{-it_2 S} \phi(\kappa_{-t_2} \varrho) | e^{-it_1 S} \phi(\kappa_{-t_1} \varrho))
$$

$$
= -i2\zeta_{-t}(\varrho).
$$

For the latter equality, we used the commutator $[\Phi_F(f), \Phi_F(g)] = i \,\mathrm{Im}(f|g)\mathbb{1}$. We remark that the combinatoric Lemma works well on D_F (on D, in tensor product with $\mathbb{1}$) for $z = is$ with $s \in \mathbb{R}$, since D_F consists of analytic vectors for the associated field operator expressions.

Finally, with Proposition 52.1-8 we arrive at

$$
e^{itH} = U_t Q(-\zeta_{-t}, -\psi_{-t}) = Q(\underbrace{-\zeta_{-t} \circ \kappa_t}_{= \, \zeta_t}, \underbrace{-e^{itS} \psi_{-t} \circ \kappa_t}_{= \, \psi_t}) U_t = Q(\zeta_t, \psi_t) U_t.
$$

The identities $-\zeta_{-t}(\kappa_t \varrho) = \zeta_t(\varrho)$ and $-e^{itS}\psi_{-t}(\kappa_t \varrho) = \psi_t(\varrho)$ may be shown most conveniently by means of the cocycle equations introduced later in Sec. 52.2.1. On the other side, they are straight forward by the definitions of ζ_t and ψ_t from the Eqs. (52.1.26) and (52.1.27) (with the help of some suitable integral substitutions and $\text{Im}(f|f) = 0$). ☐

For the unitary dynamics e^{itH} and for the propagator $Q(\zeta_t, \psi_t)$, we have by Eq. (52.1.29) the convergent Dyson expansion, which — in contradistinction to the completely non-commutative case — can be summed up to a closed expression.

To re-discover the physics, recall (from our radiation models) that the spectral ϱ-integrals offers the possibilities for the collective parameters ϱ, which are only specified by giving a state for the total material system. The entire material system exhibits a cluster structure, which here is only indicated by the form of the coupling Hamiltonian. For fixed ϱ, the coupling function $\phi(\varrho) = 2^{\frac{1}{2}} \sum_{j=1}^{M} \xi_j(\varrho)\phi_j$ contains transition functions $\phi_j(x)$, composed of the two material wave functions of the transition within a material cluster, which depend on x in the position space representation. The complex $\xi_j(\varrho)$ signify collective material (de-) excitation operators, which had become "classical" by the average over the clusters.

In the formal language, the described material expression is multiplied by the Boson field $\Phi_F(x)$ and integrated over d^3x, which is nothing else than the "smearing" of $\Phi_F(x)$. That product represents, finally, a single interaction event, which is iterated and integrated over the whole time interval in a summand of the Dyson series. The entire Dyson series describes thus the superposition of more and more iterated interaction events during a whole time interval. The time interval goes to infinity for gaining the perturbation series of the wave operators and of the S-matrix.

52.1.5. *Closed Expression for e^{itH} via Trotter's Product Formula*

In contradistinction to the Dyson series, where the single interaction events are iterated and integrated over the whole time interval, the Trotter product method represents the effects of the interaction during a small time interval t/n and iterates over time.

Trotter's product formula (e.g., [RS73b] Theorem VIII.31), is expressed by the strong operator limit on some complex Hilbert space

$$e^{it(K+\Upsilon)} = \lim_{n\to\infty} \left(e^{i\frac{t}{n}K} e^{i\frac{t}{n}\Upsilon}\right)^n, \quad \forall t \in \mathbb{R},$$

provided $K + \Upsilon$ is essentially self-adjoint on $\text{dom}(K) \cap \text{dom}(\Upsilon)$, where K and Υ both are self-adjoint.

We know from Eq. (51.2.1) together with from Assumption 52.1-1, and Proposition 51.2-1(a) that this essential self-adjointness condition, in case of our specific K and Υ, is valid, and that consequently Trotter's product formula applies.

Theorem 52.1-12 (e^{itH} via the Trotter Product Formula). *Let the assumptions and notions be as in Theorem 52.1-11. Then for each $t \in \mathbb{R}$, we have in the strong operator topology the limiting relation*

$$e^{itH} = e^{it(K+\Upsilon)} = \lim_{n\to\infty} \left(\exp\{i\tfrac{t}{n}K\} \, \exp\{i\tfrac{t}{n}\Upsilon\} \right)^n = Q(\zeta_t, \psi_t) \, e^{itK}.$$

Here, the last equality is gained by explicitly calculating the operator expressions $\left(\exp\{i\tfrac{t}{n}K\} \, \exp\{i\tfrac{t}{n}\Upsilon\} \right)^n$ and performing their limit $n \to \infty$.

Proof. The proof is already outlined in Sec. 40.1.4 on page 1414, but for completeness we give here a more detailed elaboration.

(1) Let us first treat a special approximation by Riemann sums for two integrals. Without restriction in generality we assume $t > 0$; for $t < 0$ one has to substitute $t \to -t$. Consider the norm continuous function

$$\mathbb{R} \ni s \mapsto f(s) := e^{isS} \phi(\varphi_s \varrho) \in \mathcal{V}$$

for fixed $\varrho \in \mathsf{P}$. For arbitrary $n \in \mathbb{N}$ we divide the interval $[0, t]$ into n equal parts with length $\Delta t = t/n$. Then we perform the Riemannian sums,

$$\lim_{n\to\infty} \underbrace{\frac{t}{n} \sum_{k=1}^{n} f(kt/n)}_{=:\, \psi_{t,n}(\varrho)} = \lim_{n\to\infty} \sum_{k=1}^{n} \Delta t f(k\Delta t) =$$

$$= \int_0^t ds\, f(s) = \int_0^t ds\, e^{isS} \phi(\varphi_s \varrho) = \psi_t(\varrho) =: F(t)$$

in norm. Observe that $F(l\Delta t) \approx \sum_{k=1}^{l} \Delta t f(k\Delta t)$ for large n. So, similarly,

$$\lim_{n\to\infty} \underbrace{\frac{t^2}{n^2} \sum_{l=1}^{n} \sum_{k=1}^{l} \mathrm{Im}(f(kt/n)|f(lt/n))}_{=:\, -2\zeta_{t,n}(\varrho)} = \lim_{n\to\infty} \Delta t \sum_{l=1}^{n} \mathrm{Im}\Big(\sum_{k=1}^{l} \Delta t f(k\Delta t) \big| f(l\Delta t) \Big)$$

$$= \lim_{n\to\infty} \sum_{l=1}^{n} \Delta t \, \mathrm{Im}(F(l\Delta t)|f(l\Delta t)) = \int_0^t ds \, \mathrm{Im}(F(s)|f(s))$$

$$= \int_{t_1=0}^t dt_1 \int_{t_2=0}^{t_1} dt_2 \, \mathrm{Im}(f(t_2)|f(t_1)) = -2\zeta_t(\varrho).$$

(2) Using the spectral integral formulation for Υ of Corollary 52.1-6, then by the spectral calculus for $dP(\varrho) \otimes \mathbb{1}$, and by summing up the exponential powers

F-continuously on D, and by the $\mathbb{R}$-linearity of $f \mapsto \Phi_F(f)$, we get

$$\exp\{i\tfrac{t}{n}\Upsilon\} = \int_{\mathsf{P}} \exp\{i\tfrac{t}{n}[\mathbb{1} \otimes \Phi_F(\phi(\varrho))]\}(dP(\varrho) \otimes \mathbb{1}) = \int_{\mathsf{P}} [\mathbb{1} \otimes W_F(\tfrac{t}{n}\phi(\varrho))](dP(\varrho) \otimes \mathbb{1}).$$

For the free time evolutions $\alpha_s^{\text{free}}(.) = e^{isK} \cdot e^{-isK}$ we obtain

$$\alpha_s^{\text{free}}(\exp\{i\tfrac{t}{n}\Upsilon\}) = \int_{\mathsf{P}} [\mathbb{1} \otimes W_F(\tfrac{t}{n}e^{isS}\phi(\varphi_s\varrho))](dP(\varrho) \otimes \mathbb{1}).$$

We are now able to calculate the Trotter powers directly,

$$\left(\exp\{i\tfrac{t}{n}K\} \exp\{i\tfrac{t}{n}\Upsilon\}\right)^n e^{-itK}$$

$$= \alpha_{\frac{t}{n}}^{\text{free}}(\exp\{i\tfrac{t}{n}\Upsilon\})\, \alpha_{2\frac{t}{n}}^{\text{free}}(\exp\{i\tfrac{t}{n}\Upsilon\}) \cdots \alpha_{n\frac{t}{n}}^{\text{free}}(\exp\{i\tfrac{t}{n}\Upsilon\})$$

$$\overset{\star}{=} \int_{\mathsf{P}} \left[\mathbb{1} \otimes \prod_{k=1}^{n} W_F\left(\tfrac{t}{n} \underbrace{\exp\{ik\tfrac{t}{n}S\}\phi(\varphi_{k\frac{t}{n}}\varrho)}_{= f(kt/n)}\right)\right](dP(\varrho) \otimes \mathbb{1})$$

$$= Q(\zeta_{t,n}, \psi_{t,n}),$$

where the equality sign with the $\star$ is explained just now. The Weyl relations

$$W_F(f)W_F(g) = \exp\{-\tfrac{i}{2}\operatorname{Im}(f|g)\}W_F(f+g), \quad \forall f, g \in \mathcal{V},$$

and $\operatorname{Im}(f|f) = 0$ (allowing also $k = l$ in the double sum here) lead to

$$\prod_{k=1}^{n} W_F\left(\tfrac{t}{n}f(kt/n)\right)$$

$$= \exp\left\{\underbrace{-\tfrac{i}{2}\tfrac{t^2}{n^2}\sum_{l=1}^{n}\sum_{k=1}^{l}\operatorname{Im}(f(kt/n)|f(lt/n))}_{= i\zeta_{t,n}(\varrho)}\right\}W_F\left(\underbrace{\tfrac{t}{n}\sum_{k=1}^{n}f(kt/n)}_{= \psi_{t,n}(\varrho)}\right)$$

$$= \exp\{i\zeta_{t,n}(\varrho)\}\, W_F(\psi_{t,n}(\varrho)) \overset{n\to\infty}{\longrightarrow} \exp\{i\zeta_t(\varrho)\}\, W_F(\psi_t(\varrho))$$

approximating strongly with (1). Finally use Proposition 52.1-8 for

$$\lim_{n\to\infty} Q(\zeta_{t,n}, \psi_{t,n}) = Q(\zeta_t, \psi_t), \quad \forall t \in \mathbb{R},$$

in the strong operator topology. $\qquad\square$

52.2. Generalization of the Interaction Operator

With the exception of the interaction Υ, we assume here the identical partially commutative situation as in Assumption 52.1-1. It consists of the total Hilbert space $\mathcal{H} \otimes F_+(\mathcal{V})$, and a commutative sub-C*-algebra $\mathcal{A}_{\text{com}}$ of $\mathcal{L}(\mathcal{H})$, which coincides with the C*-algebra $C_b(\mathsf{P}, \mathbb{C})$. The material Heisenberg dynamics $\alpha_t^{\text{mat}}(.) = e^{itA} \cdot e^{-itA}$ restricted to $\mathcal{A}_{\text{com}}$ is given by a flow κ_t on the "classical configuration space" P. We know the free Hamiltonian $K = A \otimes \mathbb{1} + \mathbb{1} \otimes d\Gamma(S)$, with some self-adjoint one-Boson operator S on $\mathcal{V}$.

Let us neglect at first our knowledge of the origin of $e^{itH}e^{-itK} = Q(\zeta_t, \psi_t)$, which we determined in the previous section from a specified interaction Υ. We want to proceed here in the opposite direction and start with the unitaries

$$Q(\zeta, \psi) = \int_{\mathsf{P}} e^{i\zeta(\varrho)} \big[\mathbb{1} \otimes W_F(\psi(\varrho))\big] (dP(\varrho) \otimes \mathbb{1}) \qquad (52.2.1)$$

on $\mathcal{H} \otimes F_+(\mathcal{V})$, constructed by means of the continuous $\varrho \mapsto \zeta(\varrho) \in \mathbb{R}$ and (norm) continuous $\varrho \mapsto \psi(\varrho) \in \mathcal{V}$ as input information. With these unitaries, which play the role of propagators in the interaction picture, we want to construct unitary one-parameter groups of the type $t \mapsto Q(\zeta_t, \psi_t)e^{itK}$ for the total dynamics, and determine then their self-adjoint generators, and their interaction operators.

52.2.1.   *Cocycle Equations for Unitary One-Parameter Groups*

The requirement of the group property for $V_t := Q(\zeta_t, \psi_t)\, e^{itK}$, $t \in \mathbb{R}$, leads to the so-called "cocycle equations".

Proposition 52.2-1 (Group Property and Cocycle Equations). *Let be given two continuous functions (ψ with respect to the norm):*

$$\psi : \mathbb{R} \times \mathsf{P} \to \mathcal{V}, \ (t, \varrho) \mapsto \psi_t(\varrho) \equiv \psi(t, \varrho), \quad \text{and}$$
$$\zeta : \mathbb{R} \times \mathsf{P} \to \mathbb{R}, \ (t, \varrho) \mapsto \zeta_t(\varrho) \equiv \zeta(t, \varrho).$$

Then $V_t := Q(\zeta_t, \psi_t)\, e^{itK}$, $t \in \mathbb{R}$, defines a strongly continuous unitary one-parameter group on $\mathcal{H} \otimes F_+(\mathcal{V})$, especially $V_t^* = V_{-t}$ and $V_0 = \mathbb{1}$, if and only if ψ_t and ζ_t satisfy the cocycle relations

$$\psi_{s+t}(\varrho) = \psi_s(\varrho) + e^{isS}\psi_t(\kappa_s \varrho), \qquad (52.2.2)$$

$$\zeta_{s+t}(\varrho) = \zeta_s(\varrho) + \zeta_t(\kappa_s \varrho) - \frac{1}{2}\operatorname{Im}(\psi_s(\varrho)|e^{isS}\psi_t(\kappa_s \varrho)), \qquad (52.2.3)$$

for each $\varrho \in \mathsf{P}$ and all $s, t \in \mathbb{R}$.

Remark that by inserting $s = t = 0$, the cocycle equations imply vanishing initial values, $\psi(0, \varrho) = 0$ and $\zeta(0, \varrho) = 0$ for every $\varrho \in \mathsf{P}$.

Proof.   We use Proposition 52.1-8 to calculate

$$\begin{aligned}
V_s\, V_t &= Q(\zeta_s, \psi_s)\, e^{isK} Q(\zeta_t, \psi_t)\, e^{itK} \\
&= Q(\zeta_s, \psi_s)\, Q(\zeta_t \circ \kappa_s, e^{isS}\psi_t \circ \kappa_s)\, e^{i(s+t)K} \\
&= Q(\zeta_s \diamond \zeta_t, \psi_s + e^{isS}\psi_t \circ \kappa_s)\, e^{i(s+t)K},
\end{aligned}$$

with $\zeta_s \diamond \zeta_t(\varrho) := \zeta_s(\varrho) + \zeta_t(\kappa_s \varrho) - \frac{1}{2}\operatorname{Im}(\psi_s(\varrho)|e^{isS}\psi_t(\kappa_s \varrho))$. This coincides with V_{s+t}, if and only if the cocycle equations are fulfilled. Finally, the strong continuity of $t \mapsto Q(\zeta_t, \psi_t)$, and thus of $t \mapsto V_t$, follows from the supposed continuity of $(t, \varrho) \mapsto \zeta_t(\varrho)$ and $(t, \varrho) \mapsto \psi_t(\varrho)$.

With the vanishing initial values, $\psi(0, \varrho) = 0$ and $\zeta(0, \varrho) = 0$, it follows $V_0 = \mathbb{1}$, and thus the group property gives $V_t^* = V_{-t}$. $\qquad\square$

The first cocycle Eq. (52.2.2) stands for its own. In contrast, the second one (52.2.3) is coupled to the first one. So a solution of the second cocycle equation needs the solution of the first one. The cocycle relations are uniquely solvable under certain initial values.

Proposition 52.2-2 (The Solutions of the Cocycle Equations).

(a) *[First Cocycle Equation] The initial value*

$$\phi : P \to V, \ \varrho \mapsto \phi(\varrho) := \left.\frac{\partial \psi_t(\varrho)}{\partial t}\right|_{t=0}$$

be a (norm) continuous function, where the derivation exists in norm. Then the first cocycle Eq. (52.2.2) is uniquely solvable by

$$\psi_t(\varrho) \equiv \psi(t, \varrho) = \int_{t_1=0}^{t} dt_1 \, e^{it_1 S} \phi(\kappa_{t_1} \varrho) \in V \tag{52.2.4}$$

for each $t \in \mathbb{R}$ (cf. Eq. (52.1.26)).

(b) *[Second Cocycle Equation] Suppose that the first cocycle equation be solved by (52.2.4), and moreover, that the initial value*

$$\lambda : P \to \mathbb{R}, \ \varrho \mapsto \lambda(\varrho) := \left.\frac{\partial \zeta_t(\varrho)}{\partial t}\right|_{t=0} \tag{52.2.5}$$

be a continuous function. Then the unique solution for the second cocycle Eq. (52.2.3) is given by

$$\zeta_t(\varrho) \equiv \zeta(t, \varrho) = \int_{t_1=0}^{t} dt_1 \, \lambda(\kappa_{t_1} \varrho) - \frac{1}{2} \int_{t_1=0}^{t} dt_1 \int_{t_2=0}^{t_1} dt_2 \, \mathrm{Im}(e^{it_2 S} \phi(\kappa_{t_2} \varrho) | e^{it_1 S} \phi(\kappa_{t_1} \varrho))$$

$$= \int_{t_1=0}^{t} dt_1 \, \lambda(\kappa_{t_1} \varrho) - \frac{1}{2} \int_{t_1=0}^{t} dt_1 \, \mathrm{Im}(\psi_{t_1}(\varrho) | e^{it_1 S} \phi(\kappa_{t_1} \varrho))$$

$$\tag{52.2.6}$$

for each $t \in \mathbb{R}$. (That is similar to Eq. (52.1.27), but there $\lambda = 0$.)

Proof. (a) That (52.2.4) fulfills the first cocycle equation is easily checked. We proceed in opposite direction and start from the first cocycle equation. The partial derivative $\frac{\partial \psi(s, \varrho)}{\partial s}$ exists at $s = 0$ by assumption in terms of the initial value. We show that then the partial derivative $\frac{\partial \psi(s, \varrho)}{\partial s}$ exists for $s \neq 0$, too. Recall, $\psi(0, \varrho) = 0$ for all ϱ. So, applying the first cocycle relation and using the initial value at $\kappa_s \varrho$ instead at ϱ, we conclude

$$\left.\frac{\partial \psi(s, \varrho)}{\partial s}\right|_{s \neq 0} = \lim_{t \to 0} \frac{\psi(s + t, \varrho) - \psi(s, \varrho)}{t} = e^{isS} \lim_{t \to 0} \frac{\psi(t, \kappa_s \varrho)}{t}$$

$$= e^{isS} \left.\frac{\partial \psi(t, \kappa_s \varrho)}{\partial t}\right|_{t=0} = e^{isS} \phi(\kappa_s \varrho).$$

Consequently, $s \mapsto \mathrm{e}^{isS}\phi(\kappa_s\varrho)$ is the norm derivative of $s \mapsto \psi(s,\varrho)$, for ϱ being fixed. Thus, $\psi(0,\varrho) = 0$ and the integration $\int_0^t ds\ldots$ yields (52.2.4).

(b) That (52.2.6) fulfills the second cocycle equation one checks directly. For the converse direction, first recall $\zeta(0,\varrho) = 0$. Now the second cocycle equation gives

$$
\left.\frac{\partial\zeta(s,\varrho)}{\partial s}\right|_{s\neq 0} = \lim_{t\to 0}\frac{\zeta(s+t,\varrho) - \zeta(s,\varrho)}{t}
$$

$$
= \lim_{t\to 0}\frac{\zeta(t,\kappa_s\varrho)}{t} - \frac{1}{2}\mathrm{Im}\Big(\psi_s(\varrho)\Big|\mathrm{e}^{isS}\lim_{t\to 0}\frac{\psi(t,\kappa_s\varrho)}{t}\Big)
$$

$$
= \underbrace{\left.\frac{\partial\zeta(t,\kappa_s\varrho)}{\partial t}\right|_{t=0}}_{=\ \lambda(\kappa_s\varrho)} - \frac{1}{2}\mathrm{Im}(\psi(s,\varrho)|\mathrm{e}^{isS}\phi(\kappa_s\varrho)).
$$

Now we take $\zeta(0,\varrho) = 0$ for the evaluation of the integral $\int_0^t ds\ldots$, which leads to (52.2.6).   □

In order to deduce the generator of $V_t = Q(\zeta_t,\psi_t)\,\mathrm{e}^{itK}$, the initial value functions λ and ϕ need to be bounded, because only then the spectral integral expression for the interaction in the following Theorem is well defined. Recall that we expressed boundedness by finite supremum norms,

$$
\|\lambda\|_\infty = \sup\{|\lambda(\varrho)|\mid \varrho \in \mathsf{P}\} < \infty, \qquad \|\phi\|_\infty = \sup\{\|\phi(\varrho)\|\mid \varrho \in \mathsf{P}\} < \infty.
$$

With the help of Lemma 51.3-2 and Corollary 52.1-9 it immediately follows that $t \mapsto V_t$ is a strongly F-continuous one-parameter group on D.

Theorem 52.2-3 (Self-adjoint Generator for the Total Unitary Group).
Suppose initial values $[\varrho \mapsto \lambda(\varrho)] \in C_b(\mathsf{P},\mathbb{R})$ and $[\varrho \mapsto \phi(\varrho)] \in C_b(\mathsf{P},\mathcal{V})$, with uniquely associated solutions ψ_t and ζ_t of the cocycle relations given by (52.2.4) and (52.2.6). Then the self-adjoint generator H of the strongly continuous unitary one-parameter group $\mathrm{e}^{itH} \equiv V_t = Q(\zeta_t,\psi_t)\,\mathrm{e}^{itK}$ is given by

$$
H = \underbrace{A\otimes\mathbb{1} + \mathbb{1}\otimes d\Gamma(S)}_{=\ K,\ \text{free Hamiltonian}} + \Upsilon,
$$

where the interaction operator (with domain $\mathrm{dom}(\Upsilon) = D$) is given by

$$
\Upsilon = \underbrace{\left[\int_{\mathsf{P}}\lambda(\varrho)\,dP(\varrho)\right]\otimes\mathbb{1}}_{\in\ \mathcal{A}_{com}} + \int_{\mathsf{P}}\left[\mathbb{1}\otimes\Phi_F(\phi(\varrho))\right](dP(\varrho)\otimes\mathbb{1}),
$$

and where H is essentially self-adjoint on $\mathrm{dom}(K)\cap\mathrm{dom}(\Upsilon)$.

Before giving the proof, let us remark that also the Dyson expansion, as well as the Trotter product formula method, from Theorems 52.1-11, and 52.1-12, work well for the generalized interaction operator Υ here. The reason is, that we did not use any specific form of the (bounded) coupling function $\varrho \mapsto \phi(\varrho)$ in the proofs there.

Nevertheless, we have for the proof to take the opposite direction, i.e., to start from the unitary one-parameter group $V_t = Q(\zeta_t, \psi_t) e^{itK}$, in order to ensure self-adjointness of its generator $H = K + \Upsilon$, what is not *a priori* clear for our generalized Υ. Moreover, we get in this manner the most general form for an interaction operator in the partially commutative situation. That determines, besides other things, the range of applicability for our treatment of mesoscopic radiation models.

Proof. The proof is divided into three parts.

(1) Eq. (52.2.4) yields

$$\left\| \frac{\psi_t(\varrho)}{t} \right\| \le \|\phi\|_\infty, \quad \text{thus} \quad \|\psi_t(\varrho)\| \le \|\phi\|_\infty |t|.$$

Moreover, for $t > 0$ (without restriction in generality, otherwise substitute $t \to -t$)

$$\left\| \frac{\psi_t(\varrho)}{t} - \phi(\varrho) \right\| \le \frac{1}{t} \int_0^t ds \|e^{isS}\phi(\kappa_s \varrho) - \phi(\varrho)\| \xrightarrow{t \to 0} 0$$

by the mean value theorem (cf. the same argument in the proof of Theorem 51.3-5). From Eq. (52.2.6) we conclude that

$$|\zeta_t(\varrho)| \le \left(\|\lambda\|_\infty + \frac{1}{2}\|\phi\|_\infty^2 |t| \right)|t|,$$

which leads to ($t > 0$, without restriction in generality)

$$\left| \frac{e^{i\zeta_t(\varrho)} - 1}{t} - i\lambda(\varrho) \right|$$

$$= \left| \frac{i}{t} \int_0^t ds[\lambda(\kappa_s \varrho) - \lambda(\varrho)] - \frac{i}{2t} \int_0^t ds\,\mathrm{Im}(\psi_s(\varrho)|e^{isS}\phi(\kappa_s \varrho)) + \frac{1}{t} \sum_{n=2}^\infty \frac{i^n}{n!} \zeta_t(\varrho)^n \right|$$

$$\le \underbrace{\frac{1}{t} \int_0^t ds|\lambda(\kappa_s \varrho) - \lambda(\varrho)|}_{\xrightarrow{t \to 0} 0,\ \text{mean value th.}} + \underbrace{\frac{1}{2}\|\phi\|_\infty^2 |t| + \sum_{n=2}^\infty \frac{\left(\|\lambda\|_\infty + \frac{1}{2}\|\phi\|_\infty^2 |t|\right)^n}{n!} |t|^{n-1}}_{\xrightarrow{t \to 0} 0}.$$

Analogously, $\left| \frac{e^{i\zeta_t(\varrho)} - 1}{t} \right| \le \sum_{n=1}^\infty \frac{\left(\|\lambda\|_\infty + \frac{1}{2}\|\phi\|_\infty^2 |t|\right)^n}{n!} |t|^{n-1} \le k$, for a constant $k > 0$ and for $|t| \le 1$ at the last inequality sign. What we have demonstrated are the relations

$$\frac{\partial \psi_t(\varrho)}{\partial t}\bigg|_{t=0} = \phi(\varrho), \qquad \frac{\partial e^{i\zeta_t(\varrho)}}{\partial t}\bigg|_{t=0} = i\lambda(\varrho),$$

together with some estimations, uniform in $\varrho \in \mathsf{P}$.

(2) In the second part we show $\frac{dQ(\zeta_t, \psi_t)}{dt}\bigg|_{t=0} = i\Upsilon$ with respect to the F-topology on D, and that for each $a \ge 1$ there is a constant $c_a > 0$ such that the differential

quotient is uniformly F-bounded in t by

$$\left\|(\mathbb{1}\otimes a^{N_F})\frac{Q(\zeta_t,\psi_t)-\mathbb{1}}{t}\psi\right\| \le c_a\|(\mathbb{1}\otimes(2^{\frac{1}{2}}a)^{N_F})\psi\|, \quad \forall\psi\in D, \quad \forall|t|\le 1. \quad (52.2.7)$$

With the F-continuous decomposition $\mathbb{1}\otimes W_F(f) = \sum\limits_{n=0}^{\infty}\frac{i^n}{n!}\mathbb{1}\otimes\Phi_F(f)^n$, where we recall that D consists of analytic vectors for the self-adjoint $\mathbb{1}\otimes\Phi_F(f))$, we obtain

$$\frac{Q(\zeta_t,\psi_t)-\mathbb{1}}{t} - i\Upsilon = \frac{Q(\zeta_t,0)-\mathbb{1}}{t}Q(0,\psi_t) + \frac{Q(0,\psi_t)-\mathbb{1}}{t} - i\Upsilon$$

$$= \left\{\int_P\left[\frac{e^{i\zeta_t(\varrho)}-1}{t} - i\lambda(\varrho)\right]dP(\varrho)\otimes\mathbb{1}\right\}Q(0,\psi_t)$$

$$+ i\left\{\int_P\lambda(\varrho)\,dP(\varrho)\otimes\mathbb{1}\right\}[Q(0,\psi_t)-\mathbb{1}]$$

$$+ \frac{Q(0,\psi_t)-\mathbb{1}}{t} - i\int_P[\mathbb{1}\otimes\Phi_F(\phi(\varrho))](dP(\varrho)\otimes\mathbb{1}).$$

Inserting the series for $Q(0,\psi_t)$ continues the relation as

$$\cdots = \sum_{n=0}^{\infty}\frac{i^n}{n!}\int_P\left[\frac{e^{i\zeta_t(\varrho)}-1}{t} - i\lambda(\varrho)\right][\mathbb{1}\otimes\Phi_F(\psi_t(\varrho))^n](dP(\varrho)\otimes\mathbb{1})$$

$$+ i\sum_{n=1}^{\infty}\frac{i^n}{n!}\int_P\lambda(\varrho)[\mathbb{1}\otimes\Phi_F(\psi_t(\varrho))^n](dP(\varrho)\otimes\mathbb{1})$$

$$+ \frac{1}{t}\sum_{n=2}^{\infty}\frac{i^n}{n!}\int_P[\mathbb{1}\otimes\Phi_F(\psi_t(\varrho))^n](dP(\varrho)\otimes\mathbb{1})$$

$$+ i\int_P[\mathbb{1}\otimes\Phi_F(\tfrac{\psi_t(\varrho)}{t} - \phi(\varrho))](dP(\varrho)\otimes\mathbb{1}).$$

Using part (1) of the proof, and the F-bounds of Theorem 52.1-5, we get (for $|t|\le 1$)

$$\left\|(\mathbb{1}\otimes a^{N_F})\left[\frac{Q(\zeta_t,\psi_t)-\mathbb{1}}{t} - i\Upsilon\right]\psi\right\|$$

$$\le \sum_{n=0}^{\infty}\frac{(2a\|\phi\|_\infty|t|)^n}{\sqrt{n!}}\underbrace{\left\{\int_P\left|\frac{e^{i\zeta_t(\varrho)}-1}{t} - i\lambda(\varrho)\right|^2 d\mu_\psi^a(\varrho)\right\}^{\frac{1}{2}}}$$

$$\le (k+\|\lambda\|_\infty)\|(\mathbb{1}\otimes(2^{\frac{1}{2}}a)^{N_F})\psi\|$$

$$+ \|\lambda\|_\infty\sum_{n=1}^{\infty}\frac{(2a\|\phi\|_\infty|t|)^n}{\sqrt{n!}}\|(\mathbb{1}\otimes(2^{\frac{1}{2}}a)^{N_F})\psi\|$$

$$+ \sum_{n=2}^{\infty} \frac{(2a\|\phi\|_\infty)^n |t|^{n-1}}{\sqrt{n!}} \|(\mathbb{1} \otimes (2^{\frac{1}{2}}a)^{N_F})\psi\|$$

$$+ 2a \left\| \frac{\psi_t(\varrho)}{t} - \phi(\varrho) \right\| \|(\mathbb{1} \otimes (2^{\frac{1}{2}}a)^{N_F})\psi\|$$

$$\xrightarrow{t \to 0} 0,$$

for all $\psi \in D$ and $a \geq 1$. Of course, Eq. (52.2.7) is obtained in the same way with a suitable c_a.

(3) Finally we conclude for $|t| \leq 1$ that

$$\left\| (\mathbb{1} \otimes a^{N_F}) \left[\frac{V_t - \mathbb{1}}{t} - \frac{e^{itK} - \mathbb{1}}{t} - i\Upsilon \right] \psi \right\|$$

$$= \left\| (\mathbb{1} \otimes a^{N_F}) \left[\frac{Q(\zeta_t, \psi_t) - \mathbb{1}}{t} e^{itK} - i\Upsilon \right] \psi \right\|$$

$$\leq \left\| (\mathbb{1} \otimes a^{N_F}) \frac{Q(\zeta_t, \psi_t) - \mathbb{1}}{t} [e^{itK} - \mathbb{1}] \psi \right\| + \left\| (\mathbb{1} \otimes a^{N_F}) \left[\frac{Q(\zeta_t, \psi_t) - \mathbb{1}}{t} - i\Upsilon \right] \psi \right\|$$

$$\leq c_a \left\| (\mathbb{1} \otimes a^{N_F}) [e^{itK} - \mathbb{1}] \psi \right\| + \left\| (\mathbb{1} \otimes a^{N_F}) \left[\frac{Q(\zeta_t, \psi_t) - \mathbb{1}}{t} - i\Upsilon \right] \psi \right\| \xrightarrow{t \to 0} 0.$$

Now the conclusion is the same as at the end of the proof of Theorem 51.3-5. With $a = 1$ we find $\mathrm{dom}(H) \cap D = \mathrm{dom}(K) \cap D$. Since both $\mathrm{dom}(H)$ and $D = \mathrm{dom}(\Upsilon)$ are left invariant by $V_t = e^{itH}$, it follows that H is essentially self-adjoint on $\mathrm{dom}(H) \cap D$ (by the already mentioned standard result [RS73b] Theorem VIII.10, or by our Theorem 43.6-1 on page 1550). □

52.2.2. *Cocycle Equations and Heisenberg Automorphisms*

For the total Heisenberg dynamics, we have

$$\alpha_t^{\mathrm{tot}}(.) = e^{itH} \cdot e^{-itH} = Q(\zeta_t, \psi_t) \underbrace{e^{itK} \cdot e^{-itK}}_{= \alpha_t^{\mathrm{free}}(.)} Q(\zeta_t, \psi_t)^*, \quad t \in \mathbb{R}. \qquad (52.2.8)$$

Concerning the material observables, there are the inclusions

$$\mathcal{A}_{\mathrm{com}} \subset \mathcal{M}_{\mathrm{com}} = \mathcal{A}''_{\mathrm{com}} \subset \mathcal{M}'_{\mathrm{com}} = \mathcal{A}'_{\mathrm{com}}, \qquad (52.2.9)$$

(where the "prime" indicates — as always in the book — the commutant). In our radiation models $\mathcal{A}_{\mathrm{com}}$ indicates the algebra of collective observables, gained by the classical extension of the quasilocal electron algebra $\mathcal{A}$ to $\mathcal{A}_e \supset \mathcal{A}_{\mathrm{com}}$. Since $\mathcal{A}$ commutes with $\mathcal{A}_{\mathrm{com}}$, the von Neumann algebra $\mathcal{A}'_{\mathrm{com}}$ comprises $\mathcal{A}_e$, if the latter is faithfully represented in the material Hilbert space $\mathcal{H}$.

Concerning the represented observables of the total system "matter-plus-Bosons", we conclude

$$\mathcal{A}_{\mathrm{com}} \overline{\otimes} \mathbb{1} \subset \mathcal{M}_{\mathrm{com}} \overline{\otimes} \mathcal{L}(F_+(\mathcal{V})) \subset \mathcal{M}'_{\mathrm{com}} \overline{\otimes} \mathcal{L}(F_+(\mathcal{V})) = (\mathcal{A}_{\mathrm{com}} \overline{\otimes} \mathbb{1})', \qquad (52.2.10)$$

(using the W*-tensor product). We consider $(\mathcal{A}_{com}\overline{\otimes}\mathbb{1})'$ — and not $\mathcal{L}(\mathcal{H})\overline{\otimes}$
$\mathcal{L}(F_+(\mathcal{V})) = \mathcal{L}(\mathcal{H}\otimes F_+(\mathcal{V}))$ — as the largest observable algebra, fitting to our
"partially commutative scenario".

Theorem 52.2-4 (The Automorphisms on the Commutant $(\mathcal{A}_{com}\otimes\mathbb{1})'$).
*The *-automorphism groups, α^{tot} and α^{free}, leave the von Neumann algebra $(\mathcal{A}_{com}\otimes$
$\mathbb{1})'$ invariant, that is, both perform a well-defined Heisenberg dynamics on $(\mathcal{A}_{com}\otimes$
$\mathbb{1})'$.*

*Furthermore, in restriction to the commutant $(\mathcal{A}_{com}\otimes\mathbb{1})'$, the phase factors ζ_t
in (52.2.8) drop out from the Heisenberg automorphisms leading to*

$$\alpha_t^{tot}(Z) = Q(\eta,\psi_t)\,\alpha_t^{free}(Z)\,Q(\eta,\psi_t)^*, \quad \forall Z \in (\mathcal{A}_{com}\otimes\mathbb{1})', \tag{52.2.11}$$

*for arbitrary continuous $\eta : \mathsf{P}\to\mathbb{R}$ (not necessarily bounded), including especially
the case $\eta = 0$.*

Proof. By assumption $\alpha_t^{mat}(.) = e^{itA}\cdot e^{-itA}$ leaves $\mathcal{A}_{com}$, and thus also $\mathcal{M}_{com}$
and its commutant $\mathcal{M}'_{com}$ invariant. Consequently, α_t^{free} leaves $\mathcal{M}_{com}\otimes\mathcal{L}(F_+(\mathcal{V}))$
and also $\mathcal{M}'_{com}\otimes\mathcal{L}(F_+(\mathcal{V}))$ invariant. Since $Q(\zeta_t,\psi_t)\in\mathcal{M}_{com}\otimes\mathcal{L}(F_+(\mathcal{V}))$, the
interacting dynamics α_t^{tot} leaves both $\mathcal{M}_{com}\otimes\mathcal{L}(F_+(\mathcal{V}))$ and $\mathcal{M}'_{com}\otimes\mathcal{L}(F_+(\mathcal{V}))$
invariant, too.

With Proposition 52.1-8 we obtain for $Z\in\mathcal{M}'_{com}\otimes\mathcal{L}(F_+(\mathcal{V}))$

$$Q(\eta,\psi_t)\,\alpha_t^{free}(Z)\,Q(\eta,\psi_t)^* = Q(0,\psi_t)Q(\eta,0)\,\alpha_t^{free}(Z)\,Q(-\eta,0)Q(0,\psi_t)^*$$
$$= Q(0,\psi_t)\,\underbrace{Q(\eta,0)Q(-\eta,0)}_{=\,\mathbb{1}\otimes\mathbb{1}}\alpha_t^{free}(Z)\,Q(0,\psi_t)^* = Q(0,\psi_t)\,\alpha_t^{free}(Z)\,Q(0,\psi_t)^*,$$

since $\alpha_t^{free}(Z)\in\mathcal{M}'_{com}\otimes\mathcal{L}(F_+(\mathcal{V}))$ commutes with $Q(-\eta,0)\in\mathcal{A}_{com}\otimes\mathbb{1}$. $\square$

Observation 52.2-5 (On the Role of the Phase Factors ζ_t). Let us draw a
conclusion of the preceding Theorem.

(a) The phase factors ζ_t are exclusively needed for the interacting unitary one-
    parameter group e^{itH}, as well as for α^{tot} on all of $\mathcal{L}(\mathcal{H}\otimes F_+(\mathcal{V}))$.
(b) For α^{tot} restricted to the von Neumann algebra $(\mathcal{A}_{com}\otimes\mathbb{1})'$, the ζ_t are superflu-
    ous. So, here the interaction comes into play only via ψ_t from the first cocycle
    Eq. (52.2.2). With Proposition 52.1-8 (e) we have for all $X\in\mathcal{M}'_{com}$ and all
    $f\in\mathcal{V}$,

$$\alpha_t^{tot}(X\otimes W_F(f)) = \Big\{\overbrace{\Big[\int_\mathsf{P}\exp\{-i\operatorname{Im}(\psi_t(\varrho)|f)\}\,dP(\varrho)\Big]}^{\in\,\mathcal{A}_{com}}\otimes\mathbb{1}\Big\}\,\alpha_t^{free}(X\otimes W_F(f))\,\cdot$$
$$\underbrace{\phantom{\Big[\int_\mathsf{P}\exp\{-i\operatorname{Im}(\psi_t(\varrho)|f)\}\,dP(\varrho)\Big]}}_{=\,Q(-\operatorname{Im}(\psi_t|f),0)}\qquad\qquad {}_{=\,\alpha_t^{mat}(X)\otimes W_F(e^{itS}f)}$$

$$(52.2.12)$$

52.2.3. *Supplements on Cocycles and Automorphisms*

One knows quite generally, that in quantum theory the symmetry groups are implemented in terms of *projective* representations, taking into account the arbitrariness of the phases of the state vectors. Then, in case of the group $\mathbb{R}$, one has the *composition law* for the projectively representing unitaries

$$U(t)U(s) = \exp\{iz(t,s)\}U(t+s),$$

with a 2-cocycle $\mathbb{R} \times \mathbb{R} \ni (t,s) \mapsto z(t,s) \in \mathbb{R}$,

satisfying the characterizing relation $z(t,s) + z(t+s,r) = z(t, s+r) + z(s,r)$.

$$(52.2.13)$$

The associativity law for the product of 3 implementing unitaries is equivalent to the 2-cocycle equations. If one replaces $z(t,s)$ by $z'(t,s) = z(t,s) + [c(t) + c(s)] - c(t+s)$, then one obtains an *equivalent* 2-cocycle. Because then the "equivalent" (= only inessentially modified) implementing unitaries $\exp\{ic(t)\}U(t)$ satisfy the composition law with $z'(t,s)$.

Relation Eq. (52.2.13) is a special case of the general 2-cocycle equation for groups.

Definition 52.2-6 (General 2-Cocycle). Let G be an arbitrary group and $\mathcal{Z}$ an (additive) Abelian group in which G acts (written as multiplication from the left).

A function $z : G \to \mathcal{Z}$ is called a *2-cocycle*, if and only if for all $g_1, g_2, g_3 \in G$

$$z(g_1, g_2) + z(g_1 g_2, g_3) = z(g_1, g_2 g_3) + g_1 \cdot z(g_2, g_3) \qquad (52.2.14)$$

is valid.

Notice that the action of G on $\mathcal{Z}$ may be also a trivial one (as in the earlier case of implementing unitaries).

As concerns the implementation of automorphisms $U(t)AU^*(t) = \alpha_t(A)$, $A \in \mathcal{L}(\mathcal{H})$, the composition law for the $U(t)$ with a general 2-cocycle is sufficient for the group law $\alpha_t \circ \alpha_s = \alpha_{t+s}$, since the phases drop out. But in order to have a self-adjoint generator one has to require that the $U(t)$ for themselves satisfy the group law $U(t)U(s) = U(t+s)$ (besides being strongly continuous in t). If the original $U(t)$ display a composition law with the 2-cocycle $z(t,s)$ then the slightly modified $\exp\{ic(t)\}U(t)$ satisfy the group law if $[c(t) + c(s)] - c(t+s) = -z(t,s)$. Especially, if the original $U(t)$ satisfy already the group law, then do so the $\exp\{ic(t)\}U(t)$.

For general unitaries in the interaction picture $U_t^{\text{int}} = e^{itH} e^{-itK}$ — called "unitary propagators" — the total dynamics $U(t) = U_t^{\text{int}} e^{itK}$ satisfies the group law, if and only if there hold the **multiplicative cocycle equations**

$$U_{s+t}^{\text{int}} = \left(e^{isH} e^{itH} e^{-isK} e^{-itK} = e^{isH} e^{-isK} e^{isK} e^{itH} e^{-itK} e^{-isK} = \right)$$
$$= U_s^{\text{int}} \left[e^{isK} U_t^{\text{int}} e^{-isK} \right]. \qquad (52.2.15)$$

Recapitulating Proposition 52.2-1, we test this relation directly for the $e^{itH}\,e^{-itK} = Q(\zeta_t, \psi_t)$ where we express the spectral integral $Q(\zeta_t, \psi_t) = \int_{\mathsf{P}} e^{i\zeta_t(\varrho)} \big[\mathbb{1} \otimes W_F(\psi_t(\varrho))\big](dP(\varrho) \otimes \mathbb{1})$ (cf. relation following Eq. (52.1.28)) as the function $\varrho \mapsto e^{i\zeta(t,\varrho)} W_F(\psi(t,\varrho))$ and calculate

$$e^{i\zeta(s,\varrho)} W_F(\psi(s,\varrho))\, e^{isK} e^{i\zeta(t,\varrho)} W_F(\psi(t,\varrho)) e^{-isK}$$

$$= e^{i\zeta(s,\varrho)+i\zeta(t,\kappa_s\varrho)} W_F(\psi(s,\varrho))\, W_F(e^{isS}\psi(t,\kappa_s\varrho)) \qquad (52.2.16)$$

$$= e^{i\zeta(s)+i\zeta(t,\kappa_s\varrho)} \exp\{-\tfrac{i}{2}\,\mathrm{Im}(\psi(s,\varrho)|e^{isS}\psi(t,\kappa_s\varrho))\} W_F(\psi(s,\varrho) + e^{isS}\psi(t,\kappa_s\varrho))$$

$$= e^{i\zeta(s+t)} W_F(\psi(s+t,\varrho)).$$

In the second step we have used that the composite free dynamics acts as a combination of the material central dynamics and the free photon dynamics, in the third step we have employed the Weyl commutation relations, and in the fourth step the cocycle equations, Eqs. (52.2.2) and (52.2.3), namely

$$\psi_{s+t}(\varrho) = \psi_s(\varrho) + e^{isS}\psi_t(\kappa_s\varrho),$$

$$\zeta_{s+t}(\varrho) = \zeta_s(\varrho) + \zeta_t(\kappa_s\varrho) - \frac{1}{2}\,\mathrm{Im}(\psi_s(\varrho)|e^{isS}\psi_t(\kappa_s\varrho)),$$

have been applied.

In other words: The preceding "cocycle equations" for the phases $\zeta_t(\varrho) \equiv \zeta(t,\varrho)$ in combination with the $\psi_t(\varrho) \equiv \psi(t,\varrho)$ (physically "polarization densities") *express the multiplicative cocycle equations for unitary propagators.*

On the Hilbert space $\mathcal{H} \otimes F_+(\mathcal{V})$ we have constructed in the foregoing investigations the total Heisenberg dynamics in the form of a unitary implementation $\alpha_t^{\mathrm{tot}}(Z) = Q(\zeta_t, \psi_t) \exp\{itK\} Z \exp\{-itK\} Q(\zeta_t, \psi_t)^*$ for all $Z \in \mathcal{M}\overline{\otimes}\mathcal{L}(F_+(\mathcal{V}))$, where $\mathcal{M}$ is a von Neumann algebra on $\mathcal{H}$. For our model expositions, we are interested in the abstract Heisenberg automorphisms on the C*-algebra $\mathcal{A}^{\mathrm{tot}} = \mathcal{A}_e \otimes \mathcal{W}(E, \mathrm{Im}(.|.))$. Since the composite free dynamics leaves $\mathcal{A}^{\mathrm{tot}}$ invariant, the total dynamics leaves $\mathcal{A}^{\mathrm{tot}}$ invariant if $Q(\zeta_t, \psi_t) \in \mathcal{A}^{\mathrm{tot}}$, as a sufficient condition.

A weaker sufficient condition may be found by choosing for $Z \in \mathcal{A}^{\mathrm{tot}}$ factorizing elements as in Eq. (52.2.12), getting

$$\alpha_t^{\mathrm{tot}}(X \otimes W_F(f)) = \left\{ \underbrace{\left[\overbrace{\int_{\mathsf{P}} \exp\{-i\,\mathrm{Im}(\psi_t(\varrho)|f)\}\,dP(\varrho)}^{\in\,\mathcal{A}_{\mathrm{com}}} \right] \otimes \mathbb{1}}_{=\,Q(-\mathrm{Im}(\psi_t|f),0)} \right\} \underbrace{\alpha_t^{\mathrm{free}}(X \otimes W_F(f))}_{=\,\alpha_t^{\mathrm{mat}}(X) \otimes W_F(e^{itS}f)}.$$

Therefore, a sufficiency criterion is also satisfied, if the exclusively material condition $\int_{\mathsf{P}} \exp\{-i\,\mathrm{Im}(\psi_t(\varrho)|f)\}\,dP(\varrho) \in \mathcal{Z}(\mathcal{A}_e) = \mathcal{A}_{\mathrm{com}} \subset \mathcal{M}_{\mathrm{com}}$ is valid, which amounts to $\mathsf{P} \ni \varrho \mapsto \exp\{-i\,\mathrm{Im}(\psi_t(\varrho)|f)\}$ being continuous for each $t \in \mathbb{R}$ and $f \in \mathcal{V}$. Since the linear combinations of those factorizing elements are norm dense in $\mathcal{A}^{\mathrm{tot}}$ and the

*-isomorphic action is norm continuous, α_t^{tot} leaves then the faithfully represented $\mathcal{A}^{\text{tot}}$ in fact invariant. Under this simple condition, one gains the total Heisenberg dynamics also in all representations Π of $\mathcal{A}^{\text{tot}}$, for which $\ker(\Pi)$ is α^{tot}-invariant (but the dynamics does not always arise in form of a unitary implementation).

In the foregoing investigation we have elaborated a more detailed picture, in which the total Heisenberg dynamics is introduced via unitaries in Dyson expansions, acting on von Neumann algebras of the form $\mathcal{M}'_{\text{com}} \otimes \mathcal{L}(F_+(\mathcal{V}))$. That would allow for more general interaction functions and polarization expressions.

Most importantly, the method by unitaries in Dyson expansions applies also — as demonstrated in Sec. 51.3 — to the entirely non-commutative coupling ansatzes. To extend this strategy also to other than Fock representations for the Bosons, one has to estimate the Dyson expansion anew, in application on the now altered state vectors, what is the topic of the following chapter.

Chapter 53

Further Bosonic Representations

The material system on the Hilbert space $\mathcal{H}$ be as before. But for the Boson field we generalize our ansatz, which we prepare in algebraic terms. Instead of using the Fock representation, we describe now the Boson observables by the C*-Weyl algebra

$$\mathcal{W}(E, \mathrm{Im}(.|.)), \qquad \text{with test function space } E,$$

where E is a complex pre-Hilbert space, norm-dense in the one-Boson Hilbert space $\mathcal{V}$. The symplectic form is the imaginary part of the inner product $(.|.)$ of $\mathcal{V}$ restricted to E. The complex unit i of E induces the physical particle structure. As before, we set $\hbar = 1$ for convenience.

The test function space E should be invariant under the one-Boson unitary time evolution e^{itS} generated by the one-Boson Hamiltonian S on $\mathcal{V}$, such that $\mathrm{e}^{itS} E = E$ for all $t \in \mathbb{R}$. Then the free Bosonic Heisenberg dynamics is given by the Bogoliubov automorphisms on $\mathcal{W}(E, \mathrm{Im}(.|.))$, satisfying for each Weyl element

$$\alpha_t^{\mathrm{bos}}(W(f)) = W(\mathrm{e}^{itS} f), \quad \forall f \in E, \quad \forall t \in \mathbb{R}.$$

In order to obtain a self-adjoint multi-Boson Hamiltonian R, we have to go into a regular, non-degenerate representation $(\Pi, \mathcal{K})$ of $\mathcal{W}(E, \mathrm{Im}(.|.))$ in which α^{bos} is implemented by a strongly continuous unitary group e^{itR}, that is,

$$\alpha_t^{\mathrm{bos}}(Y) = \mathrm{e}^{itR} Y \mathrm{e}^{-itR}, \quad \forall Y \in \mathcal{W}(E, \mathrm{Im}(.|.)), \quad \forall t \in \mathbb{R}. \tag{53.0.1}$$

As we did before, we omit the representation symbol Π what is supported by every representation of $\mathcal{W}(E, \mathrm{Im}(.|.))$ being faithful.

In general, R is non-unique, (see Sec. 20.1.1 on page 484). This non-uniqueness arises, if and only if the von Neumann algebra

$$\mathcal{M}_{\mathrm{bos}} := \mathcal{W}(E, \mathrm{Im}(.|.))'', \qquad \text{(bicommutant of the represented Weyl algebra)},$$

associated with our representation possesses a non-trivial commutant

$$\mathcal{M}'_{\mathrm{bos}} = \mathcal{W}(E, \mathrm{Im}(.|.))' \subseteq \mathcal{L}(\mathcal{K}).$$

Or, if one wishes to use only affiliated implementations, the non-uniqueness arises, if and only if we have a non-trivial center

$$\mathcal{Z}_{\mathrm{bos}} := \mathcal{M}_{\mathrm{bos}} \cap \mathcal{M}'_{\mathrm{bos}} \subseteq \mathcal{L}(\mathcal{K}).$$

In the Fock representation, the representation Hilbert space coincides with the Fock space, $\mathcal{K} = F_+(\mathcal{V})$, and the abstract Weyl elements $W(f) \in \mathcal{W}(E, \mathrm{Im}(.|.))$ with the Fock Weyl operators $W_F(f)$. There, however, it holds $\mathcal{M}_{\mathrm{bos}} = \mathcal{L}(F_+(\mathcal{V}))$, and hence, the implementing Hamiltonian is uniquely given by

$$R = d\Gamma(S), \quad \text{(in the Fock representation).}$$

So, when taking the Fock representation, we indeed are back in the setup of the previous two chapters.

But we want now to consider other representations than Fock. As candidate for a suitable representation $(\Pi, \mathcal{K})$, one may take the GNS representation of a time-invariant state ω on $\mathcal{W}(E, \mathrm{Im}(.|.))$, i.e.,

$$\omega \circ \alpha_t^{\mathrm{bos}} = \omega, \quad \forall t \in \mathbb{R}, \quad \text{(time-invariance)}. \tag{53.0.2}$$

In its GNS representation, there exists a unique implementing Hamiltonian R satisfying

$$R\Omega_\omega = 0, \quad \text{equivalently } e^{itR}\Omega_\omega = \Omega_\omega, \quad \forall t \in \mathbb{R}, \tag{53.0.3}$$

for the cyclic GNS vector Ω_ω. (We refer to Theorem 45.2-26 on page 1653.) Especially, the representation may again be the GNS representation of the dynamically invariant vacuum state (related to a complex Bosonic particle structure i).

So, in generalization to the Fock setup described in Sec. 51.2, the composite matter–Boson system is now given in the tensor product Hilbert space

$$\mathcal{H} \otimes \mathcal{K}, \quad \text{(Hilbert space of composite matter-Boson system).}$$

With bounded operators B_j on the material Hilbert space $\mathcal{H}$ and with $\phi_j \in E$ for $j \in \{1, 2, \ldots, M\}$, the interacting Hamiltonian is assumed to have the form — in generalization of (51.2.1) —

$$H = \underbrace{A \otimes \mathbb{1} + \mathbb{1} \otimes R}_{= K, \text{ free Hamilt.}} + \underbrace{\sum_{j=1}^{M} \left[B_j \otimes a_\Pi(\phi_j) + B_j^* \otimes a_\Pi^*(\phi_j) \right]}_{= \Upsilon, \text{ interaction}} \tag{53.0.4}$$

acting on $\mathcal{H} \otimes \mathcal{K}$. The annihilation and creation operators corresponding to the representation $(\Pi, \mathcal{K})$ are given with the complex unit i on $\mathcal{V}$, the unique Boson–particle structure, by

$$a_\Pi(f) = \frac{1}{\sqrt{2}} \left(\Phi_\Pi(f) + i\Phi_\Pi(if) \right), \quad a_\Pi^*(f) = \frac{1}{\sqrt{2}} \left(\Phi_\Pi(f) - i\Phi_\Pi(if) \right),$$

where $\Phi_\Pi(f) = -i\frac{d}{dt}W(tf)$ in the representation Π, for each $f \in E$.

We mentioned already at the beginning of Chapter 51, that, because the annihilation and creation operators are unbounded, in a general regular representation Π, it is not possible to control the growth of the Dyson expansion series by standard techniques, such as the Hilbert space norm or the operator norm, or to deduce convergence in the thermodynamic limit. Here we want to generalize to Fock-like representations $(\Pi, \mathcal{K})$ in which, possibly besides a classical part some Fock spaces are involved. We proceed to two representative examples.

53.1. Convergence in Fock⊗Fock Representations

A first type of a Fock-like representation is obtained as the GNS representation of a quasifree state corresponding to a regular form in the exponent of the characteristic function. Its GNS Hilbert space is of type $F_+ \otimes F_+$, as is demonstrated in Proposition 25.1-14 on page 658.

Let us take for example the photonic thermal equilibrium state ω at inverse temperature $\beta > 0$ from Chapter 30, which is a gauge–invariant, quasifree state on $\mathcal{W}(E, \mathrm{Im}(.|.))$ of this type. Its characteristic function is given by

$$\langle \omega; W(f) \rangle = \exp\{-\frac{1}{4}\|f\|^2 - \frac{1}{2}\|T^{\frac{1}{2}}f\|^2\}, \quad \forall f \in E,$$

where $E \subseteq \mathrm{dom}(T^{\frac{1}{2}})$ and $S > 0$ (that is, S is positive, not having zero as eigenvalue). Then we know that

$$T := \mathrm{e}^{-\beta S}(\mathbb{1} - \mathrm{e}^{-\beta S})^{-1}$$

is well defined, also in restriction to E. Let us remark some further operator properties.

Remark 53.1-1. It holds $\mathrm{dom}(S^{-\frac{1}{2}}) = \mathrm{dom}(T^{\frac{1}{2}}) = \mathrm{dom}((\mathbb{1}+T)^{\frac{1}{2}})$. The graph norms of $S^{-\frac{1}{2}}$, $T^{\frac{1}{2}}$, and $(\mathbb{1}+T)^{\frac{1}{2}}$ are equivalent. In addition, E is a core for each of these three self-adjoint operators on $\mathcal{V}$. Finally, $T^{\frac{1}{2}}(E)$ and $(\mathbb{1}+T)^{\frac{1}{2}}(E)$ are norm dense in $\mathcal{V}$.

Proof. The spectrum of S is a subset of $[0, \infty[$, where 0 is not an eigenvalue. Thus for $\lambda > 0$ we have the estimations

$$\beta\lambda \leq \sum_{n=1}^{\infty} \frac{(\beta\lambda)^n}{n!} = \mathrm{e}^{\beta\lambda} - 1 = \beta\lambda \sum_{n=1}^{\infty} \frac{(\beta\lambda)^{n-1}}{n!} = \beta\lambda \sum_{n=0}^{\infty} \frac{(\beta\lambda)^n}{(n+1)!} \leq \beta\lambda\,\mathrm{e}^{\beta\lambda}.$$

Taking the inverse, we have for $\lambda > 0$ that

$$\frac{1}{\beta\lambda} \geq \frac{1}{\mathrm{e}^{\beta\lambda} - 1} = \frac{\mathrm{e}^{-\beta\lambda}}{1 - \mathrm{e}^{-\beta\lambda}} \geq \frac{\mathrm{e}^{-\beta\lambda}}{\beta\lambda} \quad \Rightarrow \quad 1 + \frac{\mathrm{e}^{-\beta\lambda}}{1 - \mathrm{e}^{-\beta\lambda}} = \frac{1}{1 - \mathrm{e}^{-\beta\lambda}} \geq \frac{1}{\beta\lambda}.$$

With the spectral calculus (from Theorem 43.3-3) applied to the self-adjoint S, we thus obtain $\mathrm{dom}(S^{-\frac{1}{2}}) = \mathrm{dom}(T^{\frac{1}{2}}) = \mathrm{dom}((\mathbb{1}+T)^{\frac{1}{2}})$, and

$$\frac{1}{\beta}\|S^{-\frac{1}{2}}f\|^2 \geq \|T^{\frac{1}{2}}f\|^2, \qquad \|f\|^2 + \|T^{\frac{1}{2}}f\|^2 = \|(\mathbb{1}+T)^{\frac{1}{2}}f\|^2 \geq \frac{1}{\beta}\|S^{-\frac{1}{2}}f\|^2,$$

which finally gives the equivalence of the graph norms.

With help of [Rig77], Theorem 4, we conclude, that the assumptions $E \subseteq \mathrm{dom}(T^{\frac{1}{2}})$ and $e^{itS}E = E$ yield E to be a core of $T^{\frac{1}{2}}$, thus of $S^{-\frac{1}{2}}$ and of $(\mathbb{1}+T)^{\frac{1}{2}}$. Consequently, $B(E)^{\perp} = \mathrm{ran}(B)^{\perp} = \ker(B) = \{0\}$ for the self-adjoint $B = T^{\frac{1}{2}}$, or $B = (\mathbb{1}+T)^{\frac{1}{2}}$, but also for $B = S^{-\frac{1}{2}}$. This implies the density statements. □

For later purposes, let us briefly denote by $\|.\|_T$ the graph norm of $T^{\frac{1}{2}}$,

$$E \ni f \mapsto \|(\mathbb{1}+T)^{\frac{1}{2}}f\| = (\|f\|^2 + \|T^{\frac{1}{2}}f\|^2)^{\frac{1}{2}} =: \|f\|_T, \quad \text{(graph norm of } T^{\frac{1}{2}}\text{)}.$$

The GNS representation $(\Pi, \mathcal{K}) \equiv (\Pi_\omega, \mathcal{H}_\omega)$ of ω is given by

$$\mathcal{K} = F_+(\mathcal{V}) \otimes F_+(\mathcal{V}),$$

$$W(f) \equiv \Pi(W(f)) = W_F((\mathbb{1}+T)^{\frac{1}{2}}f) \otimes W_F(JT^{\frac{1}{2}}f), \quad \forall f \in E.$$

Here J is an antilinear involution on $\mathcal{V}$, satisfying

$$(Jf|Jg) = (g|f), \quad \forall f, g \in \mathcal{V}, \qquad J e^{itS} = e^{-itS} J, \quad \forall t \in \mathbb{R}.$$

The field, annihilation and creation operators associated with the GNS representation Π are expressed by those on Fock space according as

$$\Phi_\Pi(f) = \Phi_F((\mathbb{1}+T)^{\frac{1}{2}}f) \otimes \mathbb{1} + \mathbb{1} \otimes \Phi_F(JT^{\frac{1}{2}}f),$$

$$a_\Pi(f) = a_F((\mathbb{1}+T)^{\frac{1}{2}}f) \otimes \mathbb{1} + \mathbb{1} \otimes a_F^*(JT^{\frac{1}{2}}f),$$

$$a_\Pi^*(f) = a_F^*((\mathbb{1}+T)^{\frac{1}{2}}f) \otimes \mathbb{1} + \mathbb{1} \otimes a_F(JT^{\frac{1}{2}}f).$$

Since $T^{\frac{1}{2}}$ commutes with e^{itS}, we have for the characteristic function $\langle \omega; W(e^{itS}f) \rangle = \langle \omega; W(f) \rangle$, and hence our state ω is time-invariant, cf. (53.0.2). The implementing self-adjoint Hamiltonian R, satisfying $R\Omega_\omega = 0$ for the cyclic vector $\Omega_\omega = \Omega_{\mathrm{vac}} \otimes \Omega_{\mathrm{vac}}$, cf. Eq. (53.0.3), is given by

$$R = d\Gamma(S) \otimes \mathbb{1} - \mathbb{1} \otimes d\Gamma(S). \tag{53.1.1}$$

With the GNS representation $(\Pi, \mathcal{K})$ for the Boson part, let us return to our composite matter–Boson system on the tensor product Hilbert space $\mathcal{H} \otimes \mathcal{K}$, with the interacting Hamiltonian H from Eq. (53.0.4). Using the Fock number operator $N_F = d\Gamma(\mathbb{1})$, we define on the representation Hilbert space $\mathcal{K} = F_+(\mathcal{V}) \otimes F_+(\mathcal{V})$ the "number" operator

$$N := N_F \otimes \mathbb{1} + \mathbb{1} \otimes N_F \quad \Rightarrow \quad a^N = a^{N_F} \otimes a^{N_F}, \quad \forall a \geq 1.$$

With the help of N, we construct the F-space

$$D := \bigcap_{a \geq 1} \mathrm{dom}(\mathbb{1} \otimes a^N) \quad \subset \mathcal{H} \otimes \mathcal{K},$$

equipped with the F-topology arising from the directed system of norms

$$D \ni \psi \mapsto \|(\mathbb{1} \otimes a^N)\psi\|, \quad a \geq 1.$$

Using this F-space setup, we obtain at last the analogous results to Lemma 51.3-3, implying that all results from the previous sections (in the single-Fock situation) are valid here, too. Like in the single-Fock situation, in order to treat simultaneously products of Π-represented annihilation, creation and field operators, we use the unifying symbol $A_k(g_k)$ for $a_\Pi(g_k)$, or $a_\Pi^*(g_k)$, resp. for $\Phi_\Pi(g_k) = 2^{-\frac{1}{2}}(a_\Pi(g_k) + a_\Pi^*(g_k))$, that means

$$A_k(g_k) \in \{a_\Pi(g_k), a_\Pi^*(g_k), \Phi_\Pi(g_k)\}, \quad g_k \in E.$$

Lemma 53.1-2 (F-Estimations, F-Continuity). *The following two assertions are valid:*

(a) *For $C \in \mathcal{L}(\mathcal{H})$ and $g_1, \ldots g_n \in E$ (with $n \in \mathbb{N}$) the operator $C \otimes \prod_{k=1}^{n} A_k(g_k)$ acts F-continuously on D. More exactly we have the F-estimations*

$$\left\|(\mathbb{1} \otimes a^N)\left[C \otimes \prod_{k=1}^{n} A_k(g_k)\right]\psi\right\| \leq (4a)^n \sqrt{n!} \, \|g_1\|_T \cdots \|g_n\|_T \underbrace{\|(C \otimes (2^{\frac{1}{2}}a)^N)\psi\|}_{\leq \|C\| \, \|(\mathbb{1} \otimes (2^{\frac{1}{2}}a)^N)\psi\|}$$

for all $\psi \in D$ and every $a \geq 1$, where $\|.\|_T$ is the graph norm of $T^{\frac{1}{2}}$ from above.

(b) *Let $m, n \in \mathbb{N}$. The mapping*

$$(C_1, \ldots, C_m, g_1, \ldots, g_n) \longmapsto \prod_{j=1}^{m} C_j \otimes \prod_{k=1}^{n} A_k(g_k)$$

is jointly F-continuous on D, with respect to the strong operator topology on (norm) bounded subsets of $\mathcal{L}(\mathcal{H})$ for the C_j, and with respect to the graph norm $\|.\|_T$ on E for the g_k. That means: If for each $j \in \{1, \ldots, m\}$ we have a sequence $\lim_{\nu \to \infty} C_{j,\nu} = C_j$ in the strong operator topology with $\|C_{j,\nu}\| \leq c_j$ for all $\nu \in \mathbb{N}$ for some $c_j > 0$ in $\mathcal{L}(\mathcal{H})$ (also $\|C_j\| \leq c_j$), and if for each $k \in \{1, \ldots, n\}$ we have a sequence $\lim_{\nu \to \infty} \|g_{k,\nu} - g_k\|_T = 0$ in E, then it follows that

$$\lim_{\nu \to \infty} \left\|(\mathbb{1} \otimes a^N)\left[\prod_{j=1}^{m} C_{j,\nu} \otimes \prod_{k=1}^{n} A_k(g_{k,\nu}) - \prod_{j=1}^{m} C_j \otimes \prod_{k=1}^{n} A_k(g_k)\right]\psi\right\| = 0$$

for each $a \geq 1$ and every $\psi \in D$.

By part (a) the interaction operator Υ from (53.0.4) acts F-continuously on D.

Proof. [Hint] Part (a) is similarly treated to Lemma 5.1 and its proof in [Hon90c]. A further multiplicative factor $2^{\frac{n}{2}}$ in the F-estimations of (a) arises from the possibility that the $A_k(g_k)$ are not only annihilation and creation operators as in [Hon90c], but also are allowed to be field operators. Part (b) is shown analogously to Lemma 51.3-3(b). □

By construction, the representation Π is continuous with respect to the graph norm $\|.\|_T$, so we may extend E to its completion (denoted by the same symbol) with respect to some LC-topology stronger than or equal to $\|.\|_T$, in which also $t \mapsto e^{itS}$ is strongly LC-continuous. Especially, $t \mapsto e^{itS}$ is strongly $\|.\|_T$-continuous, since e^{itS} commutes with $T^{\frac{1}{2}}$. For the extension of the test function space, states, and representations we refer to Sec. 18.2.4 on page 414. This completion procedure of E ensures the convergence of the cocycle solution integral

$$\psi_t(\varrho) \equiv \psi(t, \varrho) = \int_{t=0}^{t} ds\, e^{isS} \phi(\varphi_s \varrho)$$

within the completed test function space E, for every LC-continuous initial value function $\varrho \mapsto \phi(\varrho) \in E$.

Theorem 53.1-3 (Persistence of the Results). *For LC-completed E, we get in the present $\mathcal{H} \otimes \mathcal{K}$ the completely analogous results as in the previous sections for the single Fock case.*

The only exception is the Kato–Rellich self-adjointness of Proposition 51.2-1(b), which depends essentially on the single-Fock situation, and there seems to be no analog for the double-Fock case. The main reason is that the free Boson Hamiltonian R, here from (53.1.1), cannot be semi-bounded from below, in contrast to the free Boson Hamiltonian $d\Gamma(S)$ in the single-Fock situation.

53.2.   Convergence in Fock⊗Classic Representations

A second type of a Fock-like representation is achieved as the GNS representation of a macroscopic classical state. Its GNS Hilbert space is of the type $F_+ \otimes L^2$ or $F_+ \otimes F_+ \otimes L^2$, etc., where some classical field part acts by commutative multiplication on the L^2- Hilbert space.

The most simple example is given in terms of a fully coherent state ω corresponding to an unbounded $\mathbb{C}$-linear form $L : E \to \mathbb{C}$, where the unboundedness of L is with respect to the norm $\|.\|$ on E inherited from $\mathcal{V}$, in formula,

$$\omega \in \mathcal{S}_L^{(\infty)}(E, \hbar = 1) = \mathcal{S}_{cl,L}^{(\infty)}(E, \hbar = 1), \quad \text{with unbounded } L : E \to \mathbb{C}.$$

For the results used here, we refer to Sec. 26.4. To ω there exists a unique probability measure μ_ω on the torus $U(1) = \{z \in \mathbb{C} \mid |z| = 1\}$, such that the characteristic function of ω is given by

$$\langle \omega; W(f) \rangle = \exp\{-\tfrac{1}{4}\|f\|^2\} \int_{U(1)} \exp\{i 2^{\frac{1}{2}} \operatorname{Re}(L(f)z)\}\, d\mu_\omega(z), \quad \forall f \in E.$$

In order that ω is a time-invariant state according to Eq. (53.0.2), the linear form L has to be time-invariant, in the sense of $L(e^{itS} f) = L(f)$ for all $f \in E$ and all $t \in \mathbb{R}$. An example for such a time-invariant L is given by

$$E := \mathrm{S}(\mathbb{R}^3, \mathbb{C}), \qquad S := -\Delta, \qquad L(f) := \widehat{f}(0) = \frac{1}{(2\pi)^{\frac{3}{2}}} \int_{\mathbb{R}^3} f(x)\, d^3x, \quad \forall f \in E,$$

that is, $E = \mathrm{S}(\mathbb{R}^3, \mathbb{C})$ is the Schwartz space (that are the functions $f : \mathbb{R}^3 \to \mathbb{C}$ of rapid decrease at infinity, e.g., [RS73b], [RS75]), the one-Boson Hamiltonian S is the negative Laplacian on $\mathbb{R}^3$ (thus, $e^{itS} E = E$), and the linear form $L(f) = \widehat{f}(0)$ acts by evaluation at zero momentum $k = 0$ of the Fourier transforms $\widehat{f}(k) = (2\pi)^{-3/2} \int_{\mathbb{R}^3} e^{ik \cdot x} f(x)\, d^3x$, $k \in \mathbb{R}^3$, a linear form also occurring with Bose–Einstein condensation.

The GNS representation $(\Pi, \mathcal{K}) \equiv (\Pi_\omega, \mathcal{H}_\omega)$ of the fully coherent ω is given by

$$\mathcal{K} = F_+(\mathcal{V}) \otimes \mathrm{L}^2(U(1), \mathbb{C}; \mu_\omega),$$

$$W(f) \equiv \Pi(W(f)) = W_F(f) \otimes \exp\{i2^{\frac{1}{2}} \operatorname{Re}(L(f)u)\}, \quad \forall f \in E.$$

Here u is the unitary on $\mathrm{L}^2(U(1), \mathbb{C}; \mu_\omega)$ acting by multiplication with z, that is, $(u\xi)(z) = z\xi(z)$ for all $z \in U(1)$ and every $\xi \in \mathrm{L}^2(U(1), \mathbb{C}; \mu_\omega)$. The field, annihilation, and creation operators associated with the GNS representation Π are expressed by those on Fock space and with the unitary u according to

$$\Phi_\Pi(f) = \Phi_F(f) \otimes \mathbb{1} + \mathbb{1} \otimes 2^{\frac{1}{2}} \operatorname{Re}(L(f)u),$$

$$a_\Pi(f) = a_F(f) \otimes \mathbb{1} + \mathbb{1} \otimes \overline{L(f)}u^*,$$

$$a_\Pi^*(f) = a_F^*(f) \otimes \mathbb{1} + \mathbb{1} \otimes L(f)u.$$

Because of the time-invariance of L, the implementing self-adjoint Hamiltonian R, satisfying $R\Omega_\omega = 0$ for the cyclic vector $\Omega_\omega = \Omega_{\mathrm{vac}} \otimes 1$ (here $1(z) = 1$ for all $z \in U(1)$ is the constant 1-function), according to Eq. (53.0.3), is simply given by

$$R = d\Gamma(S) \otimes \mathbb{1}.$$

Using this GNS representation Π for the Boson side, let us return to our composite matter–Boson system on the tensor product Hilbert space $\mathcal{H} \otimes \mathcal{K}$, with the interacting Hamiltonian H from Eq. (53.0.4). Here we define the "number" operator N on the representation Hilbert space $\mathcal{K} = F_+(\mathcal{V}) \otimes \mathrm{L}^2(U(1), \mathbb{C}; \mu_\omega)$ by

$$N := N_F \otimes \mathbb{1} \qquad \Rightarrow \qquad a^N = a^{N_F} \otimes \mathbb{1}, \ \forall a \geq 1.$$

This leads in $\mathcal{H} \otimes \mathcal{K}$ to the F-space

$$D := \bigcap_{a \geq 1} \operatorname{dom}(\mathbb{1} \otimes a^N) \quad \subset \mathcal{H} \otimes \mathcal{K},$$

equipped with the F-topology arising from the directed system of norms

$$D \ni \psi \mapsto \|(\mathbb{1} \otimes a^N)\psi\|, \quad a \geq 1.$$

With this F-space setup, we finally arrive at the subsequent analog to Lemma 51.3-3, and thus at the validity of all other results from the previous sections in the single-Fock situation. For their formulation, we introduce on E the two norms $\|f\|_L$ and $\|f\|'_L$, the first one arising from an inner product,

$$(f|g)_L := (f|g) + \overline{L(f)}L(g) \quad \Rightarrow \quad \|f\|_L = \sqrt{(f|f)_L}, \qquad \|f\|'_L := \|f\| + |L(f)|.$$

These norms are equivalent via $\|f\|_L \le \|f\|'_L \le 2^{\frac{1}{2}}\|f\|_L$ for all $f \in E$. Like for the single-Fock situation, in order to treat simultaneously products of Π-represented annihilation, creation, and field operators, we write $\mathsf{A}_k(g_k)$ for $a_\Pi(g_k)$, or $a_\Pi^*(g_k)$, and $\Phi_\Pi(g_k) = 2^{-\frac{1}{2}}(a_\Pi(g_k) + a_\Pi^*(g_k))$, i.e.,

$$\mathsf{A}_k(g_k) \in \{a_\Pi(g_k),\ a_\Pi^*(g_k),\ \Phi_\Pi(g_k)\}, \qquad g_k \in E.$$

Lemma 53.2-1 (F-Estimations, F-Continuity). *The following two assertions are valid:*

(a) *For $C \in \mathcal{L}(\mathcal{H})$ and $g_1, \ldots g_n \in E$ (with $n \in \mathbb{N}$) the operator $C \otimes \prod\limits_{k=1}^{n} \mathsf{A}_k(g_k)$*

acts F-continuously on D, and we have the F-estimations

$$\left\|(\mathbb{1} \otimes a^N)\big[C \otimes \prod_{k=1}^{n} \mathsf{A}_k(g_k)\big]\psi\right\| \le (2a)^n \sqrt{n!}\,\|g_1\|'_L \ \cdots\ \|g_n\|'_L \underbrace{\left\|(C \otimes (2^{\frac{1}{2}}a)^N)\psi\right\|}_{\le \|C\|\,\|(\mathbb{1}\otimes(2^{\frac{1}{2}}a)^N)\psi\|}$$

for all $\psi \in D$ and every $a \ge 1$.

(b) *Let $m, n \in \mathbb{N}$. The mapping*

$$(C_1, \ldots, C_m, g_1, \ldots, g_n) \longmapsto \prod_{j=1}^{m} C_j \otimes \prod_{k=1}^{n} \mathsf{A}_k(g_k)$$

is jointly F-continuous on D, with respect to the strong operator topology on (norm) bounded subsets of $\mathcal{L}(\mathcal{H})$ for the C_j, and with respect to the norm $\|.\|'_L$ or $\|.\|_L$ on E for the g_k. That means: If for each $j \in \{1, \ldots, m\}$ we have a sequence $\lim\limits_{\nu \to \infty} C_{j,\nu} = C_j$ in the strong operator topology with $\|C_{j,\nu}\| \le c_j$ for all $\nu \in \mathbb{N}$ for some $c_j > 0$ in $\mathcal{L}(\mathcal{H})$ (also $\|C_j\| \le c_j$), and if for each $k \in \{1, \ldots, n\}$ we have a sequence $\lim\limits_{\nu \to \infty} \|g_{k,\nu} - g_k\|'_L = 0$ in E, then it follows that

$$\lim_{\nu \to \infty} \left\|(\mathbb{1} \otimes a^N)\left[\prod_{j=1}^{m} C_{j,\nu} \otimes \prod_{k=1}^{n} \mathsf{A}_k(g_{k,\nu}) - \prod_{j=1}^{m} C_j \otimes \prod_{k=1}^{n} \mathsf{A}_k(g_k)\right]\psi\right\| = 0$$

for each $a \ge 1$ and every $\psi \in D$.

Note, by part (a) the interaction operator Υ from (53.0.4) acts F-continuously on D.

Proof. We generalize the proof of Lemma 51.3-3. Instead of (51.3.5) we obtain here for the ℓ-particle vectors $\eta \in P_+(\otimes_\ell \mathcal{V}) \otimes \mathrm{L}^2(U(1), \mathbb{C}; \mu_\omega)$,

$$\|a_\Pi^*(f)\eta\| \le \|(a_F^*(f) \otimes \mathbb{1})\eta\| + \|L(f)(\mathbb{1} \otimes u)\eta\| \le (\ell+1)^{\frac{1}{2}}\|f\|\,\|\eta\| + |L(f)|\,\|\eta\|$$
$$\le (\ell+1)^{\frac{1}{2}}(\|f\| + |L(f)|)\,\|\eta\| = (\ell+1)^{\frac{1}{2}}\|f\|'_L\,\|\eta\|,$$

analogously for $a_\Pi(f)$. Consequently, for all $f \in E$ and all $\ell \in \mathbb{N}_0$,

$$\|\mathsf{A}(f)\eta\| \leq 2^{\frac{1}{2}}(\ell+1)^{\frac{1}{2}}\|f\|'_L\|\eta\|, \quad \forall \eta \in P_+(\otimes_\ell \mathcal{V}) \otimes \mathrm{L}^2(U(1), \mathbb{C}; \mu_\omega).$$

Again the factor $2^{\frac{1}{2}}$ arises from the fact that possibly $\mathsf{A}(f) = \Phi_\Pi(f) = 2^{-\frac{1}{2}}(a_\Pi(f) + a_\Pi^*(f))$ is a field operator. The rest of the proof is the same as before. $\qquad\square$

By construction, the representation Π is $\|.\|_L$-continuous, and so we have to complete E with respect to an LC-topology stronger than or equal to $\|.\|_L$, in accordance with the extension technique in Sec. 18.2.4. The only condition on the LC-topology is that $t \mapsto e^{itS}$ has to be strongly LC-continuous (note, $t \mapsto e^{itS}$ is strongly $\|.\|_L$-continuous). This becomes necessary for the same reason as before, the convergence of the cocycle solution integral $\psi_t(\varrho) = \int_0^t ds\, e^{isS}\phi(\varphi_s\varrho)$ for every LC-continuous initial value function $\varrho \mapsto \phi(\varrho) \in E$.

Theorem 53.2-2 (Persistence of the Results). *It follows that in $\mathcal{H} \otimes \mathcal{K}$ we obtain for LC-completed E the completely analogous results as in the single=Fock case of the previous sections. The only exception is the "Kato–Rellich" self-adjointness outlined in Proposition 51.2-1(b).*

Of course, with our two examples in the present and the section before, we only scratched at the potential for generalizations from the present representations to further Bosonic Fock-like representations $(\Pi, \mathcal{K})$.

53.3. The Partially Commutative Situation

Let us finally return to our partially commutative situation for the material part as in Assumption 52.1-1. There we do not need all the convergence investigations for Dyson perturbation expansions in order to formulate the interacting unitary dynamical evolutions. On the other side, this global generalization has other disadvantages.

For the partially commutative material system, we suppose again the commutative sub-C*-algebra $\mathcal{A}_{\mathrm{com}}$ of $\mathcal{L}(\mathcal{H})$ isomorphic to the C*-algebra $C_b(\mathrm{P}, \mathbb{C})$ via the spectral measure $dP(\varrho)$, and the flow κ_t on the "classical phase space" P determined by the Heisenberg dynamics $\alpha_t^{\mathrm{mat}}(.) = e^{itA} \cdot e^{-itA}$ in restriction to $\mathcal{A}_{\mathrm{com}} \cong C_b(\mathrm{P}, \mathbb{C})$.

For the Boson system, the complex test function space E be a complete LC-space for an LC-topology stronger than the norm inherited from $\mathcal{V}$. Moreover, the restriction $t \mapsto e^{itS}|_E$ of the unitary one-Boson dynamics to E be a strongly LC-continuous one-parameter group on E. We choose the representation $(\Pi, \mathcal{K})$ of $\mathcal{W}(E, \mathrm{Im}(.|.))$ to be LC-continuous, such that in addition the Hamiltonian implementation (53.0.1) exists. In the representation, $E \ni f \mapsto W(f)$ is strongly continuous with respect to the LC-topology on E, and consequently, the unitaries of type

$$Q(\zeta, \psi) = \int_P e^{i\zeta(\varrho)} \left[\mathbb{1} \otimes W(\psi(\varrho)) \right] (dP(\varrho) \otimes \mathbb{1}) \in \mathcal{M}_{\mathrm{com}} \otimes \mathcal{M}_{\mathrm{bos}},$$

now acting on $\mathcal{H} \otimes \mathcal{K}$, are well defined by Sec. 52.1.1, and possess the analogous properties as in Proposition 52.1-8 on page 1956. However, here $\varrho \mapsto \psi(\varrho) \in E$ has to be LC-continuous.

This allows to proceed in the same way as in Sec. 52.2, which we present in terms of a summarizing result.

Proposition 53.3-1 (Cocycle Equations, Group Property, and Solutions).
The unitaries $V_t := Q(\zeta_t, \psi_t) e^{itK}$, where $t \in \mathbb{R}$, define a strongly continuous unitary one-parameter group on $\mathcal{H} \otimes \mathcal{K}$ (with $V_t^* = V_{-t}$ and $V_0 = \mathbb{1}$), if and only if ψ_t and ζ_t satisfy the cocycle relations

$$\psi_{s+t}(\varrho) = \psi_s(\varrho) + e^{isS} \psi_t(\varphi_s \varrho), \tag{53.3.1}$$

$$\zeta_{s+t}(\varrho) = \zeta_s(\varrho) + \zeta_t(\varphi_s \varrho) - \frac{1}{2} \operatorname{Im}(\psi_s(\varrho)|e^{isS}\psi_t(\varphi_s \varrho)), \tag{53.3.2}$$

for each $\varrho \in P$ and all $s, t \in \mathbb{R}$. Here $\psi : \mathbb{R} \times P \to E$ has to be LC-continuous, and $\zeta : \mathbb{R} \times P \to \mathbb{R}$ be continuous as before.

With the LC-continuous initial value $\phi : P \to E$, $\varrho \mapsto \phi(\varrho) := \frac{\partial \psi_t(\varrho)}{\partial t}\big|_{t=0}$, where the derivation exists in LC-topology, the first cocycle Eq. (53.3.1) is uniquely solvable by

$$\psi_t(\varrho) \equiv \psi(t, \varrho) = \int_{t_1=0}^{t} dt_1 \, e^{it_1 S} \phi(\varphi_{t_1} \varrho) \in E.$$

(It is just here for the LC-convergence of differentiation and integral that we essentially need the LC-completeness of E.)

The solution of the second cocycle Eq. (53.3.2) is given as in Proposition 52.2-2(b).

A formal calculation, mimicking the proof of Theorem 52.2-3, demonstrates that then the self-adjoint generator H of the strongly continuous unitary one-parameter group

$$e^{itH} = Q(\zeta_t, \psi_t) e^{itK}, \quad \forall t \in \mathbb{R}, \tag{53.3.3}$$

turns out to have the shape (for λ see Eq. (52.2.5))

$$H = \underbrace{A \otimes \mathbb{1} + \mathbb{1} \otimes R}_{= K,\ \text{free Hamilton.}} + \underbrace{\left[\int_P \lambda(\varrho)\, dP(\varrho) \right] \otimes \mathbb{1} + \int_P \left[\mathbb{1} \otimes \Phi_\Pi(\phi(\varrho)) \right] (dP(\varrho) \otimes \mathbb{1})}_{= \Upsilon,\ \text{interaction}}.$$

But here the spectral integral operator in Υ is subtle to define in a mathematically precise manner by always the same reason, namely, the unboundedness of the field operators $\Phi_\Pi(f)$ (see e.g., [Bös76]).

Choosing $\lambda = 0$ and the coupling function to be

$$\phi : \mathsf{P} \to E, \quad \varrho \mapsto \phi(\varrho) := 2^{\frac{1}{2}} \sum_{j=1}^{M} \xi_j(\varrho)\phi_j$$

with $\xi_j \in C_b(\mathsf{P}, \mathbb{C})$ and $\phi_j \in E$, we finally regain H from Eq. (53.0.4) with

$$B_j = \int_{\mathsf{P}} \overline{\xi_j(\varrho)} \, dP(\varrho) \in \mathcal{A}_{\mathrm{com}}. \quad \forall j \in \{1, \dots, M\}.$$

Summary 53.3-2. In the partially commutative situation we are able to introduce strongly continuous unitary one-parameter groups of type (53.3.3) on $\mathcal{H} \otimes \mathcal{K}$ for the interacting Schrödinger dynamics. But, because of the lack of some kind of growth control for the field, annihilation, and creation operators in such a general Bosonic representation Π, we cannot deduce their generators in a mathematically precise manner.

The latter difficulty, however, may be overcome by choosing a Fock-like representation Π, as we have recognized in the previous sections.

Nevertheless, the results of Sec. 52.2.2 remain valid, when replacing $F_+(\mathcal{V})$ by $\mathcal{K}$, and also when replacing $\mathcal{L}(\mathcal{K})$ by $\mathcal{M}_{\mathrm{bos}}$. We have the inclusions

$$\mathcal{A}_{\mathrm{com}} \otimes \mathbb{1} \subset \mathcal{M}_{\mathrm{com}} \overline{\otimes} \mathcal{M}_{\mathrm{bos}} \subset \mathcal{M}'_{\mathrm{com}} \overline{\otimes} \mathcal{M}_{\mathrm{bos}}$$

(here $\overline{\otimes}$ is the W*-tensor product), and the interacting, respectively the free one-parameter *-automorphism group for the related Heisenberg dynamics, cf. Eq. (52.2.8), is

$$\alpha_t^{\mathrm{int}}(.) = e^{itH} \cdot e^{-itH} = Q(\zeta_t, \psi_t) \underbrace{e^{itK} \cdot e^{-itK}}_{= \alpha_t^{\mathrm{free}}(.)} Q(\zeta_t, \psi_t)^*, \quad t \in \mathbb{R}.$$

By the construction in Eq. (53.0.1), $\alpha_t^{\mathrm{bos}}(.) = e^{itR} \cdot e^{-itR}$ leaves $\mathcal{M}_{\mathrm{bos}}$ invariant, and thus its commutant, too.

Corollary 53.3-3 (Automorphism Group on $\mathcal{M}'_{\mathrm{com}} \otimes \mathcal{M}_{\mathrm{bos}}$, $\mathcal{M}'_{\mathrm{com}} \otimes \mathcal{L}(\mathcal{K})$). *The free and interacting *-automorphism groups, α^{tot} resp. α^{free}, leave both von Neumann algebras $\mathcal{M}'_{\mathrm{com}} \otimes \mathcal{M}_{\mathrm{bos}}$ and $\mathcal{M}'_{\mathrm{com}} \otimes \mathcal{L}(\mathcal{K})$ invariant. Furthermore,*

$$\alpha_t^{\mathrm{tot}}(Z) = Q(\eta, \psi_t)\, \alpha_t^{\mathrm{free}}(Z)\, Q(\eta, \psi_t)^*, \quad \forall Z \in \mathcal{M}'_{\mathrm{com}} \otimes \mathcal{L}(\mathcal{K}),$$

*for arbitrary continuous $\eta : \mathsf{P} \to \mathbb{R}$ (not necessarily bounded), especially for $\eta = 0$. So, for the restricted *-automorphism group α^{tot}, the previous phase factors ζ_t are superfluous. They are, however, needed to make $\mathbb{R} \ni t \mapsto V_t := Q(\zeta_t, \psi_t)\, e^{itK}$ to an implementing unitary group (provided the cocycle equations of Proposition 53.3-1 are satisfied).*

PART P
Gauges and Fiber Bundles

Chapter 54

Manifolds and Fibre Bundles
over CLC-Spaces

54.1. Differentiable Mappings on CLC-Spaces

Let us consider a mapping $A : E \to F$ between CLC-spaces (= complete, locally convex Hausdorff topological vector spaces). The directional derivative (Gateaux derivative), at the point $f \in E$ in the direction $g \in E$ is introduced as

$$d_f A(g) \equiv \delta_f A(g) := \lim_{\varepsilon \to 0} \frac{A(f + \varepsilon g) - A(f)]}{\varepsilon} , \qquad (54.1.1)$$

if the limit exists in F. (The second "functional" notation of the differential is frequently used in physical contexts, if E is an infinite-dimensional function space.) Even if the limit exists for all $g \in E$, the derivative at the point f, that is the function $g \mapsto d_f A(g) \in F$, need not be linear in g. That kind of linearity, as well as certain continuity properties, and even some estimations have to be demanded for a well behaved differential calculus (e.g., [Kel74], [Fis76], [Gut77], [Sch78a], [Sch79], [Ham82], [Sch83], [Nee01]).

The existence of the limit (54.1.1) and its linearity and continuity with respect to the direction g may be combined into the following requirement: There is a linear function $E \ni g \mapsto d_f A(g) \in F$ such that the real function on an open neighborhood of zero $U(0,0) \subset \mathbb{R} \times E$

$$R(\varepsilon, g) := \begin{cases} [A(f + \varepsilon g) - A(f) - d_f A(\varepsilon g)] / \varepsilon , & \varepsilon \neq 0 , \\ 0 , & \varepsilon = 0 , \end{cases} \qquad (54.1.2)$$

be continuous. In this manner we formulate a recursive definition of C^n-mappings.

Definition 54.1-1. Let be given the CLC-spaces E and F and a map $A : U \to F$, where U is open in E.

(a) We say A is a $C^0(U, F)$-*mapping*, if it is continuous.
(b) We say A is a $C^n(U, F)$-*mapping*, if it is a $C^{n-1}(U, F)$-mapping and if there exists a symmetric n-linear mapping $d_f^n A \equiv \delta_f^n A : E \times \overset{n}{\cdots} \times E \to F$ for all

$f \in U$, such that the real function R on an open neighborhood of zero $U(0,0) \subset \mathbb{R} \times E$, defined by

$$R(\varepsilon, g) := \varepsilon^{-n} \left[A(f + \varepsilon g) - A(f) - d_f A(\varepsilon g) - \cdots - \tfrac{1}{n!} d_f^n A(\varepsilon g, \cdots, \varepsilon g) \right] \quad (54.1.3)$$

for $\varepsilon \neq 0$ and $R(0, g) := 0$ for $\varepsilon = 0$ is continuous. Further on, the function

$$d_{\cdot}^n A(\cdot, \ldots, \cdot) := U \times E \times \overset{n}{\cdots} \times E \to F \qquad (54.1.4)$$

is to be continuous.

If E and F are Banach spaces, then the $R(\varepsilon, g)$ are by assumption norm continuous, and the difference quotients converge in norm to the differential quotients.

If E is a subspace of the continuous real functions $C^0(\mathcal{M}, \mathbb{R})$ on the topological space $\mathcal{M}$, the Dirac measure δ_m is an element in E', such that $\delta_m(f) = f(m)$ for all $m \in \mathcal{M}$. If there is a scalar product $(\cdot|\cdot)$ on E, such that all evaluation maps $f \mapsto f(m)$ are norm continuous, then there is a reproducing kernel $m \mapsto \Delta_m \in \overline{E}^{\|\cdot\|}$ such that

$$f(m) = (\Delta_m | f) =: \int_{\mathcal{M}} \Delta_m(m') f(m') dm' , \qquad (54.1.5)$$

where the *formal* integration is a useful *symbolism* for calculations. The map $m' \mapsto \Delta_m(m')$ is often called the "delta function" or the "Dirac function" at the point m. In quantum optics, the "transversal delta function" $\mathbb{R}^3 \ni x' \to \delta_x^\top(x') = \sum_{n=1}^\infty |\mathbf{f}_n(x)\rangle\langle\mathbf{f}_n(x')|$, with $\{\mathbf{f}_n(x) \,|\, n \in \mathbb{N}\}$ an orthonormal basis in the transversal test function space, plays an important role. Then one writes formally

$$\delta_f^n A(\Delta_{m_1}, \cdots, \Delta_{m_n}) =: \frac{\delta^n A(f)}{\delta f(m_1) \cdots \delta f(m_n)} , \qquad (54.1.6)$$

which leads, in view of the n-linearity of the derivative, to the symbolic equation

$$\delta_f^n A(g_1, \cdots, g_n) = \int_{\mathcal{M}^n} \frac{\delta^n A(f)}{\delta f(m_1) \cdots \delta f(m_n)} \, g_1(m_1) \cdots g_n(m_n) dm_1 \cdots dm_n. \qquad (54.1.7)$$

The general differential calculus on infinite-dimensional spaces is a concise version of the so-called functional differentiation.

In frequent applications, E is a subspace of the continuous real functions $C^0(\mathcal{M}, \mathbb{R})$, where $\mathcal{M}$ equals a Cartesian product of a finite set of indices $\{1, \cdots, r\}$ times a continuous configuration space $\mathcal{O}$, and one writes $f(m) = f_\alpha(x)$, as well as

$$\frac{\delta A(f)}{\delta f(m)} = \frac{\delta A(f)}{\delta f_\alpha(x)} .$$

If $f_\alpha(x)$ is independent of $x \in \mathcal{O}$, then f is an r-tuple $f = (f_1, \cdots, f_r) \in \mathbb{R}^r \equiv E$ and one writes

$$\frac{\delta A(f)}{\delta f(m)} = \frac{\partial A(f)}{\partial f_\alpha} ,$$

which makes explicit that the partial differentiation is a special case of the functional differentiation. We use this in the Lagrange formalism for a unified notation to differentiate either to the position maps $\mathbf{q}(x)$ or to the position vectors $\mathbf{q}^j$ of the point charges in Sec. 7.1 on page 119. The formal integration of Eq. (54.1.7) goes then over into a finite sum

$$\delta_f^n A(g^1, \cdots, g^n) \equiv d_f^n A(g^1, \cdots, g^n) = \sum_{\alpha_1, \cdots, \alpha_n = 1}^{r} \frac{\partial^n A(f)}{\partial f_{\alpha_1} \cdots \partial f_{\alpha_n}} g_{\alpha_1}^1 \cdots g_{\alpha_n}^n .$$

Definition 54.1-2 (Diffeomorphisms). A map $A \in C^n(U, F)$, with $U \subset E$ open and with an open image $A(U) = V \subset F$, which has an inverse map $A^{-1} \in C^n(V, U)$ is called an *n-diffeomorphism*, which we denote by $A \in \mathrm{Diff}^n(U, V)$.
    If $V = U$, we write $\mathrm{Diff}^n(U) := \mathrm{Diff}^n(U, U)$.

Proposition 54.1-3 (Chain Rule). *Let E, F, G be three CLC-spaces and U an open subset of E, and V an open subset of F. Let $A : U \to F$ and $B : V \to G$, with $A(U) \subset V$, be two n-differentiable mappings between CLC-spaces, according to Definition 54.1-1. Then the composite map $C = B \circ A : U \to G$ is n-differentiable and it holds:*

$$\delta_f C(g) = \delta_{A(f)} B\big(\delta_f A(g)\big) . \tag{54.1.8}$$

(*Observe that both $A(f)$ and $\delta_f A(g)$ are elements in F, on which B is defined.*) *If $E \ni f$ is a real function on $\mathcal{M}$ and each $h \in F$ is a real function on $\mathcal{W} \ni w$, then $w \mapsto A(f)(w)$ is a real function on $\mathcal{W}$, and we may write a point-wise formal version of the chain rule*

$$\delta_f C(\Delta_m) \equiv \frac{\delta C(f)}{\delta f(m)} = \int_{\mathcal{W}} \frac{\delta B(A(f))}{\delta A(f)(w)} \frac{\delta A(f)(w)}{\delta f(m)} \, dw , \quad m \in \mathcal{M} . \tag{54.1.9}$$

(*Only under very stringent conditions can this formulation be made mathematically meaningful in a literal manner, where e.g., dw may be the Lebesgue measure on $\mathbb{R}^n$.*)

Remark 54.1-4 (Relation to the Composition Formula of Tangent Maps). Assume the situation of Proposition 54.1-3. The differential of $A : U \to F$ may be viewed as the map $\delta . A(.) \equiv \delta A \equiv dA : U \times E \to V \times F$, that is, the tangent map of A over linear coordinate spaces (cf. Definition 54.4-5 on page 2015). That means explicitly $dA(f, \hat{f}) = (A(f), d_f A(\hat{f}))$. Likewise we have the tangent map of $B : V \to G$, namely $\delta B \equiv dB : V \times F \to B(V) \times G$. In this notation, the chain rule (54.1.8) assumes the simple form

$$dC = dB \circ dA \quad \text{if} \quad C = B \circ A , \tag{54.1.10}$$

and is a special case of the composition formula of tangent maps.

The chain rule enables to compose ($=$ multiply) n-diffeomorphisms to n-diffeomorphisms, whenever the domains and images fit together. The pertinent concept is as follows (cf. [KN69], also [Kob72]).

Definition 54.1-5 (Pseudo Group).   A pseudo group of transformations over a topological space $\mathcal{S}$ is a set Υ of transformations with the following properties:

(1) Each $f \in \Upsilon$ is a homeomorphism between open subsets of $\mathcal{S}$.
(2) If f is in Υ, then each restriction of f to an open subset of its domain is in Υ.
(3) If $\{U_\alpha | \alpha \in J\}$ is a family of open subsets of $\mathcal{S}$ and $U = \cup_\alpha U_\alpha$, then a homeomorphism $f : U \to V \subset \mathcal{S}$ is in Υ if and only if $f|_{U_\alpha} \in \Upsilon$ for all $\alpha \in J$.
(4) For each open U, the identity map $\mathbb{1}_U$ is in Υ.
(5) If $f \in \Upsilon$, then f^{-1} is in Υ.
(6) If $f, g \in \Upsilon$ and the image of f has a non-empty intersection V with the domain of g, then $g \circ f$, with domain $f^{-1}(V)$ (and image $g(V)$), is in Υ.

We conclude:

Proposition 54.1-6. *Let E be an arbitrary CLC-space. Then for fixed $n \in \mathbb{N}$, the set* $\mathrm{Diff}^n(U,V)$, *with the domains U varying among all open subsets of E, is a pseudo group, denoted* $\Upsilon^n(E)$.

Especially for E being a Banach space $\Upsilon^n(E)$ is a pseudo group, which has the same nice properties as the n-diffeomorphisms in finite-dimensional vector spaces.

In a general CLC-space E, some important theorems like the inverse mapping theorem and the implicit function theorem are not valid ([Sch60], [Ham82]). That leads to sharpen the conditions on the derivatives. For E being a so-called ILB-chain, that is a B-I-chain (see Definition 49.1-5 on page 1882) with I an infinite strictly ordered subset of $\mathbb{N}$, Omori in [Omo97] has formulated linear estimates leading to his ILB-normal mappings. For these, he establishes an ILB-inverse mapping theorem (Theorem 6.5) and an ILB-implicit function theorem (Theorem 6.9).

54.2.   Differentiable Manifolds and Fiber Bundles

54.2.1.   *Differentiable Manifolds*

We give a selection of basic concepts in the theory of differentiable manifolds in a manner, which seems appropriate also for the infinite-dimensional case. Infinite-dimensional manifolds have a canonical form only when modeled on a Banach space. We found that for classical and quantum field theories, more general model spaces should be used to avoid unphysical restrictions. This is why certain parts of our developments deal with a general LC-space (locally convex Hausdorff topological vector space) as model space of the manifold. In the present differential geometric exposition we use only complete LC-spaces, that are CLC-spaces.

As in the previous Chapter, we characterize a CLC-space by the symbol $E = E[(p_i)_I]$ which indicates the family $\{p_i \mid i \in I\}$ of semi-norms defining the topology in E. In this general context, our exposition has sometimes a tentative character.

Since in the finite-dimensional case, manifolds are popular in Mathematical Physics, we treat those considerations, which run parallel to the finite-dimensional case rather sketchy.

Just for this very broad and variable ansatz, the notion of a pseudo group, as introduced in the preceding section, seems adequate.

Definition 54.2-1 (Differentiable Manifold). Assume a CLC-space E and consider the pseudo group $\Upsilon^r(E)$ (consisting of all r-diffeomorphisms on any open subset of E onto its open image, where $r \in \{0, 1, 2, \ldots, \infty\}$).
A topological Hausdorff space $\mathcal{M}$ is called a C^r-*manifold* modeled on the CLC-space E, or shortly a C^r-E-*manifold*, if it is equipped with the following collection of structures.

(a) $\mathcal{M}$ is covered by an indexed family of open subsets $\{U_\alpha \mid \alpha \in J\}$ such that there is for each $\alpha \in J$ a homeomorphism $\phi_\alpha : U_\alpha \overset{onto}{\rightarrow} V_\alpha$, where $V_\alpha \subset E$ is open.
(b) If $U_\alpha \cap U_\beta \neq \emptyset$, the *transition function*

$$\phi_{\beta\alpha} \equiv \phi_\beta \circ \phi_\alpha^{-1} : \phi_\alpha(U_\alpha \cap U_\beta) \rightarrow \phi_\beta(U_\alpha \cap U_\beta)$$

is in $\Upsilon^r(E)$ (implying that $\phi_\alpha(U_\alpha \cap U_\beta)$ and $\phi_\beta(U_\alpha \cap U_\beta)$ are open in E).
(c) A family $\{(U_\alpha, \phi_\alpha) \mid \alpha \in J\}$ satisfying (a) and (b) above is called an *atlas* A and each pair (U_α, ϕ_α) a *chart* of $\mathcal{M}$. (Sometimes one calls $\{(V_\alpha, \phi_\alpha^{-1}) \mid \alpha \in J\}$ the atlas, or even so $\{(V_\alpha, \phi_\alpha) \mid \alpha \in J\}$.)
(d) A pair (U, ϕ), consisting of any open subset of $\mathcal{M}$ with an homeomorphism $\phi : U \overset{onto}{\rightarrow} V$, with V an open subset of E (also called *chart*), is *compatible* with an atlas A $= \{(U_\alpha, \phi_\alpha) \mid \alpha \in J\}$, if all transition functions $\phi \circ \phi_\alpha^{-1}$ are in $\Upsilon^r(E)$.
(e) An atlas A_c of $\mathcal{M}$ is called *complete*, if it is not strictly contained in any other atlas of $\mathcal{M}$, that is, if it contains all charts which are compatible with it.

The choice of a complete atlas A_c gives the *differentiable structure* on $\mathcal{M}$. More precisely, the pair $(\mathcal{M}, A_c)$ makes up the *differentiable manifold* (where we usually omit the symbol A_c and include still the case $r = 0$ for convenience.)

If we henceforth speak of an *(admissible) atlas* A *of a differentiable manifold*, it is understood that its charts are compatible with the chosen complete Atlas A_c (these are *admissible* charts).

If $\mathcal{M}$ has several connected components, the preceding definition implies that we take the same model space E for each component. If $\mathcal{M}$ is a discrete set, the connected components are the singletons and the model space is $E = \{0\}$ in each component.

Since the transition diffeomorphisms $\phi_{\beta\alpha}$ are taken from a pseudo group on the model space E, all restrictions of them to open subsets of the $\phi_\alpha(U_\alpha \cap U_\beta)$ are in this pseudo group. So, if (U, ϕ) is an admissible chart, then also $(U', \phi|_{U'})$ is an admissible chart if U' is an open subset of U. That shows that the refinement of an (admissible) atlas is again an (admissible) atlas. In practice, it is sufficient to specify a peculiar atlas on $\mathcal{M}$ (with as few cards as possible), since it already determines a differentiable structure (complete atlas) for $\mathcal{M}$.

Remark 54.2-2 (Refined Open Coverings). One often appeals to the fact, that for any open covering $\{U_\alpha | \alpha \in J\}$ of $\mathcal{M}$, there exists an admissible atlas, the chart patches of which are each contained in some U_α: If $\{(U'_\beta, \phi_\beta)| \beta \in J'\}$ is an admissible atlas take e.g., the atlas $\{(U_\alpha \cap U'_\beta, \phi^r_{\alpha\beta})| (\alpha, \beta) \in J \times J'\}$, with the restrictions of ϕ_β as chart maps.

Since all operations on the points of a differentiable manifold are performed via the operations in the chart images $V_\alpha \subset E$ the set $\dot{\cup}_{\alpha \in J} V_\alpha$ (the dot means disjoint union) may be viewed as the accessible aspect of the manifold. Each $x_\beta \in \dot{\cup}_{\alpha \in J} V_\alpha$ signifies a point $x = \phi_\beta^{-1}(x_\beta)$ in the "abstract" manifold $\mathcal{M}$. We consider x_β as a coordination of $x \in \mathcal{M}$. If also $x = \phi_\gamma^{-1}(x_\gamma)$, then this is the same as

$$x_\gamma = \phi_{\gamma\beta}(x_\beta), \quad \text{written as} \quad x_\gamma \approx x_\beta.$$

This symmetric binary relation is in fact an equivalence relation, since reflexivity and transitivity follow from

$$\phi_{\gamma\beta} \circ \phi_{\beta\gamma} = \mathrm{id}_{V_\gamma}, \quad \phi_{\gamma\beta} \circ \phi_{\beta\alpha} = \phi_{\gamma\alpha}. \tag{54.2.1}$$

Thus, there is a biunivocal correspondence between the $x \in \mathcal{M}$ and the equivalence classes $[x_\beta]$, which provide a complete and disjoint covering of $\dot{\cup}_{\alpha \in J} V_\alpha$. In certain cases — especially for fiber bundles (cf. below) — the *manifold is constructed* in terms of equivalence classes.

Let us give only a hint on how to proceed in the general case: Given $\dot{\cup}_{\alpha \in J} V_\alpha$ and the transition functions (54.2.1), one sets $\mathcal{M} := \dot{\cup}_{\alpha \in J} V_\alpha / \approx$. From (54.2.1), it follows that $\phi_{\alpha\alpha} = \mathrm{id}_{V_\alpha}$. This implies that in each $[x_\beta]$ dwells at most one element from V_α and this is denoted by $\phi_\alpha([x_\beta])$. This defines the chart mapping ϕ_α from the classes, with a representative in V_α, onto V_α. The topology is then the weakest topology in $\mathcal{M}$, which makes all chart mappings continuous.

If E is n-dimensional, the coordination can be performed in terms of n-tuples $x_\beta \in \mathbb{R}^n$. Especially for the space–time coordinates of a point event, one needs a prescription (appropriate for physical measurements), telling which of the employed real quadruples are equivalent, in order to formulate an abstract space–time manifold $\mathcal{O}$. The same applies for a 3-dimensional space manifold Λ, like our spatial domains for radiation, which are assumed to be open subsets of the Euclidean space $\mathbb{E}^3$.

Definition 54.2-3 (Submanifold). Let $\mathcal{M}$ be an E-manifold. A subset $\mathcal{S} \subset \mathcal{M}$ is a *submanifold*, if there is a closed subspace $F \subset E$ such that for each $x \in \mathcal{S}$, there is an admissible chart $\phi_\alpha : U_\alpha \to V_\alpha \subset F \oplus F^c = E$ such that $x \in U_\alpha$ and $\phi_\alpha(U_\alpha \cap S) = \phi_\alpha(U_\alpha) \cap (F \oplus \{0\})$.

If $\mathcal{M}$ is an E-manifold, an arbitrary open subset $\mathcal{S} \subset \mathcal{M}$ is a submanifold in the described sense, where $F = E$: For $x \in S$, any admissible chart $\phi_\alpha : U_\alpha \to V_\alpha \subset E \oplus \{0\}$ with $x \in U_\alpha$ will satisfy the requirements of Definition 54.2-3. Since the Euclidean space $\mathbb{E}^3$ is an $\mathbb{R}^3$-manifold (with an atlas $\{(U_\alpha, \phi_\alpha)| \alpha \in J\}$ say), any open $\Lambda \subset \mathbb{E}^3$ is a submanifold (with an atlas e.g., given by $\{(U_\alpha \cap \Lambda, \phi_\alpha|_{U_\alpha \cap \Lambda})| \alpha \in J\}$).

Only under additional regularity assumptions, of course, one may find admissible charts $\phi_\alpha : U_\alpha \to \mathbb{R}^3$ which make the boundary $\partial\Lambda$ piece-wise a two-dimensional submanifold of $\mathbb{E}^3$.

Definition 54.2-4 (Orientable Manifolds). We shall use an orientation of a manifold only in the finite-dimensional case.

So, let E be a finite-dimensional real vector space. Then a collection of its basis systems is called an *orientation*, if two basis systems of it are transformed into each other by means of a linear transformation with positive determinant.

A finite-dimensional manifold $\mathcal{M}$ on the finite-dimensional real vector space E is called *orientable* if there is an atlas $\{(U_\alpha, \phi_\alpha)| \alpha \in J\}$ such that, for all $\alpha, \beta \in J$, the transition functions (if they are definable)

$$\phi_{\beta\alpha} : \phi_\alpha(U_\alpha \cap U_\beta) \to \phi_\beta(U_\alpha \cap U_\beta)$$

have a derivative with positive determinant $d_x\phi_{\beta\alpha}$ for all $x \in U_\alpha \cap U_\beta$.

The choice of such an atlas defines then an *orientation* of $\mathcal{M}$.

In terms of the tangent spaces (see Definition 54.4-2 on page 2012): $\mathcal{M}$ is orientable, if its tangent spaces allow for a compatible orientation.

Up to now we had defined differentiable mappings only on CLC-spaces.

Definition 54.2-5 (Differentiable Manifold Mappings and Curves).

(a) A mapping f of an E-manifold $\mathcal{M}$, with atlas $\{(U_\alpha, \phi_\alpha)| \alpha \in J\}$, into another E'-manifold $\mathcal{M}'$, with atlas $\{(U'_\beta, \phi'_\beta)| \beta \in J'\}$, is a C^k-mapping, if for any pair $(\alpha, \beta) \in J \times J'$, for which the mapping $f_{\beta,\alpha} := \phi'_\beta \circ f \circ \phi_\alpha^{-1} : V_\alpha \to V'_\beta$ is defined (which requires $f(U_\alpha) \subset U'_\beta$), $f_{\beta,\alpha}$ is in the class C^k (in the sense of mappings between CLC-spaces).

(b) A C^k-bijection, $k \in \{0, 1, \ldots \infty\}$, f of an E-manifold $\mathcal{M}$ onto an E'-manifold $\mathcal{M}'$ is called *k-diffeomorphism*, or an element of $\text{Diff}^k(E, E')$ if its inverse is also C^k. If the degree of differentiability is left open, we speak simply of a *diffeomorphism*.

(c) A C^k-mapping, $k \in \{0, 1, \ldots \infty\}$, $c :] - a, a[\to \mathcal{M}$ for some $a > 0$, $\mathcal{M}$ an E-Manifold, is called a *smooth curve* through $c(0) =: m \in \mathcal{M}$.

54.2.2. *Fiber Bundles*

A large class of manifolds is fibred. In the subsequent discussions, the restriction to finite-dimensional fibred manifolds would not make much of the formulations simpler, what we take also as a justification for our more general approach, besides having in mind some applications to infinite-dimensional phase spaces.

Definition 54.2-6 (Coordinated Fiber Bundles). The three differentiable manifolds $\mathcal{B}$ (*total space*), $\mathcal{M}$ (*base space*), $\mathcal{F}$ (*standard or typical fiber*) and the smooth *projection* mapping $\pi : \mathcal{B} \overset{onto}{\to} \mathcal{M}$ make up a *coordinated fiber bundle*

$$\mathcal{B} = \mathcal{B}(\pi, \mathcal{M}, \mathcal{F}, \tau),$$

if there is given the following collection of structures. (The order k of differentiability is fixed throughout the general discussion of bundle theory, including the values $k = 0$ and $k = \infty$.)

There is an open, indexed covering $\{U_\alpha \,|\, \alpha \in J\}$ of $\mathcal{M}$, such that for each $\alpha \in J$, there exists a diffeomorphism (*local trivialization map*)

$$\tau_\alpha : \pi^{-1}(U_\alpha) \overset{onto}{\to} U_\alpha \times \mathcal{F} \tag{54.2.2}$$

with

$$(\pi \circ \tau_\alpha^{-1})(x, f) = x \,, \quad \forall (x, f) \in U_\alpha \times \mathcal{F} \,. \tag{54.2.3}$$

This trivialization structure is indicated by the symbol $\tau = \{(U_\alpha, \tau_\alpha) \,|\, \alpha \in J\}$.

The submanifold $\mathcal{F}_x := \pi^{-1}(x) \subset \mathcal{B}$ is called the *fiber at* $x \in \mathcal{M}$.

We assume in what follows that $\mathcal{M}$ is modeled over the CLC-space E, and $\mathcal{F}$ is modeled over the CLC-space F.

Remark 54.2-7 (Fiber Bundles and Coordination). In the preceding definition we have termed a fiber bundle $\mathcal{B} = \mathcal{B}(\pi, \mathcal{M}, \mathcal{F}, \tau)$, with a fixed trivialization structure τ, a "coordinated fiber bundle" in reference to Steenrod [Ste51]. (Steenrod designated these bundles as "coordinate bundles". We changed this term a little for avoiding a confusion with "frame bundles".) We adhere to this denomination in spite of the trivialization maps being only an intermediate step in forming true coordination maps, and this only, if the open covering $\{U_\alpha \,|\, \alpha \in J\}$ of the base manifold $\mathcal{M}$, as part of the trivialization structure τ, is meant to be an atlas of $\mathcal{M}$. To assume that — what we will do henceforth — is no restriction, since for any open covering $\{U_\alpha \,|\, \alpha \in J\}$, there exists an atlas of the differentiable manifold $\mathcal{M}$, each chart patch V_γ of which is contained in a U_α (see Remark 54.2-2). The τ_α restricted to $\pi^{-1}(V_\gamma)$ act then as refined trivialization maps.

Since $\{U_\alpha \,|\, \alpha \in J\}$, with certain chart maps $\phi_\alpha : U_\alpha \to E$, is now an atlas of $\mathcal{M}$, one can show that $\{(\pi^{-1}(U_\alpha), \tau_\alpha) \,|\, \alpha \in J\}$ provides an atlas for the total space $\mathcal{B}$, a so-called *bundle atlas*, if the τ_α are prolonged by chart maps of $\mathcal{M}$ and $\mathcal{F}$ into the respective model spaces E and F. This atlas is admissible for the original differentiable structure of $\mathcal{B}$ (on the model space $E \oplus F$).

To refer for a while to a fixed trivializing open covering, that is to a coordinated bundle, appears useful for a constructive approach to bundle theory.

The subsequent relations are *consequences* (combined with further definitions) of Definition 54.2-6.

The total space of a fiber bundle decomposes into a disjoint union (indicated by a dot over $\cup$) of fibers: $\mathcal{B} = \dot{\cup}\mathcal{F}_x$, $x \in \mathcal{M}$. It holds for $x \in U_\alpha$ that $\tau_\alpha(\mathcal{F}_x)$ is not only contained in, but is all of $\{x\} \times \mathcal{F}$, since each $b \in \tau_\alpha^{-1}(x, f)$ satisfies $\pi b = x$ and is thus an element of $\mathcal{F}_x$ for all $f \in \mathcal{F}$. So all (x, f), with $f \in \mathcal{F}$, are gained by $\tau_\alpha(b)$, for some $b \in \mathcal{F}_x$. Observe that each singleton $\{x\}$ is closed in $\mathcal{M}$. (Each point in the complement of $\{x\}$ has an open neighborhood within this complement in virtue of the Hausdorff property of $\mathcal{M}$. Thus, this complement is open, and $\{x\}$ is closed.) Thus each fiber $\mathcal{F}_x$ is closed in $\mathcal{B}$, since the projection π is continuous.

For $x \in U_\alpha$, we may introduce the diffeomorphism which associates the abstract (typical) fiber $\mathcal{F}$ with the fiber $\mathcal{F}_x$ embedded into the bundle space $\mathcal{B}$,

$$\tau_{\alpha x}^{-1} : \mathcal{F} \to \mathcal{F}_x, \quad \tau_{\alpha x}^{-1} f := \tau_\alpha^{-1}(x, f), \tag{54.2.4}$$

where τ_α^{-1} is the inverse trivialization map, so that $\tau_{\alpha x}^{-1}$ is a restriction of the latter. This leads to the *x-dependent fiber diffeomorphism*

$$\tau_{\alpha x} : \mathcal{F}_x \overset{onto}{\to} \mathcal{F}, \quad \text{expressing the trivialization map as}$$
$$\tau_\alpha b = (\pi b, \tau_{\alpha x} b) =: (x, f_{x,b}^\alpha) \in U_\alpha \times \mathcal{F}, \quad b \in \mathcal{F}_x. \tag{54.2.5}$$

Remark 54.2-8 (On b as a Quality Index). Our uncommon symbol $f_{x,b}^\alpha$ is meant to visualize the fact that the local trivializations associate with a bundle element $b \in \mathcal{B}$ an element of the typical fiber $\mathcal{F}$, which depends not only on the base space point $x \in \mathcal{M}$ and the index α of the trivialization map, but also on a further quality, inherited by b.

The role of b will be important to understand the non-triviality of fiber bundles.

Intuitively speaking, b represents a new quality associated with x — being in physics often a space-time point — which is only partially expressed by the fiber attached to x. In elementary particle physics, the fiber consists mostly of elements of an internal symmetry. The index b refers there to an entanglement of the symmetry states of the particle with surrounding space–time. That will become clearer in the discussion of gauge bundles.

Since $\tau_{\alpha x}^{-1}$ originates from the restriction of $\tau_\alpha^{-1} : U_\alpha \times \mathcal{F}$ to $\{x\} \times \mathcal{F}$, one concludes that

$$U_\alpha \times \mathcal{F} \ni (x, f) \mapsto \tau_{\alpha,x}^{-1} f \in \mathcal{F}_x \subset \pi^{-1}(U_\alpha) \tag{54.2.6}$$

is continuous in the two arguments.

For notational convenience, let us define for each $x \in \mathcal{M}$ the corresponding index set

$$J_x := \{\alpha \in J \,|\, x \in U_\alpha\}. \tag{54.2.7}$$

Since the U_α cover $\mathcal{M}$, we have $J_x \neq \emptyset, \forall x \in \mathcal{M}$. Then we have for each $x \in \mathcal{M}$ the *transition diffeomorphisms*

$$\tau_{\beta\alpha,x} := \tau_{\beta x} \circ \tau_{\alpha x}^{-1} : \mathcal{F} \to \mathcal{F}, \quad \forall \alpha, \beta \in J_x. \tag{54.2.8}$$

The interesting case is that where J_x contains more than a single element so that x is in overlapping trivializing neighborhoods of the kind $U_\alpha \cap U_\beta$. Only then, $\tau_{\beta\alpha,x}$ may be different from the *identity* $\mathrm{id}_{\mathcal{F}} = \tau_{\alpha\alpha,x}$.

Keeping the indices $\alpha, \beta \in J_x$ fixed, one may vary x in $U_\alpha \cap U_\beta$. The mapping

$$(U_\alpha \cap U_\beta) \times \mathcal{F} \ni (x, f) \mapsto \tau_{\beta\alpha,x}f \in \mathcal{F}, \tag{54.2.9}$$

is then continuous in both arguments. (We avoid introducing a topology into the group $\mathrm{Diff}(\mathcal{F})$.) By (54.2.8) there hold the *transition relations*

$$\tau_{\gamma\beta,x} \circ \tau_{\beta\alpha,x} = \tau_{\gamma\alpha,x}, \quad \forall x \in \mathcal{M}, \ \forall\, \alpha, \beta, \gamma \in J_x. \tag{54.2.10}$$

Setting $\gamma = \alpha$, we obtain

$$\tau_{\gamma\beta,x} \circ \tau_{\beta\gamma,x} = \tau_{\gamma\gamma,x} = \mathrm{id}_{\mathcal{F}}, \quad \text{i.e.,} \quad \tau_{\gamma\beta,x}^{-1} = \tau_{\beta\gamma,x}, \quad \forall x \in \mathcal{M}, \ \forall\, \beta, \gamma \in J_x. \tag{54.2.11}$$

The transition diffeomorphisms constitute, so to speak, the backbone of the fiber bundle, as is demonstrated by the following Proposition.

Proposition 54.2-9 (Coordinated Bundle Reconstruction). *Let there be given two differentiable manifolds $\mathcal{F}$ and $\mathcal{M}$ and an open covering $\{U_\alpha \,|\, \alpha \in J\}$ of $\mathcal{M}$.*

Then there is a one–one correspondence between all possible coordinated fiber bundles $\mathcal{B}(\pi, \mathcal{M}, \mathcal{F}, \tau)$, with the τ-structure built on the given open covering of $\mathcal{M}$, on the one hand, and all families of transition diffeomorphisms $\tau_{\beta\alpha,x} : \mathcal{F} \to \mathcal{F}, x \in \mathcal{M}, \beta, \alpha \in J_x \times J_x$, satisfying (54.2.10) and the continuity relation (54.2.9), on the other hand. This correspondence is provided by the bijection

$$\mathcal{B}(\pi, \mathcal{M}, \mathcal{F}, \tau) \overset{\varrho}{\longleftrightarrow} \hat{\mathcal{B}}(\hat{\pi}, \mathcal{M}, \mathcal{F}, \hat{\tau}) = [\dot{\cup}_{\alpha \in J}(\{\alpha\} \times U_\alpha \times \mathcal{F})]\,/\tau \tag{54.2.12}$$

which associates each $b \in \mathcal{B}(\pi, \mathcal{M}, \mathcal{F}, \tau)$ with the equivalence class $\varrho(b) = \hat{b} = [(\alpha, \pi b, f)]$ if $\pi b = x \in U_\alpha$ where $f = \tau_{\alpha x}b$. Here two triples (α, x, f), (β, y, h) are defined τ-equivalent, if $x = y$ and $h = \tau_{\beta\alpha,x}f$, for some $\beta \in J_x$, where $\tau_{\beta\alpha,x}$ from (54.2.8).

That means that the set of equivalence classes on the right-hand side of Eq. (54.2.12) can be equipped with the structure of a coordinated bundle $\hat{\mathcal{B}}(\hat{\pi}, \mathcal{M}, \mathcal{F}, \hat{\tau})$, a special differentiable manifold, such that ϱ is a diffeomorphism with

$$\pi b = (\hat{\pi} \circ \varrho)b, \; \forall b \in \mathcal{B} \quad \Longleftrightarrow \quad \hat{\mathcal{F}}_x = \varrho(\mathcal{F}_x), \quad \forall x \in \mathcal{M}, \tag{54.2.13}$$

$$\tau_{\alpha,x} b = (\hat{\tau}_{\alpha,x} \circ \varrho)b, \quad \forall b \in \mathcal{B} \;\; \text{and} \;\; \forall \alpha \in J_x, \;\; \text{where} \; x = \pi b = (\hat{\pi} \circ \varrho)b. \tag{54.2.14}$$

Let us call two coordinated bundles, which are diffeomorphic, with the diffeomorphism ϱ satisfying Eqs. (54.2.13) and (54.2.14), "isomorphic". It means that ϱ does not only map fibers onto fibers but also maps bundle elements onto those with the same trivialization images (in $U_\alpha \times \mathcal{F}$).

Proof. Given $\mathcal{B}(\pi, \mathcal{M}, \mathcal{F}, \tau)$, we have already derived the family of transition diffeomorphisms. Because of (54.2.10), the asserted τ-equivalence for triples is in fact an equivalence relation in $\bigcup_{\alpha \in J}(\{\alpha\} \times U_\alpha \times \mathcal{F})$, and each $b \in \mathcal{B}$ determines uniquely an equivalence class $\hat{b}$ of triples.

To equip the set of equivalence classes with a coordinated bundle structure, we want to keep the typical fiber $\mathcal{F}$ and the smoothly partitioned base manifold $\mathcal{M}$. We may define the projection mapping $\hat{\pi}[(\alpha, x, f)] := x \in U_\alpha \subset \mathcal{M}$, since τ-equivalent triples have the same x. This map is onto $\mathcal{M}$ and leads to the embedded fiber $\hat{\mathcal{F}}_x := \hat{\pi}^{-1}x$, for all $x \in \mathcal{M}$. Clearly relation Eq. (54.2.13) is satisfied.

From (54.2.10), it follows that $\tau_{\alpha\alpha,x} = \mathrm{id}_{\mathcal{F}}$ for $x \in U_\alpha \subset \mathcal{M}$. This implies that for a given $\alpha \in J$ and $x \in U_\alpha$, there is at most one $f \in \mathcal{F}$ such that (α, x, f) is in a class. Thus the trivialization mapping $\hat{\pi}^{-1}(U_\alpha) \ni [(\alpha, x, f)] \stackrel{\hat{\tau}_\alpha}{\longmapsto} (x, f)$ is well defined. Since x varies here in U_α and f varies in all of $\mathcal{F}$ we have in fact:

$$\hat{\tau}_\alpha : \hat{\pi}^{-1}(U_\alpha) \stackrel{\text{onto}}{\longrightarrow} U_\alpha \times \mathcal{F}.$$

Likewise we may define $\hat{\tau}_{\alpha,x}[(\alpha, x, f)] = f$, which gives Eq. (54.2.14).

Since the coordinated fiber bundle $\hat{\mathcal{B}}$ has the identical local trivializations as $\mathcal{B}$, and these are the intermediate step to construct an atlas, also $\hat{\mathcal{B}}$ is a differentiable manifold and all considered mappings are smooth.

Given $\varrho(b) = [(\alpha, \pi b, f)] = \hat{b} \in \hat{\mathcal{B}}$, we know from $\hat{b}$ the trivialization images of $b \in \mathcal{B}$; that determines b uniquely. Thus ϱ is invertible and clearly smooth, in virtue of the smooth τ-structure. $\qquad\square$

The construction of a coordinated fiber bundle in terms of equivalent triples is important for introducing physical bundles, such as gauge bundles, starting from the base and fiber spaces. The transition diffeomorphisms must be derived from the physical situation.

The construction of a coordinated fiber bundle is, however, only the first step to introduce a geometric (uncoordinated) fiber bundle. There is still required a further step, for which we need the notions of "structure groups", which express, in some way, the local and global complexity of the coordinated fiber bundles.

Definition 54.2-10 (Structure Groups). For a given coordinated fiber bundle $\mathcal{B}(\pi, \mathcal{M}, \mathcal{F}, \tau)$, let us introduce the *structure group at* x by

$$G_x^{\mathcal{B}} := \{\tau_{\beta\alpha, x} \,|\, \alpha, \beta \in J_x\} \subset \mathrm{Diff}(\mathcal{F}). \tag{54.2.15}$$

Since the elements of two structure groups at different points x of the base manifold may be multiplied like diffeomorphisms of $\mathcal{F}$, the union of structure groups over varying x constitutes again a subgroup of diffeomorphisms of $\mathcal{F}$. Thus we define the *global structure group* of the bundle

$$G^{\mathcal{B}} := \cup_{x \in \mathcal{M}} \, G_x^{\mathcal{B}}. \tag{54.2.16}$$

There is a fine point in the introduction of the structure group: Since $G^{\mathcal{B}}$ is defined by its action in the fiber $\mathcal{F}$, its unit coincides with the identity transformation. That is, $G^{\mathcal{B}}$ acts *effectively* in $\mathcal{F}$.

In this context, let us recall the following types of group actions.

Definition 54.2-11 (Transitive, Effective, and Free Group Actions). The action T of a group G in a set $\mathcal{F}$, namely $T_g : \mathcal{F} \to \mathcal{F}$, $g \in G$, is said to be

(a) *transitive* if there is only one orbit; that is $T_G f = \mathcal{F}$, $\forall f \in \mathcal{F}$;
(b) *effective* if $T_g = \mathrm{id}_{\mathcal{F}}$ implies that g equals the group unit e; that is $g \mapsto T_g$ is one-to-one;
(c) *free* if it has no fixed points; that is $T_g f = f$ implies $g = e$ for any $f \in \mathcal{F}$. That means, that the stability group $G_f = \{g \in G \,|\, T_g f = f\}$ equals $\{e\}$ for all $f \in \mathcal{F}$.

Clearly, a free action is effective, but not necessarily transitive.

Remark 54.2-12 (Topological Structure Group). The structure group $G^{\mathcal{B}}$ of a bundle $\mathcal{B} = \mathcal{B}(\pi, \mathcal{M}, \mathcal{F}, \tau)$ is here introduced as a transformation group acting on $\mathcal{F}$. As can be seen from the reconstruction Theorem 54.2-9, we have in general no need to equip these groups with a topology. For finite-dimensional fiber bundles, a topology of the structure group, characterizes *Ehresmann–Feldbau bundles* (according to [Ste51]). Whether the structure group is topological, or not, leads to different bundle classification theorems. We deal here mostly with topological structure groups, even with Lie groups, and assume then that $\lim_{i \in I} g_i f = (\lim_{i \in I} g_i) f$, $\forall f \in \mathcal{F}$, whenever the net $(g_i)_I$ is convergent in the topology of $G^{\mathcal{B}}$.

Proposition 54.2-9 tells us, that each coordinated fiber bundle $\mathcal{B}$ is "isomorphic" in a certain sense to the bundle $\hat{\mathcal{B}}$ of equivalent triples, gained from the local trivializations. We investigate now these "bundle isomorphisms".

54.3.   Geometric Bundles and Equivalence of Bundles

54.3.1.   *Strict Equivalence and Geometric Bundles*

Equivalence of bundles is expressed by certain maps between bundles.

Observation 54.3-1 (Structure of Bundle Maps). Any diffeomorphic bundle
map $\varrho : \mathcal{B}(\pi, \mathcal{M}, \mathcal{F}, \tau) \to \mathcal{B}^*(\pi^*, \mathcal{M}^*, \mathcal{F}^*, \tau^*)$ which satisfies as additional condition

$$\pi b = \pi b' \iff \pi^* \varrho(b) = \pi^* \varrho(b'), \qquad \forall b, b' \in \mathcal{B}, \tag{54.3.1}$$

(that is, in generalization of Eq. (54.2.13), the preservation of the fiber structure)
is called a *bundle map*.

For further conclusions, we remark that for all $\alpha \in J$ there exist local sections
$s_\alpha : U_\alpha \to \pi^{-1}(U_\alpha) \subset \mathcal{B}$ (such that $\pi s_\alpha(x) = x$). One may e.g., set $s_\alpha(x) := \tau_\alpha^{-1}(x, f) \in \mathcal{B}, \forall x \in U_\alpha$, letting $f \in \mathcal{F}$ be fixed.

If we define

$$x^* := (\pi^* \circ \varrho \circ s_\alpha)(x) =: \varrho_\alpha^{\mathcal{M}}(x) \in \mathcal{M}^*, \qquad \forall x \in U_\alpha, \tag{54.3.2}$$

we may patch that together to a diffeomorphism $\varrho^{\mathcal{M}} : \mathcal{M} \to \mathcal{M}^*$, since the trivializing open covering $\{U_\alpha \,|\, \alpha \in J\}$ belongs to an atlas for $\mathcal{M}$.

That in turn leads to the diffeomorphism between the fibers

$$\varrho(\mathcal{F}_x) = \mathcal{F}_{x^*}^* =: \varrho_x(\mathcal{F}_x) \qquad (\textit{fiber map}). \tag{54.3.3}$$

Of interest are also the following *mapped transition functions* from $\mathrm{Diff}(\mathcal{F}, \mathcal{F}^*)$,
generalizations of the transition diffeomorphisms of a single bundle, now with an
inserted fiber map in between,

$$\kappa_{\gamma\alpha, x} f := (\tau_{\gamma x^*}^* \circ \varrho_x \circ \tau_{\alpha x}) f, \quad \forall f \in \mathcal{F}, \quad x \in U_\alpha \cap \varrho^{\mathcal{M}\,-1}(U_\gamma^*). \tag{54.3.4}$$

They behave similarly to transition diffeomorphisms under coordinate changes

$$\begin{aligned}
\kappa_{\gamma\beta, x} &= \kappa_{\gamma\alpha, x} \circ \tau_{\alpha\beta, x}, & x &\in U_\alpha \cap U_\beta \cap \varrho^{\mathcal{M}\,-1}(U_\gamma^*); \\
\kappa_{\delta\alpha, x} &= \tau_{\delta\gamma, x^*}^* \circ \kappa_{\gamma\alpha, x}, & x &\in U_\alpha \cap \varrho^{\mathcal{M}\,-1}(U_\delta^*) \cap \varrho^{\mathcal{M}\,-1}(U_\gamma^*).
\end{aligned} \tag{54.3.5}$$

Since for a bundle diffeomorphism, the fibers are diffeomorphic, it is no restriction to
identify them. Then the above map diffeomorphisms $\kappa_{\gamma\alpha, x}$ are elements of $\mathrm{Diff}(\mathcal{F})$
and may be multiplied with each other.

Similarly as the transition diffeomorphisms characterize a bundle, the map diffeomorphisms characterize a bundle diffeomorphism, if the base space transformation $\varrho^{\mathcal{M}}$ is already specified.

Theorem 54.3-2 (Reconstruction of Bundle Maps). *Let be given two coordinated fiber bundles* $\mathcal{B} = \mathcal{B}(\pi, \mathcal{M}, \mathcal{F}, \tau)$ *and* $\mathcal{B}^* = \mathcal{B}^*(\pi^*, \mathcal{M}^*, \mathcal{F}, \tau^*)$ *such that* $G^{\mathcal{B}} = G^{\mathcal{B}^*} = G$, *and let* $\varrho^{\mathcal{M}} : \mathcal{M} \to \mathcal{M}^*$ *be a diffeomorphism between the base spaces.*

Furtheron, let

$$\{\kappa_{\gamma\alpha,x} : U_\alpha \cap \varrho^{\mathcal{M}\,-1}(U_\gamma^*) \to G\} \mid \gamma \in J^*, \alpha \in J\} \tag{54.3.6}$$

be a set of differentiable maps satisfying the relations Eq. (54.3.5).

Then there exists one and only one bundle diffeomorphism $\varrho : \mathcal{B} \to \mathcal{B}^*$ which induces $\varrho^{\mathcal{M}}$ and possesses the $\kappa_{\gamma\alpha,x}$ as mapped transition functions.

Proof. [Sketch] For each $b \in \mathcal{B}$ with $\pi b \in U_\alpha \cap \varrho^{\mathcal{M}\,-1}(U_\gamma^*)$, we define

$$\varrho_{\gamma\alpha}b := (\tau_{\gamma x^*}^{*\,-1} \circ \kappa_{\gamma\alpha,x} \circ \tau_{\alpha x})b, \quad x^* := \varrho^{\mathcal{M}}(x). \tag{54.3.7}$$

Then $\varrho_{\gamma\alpha}$ acts smoothly on b and $\pi^* \varrho_{\gamma\alpha}b = \varrho^{\mathcal{M}}(\pi b)$.

For index combinations where the occurring expressions are defined, we obtain $\varrho_{\gamma\alpha}b = \varrho_{\delta\beta}b$. Therefore, we can patch the $\varrho_{\gamma\alpha}$ to a well-defined bundle diffeomorphism which has the prescribed mapping diffeomorphisms.

Conversely, any bundle diffeomorphism $\varrho : \mathcal{B} \to \mathcal{B}^*$, which owns the prescribed mapping diffeomorphisms must satisfy Eq. (54.3.7) and thus is unique. □

It is the idea, that, in contrast to the global structure group $G^{\mathcal{B}}$, the local structure groups $G_x^{\mathcal{B}}$ depend too sensitively on the coordination as to convey a geometrical meaning.

Definition 54.3-3 (Strict Equivalence and Fiber Bundles). We presuppose the notion of a coordinated fiber bundle.

(i) Two coordinated bundles of the form $\mathcal{B}(\pi, \mathcal{M}, \mathcal{F}, \tau)$ with $\tau = \{(U_\alpha, \tau_\alpha) \mid \alpha \in J\}$ and $\mathcal{B}(\pi, \mathcal{M}, \mathcal{F}, \tau')$ with $\tau' = \{(U_\beta', \tau_\beta') \mid \beta \in J'\}$ are *strictly equivalent* if the following three conditions are satisfied:

(a) they have the same global structure group $G^{\mathcal{B}}$;

(b) all "*mixed transition diffeomorphisms*"

$$\sigma_{\beta\alpha,x} := \tau_{\beta,x}' \circ \tau_{\alpha,x}^{-1} \tag{54.3.8}$$

are elements of $G^{\mathcal{B}}$ for all $(\beta, \alpha, x) \in J' \times J \times \mathcal{M}$ with $x \in U_\beta' \cap U_\alpha$;

(c) each of the maps $\sigma_{\beta\alpha,\bullet}$ and $\sigma_{\beta\alpha,\bullet}^{-1} : (U_\beta' \cap U_\alpha) \times \mathcal{F} \to \mathcal{F}$ is continuous.

(ii) A strict equivalence class of coordinated fiber bundles $\mathcal{B}(\pi, \mathcal{M}, \mathcal{F}, \tau)$ is called a *fiber bundle* and denoted $\mathcal{B}(\pi, \mathcal{M}, \mathcal{F}, G^{\mathcal{B}})$, with $G^{\mathcal{B}} \subset \mathrm{Diff}(\mathcal{F})$ the global structure group of the participating coordinated bundles.

In the last part of the preceding definition, the required "strict equivalence" for a family of coordinated fiber bundles constitutes the decisive second step to get the (geometric) notion of a "fiber bundle" by abstraction from the coordination. (The proof for the symmetry, reflexivity, and transitivity of "strict equivalence" is recommended as an exercise.)

Whereas for a coordinated fiber bundle $\mathcal{B}(\pi, \mathcal{M}, \mathcal{F}, \tau)$ the (local and global) structure groups follow from the trivialization structure τ, we must indicate for a fiber bundle $\mathcal{B}(\pi, \mathcal{M}, \mathcal{F}, G^{\mathcal{B}})$, what subgroup $G^{\mathcal{B}}$ of $\text{Diff}(\mathcal{F})$ is chosen as global structure group. The choice of the local structure groups may then be varied to a large extent within the strict equivalence class defining the fiber bundle.

Example 54.3-4 (Möbius Strip). A popular example is the Möbius strip, where $\mathcal{M}$ is the unit circle S^1 and $\mathcal{F}$ is the open interval $]-1, +1[$, which may be mirrored about zero by the inversion $\iota \in \text{Diff}(\mathcal{F})$, i.e. $\iota f = -f$, $\forall f \in]-1, +1[$. We want to construct the Möbius strip explicitly as a strict equivalence class $\mathcal{B}^{\text{Möb}}(\pi, S^1,]-1, +1[, G^{\mathcal{B}}) \equiv \mathcal{B}^{\text{Möb}}$ of coordinated fiber bundles $\mathcal{B}^{\text{Möb}}(\pi, S^1,]-1, +1[, \tau) \equiv \mathcal{B}^{\text{Möb}}(\tau)$. Each $\mathcal{B}^{\text{Möb}}(\tau)$ in turn is constructed via τ-equivalent triples (in the sense of Proposition 54.2-9).

First we remark that the manifold S^1 is not quite trivial. A minimal atlas of S^1 consists of two open subsets U_1 and U_2 of S^1, with the coordinate mappings $\phi_\alpha : U_\alpha \to I_\alpha \subset \mathbb{R}$, $\alpha \in J = \{1, 2\}$. Note that the intersection $U_1 \cap U_2$ decomposes at least into two disjoint open parts D_1 and D_2, also if the U_α are connected, as we assume so.

For specifying τ, we seek a covering of S^1 by local factorizing neighborhoods. We need at least two open subsets of S^1, for which we take the above $U_\alpha, \alpha \in J$. We must then define the mappings $\tau_\alpha : \pi^{-1}(U_\alpha) \to U_\alpha \times \mathcal{F}$, which reduce to the $\tau_{\alpha,x}$ of Eq. (54.2.5), since $\tau_\alpha b = (x, \tau_{\alpha,x} b) = (x, f^\alpha_{x,b})$, if $\pi b = x$, $b \in \mathcal{B}^{\text{Möb}}(\tau)$. But, in the constructive procedure, especially b is at first completely unknown, whereas for $f^\alpha_{x,b}$ something is known, namely that it is a b-dependent element in $]-1, +1[$, which runs through all of $\mathcal{F}$ if the mysterious parameter b is varied.

Combining the known facts, we find that each b is something that is given by triples $(\alpha, x, f) \in J \times \mathcal{M} \times \mathcal{F}$ which are identified under an equivalence relation. As we have described in the bundle reconstruction of Proposition 54.2-9, the equivalence relation uses the local structure groups $G^{\mathcal{B}}_x$: Two triples (α, x, f) and (β, y, h) are defined "equivalent", if $x = y$ and $h = \tau_{\beta\alpha,x} f$, with $\tau_{\beta\alpha,x} \in G^{\mathcal{B}}_x$. If the local trivializations $\tau_{\alpha,x}$ are given, then $\tau_{\beta\alpha,x}$ is definable by the product $\tau_{\beta,x} \circ \tau_{\alpha,x}^{-1}$. In many applications, the structure group is, however, given first and the local trivializations $\tau_{\alpha,x}$ are to be derived from it. This is just the point of view in the proof of Proposition 54.2-9, and it fits to the present construction of the Möbius strip (and to the construction of gauge bundles).

The bundle $\mathcal{B}^{\text{Möb}}(\tau)$ is illustrated in the most simple fashion as a circular rubber ribbon with a single twist at a certain, fixed overlap region. We take D_1 as that region with the twist, which means that neither the old orientation of the fibers are valid nor the new orientation is reached. That is mathematically expressed as follows: Above D_1, the structure group contains besides the identity e also the inversion ι and $G^{\mathcal{B}}_x = G_2$, for $x \in D_1$, whereas all other $G^{\mathcal{B}}_x$ are assumed trivial. Thus also the total structure group $G^{\mathcal{B}}$ is merely G_2. So we select just the smallest non-trivial group G_2 from the huge group $\text{Diff}(]-1, +1[)$ as the structure group.

Since $x \mapsto \tau_{\beta\alpha,x} \in G_2$ should be continuous, and G_2 is discrete, the group elements must in fact be constant in each of the simply connected overlap regions D_1 and D_2.

Having fixed the $G_x^\mathcal{B}$, we have specified the equivalence classes $[(\alpha,x,f)]$ which make up the bundle elements $b \in \mathcal{B}^{\text{Möb}}(\tau)$. For given $(\alpha,x) \in J \times S^1$, we define $\tau_{\alpha,x}b := \tau_{\alpha,x}[(\alpha,x,f)] = f$. Then, with the same b, $\tau_{\beta,x}b = \tau_{\beta\alpha,x}f$, and the specification of $\mathcal{B}^{\text{Möb}}(\tau)$ is completed.

The region with the non-trivial local structure group $G_x^\mathcal{B} = \{e,\iota\}$ may be shifted along the circle S^1, by using different trivializing coverings of S^1. The strict equivalence to the previous $\mathcal{B}^{\text{Möb}}(\tau)$ is reached by making each $G_y^\mathcal{B}$, with $y \in S^1$, either trivial or non-trivial with the help of transformations from $G^\mathcal{B} = G_2$.

A bit surprising is perhaps the strict equivalence of the described $\mathcal{B}^{\text{Möb}}(\tau)$ to all coordinated Möbius bundles $\mathcal{B}^{\text{Möb}}(\tau')$ which have more than one twisted region. The proof for this strict equivalence goes as just formulated for shifting a twist. From our 3-dimensional insight, however, different numbers of twists seem to produce different geometric objects. The situation is changed for the 2-dimensional inhabitant of the rubber ribbon: Once twisted, he has lost his orientation and does not realize an additional twist in a further overlap region. Mathematically the loss of orientation is expressed by the non-triviality of the global structure group $G^{\text{Möb}} = G^\mathcal{B} = G_2$.

Altogether the resulting strict equivalence class, which constitutes by definition the geometric fiber bundle $\mathcal{B}^{\text{Möb}}(\pi, S^1,]-1,+1[, G_2)$, comprises intuitively speaking all rubber ribbons which are at least once twisted, at local transition regions whatsoever. That means: We can visually imagine a coordinated Möbius strip, but not the geometric Möbius strip.

Our discussion reveals a big redundancy in the construction of the Möbius strip: The fiber $]-1,+1[$, chosen for intuitive visualization by a rubber band, is unnecessarily large for defining the global structure group G_2. For introducing G_2, it would suffice to set $\mathcal{F} = \{-1,+1\}$ or to take even the global structure group G_2 for itself. The latter idea is taken up by the notion of a "principal fiber bundle".

Although the structure group is basic for the geometrical meaning of a fiber bundle $\mathcal{B}(\pi, \mathcal{M}, \mathcal{F}, G)$, it does not characterize the bundle sufficiently (in spite of our symbolic notation). On the other side, "strict equivalence" is too stringent as to represent the geometry of a fiber bundle. A notion between "to have the same structure group" and "strict equivalence" is the "equivalence" of bundles.

54.3.2.   *Equivalence and (Non-)Triviality*

Definition 54.3-5 (Equivalent Bundles). We presuppose the notion of a fiber bundle.

(a) Two coordinated fiber bundles $\mathcal{B}(\pi, \mathcal{M}, \mathcal{F}, \tau)$ and $\mathcal{B}'(\pi', \mathcal{M}', \mathcal{F}', \tau')$ are *equivalent* if $(\mathcal{M}, \mathcal{F}, G^\mathcal{B})$ equals $(\mathcal{M}', \mathcal{F}', G^{\mathcal{B}'})$ and if there exists a bundle diffeomorphism $\varrho : \mathcal{B} \to \mathcal{B}'$ for which the induced bases space map $\varrho^{\mathcal{M}} : \mathcal{M} \to \mathcal{M}$ is the identity. (The global structure groups G^B and $G^{B'}$ result from the respective trivialization structures.)

(b) Two (geometric) fiber bundles $\mathcal{B}(\pi, \mathcal{M}, \mathcal{F}, G)$ and $\mathcal{B}'(\pi', \mathcal{M}', \mathcal{F}', G')$ are *equivalent*, if a coordinated fiber bundle associated with $\mathcal{B}$ is equivalent to a coordinated fiber bundle associated with $\mathcal{B}'$. (Then we have $(\mathcal{M}, \mathcal{F}, G) = (\mathcal{M}', \mathcal{F}', G')$.)

The proof that "equivalence" for coordinated and geometric fiber bundles is indeed an equivalence relation is recommended as an exercise.

Since equivalent bundles require besides equal fibers also equal base spaces, we obtain by specializing Theorem 54.3-2 to that case the following.

Lemma 54.3-6 (Mapped Transition Functions for Equivalent Bundles). *Let be given two coordinated fiber bundles* $\mathcal{B} = \mathcal{B}(\pi, \mathcal{M}, \mathcal{F}, \tau)$ *and* $\mathcal{B}^* = \mathcal{B}^*(\pi^*, \mathcal{M}, \mathcal{F}, \tau^*)$ *such that* $G^B = G^{B^*} = G$. *Then they are equivalent if and only if there exist smooth maps* $\{\kappa_{\gamma\alpha,x} : U_\alpha \cap U_\gamma^* \to G \,|\, \gamma \in J^*, \alpha \in J\}$ *(used as mapped transition functions for the equivalence generating bundle map) such that Eq. (54.3.5) is valid, namely*

$$\kappa_{\gamma\beta,x} = \kappa_{\gamma\alpha,x} \circ \tau_{\alpha\beta,x}, \quad x \in U_\alpha \cap U_\beta \cap U_\gamma^*;$$
$$\kappa_{\delta\alpha,x} = \tau_{\delta\gamma,x}^* \circ \kappa_{\gamma\alpha,x}, \quad x \in U_\alpha \cap U_\delta^* \cap U_\gamma^*.$$

Definition 54.3-7 (Refined Coordinated Bundles). We consider again coordinated fiber bundles.

(a) A *refinement* of a coordinated fiber bundle $\mathcal{B}(\pi, \mathcal{M}, \mathcal{F}, \tau)$ is a coordinated fiber bundle of the form $\mathcal{B}(\pi, \mathcal{M}, \mathcal{F}, \tau^r)$, where the trivialization structure τ^r consists of a refinement $\{U_\gamma^r\}$ of the original $\{U_\alpha\}$ with trivialization maps $\tau_\gamma^r := \tau_\alpha|_{U_\gamma^r}$ for a chosen $U_\alpha \supset U_\gamma^r$.

(It follows that the refined bundle keeps the global structure group and is strictly equivalent to the original one.)

(b) Given two coordinated fiber bundles $\mathcal{B}(\pi, \mathcal{M}, \mathcal{F}, \tau)$ and $\mathcal{B}(\pi, \mathcal{M}, \mathcal{F}, \tau')$, then we introduce the *mutual refinements* $\mathcal{B}(\pi, \mathcal{M}, \mathcal{F}, \tau^r)$ and $\mathcal{B}(\pi, \mathcal{M}, \mathcal{F}, \tau'^r)$ as the respective refined coordinated fiber bundles which both have as open covering the sets $U_\gamma = U_\alpha \cap U_\beta'$, where γ replaces the pair of indices (α, β), $\alpha \in J$, $\beta \in J'$.

A valuable criterion for bundle equivalence goes in terms of a factorization structure of the mapped transition functions.

Proposition 54.3-8 (Multiplier Criterion for Bundle Equivalence). *Two coordinated fiber bundles* $\mathcal{B}(\pi, \mathcal{M}, \mathcal{F}, \tau)$ *and* $\mathcal{B}^*(\pi, \mathcal{M}, \mathcal{F}, \tau^*)$ *are equivalent if and only if the following is true:* $G^B = G^{B^*} = G$ *and for the mutual refinements*

$\mathcal{B}(\pi, \mathcal{M}, \mathcal{F}, \tau^r)$ and $\mathcal{B}(\pi, \mathcal{M}, \mathcal{F}, \tau^{*r})$, *there exist continuous functions* $\lambda_\gamma : U_\gamma \to G$ (*multipliers*) *such that for each fixed* $x \in \mathcal{M}$

$$\tau^{*r}_{\gamma\delta,x} = \lambda_{\gamma x}^{-1} \circ \tau^r_{\gamma\delta,x} \circ \lambda_{\delta x} \qquad (\textit{product again in } G \subset \text{Diff}(\mathcal{F})), \qquad (54.3.9)$$

for all indices $\gamma, \delta \in J_x$ *of the refined open covering.*

Proof. If $\mathcal{B}$ and $\mathcal{B}^*$ are equivalent, the mapped transition functions (provided by Lemma 54.3-6) for their mutual refinements enable us to define $\lambda_{\gamma x} := \kappa_{\gamma\gamma,x}^{-1}$. Then Eq. (54.3.5) leads to $\kappa_{\gamma\beta,x} = \lambda_{\gamma x}^{-1} \circ \tau_{\gamma\beta,x}$ and $\kappa_{\gamma\beta,x} = \tau^*_{\gamma\beta,x} \circ \lambda_{\gamma x}^{-1}$, which combined give Eq. (54.3.9), if one goes over to the refined transition functions.

Let conversely a set of $\lambda_{\alpha x}$ be given satisfying Eq. (54.3.9). Then we define

$$\kappa_{\gamma\delta,x} := \lambda_{\gamma x}^{-1} \circ \tau_{\gamma\delta,x} \qquad (54.3.10)$$

and write this relation $\kappa_{\gamma\beta,x} := \lambda_{\gamma x}^{-1} \circ \tau_{\gamma\alpha,x} \circ \tau_{\alpha\beta,x} = \kappa_{\gamma\alpha,x} \circ \tau_{\alpha\beta,x}$ (using the transition relations Eq. (54.2.10)) and arrive at the first line of Eq. (54.3.5). The second line of Eq. (54.3.5) follows from Eq. (54.3.9) in the form $\tau^*_{\gamma\delta,x} = \lambda_{\gamma x}^{-1} \circ \tau_{\gamma\alpha,x} \circ \tau_{\alpha\delta,x} \circ \lambda_{\delta x} = \kappa_{\gamma\alpha,x} \circ \kappa_{\delta\alpha,x}^{-1}$. $\square$

From that criterion we see directly that strict equivalence implies equivalence, since we have by Eqs. (54.2.8) and (54.3.8) (without needing a mutual reduction): $\tau'_{\gamma\delta,x} = \tau'_{\gamma,x} \circ \tau'^{-1}_{\delta,x} = \sigma_{\gamma\gamma,x} \circ \tau_{\gamma\delta,x} \circ \sigma_{\delta\delta,x}^{-1}$, that is a version of Eq. (54.3.9).

The following bundle class is often devaluated as being "trivial". In physical applications, these bundles exhibit, however, most interesting effects.

Definition 54.3-9 (Product Bundles). A special type of a coordinated fiber bundles is given by a *"product bundle"*, which is the Cartesian product $\mathcal{M} \times \mathcal{F}$ considered as a (coordinated) bundle $\mathcal{B}_0 = \mathcal{B}(\pi_0, \mathcal{M}, \mathcal{F}, \tau_0)$. Generalizing $\mathcal{M} \times \mathcal{F}$, we characterize a product bundle $\mathcal{B}_0$ as follows. The projection $\pi_0 : \mathcal{B}_0 \to \mathcal{M}$ is not further specified (in contradistinction to $\pi_0(x, f) = x$). The trivialization structure has the form $\tau_0 = \{(\mathcal{M}, \tau^0)\}$ with $\tau^0 : \mathcal{B}_0 \overset{onto}{\to} \mathcal{M} \times \mathcal{F}$, and we write $\tau^0 b = (x, f_{x,b})$, $\pi_0 b = x$. Then $G^{\mathcal{B}} = \{\text{id}_{\mathcal{F}}\}$, since each $x \in \mathcal{M}$ is just in one trivializing neighborhood so that each local structure group $G_x^{\mathcal{B}}$ equals $\{\text{id}_{\mathcal{F}}\}$. If $\mathcal{B}(\pi_0, \mathcal{M}, \mathcal{F}, \tau_0)$ is a coordinated product bundle then also $\mathcal{B}(\pi_0, \mathcal{M}, \mathcal{F}, \tau_0')$ is a coordinated product bundle, where $\tau^{0'} = (\text{id}_{\mathcal{M}} \times \varrho^{\mathcal{F}}) \circ \tau^0$ with $\varrho^{\mathcal{F}}$ any diffeomorphism on $\mathcal{F}$.

Since the global structure groups may not differ from each other for equivalent (coordinated) fiber bundles, any bundle $B = \mathcal{B}(\pi, \mathcal{M}, \mathcal{F}, \tau)$ with a non-trivial structure group $G^{\mathcal{B}}$ cannot be equivalent to a product bundle.

Proposition 54.3-10 (Trivial Structure Group Versus Product Form). *A* (*coordinated*) *fiber bundle* $B = \mathcal{B}(\pi, \mathcal{M}, \mathcal{F}, G^{\mathcal{B}})$ (*respectively a* $B = \mathcal{B}(\pi, \mathcal{M}, \mathcal{F}, \tau)$) *is equivalent to a product bundle if and only if* $G^{\mathcal{B}} = \{\text{id}_{\mathcal{F}}\}$.

But $G^B = \{id_\mathcal{F}\}$ does not imply strict equivalence of a coordinated fiber bundle B to a product bundle.

Proof. If $G^B = \{id_\mathcal{F}\}$, we have in $\mathrm{Diff}(\mathcal{F})$ for the given bundle B the relations $\tau_{\beta\alpha,x} = id_\mathcal{F} = \tau_{\beta,x} \circ id_\mathcal{F} \circ \tau_{\alpha,x}^{-1}$, for all $x \in \mathcal{M}$ and $\alpha, \beta \in J_x$. Hence $\tau_{\beta,x} = \tau_{\alpha,x}$ for $x \in U_\alpha \cap U_\beta$.

To compare that with a product bundle $\mathcal{B}_0 = \mathcal{B}(\pi_0, \mathcal{M}, \mathcal{F}, \tau_0)$, we introduce the refined product bundle $\mathcal{B}_0^r = \mathcal{B}(\pi_0, \mathcal{M}, \mathcal{F}, \tau_0^r)$ which refers to the $\mathcal{M}$-covering $\{U_\alpha \,|\, \alpha \in J\}$ of the first bundle. We have now common refinements for the two bundles. The transformations $\tau_{\beta\alpha,x}^{0r}$ for $\mathcal{B}_0^r$ equal also $id_\mathcal{F}$ and we may write $\tau_{\beta\alpha,x} = \tau_{\beta,x} \circ \tau_{\beta\alpha,x}^{0r} \circ \tau_{\alpha,x}^{-1}$, for all $x \in \mathcal{M}$ and $\alpha, \beta \in J_x$. Thus Eq. (54.3.9) for equivalence is satisfied.

But we cannot demonstrate Eq. (54.3.8) for the strict equivalence of the mutual refinements, i.e., that

$$\sigma_{\beta\alpha,x} = \tau_{\beta,x} \circ \tau_{\alpha,x}^{0r\ -1} = id_\mathcal{F} ,$$

for all $(\beta, \alpha, x) \in J \times J \times \mathcal{M}$ with $x \in U_\beta \cap U_\alpha$, since in general $\tau_{\beta,x} b$ differs from $\tau_{\alpha,x}^{0r} b$ for $b \in \mathcal{F}_x \subset \mathcal{B}$ (or $\sigma_{\beta\alpha,x}$ is not defined at all). □

The restriction imposed by equal structure groups is overcome by the weaker notion of "G-equivalence" [Ste51], where G may be a larger group than the now possibly different structure groups of the compared bundles.

Definition 54.3-11 (G-Images of Bundles and G-Equivalence). We work again with coordinated fiber bundles.

(a) Let $B = B(\pi, \mathcal{M}, \mathcal{F}, \tau)$ be a coordinated bundle with structure group G^B, and G a group which contains G^B.
   Then the same factorizing neighborhoods, and the same transition functions, altered only by regarding their values as belonging to G, define a new bundle called the G *image of B*.
(b) Let B and B' be bundles with their structure groups G^B and $G^{B'}$ contained in the group G. Then B and B' are said G-*equivalent*, if their respective G-images are equivalent.

Also G-equivalence, with variable G, is an equivalence relation. If B and B' are equivalent, then they are also G-equivalent, with $G = G^B = G^{B'}$.

Theorem 54.3-12 (Factorization Criterion for Bundle Triviality). *A given (coordinated) fiber bundle $\mathcal{B} = \mathcal{B}(\pi, \mathcal{M}, \mathcal{F}, G^\mathcal{B})$ (respectively a $\mathcal{B}(\pi, \mathcal{M}, \mathcal{F}, \tau)$), the global structure group $G^\mathcal{B}$ of which is contained in a group G, is G-equivalent to a product bundle, if and only if there exist — for some trivializing open covering $\{U_\alpha | \alpha \in J\}$ — continuous functions $\lambda_\alpha : U_\alpha \to G$ such that for each fixed $x \in \mathcal{M}$ the transition functions factorize as*

$$\tau_{\beta\alpha,x} = \lambda_{\beta x} \circ \lambda_{\alpha x}^{-1}, \qquad \forall \alpha, \beta \in J_x . \tag{54.3.11}$$

Proof.   We compare the given $\mathcal{B}$ with a product bundle $\mathcal{B}_0$, where we form the refinement $\mathcal{B}_0^r$ with the same open covering $\{U_\alpha \,|\, \alpha \in J\}$ of the basis $\mathcal{M}$ as for $\mathcal{B}$. The G-images of $\mathcal{B}$ and $\mathcal{B}_0^r$ retain their transition functions, where $\tau^{0r}_{\beta\alpha,x} = \mathrm{id}_{\mathcal{F}}$ for all indices. Then, in view of Proposition 54.3-8, the equivalence of the G-images is true if and only if Eq. (54.3.11) is satisfied (where the product bundle plays the role of the image bundle). $\qquad\qquad\qquad\qquad\qquad\qquad\qquad\qquad\qquad\qquad$ □

54.4.   (Co-)Tangent Vectors and Differential Forms

Some types of fiber bundles $\mathcal{B}(\pi, \mathcal{M}, \mathcal{F})$ can be classified by specifying the fiber manifolds $\mathcal{F}$ and the transition functions $\tau_{\beta\alpha,x}$, while letting the base $\mathcal{M}$ often be an arbitrary differentiable manifold.

Definition 54.4-1 (Vector Bundles).   Let be given a differentiable manifold $\mathcal{M}$.

(a) A *coordinated vector bundle* $\mathcal{B} \equiv \mathcal{B}(\pi, \mathcal{M}, F, \tau)$ is a fiber bundle with base manifold $\mathcal{M}$ and with a (linear) CLC-space F as typical fiber, where the family of local trivializations $\tau = \{(U_\alpha, \tau_\alpha) \,|\, \alpha \in J\}$ lead, for each fixed $x \in \mathcal{M}$, to a group $G_x^{\mathcal{B}}$ of *linear* transition diffeomorphisms $\tau_{\beta\alpha,x} \in \mathrm{Diff}(F)$.
It follows that each fiber $F_x = \tau_\alpha^{-1}(\{x\} \times F)$ is naturally equipped with a linear structure, by transporting the linear structure from F by means of the $\tau_{\alpha,x}^{-1}$, that are the same mappings, which transfer the CLC-topology in the reconstruction theorem. So each F_x inherits the structure of a CLC-space.

(b) The usual notion of a *vector bundle*, here denoted $\mathcal{B} \equiv \mathcal{B}(\pi, \mathcal{M}, F)$, with the CLC-space F as typical fiber, is apparently meant as a coordinated vector bundle with a certain maximality of the trivialization structure.
Then each $x \in \mathcal{M}$ seems to be in so many charts, that the local and global structure groups are equal to $\mathrm{GL}(F, F)$, that are *all* linear transformations of $\mathrm{Diff}(F)$.

54.4.1.   *Tangent and Cotangent Vectors*

Definition 54.4-2 (Tangent- and Cotangent-Bundles).   Let be given a differentiable manifold $\mathcal{M}$ modeled on the CLC-space E with atlas $\{\phi_\alpha : U_\alpha \to V_\alpha \,|\, \alpha \in J\}$ and transition coordinate mappings $\phi_{\beta\alpha}$. We assume that the atlas is complete.

(a) The *tangent bundle of* $\mathcal{M}$ may now be elegantly introduced as follows: It is the coordinated vector bundle

$$T\mathcal{M} := \mathcal{B}(\pi, \mathcal{M}, E, \tau)\,,$$

with typical fiber E, referring to the mentioned maximal atlas, and constructed by means of the x-indexed linear transition diffeomorphisms

$$\tau_{\beta\alpha,x} := d_{\phi_\alpha(x)}\phi_{\beta\alpha}, \quad \text{with } \phi_\alpha(x) \in V_\alpha \text{ the coordinates of } x \in U_\alpha \subset \mathcal{M}.$$
(54.4.1)

The fibers $\tau_{\alpha,x}^{-1}E$ are denoted by $T_x\mathcal{M}$.

By the completeness of the atlas, the local and global structure groups are $GL(E, E)$.

(b) The *cotangent bundle of* $\mathcal{M}$ is obtained by duality from $T\mathcal{M}$ if one refers to the same complete atlas, that means

$$T^*\mathcal{M} := \mathcal{B}(\pi^*, \mathcal{M}, E', \tau^*)$$

is the coordinated vector bundle, constructed by the x-indexed linear transition diffeomorphisms

$$\tau_{\beta\alpha,x}^* : E' \to E',$$

where E' is the topological dual space of E and $\tau_{\beta\alpha,x}^*$ are the dual mappings of the $\tau_{\beta\alpha,x}$. The fibers $\tau_{\alpha,x}^{*-1}E'$ are denoted by $T_x^*\mathcal{M}$.

The local and global structure groups, resulting from this definition, are $GL(E', E')$, consisting of all linear diffeomorphisms of E' in the $\sigma(E', E)$-topology.

Since E' is equipped with the $\sigma(E', E)$-topology, $GL(E', E')$ is naturally isomorphic to $GL(E, E)$. Since, however, E' is in general not isomorphic to E, the tangent and the cotangent bundles have different fibers and are not in general equivalent bundles, in contrast to the finite-dimensional case. (More details on dual topologies for the cotangent bundle are given in [Nee01].)

Using here the characterization of coordinated bundles in terms of the transition diffeomorphisms $\tau_{\beta\alpha,x}$ for the tangent bundle (resp. $\tau_{\beta\alpha,x}^*$ for the cotangent bundle), the concept of a (co-) tangent vector seems somewhat unfamiliar. According to the general scheme of Theorem 54.2-9, a tangent vector at $x \in U_\alpha \subset \mathcal{M}$ is an element $b \in T\mathcal{M}$ with $\pi b = x$, where $b = [(\alpha, x, f)]$, $\alpha \in J_x$, $f \in E$. So, if you have chosen a chart patch $U_\alpha \ni x$, you can take *any* $f \in E$ and declare it a tangent vector at x in a certain trivialization. Essential is only its behavior under coordinate transformations, which is what leads to the concept of a coordinate-independent b.

A more common approach for a tangent vector $b \in T_x\mathcal{M}$ is usually formulated with the help of differentiable curves. In an arbitrary differentiable manifold $\mathcal{M}$, with atlas $\{(U_\alpha, \phi_\alpha)\}$, a piece of a differentiable curve c through $x \in \mathcal{M}$ is given by a set $c = \{c(t') \in \mathcal{M} \mid t' \in]-a, a[, \ a > 0\}$, with $c(t) = x$ for some $t \in]-a, a[$, such that the chart image curves $c_\alpha = \phi_\alpha(c) \subset E$ are continuously differentiable for all chart patches $U_\alpha \ni x$. The derivatives $\dot{c}_\beta(t')$, $t' \in]-a, a[$, are continuous curves in E, which transform like $\dot{c}_\beta(t) = d_{\phi_\alpha(x)}\phi_{\beta\alpha}\,\dot{c}_\alpha(t)$ under a chart change. By the smoothness of the transition maps $\phi_{\beta\alpha}$, the existence of a single continuously differentiable chart image curve c_α is sufficient for the continuous differentiability of the coordinate-free c.

That demonstrates that for given $t \in \,]-a,a[$, the equivalence relation $(\alpha, c(t), \dot{c}_\alpha(t)) \approx (\beta, c(t), \dot{c}_\beta(t))$ for defining a tangent vector is fulfilled. Thus the set of equivalent triples $[(\alpha, c(t), \dot{c}_\alpha(t))] \subset \bigcup_\alpha(\{\alpha\} \times U_\alpha \times E)$ constitutes an equivalence class in the sense of the tangent bundle reconstruction. Instead of merely writing $b = [(\alpha, x, f)]$ for a bundle element, one denotes here $b = [(\alpha, c(t), \dot{c}_\alpha(t))]$, that is, one has the additional information: the base space element x sits on a certain curve, which we have chosen. This choice of a curve in the base space $\mathcal{M}$ gives then the constructive expression $f = \dot{c}_\alpha(t) = \tau_{\alpha,x}b$ in the typical fiber E.

We conform with the usual notation, if we set

$$X_{c(t)} \equiv \dot{c}(t) := b = [(\alpha, c(t), \dot{c}_\alpha(t))], \quad t \in \,]-a,a[. \tag{54.4.2}$$

One should be aware of the fact, that the constructive expression needs a trivialization, whereas the tangent vector $X_{c(t)} = \dot{c}(t) = b$ as element of the total bundle space, is as "abstract" as before. (Even for a 2-dimensional manifold, as e.g., the Möbius strip, we can visualize a tangent vector only in terms of a chosen coordination with fixed transition region, whereas the tangent vector as a geometric object is abstracted from the transition regions.)

We have now shown that the derivatives of curves are tangent vectors. If reversely $X_x = b = [(\alpha, x, f)] \in T_x\mathcal{M}$ is a given tangent vector at $x \in U_\alpha \subset \mathcal{M}$, then we can form the chart curve $\{c_\alpha(t') := \phi_\alpha(x) + (t'-t)f \,|\, t' \in]-a,a[\} \subset E$, which defines the abstract curve $c \subset \mathcal{M}$ giving $X_x = \dot{c}(t)$, as desired. This is obviously possible also for infinite-dimensional model spaces E.

Thus tangent vectors may always be viewed as derivatives of curves at a given point x of the differentiable manifold $\mathcal{M}$. A much harder problem, especially for infinite-dimensional manifolds, is to find an "integral curve" for a "(local) field of tangent vectors".

Definition 54.4-3 (Cross Sections and Vector Fields). Let be given a differentiable manifold $\mathcal{M}$ with an atlas $\{(U_\alpha, \phi_\alpha)\}$.

(a) For a fiber bundle $\mathcal{B} \equiv \mathcal{B}(\pi, \mathcal{M}, \mathcal{F}, G^\mathcal{B})$ of any kind, a smooth *section map* s is a C^k-mapping $\mathcal{M} \to \mathcal{B}$ such that $\pi \circ s = \mathrm{id}_\mathcal{M}$. The image $s(\mathcal{M}) \subset \mathcal{B}$ is a *cross section* — or simply *section* — of $\mathcal{B}$. The set of all sections is denoted by $\Gamma(\mathcal{B})$. If s is only defined on a local region $U \subset \mathcal{M}$, then we speak of a *local section*.
(b) Especially, a smooth *vector field* $X_\bullet \equiv X$ of a differentiable manifold $\mathcal{M}$ is the image $s(\mathcal{M})$ of a smooth section map $s : \mathcal{M} \to T\mathcal{M}$, that is $X_x = s(x)$, $\forall x \in \mathcal{M}$. The set of vector fields is denoted by $\Gamma(T\mathcal{M})$ or by $\mathsf{X}(\mathcal{M})$.
(c) For a given smooth vector field X, a local *integral curve* at $x \in \mathcal{M}$ is a smooth curve $c = \{c(t') \in \mathcal{M} \,|\, t' \in]-a,a[, \; a > 0\}$, with $c(t) = x$ for some $t \in]-a,a[$, such that Eq. (54.4.2) is valid for all $t' \in]-a,a[$.

(d) A smooth vector field is called *complete*, if for each $x \in \mathcal{M}$, it gives rise to a smooth integral curve through x for all $t \in \mathbb{R}$.

For an E-manifold $\mathcal{M}$, let $\{\varphi_t | t \in \mathbb{R}\}$ be a one-parameter group of diffeomorphisms in $\mathcal{M}$, such that $\mathbb{R} \times \mathcal{M} \ni (t, x) \to \varphi_t x \in \mathcal{M}$ is a C^∞-map. Then $X_x := d\varphi_t x/dt|_{t=0}$ is clearly a complete vector field.

The inverse problem, however, concerning the existence of local integral curves for a given smooth vector field can be dealt with in a general manner, only for finite-dimensional manifolds or for infinite-dimensional Banach manifolds. The piece of integral curve for a local vector field, with its smooth dependence on the curve parameter and initial points in a local region, is called a *flow box*. The uniqueness and existence of flow boxes concerns the so-called *flow box theorems* (see e.g., section on "Vector Fields as Dynamical Systems" in [AM78]). For infinite-dimensional CLC-manifolds, there is no general theory. Special results are given in [Omo74], from which we cite Theorem 7.2 (in a somewhat loose manner):

Theorem 54.4-4 (ILB-Chain Flow Box Theorem). *Let $\mathcal{M}$ be an E-manifold, where E is an ILB-chain (for which the LC-topology is given by an increasing sequence of Banach space norms). Assume that in a chart patch U_α there is given for a $r \geq 1$ a C^r vector field X. Then there is an open subset $U_0 \subset U_\alpha$, an interval $]-a, a[$, $a > 0$, and a C^r-map*

$$c : U_0 \times]-a, \quad a[\to U_\alpha$$

such that for all $x \in U_0$ the set $\{c(x, t') \in \mathcal{M} \,|\, t' \in \,]-a, a[\}$ is an integral curve for X through x, and the only one.

In our treatment of flows in a physical field space, we do not appeal to a general flow box theorem but perform direct discussions of the special situations. In the case of classical Maxwell theory, the vector field is given in terms of spatial differential operators and the manifold is the restriction of a linear space to a subset identified by boundary conditions. Let us mention merely Theorem 4.2-5 on page 61 as an example. It is typical for physical applications, that the vector field is not defined on all of the manifold.

Definition 54.4-5 (Tangent Map). Let $f : \mathcal{M} \to \mathcal{N}$ be a C^1-map between differentiable manifolds. Then one defines the tangent map at $x \in \mathcal{M}$ by the following prescription:

$$d_x f(X_x) := df(c(t))/dt|_{t=0}, \quad \text{if } c \subset \mathcal{M} \text{ is a curve with } c(0) = x \text{ and } \dot{c}(0) = X_x \,.$$
$$(54.4.3)$$

Here one makes use of $t \to f(c(t))$ being a differentiable piece of curve in $\mathcal{N}$, if $t \mapsto c(t)$ is so in $\mathcal{M}$. One can show that this does not depend on the special choice of the curve c (equivalence for tangent vectors).

The collection of $\{d_x f \,|\, x \in \mathcal{M}\}$ constitutes the *tangent map*

$$df : T\mathcal{M} \to T\mathcal{N} . \tag{54.4.4}$$

Sometimes, df is also denoted by f_* in the literature.

If f is even a C^k-map, with $1 < k \le \infty$, then df is a C^{k-1}-map between the tangent bundles.

We may now derive the product formula for tangent maps from the chain rule for the coordinate mappings of Proposition 54.1-3 on page 1995; see also Remark 54.1-4.

Proposition 54.4-6 (Composition Formula of Tangent Maps). *Assume the three differentiable manifolds $\mathcal{M}, \mathcal{N}, \mathcal{O}$ and the two differentiable mappings $A : \mathcal{M} \to \mathcal{N}$ and $B : \mathcal{N} \to \mathcal{O}$. Then the composed map $C = B \circ A : \mathcal{M} \to \mathcal{O}$ is also differentiable and its tangent map satisfies*

$$dC : T\mathcal{M} \to T\mathcal{O}, \quad dC = dB \circ dA . \tag{54.4.5}$$

We give the definition of the *Lie bracket* of two given smooth vector fields $X, Y \in \mathsf{X}(\mathcal{M})$ by means of the local coordinate expressions referring to an atlas $\{(U_\alpha, \phi_\alpha) \,|\, \alpha \in J\}$ of $\mathcal{M}$. For $U_\alpha \ni x$, one has $X_x = [(\alpha, x, f_x^\alpha)]$ with a smooth function $f^\alpha : U_\alpha \to E$, and similarly $Y_x = [(\alpha, x, g_x^\alpha)]$, $x \in U_\alpha$. Defining $[f^\alpha, g^\alpha]_x :=$ $d_x f^\alpha(g_x^\alpha) - d_x g^\alpha(f_x^\alpha)$, we observe that the two relations $(\alpha, x, f_x^\alpha) \approx (\beta, x, f_x^\beta)$ and $(\alpha, x, g_x^\alpha) \approx (\beta, x, g_x^\beta)$, $x \in U_\beta \cap U_\alpha$ imply $(\alpha, x, [f^\alpha, g^\alpha]_x) \approx (\beta, x, [f^\beta, g^\beta]_x)$.

To prove that, we use Eq. (54.4.1) to get $f_x^\beta = d_{\phi_\alpha(x)}\phi_{\beta\alpha}(f_x^\alpha)$, and the same for g_x^β. We observe that the second derivatives in the Lie bracket cancel each other and only $[f^\beta, g^\beta]_x = d_{\phi_\alpha(x)}\phi_{\beta\alpha}([f^\alpha, g^\alpha]_x)$ survives. Thus we conclude that

$$\mathcal{M} \ni x \mapsto [X, Y]_x := [(\alpha, x, [f^\alpha, g^\alpha]_x)]$$

is a well-defined vector field on $\mathcal{M}$, called the "Lie bracket" of X and Y.

If we generalize $\phi_{\beta\alpha}$ to a smooth map $\phi : \mathcal{M} \to \mathcal{M}'$ we obtain by an analogous calculation for the commutator of two vector fields $X, Y \in \mathsf{X}(\mathcal{M})$, which are by $d\phi$ transformed into $X', Y' \in \mathsf{X}(\mathcal{M}')$ the formula

$$[X', Y'] \circ \phi = d\phi \circ [X, Y] . \tag{54.4.6}$$

The following two relations, involving the three vector fields $X, Y, Z \in \mathsf{X}(\mathcal{M})$, are easily gained from their coordinate expressions

$$[X, Y] = -[Y, X] , \qquad \text{(anti-symmetry)}, \tag{54.4.7}$$
$$[X, [Y, Z]] + [Y, [Z, X]] + [Z, [X, Y]] = 0 , \qquad \text{(Jacobi identity)} . \tag{54.4.8}$$

Let us now turn to the cross sections of the cotangent bundles.

54.4.2. *Differential Forms*

Definition 54.4-7 (Generalized Covectors and Differential Forms). Let $\mathcal{M}$ be a given differentiable manifold, modeled on the CLC-space E with a complete atlas $\{(U_\alpha, \phi_\alpha)\}$, and with its cotangent bundle $T^*\mathcal{M}$.

(a) A smooth section map $s : \mathcal{M} \to T^*\mathcal{M}$, with images $\omega_x = s(x) \in T^*_x\mathcal{M}$, $\forall x \in \mathcal{M}$, defines a *covector field*, or *differential form*, or *one-form* on $\mathcal{M}$, denoted by ω. The set of all differential forms is then $\Gamma(T^*\mathcal{M})$, also denoted by the symbol $\Omega^1(\mathcal{M})$.

(b) If $\mathcal{V}$ is any real topological vector space, we form the set $E'_\mathcal{V}$ of all $\mathbb{R}$-linear continuous functionals $\alpha : E \to \mathcal{V}$.

(c) For a real topological vector space $\mathcal{V}$, we introduce the *generalized cotangent bundle of* $\mathcal{M}$ as the coordinated vector bundle

$$T^*(\mathcal{M}, \mathcal{V}) := \mathcal{B}(\pi^*, \mathcal{M}, E'_\mathcal{V}, \tau^*). \qquad (54.4.9)$$

The x-indexed linear transition diffeomorphisms

$$\tau^*_{\beta\alpha,x} : E'_\mathcal{V} \to E'_\mathcal{V}, \qquad (54.4.10)$$

are the pull backs of the $\tau_{\beta\alpha,x}$ of Definition 54.4-2 on page 2012 , that is, $(\tau^*_{\beta\alpha,x}\alpha)(f) = \alpha(\tau_{\beta\alpha,x}f)$, for all $\alpha \in E'_\mathcal{V}$, $f \in E$.

(d) The set of smooth sections $\Gamma(T^*(\mathcal{M}, \mathcal{V})) =: \Omega^1(\mathcal{M}, \mathcal{V})$ constitutes by definition the $\mathcal{V}$-*valued differential forms.* (Then $\Omega^1(\mathcal{M}, \mathbb{R}) = \Omega^1(\mathcal{M})$.)
That is, an $\omega \in \Omega^1(\mathcal{M}, \mathcal{V})$ assigns to each $X_x \in T_x\mathcal{M}$ an element $\omega(X_x) = v_x \in \mathcal{V}$, which smoothly depends on $x \in \mathcal{M}$.

(e) A $\mathcal{V}$-*valued differential form* ω *of degree* $k \in \mathbb{N}$, or $\mathcal{V}$-*valued* k-*form*, on $\mathcal{M}$, assigns to each $x \in \mathcal{M}$ a skew-symmetric k-multilinear map $\omega_x : T_x\mathcal{M} \times \overset{k}{\cdots} \times T_x\mathcal{M} \to \mathcal{V}$.
The set of all $\mathcal{V}$-valued k-forms on $\mathcal{M}$ is denoted by $\Omega^k(\mathcal{M}, \mathcal{V})$. Additionally, we define $\Omega^0(\mathcal{M}, \mathcal{V})$ as the set of all smooth $\mathcal{V}$-valued functions on $\mathcal{M}$.

(f) The set of all $\mathcal{V}$-valued differential forms is denoted

$$\Omega(\mathcal{M}, \mathcal{V}) := \cup_{k=0}^\infty \Omega^k(\mathcal{M}, \mathcal{V}). \qquad (54.4.11)$$

With slight alterations, one defines also differential forms which take values in a complex linear space $\mathcal{V}$.

We remark that an element $\omega \in \Omega^k(\mathcal{M}, \mathbb{R}) \equiv \Omega^k(\mathcal{M})$ is a usual differential form (of degree k). Beside the case $\mathcal{V} = \mathbb{R}$, the $\mathcal{V}$-valued differential forms, with $\mathcal{V}$ the Lie algebra of a Lie group, are especially important.

If $\mathcal{V}$ is a real, finite-dimensional, associative algebra, one introduces a wedge product for $\omega \in \Omega^k(\mathcal{M}, \mathcal{V})$ and $\omega' \in \Omega^l(\mathcal{M}, \mathcal{V})$ as follows. Each $\omega \in \Omega^k(\mathcal{M}, \mathcal{V})$ is decomposed into a finite sum of product elements $\omega = \sum_i \eta_i \otimes v_i$, $\eta_i \in \Omega^k(\mathcal{M})$,

$v_i \in \mathcal{V}$, and analogously for ω'. The wedge product $\omega \wedge \omega'$ is now defined by

$$(\eta_i \otimes v_i) \wedge (\eta'_j \otimes v'_j) := (\eta_i \wedge \eta'_j) \otimes v_i \cdot v_j, \quad \eta_i \in \Omega^k(\mathcal{M}), \eta'_j \in \Omega^l(\mathcal{M}), \quad (54.4.12)$$

and distributive extension. That makes $\Omega(\mathcal{M}, \mathcal{V})$ to a graded algebra.

The usual commutation relation

$$\omega \wedge \omega' = (-1)^{kl} \omega' \wedge \omega$$

is, however, no longer valid in the general case. A commutator is therefore defined by

$$[\omega, \omega'] := \omega \wedge \omega' - (-1)^{kl} \omega' \wedge \omega, \quad\quad (54.4.13)$$

which vanishes identically, if and only if $\mathcal{V}$ is a commutative algebra. In particular, one has the general self-commutator for $\omega \in \Omega^k(\mathcal{M}, \mathcal{V})$

$$[\omega, \omega] := \begin{cases} 2\omega \wedge \omega, & k \text{ odd} \\ 0, & k \text{ even} \end{cases}. \quad\quad (54.4.14)$$

The exterior derivative for $\omega \in \Omega^k(\mathcal{M}, \mathcal{V})$ is given by $\mathbf{d}\omega = \sum_i \mathbf{d}\eta_i \otimes v_i \in \Omega^{k+1}(\mathcal{M}, \mathcal{V})$. Thus $\mathbf{d}$ maps $\Omega(\mathcal{M}, \mathcal{V})$ into $\Omega(\mathcal{M}, \mathcal{V})$. Especially $\mathbf{d}^2\omega = 0$ for all $\omega \in \Omega(\mathcal{M}, \mathcal{V})$. If $\omega \equiv f \in \Omega^0(\mathcal{M}, \mathcal{V})$ (a $\mathcal{V}$-valued function), then $\mathbf{d}f \in \Omega^1(\mathcal{M}, \mathcal{V})$ equals the differential respectively tangent map $df : T\mathcal{M} \to \mathcal{V}$.

Let us recall that $\omega \in \Omega(\mathcal{M}, \mathcal{V})$ is *closed*, if $\mathbf{d}\Omega = 0$ and *exact*, if there is an $\omega' \in \Omega(\mathcal{M}, \mathcal{V})$ with $\omega = \mathbf{d}\omega'$. Thus, all exact forms are closed, but not vice versa, a distinction which gives rise to profound insights into the topology of a manifold.

54.5.   Lie Groups, Principal Bundles, and Connections

54.5.1.   *Lie Groups*

Definition 54.5-1 (Lie-Group). A Lie group G is a group, which is a differentiable manifold modeled on a CLC-space E such that $G \times G \ni (g, h) \to g \cdot h^{-1}$ is a smooth (C^∞-) map. (The unit element of G is denoted by e.)

Definition 54.5-2 (Group Actions). A Lie group G is said to act from the left (or homomorphically) on a differentiable manifold $\mathcal{M}$, if there is a smooth mapping $l : G \times \mathcal{M} \to \mathcal{M}$ such that $l_e x = x$ and $l_{g \cdot h} x = (l_g \circ l_h)x$ for all $x \in \mathcal{M}$ and all $g, h \in G$. A right (also homomorphic) action is a smooth mapping $r : G \times \mathcal{M} \to \mathcal{M}$ such that $r_e x = x$ and $r_{g \cdot h} x = (r_g \circ r_h)x$ for all $x \in \mathcal{M}$ and all $g, h \in G$. One often writes $l_g x \equiv gx$ and $r_g x \equiv xg^{-1}$.

If G acts on itself, i.e., $\mathcal{M} = G$, we have $l_g h = gh$, $r_g h = hg^{-1}$, where the right-hand sides designate now group products, and we denote $\mathrm{ad}_g h := ghg^{-1}$, and all of the actions constitute diffeomorphisms on G. The *corresponding tangent maps* are written $L_g X = gX, R_g X = Xg^{-1}$, $X \in \Gamma(TG)$. Explicitly, we have for the local expressions in terms of a smooth local curve $c(t)$ in G, with $\dot{c}(0) = X_h$, $h \in G$, the defining relations

$$gX_h := d(g \cdot c(t))/dt|_{t=0}, \quad X_h g := d(c(t) \cdot g)/dt|_{t=0}, \quad Ad_g X_h := gX_h g^{-1}. \quad (54.5.1)$$

Because of the formula for composing tangent maps, L_g and R_g are G-actions from the left and from the right respectively on $\Gamma(TG)$.

Definition 54.5-3 (Left-Invariant Vector Fields). Let G be a Lie group. A vector field $X_\bullet \equiv X \in \Gamma(TG)$ is called *left-invariant* if $L_g X_h = X_{gh}$ for all $g, h \in G$. The set of all left-invariant vector fields is denoted by $\Gamma_L(TG)$.

Proposition 54.5-4. *For a Lie group G, the map $X \equiv X_\bullet \mapsto X_e$, with the inverse mapping $X_e \mapsto L_\bullet X_e$ (the vector field which takes at $g \in G$ the value $L_g X_e$), constitutes a linear diffeomorphism between the set of left invariant vector fields $\Gamma_L(TG)$ and the tangent space $T_e G$. (Only occasionally we indicate the empty argument by $\bullet$ for better readability.)*

Definition 54.5-5 (Lie Algebra). The Lie algebra $\mathcal{G}$ of a Lie group G (modeled on the CLC-space E) is the CLC-space $T_e G$ (linearly diffeomorphic to E), which is — beside the linear structure — equipped with the Lie product

$$[X_e, Y_e] := [L_\bullet X_e, L_\bullet Y_e]_e, \quad (54.5.2)$$

where the bracket on the right-hand side is the Lie bracket of vector fields, evaluated at e.

Definition 54.5-6. Given a smooth curve $X(t)$ (shorthand for a function on an arbitrary interval $[a, b] \subset \mathbb{R}$) in $\mathcal{G}$, we call a curve $p(t)$ in G, which is a solution of the differential equation

$$p(t)^{-1} \dot{p}(t) = X(t)$$

a *product integral* of $X(t)$ and write

$$\prod_{t_0}^{t} \exp[X(t)]\, dt := p^{-1}(t_0) \cdot p(t).$$

The existence of the product integrals singles out a certain class of Lie groups (cf. [Mil83], [Omo97]).

Definition 54.5-7. A Lie group G is called *regular*, if every smooth path $X(t)$ in $\mathcal{G}$ has a product integral and if the correspondence $X(t) \mapsto p^{-1}(0) \cdot p(1)$ defines a smooth map $C^\infty([a, b], \mathcal{G}) \to G$.

In a regular Lie group exist especially the product integrals of the constant paths $\{X(t) = X \mid t \in [a, b], X \in \mathcal{G}\}$. If we write in this case

$$\prod_{a}^{t} \exp[Xt]\, dt =: \exp[(t - a)X],$$

we obtain $p(t) = \exp[tX]$ as the existing solution of the differential equation $\dot{p}(t) = p(t)X$. We have here a global existence of the *exponential map*.

Reversely, if a product integral is a one-parameter subgroup of G, it must be the exponential for some Lie algebra element X, because we have by differentiation of the group relation $p(t'+t) = p(t')\cdot p(t)$ to t, that $p(t')(p(t)X(t)) = p(t'+t)X(t'+t)$, which implies the constancy of $X(t)$. But one knows that every finite dimensional Lie algebra acting on an arbitrary G is a differential. Thus all one-parameter subgroups are exponentials in a regular Lie group.

Only for simply-connected regular Lie groups we have the biunivocal correspondence between Lie groups and their Lie algebras.

Theorem 54.5-8. *A regular Lie group G, which is simply-connected, is uniquely determined by its Lie algebra $\mathcal{G}$: If there is another regular Lie group G', the Lie algebra $\mathcal{G}'$ of which is a homomorphic image of $\mathcal{G}$, then G' is a homomorphic image of G.*

Observe that all finite-dimensional Lie groups are regular and that this holds also for 0-dimensional Lie groups, which form a discrete topological space. The connected component of the unit element is in the latter case $\{e\}$ and the Lie algebra is $\{0\}$. The exponential $\exp(0) = e$ exists and may be shifted to the other connected components.

54.5.2.   *Principal Fiber Bundles*

A most important type of fiber bundles are the so-called *principal bundles*.

Definition 54.5-9 (Principal Fiber Bundles).   A fiber bundle $\mathcal{B} = \mathcal{B}(\pi, \mathcal{M}, \mathcal{F}, G^{\mathcal{B}})$ is a *principal bundle*, if $G^{\mathcal{B}} \equiv G$ is a regular Lie group (including the discrete case for G) which is also taken as the typical fiber $G = \mathcal{F}$, on which it acts by left multiplication.

A principal bundle is denoted by the symbol $\mathcal{P}(\pi, \mathcal{M}, G) := \mathcal{B}(\pi, \mathcal{M}, G, G)$, and a coordinated principal bundle, taken of its strict equivalence class, by $\mathcal{P}(\pi, \mathcal{M}, G, \tau)$ (where $\tau = \{(U_\alpha, \tau_\alpha)\,|\,\alpha \in J\}$ indicates still the trivialization structure).

For clarity, we denote occasionally the product in $G \ni f, g$ by $f \cdot g \in G$.

The induced right action of G on $\mathcal{P} \ni b$ is *defined* by

$$r_{h^{-1}}b \equiv bh := \tau_\alpha^{-1}(x, f \cdot h), \quad \text{if } \tau_\alpha b = (x, f), \quad f, h \in G, \tag{54.5.3}$$

(without a dot between b and h).

We keep the notation $\tau_\alpha b = (x, \tau_{\alpha x} b)$, if $\pi b = x$, where now $\tau_{\alpha x} b \in G$ (but still $\tau_{\alpha x} : \pi^{-1}x \to G$ is a transformation from a part of $\mathcal{P}$ into G, and not on $\mathcal{F} \equiv G$). We change the notation

$$\tau_{\beta\alpha,x} \to g_{\beta\alpha,x} := \tau_{\beta x} \circ \tau_{\alpha x}^{-1} \in G. \tag{54.5.4}$$

(Observe that, of course, the transition group elements of principal bundles do in general not satisfy the factorization criterion for triviality since the $\tau_{\alpha\bullet}$ are not functions from U_α into G.)

The transition relations Eq. (54.2.10) may now be written as

$$g_{\gamma\beta,x} \cdot g_{\beta\alpha,x} = g_{\gamma\alpha,x}, \quad \forall x \in \mathcal{M}, \quad \forall \ \alpha, \beta, \quad \gamma \in J_x. \tag{54.5.5}$$

One concludes directly from Definition 54.5-9 that for all $b \in \mathcal{P}$ and all $h \in G$

$$\pi(bh) = \pi b, \quad \text{and} \quad \tau_{\alpha x}(bh) = (\tau_{\alpha x}b) \cdot h, \quad \text{for} \quad \pi b = x. \tag{54.5.6}$$

Definition 54.5-10 (Regular Bundle and Related Principal Bundle).

(a) Let $\mathcal{B} = \mathcal{B}(\pi, \mathcal{M}, \mathcal{F}, \tau)$ be a given coordinated fiber bundle, with $\tau = \{(U_\alpha, \tau_\alpha) \,|\, \alpha \in J\}$, and with the additional assumption that the structure group $G^{\mathcal{B}}$ be a regular Lie group such that the maps $U_\beta \cap U_\alpha \ni x \mapsto \tau_{\beta\alpha,x} \in G^{\mathcal{B}}$ be continuous. Then $\mathcal{B} = \mathcal{B}(\pi, \mathcal{M}, \mathcal{F}, \tau)$ is called *regular*.

(b) Let $\mathcal{B} = \mathcal{B}(\pi, \mathcal{M}, \mathcal{F}, \tau)$ be a given regular coordinated fiber bundle. Then one can construct a coordinated bundle $\mathcal{B}(\pi, \mathcal{M}, \mathcal{F} = G^{\mathcal{B}}, \tau')$ in terms of the given open covering $\{U_\alpha\}$ of $\mathcal{M}$ and the equivalence relation (α, x, g) is equivalent to (β, y, g') if and only if $x = y$ and $g' = \tau_{\beta\alpha,x} \circ g$, $g, g' \in G^{\mathcal{B}} \subset \text{Diff}(\mathcal{F})$.

By means of the assumed regularity, this action of $G^{\mathcal{B}}$ is jointly continuous in (x, g) and the reconstruction theorem of Proposition 54.2-9 applies.

Taken $G^{\mathcal{B}}$ as an abstract group, we may identify $\circ$ with the abstract group multiplication $\cdot$, denote $\tau_{\beta\alpha,x} \equiv g_{\beta\alpha,x}$, and view $\mathcal{B}(\pi, \mathcal{M}, \mathcal{F} = G^{\mathcal{B}}, \tau')$ as a coordinated principal bundle $\mathcal{P}^{\mathcal{B}}(\tau') = \mathcal{P}(\pi, \mathcal{M}, G^{\mathcal{B}}, \tau')$ *associated with* $\mathcal{B}$. By this, we have also related with $\mathcal{B}(\pi, \mathcal{M}, \mathcal{F}, G^{\mathcal{B}})$ the *associated principal bundle* $\mathcal{P}^{\mathcal{B}} = \mathcal{P}(\pi, \mathcal{M}, G^{\mathcal{B}})$.

Since the equivalence of a bundle $\mathcal{B}(\pi, \mathcal{M}, \mathcal{F}, G^{\mathcal{B}})$ to another bundle is merely a matter of the transition diffeomorphisms if the quantities $(\mathcal{M}, \mathcal{F}, G^{\mathcal{B}})$ are kept fixed, one needs then only to study equivalence for principal bundles.

Proposition 54.5-11 (Transfer of Equivalence). *Two regular fiber bundles with the same base manifold, typical fiber, and global structure group, are equivalent, if and only if their associated principal bundles are equivalent.*

In the language of principal bundles, most important concepts for physical applications are formulated, where fiber bundles which are bundle diffeomorphic to a product bundle are called *trivial*, (in spite describing non-trivial physics, as we shall demonstrate later on).

Proposition 54.5-12 (Trivial Principal Bundles).

(a) *A coordinated principal fiber bundle $\mathcal{P}(\pi, \mathcal{M}, G, \tau)$ is trivial, if and only if its transition group elements factorize. That means that for each coordinate patch*

U_α of τ, there is a continuous function $U_\alpha \ni x \mapsto g_{\alpha x} \in G$ such that

$$g_{\beta\alpha,x} = g_{\beta x} \cdot g_{\alpha x}^{-1}, \quad \forall x \in U_\beta \cap U_\alpha . \tag{54.5.7}$$

(b) *A principal bundle $\mathcal{P}(\pi, \mathcal{M}, G)$ is trivial, if and only if it admits a global continuous section $s : \mathcal{M} \to \mathcal{P}$ (with $\pi \circ s = id_\mathcal{M}$).*

Proof. (a) That follows from Proposition 54.3-12 on page 2011, where the G-equivalence is expressed in terms of a bundle map.

(b) Suppose $s : \mathcal{M} \to \mathcal{P}$ is given and define for each $x \in \mathcal{M}$ and $\alpha \in J_x$

$$g_{\alpha x} := (\tau_{\alpha x} \circ s_\alpha)(x) . \tag{54.5.8}$$

We obtain then

$$(\tau_{\beta\alpha,x} \circ \tau_{\alpha x}) s_\alpha(x) = \tau_{\beta\alpha,x}(e \cdot g_{\alpha x}) = \tau_{\beta x} s_\alpha(x) \implies g_{\beta\alpha,x} \cdot g_{\alpha x} = g_{\beta x} , \quad x \in U_\beta \cap U_\alpha , \tag{54.5.9}$$

since $s_\alpha(x) = s_\beta(x)$ on $U_\beta \cap U_\alpha$ for the restrictions of the global section.

Conversely, let Eq. (54.5.7) be given. Define

$$s_{\alpha x} := \tau_{\alpha x}^{-1} g_{\alpha x}, \quad \forall \alpha \in J_x , \tag{54.5.10}$$

which is continuous in $x \in U_\alpha$ and satisfies $s_{\beta x} = s_{\alpha x}, x \in U_\beta \cap U_\alpha$. Thus, the $s_\alpha, \alpha \in J$, combine to a global, single-valued, continuous cross section. $\square$

Since there is for a non-trivial principal bundle no global cross section one needs a more general substitute for it, what leads to the notion of a *connection*.

54.5.3. *Connections in Principal Bundles*

Definition 54.5-13 (Vertical Tangent Vectors and Connections). Let $\mathcal{P}(\pi, \mathcal{M}, G) = \mathcal{P}$ be the given principal bundle. Then the tangent map at $b \in \mathcal{P}$ of the bundle projection, that is $d_b\pi : T_b\mathcal{P} \to T_{\pi b}\mathcal{M}$, is a smooth surjection with its kernel denoted by $V_b\mathcal{P} \subset T_b\mathcal{P}$.

The elements of $V_b\mathcal{P}$ are called *vertical tangent vectors* at b. The vector bundle $V\mathcal{P} := \cup_{b\in\mathcal{P}} V_b \subset T\mathcal{P}$ is the *vertical tangent bundle*.

The choice of a smooth sub-bundle $H\mathcal{P} \subset T\mathcal{P}$

(1) such that at each $b \in \mathcal{P}$ we have the direct sum $T_b\mathcal{P} = V_b\mathcal{P} \oplus H_b\mathcal{P}$, giving the bundle decomposition

$$T\mathcal{P} = V\mathcal{P} \oplus H\mathcal{P} , \tag{54.5.11}$$

(2) and such that we have the right-shift relation

$$H_{bg}\mathcal{P} = (R_{g^{-1}})H_b\mathcal{P}, \quad \forall b \in \mathcal{P}, \quad \forall g \in G , \tag{54.5.12}$$

is called a *connection* of $\mathcal{P}$. (Recall: $R_{g^{-1}}$ is the tangent map of $r_{g^{-1}}b = bg$.)

Notational Remark 54.5-14 (Vectors on $\mathcal{P}$). We discriminate the vectors $\bar{X}$ in $T\mathcal{P}$ by means of a *bar* from the vectors X in $T\mathcal{M}$.

Observe that with varying connection $H\mathcal{P}$ the unique decompositions $\bar{X}_b = \bar{X}_b^V \oplus \bar{X}_b^H$, for fixed $\bar{X}_b \in T_b\mathcal{P}$, contain not only a varying horizontal component $\bar{X}_b^H$ but also a varying vertical component $\bar{X}_b^H$.

We employ now that for a regular Lie group G, with Lie algebra $\mathcal{G} \ni a$, the exponentials $\exp\{ta\} \in G$ are defined for all $t \in \mathbb{R}$ and constitute a one-parameter subgroup of G.

Definition 54.5-15 (Connection Forms). Let $\mathcal{P}(\pi, \mathcal{M}, G)$ be a given principal bundle, where $\mathcal{G}$ is the Lie algebra of the regular Lie group G, acting smoothly from the right in $\mathcal{P}$ along the fibers $G_x = bG$, $\pi b = x$, that is, in the vertical direction.

(a) For each $f \in C^\infty(\mathcal{P}, \mathcal{G})$, one defines the *fundamental vector field*

$$\bar{X}_b^f := \frac{d\left(b\exp[tf(b)]\right)}{dt}\Big|_{t=0} \in V_b\mathcal{P}, \quad b \in \mathcal{P}, \tag{54.5.13}$$

where the derivative of a smooth curve has been employed. By varying f, the $\bar{X}_b^f$ exhaust $V_b\mathcal{P}$: They are in $V_b\mathcal{P}$, because by varying $t \in \mathbb{R}$ we have $\pi(b\exp[tf(b)]) = \pi(b)$ and differentiation to t gives 0. By $f(b)$ running through $\mathcal{G}$ and t through $\mathbb{R}$, $b\exp[tf(b)]$ gives the fiber $bG = \pi^{-1}(\pi b)$. Any curve $t \mapsto b(t)$ with $\pi b(t) = x = \pi b(0)$ (owning vertical tangent vectors) lies in $b(0)G$.

(b) A one-form $\omega \in \Omega^1(\mathcal{P}, \mathcal{G})$ is called *horizontal* (that is, $\omega \in \Omega_H^1(\mathcal{P}, \mathcal{G})$), if

$$\omega_b(\bar{X}_b^f) = f(b) \in \mathcal{G}, \quad \forall b \in \mathcal{P}, \quad \forall f \in C^\infty(\mathcal{P}, \mathcal{G}). \tag{54.5.14}$$

(c) A one-form $\omega \in \Omega^1(\mathcal{P}, \mathcal{G})$ is called *equivariant* (that is $\omega \in \Omega_G^1(\mathcal{P}, \mathcal{G})$), if

$$r_g^*\omega = Ad(g^{-1})\omega, \tag{54.5.15}$$

which means in explicit terms

$$(r_g^*\omega)_b(\bar{X}_b) \equiv \omega_{r_gb}(R_g\bar{X}_b) = g^{-1}\omega_b(\bar{X}_b)g, \tag{54.5.16}$$

where the last term is the $Ad(g^{-1})$-multiplication in $\mathcal{G}$.

(d) A one-form $\omega \in \Omega^1(\mathcal{P}, \mathcal{G})$ is called a *connection form* (that is, $\omega \in \Omega_{H,G}^1(\mathcal{P}, \mathcal{G})$), if it is horizontal and equivariant.

One obtains the following bijective relation.

Proposition 54.5-16. *Given a connection form $\omega \in \Omega_{H,G}^1(\mathcal{P}, \mathcal{G})$, then*

$$H_b\mathcal{P} := \{\bar{X}_b \in T_b\mathcal{P} \mid \omega(\bar{X}_b) = 0\} \tag{54.5.17}$$

defines a connection on $\mathcal{P}$.

Reversely, if a connection $H\mathcal{P}$ is given, then a connection form $\omega \in \Omega^1_{H,G}(\mathcal{P}, \mathcal{G})$ is uniquely determined by Eqs. (54.5.17) and (54.5.14). We often also designate the connection by means of the connection form symbol ω.

In terms of a connection, or equivalently connection form, one introduces the covariant derivatives.

Definition 54.5-17 (Covariant Derivatives). Let again be given a principal bundle $\mathcal{P}(\pi, \mathcal{M}, G) = \mathcal{P}$, together with a connection form $\omega \in \Omega^1_{H,G}(\mathcal{P}, \mathcal{G})$.

(a) Let F denote a CLC-space. The *"horizontal part"* α^H of $\alpha \in \Omega^k(\mathcal{P}, F)$ (F-valued k-form) is defined by its taking into account only the horizontal parts of the tangent vectors, i.e.,

$$\alpha^H_b(\bar{X}^1_b, \dots, \bar{X}^k_b) := \alpha_b(\bar{X}^{1H}_b, \dots, \bar{X}^{kH}_b), \quad \bar{X}^i_b \in T_b\mathcal{P}, \quad \bar{X}^{iH}_b \in H_b\mathcal{P}.$$

Thus a connection form $\omega \in \Omega^1_{H,G}(\mathcal{P}, \mathcal{G})$ has $F = \mathcal{G}$ and displays a vanishing horizontal part $\omega^H = 0$.

(b) The *"horizontal or covariant"* derivative $\nabla_\omega \alpha$ of $\alpha \in \Omega^k(\mathcal{P}, F)$ is defined, by means of the exterior derivative for F-valued forms, as

$$\nabla_\omega \alpha := (\mathbf{d}\alpha)^H. \tag{54.5.18}$$

(Recall that the exterior derivative $\mathbf{d}$ maps an F-valued k-form α onto an F-valued $k+1$-form $\mathbf{d}\alpha$.)

(c) Especially the $\mathcal{G}$-valued two-form

$$\nabla_\omega \omega = \Omega \tag{54.5.19}$$

is called the *"curvature of the connection"* ω.

The curvature introduced by a connection coincides in special cases with the curvature on a Riemannian manifold.

The Lie bracket for $\alpha, \alpha' \in \Omega^1(\mathcal{P}, \mathcal{G})$ is defined by that in $\mathcal{G}$ via $[\alpha, \alpha'](\bar{X}) := [\alpha(\bar{X}), \alpha'(\bar{X})]$, $\forall \bar{X} \in T\mathcal{P}$, which coincides in the present special case with the general definition in Eq. (54.4.13). By direct calculations, one obtains the following.

Theorem 54.5-18. *Let ω be a connection on the principal bundle $\mathcal{P}$. Then it holds for the curvature two-form*

$$\Omega = \mathbf{d}\omega + \frac{1}{2}[\omega, \omega], \qquad (\textit{Maurer–Cartan}), \tag{54.5.20}$$

$$\nabla_\omega \Omega = 0, \qquad (\textit{Bianchi identity}). \tag{54.5.21}$$

The geometric meaning of a connection is related to that of the base manifold of the principal bundle. Thus one has need for a systematic method to pull back the connection from the principal bundle $\mathcal{P} = \mathcal{P}(\pi, \mathcal{M}, G)$ to the base $\mathcal{M}$. We do this by means of distinguished families of local sections, which are associated with the families of local trivializations.

Proposition 54.5-19 (Distinguished Local Sections and Trivializations).
Let be given a coordinated principal bundle $\mathcal{P}(\pi, \mathcal{M}, G, \tau) \equiv \mathcal{P}(\tau)$ (referring to an open covering $\{U_\alpha\}_J$ of $\mathcal{M}$, with associated trivialization structure $\tau = \{(U_\alpha, \tau_\alpha) \,|\, \alpha \in J\}$, and $g_{\alpha\beta,x} = \tau_{\beta,x} \circ \tau_{\alpha,x}^{-1}(e) \in G$).

Then there is a distinguished family of local sections $\sigma = \{\sigma_\alpha : U_\alpha :\to \mathcal{P}(\tau) \,|\, \alpha \in J\}$, which satisfies

$$\sigma_\beta(x) := \sigma_\alpha(x) g_{\alpha\beta,x}, \quad \forall \alpha, \beta \in J, \quad \forall x \in U_\alpha \cap U_\beta. \tag{54.5.22}$$

Let reversely be given a principal bundle $\mathcal{P}(\pi, \mathcal{M}, G) \equiv \mathcal{P}$ with a family of local sections $\sigma = \{\sigma_\alpha : U_\alpha :\to \mathcal{P} \,|\, \alpha \in J\}$, referring to an open covering $\{U_\alpha\}_J$ of $\mathcal{M}$. Then this fixes a τ-structure on $\mathcal{P}$, which means a selection of a coordinated principal fiber bundle in the class of $\mathcal{P}$.

Proof. If τ is given, then we define for each $\alpha \in J$:

$$\sigma_\alpha(x) := \tau_\alpha^{-1}(x, e) \equiv \tau_{\alpha,x}^{-1}(e), \quad \forall x \in U_\alpha. \tag{54.5.23}$$

From the discussion near Eq. (54.2.6) on page 2001 it follows that this is a smooth mapping with $\pi \circ \sigma_\alpha(x) = x$, $\forall x \in U_\alpha$. It holds that

$$\sigma_\beta(x) = \tau_{\beta,x}^{-1}(e) = \tau_{\alpha,x}^{-1} \circ (\tau_{\alpha,x} \circ \tau_{\beta,x}^{-1})(e) = \tau_{\alpha,x}^{-1}(g_{\alpha\beta,x}) = \sigma_\alpha(x) g_{\alpha\beta,x}.$$

If, reversely, σ is given on $\mathcal{P}$, then define for all $\alpha \in J$

$$\tau_\alpha^{-1}(x, g) := \sigma_\alpha(x) g, \quad x \in U_\alpha, \quad g \in G. \tag{54.5.24}$$

Since both $\sigma_\alpha(x)$ and $\sigma_\beta(x)$ are in G_x, there is a uniquely determined $g_{\alpha\beta,x} \in G$ such that (54.5.22) is satisfied. The $g_{\alpha\beta,x}$ satisfy the transition relations. They determine the local structure groups $G_x^\mathcal{P}$. □

We remark that from Eq. (54.5.23), we obtain $g = \tau_{\alpha,x}(\sigma_\alpha(x)g) = \tau_{\alpha,x} s_\alpha(x)$ with the g-shifted local section s_α, that looks similar to Eq. (54.5.8) $g_{\alpha x} := (\tau_{\alpha x} \circ s_\alpha)(x)$. The factorization of the transition functions would follow, however, only if $\sigma_\alpha(x) = \sigma_\beta(x)$ on $U_\beta \cap U_\alpha$, which would mean that the σ_α, $\alpha \in J$, combine to a global section.

Definition 54.5-20 (Local Potentials and Local Fields). For a principal bundle $\mathcal{P}(\pi, \mathcal{M}, G) = \mathcal{P}$, with a family of distinguished local sections $\sigma = \{\sigma_\alpha : U_\alpha :\to \mathcal{P} \,|\, \alpha \in J\}$, we introduce the following notions.

(a) The family of *local potentials* associated with a connection $\omega \in \Omega_{H,G}^1(\mathcal{P}, \mathcal{G})$ is given by

$$A_\alpha := \sigma_\alpha^* \omega \in \Omega^1(U_\alpha, \mathcal{G}), \quad \text{i.e.,}$$
$$A_{\alpha x}(X_x) := \omega_{\sigma_\alpha(x)}(d_x \sigma_\alpha(X_x)) \in \mathcal{G}, \quad X_x \in T_x \mathcal{M}. \tag{54.5.25}$$

(b) The family of *local fields* associated with a connection $\omega \in \Omega^1_{H,G}(\mathcal{P}, \mathcal{G})$ is given by

$$F_\alpha := \sigma_\alpha^* \Omega \in \Omega^2(U_\alpha, \mathcal{G}). \qquad (54.5.26)$$

Recall that the transition elements constitute a smooth mapping $g_{\alpha\beta} : U_\beta \cap U_\alpha \to G$, which has a well-defined tangent map

$$d_x g_{\alpha\beta} : T_x(U_\beta \cap U_\alpha) \to T_{g_{\alpha\beta},x} G. \qquad (54.5.27)$$

Since the elements in TG may be left and right multiplied by elements of G (for $A \in \mathcal{G} = T_e G$, we have $gA = gd\exp(tA)/dt|_{t=0} \in T_g G$), the expression $g_{\alpha\beta,x}^{-1} d g_{\alpha\beta,x}$ is a well-defined element in $T_e G \equiv \mathcal{G}$.

Proposition 54.5-21 (Construction from Local Potentials). *Let be a given coordinated principal bundle $\mathcal{P}(\tau) = \mathcal{P}(\pi, \mathcal{M}, G, \tau)$ with transition elements $g_{\alpha\beta,x} \in G$, $\beta, \alpha \in J$.*

A family of local one-forms $\{A_\alpha \in \Omega^1(U_\alpha, \mathcal{G}) \mid \alpha \in J\}$ is the set of local potentials of a connection $\omega \in A^1_{H,G}(\mathcal{P}, \mathcal{G})$, if and only if

$$A_{\beta,x} = g_{\alpha\beta,x}^{-1} A_{\alpha,x} g_{\alpha\beta,x} + g_{\alpha\beta,x}^{-1} d g_{\alpha\beta,x}, \quad \forall \beta, \alpha \in J, \quad \forall x \in U_\beta \cap U_\alpha. \qquad (54.5.28)$$

The family of local potentials is the constructive form of a connection. In fact, if we have given the family $\{A_\alpha \in \Omega^1(U_\alpha, \mathcal{G}) \mid \alpha \in J\}$, together with the distinguished local sections $\sigma_\alpha : U_\alpha \to \mathcal{P}$, then we get a connection form ω locally as follows. We choose $x \in U_\alpha$ and set $b := \sigma_\alpha(x) \in \mathcal{P}$. If $\bar{X}_b \in T_b \mathcal{P}$ has the decomposition

$$\bar{X}_b = d_x \sigma_\alpha(X_x) + \bar{X}_b^A, \qquad (54.5.29)$$

where $\bar{X}_b^A$ denotes the fundamental vector from Eq. (54.5.13) with $f(b) = A \in \mathcal{G}$, we set

$$\omega_\alpha(\bar{X}_b) = A_\alpha(X_x) + A, \quad \text{and} \quad \omega_\alpha(\bar{X}_{bg}) = g^{-1} \omega_\alpha(R_{g^{-1}} \bar{X}_b) g. \qquad (54.5.30)$$

Whereas the $\bar{X}_b^A$, $A \in \mathcal{G}$, exhaust V_b, we have $(\pi \circ \sigma_\alpha)x(t) = x(t)$ and $d_x \sigma_\alpha(X_x) \neq 0$ if and only if $X_x \neq 0$. Thus Eq. (54.5.29) constitutes a direct decomposition of $\bar{X}_b$ into a vertical component and a component for which there exists a linear isomorphism to $T_x \mathcal{M}$, $\pi b = x$. By varying $x \in U_\alpha$ we can prove that ω_α is a connection form on $\pi^{-1} U_\alpha$.

The analogous construction can be performed in terms of the distinguished section $\sigma_\beta : U_\beta \to \mathcal{P}$ to give a local connections form ω_β on $\pi^{-1} U_\beta$. Both local connections forms coincide immediately on vertical vectors. They also coincide for $b \in \pi^{-1}(U_\alpha \cap U_\beta)$ because of Eq. (54.5.28) (cf. [Ble81]). Thus the family $\{\omega_\alpha \mid \alpha \in J\}$ defines a unique element $\omega \in \Omega^1(\mathcal{P}, \mathcal{G})$. It satisfies the assumptions for a connection form required in Definition 54.5-15(b) and (c).

After having pulled down the connection 1-form we may pull down the Maurer–Cartan formula to get the relation

$$F_\alpha := \mathbf{d}A_\alpha + \frac{1}{2}[A_\alpha, A_\alpha] = \mathbf{d}A_\alpha \,, \quad \text{(local Maurer–Cartan)}, \qquad (54.5.31)$$

where the last equation holds for Abelian structure groups G exhibiting the gauge independence of the curvature and field strength.

Proposition 54.5-22 (Horizontal Lift of a Vector Field). *Let be given a principal bundle $\mathcal{P} = \mathcal{P}(\pi, \mathcal{M}, G)$ with a connection $\omega \in \Omega^1_{H,G}(\mathcal{P}, \mathcal{G})$ and a vector field $X \in \mathsf{X}(\mathcal{M})$.*

Then there is a unique horizontal vector field $\bar{X} \in \mathsf{X}^H(\mathcal{P})$ (satisfying $\omega(\bar{X}) \equiv 0$) with $d_b\pi(\bar{X}_b) = X_{\pi b}$ for all $b \in \mathcal{P}$. Necessarily it holds then $R_g\bar{X} = \bar{X}$ for all $g \in G$.

$\bar{X}$ is called the horizontal lift *of X and is denoted by $\bar{X} = \mathsf{l}(X)$. More precisely, we write $\bar{X}_b = \mathsf{l}_b(X_x)$, for a given vector $X_x \in T_x\mathcal{M}$ and given $b \in \pi^{-1}x$. It holds $\mathsf{l}_{r_gb}(X) = R_g\mathsf{l}_b(X)$ for all $g \in G$.*

Proof. The tangent projection $d_b\pi : H_b\mathcal{P} \overset{\text{onto}}{\to} T_{\pi b}\mathcal{M}$ is an isomorphism, since $\bar{X}_b = \bar{X}_b^V \oplus \bar{X}_b^H$ is unique and $V_b\mathcal{P} = \ker(d_b\pi)$. Let us denote $d_b\pi$ restricted to $H_b\mathcal{P}$ by $d_b\pi_H$. Thus we may define $\mathsf{l}_b(X_x) := d_b\pi_H^{-1}(X_x)$. Smoothness of the vector field $\bar{X}$ originates from that of $d_b\pi$.

The right-covariance arises as follows: If $\bar{X}_b = \mathsf{l}_b(X_x)$, then $R_g\bar{X}_b = \bar{X}'_{r_gb}$ for some $\bar{X}'_{r_gb} \in H_{r_gb}\mathcal{P}$, because of Eq. (54.5.12). But $d_{(r_gb)}\pi(R_g\bar{X}_b) = d_b(\pi \circ r_g)\bar{X}_b = d_b\pi\bar{X}_b = X_x$, where the product rule of tangent maps and Eq. (54.5.6) have been employed. Since the horizontal lift $\mathsf{l}_{r_gb}(X_x)$ is unique, it equals $\bar{X}'_{r_gb}$. $\qquad\square$

The above expression $d_b\pi_H^{-1}(X_x)$ for horizontally lifted vectors is not constructive, since $d_b\pi_H^{-1}$ is only introduced by a logical argument.

In the proof for the subsequent Proposition 54.5-23, the local sections appear better suited for applications.

Proposition 54.5-23 (Horizontal Lift of a Curve and Parallel Transport).
Let be given a principal bundle $\mathcal{P} = \mathcal{P}(\pi, \mathcal{M}, G)$ with a connection form $\omega \in \Omega^1_{H,G}(\mathcal{P}, \mathcal{G})$ and a differentiable curve $c : [0,1] \to \mathcal{M}$.

Then there is a differentiable "lifted curve" $\bar{c} : [0,1] \to \mathcal{P}$ with $\dot{\bar{c}}(t) \in H_{\bar{c}(t)}\mathcal{P}$ and with $\pi\bar{c}(t) = c(t)$ for all $t \in [0,1]$. Such a lifted curve is unique if one specifies the initial value $\bar{c}(0) \in \mathcal{P}$ (with $\pi\bar{c}(0) = c(0)$).

The horizontally lifted curve with initial value $\bar{c}(0)g$ is then given by $\bar{c}(t)g$, for all $g \in G$.

Thus there exists the "parallel transport" of an element $b \in \mathcal{P}$ along a base curve $c : [0,1] \to \mathcal{M}$. It is defined by the values of the unique horizontally lifted curve $\bar{c}(t) \in \mathcal{P}$, $t \in [0, 1]$, *with $\bar{c}(0) = b$. The parallel transport of a fiber $\pi^{-1}c(0)$ along the curve c is the fiber $\pi^{-1}c(t)$, $t \in [0, 1]$.*

Proof. [Hint] We indicate a proof in terms of the distinguished local sections $\sigma_\alpha : U_\alpha \to \mathcal{P}$, which have already been used to construct the connection form from given local potentials. The latter procedure is made, in fact, more evident by the following curve lifting.

We divide the curve $c : [0, 1] \to \mathcal{M}$ into a finite number of small pieces c_i such that each c_i lies in some U_α. We define the lifted piece of curve by $\bar{c}_i(t) :=$ $\sigma_\alpha(c_i(t))g_i(t)$, where the curve $g_i : t \mapsto G$ has to be still determined. For each local t, the derivative has the form

$$\frac{d\bar{c}_i(t)}{dt} = R^{-1}_{g_i(t)}\left[d\sigma_\alpha\left(\frac{dc_i(t)}{dt}\right)\right] + \bar{X}^{a(t)}_{\bar{c}_i(t)}, \quad a(t) := g_i^{-1}(t)\frac{dg_i(t)}{dt}. \tag{54.5.32}$$

Applying the connection form and using horizontality and right-equivariance (Definition 54.5-15 (c)) leads to

$$0 = \omega\left(\frac{d\bar{c}_i(t)}{dt}\right) = g_i(t)^{-1}\omega\left(d\sigma_\alpha\left(\frac{dc_i(t)}{dt}\right)\right)g_i(t) + g_i^{-1}(t)\frac{dg_i(t)}{dt}, \tag{54.5.33}$$

and then to the differential equation for $g_i(t)$

$$\frac{dg_i(t)}{dt} = -\omega\left(d\sigma_\alpha\left(\frac{dc_i(t)}{dt}\right)\right)g_i(t) = -A_\alpha\left(\frac{dc_i(t)}{dt}\right)g_i(t). \tag{54.5.34}$$

The existence of the local solutions and of the composed global solution is proved in [KN69]. Since the pulled down connections vary along $c(t)$, one should also associate $g(t)$ with $c(t)$.

Because of the right-equivariance of the connection form, we obtain the lift through the g-shifted initial point by g-shifting the entire lift. That also implies that fibers are parallely transported into fibers. □

54.6.   Associated Bundles

For the description of interacting physical systems, the notion of an "associated bundle" is often employed.

Definition 54.6-1. Given a principal bundle $\mathcal{P} = \mathcal{P}(\pi, \mathcal{M}, G)$ and some differentiable manifold $\mathcal{W}$, together with a smooth action $l : G \times \mathcal{W} \to \mathcal{W}$, then the associated bundle is defined as $(\mathcal{P} \times \mathcal{W})/G \equiv \mathcal{P} \times_G \mathcal{W}$, where the G-action on $\mathcal{P} \times \mathcal{W}$ is introduced by $T_g(b, w) := (bg^{-1}, l_g w)$.

This is a bundle over $\mathcal{M}$ with typical fiber $\mathcal{W}$ (in our notation written $\mathcal{B}(\varrho, \mathcal{M}, \mathcal{W}, G)$), where the projection $\varrho : \mathcal{P} \times_G \mathcal{W} \to \mathcal{M}$ is defined by $\varrho[b, w]_G = \pi b$. (Notice that $\pi(bg) = \pi b$, $\forall b \in \mathcal{P}$, $\forall g \in G$.)

Concerning the fibers of $\mathcal{P} \times_G \mathcal{W}$, we remark that $(\varrho^{-1} \circ \pi)\, b$ is a set of classes of tuples (b, w), in which $w \in \mathcal{W}$ undergoes no restriction by the G reduction whereas each fiber of $\mathcal{P}$ is reduced to a point, say b.

In the physical applications, $\mathcal{W}$ is mostly a vector space. A typical example is given by $\mathcal{P} = \mathcal{P}(\pi, \mathcal{O}, G)$, where $\mathcal{O}$ is a space-time manifold and G a group of internal symmetries of particles (cf. also the following section), whereas $\mathcal{W} = \mathbb{C}^n$, $n \in \mathbb{N}$. Then we have $\mathcal{P} \times_G \mathbb{C}^n = \mathcal{B}(\varrho, \mathcal{O}, \mathbb{C}^n)$, that is a bundle over space-time with fibers isomorphic to $\mathbb{C}^n$, in which the internal G-value is not specified for the bundle elements by forming the classes. The local sections of that bundle are, however, initially given by the local wave functions $l(g(x))\psi(x)$ of the particles, with specified internal G-value at each space–time point $x \in \mathcal{O}$, where $l : G \times \mathbb{C}^n \to \mathbb{C}^n$ is a (matrix) representation of G. The formation of the G-classes expresses the point of view, that the physical meaning of these wave functions be — at least in some respects — independent from the internal state variables $g(x)$.

The latter interpretation is supported by the following result, which derives from the given definitions (cf. [Lan98a]).

Proposition 54.6-2 (Sections of the Associated Bundle). *Let* $\mathcal{P} \times_G \mathcal{W}$, *written* $\mathcal{B} = \mathcal{B}(\varrho, \mathcal{M}, \mathcal{W}, G)$, *be a bundle associated to the principal bundle* $\mathcal{P} = \mathcal{P}(\pi, \mathcal{M}, G)$.

In the following, we deal in general with "local" sections, but drop this restricting adjective.

Then a section $\sigma : \mathcal{M} \to \mathcal{B}$ *is biunivocally given by a map* $\sigma_\mathcal{W} : \mathcal{M} \to \mathcal{W}$ *together with a map* $\sigma_\mathcal{P} : \mathcal{M} \to \mathcal{P}$, *such that*

$$\sigma(\pi\, b) = [b, l(\sigma_G(b))\, \sigma_\mathcal{W}(\pi\, b)]_G, \quad \forall b \in \mathcal{P}, \qquad (54.6.1)$$

where $\sigma_G : \mathcal{P} \to G$ *is uniquely given by the relation* $b\, \sigma_G(b) = \sigma_\mathcal{P}(\pi\, b)$ *for all* $b \in \mathcal{P}$.

Observe that the consistency of Eq. (54.6.1) is assured as follows. For another $b' \in \pi^{-1}x$ there is a $g^{-1} \in G$ with $b' = bg^{-1}$. Then $bg^{-1}\sigma_G(bg^{-1}) = \sigma_\mathcal{P}(\pi\, b)$ and $\sigma_G(bg^{-1}) = g\sigma_G(b)$, wherefrom Eq. (54.6.1) changes into $\sigma(\pi\, b') = [bg^{-1}, l(g)l(\sigma_G(b))\, \sigma_\mathcal{W}(\pi\, b)]_G = \sigma(\pi\, b)$, due to the G factorizing.

The role of the particle wave function is then played by $\psi(x) = \sigma_{\mathbb{C}^n}(\pi\, b)$, $\pi\, b = x$, but the specified G-values are given by $g(\pi\, b) = \sigma_G(b)$, that is, one has to select a $b \in \pi^{-1}x$. The consistency check assures us only that the wave function is associated with a bundle cross section $\sigma : \mathcal{M} \to \mathcal{B}$.

The bundle section $\sigma : \mathcal{O} \to \mathcal{B}$ brings into play also the b's as an additional "quality index", referring also to the topological influences on space–time $\mathcal{O}$, which is related to the internal states of the particle. Even in the simple case of a complex line bundle in non-relativistic quantum physics, with $\mathcal{O} = \mathsf{T} \times \Lambda$ and $G = U(1)$, the b-values may be related with the additional information "number of flux quanta somewhere in a neighborhood of Λ" (cf. Sec. 37.4 on page 1199).

To the advantages of associating the internal state of a quantum particle not merely with a group element $g \in G$ but with an element b of a principal fiber bundle $\mathcal{P} = \mathcal{P}(\pi, \mathcal{O}, G)$ belong the notions of a horizontal lift and of a parallel transport, which may be applied to calculate the g-values above paths $c : [-a, a] \to \mathcal{O}$.

If $c : [-a, a] \to \mathcal{O}$ is horizontally lifted — via a connection — to $\bar{c} : [-a, a] \to \mathcal{P}$, then it may be also lifted to the curve $[\bar{c}(t), w]/G$, $t \in [-a, a]$, of the associated bundle $\mathcal{P} \times_G \mathcal{W}$.

Chapter 55

Gauge Bundles for (Q)ED

55.1. Bundles above Space–Time

55.1.1. *General Remarks*

For many applications, one has to generalize the setup for electrodynamics to a more general space-time manifold than $\mathbb{R}^4$. For large regions, one has to employ General Relativity. Already for satellite communication, one has to observe the curvature induced by the gravitational forces [Sch88a]. For smaller regions of everyday physics, one is often concerned with multiply-connected cavities, with obstacles inserted, what also requires generalized coordinates.

It is then appropriate to work with a rather arbitrary space-time manifold $(\mathcal{O}, g)$, where g is a pseudo-Riemannian metric as e.g., in the case of a Lorentz manifold.

As described before, the vector potential plays the role of the position field variable in the Lagrangian and Hamiltonian formulation of ED. Like in general mechanics, one should also here consider the position (field) manifold as the input information, upon which a general geometric dynamical formalism is to be constructed. The problem is that the vector potential is rather an intricate concept. Even in flat Minkowsky space, the 4-potential is not simply a relativistic covector field in the strict sense (cf. Sec. 6.3.4). For, let be given a physical state of the electrodynamic field, then the vector potential A is not specified as a well-defined function on $\mathcal{O}$ because of the gauge arbitrariness. That means in other words, that A has no well-defined geometric meaning within the conceptual frame of the space-time manifold $\mathcal{O}$ alone.

Having specified a special A for the electromagnetic field state, then — in sloppy notation — the equivalent potentials have locally the form $A(y) - \mathbf{d}\lambda(y)$, with λ a gauge function of $y \in \mathcal{O}$. (We denote the differential in bold face, if it must be considered an external derivative.) As is especially revealed by coupling the field to material sources, the real purpose of the gauge function λ is to introduce an additional new coordinate, a phase given by an element in $U(1)$, for each space-time point. That is nothing else but Weyl's original point of view (see [Wey18], [Wey53]) for gauging space-time. Since $\mathcal{O}$ is to be treated geometrically (without using coordinates) the gauge angle selection should be also formulated geometrically, and both categories, space-time points and gauge angles, should be combined to a workable geometric structure.

Let us emphasize, that already purely electrodynamic field states in non-trivial space time manifolds demand for further geometric elaboration. The very general and elegant form of the local Maxwell differential equations (in general Lorentz manifolds $\mathcal{O}$, cf. e.g., [MTW73], [Sch96]) should not distract from the fact, that certain global quantities, as especially the magnetic flux through a surface, require the introduction and careful handling of the vector potential. This is also intended by introducing the gauged space-time manifold.

Having now given a base manifold $\mathcal{O}$, which usually is assumed smooth, and a Lie group $U(1)$, it is suggestive to form a principal fiber bundle with these attributes and to relate the gauge- and coordinate-independent content of the vector potential A with the bundle geometry.

The first step for a (geometric) bundle construction is to form a *coordinated* fiber bundle. The natural starting point in our situation is certainly the choice of an atlas $\{(U_\alpha, \phi_\alpha) \,|\, \alpha \in J\}$ of $\mathcal{O}$. Then one has to select the element z in $U(1)$ over each element y in the open chart region U_α of the atlas. These two data (y, z_α) characterize an element b of the intended gauge bundle in a separated (factorized) form. But to proceed into another chart region U_β, with an overlap with U_α, one has often to choose another factorization (y, z_β) for the same b. By varying b above $y \in U_\alpha$, we obtain an unknown region $\bar{U}_\alpha$, indirectly characterized by a factorization

$$\tau_\alpha : \bar{U}_\alpha \to U_\alpha \times U(1), \quad \tau_\alpha(b) = (y, z_\alpha). \tag{55.1.1}$$

The domains $\bar{U}_\alpha$ of the trivialization maps are then charts of a bundle atlas.

We introduce, therefore, the following definition.

Definition 55.1-1 (Electrodynamic Gauge Bundles).

(a) Under a *gauged space-time manifold*, with gauge group $U(1)$, we understand a coordinated principal bundle (cf. Definition (54.5-9)) of the form $\mathcal{P}(\pi, \mathcal{O}, U(1), \tau) \equiv \mathcal{P}(\tau)$, where the *base manifold* $\mathcal{O}$ is the given Lorentz manifold for space-time and

$$\tau = \{\tau_\alpha : \pi^{-1}(U_\alpha) \xrightarrow{\text{onto}} U_\alpha \times U(1) \,|\, \alpha \in J\}$$

is an indexed family of *local trivialization diffeomorphisms* corresponding to an atlas $\{(U_\alpha, \phi_\alpha) \,|\, \alpha \in J\}$ of $\mathcal{O}$.

(b) Under an *electrodynamic gauge bundle*, we understand the strict equivalence class $\mathcal{P}(\pi, \mathcal{O}, U(1))$ of the coordinated bundles $\mathcal{P}(\pi, \mathcal{O}, U(1), \tau)$.

Observe that the existence of different factorizations $\tau_\alpha(b) = (y, z_\alpha)$ and $\tau_\beta(b) = (y, z_\beta)$ of the bundle element $b \in \mathcal{P}(\tau)$ does not merely mean different coordinates for b. A factorization is in fact viewed as a first step for coordination (wherefrom originates "coordinated fiber bundle"), but different factorizations for b express a genuine topological feature inherent in neighborhoods of b, respectively in space-time neighborhoods of $\pi b = y$.

In analytical model discussions, one prefers an atlas with as few charts as possible. If the topological structures of $\mathcal{O}$, as well as electrodynamic reasons, require several charts $\{(U_\alpha, \phi_\alpha) \mid \alpha \in J\}$, the decisive question is, how to select the phases in the overlap regions $U_\beta \cap U_\alpha$.

The electrodynamic gauge bundles represent the simplest case where an internal structure (here charge, respectively the capability to interact with photons) of particles is intertwined with the space-time geometry. More generally, in the point-particle approach to elementary particles, the internal structure of the particles is pure group theory. And the more comprising the tableau of elementary particles under consideration, the larger must be the internal symmetry group, intimately connected with the type of possible interactions. By the concept of principal fiber bundles, where the structure group of the bundle corresponds to the internal symmetry group of the particle, the forces are related to the curvature of the gauged space time, that is, with the bundle geometry. The fields of the particles are then *associated* with the principal fiber bundle (cf. Section 54.6), and the connections of the latter correspond — in the quantized theory — to the Bosons which mediate the interactions.

After the first step beyond the electrodynamic $U(1)$-case to the already non-commutative isospin group $SU(2)$ of nuclear force in [YM54], that idea has guided much research in particle physics and cosmology (e.g., [Fel81], [Gro92], [Fra97], [Fra08] and references therein). In the Standard Model of elementary particles, one has the gauge group $U(1) \times SU(2) \times SU(3)$, which leads to the 12 gauge Bosons: 1 photon, 3 weak Bosons, and 8 gluons. These gauge Bosons are initially massless, but the non-electrodynamical ones should acquire a mass via the Higgs mechanism.

Our purpose is here merely to analyze the gauge bundle concept in non-relativistic (Q)ED, where just on the mesoscopic stage topological effects are of increasing interest.

55.1.2. *Gauge Bundles above General Space-Time*

As an intermediate step, let us have a short look on ED over a pseudo-Riemannian Minkowsky manifold $(\mathcal{O}, g) \equiv \mathcal{O}$ on $\mathbb{R}^4$, which is locally flat. In local coordinates, a point $y \in \mathcal{O}$ is written $y = (y^\mu) = (ct, x)$, $x \in \mathbb{R}^3$, and a tangent vector denotes $X_y = y^\mu \partial_\mu$. Then

$$g_y(\partial_\mu, \partial_\nu) \equiv g_{\mu,\nu}(y) = \begin{pmatrix} 1 & 0 & 0 & 0 \\ 0 & -1 & 0 & 0 \\ 0 & 0 & -1 & 0 \\ 0 & 0 & 0 & -1 \end{pmatrix} = (g^{-1})_{\mu,\nu}(y). \tag{55.1.2}$$

If the space-time manifold is gauged by $\mathcal{P}(\pi, \mathcal{O}, U(1), \tau) \equiv \mathcal{P}(\tau)$, a vector potential may be introduced in terms of a connection $\omega \in \Omega^1_{H,U(1)}(\mathcal{P}, \mathbb{R}a_0)$, where $\mathbb{R}a_0$ signifies the Lie algebra $\mathrm{Lie}\, U(1) = \mathcal{U}(1)$ of $U(1)$. (The basis element a_0 of the Lie algebra equals i, if $U(1)$ is realized as the complex unit circle $\mathbb{C}_1 = \{z \in \mathbb{C} \mid |z| = 1\}$.)

Let $\sigma = \{\sigma_\alpha : U_\alpha \to \mathcal{P} \mid \alpha \in J\}$ be the family of local sections corresponding to the system of local trivializations τ. The local pulled down potentials are here first denoted by $\omega_\alpha := \sigma_\alpha^* \omega \in \Omega^1(U_\alpha, \mathbb{R}a_0)$ (cf. Eq. (54.5.25)). Let us write the transition elements as $z_{\alpha\beta,y} = \exp\{a_0 \lambda_{\alpha\beta,y}\} \in U(1)$. Then the compatibility Eqs. (54.5.28) take the form

$$\omega_{\beta,y} = \omega_{\alpha,y} + z_{\alpha\beta,y}^{-1} \mathbf{d} z_{\alpha\beta,y} = \omega_{\alpha,y} + a_0 \, \mathbf{d}\lambda_{\alpha\beta,y}, \quad \forall \beta, \alpha \in J, \quad \forall y \in U_\beta \cap U_\alpha. \,\, (55.1.3)$$

Physically, we change to the potential (cf. Sec. 37.4.7 on page 1220) $\omega_{\alpha,y} = -i(e/\hbar)A_{\alpha,y}$, where now $A_\alpha \in \Omega^1(U_\alpha, \mathbb{R})$ is a usual 1-form and $e \in \mathbb{R}$ a constant with the meaning of an electrical charge. *We set here* $(e/\hbar) = 1$. In coordinates one writes $A_\alpha = A_{\alpha,\mu} dy^\mu = (u_\alpha/c)cdt + A_{\alpha,i} dx^i$. (The space indices i run from 1 to 3.) If $y \in U_\beta \cap U_\alpha$, we obtain the compatibility equations

$$A_{\beta,y} = A_{\alpha,y} - \mathbf{d}\lambda_{\alpha\beta,y} = \left(\frac{u_\alpha}{c} - \frac{\partial\lambda_{\alpha\beta}}{\partial y^0}\right) dy^0 + (A_{\alpha,i} - \frac{\partial\lambda_{\alpha\beta}}{\partial y^i}) dy^i, \quad \forall \beta, \alpha \in J.$$
$$(55.1.4)$$

(The 3-potential (A_α^i) in vector form is then gauge transformed by $+(\frac{\partial\lambda_{\alpha\beta}}{\partial y^i})$.)

The local Maurer–Cartan relation Eq. (54.5.31), in which the commutator expression vanishes, gives then the force field $F_\alpha = \mathbf{d}A_\alpha$ in terms of the following 2-form (where we drop now the index α, which is for a local F_α not necessary anyway)

$$F = \frac{\partial A_\mu}{\partial y^\nu} dy^\nu \wedge dy^\mu, \quad (\nu, \mu) \text{ ordered,}$$
$$= ((\mathbf{E}/c) \cdot dx) \wedge dy^0 + \mathbf{B} \cdot dS, \quad\quad (55.1.5)$$
$$dx := (dx^1, dx^2, dx^3), \quad dS := (dx^2 \wedge dx^3, dx^3 \wedge dx^1, dx^1 \wedge dx^2).$$

Since F is exact its derivative vanishes and we find

$$0 = \mathbf{d}F = \left(\nabla \times \frac{\mathbf{E}}{c} + \frac{\partial\mathbf{B}}{\partial y^0}\right) \cdot dS \wedge dy^0 + \nabla \cdot \mathbf{B}\, d^3 x \,;$$

$$\Longleftrightarrow \quad\quad\quad (55.1.6)$$

$$\nabla \times \mathbf{E} = -\frac{\partial\mathbf{B}}{\partial t}, \quad \nabla \cdot \mathbf{B} = 0.$$

That are the source-free Maxwell equations, which follow here merely from the structure of the gauge bundle (as they follow in the usual formulation of ED from the introduction of the potentials).

To obtain the inhomogeneous Maxwell equations, one invokes the principle of stationary action, also in gauge theory. These equations are formulated in terms of a dual field 2-form $*F$, which is — roughly speaking — obtained from F by replacing the original differentials by those which complete them to the 4-volume, decorated with certain $(-1)^n$ depending on the metric. One arrives at ([Ble81])

$$*F = -\mathbf{B} \cdot dx \wedge dy^0 + \mathbf{E}/c \cdot dS \,;$$

$$\mathbf{d} * F = -\left((\nabla \times \mathbf{B} - \frac{\partial \mathbf{E}}{c \partial y^0}) \cdot dS \right) \wedge dy^0 + \nabla \cdot \frac{\mathbf{E}}{c} d^3 x \,; \qquad (55.1.7)$$

$$*\mathbf{d} * F = -\left(\nabla \times \mathbf{B} - \frac{\partial \mathbf{E}}{c \partial y^0} \right) \cdot dx + \nabla \cdot \frac{\mathbf{E}}{c} dy^0.$$

The source 1-form is in our notation $j_\mu dy^\mu = c\varrho \, dy^0 - \mathbf{j} \cdot dx$, with ϱ the electric charge density and $\mathbf{j}$ the 3-current density. From an appropriate action ansatz ([Ble81]), the stationarity is equivalent to the relations

$$0 = *\mathbf{d} * F - \mu_0 \, j_\mu dy^\mu \quad \Longleftrightarrow$$

$$\nabla \cdot \frac{\mathbf{E}}{c} = \mu_0 c\varrho, \quad \nabla \times \mathbf{B} - \frac{\partial \mathbf{E}}{c \partial y^0} = \mu_0 \mathbf{j}. \qquad (55.1.8)$$

Observing $\epsilon_0 \mu_0 c^2 = 1$, we arrive at the usual version of the inhomogeneous Maxwell equations, but only locally above a smooth space-time manifold in Cartesian coordinates, and not Helmholtz–Hodge decomposed.

For global relations, the "twisted structure" of the gauge bundle comes into play and one has to lift the formalism to the 5-dimensional level of the connection ω.

Let us first write down the Cartesian coordinates for $b \in \mathcal{P}(\pi, \mathcal{O}, U(1)) = \mathcal{P}$ — where we refer to the coordinated principal bundle $\mathcal{P}(\tau)$ — in a local region $\bar{U}_\alpha = \pi^{-1}(U_\alpha)$. The first step is the local trivialization $\tau_\alpha b = (y, z) \in U_\alpha \times U(1)$. As above, we identify y with (y^μ). In spite of depending on α, we simply write for the moment $z = \exp\{i\lambda\}$, with $\lambda \in \mathbb{R}$ being the coordinate of z.

In coordinates, we write for a vector $\bar{X}_b \in T\mathcal{P}$ the expression $\bar{X}_b = y^\mu \partial_\mu + \lambda \partial_\lambda$. For a fundamental vector $\bar{X}_b^{i\lambda_0}$, we obtain the coordinate expression $\lambda_0 \partial_\lambda$, $\forall \lambda_0 \in \mathbb{R}$. For an $\omega \in \Omega^1(\mathcal{P}, i\mathbb{R})$, we go over to the physical form by setting $\omega =: -i\bar{A}$, with $\bar{A} \in \Omega^1(\mathcal{P}, \mathbb{R})$, and use the expression $\bar{A} = A_\mu dy^\mu + \kappa d\lambda$. Thus $\bar{A}(\bar{X}_b) = A_\mu y^\mu + \kappa \lambda \in \mathbb{R}$.

For ω respectively $\bar{A}$ to be a connection form, a necessary condition is $\bar{A}(\bar{X}_b^{\lambda_0}) = \lambda_0$, wherefrom in general $\bar{A}(\bar{X}_b) = A_\mu y^\mu + 1\lambda$.

In applications, one mostly concludes from relations in $\mathcal{O}$ to those in $\mathcal{P}$, as one does for horizontally lifting curves and vectors. For that purpose, one employs most conveniently the local sections $\sigma_\alpha : U_\alpha \to \bar{U}_\alpha$ and works with connection forms $\bar{A}$ in application on tangent vectors which are associated to a piece of a lifted curve $c \subset U_\alpha$. We get from Eqs. (54.5.32) and (54.5.33), now for the $U(1)$ structure group with $g_\alpha(s) \equiv z_\alpha(s) = \exp\{i\lambda_\alpha(s)\}$,

$$\frac{d\bar{c}(s)}{ds} = R^{-1}_{z_\alpha(s)}\left[d_{c(s)}\sigma_\alpha\left(\frac{dc(s)}{ds}\right)\right] + \bar{X}^{a(s)}_{\bar{c}(s)}, \quad a(s) := g_\alpha^{-1}(s)\frac{dg_\alpha(s)}{ds} = i\dot{\lambda}_\alpha(s).$$

$$(55.1.9)$$

Applying the local connection in the physical version to the tangent vector leads to

$$\bar{A}\left(d_{c(s)}\sigma_\alpha(\dot{c}(s)) + \bar{X}^{a(s)}_{\bar{c}(s)}\right) = A_\alpha(\dot{c}(s)) - \dot{\lambda}_\alpha(s), \quad A_\alpha \in \Omega^1(U_\alpha, \mathbb{R}). \qquad (55.1.10)$$

Since for horizontal vectors the last expression must vanish, we obtain a condition for the local phase coordinate function $\lambda_\alpha(s)$. That leads to the following insights.

Proposition 55.1-2 (Phases for Horizontally Lifted Trajectories). *Consider the gauge bundle* $\mathcal{P}(\pi, \mathcal{O}, U(1)) = \mathcal{P}$ *and specify a coordinated bundle of its strict equivalence class* $\mathcal{P}(\pi, \mathcal{O}, U(1), \tau)$ *with* $\tau = \{\tau_\alpha : \bar{U}_\alpha \xrightarrow{\text{onto}} U_\alpha \times U(1) \,|\, \alpha \in J\}$.

Let $c : [0, 1] \to \mathcal{O}$ *be a differentiable curve in the space-time manifold and let* $A_\alpha \in \Omega^1(U_\alpha, \mathbb{R})$ *be a locally pulled down connection form related to the connection* $\bar{A} \in \Omega^1_{U(1)H}(\mathcal{P}, \mathbb{R})$. *Assume that there is a piece of curve* $c : [s_i, s_{i+1}] \to U_\alpha$, *which is lifted to* $\bar{c} : [s_i, s_{i+1}] \to \bar{U}_\alpha \subset \mathcal{P}$ *via the local section* $\sigma_\alpha : U_\alpha \to \bar{U}_\alpha$.

Then the condition that the lifted tangent vectors $\dot{\bar{c}}(s)$, $s \in [s_i, s_{i+1}]$ *are horizontal leads to the following equation for the phase coordinate* $\lambda_\alpha(s)$ *of* $\bar{c}(s)$, *a part of its local bundle coordinates,*

$$\dot{\lambda}_\alpha(s) = A_\alpha(\dot{c}(s)), \quad \forall s \in [s_i, s_{i+1}]. \qquad (55.1.11)$$

If also $c : [s_i, s_{i+1}] \to U_\beta$, *then Eq. (55.1.11), with* α *replaced by* β, *gives the local equation* $\dot{\lambda}_\beta(s) = \dot{\lambda}_\alpha(s) - \mathbf{d}\lambda_{\alpha\beta,c(s)}(\dot{c}(s))$, *where* $\lambda_{\alpha\beta,y}$ *is the coordinate function of the transition element* $z_{\alpha\beta,y} \in U(1)$ *for* y *varying in* $U_\alpha \cap U_\beta$.

Since $\mathcal{P}$ *is trivial, if and only if there are phase functions* $\lambda_{\alpha,y}$, $y \in U_\alpha$, *for all* $\alpha \in J$, *such that* $\lambda_{\alpha\beta,y} = \lambda_{\alpha,y} - \lambda_{\beta,y}$, *if* $y \in U_\alpha \cap U_\beta$, *one has only in that case*

$$\dot{\lambda}_\beta(s) - \mathbf{d}\lambda_{\beta,c(s)}(\dot{c}(s)) = \dot{\lambda}_\alpha(s) - \mathbf{d}\lambda_{\alpha,c(s)}(\dot{c}(s)). \qquad (55.1.12)$$

That is, one has in that case a global phase coordinate above the path $c : [0, 1] \to \mathcal{O}$, *which is gained by integrating Eq. (55.1.12) over* s *and patching the solutions together.*

The global phase corresponds then to the renormalized global section $\sigma^r(y) = \sigma_\alpha(y)\exp\{-i\lambda_{\alpha,y}\} = \sigma_\beta(y)\exp\{-i\lambda_{\beta,y}\}$ *for* $y \in U_\alpha \cap U_\beta$ *respectively to the renormalized global pulled down 1-form*

$$A^r = A_\alpha - \mathbf{d}\lambda_\alpha = A_\beta - \mathbf{d}\lambda_\beta, \quad \text{if applied to } X_y, \ y \in U_\alpha \cap U_\beta. \qquad (55.1.13)$$

Proof. Employ Proposition 54.5-23 to get the lifted curve and its (horizontal) tangent vectors, take into account Eq. (55.1.10), and observe the gauge behavior Eqs. (55.1.3) and (55.1.4).

For the triviality condition invoke Proposition 54.5-12. □

We have now emphasized the constructive means to discuss the phase changes in terms of parallel transport in *local* regions, if the local vector potentials are given. In the proof of Proposition 54.5-23, this method has been used to lift curves $c : [0, 1] \to \mathcal{O}$ *globally* to $\bar{c} : [0, 1] \to \mathcal{P}$, by patching the local lifts together. Globally defined are the elements $\bar{c}(s) \in \mathcal{P}$, not the (phase) coordinates.

Globally defined is also the (physical) connection form $\bar{A} \in \Omega^1_{U(1)H}(\mathcal{P}, \mathbb{R})$, if one starts from a family $A_\alpha \in \Omega^1(U_\alpha, \mathbb{R})$, $\alpha \in J$, of local potentials with the correct gauge behavior. And there exists a well-defined curve integral $\int_{\bar{c}} \bar{A}$ (with here the value 0) (for integration over differential forms cf. e.g., [AMR88].) That is so, because the overlap integrals over the global $\bar{A}$ satisfy for $c(s) \in U_\alpha \cap U_\beta$ the local equations

$$\int \bar{A}\big(d_{c(s)}\sigma_\alpha(\dot{c}(s)) + \bar{X}^{a(s)}_{\bar{c}(s)}\big)\, ds = \int [A_\alpha(\dot{c}(s)) - \dot{\lambda}_\alpha(s)]\, ds = \int [A_\beta(\dot{c}(s)) - \dot{\lambda}_\beta(s)]\, ds.$$

(55.1.14)

In order to calculate globally the curve integral of the pulled down potentials A_α *alone*, what is of great physical interest, one has to choose a special factorization in the overlap regions, in which more than one possibility exists. That amounts to a choice of the transition elements $\exp\{i\lambda_{\alpha\beta,c(s)}\} \in U(1)$ and structure constants respectively. The global curve integral depends then on that choice because that is not merely a choice of coordinates. The same can be said about a global curve integral of the related family $\dot{\lambda}_\alpha$, $\alpha \in J$. If $c : [0, 1] \to \mathcal{O}$ is a closed curve with $c(0) = c(1)$, the lifted curve $\bar{c}$ may fail to be closed displaying $\bar{c}(0) \neq \bar{c}(1)$. Since $\bar{c}(1)$ is above the same base point y as $\bar{c}(0)$ there is a unique element $z_c \in U(1)$ such that $\bar{c}(1) = \bar{c}(0)z_c$. z_c represents the difference in phase between $\bar{c}(1)$ and $\bar{c}(0)$.

Let us study the elements z_c more closely (following [KN69]).

Definition 55.1-3 (Holonomy Groups).
For a given $\mathcal{P}(\pi, \mathcal{O}, U(1)) = \mathcal{P}$, we denote the set of all piece-wise differentiable closed curves c in $\mathcal{O}$ starting and ending at y by $C(y)$. If $c, c' \in C(y)$, then the composite curve $c' \cdot c$ (where one runs first through c' and then through c) is also in $C(y)$. Since the inverse curves c^{-1} (where one runs through c in the reverse direction) and the identity $c^0_y : [0, 1] \to \{y\}$ are also in $C(y)$, $C(y)$ is a group.

For the following definitions, we specify a connection $\omega \in \Omega^1_{U(1)H}(\mathcal{P}, i\mathbb{R})$.

Consider $b \in \pi^{-1}y$. Then $c' \cdot c$ induces the parallel displaced $bz_{c' \cdot c}$. The iterated runs in $\mathcal{O}$ induce $(bz_{c'})z_c = b(z'_c \cdot z_c)$ (because of the right multiplication law in principal bundles), wherefrom $z_{c'.c} = z_{c'} \cdot z_c$. Similarly $z_{c^{-1}} = z_c^{-1}$ and $z_{c_y^0} = 1$ are derived.

(a) The holonomy group $\Phi(b)$ of ω at $b \in \pi^{-1}y$ is the set $\{z_c \,|\, c \in C(y)\} \subset U(1)$.
(b) The restricted holonomy group $\Phi^0(b)$ of ω at $b \in \pi^{-1}y$ is the set $\{z_c \,|\, c \in C^0(y)\} \subset \Phi(y)$, where $C^0(y)$ consists of all curves in $C(y)$ which may be continuously shrunk within $\mathcal{O}$ to c_y^0 (which are "null-homotopic").

Recall that the *first homotopy group* $\pi_1(\mathcal{O})$ consists of classes $[c]$ of closed curves, where $[c]$ is all curves which may continuously be deformed to c within $\mathcal{O}$. (One sets $[c' \cdot c] =: [c'] \cdot [c]$.) If $\mathcal{O}$ is (path) connected and paracompact (closure is compact), then it is second countable (has a countable topological base) and it follows that $\pi_1(\mathcal{O})$ is countable.

The following facts are taken from [KN69], specialized to $G = U(1)$.

Theorem 55.1-4 (Holonomy and Homotopy). *Consider* $\mathcal{P}(\pi, \mathcal{O}, U(1)) = \mathcal{P}$ *with* $\mathcal{O}$ *connected and paracompact and choose a connection* ω *on* $\mathcal{P}$.
Then the following is true.

(a) $\Phi(b) = \Phi(bz)$ *and* $\Phi^0(b) = \Phi^0(bz)$, *for all* $z \in U(1)$ *and for all* $b \in \mathcal{P}$.
(b) *If* $b, b' \in \mathcal{P}$ *may be connected by a horizontal curve — what is denoted by* $b \sim b'$, *an equivalence relation — then* $\Phi(b) = \Phi(b')$ *and* $\Phi^0(b) = \Phi^0(b')$.
(c) *There is a natural homomorphism of* $\pi_1(\mathcal{O})$ *onto* $\Phi(b)/\Phi^0(b)$.
(d) $\Phi^0(b)$ *is a normal Lie subgroup of* $\Phi(b)$ *and* $\Phi(b)/\Phi^0(b)$ *is countable.*
(e) $\Phi(b)$ *is a Lie subgroup of* $U(1)$ *whose identity component is* $\Phi^0(b)$.
(f) *Let* $P_b := \{b' \in \mathcal{P} \,|\, b' \sim b\}$. *Then* $\mathcal{P}_b := \mathcal{B}(\pi, \mathcal{O}, \Phi(b))$ *is a reduced subbundle of* $\mathcal{P} = \mathcal{P}(\pi, \mathcal{O}, U(1))$ *with structure group* $\Phi(b)$, *to which the connection* ω *may be restricted.*
Then the Lie algebra of $\Phi(b)$ *(being the same as for* $\Phi^0(b)$*) is spanned by all elements, which are assumed by the curvature* Ω_b *of* ω *reduced to* $\mathcal{P}_b$, *if the two arguments of* Ω_b *run through all horizontal vectors to* $\mathcal{P}_b$ *(Holonomy Theorem of Ambrose and Singer).*

For our applications, observe that each (Lie) subgroup of $U(1)$ is normal and is either $U(1)$ or discrete. Physically it is interesting, under which conditions $\Phi(b)$ is discrete, what would amount to a quantization of the phase coordinates in $b\Phi(b)$ and of the curve integrals over pulled down vector potentials.

If $\mathcal{P} = \mathcal{P}(\pi, \mathcal{O}, U(1))$ is equipped with a *flat connection* ω, that is $\mathbf{d}\omega = 0$, then Proposition 55.1-4 (f) tells us that the Lie algebra of $\Phi(b)$ is $\{0\}$. Then the identity component of $\Phi(b)$ — that is the Lie subgroup connected with 1 — is trivial, but $\Phi(b)$ must not be trivial. Thus we know then that $\Phi^0(b) = \{1\}$, and (c) implies that $\Phi(b)$ is discrete for all $b \in \mathcal{P}$.

For a further analysis, we restrict the discussion to fixed time t.

55.1.3.   *Gauge Bundles for Fixed Time*

We restrict $\mathcal{P} = \mathcal{P}(\pi, \mathcal{O}, U(1))$ to the subbundle $\mathcal{P}_t = \mathcal{P}(\pi, \mathcal{O}_t, U(1))$ with $\mathcal{O}_t = \{t\} \times \Lambda$ (a "related bundle" according to [Ste51]), where the time $t \in \mathbb{R}$ is fixed (respectively an adiabatic parameter to which the derivatives vanish) and again $\Lambda \subset \mathbb{R}_x^3$ is open and connected. In $\mathcal{O}_t$, we employ the relative topology from $\mathcal{O}$. A trivialization structure for $\mathcal{P}_t$ has the general shape $\tau_t = \{(U_\alpha^t, \tau_\alpha^t) \,|\, \alpha \in J\}$, with $U_\alpha^t = \{t\} \times U_\alpha$, $U_\alpha \subset \Lambda$, and $\tau_\alpha^t : \pi^{-1} U_\alpha^t \to U_\alpha^t \times U(1)$.

We set from now on until the end of the present Chapter $c = 1$ such that $y = (t, x)$, $\forall y \in \mathcal{O}_t$.

The connections of $\mathcal{P}_t$ provide the local vector potentials as 1–forms $\{\mathbf{A}_{\alpha,y} \equiv \mathbf{A}_\alpha(y) \,|\, \alpha \in J, \, y \in U_\alpha^t\}$, in coordinates $A_{\alpha,i}(y)dx^i$, $1 \leq i \leq 3$, which in usual bundle theory have to be smooth functions, that means to be at least continuous. They have to satisfy the compatibility relations

$$\mathbf{A}_{\beta,y} = \mathbf{A}_{\alpha,y} - z_{\alpha\beta,y}^{-1} dz_{\alpha\beta,y} = \mathbf{A}_{\alpha,y} - d\lambda_{\alpha\beta,y}, \quad \forall \beta, \alpha \in J, \quad \forall y \in U_\beta^t \cap U_\alpha^t. \quad (55.1.15)$$

The transition elements $z_{\alpha\beta,y} \in U(1)$ must then be at least C^1-functions of x. (In our later bundle construction in Sec. 55.1.4, we allow for a slight generalization of differentiability.)

The exterior derivative of a 3-vector, considered as 1-form, produces the rotation, considered as 2-form. By fixing time the 4-rotation in Eq. (6.3.17) on page 116 reduces to its spatial part and we find in a local chart U_α^t

$$(F^{i,j}) := (\partial^i A^j - \partial^j A^i) = \begin{pmatrix} 0 & -B^3 & B^2 \\ B^3 & 0 & -B^1 \\ -B^2 & B^1 & 0 \end{pmatrix}, \quad 1 \leq i, j \leq 3. \quad (55.1.16)$$

The 2-form is obtained by changing the sign, due to the Minkowsky metric, and by forming

$$\mathbf{d}_0\mathbf{A} = \begin{pmatrix} dx^1, & dx^2, & dx^3 \end{pmatrix} \begin{pmatrix} 0 & B^3 & -B^2 \\ -B^3 & 0 & B^1 \\ B^2 & -B^1 & 0 \end{pmatrix} \begin{pmatrix} dx^1 \\ dx^2 \\ dx^3 \end{pmatrix},$$

$$= \mathbf{B} \cdot dS, \quad dS := (dx^2 \wedge dx^3, dx^3 \wedge dx^1, dx^1 \wedge dx^2). \quad (55.1.17)$$

For some spatial coordinate patches in Λ must hold $\partial U_\alpha \cap \partial \Lambda \neq \emptyset$, and we would have to observe in our applications the conductor boundary condition (for a subset of $\mathbb{R}_x^3$) in forming the exterior derivative (so that the normal boundary values of $\mathbf{B}$ vanish). We have indicated that subsidiary condition by the subscript 0 in $\mathbf{d}_0\mathbf{A}$.

In order to apply theorems of the usual smooth bundle theory, we treat in the present general considerations $\{t\} \times \Lambda = \mathcal{O}_t$ as a smooth manifold without boundary (forgetting about $\mathbb{R}_y^4$ as receptacle for $\mathcal{O}_t$). (In Sec. 55.1.4 below, we come back to this problem.)

A connection $\bar{\mathbf{A}} \in \Omega^1_{U(1)H}(\mathcal{P}_t, \mathbb{R})$ represents the spatial vector potential together with a phase variable, what we write in coordinates, in analogy to the case with the 4-dimensional base $\mathcal{O}$, as $\bar{\mathbf{A}} = A_i dx^i + \kappa d\lambda$. Again horizontality implies $\kappa = 1$.

We consider the horizontal lifting of curves $c : [0,1] \to \mathcal{O}_t$ to curves $\bar{c} : [0,1] \to \mathcal{P}_t$. It holds $\int_{\bar{c}} \bar{\mathbf{A}} \equiv \int_0^1 \bar{\mathbf{A}}(\dot{\bar{c}}(s))\, ds = 0$, because of horizontality. If $\lambda_\alpha(s)$ is the local phase coordinate of $\bar{c}(s)$, we obtain locally, in analogy to Eq. (55.1.11),

$$\dot{\lambda}_\alpha(s) = \mathbf{A}_\alpha(\dot{c}(s)), \quad \forall s \in [s_i, s_{i+1}]. \tag{55.1.18}$$

Locally we may now calculate the phase coordinate for a lifted path by integrating the pulled down 3-vector potential. *That provides us with a natural association of a phase variable with the integrals over the 3-vector potential in a purely classical theory.* (Usually one invokes for that purpose the Schrödinger equation with a classical vector potential.)

A global integral, like a closed curve integral $\oint_c \mathbf{A}(\dot{c}(s))ds$ over $\mathbf{A}$, is, however, only obtainable by combining the local integrals. In transition regions $U^t_\alpha \cap U^t_\beta$, we have several possibilities $\mathbf{A}_\alpha$ respectively $\mathbf{A}_\beta$, where $\mathbf{A}_\beta = \mathbf{A}_\alpha - \mathbf{d}\lambda_{\alpha\beta}$.

In the following paragraphs, we make occasionally some remarks in terms of the position domain Λ alone and do not indicate t.

The combination of the local integrals is in general a cumbersome task, involving a smooth partition of unity $e_\alpha(x), \sum_\alpha e_\alpha(x) = 1, \forall x \in \Lambda$. (The partition of unity exists if Λ is assumed paracompact.) We see, however, from Eq. (55.1.18), also in our general discussion, that the outcome must be expressible by a phase difference $\lambda(1) - \lambda(0)$. For a closed curve c with $c(0) = c(1) = y$, the phase difference is given by the element z_c of the holonomy group $\Phi(b)$, with $b = \bar{c}(0) = \bar{c}(1)z_c \in \mathcal{P}_t$.

In view of the Stokes theorem, the physical meaning of $\oint_c \mathbf{A}(\dot{c}(s))ds$ is the *magnetic flux $\mathcal{F}_c$ through a surface Σ_c enclosed by c*, even if Σ_c is not entirely contained in Λ, and even if the field $\mathbf{B} = \mathbf{dA}$ vanishes identically in $\Sigma_c \cap \Lambda$. Mathematically that means, that $\oint_c \mathbf{A}(\dot{c}(s))ds$ may be different from zero also in the flat case. Since classically, there are then no magnetic forces on charged matter, flatness inside of Λ cannot dynamically be discriminated from "total flatness", with no $\mathbf{B}$ within Σ_c of a closed curve in Λ. But there are topological phase effects. It is well known that in quantum theory, a flux outside of Λ should lead to measurable phase effects for particles inside Λ, even if there are no force fields in Λ (Aharanov–Bohm effects). We are going to demonstrate that there is also an important topological phase effect in classical ED, namely the flux quantization.

In that important case of $\mathbf{B}$ *vanishing identically in* Λ the restricted holonomy group $\Phi^0(b)$ is trivial for all $b \in \mathcal{P}_t$. We know from Theorem 55.1-4 that there is a natural homomorphism of $f : \pi_1(\mathcal{O}_t) = \pi_1(\Lambda) \xrightarrow{\text{onto}} \Phi(b)/\Phi^0(b) = \Phi(b)$ and conclude from the discreteness of $\pi_1(\Lambda)$ that $\Phi(b)$ is a discrete subgroup of $U(1)$. Since the coordinates for the $z \in U(1)$ are taken from $\mathbb{R}$, we may write $\Phi(b) \sim \mathbb{Z}$.

If, on the other side, $\mathbf{B}$ does not vanish everywhere in Λ, the parallel displacement of a $b \in \mathcal{P}_t$ along a closed c of null homotopy (contractible in Λ to a point) may also induce a phase shift, expressed by $b = \bar{c}(0) = \bar{c}(1)z_c^0$, and $\Phi^0(b)$ may be now non-trivial. The quotient $\Phi(b)/\Phi^0(b)$ stays, however, discrete whereas $\Phi(b)$ and $\Phi^0(b)$ may assume continuously varying values in dependence on the internal fluxes in Λ. The non-triviality of $\Phi^0(b)$ indicates, therefore, an internal **B**-field, the influence of which is factorized out in $\Phi(b)/\Phi^0(b)$, so that the latter group expresses predominantly topological aspects.

55.1.4. *Construction of Non-relativistic Gauge Bundles*

We consider now an interior domain Λ which satisfies the Standard Assumptions of Definition 44.4-8 on page 1589 and has moreover a smooth boundary $\partial\Lambda$. We know from Theorem 44.4-10 on page 1590 that there are 2-dimensional cut manifolds $\{\Sigma_j \subset \Lambda \,|\, 1 \leq j \leq b_1\}$, with b_1 the first Betti number, which convert Λ to a simply connected manifold Λ_{cut}. (The trivial case $b_1 = 0$ is later mentioned as limiting structure.) If there are inserted conductors in Λ, its surface $\partial\Lambda$ is disconnected and decomposes into b_2 finite connected parts, with b_2 the second Betti number.

  We investigate here mainly the case, where the **B**-field in Λ vanishes (flat connection).

Observation 55.1-5 (Potentials of Flat Connections). Assume Λ to be an interior domain which satisfies the Standard Assumption.

  If **B** vanishes in all of Λ, the only non-vanishing vector potentials, which may not be gauged away, are $\mathbf{A}^{\mathrm{co}}$ and/or $\mathsf{A}^0_{\mathrm{co}}$ according to which Betti numbers are greater than 0.

  That is so because $\mathbf{A}^\|$ has vanishing curl but can be gauged away (being a global gradient $\mathrm{grad}_0 \lambda^\|$) and because there is a one-one correspondence between $\mathbf{B}^\top$ and $\mathbf{A}^\top$ (see Sec. 6.1 on page 102).

  On the other side, $\mathbf{A}^{\mathrm{co}} \in \mathbb{H}_2$ has always vanishing curl, and the part of A_{co} which gives vanishing $\mathbf{B}^{\mathrm{co}}$ is just $\mathsf{A}^0_{\mathrm{co}} \in \mathbb{H}_1$ (e.g., text near Eq. (55.2.10) below).

  Thus we get for a general flat vector potential the form $\mathbf{A}^{\mathrm{co}} + \mathsf{A}^0_{\mathrm{co}} + \mathrm{grad}_0 \lambda^\|$ which is, however, not unique.

Remark 55.1-6 (Gauge Bundles with Flat Connections). For constructing a coordinated principal bundle $\mathcal{P}_t(\tau_t) = \mathcal{P}(\pi, \mathcal{O}_t, U(1), \tau_t)$, with $\mathcal{O}_t = \{t\} \times \Lambda$, we determine first the local trivializations $\tau_\alpha : \pi^{-1}U^t_\alpha \to U^t_\alpha \times U(1), \alpha \in J$, together with the transition elements $z_{\alpha\beta,y} \in U(1), y \in U^t_\alpha \cap U^t_\beta$.

  To determine a connection, one needs in general additional information. To determine a flat connection is, however, merely a matter of the transition functions.

  We construct now *a first type of a flat connection* corresponding to the most interesting vector potential $\mathsf{A}^0_{\mathrm{co}}$, abbreviated here simply by A, which is in general not globally defined in terms of a smooth cross section of $\mathcal{P}_t(\tau_t)$.

  By Theorem 44.4-10, we have the available gradient representation of a 3-vector field from $\mathbb{H}_1$. Because of the assumed smoothness, we may convert it (after a change of sign) into $\mathsf{A}(y) = \mathbf{d}\varphi(y)$, viewed as a relation for 1-forms on $\{t\} \times \Lambda_{\mathrm{cut}}$, where $\varphi(y)$ is a solution of the spatial Laplace equation at time t. More precisely, we assume $\varphi(y)$ to be a linear combination — with possibly t-dependent coefficients — of b_1 linearly independent functions on Λ_{cut} satisfying

$$\Delta\varphi = 0 \quad \text{in} \quad \Lambda_{\mathrm{cut}}, \qquad \left.\frac{\partial\varphi}{\partial n}\right|_{\partial\Lambda} = 0, \tag{55.1.19}$$

$$[\varphi]_{\Sigma_j} = \text{constant}_j, \qquad \left[\frac{\partial\varphi}{\partial n}\right]_{\Sigma_j} = 0, \quad \forall j \in \{1, \dots, b_1\}.$$

From these ingredients, we construct a coordinated gauge bundle $\mathcal{P}_t(\tau_t) = \mathcal{P}(\pi, \mathcal{O}_t, U(1), \tau_t)$ as follows.

We specify the trivialization domains U_α, $\alpha \in J$, and choose first $U_0 := \Lambda_{\mathrm{cut}}$ and cover then the gaps in Λ, arising by the omission of the cut manifolds, by open simply connected neighborhoods $\{\Lambda \supset U_j \supset \Sigma_j \,|\, j = 1, \dots, b_1\}$ (where the case $b_1 = 0$ is later obtained as limiting structure). We require that each U_j contains just one cut, what is possible by the pair-wise disjointness of the Σ_j, which enables also the pair-wise disjointness of the U_j, $j = 1, \dots, b_1$.

Since the Σ_j have distinguished sides it is possible to decompose $U_j \backslash \Sigma_j = U_{j+} \dot\cup U_{j-} \subset U_0$, such that $\partial U_{j+} \supset \Sigma_j^+$ and $\partial U_{j-} \supset \Sigma_j^-$ (the boundaries being outside of the open $U_{j\pm}$). The analogous relations are applicable to the $U_j^t = \{t\} \times U_j$. Then $\{(U_j^t, \phi_j^t) \,|\, j = 1, \dots, b_1\}$, with the $\phi_j^t : U_j^t \to \{t\} \times \mathbb{R}^3$ (relative topology!) as embedding maps, constitutes an atlas of $\mathcal{O}_t$.

We write the trivialization maps as $\tau_\alpha^t b = (y, z_\alpha(y))$, $y = \pi b \in U_\alpha^t$, where $z_\alpha(y) = \exp\{i\lambda_\alpha(y)\} \in U(1)$. In detail, we set

$$\tau_0^t b = (y, \exp\{i\lambda_0(y)\}), \quad \pi b = y \in U_0^t, \quad \lambda_0(y) := \varphi(y),$$

and introduce for $1 \leq j \leq b_1$:

$$\tau_j^t b = (y, \exp\{i\lambda_j(y)\}), \quad \lambda_j(y) := \begin{cases} \varphi(y) & y \in U_{j-}^t \\ \varphi(y) - c_j & y \in U_{j+}^t \end{cases}. \tag{55.1.20}$$

For the jump constants c_j, note that Σ_j has two sides and we have defined

$$[\varphi]_{\Sigma_j} := \varphi|_{\Sigma_j^+} - \varphi|_{\Sigma_j^-} = c_j, \quad j = 1, \dots, b_1,$$

the values of c_j not depending on the crossing points $x \in \Sigma_j$.

Then — by continuous extension over the cuts Σ_j — the phases $\lambda_j : U_j^t \to \mathbb{R}$ are continuous and spatially differentiable in the direction normal to the cut.

Recall that a class of strictly equivalent coordinated bundles lead to a (geometric) fiber bundle. In that class, the domains of trivialization may widely be varied and refined. It is practical to start with as few trivialization domains as possible.

Theorem 55.1-7 (Construction of a Non-relativistic Flat Gauge Bundle).
Let be given an interior spatial domain $\mathcal{O}_t = \{t\} \times \Lambda$ (at fixed time t) which satisfies the Standard Assumptions 44.4-8 with a smooth boundary $\partial\Lambda$.

(a) *Then there exists a coordinated principal bundle* $\mathcal{P}(\pi, \mathcal{O}_t, U(1), \tau_t)$, *with the continuous trivialization structure given by Eq. (55.1.20), giving rise to the (geometric) principal bundle* $\mathcal{P}_t = \mathcal{P}(\pi, \mathcal{O}_t, U(1))$. $\mathcal{P}(\pi, \mathcal{O}_t, U(1), \tau_t)$ *is parameterized by an harmonic function* φ *on* Λ_{cut} *described in the text preceding Eq. (55.1.19), what we indicate occasionally by the symbol* $\mathcal{P}_t^\varphi$.
The transition elements $z_{\beta\alpha,y} \in U(1)$ *are then given by the following phase differences (where* $1 \leq j \leq b_1$*)*

$$\lambda_{j0,y} = \lambda_j(y) - \lambda_0(y) = -\lambda_{0j,y}, \quad \lambda_{00,y} = 0 = \lambda_{jj,y}, \quad \forall y \in U_j^t \cap U_0^t,. \quad (55.1.21)$$

(The overlaps $U_j^t \cap U_{j'}^t$, $1 \leq j \neq j' \leq b_1$ *are empty.)*
(b) *Since the transition elements factorize each* $\mathcal{P}_t^\varphi$ *is trivial (equivalent to the product bundle).*
(c) *With each* $\mathcal{P}_t^\varphi$ *is associated a distinguished connection form* $\bar{\mathsf{A}} \in \Omega^1_{U(1)H}(\mathcal{P}_t, \mathbb{R})$, *which provides the local cohomological vector potentials of type* A^0_{co}. *For that aim,* $\bar{\mathsf{A}}$ *is introduced via the gauge compatible family of local forms (the occurring derivatives are spatial)*

$$\mathsf{A}_j := \mathbf{d}\lambda_j \in \Omega^1(U_j^t, \mathbb{R}), \quad 0 \leq j \leq b_1 \quad (55.1.22)$$

from which one derives the gauge behavior in overlap regions

$$\mathsf{A}_j(y) = \mathsf{A}_0(y) - \mathbf{d}\lambda_{0j}(y), \quad \forall y \in U_j^t \cap U_0^t. \quad (55.1.23)$$

(d) *Since* $\mathbf{d}\bar{\mathsf{A}} = 0$, *the connection is flat and for each* $b \in \mathcal{P}_t$ *the restricted (but not necessarily the absolute) holonomy group* $\Phi^0(b)$ *for that connection is trivial.*
(e) *Since the renormalized pulled down vector potential satisfies* $\mathsf{A}^r(y) = \mathsf{A}_j(y) - \mathbf{d}\lambda_j(y) = \mathsf{A}_0(y) - \mathbf{d}\lambda_0(y)$, *in all overlap regions* $U_j^t \cap U_0^t$, $1 \leq j \leq b_1$, *there are well-defined global curve integrals for the original pulled down vector potential. One obtains for any closed curve* $c : [0,1] \to \mathcal{O}_t$

$$\oint_c \mathsf{A}(\dot{c}(s))\, ds = \sum_{\text{crossed cuts}} \pm c_j. \quad (55.1.24)$$

(f) *Since the connected and paracompact* $\mathcal{O}_t$ *is second countable, the fundamental group is discrete and thus* $\Phi(y)$ *is a discrete subgroup of* $U(1)$. *Thus we obtain for the jump constants*

$$c_j \in q 2\pi \mathbb{Z}, \quad \forall\, 1 \leq j \leq b_1, \quad \text{with } q \in \mathbb{R} \text{ some constant.} \quad (55.1.25)$$

We remark that we obtain for $b_1 = 0$ *the limiting case with only a single global trivialization and vanishing jump constants.*

Proof. We have only to say a word to (e). If we have the 3-dimensional transition regions U_{j+}^t attached with two phase values, the renormalized vector potential

$\mathsf{A}^r(y) = \mathsf{A}_j(y) - \mathbf{d}\lambda_j(y) = \mathsf{A}_0(y) - \mathbf{d}\lambda_0(y)$ gives us in both cases as phase partner $\varphi(y)$. For integration it is in fact sufficient to know $\varphi(y)$ only in $\{t\} \times \Lambda_{\mathrm{cut}}$.

From $\oint_c \mathsf{A}^r(\dot{c}(s)) \, ds = 0$ follows $\oint_c \mathsf{A}(\dot{c}(s)) \, ds = \oint_c \mathbf{d}\lambda(\dot{c}(s)) \, ds = \oint_c d\varphi(c(s))$.

If a piece of the path c, namely $c : [s_i, s_{i+1}] \to \Lambda$ (dropping t), crosses the cut Σ_j from Σ_j^- to Σ_j^+, the integration delivers the values $\varphi(c(s_{i+1})) - \varphi|_{\Sigma_j^+} + \varphi|_{\Sigma_j^-} - \varphi(c(s_i))$. (Here the continuous extensions of φ are employed, which have already been used to continuously bridge the cut by λ_j.) The other pieces of the closed c compensate the first and last term leaving the value $-c_j$. The value c_j is obtained by integrating in the reverse direction. The pieces of integration without crossing a cut compensate each other. □

It is interesting to note that the preceding construction of $\mathcal{P}_t^\varphi$ requires necessarily the constancy of the jumps c_j of φ all over the cut surface Σ_j (what we originally have learned from Theorem 44.4-10 on page 1590). For, in the bundle construction, the transition elements $z_{0j,y}$ are indexed by the $\lambda_{0j,y} = \lambda_0(y) - \lambda_j(y) = c_j(y)$ which must be continuous on the overlap region U_{j+}^t. Since each holonomy group $\Phi(b)$ is discrete, the transition elements must be constant on the overlaps.

The preceding construction of $\mathcal{P}_t^\varphi$ depends heavily on the harmonic function φ with all its boundary properties on $\partial \Sigma_{\mathrm{cut}}$, and especially depends on the positions of the virtual cuts Σ_j. By forming the strict equivalence class $\mathcal{P}_t$, one may shift the Σ_j homotopically around but must observe certain subsidiary conditions expressed by Eq. (55.1.19). The number of cuts equals the first Betti number b_1 and is certainly a topological constant.

The advantage of the smooth bundle construction, with its continuous local transition functions, lies in general topological insights within a consistent conceptual frame, for which there exists a lot of mathematical notions and theorems. Especially the assertions of Theorem 55.1-4 on the holonomy groups presuppose the structure of a principal bundle, wherefrom we come in the end to the following physical conclusions on flux quantization.

Conclusion 55.1-8 (Magnetic Flux Quantization in ED). Consider an interior multiply connected spatial domain $\mathcal{O}_t = \{t\} \times \Lambda$ (at time t) which satisfies the Standard Assumptions 44.4-8 with a smooth boundary $\partial \Lambda$. Assume that there is no **B**-field in $\mathcal{O}_t$, what implies that we may choose the vector potential A_{co} from the first cohomological space $\mathbb{H}_1$. The smooth boundary provides regularity properties for A_{co}.

Express this situation in terms of a smooth trivial gauge bundle $\mathcal{P}_t = \mathcal{P}(\pi, \mathcal{O}_t, U(1))$ with a flat connection $\bar{\mathcal{A}} \in \Omega_{U(1)H}^1(\mathcal{P}_t, \mathbb{R})$ according to Theorem 55.1-7.

Then one concludes — without any appeal to quantum mechanics — that the magnetic flux $\mathcal{F}_c$ through any surface Σ_c^t, with its boundary c being a closed curve in $\mathcal{O}_t$, arises in discrete equal steps: $\mathcal{F}_c \in q2\pi\mathbb{Z}$, for some constant $q \in \mathbb{R}$.

The described situations may physically be prepared by multiply connected superconductors filling Λ (where only the superconducting ring is the favorite example in the literature) or by external regions of (normal) current carrying coils, from where the **B**-field does not penetrate into the surrounding external space Λ (cf. subsequent Discussion and Sec. 37.4.6 on page 1218).

We have now to supplement the *second type of a flat connection*, which is related to a vector potential $\mathbf{A}^{\mathrm{co}} \in \mathbb{H}_2$ what may not be gauged away. According to Theorem 44.4-10 on page 1590 it holds $\mathbf{A}^{\mathrm{co}}(y) = \nabla_x \varphi^{\mathrm{co}}(y)$ within all of $\mathcal{O}_t = \{t\} \times \Lambda$ in the generalized sense, where $\varphi_t^{\mathrm{co}} \in W^1(\Lambda, \mathbb{C})$ is a solution of

$$\Delta_x \varphi_t^{\mathrm{co}} = 0 \text{ in } \Lambda, \qquad \varphi_t^{\mathrm{co}}|_{\partial \Lambda_j} = \text{constant}_j, \quad \forall j \in \{0, \dots, b_2\}. \qquad (55.1.26)$$

If $\partial \Lambda$ is smooth, then also φ^{co} is smooth and may be directly used for a smooth bundle construction. That is, we simply formulate the total factorization for $\mathcal{P}_t = \mathcal{P}(\pi, \mathcal{O}_t, U(1), \tau_t)$, with the only trivialization region $U_0^t = \mathcal{O}_t$,

$$\tau_0^t : \mathcal{P}_t \to \mathcal{O}_t \times U(1), \quad \tau_0^t b = y \times \exp\{i\varphi_t^{\mathrm{co}}(x)\}, \quad \pi b = y = (t, x). \qquad (55.1.27)$$

The physical content is expressed by the boundary conditions for φ_t^{co}, which attribute a constant phase value to each piece of an ideal conductor inserted into Λ. These resulting phase differences are "felt" by the condensate of a superconductor as demonstrates the Josephson effects. They must, therefore, survive a gauge transformation, what means that $\mathbf{A}^{\mathrm{co}}$, indeed, cannot be gauged away. In other words: Even that simple product bundle is physically not trivial, since it represents an experimentally relevant phase association with the points $y \in \mathcal{O}_t$. Since the phases $\varphi_t^{\mathrm{co}}(x)$ are single-valued in all of Λ, there are only trivial holonomy groups affiliated with that bundle.

Conclusion 55.1-9 (Flat Connections with Fixed Time in (Q)ED). For constructing a *general flat connection* on a time-fixed gauge bundle $\mathcal{P}_t$, which describes $\mathbf{A}^{\mathrm{co}} + \mathbf{A} + \mathrm{grad}_0 \lambda^{\|}$, we may employ the trivializations of the bundle for $\mathbf{A}$ and use Eq. (55.1.20) with φ replaced by $\varphi + \varphi^{\mathrm{co}} + \lambda^{\|}$.

Since the longitudinal gauge function is often gauged away, one may ask, whether the combination $\mathbf{A}^{\mathrm{co}} + \mathbf{A}$ makes sense in physics. That is, in fact, the case with the ring SQUID, discussed in Sec. 37.4 on page 1199. There both phase properties related to $\mathbf{A}^{\mathrm{co}}$ respectively to $\mathbf{A} = \mathbf{A}_{\mathrm{co}}^0$ are of concrete physical meaning, just on the mesoscopic stage.

Let us mention, that the parametric time dependence of the spatially constructed connection is relevant and that the quantization of $\mathbf{A}^{\mathrm{co}}$ is required by experiments.

The detailed phase information obtained by horizontally lifted, not necessarily closed, curves is most relevant in quantum theory.

55.1.5.   *Phases in Associated Line Bundles*

As mentioned before, the phases obtained by horizontal lifts of trajectories in position space are obtained by completely classical arguments. The phase changes along an horizontally lifted path describe the results of parallel transports. Especially for closed trajectories in position space, holonomy theory of flat connections predicts in ED flux quantization as an entirely classical phenomenon. It is accurately confirmed, e.g., for superconducting rings in which the **B**-field is expelled by the Meissner effect. That superconductivity may be microscopically explained only by many–body quantum statistics does not matter for deriving the flux quantum according to the foregoing arguments.

The same argumentation also works for a tightly wound solenoid, with its **B**-field shielded from the exterior space. If the solenoid is also ring shaped or traverses the total experimental space, the exterior space is not simply connected and we have a non-trivial space $\mathbb{H}_1$ for the first cohomology group. (In comparison to the superconducting ring, the interior and exterior spaces are permuted.) In any case, we may apply the construction of a gauge bundle according to Theorem 55.1-7.

As a side remark, let us mention, that the superconducting ring may inherit the twist of a *Möbius strip*. The original structure group is G_2, but if we extend it to $U(1)$, then we may perform the above described, slightly varied, trivialization structure to formulate the G-equivalence to a product bundle (with $G = U(1)$). In that manner, a flux quantization can also be derived. Already that example illustrates that *"trivial gauge bundles" — which are equivalent to product bundles — may be geometrically and physically non-trivial.*

In the force-free external space of the mentioned solenoids, there have been performed many experiments for interference phenomena with electron rays. It may be emphasized again, that already for *classically described electrons*, one can derive the phase changes by applying the notion of parallel transport along their classical trajectories.

In order to treat theoretically, however, interference experiments and to derive Aharanov–Bohm effects, one needs a *quantum theory* which is adapted to the gauge bundle structure $\mathcal{P}_t = \mathcal{P}(\pi, \mathcal{O}_t, U(1))$. That adaption is systematically realized by the notion of an "associated $\mathbb{C}^n$-bundle". For simplicity, we neglect spin effects and set $n = 1$, arriving at an "associated line bundle".

In the notation of Sec. 54.6, $U(1)$ acts on an element w of $\mathcal{W} \equiv \mathbb{C}$ as $l(z)w = zw$, $\forall z \in \mathbb{C}_1 \equiv U(1)$. The "wave function" of the electron is not simply a function $\sigma_\mathbb{C} : \mathcal{O}_t \to \mathbb{C}$ but "feels" the intertwinement of its phases with the space-time coordinates $y \in \mathcal{O}_t$. Its values w in $\mathbb{C}$ must therefore be related with the gauge bundle $\mathcal{P}_t$, and its phase changes $l(z)w$ must be accompanied by the action of $U(1)$ in $\mathcal{P}_t$ (by right-multiplication). One arrives at the bundle $\mathcal{P}_t \times_{U(1)} \mathbb{C} \equiv \mathcal{B}(\varrho, \mathcal{O}_t, \mathcal{W}, U(1)) =: \mathcal{B}$.

As expressed in Eq. (54.6.1), one works in a systematic theory with sections of the associated bundle (and not with sections with values in $\mathbb{C}$)

$$\sigma : \quad \mathcal{O}_t \to \mathcal{B}, \quad \text{given by}$$
$$\sigma(\pi\, b) = [b, l(\sigma_{U(1)}(b))\, \sigma_\mathbb{C}(\pi\, b)]_{U(1)}, \quad \forall b \in \mathcal{P}_t, \tag{55.1.28}$$

where the wave function section $\sigma_{\mathbb{C}}$ obtains phases $\sigma_{U(1)}(b) \in U(1)$, which do not depend merely on $y = \pi b$ but on the choice of a bundle point $b \in \pi^{-1}y \subset \mathcal{P}_t$. The tensoring in the bracket $[b, .]_{U(1)}$, combined with $U(1)$ factorizing, provides the association of phase changes of the wave function with those of the bundle points b. The phases are determined by a gauge bundle section $\sigma_{\mathcal{P}_t}$ according to the equation (*) $b\sigma_{U(1)}(b) = \sigma_{\mathcal{P}_t}(\pi b)$, where on the left-hand side occurs right-multiplication in $\mathcal{P}_t$.

In general, all sections involved are local. If, however, Λ in $\mathcal{O}_t = \{t\} \times \Lambda$ satisfies our Standard Assumption, the local gauge bundle sections combine to a global section $\sigma_{\mathcal{P}_t} : \mathcal{O}_t \to \mathcal{P}_t$. Equation (*) for the phases keeps, however, its local character. That means, that in transition regions there arise in general more than one phase value.

A unique local phase value is only obtained along a given electron trajectory by constructing the horizontal lift (with respect to our flat connection). We are therefore in the strange situation, that for a unique quantum phase, we need a lifted classical trajectory. What seems secretely implied by the usual discussions for the Aharonov–Bohm effect, is the definition of the classical trajectories by the Ehrenfest theorems.

The problem is realized in the physics literature under the headline of "non-integrable phases": Given a $y \in \mathcal{O}_t$, the phase $\lambda(y) = \int_0^1 \mathsf{A}(\dot{c}(s))\, ds$, $c(1) = y$, depends on the path c and may be multi-valued.

If we, in fact, presuppose a classical path $c \subset \mathcal{O}_t$ we may lift it as $\hat{c}$ to the associated bundle $\mathcal{P}_t \times_{U(1)} \mathbb{C}$ by first determining the lift $\bar{c}$ to $\mathcal{P}_t$. Even if $c : [0,1] \to \mathcal{O}_t$, has several intersections with itself, the paralleled displacements $\bar{c}(s) = bz(s)$ along $c(s)$, $s \in [0,1]$ through $\bar{c}(0) = b$ are well defined. We then define

$$
\begin{aligned}
\hat{c}(s) &:= [bz(s), \sigma_{\mathbb{C}}(\pi \, \bar{c}(s))]_{U(1)} = [b, l(z(-s))\sigma_{\mathbb{C}}(\pi \, \bar{c}(s))]_{U(1)}, \\
\hat{c}(0) &= [b, \sigma_{\mathbb{C}}(\pi \, b)]_{U(1)}
\end{aligned}
\tag{55.1.29}
$$

for the lifted curve beginning at $[b, \sigma_{\mathbb{C}}(\pi \, b)]_{U(1)} \in \mathcal{B}$. Along that curve, one then simplifies the notation $[b, l(z(-s))\sigma_{\mathbb{C}}(\pi \, \bar{c}(s))]_{U(1)} \longrightarrow z(-s)\psi(c(s))$ for the electronic wave function. But one has to keep in mind that the phases $z(-s)$ are determined by the horizontal lift in $\mathcal{P}_t$ and are not necessarily single-valued as functions on space.

With $z(-s)\psi(c(s))$ on hand, one may perform the physical discussions of electronic interference effects typical for multiply connected regions.

Let us finally mention that the wave function χ for electron pairs in Sec. 37.4.6 on page 1218 is an averaged mesoscopic one, similar to the complex Ginzburg–Landau order parameter, for which a classically determined phase is more in place than for a microscopic wave function.

The advantage of the general setup for an associated bundle is the generality of the representation space $\mathcal{W}$ for the gauge group (here $U(1)$). For be associating wave functions, one thinks in first line on $\mathcal{W} = \mathbb{C}^n$. But $\mathcal{W}$ may also be interpreted, e.g., as the partial algebra of quantized field operators for elementary particles. As long as the particle number is fixed, that reduces, however, to the approach via Schrödinger wave functions.

55.1.6. *Transition to Non–Smooth Boundaries and Sections*

In the preceding two sections, we have expounded, how in a smooth bundle theory exponentiated phases $z(s) = \exp\{i\lambda(s)\}$ may be defined along lifted trajectories.

For calculations, global discontinuous phase sections $\mathcal{O}_t \ni y \mapsto \lambda(y) = \lambda_t(x) \in \mathbb{R}$ (that are discontinuous *functions*) are more practicable, already in smooth bundle theory without boundary conditions. Using Sobolev Hilbert space theory, we demonstrate in our main text, that even global non–smooth vector potentials are tractable which satisfy conductor boundary conditions for rather irregular spatial boundaries. That includes also their gauge behavior and their decomposition into Helmholtz–Hodge components.

The present section serves only to illuminate the relationship between smooth and non–smooth gauge theory in terms of a formal limiting procedure, which is adapted to the above treatment of a flat connection respectively vector potential. But we sketch here the above described bundle construction, not by starting from a given vector potential, but by inserting phase functions above the base manifold with its given geometry. (For the general physical philosophy of a "non-integrable phase factor" as the primary field quantity, see [Ton93] and references therein.)

Let Λ satisfy the Standard Assumptions and specify the trivialization domains, as before, by choosing a minimal open covering $U_0 := \Lambda_{\text{cut}}$ and $\{U_j \supset \Sigma_j \,|\, j = 1, \ldots, b_1\}$, decomposing $U_j \backslash \Sigma_j = U_{j+} \dot{\cup} U_{j-} \subset U_0$. We apply the analogous relations to the $U_j^t = \{t\} \times U_j$.

We write the trivialization maps by specifying the phases, the exponents of the $U(1)$-elements $z_\alpha(y) = \exp\{i\lambda_\alpha(y)\}$. In the simply connected U_0, we assume a differentiable global $\lambda_0(y)$, which makes, however, jumps $[\lambda_0]_{\Sigma_j} := \lambda_0|_{\Sigma_j^+} - \lambda_0|_{\Sigma_j^-} = c_j$ while crossing the cut Σ_j from Σ_j^- to Σ_j^+. The c_j are arbitrary real constants, say non-vanishing.

In the transition regions, we introduce additionally the phases

$$\lambda_j(y) := \begin{cases} \lambda_0(y) & y \in U_{j-}^t \\ \lambda_0(y) - c_j & y \in U_{j+}^t \end{cases}. \tag{55.1.30}$$

So, a two-valued phase occurs only in the open U_{j+}^t, $j = 1, \ldots, b_1$, which have Σ_j^+ as a part of their topological boundaries.

With these quantities, the smooth coordinated gauge bundle $\mathcal{P}_t(\tau_t) = \mathcal{P}(\pi, \mathcal{O}_t, U(1), \tau_t)$ can be constructed, in which the cuts are bridged by continuous phases at the cost of two-valuedness. In the transition regions U_{j+}^t, the "transition phases" $\lambda_{0j} = \lambda_0 - \lambda_j = c_j$ are assumed constant, what fits to the necessary discreteness of the holonomy groups at the points of $\mathcal{P}_t$. They have also to belong to a subgroup of $U(1)$.

To avoid the two-valuedness, we imagine the homotopic limit of the U^t_{j+} leading to the Σ^+_j and extend simultaneously λ_0 to be also defined on Σ_j by applying continuity from the Σ^+_j-side. Then λ_0 is not only defined on all of Λ, but its jumps on the Σ_j are interpreted as the "transition phases" of an extrapolated gauge bundle. That is meant as the link to smooth bundle theory.

A (flat) connection is introduced by viewing the phase function as a generalized 0-form and setting $\mathsf{A}_t(x) := \mathbf{d}_x \lambda_0(y)$ for all $x \in \Lambda_{\text{cut}}$. If $\lambda_0(y)$ corresponds completely to a harmonic function φ of Eq. (55.1.19), then also the normal derivatives to the cut have a meaning. (If λ_0 has also an additive part of type Eq. (55.1.26) and/or of type $\lambda^\parallel$, that would not alter the conclusion.) The normal derivatives are important for the integrals $\int_c \mathsf{A}$ along curves c which traverse the Σ_j. Their continuity is implicitly assumed in usual applications.

By interpreting the derivatives as weak ones on all of Λ, according to Sobolev theory, one obtains useful generalizations for that setup, while making the link to smooth bundle theory weaker.

Another matter is, how the further parts of the total Helmholtz–Hodge decomposed vector potential are indeed introduced. Their definition and boundary behavior surpasses the possibilities of smooth bundle theory as usually described in mathematical physics. According to the applications in the present book it seems unavoidable — but also practicable — to use global non-continuous sections for vector potentials and phases to meet all needs of physics. And there must not be sacrificed any piece of mathematical rigor in gaining an immense extension of the field of application for such generalized kinds of "connections".

55.2. Bundles above General Force-Field Trajectories

55.2.1. *Trajectorial Gauge Groups with Split Gauge Functions*

We have discussed in Chapter 6, the existence of potentials from the global point of view: What conditions must be satisfied for an electromagnetic field trajectory $[\mathbb{R} \ni t \mapsto \psi_t = (\mathbf{E}_t, \mathbf{B}_t) \in \mathcal{R}]$ that it may be derived from a potential trajectory $t \mapsto (u_t, \mathbf{A}_t)$? It turns out, that only that part of the Maxwell equations is relevant for this existence problem, which does not contain material sources. Thus we can deal with electrodynamic fields alone. In order to get a manageable theory of "trajectorial gauge transformations" we have set up Assumption 6.3-1 on page 108, which we reproduce here in the following compiled formulation. If not specified otherwise we do not need any assumption on our domain $\Lambda \subseteq \mathbb{R}^3$, i.e., no smoothness of the boundary $\partial \Lambda$ is necessary, nor Λ has to be interior.

Definition 55.2-1 (Admissible Field Trajectories). Let FT be the set of all admissible field trajectories $[t \mapsto (\mathbf{E}_t, \mathbf{B}_t)]$, which own by definition the following features.

$[t \mapsto (\mathbf{E}_t, \mathbf{B}_t)]$ takes its values in the real Hilbert space $\mathcal{R} = L^2(\Lambda, \mathbb{R}^3) \boxplus L^2(\Lambda, \mathbb{R}^3)$, which is split into the longitudinal, cohomological, and transversal subspaces according to the Helmholtz–Hodge decomposition (5.1.2), and satisfies the following four requirements:

(1) $\mathbf{E}_t^{\parallel} \in \mathrm{ran}(\mathrm{grad}_0)$ for all $t \in \mathbb{R}$, that are weak gradients of a potential trajectory with $[t \mapsto u_t = \mathrm{grad}_0^{-1} \mathbf{E}_t^{\parallel}] \in C(\mathbb{R}, W_0^1(\Lambda, \mathbb{R}))$.
(2) $[t \mapsto \mathbf{E}_t^{co}] \in C(\mathbb{R}, \mathbb{H}_2)$.
(3) $\mathbf{B}_t^{\top} \in \mathrm{ran}(\mathrm{curl}_0)$ for all $t \in \mathbb{R}$, meaning the existence condition for the transversal vector potential $\mathbf{A}_t^{\top} := \mathrm{curl}_0|^{-1} \mathbf{B}_t^{\top}$ (where in general only $\mathbf{B}_t^{\top} \in \overline{\mathrm{ran}(\mathrm{curl}_0)}$).
(4) The three source-free Maxwell Eqs. (6.3.1) are fulfilled for all $t \in \mathbb{R}$ in the weak formulation

$$\mathbf{B}_t \in \mathrm{ker}(\mathrm{div}_0), \qquad \frac{d\mathbf{B}_t^{co}}{dt} = 0, \qquad \frac{d\mathbf{B}_t^{\top}}{dt} = -\mathrm{curl}_0 \mathbf{E}_t^{\top}. \qquad (55.2.1)$$

We have then shown the following existence result (cf. Theorem 6.3-4 on page 110).

Theorem 55.2-2 (Existence of Adapted Potential Trajectories). *The class* $\mathrm{PT}[t \mapsto (\mathbf{E}_t, \mathbf{B}_t)]$ *of all so-called "adapted potential trajectories"* $[t \mapsto (u_t, \mathbf{A}_t)]$, *associated with any given admissible field trajectory* $[t \mapsto (\mathbf{E}_t, \mathbf{B}_t)] \in \mathrm{FT}$ *is non-empty.*

We thus know, that there are trajectories $[t \mapsto (u_t, \mathbf{A}_t)]$, *which satisfy*

$$[t \mapsto u_t] \in C(\mathbb{R}, W_0^1(\Lambda, \mathbb{R})),$$
$$[t \mapsto \mathrm{grad}_0^{-1} \mathbf{A}_t^{\parallel}] \in C^1(\mathbb{R}, W_0^1(\Lambda, \mathbb{R})), \qquad (55.2.2)$$
$$[t \mapsto \mathbf{A}_t^{co}] \in C^1(\mathbb{R}, \mathbb{H}_2),$$

as well as the original relations, characterizing potentials with ideal conductor boundary conditions, namely

$$\mathbf{E}_t^{\parallel} = -\mathrm{grad}_0 \, u_t - \frac{d\mathbf{A}_t^{\parallel}}{dt}, \qquad \mathbf{E}_t^{co} = -\frac{d\mathbf{A}_t^{co}}{dt}, \qquad \mathbf{E}_t^{\top} = -\frac{d\mathbf{A}_t^{\top}}{dt}, \qquad (55.2.3)$$
$$\mathbf{B}_t^{\top} = \mathrm{curl}_0 \, \mathbf{A}_t = \mathrm{curl}_0 \, \mathbf{A}_t^{\top}, \qquad \forall t \in \mathbb{R}.$$

We have used here for the vector potential the Helmholtz–Hodge decomposition $\mathbf{A}_t = \mathbf{A}_t^{\parallel} \oplus \mathbf{A}_t^{co} \oplus \mathbf{A}_t^{\top}$ *(in the form of Eq. (6.0.3) on page 101). We call therefore* $\mathbf{A}_t$ *a "Helmholtz–Hodge adapted vector potential".*

Let us emphasize that, for given field trajectory $[t \mapsto (\mathbf{E}_t, \mathbf{B}_t)]$, the existing adapted potential trajectory $[t \mapsto (u_t, \mathbf{A}_t)]$ consist of globally defined potentials over all of Λ. Especially all Helmholtz–Hodge components of $\mathbf{A}_t$ are at each time t globally defined in the sense of being vectors in the pertinent Sobolev spaces. As we know, these Sobolev vectors consist of equivalence classes of functions over Λ, and the functions must not be defined at each point in Λ. In each class, a representative function may be defined on all of Λ, which displays in general, however, discontinuities. This is the big difference to connection forms in smooth gauge bundles $\mathcal{P}(\pi, \Lambda, U(1))$, which would in a global trivialization lead to continuous (even differentiable) vector potentials over $\mathsf{T} \times \Lambda$.

Notice that in the subsequent gauge transformations for adapted potentials nothing is said about the cohomological magnetic field $\mathbf{B}_t^{\mathrm{co}}$, which is in fact time-independent. As in the whole main text, we consider also here $\mathbf{B}_t^{\mathrm{co}}$ at first a fixed parameter function of the system and deal with its vector potential only later on.

Theorem 55.2-3 (Existence of the Trajectorial Gauge Group). *Let* PT *be the set of all adapted potential trajectories* $[t \mapsto (u_t, \mathbf{A}_t)]$, *which are affiliated to some admissible field trajectory of Definition 55.2-1. That is,* PT *is the union of all classes* PT$[t \mapsto (\mathbf{E}_t, \mathbf{B}_t)]$, *where* $[t \mapsto (\mathbf{E}_t, \mathbf{B}_t)]$ *varies over* FT.

For a given scalar trajectory $\bar{\lambda} \equiv [t \mapsto \lambda_t] \in \mathrm{C}^1(\mathbb{R}, \mathrm{W}_0^1(\Lambda, \mathbb{R}))$ *(functions which are one time weakly differentiable to t and to the x^i, with vanishing boundary evaluation on $\partial\Lambda$) and a given cohomological vector field* $h \in \mathbb{H}_2$, *we define the mapping*

$$G(\bar{\lambda}, h)[t \mapsto (u_t, \mathbf{A}_t)] := [t \mapsto (u_t - \tfrac{d\lambda_t}{dt}, \mathbf{A}_t + \mathrm{grad}_0\, \lambda_t + h)]. \qquad (55.2.4)$$

Then $G(\bar{\lambda}, h)$ *leaves each class of potential trajectories* PT$[t \mapsto (\mathbf{E}_t, \mathbf{B}_t)]$, *for fixed field trajectory, invariant.*

We call therefore $G(\bar{\lambda}, h)$ *a* trajectorial gauge transformation. *Obviously the set*

$$\mathrm{G}_{\mathrm{PT}} := \{G(\bar{\lambda}, h) \,|\, \bar{\lambda} \in \mathrm{C}^1(\mathbb{R}, \mathrm{W}_0^1(\Lambda, \mathbb{R})), \ h \in \mathbb{H}_2\}, \qquad (55.2.5)$$

constitutes an Abelian transformation group, acting on PT, *with the group law* $G(\bar{\lambda}, h) \circ G(\bar{\lambda}', h') = G(\bar{\lambda} + \bar{\lambda}', h + h')$ *and unit element* $G(0, 0)$. *We name* G_{PT} *the* trajectorial gauge group.

We find from Theorem 55.2-2 that G_{PT} *acts transitively and freely in each class* PT$[t \mapsto (\mathbf{E}_t, \mathbf{B}_t)]$.

Thus G_{PT} *constitutes a faithful representation of the Cartesian product of two vector groups* $\mathrm{C}^1(\mathbb{R}, \mathrm{W}_0^1(\Lambda, \mathbb{R})) \boxtimes \mathbb{H}_2$.

The subgroup $\mathbb{H}_2 =: \mathrm{G}_P^{\mathrm{co}}$ *is called the* second cohomological gauge group.

The preceding theorem reveals that the set of potential trajectories PT exhibits a bundle structure $\mathrm{PT} = \mathcal{P}(\bar{\pi}, \mathrm{FT}, \mathrm{G}_{\mathrm{PT}})$, which is similar to a principal bundle, with the infinite-dimensional base space of field trajectories FT and the infinite-dimensional group of trajectorial gauge transformations G_{PT}. The projection $\bar{\pi} : \mathrm{PT} \to \mathrm{FT}$ is constructed via Eq. (55.2.3), by means of which the fibers are expressible as PT$[t \mapsto (\mathbf{E}_t, \mathbf{B}_t)] = \bar{\pi}^{-1}([t \mapsto (\mathbf{E}_t, \mathbf{B}_t)])$. (We have made already the frequent use of inverted differential operators, which now are part of the not single-valued $\bar{\pi}^{-1}$.)

If we introduce in $L := \mathrm{C}^1(\mathbb{R}, \mathrm{W}_0^1(\Lambda, \mathbb{R}))$ a CLC-topology, then multiplication (addition) and inversion become continuous and we have a smooth topological group. As a linear space it is also a differentiable manifold, with the tangent space at 0 linear diffeomorphic to L. L is an infinite-dimensional commutative Lie group.

If we associate $\bar{\lambda} \in L$ with a function $\mathcal{O} \ni x \mapsto \exp\{a_0 \lambda(x)\}$, by choosing a representative of the function class $\bar{\lambda}$, the group L appears formally as a subgroup of the infinite Cartesian product $\mathsf{X}_{x \in \mathcal{O}} U(1)$, an infinite-dimensional, compact, commutative Lie group.

Similarly we may use Theorem 44.4-10 on page 1590 — when presupposing the Standard Assumption 44.4-8 for Λ — to associate $h \in \mathbb{H}_2$ with the 4-dimensional generalized gradient (and thus with a 4-dimensional "generalized differential" named also "singular differential" $d\lambda^{\mathrm{co}} = \partial_\mu \lambda^{\mathrm{co}} dx^\mu$, cf. [Fel81]) of a representative function $\lambda^{\mathrm{co}} : \mathsf{T} \times \Lambda \to \mathbb{R}$, which is constant in $x^0 = ct$ and satisfies with respect to the space coordinates $\Delta \lambda^{\mathrm{co}} = 0$, with constant values on each of the b_2 connected pieces of $\partial \Lambda$. In this manner also $\mathbb{H}_2$ appears formally as a subgroup of $\mathsf{X}_{x \in \mathcal{O}} U(1)$, and the similarity to a gauge group is emphasized in both cases.

55.2.2. *Tentative Extension of the Trajectorial Gauge Group*

Let us now investigate a seemingly more general situation, in which we only know that there exists a total gauge function $\bar{\lambda} \in \mathrm{C}^1(\mathbb{R}, \mathrm{W}^1(\Lambda, \mathbb{R}))$, describing the gauge behavior of the adapted potential trajectories $[t \mapsto (u_t, \mathbf{A}_t)] \in \mathrm{PT}[t \mapsto (\mathbf{E}_t, \mathbf{B}_t)]$ (for fixed, but arbitrary $[t \mapsto (\mathbf{E}_t, \mathbf{B}_t)] \in \mathrm{FT}$) in the form

$$[t \mapsto (u_t, \mathbf{A}_t)] \quad \longrightarrow \quad [t \mapsto (u_t - \tfrac{d\lambda_t}{dt}, \mathbf{A}_t + \mathrm{grad}\,\lambda_t)]. \qquad (55.2.6)$$

Then the condition that the transformed potential trajectory be again in $\mathrm{PT}[t \mapsto (\mathbf{E}_t, \mathbf{B}_t)]$ leads to the requirement $\frac{d\lambda_t}{dt} \in \mathrm{dom}(\mathrm{grad}_0) = \mathrm{W}_0^1(\Lambda, \mathbb{R})$, and a time-independent part of $\mathrm{grad}\,\lambda_t$ must be in $\mathbb{H}_2$, what we are going to demonstrate.

Proposition 55.2-4 (Splitting of Dynamical Trajectorial Gauge Group).
Let be given a gauge transformation in the form Eq. (55.2.6), where $\bar{\lambda} \in \mathrm{C}^1(\mathbb{R}, \mathrm{W}^1(\Lambda, \mathbb{R}))$.

Then for each $t \in \mathbb{R}$ there is a unique decomposition $\lambda_t = \lambda_t^{\|} + \lambda^{\mathrm{co}}$ with $\lambda_t^{\|} \in \mathrm{W}_0^1(\Lambda, \mathbb{R})$ and time-independent $\lambda^{\mathrm{co}} \in \mathrm{W}^1(\Lambda, \mathbb{R})$, such that $h := \mathrm{grad}\,\lambda^{\mathrm{co}} \in \mathbb{H}_2$. Moreover, $\bar{\lambda}^{\|} = [t \to \lambda_t^{\|}] \in \mathrm{C}^1(\mathbb{R}, \mathrm{W}_0^1(\Lambda, \mathbb{R}))$, and we may write the gauge transformation (55.2.6) in its split manner

$$[t \mapsto (u_t, \mathbf{A}_t^{\|} \oplus \mathbf{A}_t^{\mathrm{co}} \oplus \mathbf{A}_t^{\top})] \quad \longrightarrow$$

$$[t \mapsto (u_t - \tfrac{d\lambda_t^{\|}}{dt}, \mathbf{A}_t^{\|} + \mathrm{grad}_0\,\lambda_t^{\|} \oplus \mathbf{A}_t^{\mathrm{co}} + \mathrm{grad}\,\lambda^{\mathrm{co}} \oplus \mathbf{A}_t^{\top})] = G(\bar{\lambda}^{\|}, h)[t \mapsto (u_t, \mathbf{A}_t)], \qquad (55.2.7)$$

which coincides with our former type (55.2.4) *of trajectorial gauge transformations. Assuming that* $\Lambda \subseteq \mathbb{R}^3$ *satisfies the Standard Assumption, it holds* $\lambda^{\mathrm{co}} \in \mathrm{H}_c(\Lambda, \mathbb{R})$, *where* $\mathrm{H}_c(\Lambda, \mathbb{R})$ *denotes the space of harmonic Sobolev elements with constant values at each of the connected finite parts* $\partial \Lambda_j$, $j = 1, \ldots, b_2$, *of the boundary* $\partial \Lambda$ *of* Λ, *by Theorem 44.4-10.*

We recognize that gauge transformations of type (55.2.6) *do not lead to a more general gauge group than* G_{PT} (*the Standard Assumption being supposed*). *We therefore use the suggestive notation*

$$\mathrm{G}_{\mathrm{PT}} = \mathrm{G}_{\mathrm{PT}}^{\|} \times \mathrm{G}_P^{\mathrm{co}} \subset \mathsf{X}_{x \in \mathcal{O}}\, U(1), \quad \mathrm{G}_{\mathrm{PT}}^{\|} := \mathrm{C}^1(\mathbb{R}, \mathrm{W}^1(\Lambda, \mathbb{R})), \ \mathrm{G}_P^{\mathrm{co}} := \mathrm{H}_c(\Lambda, \mathbb{R}).$$
$$(55.2.8)$$

Proof. Before and after the gauge transformation (55.2.6), the transversal vector potential is the same, namely $\mathbf{A}_t^\top = \mathrm{curl}_0|^{-1}\mathbf{B}_t^\top$. Thus, according to the Helmholtz–Hodge decomposition (6.0.3) on page 101, we conclude that we have a splitting $\mathrm{grad}\,\lambda_t =: \eta_t^\| \oplus \eta_t^{\mathrm{co}} \in \overline{\mathrm{ran}(\mathrm{grad}_0)} \oplus \mathbb{H}_2$. Thus the longitudinal vector potential after the gauge transformation is given by $\tilde{\mathbf{A}}_t^\| = \mathbf{A}_t^\| + \eta_t^\|$. Since by assumption for adapted potentials it must be $\tilde{\mathbf{A}}_t^\|, \mathbf{A}_t^\| \in \mathrm{ran}(\mathrm{grad}_0)$, we conclude that $\eta_t^\| \in \mathrm{ran}(\mathrm{grad}_0)$. Consequently, there is a $\lambda_t^\| \in \mathrm{W}_0^1(\Lambda, \mathbb{R})$ with $\eta_t^\| = \mathrm{grad}_0\,\lambda_t^\|$. With $\mathrm{grad}_0 \subset \mathrm{grad}$ it follows for $\lambda_t^{\mathrm{co}} := \lambda_t - \lambda_t^\| \in \mathrm{W}^1(\Lambda, \mathbb{R})$ that $\mathrm{grad}\,\lambda_t^{\mathrm{co}} = \eta_t^{\mathrm{co}} \in \mathbb{H}_2$.

The decomposition $\lambda_t = \lambda_t^\| + \lambda_t^{\mathrm{co}}$ with $\lambda_t^\| \in \mathrm{W}_0^1(\Lambda, \mathbb{R})$ and $\mathrm{grad}\,\lambda_t^{\mathrm{co}} \in \mathbb{H}_2$ is unique, as demonstrates the following argument. Let $\lambda_t = \tilde{\lambda}_t^\| + \tilde{\lambda}_t^{\mathrm{co}}$ be a further decomposition of this type. Then $0 = \mathrm{grad}_0(\lambda_t^\| - \tilde{\lambda}_t^\|) \oplus \mathrm{grad}(\lambda_t^{\mathrm{co}} - \tilde{\lambda}_t^{\mathrm{co}}) \in \mathrm{ran}(\mathrm{grad}_0) \oplus \mathbb{H}_2$. Consequently, $0 = \mathrm{grad}_0(\lambda_t^\| - \tilde{\lambda}_t^\|) \in \mathrm{ran}(\mathrm{grad}_0)$. But grad_0 is injective (because there are no constants in $\mathrm{W}_0^1(\Lambda, \mathbb{R})$), thus $\lambda_t^\| = \tilde{\lambda}_t^\|$ leading to $\lambda_t^{\mathrm{co}} = \tilde{\lambda}_t^{\mathrm{co}}$.

The time independence of $h := \eta_t^{\mathrm{co}} \in \mathbb{H}_2$ respectively of its potential $\lambda^{\mathrm{co}} := \lambda_t^{\mathrm{co}}$ finally follows as in Theorem 6.3-4 on page 110. □

The point of all this is, that we may separate neatly two different kinds of trajectorial gauge transformations, pertaining to the two gauge dependent dynamical parts of the vector potential, and can do this only for the trajectorial gauge group (and of course not for a single $U(1)$ gauge group). We remark that certain topological features, expressed by the second cohomology group of Λ, are here integrated into the definition of $\mathrm{G}_P^{\mathrm{co}}$.

Altogether, we have motivation enough to introduce the following bundle.

Definition 55.2-5 (Trajectorial Gauge Bundle). Under the *trajectorial gauge bundle* we understand the fiberd set PT of adapted potential trajectories

$$\mathrm{PT} = \mathcal{P}(\bar{\pi}, \mathrm{FT}, \mathrm{G}_{\mathrm{PT}}), \quad \mathrm{G}_{\mathrm{PT}} = \mathrm{C}^1(\mathbb{R}, \mathrm{W}_0^1(\Lambda, \mathbb{R})) + \mathbb{H}_2 = \mathrm{G}_{\mathrm{PT}}^{\|} \times \mathrm{G}_P^{\mathrm{co}}, \quad (55.2.9)$$

where $\bar{\pi} : \mathrm{PT} \to \mathrm{FT}$ is constructed according to Eq. (55.2.3). If the Standard Assumption is satisfied, then $\mathbb{H}_2$ is isomorphic to the group $\mathrm{H}_c(\Lambda, \mathbb{R})$ of harmonic gauge functions, as described above.

In terms of the CLC-topology, G_{PT} can be made to an infinite-dimensional Abelian Lie group, which acts transitively and freely on the fibers $\bar{\pi}^{-1}([t \to (\mathbf{E}_t, \mathbf{B}_t)])$ over the force field trajectories, and thus on PT.

Theorem 55.2-2 tells us that there are global sections $\sigma : FT \to PT$. In the theory for smooth principal bundles one had then to conclude that the bundle be trivial (only as a fiber bundle, exhibiting still interesting mathematical and physical features). A global section is a gauge selection in the usual physical sense. A distinguished gauge selection, described in Sec. 6.3.1 on page 108, is the temporal gauge, which consists of a class of potential trajectories with vanishing scalar potential. If we fix it in terms of a special potential trajectory $[t \mapsto (0, \dot{\mathbf{A}}_t)]$, all other potential trajectories of the fiber $\bar{\pi}^{-1} \circ \bar{\pi}([t \mapsto (0, \dot{\mathbf{A}}_t)])$ are obtained by the (vertical) actions of G_{PT}, since the global gauge transformations add all missing trajectories $[t \mapsto \mathbf{A}_t^{\|}]$, all $[t \mapsto u_t]$, and all $[t \mapsto \mathbf{A}_t^{co}]$, to complete the fiber.

If we also vary (horizontally) the temporal potential trajectories $[t \mapsto (0, \dot{\mathbf{A}}_t)]$, such that $\bar{\pi}([t \mapsto (0, \dot{\mathbf{A}}_t)])$ runs through the base manifold FT, then we reach in this manner all of $\mathcal{P}(\bar{\pi}, FT, G_{PT})$. We have, in other words, constructed a global trivialization $\mathcal{P}(\bar{\pi}, FT, G_{PT}) \to FT \times G_{PT}$ for the non–smooth, infinite-dimensional bundle.

If we compare the bundle of all adapted potential trajectories $\mathcal{P}(\bar{\pi}, FT, G_{PT})$ with the gauge bundle $\mathcal{P} \equiv \mathcal{P}(\pi, \mathcal{O}, U(1))$, then the former corresponds to the set $\Omega^1_{H,U(1)}(\mathcal{P}, a_0\mathbb{R})$ of all connections ω which have a global (in general non–smooth) coordinate representation $A \in \Omega^1(\mathcal{O}, a_0\mathbb{R})$, where the bundle projection $\bar{\pi}$ is in analogy to the external derivative $\mathbf{d} : \Omega^1(\mathcal{O}, a_0\mathbb{R}) \to \{F\}$, projecting onto the field tensors. But the explicit realization of that bundle in Helmholtz–Hodge decomposed form, using weak derivatives, requires just all steps of the described evaluation.

55.2.3. *Gauge Bundles for Both Cohomological Vector Potentials*

Whereas in the preceding section, we came back to the original trajectorial gauge group G_{PT}, we discuss now a genuine extension of the class of trajectorial gauge transformations, motivated by the following situation.

It is well known that only distinguished sections of the bundle $\mathcal{P}(\bar{\pi}, FT, G_{PT})$ are suited to construct a field phase space, allowing for a Hamiltonian formalism, after the material position coordinates having been supplemented. The details are expounded in Sec. 7.2, where we focussed on the temporal and Coulomb gauges. These gauge sections are characterized by merely fixing the trajectories $[t \mapsto (u_t, \mathbf{A}_t^{\|})]$ to $[t \mapsto (u_t^{\Gamma}, \mathbf{A}_t^{\|\Gamma})]$, where Γ indicates the chosen gauge. The components $\mathbf{A}_t^{\top}$ are determined by the force field trajectory, and the components $\mathbf{A}_t^{co}$ may be changed by any $h_2 \in \mathbb{H}_2$ without affecting the existence problem of a (time-independent) Hamiltonian. Thus $\mathbf{A}_t^{co}$ has in this sense still the gauge freedom described by G_P^{co}.

We must now investigate the role of A_{co}, which we always treat as a parameter function of the system.

Since A_{co} is not Helmholtz–Hodge adapted, it interferes in general with the adapted A_t, and even so with u_t respectively u_t. The detailed relationships are involved and pertain to the refined Helmholtz–Hodge decompositions of Sec. 44.4.4 on page 1596. So, only if $u_t = 0 = u_t$, we know by Theorem 6.2-2 on page 106 that any vector potential may be decomposed as $A_t = \mathbf{A}_t + A_{co}$, $\forall t \in \mathbb{R}$, where $\mathbf{A}_t = \mathbf{A}_t^{\|} \oplus \mathbf{A}_t^{co} \oplus \mathbf{A}_t^{\top}$ is Helmholtz–Hodge compatible and where $A_{co} \in W(\mathrm{curl}; \Lambda, \mathbb{R})$ refers to the time invariant $B_t^{co} \equiv \mathbf{B}^{co} = \mathrm{curl}\, A_{co} \in \mathbb{H}_1$.

In order not to disturb the dynamical, Helmholtz–Hodge adapted relationships, we employ A_{co} as potential for the cohomological magnetic field alone, and describe all other force field parts in terms of the potential $\mathbf{A}_t$. In general, one has the orthogonal splitting

$$A_{co} = A_{co}^0 \oplus A_{co}^1 \in \ker(\mathrm{curl}) \oplus \overline{\mathrm{ran}(\mathrm{curl}_0)}, \qquad (55.2.10)$$

with unique $A_{co}^1 = \mathrm{curl}|^{-1} \mathbf{B}^{co} \in \overline{\mathrm{ran}(\mathrm{curl}_0)} \cap W(\mathrm{curl}; \Lambda, \mathbb{R})$, and non–unique

$$A_{co}^0 \in \ker(\mathrm{curl}) = \overline{\mathrm{ran}(\mathrm{grad})} \oplus \mathbb{H}_1 \subset W(\mathrm{curl}; \Lambda, \mathbb{R}).$$

Whereas A_{co}^1 has no gradient representation, one knows from Theorem 44.4-10 on page 1590 — with Standard Assumption for *interior* Λ presupposed — that

$$A_{co}^0 = \mathrm{grad}\, \eta \oplus \nabla\varphi \in \mathrm{ran}(\mathrm{grad}) \oplus \mathbb{H}_1 = \ker(\mathrm{curl}),$$

for unique $\eta \in W^1(\Lambda, \mathbb{R})$ and unique $\varphi \in W^1(\Lambda_{\mathrm{cut}}, \mathbb{R})$ (unique up to a constant). Here, grad is the gradient in all of Λ, whereas $\nabla\varphi \in \mathbb{H}_1$ is the gradient of φ in the cut cavity Λ_{cut} and not in the whole of our interior region Λ. φ is a harmonic element in $W^1(\Lambda_{\mathrm{cut}}, \mathbb{R})$, which makes jumps with constant height along each cut Σ_j, $j \in \{1, \ldots, b_1\}$,

$$\varphi|_{\Sigma_j^+} - \varphi|_{\Sigma_j^-} = [\varphi]_{\Sigma_j} = c_j, \quad \text{(jump constant along the cut } \Sigma_j\text{)}.$$

(The c_j depend on φ.) Especially, provided there is some suitable integrability for η and φ, a closed curve integral in Λ is calculated in terms of the jump constants,

$$\underset{\text{closed curve}}{\oint} A_{co}^0 \cdot d\mathbf{s} = \underbrace{\oint \mathrm{grad}\, \eta \cdot d\mathbf{s}}_{=0} + \oint \nabla\varphi \cdot d\mathbf{s} = \underset{\text{crossed cuts}}{\sum} \pm c_j, \qquad (55.2.11)$$

with summation over the traversed cuts by the closed curve, where the sign $\pm$ arises from crossing the cut Σ_j, from the side Σ_j^+ to the side Σ_j^-, or conversely. These relations persist also in the case of a C^∞-boundary $\partial\Lambda$, where one may show (with regularity arguments from Sec. 44.4.6 on page 1600) that automatically

$$\eta \in C^\infty(\bar{\Lambda}, \mathbb{R}), \qquad \mathbf{B}^{co}, A_{co}^0, A_{co}^1, \nabla\varphi \in C^\infty(\bar{\Lambda}, \mathbb{R}^3),$$

but that nevertheless $\varphi \in C_b^\infty(\Lambda_{\text{cut}}, \mathbb{R})$ makes constant jumps at the cuts. (Observe that the boundary of Λ_{cut} — in contradistinction to that of Λ — is never smooth at the intersections of the cuts with $\partial\Lambda$.)

The gradient term $\text{grad}\,\eta$ possibly may be shifted via the splitting of Proposition 55.2-4 to the Helmholtz–Hodge compatible potentials, leading eventually only to additional time constant scalar potentials relevant for $\mathbf{A}_t^\|$ and $\mathbf{A}_t^{\text{co}}$, but not relevant (by its time independence) for the scalar potential u_t. So the essential term in $\mathbf{A}_{\text{co}}^0$, providing additional information, is $\nabla\varphi$. This consideration suggests to renounce on the $\text{grad}\,\eta$-term and to include only $\mathbf{A}_{\text{co}}^0 = \nabla\varphi$ into the parameter function $\mathbf{A}_{\text{co}}$.

Assumption 55.2-6 (Allowed Vector Potentials for $\mathbf{B}^{\text{co}}$). The trivial part $\mathbf{A}_{\text{co}}^0 \in \ker(\text{curl})$ of the vector potential (55.2.10), corresponding to the cohomological magnetic field $\mathbf{B}^{\text{co}}$, is restricted to the first cohomological space, i.e., we only allow $\mathbf{A}_{\text{co}}^0 \in \mathbb{H}_1 \subset \ker(\text{curl})$.

Summarizing we may write $\mathbf{A}_{\text{co}}^0 = \nabla\varphi_{\text{co}}$ with φ_{co} from the specified harmonic subspace $H_c(\Lambda_{\text{cut}}, \mathbb{R}) \subset W^1(\Lambda_{\text{cut}}, \mathbb{R})$ exhibiting constant jumps along the cuts and fulfilling some more specifications found in Theorem 44.4-10. Notice that the number of cuts, but not their exact position, is fixed in the definition of $H_c(\Lambda_{\text{cut}}, \mathbb{R})$. Nevertheless one knows that $H_c(\Lambda_{\text{cut}}, \mathbb{R})$ is finite-dimensional for interior Λ satisfying the Standard Assumption.

Since in any case, we have $\mathbf{A}_{\text{co}}^0 \in \ker(\text{curl})$, it holds $\mathbf{B}^{\text{co}} = \text{curl}(\mathbf{A}_{\text{co}}^0 + \mathbf{A}_{\text{co}}^1) = \text{curl}\,\mathbf{A}_{\text{co}}^1$, so that physics does not depend on varying $\mathbf{A}_{\text{co}}^0 = \nabla\varphi_{\text{co}}$ over $\mathbb{H}_1$ by adding the gauge terms $\nabla\lambda_{\text{co}}$ with $\lambda_{\text{co}} \in H_c(\Lambda_{\text{cut}}, \mathbb{R})$.

Definition 55.2-7 (First Cohomological Gauge Group). Assume the Standard Assumption for an interior region $\Lambda \subset \mathbb{R}^3$.

The space $H_c(\Lambda_{\text{cut}}, \mathbb{R})$ — which determines the admissible scalar potential only in a chosen Λ_{cut}, but not in all of Λ — defines the group $G_{\text{P, co}}$ of gauge transformations, allowed for a fixed time-independent cohomological magnetic field $\mathbf{B}^{\text{co}} \in \mathbb{H}_1$.

Formally, we may associate again $G_{\text{PT, co}}$ with elements of $\mathsf{X}_{x \in \mathcal{O}} U(1)$, and we keep in mind that $G_{\text{P, co}}$ inherits the topological features of the first cohomology group $\mathbb{H}_1$.

Conclusion 55.2-8 (Cohomological Gauge Freedom). For the gauge behavior of a material system coupled to the electrodynamic field (both systems quantized or not) one has to take into account the full trajectorial gauge group

$$G_{\text{PT}} \times G_{\text{P, co}} = G_{\text{PT}}^\| \times G_{\text{P}}^{\text{co}} \times G_{\text{P, co}} \subset \mathsf{X}_{x \in \mathcal{O}} U(1). \qquad (55.2.12)$$

The usual global gauge fixing of Theoretical Physics concerns only $G_{\text{PT}}^\|$, which transforms $\mathbf{A}_t^\|$, as is especially the case for temporal, Coulomb, and Lorenz gauges. The mentioned gauges do not fix completely a global gauge section. A completely fixed gauge Γ determines in our interpretation just a single global section

$$\sigma^\Gamma : \mathrm{FT} \to \mathrm{PT}, \quad \text{with} \quad \bar{\pi} \circ \sigma^\Gamma = \mathrm{id}_{\mathrm{FT}}. \tag{55.2.13}$$

Under fixed $\mathbf{A}_t^{\parallel}$, the physical dynamics satisfies still the condition to be invariant against the actions of $\mathrm{G}_\mathrm{P}^{\mathrm{co}}$ and $\mathrm{G}_{\mathrm{P,\,co}}$, which correspond to time-invariant gauge "functions". That is, for $h_1 \in \mathbb{H}_1$ and $h_2 \in \mathbb{H}_2$, each potential trajectory $[t \to (u_t^\Gamma, \mathbf{A}_t^\Gamma)] \in \mathrm{PT}$ conforming to the gauge Γ, may still be transformed into $[t \to (u_t^\Gamma, \mathbf{A}_t^\Gamma + h_1 + h_2)]$, without changing the down projected path $\bar{\pi}\big([t \to (u_t^\Gamma, \mathbf{A}_t^\Gamma))]\big)$. If $h_1 \neq 0$, the transformed potential trajectory is, however, no longer in PT, by the mere definition of our set of adapted potential trajectories PT: Rather that transformation, which alters A_{co}, leads to another field "system", according to our present terminology.

We come here to a conflict between bundle geometry and usual physical practice in the non-relativistic domain. In some weaker form, that conflict is already present for $\mathrm{G}_\mathrm{P}^{\mathrm{co}}$. Let us assume that we have first $\mathbf{A}_t^{\parallel}$ fixed by a gauge Γ, which allows for a Hamiltonian and canonical formalism, and let then vary $\mathbf{A}_t^{\mathrm{co}}$ and A_{co} under the action of $\mathrm{G}_\mathrm{P}^{\mathrm{co}} \times \mathrm{G}_{\mathrm{P,\,co}}$. In order to express the geometric-topological structure of that situation, one would form a principal gauge bundle of the kind $\mathcal{P}_\Gamma :=$ $\mathcal{P}_\Gamma(\bar{\pi}, \mathrm{FT}, \mathrm{G}_\mathrm{P}^{\mathrm{co}} \times \mathrm{G}_{\mathrm{P,\,co}})$, the fibers of which arising from the action of $\mathrm{G}_\mathrm{P}^{\mathrm{co}} \times \mathrm{G}_{\mathrm{P,\,co}}$ onto $[t \to (u_t^\Gamma, \mathbf{A}_t^\Gamma)]$.

That would imply, that the states of the electrodynamic system, which includes charged matter, must then refer to associated bundles for $\mathcal{P}_\Gamma$.

Geometrically, $\mathcal{P}_\Gamma$ would describe only the basic geometric-topological features of $\mathcal{O} = \mathrm{T} \times \Lambda$, that is of Λ: That means in first line the multi-connectedness expressed by b_1 and the number b_2 of inserted conductors (if we assume the Standard Assumption). For that interpretation, $\mathrm{G}_\mathrm{P}^{\mathrm{co}} \times \mathrm{G}_{\mathrm{P,\,co}}$, as structure group, is not large enough since it depends on the locations of the "obstacles" in Λ, as do the force fields for themselves, the base manifold in the present concept of a gauge bundle.

$\mathrm{G}_{\mathrm{P,\,co}}$ is introduced to depend even on the virtual geometry of the cuts which make Λ simply connected. These cuts are, however, to a large extent arbitrary. In the theory of local smooth principal bundles the choice of the cuts would correspond to a construction of a coordinated gauge bundle $\mathcal{P} \equiv \mathcal{P}(\pi, \mathcal{O}, U(1), \tau)$, the overlap regions of which covering the cuts. (This is similar to the twist of the Möbius band.) In order to arrive at a more geometric principal gauge bundle one would be forced to admit gauge transformations, which shift and deform the cuts.

For calculations, one works with a fixed section of the associated bundle, what implies a selection of the potentials and of the two types of gauge phases, namely of φ_i^{co}, $1 \leq i \leq b_2$ and $\varphi_{\mathrm{co}\,i}$, $1 \leq i \leq b_1$, over Λ. The choice of the phases has no influence on the force fields.

The phase effects of quantum theory assign the phase selections φ_i^{co} and $\varphi_{\mathrm{co}\,j}$ of the sections of the mentioned associated bundles an additional meaning but, again, only phase differences govern the observable effects.

Let us finally mention that the transition functions (in the sense of Sec. 38.1.3) for *mesoscopic* radiating systems depend also on the topological features of the cavity. They determine the radiating current and may lead to topological aspects of the classical part of the radiation in multiply connected wave guides.

55.2.4. *Reduction to the Generalized Coulomb Gauge by Time Fixing*

We have introduced in Sec. 6.3.3 on page 113 a generalized Coulomb gauge by requiring $\frac{d\mathbf{A}_t^{\parallel}}{dt} = 0$, $\forall t \in \mathbb{R}$. (Whereas the usual more restricted Coulomb gauge condition is $\nabla \cdot \mathbf{A}_t = 0$, $\forall t \in \mathbb{R}$, which is equivalent via the Helmholtz–Hodge decomposition to $\mathbf{A}_t^{\parallel} = 0$, $\forall t \in \mathbb{R}$.) We have discussed in Chapter 21 how the merits of the usual Coulomb condition are preserved under the generalized Coulomb gauge condition, where the $\mathbf{A}_t^{\parallel}$ may be still gauge transformed by the time-independent gauge functions $\lambda^{\parallel} \in W_0^1(\Lambda, \mathbb{R})$. The scalar potential u_t can, however, no longer be gauge transformed what conforms well to its meaning as material binding potential which is especially responsible for the approximate stability of the microscopic clusters. The time parameter t has in the generalized Coulomb gauge the character of an adiabatic parameter, the derivatives to which being neglected.

So, for the gauge theory, the space-time manifold $\mathcal{O}$ is reduced to $\mathcal{O}_t = \{t\} \times \Lambda$, with fixed adiabatic time $t \in \mathbb{R}$ and with the spatial domain Λ. The various parts of the vector potential transform then under the total time-independent gauge group

$$G_P \times G_{P,co} = G_P^{\parallel} \times G_P^{co} \times G_{P,\,co} \subset X_{x \in \Lambda}\, U(1), \quad G_P^{\parallel} = W_0^1(\Lambda, \mathbb{R}), \qquad (55.2.14)$$

where the indicated inclusion relation is again only a formal one.

$G_P \times G_{P,co}$ is a genuine subgroup of $G_{PT} \times G_{P,\,co}$ from Eq. (55.2.12), since now the longitudinal gauge functions are time-independent (respectively are adiabatically dependent on time). Thus only $G_P^{\parallel} = W_0^1(\Lambda, \mathbb{R})$ survives, as part of the previous dynamical gauge group, and the projection $\bar{\pi}$ degenerates to $\pi = \mathrm{curl}_0$, a kind of 3-dimensional exterior derivative.

But also our "system function" $\mathbf{A}_{co}$ may be gauge transformed by $\nabla \lambda_{co}$, still under the headline "Coulomb gauge". In the version as a (local) 1-form, we have carried out a detailed analysis of that gauge behavior in Sec. 55.1.4, making explicit the adiabatic time parameter. The adiabatic time variation concerns in first line possible changes of external conditions comprising the enclosed magnetic fluxes outside of Λ. The boundary conditions are now definitely incorporated into the trajectorial gauge group $G_{P,co}$.

We had formulated in Sec. 55.1.6 only heuristically the homotopic limits $U_j^t \rightarrow \{t\} \times \Sigma_j, 1 \leq j \leq b_1$, indicating the convergence of a 3-dimensional transition region U_j^t of a gauge bundle $\mathcal{P}(\pi, \mathcal{O}_t, U(1))$ to a 2-dimensional cut surface Σ_j, what led us back to the non-continuous gauge functions of our approach. Nevertheless we feel justified to take over certain results of smooth bundle theory to the present non–smooth trajectory formulation.

Especially, it had turned out, that $\mathbf{A}_{co}$ is the cause for the quantization of the external magnetic flux if the interior $\mathbf{B}$-field vanishes. The external magnetic flux through a surface Σ_c, with the boundary curve c lying in Λ, is well expressible by the line integral $\oint_c \mathcal{A}_{co}$, in spite of Λ exhibiting a non-trivial geometry with the first and second cohomology groups not vanishing. (Usually only a global 1-form, as e.g., the connection form associated with the local vector potentials, allows for a well-defined line integral.)

Within the realm of non-relativistic ED, we see no possibility — and no necessity — to quantize the $\mathcal{A}_{co}$-potentials. There is no canonical formalism available for these fields. That contrasts gauge theory for elementary particles, where just the peculiar topological properties of vector potentials, like those of $\mathcal{A}_{co}$, are made responsible for internal quantum numbers and for the types of interaction forces, and one invests much efforts to quantize these fields. The present $\mathcal{A}_{co}$-fields carry, however, global features being connected with gradients of harmonic functions.

Neither $G_{P,\,co}$ nor G_P^{co} are diminished in size by time fixing. In spite of being intimately related with the second cohomological group $\mathbb{H}_2$, there are no discrete topological parameters related with the Helmholtz–Hodge compatible $\mathbf{A}^{co}$-potentials, respective, with the $\mathbf{B}^{co}$-fields. That is a consequence of the divergence-freeness of both field types (if no magnetic monopoles are included). Then the integrals over closed surfaces vanish, and topological characteristika, like Chern numbers, become trivial. Also the $\mathbf{A}^{co}$-fields are related with gradients of harmonic functions.

The $\mathbf{A}^{co}$-potentials are quantizable, but retain their global character and do not exhibit a physical particle structure. If one associates the $\mathbf{A}^{co}$ with charges at the boundaries and currents, one obtains a kind of global respectively macroscopic quantum observables.

In any case, there is still a rich gauge theory with interesting topological effects under our generalized Coulomb condition. Clearly, time fixing breaks relativistic covariance. But our experimental perception of the mesoscopic radiating systems is indeed bound to an inertial system and shows us clustered structures stabilized by classical longitudinal binding fields. That forms the basis for analyzing matter in terms of photonic radiation, even if the radiating bodies travel away from us with large velocities. As the narrow Coulomb gauge serves well in usual quantum optics, our generalized Coulomb gauge seems to be sufficient for the theory of mesoscopic radiators with non-trivial topology.

55.3. Gauges, Wave Equations and Causality in Free Space

Causality problems in the usual Coulomb Gauge are investigated in the paper: O.L. Brill and B. Goodman, Causality in the Coulomb gauge, *Am. J. Phys.* **35** (1967) 832–837. In physics, "causality" does not only mean that the effect must occur later than the cause but that — in accordance with relativity theory — the time dependent effects do not propagate faster than light from the cause. In this sense, an instantaneous action contradicts causality. An instantaneous action seems to occur for the Coulomb potentials and the longitudinal electric fields. On the other side, fields derived from a wave equation — as arising for the potentials in the Lorenz gauge — satisfy automatically causality in the concise physical sense, provided one takes into account only times later than the "initial time". If one deals with times prior to the "initial time" one gains "anti–causal" solutions.

We investigate in the present section aspects of causality in a more general context than in the cited paper continuing and sharpening our previous considerations on electrodynamic wave equations in the special case of free space, and come back to the original question only at the end of this section.

For the convenience of the reader, the present supplementary section is formulated in a self–contained manner.

55.3.1. *The Setup*

The present investigation is based on a combination of our rigorous mathematical results from Chapters 4, 5, and 44 with the usual heuristic treatments in physical textbooks on classical electrodynamics. This is justified by the fact that we discuss Maxwell's vacuum equations only in free space $\mathbb{R}^3$. Then the occurring gradient, divergence, and curl operators in L^2–Hilbert spaces are unique. That contrasts the case of a proper subregion $\Lambda \subset \mathbb{R}^3$ where the differential vector operators depend on the boundary conditions. The boundary conditions may prevent an only locally valid equation like

$$\nabla \times (\nabla \times \mathbf{G}) = \nabla(\nabla \cdot \mathbf{G}) - \Delta\mathbf{G} \qquad (55.3.1)$$

to be valid on certain operator cores and, by this, may be non-extendable. Assuming differentiable vector fields $\mathbf{G} : \mathbb{R}^3 \to \mathbb{R}^3$, we shall make use of that formula in the following calculations (see the standard relations from vector analysis summarized in Proposition 2.3-1), where the Laplacian Δ acts component–wise.

We work at first directly with the electric and magnetic force fields, for which we use the standard notation: $\mathbf{E}(t, x) \equiv \mathbf{E}_t(x) \in \mathbb{R}^3$ is the electric field at time $t \in \mathbb{R}$ and position $x \in \mathbb{R}^3$, and $\mathbf{B}(t, x) \equiv \mathbf{B}_t(x) \in \mathbb{R}^3$ is the magnetic induction, also simply called "magnetic field" (as we are working in vacuum). The current and charge densities are denoted by $\mathbf{j}(t, x) \equiv \mathbf{j}_t(x) \in \mathbb{R}^3$ and $\rho(t, x) \equiv \rho_t(x) \in \mathbb{R}$, respectively.

The occurring vector and scalar fields are supposed to be square integrable over $x \in \mathbb{R}^3$ for each $t \in \mathbb{R}$, that is,

$$\mathbf{E}_t \in L^2(\mathbb{R}^3, \mathbb{R}^3), \quad \mathbf{B}_t \in L^2(\mathbb{R}^3, \mathbb{R}^3), \quad \mathbf{j}_t \in L^2(\mathbb{R}^3, \mathbb{R}^3), \quad \rho_t \in L^2(\mathbb{R}^3, \mathbb{R}).$$

In our notation, the real Hilbert space $L^2(\mathbb{R}^3, \mathbb{R}^3)$ consists of all square integrable vector fields $\mathbf{F} : \mathbb{R}^3 \to \mathbb{R}^3$, $x \mapsto \mathbf{F}(x)$, whereas the real Hilbert space $L^2(\mathbb{R}^3, \mathbb{R})$

denotes the space of all square integrable scalar fields $\varrho : \mathbb{R}^3 \to \mathbb{R}$, $x \mapsto \varrho(x)$. Especially, the map $t \mapsto \mathbf{E}_t$ is meant as a field trajectory within the Hilbert space $L^2(\mathbb{R}^3, \mathbb{R}^3)$.

The ∇–operator turns out to act in, or between, these real Hilbert spaces in three different types as follows: The curl $\nabla \times$. acts selfadjointly in $L^2(\mathbb{R}^3, \mathbb{R}^3)$, the gradient $\nabla.$ from $L^2(\mathbb{R}^3, \mathbb{R})$ into $L^2(\mathbb{R}^3, \mathbb{R}^3)$, whereas the divergence $\nabla \cdot$. maps $L^2(\mathbb{R}^3, \mathbb{R}^3)$ into $L^2(\mathbb{R}^3, \mathbb{R})$. The gradient and the divergence are adjoint to each other. Aligning with our former notations, here in free space $\mathbb{R}^3$, the mentioned uniqueness of these unbounded but closed Hilbert operators is (due to the Sections 10.2 and 44.8)

$$\nabla \times . = \mathrm{curl} = \mathrm{curl}_0 \,, \quad \nabla \cdot . = \mathrm{div} = \mathrm{div}_0 \,, \quad \nabla. = \mathrm{grad} = \mathrm{grad}_0 \,. \qquad (55.3.2)$$

(In contrast, for a proper region $\Lambda \subset \mathbb{R}^3$ with conductor boundary conditions the operators with the index "0" are different to the one without, respectively.)

We omit a detailed discussion of the domains of definition (suitable Sobolev spaces) in order to maintain a better overview on the reasoning and to be nearer to theoretical physics treatments. Let us mention, however, that the mathematical argumentation may be sharpened in the manner of our previous elaborations of vector operators.

When performing concrete integral expression, in addition to square integrability, the fields should possess some more properties such as continuity, differentiability, or sufficiently fast vanishing at infinity, in order that certain manipulations be possible. We call such fields "sufficiently smooth".

Notational Remark 55.3-1 (IV, IVP, and WE). Occasionally we briefly write "IVP" for "initial value problem", meaning a set of differential equations together with some specified initial value(s), the latter being denoted by "IV". The symbol "WE" abbreviates "wave equation(s)".

Let us always take $t = 0$ for the initial time. One is primarily interested in solutions for the future of the initial time, that is for $t \geq 0$.

55.3.2. *The Helmholtz–Hodge Decomposition in Free Space*

The Hilbert space $L^2(\mathbb{R}^3, \mathbb{R}^3)$ decomposes uniquely into a direct sum of two orthogonal sub–Hilbert spaces, that are the spaces of longitudinal fields and of transversal fields, $L^2_\parallel(\mathbb{R}^3, \mathbb{R}^3)$ and $L^2_\top(\mathbb{R}^3, \mathbb{R}^3)$ respectively, and we write

$$L^2(\mathbb{R}^3, \mathbb{R}^3) = L^2_\parallel(\mathbb{R}^3, \mathbb{R}^3) \oplus L^2_\top(\mathbb{R}^3, \mathbb{R}^3) \,, \quad \mathbf{F} = \mathbf{F}^\parallel + \mathbf{F}^\top \,,$$

if $\mathbf{F} \in L^2(\mathbb{R}^3, \mathbb{R}^3)$. The associated orthogonal projections are denoted by $P^\parallel$ and $P^\top$, respectively. The cohomology spaces $\mathbb{H}_1$ and $\mathbb{H}_2$ are, of course, trivial for the free space $\mathbb{R}^3$. (Note that $P^\top$ coincides with P_{div} from Eq. (44.8.5), when one specializes there to $r = 3$.)

As a side remark, let us mention that also for cubic cavities with periodic boundary conditions, which most frequently replace free space in quantum optics, the spaces $\mathbb{H}_1$ and $\mathbb{H}_2$ are not completely trivial (see Section 44.7).

The longitudinal sub–Hilbert space $L_\parallel^2(\mathbb{R}^3, \mathbb{R}^3) \subset L^2(\mathbb{R}^3, \mathbb{R}^3)$ coincides with the kernel $\ker(\nabla \times .)$ of the curl and also with the closure of the image (= range) of the gradient. The transversal sub–Hilbert space $L_\top^2(\mathbb{R}^3, \mathbb{R}^3)$ coincides with the kernel $\ker(\nabla \cdot .)$ of the divergence and also with the closure of the range of the curl. In formulas

$$L_\parallel^2(\mathbb{R}^3, \mathbb{R}^3) = \ker(\nabla \times .) = \overline{\mathrm{ran}(\nabla.)}, \qquad (55.3.3)$$

$$L_\top^2(\mathbb{R}^3, \mathbb{R}^3) = \ker(\nabla \cdot .) = \overline{\mathrm{ran}(\nabla \times .)}. \qquad (55.3.4)$$

Thus the relations

$$\nabla \times \mathbf{F}^\parallel(x) = 0\,, \quad \nabla \cdot \mathbf{F}^\top(x) = 0\,, \quad \forall x \in \mathbb{R}^3 \qquad (55.3.5)$$

are necessary and sufficient for the pertinent field parts. Especially, the gradient fields $\nabla \varrho(x)$ are longitudinal, since $\nabla \times (\nabla \varrho) = 0$ for $\varrho \in L^2(\mathbb{R}^3, \mathbb{R})$, what may be expressed by $\mathrm{ran}(\nabla.) \subset L_\parallel^2(\mathbb{R}^3, \mathbb{R}^3)$ according to Eq. (55.3.3). The latter version uses the language of Hilbert space operators, which we here mix with the usual formulations in theoretical physics.

If one separates off the kernels from their domains of definition, the divergence and the curl become invertible operators. We formulate this useful observation, in combination with some notation, as a lemma.

Lemma 55.3-2 (Inverted Divergence and Inverted Curl). *If we restrict the divergence operator $\nabla \cdot .$ to the longitudinal fields $L_\parallel^2(\mathbb{R}^3, \mathbb{R}^3)$ it has a dense image in $L^2(\mathbb{R}^3, \mathbb{R})$ and is (uniquely) invertible. Its inverse is denoted by $(\nabla \cdot |^\parallel)^{-1}$.*

Analogously we have that the restricted curl $\nabla \times .$ acts injectively on the transversal fields $L_\top^2(\mathbb{R}^3, \mathbb{R}^3)$ and has a dense image in $L^2(\mathbb{R}^3, \mathbb{R}^3)$. Its (unique) inverse is denoted by $(\nabla \times |^\top)^{-1}$.

Let us also mention that the gradient operator $\nabla.$ acts injectively on $L^2(\mathbb{R}^3, \mathbb{R})$ with dense image in $L_\parallel^2(\mathbb{R}^3, \mathbb{R}^3)$.

It is immediate now that the above orthogonal projections write with the inverted divergence and curl as

$$P^\parallel = (\nabla \cdot |^\parallel)^{-1} \nabla \cdot . \quad \text{and} \quad P^\top = (\nabla \times |^\top)^{-1} \nabla \times . \qquad (55.3.6)$$

both acting on $L^2(\mathbb{R}^3, \mathbb{R}^3)$.

It is a specific feature of the free space $\mathbb{R}^3$, that the foregoing inverse operators as well as the orthogonal projections may be formulated in terms of concrete integral expressions which we want to supplement.

Proposition 55.3-3. *For sufficiently smooth scalar fields* $\varrho \in L^2(\mathbb{R}^3, \mathbb{R})$ *and sufficiently smooth transversal vector fields* $\mathbf{K}^\top \in L^2_\top(\mathbb{R}^3, \mathbb{R}^3)$ *it holds*

$$((\nabla \cdot |^\|)^{-1}\varrho)(x) = -\frac{1}{4\pi}\nabla \int_{\mathbb{R}^3} d^3y \, \frac{\varrho(y)}{|x - y|} \, ,$$

$$\hspace{8cm} \forall x \in \mathbb{R}^3. \hspace{1cm} (55.3.7)$$

$$((\nabla \times |^\|)^{-1}\mathbf{K}^\top)(x) = \frac{1}{4\pi}\nabla \times \int_{\mathbb{R}^3} d^3y \, \frac{\mathbf{K}^\top(y)}{|x - y|} \, ,$$

The orthogonal projections $P^\|$ *and* $P^\top$ *are given for sufficiently smooth fields* $\mathbf{F} \in L^2(\mathbb{R}^3, \mathbb{R}^3)$ *by the integrals*

$$(P^\|\mathbf{F})(x) = \mathbf{F}^\|(x) = -\frac{1}{4\pi}\nabla \int_{\mathbb{R}^3} d^3y \, \frac{(\nabla \cdot \mathbf{F})(y)}{|x - y|} \, ,$$

$$\hspace{8cm} \forall x \in \mathbb{R}^3. \hspace{1cm} (55.3.8)$$

$$(P^\top\mathbf{F})(x) = \mathbf{F}^\top(x) = \frac{1}{4\pi}\nabla \times \int_{\mathbb{R}^3} d^3y \, \frac{(\nabla \times \mathbf{F})(y)}{|x - y|} \, ,$$

Proof. The proof is divided into four steps.

(a) For the sufficiently smooth field $\mathbf{F} \in L^2(\mathbb{R}^3, \mathbb{R}^3)$ let us define

$$\mathbf{G}(x) := -\frac{1}{4\pi}\int_{\mathbb{R}^3} d^3y \, \frac{\mathbf{F}(y)}{|x - y|} \, , \hspace{1cm} \forall x \in \mathbb{R}^3.$$

With the well known relation

$$\delta(x - y) = -\frac{1}{4\pi}\Delta_x \frac{1}{|x - y|} \, ,$$

and with formula (55.3.1) one gets

$$\mathbf{F}(x) = \int_{\mathbb{R}^3} d^3y \, \mathbf{F}(y) \, \delta(x - y) = \Delta\mathbf{G}(x) \overset{(55.3.1)}{=} \underbrace{\nabla(\nabla \cdot \mathbf{G})(x)}_{=:\, \mathbf{F}_1} \underbrace{-\nabla \times (\nabla \times \mathbf{G})(x)}_{=:\, \mathbf{F}_2} \, .$$

Since $\mathbf{F}_1 \in \mathrm{ran}(\nabla.) \subset L^2_\|(\mathbb{R}^3, \mathbb{R}^3)$ (cf. Eq. (55.3.3)) is a gradient field, it is longitudinal, that is $\mathbf{F}_1 = \mathbf{F}^\|$. Since $\mathbf{F}_2 \in \mathrm{ran}(\nabla \times.) \subset L^2_\top(\mathbb{R}^3, \mathbb{R}^3)$ (cf. formula (55.3.4)), we conclude $\mathbf{F}_2 = \mathbf{F}^\top$. (Alternatively one may work with the unique characterization (55.3.5).)

(b) A consequence of the Gauss law is the formula for partial integration

$$\int_{\mathbb{R}^3} d^3y \, \frac{\partial^n \varphi(y)}{\partial y_1^{n_1} \partial y_2^{n_2} \partial y_3^{n_3}} \, \phi(y) = (-1)^n \int_{\mathbb{R}^3} d^3y \, \varphi(y) \, \frac{\partial^n \phi(y)}{\partial y_1^{n_1} \partial y_2^{n_2} \partial y_3^{n_3}} \, ,$$

where $n = n_1 + n_2 + n_3$ with $n_k \in \mathbb{N}_0$. Here $\varphi : \mathbb{R}^3 \to \mathbb{C}$ and $\phi : \mathbb{R}^3 \to \mathbb{C}$ are n–times continuously differentiable scalar field functions, where one of these scalar fields has to possess a *compact* support. The latter ensures that the boundary integral outside of the compact support vanishes. This partial integration may be extended via the convergence theorems of Lebesgue to less smooth scalar fields φ and ϕ, where at least one of these has to vanish sufficiently fast at infinity.

For an arbitrary function $f : \mathbb{R} \to \mathbb{C}$, $\xi \mapsto f(\xi)$ we apply partial integration (PI) to the product $\mathbb{R}^3 \ni y \mapsto \mathbf{F}(y) f(|x - y|)$ with a sufficiently smooth vector field $\mathbf{F} \in \mathrm{L}^2(\mathbb{R}^3, \mathbb{R}^3)$. First note that $\nabla_x f(|x - y|) = -\nabla_y f(|x - y|)$. Then we get

$$
\nabla \cdot \int_{\mathbb{R}^3} d^3 y \, \mathbf{F}(y) \, f(|x - y|) = \int_{\mathbb{R}^3} d^3 y \, \mathbf{F}(y) \cdot \nabla_x f(|x - y|)
$$

$$
= - \int_{\mathbb{R}^3} d^3 y \, \mathbf{F}(y) \cdot \nabla_y f(|x - y|) \overset{\mathrm{PI}}{=} \int_{\mathbb{R}^3} d^3 y \, (\nabla \cdot \mathbf{F})(y) \, f(|x - y|) .
$$

$$(55.3.9)$$

Moreover, with $\nabla_x \mathbf{F}(y) f(|x - y|) = -\mathbf{F}(y) \times \nabla_x f(|x - y|)$ by the standard vector relation (2.3.5), it follows that

$$
\nabla \times \int_{\mathbb{R}^3} d^3 y \, \mathbf{F}(y) \, f(|x - y|) = - \int_{\mathbb{R}^3} d^3 y \, \mathbf{F}(y) \times \nabla_x f(|x - y|)
$$

$$
= \int_{\mathbb{R}^3} d^3 y \, \mathbf{F}(y) \times \nabla_y f(|x - y|) \overset{\mathrm{PI}}{=} \int_{\mathbb{R}^3} d^3 y \, (\nabla \times \mathbf{F})(y) \, f(|x - y|) .
$$

$$(55.3.10)$$

(c) Specializing (b) to the special function $f(\xi) = \frac{1}{\xi}$ leads to

$$
\nabla \cdot \int_{\mathbb{R}^3} d^3 y \, \frac{\mathbf{F}(y)}{|x - y|} = \int_{\mathbb{R}^3} d^3 y \, \frac{(\nabla \cdot \mathbf{F})(y)}{|x - y|} ,
$$

$$
\nabla \times \int_{\mathbb{R}^3} d^3 y \, \frac{\mathbf{F}(y)}{|x - y|} = \int_{\mathbb{R}^3} d^3 y \, \frac{(\nabla \times \mathbf{F})(y)}{|x - y|} ,
$$

$$\forall x \in \mathbb{R}^3. \qquad (55.3.11)$$

For the field $\mathbf{G}$ defined in (a), the first expression coincides with $-4\pi \nabla \cdot \mathbf{G}$ and the second one with $-4\pi \nabla \times \mathbf{G}$. This yields (55.3.8).

(d) Set $\varrho := \nabla \cdot \mathbf{F}$ and $\mathbf{K}^\top := \nabla \times \mathbf{F}$. Then (55.3.6) ensures $(\nabla \cdot |^\|)^{-1} \varrho = P^\| \mathbf{F}$ and $(\nabla \times |^\top)^{-1} \mathbf{K}^\top = P^\top \mathbf{F}$. Now (55.3.7) follows from (55.3.8). Note that the divergence and the curl have dense images in $\mathrm{L}^2(\mathbb{R}^3, \mathbb{R})$ and $\mathrm{L}^2_\top(\mathbb{R}^3, \mathbb{R}^3)$, respectively. □

The results of the preceding Proposition demonstrate especially relations indicated in (55.3.3) and (55.3.4),

$$
(\nabla \cdot |^\|)^{-1} \varrho, \; P^\| \mathbf{F} \in \mathrm{ran}(\nabla \cdot) \subset \mathrm{L}^2_\|(\mathbb{R}^3, \mathbb{R}^3) ,
$$

$$
(\nabla \times |^\top)^{-1} \mathbf{K}^\top, \; P^\top \mathbf{F} \in \mathrm{ran}(\nabla \times \cdot) \subset \mathrm{L}^2_\top(\mathbb{R}^3, \mathbb{R}^3) .
$$

Besides that, the inverse $(\nabla \cdot)^{-1}$ (on the longitudinal fields) of the gradient operator arises by inverting the first part of (55.3.8), which leads to

$$
((\nabla \cdot)^{-1} \mathbf{K}^\|)(x) = -\frac{1}{4\pi} \int_{\mathbb{R}^3} d^3 y \, \frac{(\nabla \cdot \mathbf{K}^\|)(y)}{|x - y|} \; \in \mathrm{L}^2(\mathbb{R}^3, \mathbb{R}) ,
$$

for sufficiently smooth $\mathbf{K}^\| \in \mathrm{L}^2_\|(\mathbb{R}^3, \mathbb{R}^3)$.

Definition 55.3-4 (Non–Locality of an L²–Operator). Let be given an operator O defined on scalar or vector fields, that is on $\mathrm{L}^2(\mathbb{R}^3, \mathbb{R})$ or $\mathrm{L}^2(\mathbb{R}^3, \mathbb{R}^3)$, respectively, or between such spaces. Then O is called "non–local", if for some field function $\mathbf{F} : \mathbb{R}^3 \to \mathbb{R}^{(3)}$ with compact support $\mathrm{supp}(\mathbf{F})$, the transformed field $O\mathbf{F} : \mathbb{R}^3 \to \mathbb{R}^{(3)}$ possesses non–vanishing values outside of $\mathrm{supp}(\mathbf{F})$.

Mostly we deal, however, with a stronger form of non–locality where, for compact supp($\mathbf{F}$), supp($O\mathbf{F}$) is far from being compact.

Note, in contrast to non–locality, every differential operator acts locally. The integral formulas in the Eqs. (55.3.7) and (55.3.8) demonstrate well the stronger form of non–locality for the inverse operators $(\nabla \cdot |^{\|})^{-1}$ and $(\nabla \times |^{\top})^{-1}$, and for the orthogonal projections $P^{\|}$ and $P^{\top}$, and for the inverse gradient as well.

So, for each $t \in \mathbb{R}$, we may (uniquely) decompose the electric and magnetic fields, together with the current density, into their longitudinal and transversal field parts

$$\mathbf{E}_t = \mathbf{E}_t^{\|} + \mathbf{E}_t^{\top}\,, \quad \mathbf{B}_t = \mathbf{B}_t^{\|} + \mathbf{B}_t^{\top}\,, \quad \mathbf{j}_t = \mathbf{j}_t^{\|} + \mathbf{j}_t^{\top}\,,$$

where in each decomposition the two field types are orthogonal to each other with respect to the scalar product in $\mathrm{L}^2(\mathbb{R}^3, \mathbb{R}^3)$.

55.3.3. *Helmholtz–Hodge Decomposition of the Maxwell Equations*

55.3.3.1. *Vacuum Maxwell Equations in Free Space*

The Maxwell equations in free space $\mathbb{R}^3$, void of any matter, are given by

$$\nabla \cdot \mathbf{E}_t(x) = \frac{1}{\epsilon_0}\rho_t(x)\,, \tag{55.3.12}$$

$$\nabla \cdot \mathbf{B}_t(x) = 0\,, \tag{55.3.13}$$

$$\nabla \times \mathbf{E}_t(x) = -\frac{\partial \mathbf{B}_t(x)}{\partial t}\,, \tag{55.3.14}$$

$$\nabla \times \mathbf{B}_t(x) = \mu_0 \mathbf{j}_t(x) + \underbrace{\epsilon_0 \mu_0}_{=c^{-2}} \frac{\partial \mathbf{E}_t(x)}{\partial t}\,, \tag{55.3.15}$$

for all $x \in \mathbb{R}^3$ and $t \in \mathbb{R}$. The three constants are interrelated by $\epsilon_0 \mu_0 c^2 = 1$.

Taking the time derivative $\frac{\partial}{\partial t}$ of Maxwell Eq. (55.3.12) and the divergence $\nabla \cdot$. of Maxwell Eq. (55.3.15), and observing $\nabla \cdot (\nabla \times \mathbf{B}_t) = 0$ leads to the continuity equation, representing local charge conservation,

$$\frac{\partial \rho_t(x)}{\partial t} + \nabla \cdot \mathbf{j}_t(x) = 0\,, \quad \forall x \in \mathbb{R}^3\,, \quad \forall t \in \mathbb{R}\,. \tag{55.3.16}$$

55.3.3.2. *The Dynamical Part of the Vacuum Maxwell Equations*

The dynamical Maxwell equations are given by the Eqs. (55.3.14) and (55.3.15). Combined they write as

$$\frac{\partial}{\partial t}\underbrace{\begin{pmatrix} \mathbf{E}_t \\ \mathbf{B}_t \end{pmatrix}}_{=\,\psi_t} = \underbrace{\begin{pmatrix} c^2 & 0 \\ 0 & 1 \end{pmatrix}\begin{pmatrix} 0 & \nabla\times. \\ -\nabla\times. & 0 \end{pmatrix}}_{=\,\mathbb{A}}\underbrace{\begin{pmatrix} \mathbf{E}_t \\ \mathbf{B}_t \end{pmatrix}}_{=\,\psi_t} + \underbrace{\begin{pmatrix} -\epsilon_0^{-1}\mathbf{j}_t \\ 0 \end{pmatrix}}_{=\,\gamma_t}\,, \tag{55.3.17}$$

with the anti–selfadjoint Maxwell operator $\mathbb{A}$ for the free space $\Lambda = \mathbb{R}^3$.

In order to compare the present investigation with our previous elaborations, let us recapitulate from Section 4.3 but in specialization to vacuum instead of an arbitrary linear medium. In vacuum the dynamical part of the Maxwell equations is rewritten with the magnetic field $\mathbf{H}_t = \mu_0^{-1}\mathbf{B}_t$ as (redefining ψ_t)

$$
\underbrace{\frac{d}{dt}\begin{pmatrix}\mathbf{E}_t \\ \mathbf{H}_t\end{pmatrix}}_{=\,\psi_t} = \underbrace{\underbrace{\begin{pmatrix}\epsilon_0^{-1} & 0 \\ 0 & \mu_0^{-1}\end{pmatrix}}_{=:\,M_{\mathrm{vac}}^{-1}}\underbrace{\begin{pmatrix}0 & \mathrm{curl} \\ -\mathrm{curl}_0 & 0\end{pmatrix}}_{=\,\mathbb{A}}}_{=\,M_{\mathrm{vac}}^{-1}\mathbb{A}\,=:\,\mathbb{A}_{\mathrm{vac}}}\underbrace{\begin{pmatrix}\mathbf{E}_t \\ \mathbf{H}_t\end{pmatrix}}_{=\,\psi_t} + \underbrace{\begin{pmatrix}-\epsilon_0^{-1}\mathbf{j}_t \\ 0\end{pmatrix}}_{=\,\gamma_t} \qquad (55.3.18)
$$

(see Eq. (4.3.6)), where the current $\gamma_t = -\frac{1}{\epsilon_0}\begin{pmatrix}\mathbf{j}_t \\ 0\end{pmatrix}$ indicates the inhomogeneity.

The anti–selfadjoint generator $\mathbb{A}_{\mathrm{vac}}$ for the free dynamics is called the *vacuum Maxwell operator* (it coincides with $\mathbb{A}_M$ from Section 4.3, but specialized to vacuum). It refers to an arbitrary region $\Lambda \subseteq \mathbb{R}^3$ and — in terms of its special form and domain of definition — the conductor boundary conditions are incorporated. Presently we specialize to $\Lambda = \mathbb{R}^3$, where we know that the two curls are identical, that is $\nabla \times \,.\, = \mathrm{curl} = \mathrm{curl}_0$ according to (55.3.2). Thus in free space (55.3.18) agrees with (55.3.17), up to the conversion $\mathbf{B}_t = \mu_0\mathbf{H}_t$. (If we treat the fields as vectors in a certain Hilbert space, time t is a parameter and we write for the time derivative d/dt. In the present section we treat the fields exclusively as functions in the position or momentum space representation and employ the partial derivative $\partial/\partial t$, also when not explicitly indicating the other independent variables $x \in \mathbb{R}^3$.)

We specify the initial conditions at initial time $t = 0$,

$$
\psi_t\big|_{t=0} = \psi_0 = (\mathbf{E}_0, \mathbf{H}_0) \in \mathrm{dom}(\mathbb{A}_{\mathrm{vac}}) = \mathrm{dom}(\mathbb{A})\,,
$$

and obtain the (unique) solution in operator form

$$
\psi_t = \underbrace{\exp\{t\mathbb{A}_{\mathrm{vac}}\}\psi_0}_{=:\,\psi_t^{hom}} + \underbrace{\int_0^t \exp\{(t-s)\mathbb{A}_{\mathrm{vac}}\}\gamma_s ds}_{=:\,\psi_t^{inh}}\,, \qquad \forall t \in \mathbb{R}\,. \qquad (55.3.19)
$$

We remark that for vanishing current — that is $\gamma_s = 0$ for all $s \in \mathbb{R}$ — we obtain the solution for the homogeneous dynamical Maxwell equation with the correct initial conditions. If, on the other side, $\gamma_s \neq 0$ but $\psi_0 = 0$, then we get a solution of the inhomogeneous dynamical Maxwell equation with trivial initial values.

We conclude: *The general solution ψ_t is the sum of the solution ψ_t^{hom} for the homogeneous dynamical Maxwell equation with the correct initial conditions plus the solution ψ_t^{inh} for the inhomogeneous dynamical Maxwell equation with trivial initial values.*

We work in the following more in the manner of usual textbooks on ED.

55.3.3.3. *Helmholtz–Hodge Decomposition of the Maxwell Equations*

Using the inverse divergence operator $(\nabla \cdot |^{\parallel})^{-1}$ the Helmholtz–Hodge decomposed Maxwell equations may be written (for all $t \in \mathbb{R}$)

$$\mathbf{E}_t^{\parallel} = \frac{1}{\epsilon_0}(\nabla \cdot |^{\parallel})^{-1}\rho_t \quad \Leftrightarrow \quad \nabla \cdot \mathbf{E}_t^{\parallel} = \frac{1}{\epsilon_0}\rho_t, \tag{55.3.20}$$

$$\frac{\partial \mathbf{E}_t^{\parallel}}{\partial t} = -\frac{1}{\epsilon_0}\mathbf{j}_t^{\parallel}, \tag{55.3.21}$$

$$\mathbf{B}_t^{\top} = \mathbf{B}_t \quad \Leftrightarrow \quad \mathbf{B}_t^{\parallel} = 0 \quad \Leftrightarrow \quad \nabla \cdot \mathbf{B}_t = 0, \tag{55.3.22}$$

$$\nabla \times \mathbf{E}_t^{\top} = -\frac{\partial \mathbf{B}_t^{\top}}{\partial t}, \tag{55.3.23}$$

$$\nabla \times \mathbf{B}_t^{\top} = \mu_0 \mathbf{j}_t^{\top} + \underbrace{\epsilon_0\mu_0}_{=c^{-2}} \frac{\partial \mathbf{E}_t^{\top}}{\partial t}. \tag{55.3.24}$$

The two Eqs. (55.3.21) and (55.3.24) follow from decomposing (55.3.15).

Performing the time derivative $\frac{\partial}{\partial t}$ in the longitudinal Maxwell Eq. (55.3.20), we derive with (55.3.21) the longitudinal version of the continuity equation

$$\mathbf{j}_t^{\parallel} = -(\nabla \cdot |^{\parallel})^{-1}\frac{\partial \rho_t}{\partial t} \quad \Leftrightarrow \quad \frac{\partial \rho_t}{\partial t} + \nabla \cdot \mathbf{j}_t^{\parallel} = 0. \tag{55.3.25}$$

This formula may be also obtained directly from (55.3.16) observing that $\nabla \cdot \mathbf{j}_t^{\top} = 0$.

Obviously, one may replace the Maxwell Eq. (55.3.21) by the continuity Eq. (55.3.25), that is

$$(55.3.20) \ \& \ (55.3.21) \quad \Leftrightarrow \quad (55.3.20) \ \& \ (55.3.25).$$

55.3.3.4. *The Longitudinal Electric Part of the Maxwell Equations*

With the initial time $t = 0$ one may derive the integrated form of the longitudinal Maxwell Eq. (55.3.21) to

$$\mathbf{E}_t^{\parallel} = \frac{1}{\epsilon_0}(\nabla \cdot |^{\parallel})^{-1}\rho_t = \underbrace{\frac{1}{\epsilon_0}(\nabla \cdot |^{\parallel})^{-1}\rho_0}_{= \mathbf{E}_0^{\parallel}} + \frac{1}{\epsilon_0}\int_0^t \underbrace{(\nabla \cdot |^{\parallel})^{-1}\frac{\partial \rho_s}{\partial s}}_{= -\mathbf{j}_s^{\parallel}} ds, \tag{55.3.26}$$

provided a fixed current trajectory $t \mapsto \mathbf{j}_t$ is given. One has only to recall the relation $\rho_t = \rho_0 + \int_0^t \frac{\partial \rho_s}{\partial s}ds$.

With the help of the first formula in (55.3.7), we are able to solve the longitudinal Maxwell Eq. (55.3.20) directly by

$$\mathbf{E}_t^{\parallel}(x) = \mathbf{E}^{\parallel}(t,x) = \frac{1}{\epsilon_0}(\nabla \cdot |^{\parallel})^{-1}\rho_t(x)$$

$$= -\frac{1}{4\pi\epsilon_0}\nabla\int_{\mathbb{R}^3} d^3y \, \frac{\rho(t,y)}{|x-y|} = \frac{1}{4\pi\epsilon_0}\int_{\mathbb{R}^3} d^3y \, \rho(t,y)\frac{x-y}{|x-y|^3} \tag{55.3.27}$$

for all $x \in \mathbb{R}^3$ and $t \in \mathbb{R}$ (the last equality sign follows from $\nabla_x \frac{1}{|x-y|} = -\frac{x-y}{|x-y|^3}$).
That is, the longitudinal electric field coincides just with the well known Coulomb
field arising instantaneously from the (sufficiently smooth) charge density $\rho_t(x) \equiv$
$\rho(t, x)$.

55.3.3.5. *The Transversal Electromagnetic Part of the Maxwell Equations*

The transversal dynamical Maxwell Eqs. (55.3.23) and (55.3.24) may be combined
to the coupled dynamical differential equation,

$$\underbrace{\frac{\partial}{\partial t} \begin{pmatrix} \mathbf{E}_t^\top \\ \mathbf{B}_t^\top \end{pmatrix}}_{= \psi_t^\top} = \begin{pmatrix} c^2 & 0 \\ 0 & 1 \end{pmatrix} \underbrace{\begin{pmatrix} 0 & \nabla \times . \\ -\nabla \times . & 0 \end{pmatrix}}_{= \mathbb{A}^\top} \underbrace{\begin{pmatrix} \mathbf{E}_t^\top \\ \mathbf{B}_t^\top \end{pmatrix}}_{= \psi_t^\top} + \underbrace{\begin{pmatrix} -\epsilon_0^{-1} \mathbf{j}_t^\top \\ 0 \end{pmatrix}}_{= \gamma_t^\top}, \qquad (55.3.28)$$

involving the anti–selfadjoint transversal Maxwell operator $\mathbb{A}^\top$. This is just the
transversal part of Eq. (55.3.17). Of course, the solution theory of that Maxwell–
Cauchy problem works as in Subsection 55.3.3.2, it is part of the Chapters 4 and 5.

55.3.4. *The Inhomogeneous WE for the Force Fields*

We recapitulate first the standard deduction of the inhomogeneous electromagnetic
wave equations from the Maxwell equations. Later on we proceed in the opposite
direction.

55.3.4.1. *Wave Equations for the Electric and Magnetic Fields*

From (55.3.1), with the free space Laplacian Δ acting in each component of the
electric field $\mathbf{E}_t$, it follows via the first Maxwell Eq. (55.3.12) that

$$\nabla \times (\nabla \times \mathbf{E}_t) = \nabla(\nabla \cdot \mathbf{E}_t) - \Delta \mathbf{E}_t = \frac{1}{\epsilon_0} \nabla \rho_t - \Delta \mathbf{E}_t . \qquad (55.3.29)$$

Now we take the curl $\nabla \times .$ of Maxwell Eq. (55.3.14) and the time derivative $\frac{\partial}{\partial t}$ of
Maxwell Eq. (55.3.15) in order to get

$$\frac{1}{\epsilon_0} \nabla \rho_t - \Delta \mathbf{E}_t = \nabla \times (\nabla \times \mathbf{E}_t) = -\nabla \times \frac{\partial \mathbf{B}_t}{\partial t} , \quad \nabla \times \frac{\partial \mathbf{B}_t}{\partial t} = \mu_0 \frac{\partial \mathbf{j}_t}{\partial t} + \frac{1}{c^2} \frac{\partial^2 \mathbf{E}_t(x)}{\partial t^2} .$$

Putting things together by eliminating $\nabla \times \frac{\partial \mathbf{B}_t}{\partial t}$, we arrive at the inhomogeneous
wave equation (WE) for $\mathbf{E}_t$,

$$\square \mathbf{E}_t = -\mu_0 \frac{\partial \mathbf{j}_t}{\partial t} - \frac{1}{\epsilon_0} \nabla \rho_t \qquad \text{(electric WE in } \mathrm{L}^2(\mathbb{R}^3, \mathbb{R}^3)), \qquad (55.3.30)$$

where we have used the d'Alembert or wave operator

$$\square := \frac{1}{c^2} \frac{\partial^2}{\partial t^2} - \Delta .$$

Similarly, by applying $\nabla \times \,.$ to Maxwell Eq. (55.3.15) and $\frac{\partial}{\partial t}$ to Maxwell Eq. (55.3.14), we obtain the inhomogeneous wave equation for the magnetic induction $\mathbf{B}_t$,

$$\Box \mathbf{B}_t = \mu_0 \nabla \times \mathbf{j}_t \qquad \text{(magnetic WE in } L^2(\mathbb{R}^3, \mathbb{R}^3)). \tag{55.3.31}$$

55.3.4.2. *Helmholtz–Hodge Decomposition of the Wave Equations*

Since $\nabla \rho_t$ is a longitudinal field, we conclude that the wave Eq. (55.3.30) decomposes into its longitudinal and transversal field parts according to

$$\Box \mathbf{E}_t^{\|} = -\mu_0 \frac{\partial \mathbf{j}_t^{\|}}{\partial t} - \frac{1}{\epsilon_0} \nabla \rho_t \quad \text{(longitudinal electric WE in } L_{\|}^2(\mathbb{R}^3, \mathbb{R}^3)), \tag{55.3.32}$$

$$\Box \mathbf{E}_t^{\top} = -\mu_0 \frac{\partial \mathbf{j}_t^{\top}}{\partial t} \qquad \text{(transversal electric WE in } L_{\top}^2(\mathbb{R}^3, \mathbb{R}^3)). \tag{55.3.33}$$

Since $\mathbf{B}_t^{\|} = 0$ (according to (55.3.22)) and since $\nabla \times \mathbf{j}_t^{\|} = 0$, the magnetic wave equation from (55.3.31) is automatically transversal:

$$\Box \mathbf{B}_t^{\top} = \mu_0 \nabla \times \mathbf{j}_t^{\top} \qquad \text{(transversal magnetic WE in } L_{\top}^2(\mathbb{R}^3, \mathbb{R}^3)). \tag{55.3.34}$$

Note that the transversal wave Eqs. (55.3.33) and (55.3.34) may alternatively be obtained – by an analogous procedure as in the previous Subsection – from the transversal dynamical Maxwell Eqs. (55.3.23) and (55.3.24).

Theorem 55.3-5 (Equivalence of Transversal IVP's). *Let be given* $\mathbf{E}_0^{\top}, \mathbf{B}_0^{\top} \in L_{\top}^2(\mathbb{R}^3, \mathbb{R}^3)$. *Then for a transversal field trajectory* $t \mapsto \psi_t^{\top} = \begin{pmatrix} \mathbf{E}_t^{\top} \\ \mathbf{B}_t^{\top} \end{pmatrix}$ *in* $L_{\top}^2(\mathbb{R}^3, \mathbb{R}^3) \oplus L_{\top}^2(\mathbb{R}^3, \mathbb{R}^3)$ *the following two assertions are equivalent:*

(i) *The Maxwell differential equation (55.3.28) is fulfilled for* $t \geq 0$ *(or for* $t \in \mathbb{R}$*) with the initial value(s)* $\psi_t^{\top}|_{t=0} = \psi_0^{\top} = \begin{pmatrix} \mathbf{E}_0^{\top} \\ \mathbf{B}_0^{\top} \end{pmatrix}$ *at* $t = 0$.

(ii) *The transversal inhomogeneous wave Eqs. (55.3.33) and (55.3.34) are satisfied for* $t \geq 0$ *(or for* $t \in \mathbb{R}$*) with the initial values*

$$\mathbf{E}_t^{\top}|_{t=0} = \mathbf{E}_0^{\top}, \qquad \frac{\partial \mathbf{E}_t^{\top}}{\partial t}\bigg|_{t=0} = c^2 \nabla \times \mathbf{B}_0^{\top} - \mu_0 \mathbf{j}_0^{\top},$$

$$\mathbf{B}_t^{\top}|_{t=0} = \mathbf{B}_0^{\top}, \qquad \frac{\partial \mathbf{B}_t^{\top}}{\partial t}\bigg|_{t=0} = -\nabla \times \mathbf{E}_0^{\top}.$$

Proof. For convenience we set $c = \epsilon_0 = \mu_0 = 1$ in the proof.

$(i) \Rightarrow (ii)$. We have this already shown for the differential equations. It also follows by applying (55.3.28) two times for getting $\frac{\partial^2 \psi_t^{\top}}{\partial t^2}$. The correspondence of initial values in $(i) \Rightarrow (ii)$ is immediate.

$(ii) \Rightarrow (i)$. Take the curl $\nabla \times \,.$ of (55.3.33) and $\frac{\partial}{\partial t}$ of (55.3.34), then — noting that the component–wise acting wave operator $\Box$ commutes with the curl operator

$\nabla \times .$ — we get

$$\Box(\nabla \times \mathbf{E}_t^\top) = -\nabla \times \frac{\partial \mathbf{j}_t^\top}{\partial t}, \qquad \Box\frac{\partial \mathbf{B}_t^\top}{\partial t} = \nabla \times \frac{\partial \mathbf{j}_t^\top}{\partial t}.$$

Combining these equations yields the homogeneous wave equation

$$\Box\underbrace{\left(\frac{\partial \mathbf{B}_t^\top}{\partial t} + \nabla \times \mathbf{E}_t^\top\right)}_{=:\,\mathbf{U}_t} = 0.$$

Let us show that the initial values for $\mathbf{U}_t$ are trivial. $\mathbf{U}_0 = \frac{\partial \mathbf{B}_t^\top}{\partial t}\big|_{t=0} + \nabla \times \mathbf{E}_0^\top = 0$ is immediate. We obtain for transversal fields $\mathbf{F}^\top$ from (55.3.1) that $\Delta \mathbf{F}^\top = -\nabla \times (\nabla \times \mathbf{F}^\top)$. From the wave Eq. (55.3.34) we conclude that

$$\frac{\partial^2 \mathbf{B}_t^\top}{\partial t^2}\Big|_{t=0} = \overbrace{-\nabla \times (\nabla \times \mathbf{B}_t^\top)}^{=\,\Delta}\Big|_{t=0} + \nabla \times \mathbf{j}_t^\top\Big|_{t=0}$$

$$= -\nabla \times (\nabla \times \mathbf{B}_t^\top - \mathbf{j}_t^\top)\Big|_{t=0} = -\nabla \times \frac{\partial \mathbf{E}_t^\top}{\partial t}\Big|_{t=0},$$

where the last equality sign follows from the above given initial values. Consequently,

$$\frac{\partial \mathbf{U}_t}{\partial t}\Big|_{t=0} = \frac{\partial^2 \mathbf{B}_t^\top}{\partial t^2}\Big|_{t=0} + \nabla \times \frac{\partial \mathbf{E}_t^\top}{\partial t}\Big|_{t=0} = 0.$$

Since the homogeneous wave equation $\Box\mathbf{U}_t = 0$ is uniquely solvable under given initial values $\mathbf{U}_0$ and $\frac{\partial \mathbf{U}_t}{\partial t}\big|_{t=0}$ (by Section 4.4), it follows from the triviality of the derived trivial initial values that $\mathbf{U}_t = 0$, thus $\frac{\partial \mathbf{B}_t^\top}{\partial t} = -\nabla \times \mathbf{E}_t^\top$ for all t.

Now take $\frac{\partial}{\partial t}$ of (55.3.33) and the rotation $\nabla \times .$ of (55.3.34), then, noting that the component-wise acting wave operator $\Box$ commutes with the rotation operator $\nabla \times .$, we arrive at

$$\Box\frac{\partial \mathbf{E}_t^\top}{\partial t} = -\frac{\partial^2 \mathbf{j}_t^\top}{\partial t^2}, \qquad \Box(\nabla \times \mathbf{B}_t^\top) = \nabla \times (\nabla \times \mathbf{j}_t^\top) = -\Delta \mathbf{j}_t^\top.$$

Subtracting these equations finally leads to the homogeneous wave equation

$$\Box\underbrace{\left(\frac{\partial \mathbf{E}_t^\top}{\partial t} - \nabla \times \mathbf{B}_t^\top + \mathbf{j}_t^\top\right)}_{=:\,\mathbf{V}_t} = 0.$$

The initial value $\mathbf{V}_0 = 0$ is immediate. From the wave Eq. (55.3.33) we conclude

$$\frac{\partial^2 \mathbf{E}_t^\top}{\partial t^2}\Big|_{t=0} = \underbrace{-\nabla \times (\nabla \times \mathbf{E}_t^\top)}_{=\,\Delta} - \frac{\partial \mathbf{j}_t^\top}{\partial t}\Big|_{t=0} = \nabla \times \frac{\partial \mathbf{B}_t^\top}{\partial t}\Big|_{t=0} - \frac{\partial \mathbf{j}_t^\top}{\partial t}\Big|_{t=0},$$

where the last equality sign follows from the above given initial values. Thus $\frac{\partial \mathbf{V}_t}{\partial t}\big|_{t=0} = 0$. Again, with the trivial initial values the homogeneous wave equation leads to $\mathbf{V}_t = 0$, which finally implies $\frac{\partial \mathbf{E}_t^\top}{\partial t} = \nabla \times \mathbf{B}_t^\top - \mathbf{j}_t^\top$ for all t. $\qquad\Box$

Remark 55.3-6 (Diagonalization into Wave Equations for $\mathbf{E}^\top$ and $\mathbf{B}^\top$).
The transition to wave equations resembles in some sense a matrix diagonalization
of the transversal Maxwell operator $\mathbb{A}^\top$. For a wave equation we need the twofold
time derivation, given by $(\mathbb{A}^\top)^2$. From the transversal dynamical Maxwell equation
(55.3.28),

$$
\frac{\partial}{\partial t} \underbrace{\begin{pmatrix} \mathbf{E}_t^\top \\ \mathbf{B}_t^\top \end{pmatrix}}_{= \,\psi_t^\top} = \underbrace{\begin{pmatrix} c^2 & 0 \\ 0 & 1 \end{pmatrix} \begin{pmatrix} 0 & \nabla\times. \\ -\nabla\times. & 0 \end{pmatrix}}_{= \,\mathbb{A}^\top} \underbrace{\begin{pmatrix} \mathbf{E}_t^\top \\ \mathbf{B}_t^\top \end{pmatrix}}_{= \,\psi_t^\top} + \underbrace{\begin{pmatrix} -\epsilon_0^{-1}\mathbf{j}_t^\top \\ 0 \end{pmatrix}}_{= \,\gamma_t^\top}, \tag{55.3.35}
$$

we arrive then at the combined ("diagonalized") wave equation for the transverse
fields

$$
\frac{\partial^2}{\partial t^2} \underbrace{\begin{pmatrix} \mathbf{E}_t^\top \\ \mathbf{B}_t^\top \end{pmatrix}}_{= \,\psi_t^\top} = \underbrace{c^2 \begin{pmatrix} \Delta & 0 \\ 0 & \Delta \end{pmatrix} \begin{pmatrix} \mathbf{E}_t^\top \\ \mathbf{B}_t^\top \end{pmatrix}}_{=\,(\mathbb{A}^\top)^2 = \,\psi_t^\top} + \underbrace{\begin{pmatrix} 0 \\ \epsilon_0^{-1}\nabla\times\mathbf{j}_t^\top \end{pmatrix}}_{= \,\mathbb{A}^\top \gamma_t^\top} + \underbrace{\begin{pmatrix} -\epsilon_0^{-1}\frac{\partial}{\partial t}\mathbf{j}_t^\top \\ 0 \end{pmatrix}}_{=\,\frac{\partial}{\partial t}\gamma_t^\top}. \tag{55.3.36}
$$

Whereas in the Maxwell differential equation (55.3.35) the transversal electric and
magnetic fields are intertwined they appear as decoupled in the wave Eq. (55.3.36).
But the initial values of the wave equation have to be chosen very specifically. Then
and only then the intertwining of the $\mathbf{E}_t^\top$– and $\mathbf{B}_t^\top$–fields arising from (55.3.35) can
be reconstructed from the wave solutions for all times.

A careful mathematical analysis of the connection between Maxwell and wave solu-
tions in arbitrary cavities $\Lambda \subseteq \mathbb{R}^3$, but for the curlcurl operator instead of the
Laplacian and for the homogeneous case only, is executed in our Section 4.4.

55.3.5. *Charge Conservation is Basic for WE*

According to the Eqs. (55.3.26) and (55.3.27) the longitudinal electric Coulomb field
$\mathbf{E}_t^\|$ arises instantaneously from the time dependent charge distribution $t \mapsto \rho_t(x)$.
On the other side, we derived a wave equation for the longitudinal electric field $\mathbf{E}_t^\|$
in Eq. (55.3.32), the solutions of which propagate with the velocity of light. That
there is no contradiction is the content of the next result.

Theorem 55.3-7 (Equivalence of Longitudinal IVP's). *Suppose the local
charge conservation to be valid, which is expressed by*

$$
\mathbf{j}_t^\| = -(\nabla\cdot|^\|)^{-1}\frac{\partial\rho_t}{\partial t} \quad \Leftrightarrow \quad \frac{\partial\rho_t}{\partial t} + \nabla\cdot\mathbf{j}_t^\| = 0, \quad \forall t \geq 0. \tag{55.3.37}
$$

*For a longitudinal electric field trajectory $t \mapsto \mathbf{E}_t^\|$ the following two assertion are
then equivalent:*

(i) The first Maxwell Eq. (55.3.20) is fulfilled,

$$
\mathbf{E}_t^\| = \frac{1}{\epsilon_0}(\nabla\cdot|^\|)^{-1}\rho_t \quad \Leftrightarrow \quad \nabla\cdot\mathbf{E}_t^\| = \frac{1}{\epsilon_0}\rho_t, \quad \forall t \geq 0,
$$

leading to the instantaneous Coulomb field $\mathbf{E}_t^\|(x) = -\frac{1}{4\pi\epsilon_0}\nabla\int_{\mathbb{R}^3} d^3y \frac{\rho(t,y)}{|x-y|}$.

(ii) The initial value problem with the wave equation from (55.3.32) in $L^2_\parallel(\mathbb{R}^3, \mathbb{R}^3)$ is satisfied,

$$
\begin{cases}
\Box \mathbf{E}^\parallel_t = -\mu_0 \dfrac{\partial \mathbf{j}^\parallel_t}{\partial t} - \dfrac{1}{\epsilon_0} \nabla \rho_t, & \text{(WE for } t \geq 0), \\[2mm]
\mathbf{E}^\parallel_t \big|_{t=0} = \mathbf{E}^\parallel_0 = \dfrac{1}{\epsilon_0}(\nabla \cdot |^\parallel)^{-1} \rho_0, \quad \dfrac{\partial \mathbf{E}^\parallel_t}{\partial t}\Big|_{t=0} = -\dfrac{\mathbf{j}^\parallel_0}{\epsilon_0}, & \text{(IV at } t = 0).
\end{cases}
$$

Proof. (i)$\Rightarrow$(ii). From (55.3.37) follows $\mu_0 \frac{\partial^2 \rho_t}{\partial t^2} = -\mu_0 \nabla \cdot \frac{\partial \mathbf{j}^\parallel_t}{\partial t}$, to which we add $-\frac{1}{\epsilon_0}\Delta \rho_t$ in order to obtain (with $\Delta = \nabla \cdot (\nabla.)$ for the last equality sign) that

$$
\frac{1}{\epsilon_0}\Box \rho_t = \mu_0 \frac{\partial^2 \rho_t}{\partial t^2} - \frac{1}{\epsilon_0}\Delta \rho_t = -\mu_0 \nabla \cdot \frac{\partial \mathbf{j}^\parallel_t}{\partial t} - \frac{1}{\epsilon_0}\Delta \rho_t = \nabla \cdot \left(-\mu_0 \frac{\partial \mathbf{j}^\parallel_t}{\partial t} - \frac{1}{\epsilon_0}\nabla \rho_t\right).
$$

We insert $\rho_t = \epsilon_0 \nabla \cdot \mathbf{E}^\parallel_t$ on the left–hand side into $\frac{1}{\epsilon_0}\Box \rho_t$, and use the fact that the component–wise acting operator $\Box$ commutes with the divergence $\nabla \cdot .$, leading to

$$
\nabla \cdot \Box \mathbf{E}^\parallel_t = \nabla \cdot \left(-\mu_0 \frac{\partial \mathbf{j}^\parallel_t}{\partial t} - \frac{1}{\epsilon_0}\nabla \rho_t\right).
$$

Now we may take the inverse $(\nabla \cdot |^\parallel)^{-1}$, since all occurring fields are longitudinal.

The first initial value is immediate. For the second one, note that the assumptions yield (apply $\frac{\partial}{\partial t}$ to the first Maxwell equation, and use the continuity equation)

$$
\frac{\partial \mathbf{E}^\parallel_t}{\partial t} = \frac{1}{\epsilon_0}(\nabla \cdot |^\parallel)^{-1}\frac{\partial \rho_t}{\partial t} = -\frac{\mathbf{j}^\parallel_t}{\epsilon_0},
$$

and set then $t = 0$.

(ii)$\Rightarrow$(i). We take the divergence of the inhomogeneous wave equation and replace $\nabla \cdot \frac{\partial \mathbf{j}^\parallel_t}{\partial t}$ by $\nabla \cdot \frac{\partial \mathbf{j}^\parallel_t}{\partial t} = -\frac{\partial^2 \rho_t}{\partial t^2}$ according to (55.3.37). This gives

$$
\Box \nabla \cdot \mathbf{E}^\parallel_t = \mu_0 \frac{\partial^2 \rho_t}{\partial t^2} - \frac{1}{\epsilon_0}\underbrace{\nabla \cdot (\nabla \rho_t)}_{= \Delta} \qquad \Longleftrightarrow \qquad \Box \underbrace{\left(\nabla \cdot \mathbf{E}^\parallel_t - \frac{1}{\epsilon_0}\rho_t\right)}_{=: \, w_t} = 0.
$$

The relation $w_t\big|_{t=0} = w_0 = 0$ is immediate. For showing $\frac{\partial w_t}{\partial t}\big|_{t=0} = 0$, use $\frac{\partial \rho_t}{\partial t}\big|_{t=0} = -\nabla \cdot \mathbf{j}^\parallel_0$. But the homogeneous wave equation $\Box w_t = 0$ is uniquely solvable under given initial values w_0 and $\frac{\partial w_t}{\partial t}\big|_{t=0}$ (shown as in Section 4.4, but demonstrated also in the next subsection). Since here the initial values for w_t vanish, we get $w_t = 0$ for all t, that is (i). $\qquad\square$

It is clear that also here the initial values of the wave equation have to be chosen suitably, so that the return to the first Maxwell equation is possible.

The foregoing proof demonstrates that the equivalence (i)$\Leftrightarrow$(ii) is also valid if we vary t in *all* of $\mathbb{R}$, instead of taking only $t \geq 0$.

We are now able, to reformulate the total set of Maxwell equations entirely in terms of wave equations.

Theorem 55.3-8 (Equivalence of Maxwell Equations and WE). *The full set of vacuum Maxwell equations in free space* $\mathbb{R}^3$ *(that are the Eqs. (55.3.12) to (55.3.15)), considered as an IVP, is equivalent to the IVP for the two wave Eqs. (55.3.30), (55.3.31), combined with the local charge conservation of Eq. (55.3.16). The latter IVP is written in formulas as*

$$\Box \mathbf{E}_t = -\mu_0 \frac{\partial \mathbf{j}_t}{\partial t} - \frac{1}{\epsilon_0} \nabla \rho_t, \qquad \Box \mathbf{B}_t = \mu_0 \nabla \times \mathbf{j}_t, \qquad \frac{\partial \rho_t}{\partial t} + \nabla \cdot \mathbf{j}_t = 0,$$

for the set of differential equations, together with the initial values at $t = 0$

$$\mathbf{E}_t\big|_{t=0} = \mathbf{E}_0 = \frac{1}{\epsilon_0} (\nabla \cdot |^{\|})^{-1} \rho_0 + \mathbf{E}_0^{\top}, \qquad \frac{\partial \mathbf{E}_t}{\partial t}\bigg|_{t=0} = c^2 \nabla \times \mathbf{B}_0 - \frac{1}{\epsilon_0} \mathbf{j}_0,$$

$$\mathbf{B}_t\big|_{t=0} = \mathbf{B}_0 = \mathbf{B}_0^{\top} \quad (\Leftrightarrow \nabla \cdot \mathbf{B}_0 = 0), \qquad \frac{\partial \mathbf{B}_t}{\partial t}\bigg|_{t=0} = -\nabla \times \mathbf{E}_0.$$

Proof. We stick together the different Helmholtz–Hodge parts from the above Theorems 55.3-5 and 55.3-7. It remains to show the transversality condition of the magnetic field, $\nabla \cdot \mathbf{B}_t = 0$ for all times t. But that arises automatically from the transversality of the initial condition $\mathbf{B}_0 = \mathbf{B}_0^{\top}$, which is transported to other times $t \neq 0$ by the wave equation for $\mathbf{B}_t$. $\qquad\qquad\square$

Conclusion 55.3-9 (Initial Conditions in the Maxwell Dynamics). Whereas it had been easy to derive the WE for the $\mathbf{E}_t$– and $\mathbf{B}_t$–fields from the Maxwell equations, the recovery of the latter from the WE required more efforts, and displayed the important role of charge conservation, which is incorporated into the Maxwell equations, but must additionally be required for the WE. And only specifically chosen initial values for the WE, including also the time derivatives, were necessary to restore the intertwining between the $\mathbf{E}_t$– and $\mathbf{B}_t$–fields, inherent in the Maxwell dynamics.

The necessity to specify also $\frac{\partial \mathbf{E}_t}{\partial t}\big|_{t=0}$ and $\frac{\partial \mathbf{B}_t}{\partial t}\big|_{t=0}$ is due to the second time derivative in the WE. In the Maxwell equations for themselves, given in the Eqs. (55.3.17) or (55.3.18) in operator form, only the first time derivative is included, and the solutions from Eq. (55.3.19) contain only $\mathbf{E}_t\big|_{t=0}$ and $\mathbf{B}_t\big|_{t=0}$ as initial values. By the action of the Maxwell dynamics for an infinitesimal time the values of $\frac{\partial \mathbf{E}_t}{\partial t}\big|_{t=0}$ and $\frac{\partial \mathbf{B}_t}{\partial t}\big|_{t=0}$ are calculable.

Especially in the wave form of the Maxwell dynamics, there is a tendency to interpret the initial conditions as "cause" for the later time evolution. For the inverted time evolution, the "initial conditions" appear as the "result" of the foregoing time developments, which one may follow more and more into the past — identifying previous "causes" — while $t \leq 0$ approaches $-\infty$. For analyzing those aspects we sketch the general solution theory of the inhomogeneous wave equation.

55.3.6. *Causality in Wave Solutions*

In our introductory Section 2.2 we mentioned already the well known existence of *retarded* and *advanced* solutions for an inhomogeneous wave equation (WE), there denoted as *causal* and *anti–causal* respectively. We treat here the initial value problem (IVP) for the inhomogeneous wave equation in more general terms, emphasizing the time development into the future.

55.3.6.1.   *Solution of the IVP for the Inhomogeneous Wave Equation*

Suppose for the wave equation a sufficiently smooth inhomogeneity function f : $\mathbb{R} \times \mathbb{R}^3 \to \mathbb{R}$, $(t, x) \mapsto f_t(x) \equiv f(t, x)$, and let be given at $t = 0$ the initial value functions $w_0 : \mathbb{R}^3 \to \mathbb{R}$ and $\dot{w}_0 : \mathbb{R}^3 \to \mathbb{R}$. Then the initial value problem for the inhomogeneous wave equation is expressed as

$$\begin{cases} \Box w_t(x) = f_t(x) \,, & \forall t \geq 0 \,, \forall x \in \mathbb{R}^3 \,, \\ w(0, x) = w_0(x) \,, \quad \dfrac{\partial w}{\partial t}(0, x) = \dot{w}_0(x) \,, & t = 0 \,, \forall x \in \mathbb{R}^3 \,, \end{cases} \quad \text{(IVP inhom.WE)}.$$

$$(55.3.38)$$

For the development into the **future**, we want to determine the causal Green's function which satisfies $c^2 \Box \mathcal{G}^c(t, x) = \delta(t)\,\delta(x)$ for $t \in \mathbb{R}$. As shown in Section 2.2 it has the form

$$\mathcal{G}^c(t, x) = \theta(t)G^c(t, x), \quad G^c(t, x) = \frac{1}{4\pi c^3} \frac{\delta(t - \frac{1}{c}|x|)}{t} = \frac{1}{4\pi c^2} \frac{\delta(t - \frac{1}{c}|x|)}{|x|} \,.$$

$$(55.3.39)$$

The product of Heaviside's step function $\theta(t)$ with the distribution G^c is known to be a mathematically delicate operation and constitutes, in fact, an inherent complication of causal solution theory. Usually, one attempts in distribution theory the definition $(\theta G^c)(g) := G^c(\theta g)$, where g is an appropriate test function (from the Schwartz space $\mathcal{S}(\mathbb{R}^3, \mathbb{R})$ say), and the smearing by it is expressed as a functional application. If θg would be also an appropriate test function, then we would be ready. It is clear, however, that we need in this case additional regularity conditions for the test functions at $t = 0$.

The solution procedure of the initial value problem (55.3.38) is divided in two steps (see, e.g., [Lei86] Section 5.2 or [FK08] § 17). We do not plunge into mathematical details and do not distinguish here between distributional, weak, and classical solutions (what we carefully elaborated in the case of the Maxwell equations).

First one solves the homogeneous wave equation $\Box w_t^{\text{hom}} = 0$ with the possibly inhomogeneous initial values $w^{\text{hom}}(0, x) = w_0(x)$ and $\frac{\partial w^{\text{hom}}}{\partial t}(0, x) = \dot{w}_0(x)$, leading to the *unique* solution

$$w_t^{\text{hom}} = \frac{\partial}{\partial t} I(t)w_0 + I(t)\dot{w}_0 \,, \quad \forall t \geq 0 \,, \tag{55.3.40}$$

(which vanishes for trivial initial values). The functions $I(t)v$ for $v = w_0$ and $v = \dot{w}_0$ are given by the convolution with the causal Green's function $G^c(t, x)$, but only with respect to the spatial variable $x \in \mathbb{R}^3$, where

$$(I(t)v)(x) := \int_{\mathbb{R}^3} d^3y \, G^c(t, x - y) \, v(y) = \frac{1}{4\pi c^2 t} \int_{S(x, ct)} da(y) \, v(y), \quad \forall x \in \mathbb{R}^3.$$

The latter expression means the surface integral over the sphere

$$S(x, ct) = \{y \in \mathbb{R}^3 \mid |x - y| = ct\}, \tag{55.3.41}$$

the boundary of the ball $B(x, ct)$ with radius $ct > 0$ about the center point $x \in \mathbb{R}^3$,

$$B(x, ct) = \{y \in \mathbb{R}^3 \mid |x - y| \le ct\} = \{y \in \mathbb{R}^3 \mid t - \tfrac{1}{c}|x - y| \ge 0\}. \tag{55.3.42}$$

In a second step one solves the inhomogeneous wave equation $\Box w_t^c = f_t$ but for trivial, so–called *homogeneous* initial values $w^c(0, x) = 0$ and $\frac{\partial w^c}{\partial t}(0, x) = 0$. We give here an heuristic, but intuitive, approach in terms of singular functions. In shorthand notation one has

$$w^c = c^2 \mathcal{G}^c \star f, \quad \text{since} \quad \Box w^c = (\Box c^2 \mathcal{G}^c) \star f = \mathbb{1} \star f = f. \tag{55.3.43}$$

In explicit notation, writing out the convolution product $\star$, that reads

$$w_t^c(x) = \frac{1}{4\pi} \int_{\mathbb{R}} ds \int_{\mathbb{R}^3} d^3y \, \theta(t - s) \frac{\delta(t - s - \frac{1}{c}|x - y|)}{|x - y|} f(s, y), \quad \forall x \in \mathbb{R}^3, \ \forall t \ge 0.$$
$$\tag{55.3.44}$$

Since the s–integration ranges — due to the δ–function — automatically only over positive $(t - s)$–values the step function θ seems here superfluous and is usually omitted in ED–text books. If one performs first the s–integration, one obtains — by the action of the δ–distribution via the time argument —

$$w_t^c(x) = \frac{1}{4\pi} \int_{\mathbb{R}^3} d^3y \, \frac{f(t - \frac{1}{c}|x - y|, y)}{|x - y|}, \quad \forall x \in \mathbb{R}^3, \ \forall t \ge 0, \tag{55.3.45}$$

without any assumption on f for the past.

If one first takes into account the action of the δ–distribution via the y–argument (recalling the correct definition of δ with respect to the y–argument) one arrives for all $x \in \mathbb{R}^3$ and for all $t \ge 0$ at the correct mathematical solution expression

$$w_t^c(x) = \frac{1}{4\pi} \int_{\mathbb{R}} ds \, \theta(t - s) \int_{S(x, c(t - s))} da(y) \, \frac{f(s, y)}{|x - y|}$$
$$= \frac{1}{4\pi} \int_{B(x, ct)} d^3y \, \frac{f(t - \frac{1}{c}|x - y|, y)}{|x - y|}. \tag{55.3.46}$$

Since the integral ranges over the ball $B(x, ct)$, the solution $w_t^c(x)$ at the space–time point (t, x) is influenced only by those values of f on arguments (s, y) from which (t, x) is reached with the velocity of light c. Especially, no quantity of $f(t, x)$ from the past $t < 0$ comes into play. It is a distinguished feature of wave solutions, that the time integration can be replaced by a modified space integration. (Compare this, however, with the Maxwell solution Eq. (55.3.19), where one needs the time integration over the current.)

Only if we cut the past out of f, by resetting $f_t := 0$ for $t < 0$, we equivalently arrive in (55.3.46) at an integral over the whole free space $\mathbb{R}^3$, instead over the ball $B(x, ct)$, that is at Eq. (55.3.45).

For $t = 0$, the y–integration in Eq. (55.3.46) and — if the past is cut out of f — in Eq. (55.3.45) shrinks to the point $y = x$. Under appropriate regularity conditions of the integrand and its time derivative at $t = 0$ we arrive at an empty integration and obtain then the homogeneous initial values $w^c(0, x) = 0$ and $\frac{\partial w^c}{\partial t}(0, x) = 0$.

Finally, the total unique solution of the initial value problem (55.3.38) is the sum

$$w_t = w_t^{\mathrm{hom}} + w_t^{\mathrm{c}}, \quad \forall t \geq 0, \tag{55.3.47}$$

where — like in Eq. (55.3.19) for the Maxwell dynamics — a special homogeneous solution w_t^{hom} incorporates the initial conditions, whereas the inhomogeneous solution w_t^{c} satisfies trivial initial conditions.

For the development into the **past** let us only mention that the *anti–causal* or *advanced* Green's function has for $t \in \mathbb{R}$ the form

$$\mathcal{G}^a(t, x) = \theta(-t) G^a(t, x), \quad G^a(t, x) = \frac{-1}{4\pi c^3} \frac{\delta(t + \frac{1}{c}|x|)}{t} = \frac{1}{4\pi c^2} \frac{\delta(t + \frac{1}{c}|x|)}{|x|}. \tag{55.3.48}$$

The total unique solution of the "initial value" problem (55.3.38) is the sum

$$w_t = w_t^{\mathrm{hom}} + w_t^{\mathrm{a}}, \quad \forall t \leq 0, \tag{55.3.49}$$

where again a special homogeneous solution w_t^{hom} incorporates the "initial conditions", whereas the inhomogeneous solution w_t^{a} satisfies trivial "initial conditions" and has the universal form

$$w_t^{\mathrm{a}}(x) = \frac{1}{4\pi} \int_{\mathbb{R}^3} d^3 y \, \frac{f(t + \frac{1}{c}|x - y|, y)}{|x - y|}, \quad \forall x \in \mathbb{R}^3, \quad \forall t \leq 0, \tag{55.3.50}$$

where $f : \mathbb{R} \times \mathbb{R}^3 \to \mathbb{R}$, $(t, x) \mapsto f_t(x) \equiv f(t, x)$ denotes the inhomogeneity from which the future has been cut out, that is $f_t = 0$ for $t > 0$.

55.3.6.2. *Instantaneous Versus Propagating Electrodynamic Fields*

In the following, we neglect homogeneous solutions and for the inhomogeneous one (with trivial initial values) we again concentrate ourselves mainly on the **future** and discuss first retarded solutions. We suppose to be given a sufficiently smooth charge density $t \mapsto \rho_t$ and current density $t \mapsto \mathbf{j}_t$ connected with each other via the continuity equation (55.3.16). Then, for $t \geq 0$, the causal solution of the electric wave equation (55.3.30) is given — by means of the general solution formulas of the preceding considerations — as

$$\mathbf{E}_t^c(x) \equiv \mathbf{E}^c(t, x)$$

$$= -\frac{\mu_0}{4\pi} \int_{\mathbb{R}^3} d^3y \frac{(\frac{\partial}{\partial t}\mathbf{j})(t - \frac{1}{c}|x - y|, y)}{|x - y|} - \frac{1}{4\pi\epsilon_0} \int_{\mathbb{R}^3} d^3y \frac{(\nabla\rho)(t - \frac{1}{c}|x - y|, y)}{|x - y|}.$$

$$(55.3.51)$$

For the causal **B**–field solutions of the magnetic wave equation (55.3.31) one obtains

$$\mathbf{B}_t^c(x) = \mathbf{B}^c(t, x) = \frac{\mu_0}{4\pi} \int_{\mathbb{R}^3} d^3y \frac{(\nabla \times \mathbf{j})(t - \frac{1}{c}|x - y|, y)}{|x - y|}. \qquad (55.3.52)$$

Since we integrate over all of $\mathbb{R}^3$, the source expressions have to be switched on smoothly at $t = 0$.

Note, $(\frac{\partial}{\partial t}\mathbf{j})(t \mp \frac{1}{c}|x - y|, y)$ means to make first the partial differentiation $\frac{\partial}{\partial t}$ of $\mathbf{j}_t(x) = \mathbf{j}(t, x)$, and then in the next step, to insert the arguments $(t \mp \frac{1}{c}|x - y|, y)$. Analogously, $(\nabla\rho)(t\mp\frac{1}{c}|x-y|, y)$ and $(\nabla\times\mathbf{j})(t\mp\frac{1}{c}|x-y|, y)$ are meant to take first the x–gradient or x–curl respectively, and to insert then the arguments $(t \mp \frac{1}{c}|x - y|, y)$. (We take both signs $\mp$ in order to be prepared also for the advanced case.)

We demonstrate now, that we may shift the various ∇–operations in front of the integrals.

Lemma 55.3-10. *For all $x \in \mathbb{R}^3$ it holds*

$$\int_{\mathbb{R}^3} d^3y \frac{(\nabla\rho)(t \mp \frac{1}{c}|x - y|, y)}{|x - y|} = \nabla \int_{\mathbb{R}^3} d^3y \frac{\rho(t \mp \frac{1}{c}|x - y|, y)}{|x - y|},$$

$$\int_{\mathbb{R}^3} d^3y \frac{(\nabla \times \mathbf{j})(t \mp \frac{1}{c}|x - y|, y)}{|x - y|} = \nabla \times \int_{\mathbb{R}^3} d^3y \frac{\mathbf{j}(t \mp \frac{1}{c}|x - y|, y)}{|x - y|}.$$

$$(55.3.53)$$

Proof. We prove the second formula, the first one is obtained in the same way.

For each $x \in \mathbb{R}^3$ we perform the Fourier transformation of $t \mapsto \mathbf{j}(t, x)$ with respect to the time parameter $t \in \mathbb{R}$. A single Fourier component is then given by $\exp\{-it\omega\}\mathbf{j}(\omega, x) =: \mathbf{j}_\omega(t, x)$ for an arbitrary $\omega \in \mathbb{R}$. We prove the result for each Fourier component separately, then, in a last step, we have only to integrate over $\omega \in \mathbb{R}$ to return to the complete $\mathbf{j}(t, x)$.

With $\mathbf{j}(t, x)$ replaced by $\mathbf{j}_\omega(t, x)$ we arrive at

$$\int_{\mathbb{R}^3} d^3y \frac{(\nabla \times \mathbf{j}_\omega)(t \mp \frac{1}{c}|x - y|, y)}{|x - y|} = e^{-it\omega} \int_{\mathbb{R}^3} d^3y\, (\nabla \times \mathbf{j})(\omega, y) \frac{\exp\{\pm i\frac{1}{c}|x - y|\}}{|x - y|}$$

$$= e^{-it\omega} \nabla \times \int_{\mathbb{R}^3} d^3y\, \mathbf{j}(\omega, y) \frac{\exp\{\pm i\frac{1}{c}|x - y|\}}{|x - y|} = \nabla \times \int_{\mathbb{R}^3} d^3y \frac{\mathbf{j}_\omega(t \mp \frac{1}{c}|x - y|, y)}{|x - y|},$$

where we applied Eq. (55.3.10) of the proof of Proposition 55.3-3 for the function $f(\xi) = \frac{\exp\{\pm ic^{-1}\xi\}}{\xi}$, in order to obtain the desired result. $\qquad \square$

We have shown in Theorem 55.3-7 the equivalence of instantaneous and wave *differential equations* for the longitudinal electric field. Since we know now how the

wave solutions are uniquely determined by the charge and current trajectories we
may draw the following conclusion on the field *solutions*.

Proposition 55.3-11 (Equivalence of E–Field Solutions in the Future). *Let
us still specialize to free space* $\Lambda = \mathbb{R}^3$ *in which we assume to be given the charge
and current trajectories* $t \mapsto \varrho(t,x)$ *and* $t \mapsto \mathbf{j}(t,x)$ *for all* $x \in \mathbb{R}^3$ *such that the
continuity equation* (55.3.16) *is satisfied.*

*Then we have the following two forms for the longitudinal electric field solutions
of the Maxwell equations, valid for all* $t \geq 0$,

$$
\mathbf{E}_t^{\|}(x) \equiv \mathbf{E}^{\|}(t,x) = \frac{1}{\epsilon_0} (\nabla \cdot |^{\|})^{-1} \rho_t(x)
$$

$$
= -\frac{1}{4\pi\epsilon_0} \nabla \int_{\mathbb{R}^3} d^3 y \, \frac{\rho(t,y)}{|x-y|}
$$

$$
= -\frac{\mu_0}{4\pi} \frac{\partial}{\partial t} \int_{\mathbb{R}^3} d^3 y \, \frac{\mathbf{j}^{\|}(t-\frac{1}{c}|x-y|,y)}{|x-y|} - \frac{1}{4\pi\epsilon_0} \nabla \int_{\mathbb{R}^3} d^3 y \, \frac{\rho(t-\frac{1}{c}|x-y|,y)}{|x-y|} \, .
$$

$$
(55.3.54)
$$

*For the total electric field solutions we obtain then the two equivalent versions
(renouncing to pull out the differential operators acting on the sources)*

$$
\mathbf{E}_t^c(x) \equiv \mathbf{E}^c(t,x)
$$

$$
= -\frac{\mu_0}{4\pi} \int_{\mathbb{R}^3} d^3 y \, \frac{(\frac{\partial}{\partial t}\mathbf{j})(t-\frac{1}{c}|x-y|,y)}{|x-y|} - \frac{1}{4\pi\epsilon_0} \int_{\mathbb{R}^3} d^3 y \, \frac{(\nabla\rho)(t-\frac{1}{c}|x-y|,y)}{|x-y|}
$$

$$
= -\frac{\mu_0}{4\pi} \int_{\mathbb{R}^3} d^3 y \, \frac{(\frac{\partial}{\partial t}\mathbf{j}^{\top})(t-\frac{1}{c}|x-y|,y)}{|x-y|} - \frac{1}{4\pi\epsilon_0} \int_{\mathbb{R}^3} d^3 y \, \frac{(\nabla\rho)(t,y)}{|x-y|} \, ,
$$

$$
(55.3.55)
$$

*where the two terms in the last line give us the transversal and longitudinal field
parts respectively.*

*(Recall that in all source expressions appearing in the causal form of the solu-
tions, the time argument* $t - \frac{1}{c}|x-y|$ *has to be restricted to positive values.)*

Proof.   We obtain the equality of the two fields in Eq. (55.3.54) immediately from
Theorem 55.3-7 and Lemma 55.3-10.

To prove the equality of the fields in Eq. (55.3.55), we pick out the transversal
part of Eq. (55.3.51)

$$
\mathbf{E}^{c\top}(t,x) = -\frac{\mu_0}{4\pi} \int_{\mathbb{R}^3} d^3 y \, \frac{(\frac{\partial}{\partial t}\mathbf{j}^{\top})(t-\frac{1}{c}|x-y|,y)}{|x-y|}
$$

$$
(55.3.56)
$$

and add it to the first line in Eq. (55.3.54).   □

For discussing the result of the preceding Proposition 55.3-11, one should first
recall that the decomposition of a physical vector field into its longitudinal and

transversal parts has often a virtual character. We consider especially the total current density $\mathbf{j}_t$ and charge density ρ_t (together with $\nabla\rho_t$) which mostly have compact support. Then the longitudinal and transversal current parts $\mathbf{j}_t^{\parallel} = P^{\parallel}\mathbf{j}_t$ and $\mathbf{j}_t^{\top} = P^{\top}\mathbf{j}_t$ possess in general non–compact supports (non–locality of the pertinent projections). So already the Helmholtz–Hodge splitting $\mathbf{j}_t = \mathbf{j}_t^{\parallel} + \mathbf{j}_t^{\top}$ of the current may give rise to a non–physical "instantaneous" spatial expansion of each of the two different current parts. That is, the longitudinal conversion from instantaneousness to propagation with light velocity in Eq. (55.3.54) for itself may be physically problematic. Only the complete expression in the first line of (55.3.55) is physically ensured.

In a completely analogous manner, we obtain for the **past** the following field expressions, using the anti–causal Green's function.

Proposition 55.3-12 (Equivalence of E–Field Solutions in the Past). *Let us still specialize to free space $\Lambda = \mathbb{R}^3$ in which we assume to be given the charge and current trajectories $t \mapsto \varrho(t, x)$ and $t \mapsto \mathbf{j}(t, x)$ for all $x \in \mathbb{R}^3$ such that the continuity equation (55.3.16) is satisfied.*

Then we have the following two forms for the longitudinal electric field solutions of the Maxwell equations, valid for all $t \leq 0$,

$$\mathbf{E}_t^{\parallel}(x) \equiv \mathbf{E}^{\parallel}(t, x) = \frac{1}{\epsilon_0}(\nabla \cdot |^{\parallel})^{-1}\rho_t(x)$$

$$= -\frac{1}{4\pi\epsilon_0}\nabla\int_{\mathbb{R}^3} d^3y\,\frac{\rho(t, y)}{|x - y|}$$

$$= -\frac{\mu_0}{4\pi}\frac{\partial}{\partial t}\int_{\mathbb{R}^3} d^3y\,\frac{\mathbf{j}^{\parallel}(t + \frac{1}{c}|x - y|, y)}{|x - y|} - \frac{1}{4\pi\epsilon_0}\nabla\int_{\mathbb{R}^3} d^3y\,\frac{\rho(t + \frac{1}{c}|x - y|, y)}{|x - y|}.$$
$$(55.3.57)$$

For the total electric field solutions we obtain then the two equivalent versions

$$\mathbf{E}_t^a(x) \equiv \mathbf{E}^a(t, x)$$

$$= -\frac{\mu_0}{4\pi}\int_{\mathbb{R}^3} d^3y\,\frac{(\frac{\partial}{\partial t}\mathbf{j})(t + \frac{1}{c}|x - y|, y)}{|x - y|} - \frac{1}{4\pi\epsilon_0}\int_{\mathbb{R}^3} d^3y\,\frac{(\nabla\rho)(t + \frac{1}{c}|x - y|, y)}{|x - y|}$$

$$= -\frac{\mu_0}{4\pi}\int_{\mathbb{R}^3} d^3y\,\frac{(\frac{\partial}{\partial t}\mathbf{j}^{\top})(t + \frac{1}{c}|x - y|, y)}{|x - y|} - \frac{1}{4\pi\epsilon_0}\int_{\mathbb{R}^3} d^3y\,\frac{(\nabla\rho)(t, y)}{|x - y|}, \quad (55.3.58)$$

where the two terms in the last line give us the transversal and longitudinal field components respectively.

(Recall that in all source expressions appearing in the anti–causal form of the solutions, the time argument $t + \frac{1}{c}|x - y|$ has to be restricted to negative values.)

55.3.7. *Potentials and Causality*

The usual ansatz for the potentials (see Eqs. (6.0.1) and (6.0.2)) goes in terms of the following expressions for the force fields

$$\mathbf{E}_t = -\nabla u_t - \frac{\partial \mathbf{A}_t}{\partial t}\,, \tag{55.3.59}$$

$$\mathbf{B}_t = \nabla \times \mathbf{A}_t\,, \tag{55.3.60}$$

valid for all times $t \in \mathbb{R}$. Inserting the force field expressions into the two inhomogeneous Maxwell Eqs. (55.3.12) and (55.3.15) leads with $\nabla \cdot (\nabla u_t) = \Delta u_t$ and Eq. (55.3.1) to

$$\Delta u_t + \nabla \cdot \frac{\partial \mathbf{A}_t}{\partial t} = -\frac{1}{\epsilon_0}\rho_t\,, \tag{55.3.61}$$

$$\underbrace{\nabla(\nabla \cdot \mathbf{A}_t) - \Delta \mathbf{A}_t}_{= \nabla \times (\nabla \times \mathbf{A}_t)} + \frac{1}{c^2}\frac{\partial^2 \mathbf{A}_t}{\partial t^2} + \frac{1}{c^2}\nabla\frac{\partial u_t}{\partial t} = \mu_0 \mathbf{j}_t\,. \tag{55.3.62}$$

These equations are valid in any gauge, but simplify if appropriate gauge subsidiary conditions are imposed.

In a relativistic covariant formulation one chooses the **Lorenz condition**

$$\nabla \cdot \mathbf{A}_t + \frac{1}{c^2}\frac{\partial u_t}{\partial t} = 0\,. \tag{55.3.63}$$

That subsidiary condition leads to the two inhomogeneous wave equations

$$\Box u_t = \frac{1}{\epsilon_0}\rho_t\,, \tag{55.3.64}$$

$$\Box \mathbf{A}_t = \mu_0 \mathbf{j}_t\,. \tag{55.3.65}$$

Recall that in four–vector notation one may write, using $y := (ct, x) \in \mathbb{R}^4$ and the variable superscript $\mu \in \{0, 1, 2, 3\}$,

$$\Box A^\mu(y) = \Box\left(\tfrac{u_t(x)}{c}, \mathbf{A}_t(x)\right) = \mu_0\left(c\rho_t(x), \mathbf{j}_t(x)\right) = \mu_0 j^\mu(y)\,, \tag{55.3.66}$$

where, in Einstein's sum convection,

$$\Box = \partial/\partial y^\mu \partial/\partial y_\mu\,.$$

Each of the four potential components is then a solution of an inhomogeneous wave equation with trivial initial conditions and may be written — for positive times — as in Eq. (55.3.38). That gives

$$u_t^c(x) = \frac{1}{4\pi\epsilon_0}\int_{\mathbb{R}^3} d^3y \frac{\rho(t - \frac{1}{c}|x - y|, y)}{|x - y|}\,, \tag{55.3.67}$$

$$\mathbf{A}_t^c(x) = \frac{\mu_0}{4\pi}\int_{\mathbb{R}^3} d^3y \frac{\mathbf{j}(t - \frac{1}{c}|x - y|, y)}{|x - y|}\,. \tag{55.3.68}$$

The curl of Eq. (55.3.68) reproduces the solution Eq. (55.3.52) of the **B**–field, and insertion of Eq. (55.3.67) and Eq. (55.3.68) into Eq. (55.3.59) leads to the causal solution for the **E**–field, that is the first version of Eq. (55.3.55).

Relativistic covariance is broken from the outset by the usual **Coulomb gauge condition**

$$\nabla \cdot \mathbf{A}_t = 0 \quad \Longleftrightarrow \quad \mathbf{A}_t^{\parallel} = 0, \qquad \forall t \in \mathbb{R}, \tag{55.3.69}$$

as well as by our **generalized Coulomb gauge condition**

$$\mathbf{A}_t^{\parallel} = \mathbf{A}_0^{\parallel}, \quad \forall t \in \mathbb{R}. \tag{55.3.70}$$

In both cases, Eq. (55.3.61) reduces to the Coulomb potential condition

$$-\Delta u_t = \frac{1}{\epsilon_0}\rho_t, \quad \forall t \in \mathbb{R}, \tag{55.3.71}$$

the basic equation for non–relativistic matter models. Its solution in the present free space

$$u_t(x) = \frac{1}{4\pi\epsilon_0} \int_{\mathbb{R}^3} d^3 y \frac{\rho(t,y)}{|x-y|} \tag{55.3.72}$$

may be also gained by the limit $c \to \infty$ for the light velocity from the causal form (55.3.67).

The fourth Maxwell equation in terms of potentials in unspecified gauge Eq. (55.3.62) reduces in the usual Coulomb gauge to

$$\Box \mathbf{A}_t = \mu_0 \mathbf{j}_t - \frac{1}{c^2}\nabla\frac{\partial u_t}{\partial t}. \tag{55.3.73}$$

By commuting the curl with the $\Box$ we regain

$$\Box \mathbf{B}_t = \mu_0 \nabla \times \mathbf{j}_t, \tag{55.3.74}$$

possessing the causal solution Eq. (55.3.52).

Since $\mathbf{A}_t = \mathbf{A}_t^{\top}$ in the *usual Coulomb gauge*, Eq. (55.3.59) provides us just with the longitudinal and transversal components of $\mathbf{E}_t$. But $\mathbf{E}_t^{\parallel}$ is the negative gradient of Eq. (55.3.72), and $\mathbf{E}_t^{\top} = -\frac{\partial \mathbf{A}_t^{\top}}{\partial t}$, where $\mathbf{A}_t^{\top}$ obeys the wave equation with only the current as inhomogeneity. Adding together $\mathbf{E}_t^{\parallel}$ and $\mathbf{E}_t^{\top}$, the total $\mathbf{E}_t$ arises then in the second form of Eq. (55.3.55). Since the latter equals the first form of Eq. (55.3.55) we have directly proved that the Lorenz and Coulomb potentials produce the same force fields.

In the cited article of Brill and Goodman, one argues in the reverse direction and concludes from the equivalence of the Lorenz and Coulomb gauges to the equality of the two $\mathbf{E}_t$–versions in Eq. (55.3.55), but there that is also derived by a direct computation. In an analogous manner they could have derived that the instantaneous form of $\mathbf{E}_t^{\parallel}$ may be expressed in an anti–causal, or advanced, form, what we again concluded from the force field structures alone.

In the *generalized Coulomb gauge*, $\mathbf{A}_t^{\parallel}$ is constant in time, and we obtain as in the usual Coulomb gauge

$$\mathbf{E}_t^{\parallel} = -\nabla u_t \quad \text{and} \quad \mathbf{E}_t^{\top} = -\frac{\partial \mathbf{A}_t^{\top}}{\partial t}. \tag{55.3.75}$$

In the general Eq. (55.3.62), the first term does not vanish now, but the transverse form of the equation is the same as in the usual Coulomb and Lorenz gauge. Thus we obtain also in this case the correct force fields.

In the **temporal gauge** one sets

$$u_t = 0, \quad \forall t \in \mathbb{R}, \tag{55.3.76}$$

and obtains

$$\mathbf{E}_t^{\parallel} = -\frac{\partial \mathbf{A}_t^{\parallel}}{\partial t} \quad \text{and} \quad \mathbf{E}_t^{\top} = -\frac{\partial \mathbf{A}_t^{\top}}{\partial t}. \tag{55.3.77}$$

Then

$$\frac{1}{\epsilon_0}\rho_t = -\nabla \frac{\partial \mathbf{A}_t^{\parallel}}{\partial t} = \nabla \cdot \mathbf{E}_t^{\parallel}, \tag{55.3.78}$$

and we obtain the usual electric Coulomb field $\mathbf{E}_t^{\parallel}$, without bothering about its potential.

Again the transversal form of the general Eq. (55.3.62) is the same as in the Coulomb and Lorenz gauges, and we may directly confirm the correct force fields.

Conclusion 55.3-13 (Force Fields from the Potential Equations). For free space, we have explicitly demonstrated that in all of the considered four gauge classes (Lorenz, Coulomb, generalized Coulomb, temporal) we obtain for the transversal vector potential the WE

$$\Box\mathbf{A}_t^{\top} = \mu_0 \mathbf{j}_t^{\top}. \tag{55.3.79}$$

That is even universally gauge independent, since the WE (55.3.79) is just the transversal part of (55.3.62) and thus is valid for any gauge.

From there, one obtains the WE for $\mathbf{B}_t^{\top} = \mathbf{B}_t$ by applying the curl, as well as for $\mathbf{E}_t^{\top}$ by applying the negative time derivative. For the remaining $\mathbf{E}_t^{\parallel}$ we obtain in the *Lorenz gauge class* the WE

$$\Box\mathbf{E}_t^{\parallel} = -\mu_0 \frac{\partial \mathbf{j}^{\parallel}}{\partial t} - \frac{1}{\epsilon_0}\nabla\rho_t, \tag{55.3.80}$$

which combines with the WE for $\mathbf{E}_t^{\top}$ to the WE for the total $\mathbf{E}_t$.

By the equivalence theorem 55.3-8 we regain from the WE for $\mathbf{E}_t$ and $\mathbf{B}_t$ the Maxwell equations, *provided* we have local charge conservation and the correct initial conditions for the two fields and their time derivatives.

In the *(generalized) Coulomb and temporal gauge classes* we obtain for $\mathbf{E}_t^{\parallel}$ the instantaneous relation

$$\nabla \cdot \mathbf{E}_t^{\parallel} = \frac{1}{\epsilon_0}\rho_t. \tag{55.3.81}$$

By Theorem 55.3-7 that relation is equivalent to the WE (55.3.80), *provided* we have local charge conservation and the correct initial conditions for the longitudinal $\mathbf{E}_t^{\parallel}$–field and its time derivative.

Taking into account the already proven WE for $\mathbf{E}_t^{\top}$ and $\mathbf{B}_t$, we can proceed as in the Lorenz gauge class and arrive at the complete set of the Maxwell equations also for the Coulomb and temporal gauges.

The preceding discussion clearly reveals the universal character, not only of the $\mathbf{E}_t^\top-$ and $(\mathbf{B}_t = \mathbf{B}_t^\top)$–fields, but also that of the $\mathbf{E}_t^\top$ and $\mathbf{A}_t^\top$–fields. On the latter pair of field variables we have founded (even in arbitrary cavities) the canonical formalism, using the pairs $(\mathbf{A}_t^\top, \mathbf{Y}_t^\top = -\epsilon_0 \mathbf{E}_t^\top)$ as those part of the phase space, which ultimately leads to the photon concept. That only these phase space variables provide us — after canonical quantization — with a physically well founded photonic particle notion, with the appropriate complex wave functions, requires also in free space a thorough investigation (which is included in our general elaboration). In spite of having in free space also a kind of a diagonalization by working with the separated wave equations for the $\mathbf{E}_t^\top-$ and $\mathbf{B}_t$–fields, that can neither serve for a canonical formalism, nor for a quantization with complex wave functions formed in terms of these fields.

In the two considered Coulomb gauge classes, the transversal canonical fields constitute all of the phase space.

In our generalized Coulomb gauge, $\mathbf{A}_t^\|$ is non–vanishing but must be time–independent as a subsidiary condition. Since it is not part of the canonical formalism it cannot be quantized. In quantum mechanics the values of $\mathbf{A}_t^\| = \mathbf{A}_0^\|$ are not irrelevant since their differences may lead to phase effects. For this one needs, however, a topologically non–trivial cavity $\Lambda \subset \mathbb{R}^3$ with non–vanishing cohomological vector potential $\mathbf{A}_t^{co}$, which we found more important than $\mathbf{A}_0^\|$ for discussing quantum phases in superconductivity.

In the temporal gauge, the pair $(\mathbf{A}_t^\|, \mathbf{Y}_t^\| = -\epsilon_0 \mathbf{E}_t^\|)$ adds to the field phase space variables and undergoes also canonical quantization. The peculiar role of these quantum fields in QED seems still to be not clarified completely, but certainly requires first of all a concise structural analysis.

The Lorenz gauge is usually considered as the starting point for a relativistic quantization of ED. By that procedure, even the scalar potential is quantized. But necessary subsidiary conditions for gaining something like a Fock vacuum break, in fact, Lorentz invariance. The usefulness of including the quantized scalar potential into a photon concept is more than questionable, if one sticks to conventional particle features.

In the strictly non–relativistic formulation of our treatise, the still classical longitudinal $\mathbf{E}_t^\|$ plays the decisive role for matter models, both in the classical and the quantized formulation. The instantaneous form of its dynamics seems to fit to that role. The equivalent formulation of that dynamics as an inhomogeneous wave equation, a main topic of the present section, is, however, basic for the intrinsic consistency of the electrodynamic formalism.

In the main part of the three volumes treatise we deal with Maxwell's dynamics — classically as well as quantum mechanically — directly in operator form (like in Eq. (55.3.18), where $\mathbb{A}$, $\mathbb{A}_{\text{vac}}$, or $\mathbb{A}_M$ denote the dynamical Maxwell operators without current) and prove in this manner, e.g., the exact equivalence of certain phase space flows with the original Maxwell equations. The mathematical efforts to discuss the various stages of solution theory are considerable, but are comparable with those for the hyperbolic wave equation in mathematical physics. For the photon theory, the discrimination between L^2–solutions and generalized solutions in appropriate dual spaces (over test functions which smooth out the infrared and ultraviolet divergences) are especially important: The L^2–solutions have finite energies and correspond in QED to normalizable microscopic photon wave functions, whereas the generalized solutions describe classically scattering fields, which in QED arise only via collective photonic excitations. On the macroscopic level, the collective photonic fields are not normalizable and are neatly separated off from the quantum fluctuations which still are present. A special amount of operator algebraic formalism is needed for the intermediate stage of photon theory, on which collective photonic fields already exist which are normalizable, but closely intertwined with the quantum operators. They constitute still a challenge for mathematical physics.

Bibliography

[AA12]   M. Aspelmeyer and M. Arndt, Schrödingers Katze auf dem Prüfstand, *Spektrum der Wissenschaft* **10** (2012).

[ABM13]   U. Akram, W.P. Bowen and G.J. Milburn, Entangled mechanical cat states via conditional single photon optomechanics, arXiv:quant-ph **1305.3781** (2013).

[Ada75]   R.A. Adams, *Sobolev spaces*. New York: Academic Press (1975).

[ADR82]   A. Aspect, J. Dalibard and G. Roger, Experimental test of Bell's inequalities using time–varying analyzers, *Phys. Rev. Lett.* **49** (1982) 1804–1807.

[AGJ71]   W.O. Amrein, V. Georgescu and J.M. Jauch, Stationary state scattering theory, *Helv. Phys. Acta* **44** (1971) 407–434.

[AGR82]   A. Aspect, P. Grangier and G. Roger, Experimental realization of Einstein–Podolsky–Rosen–Bohm Gedankenexperiment: a new violation of Bell's inequalities, *Phys. Rev. Lett.* **49** (1982) 91–98.

[AH⁺77]   H. Araki, R. Haag, D. Kastler and M.A. Takesaki, Extension of KMS states and chemical potential, *Commun. Math. Phys.* **53** (1977) 97–134.

[AJS77]   W.O. Amrein, J.M. Jauch and K.B. Sinha, Scattering theory in quantum mechanics, *Lecture notes and supplements in physics* 16, Dordrecht, Holland: W.A. Benjamin Inc., (1977).

[AK77]   H. Araki and A. Kishimoto, Symmetry and equilibrium states, *Commun. Math. Phys.* **52** (1977) 211–232.

[AKM13]   M. Aspelmeyer, T.J. Kippenberg and F. Marquardt, Cavity optomechanics, arXiv:quant-ph **130.0733v1** (2013).

[Alb83]   P.M. Alberti, A note on the transition probability over C*–algebras, *Lett. Math. Phys.* **7** (1983) 25–32.

[Alb92]   P.M. Alberti, A study on the geometry of pairs of positive linear forms, algebraic transition probability and geometrical phase over non–commutative operator algebras (I), *Zeitschr. Anal. Anw.* **11** (1992) 293–334.

[Alf71]   E.M. Alfsen, *Compact convex sets and boundary integrals*. Berlin, Heidelberg, New York: Springer (1971).

[AM76]   N.W. Ashcroft and N.D. Mermin, *Solid state physics*. Philadelphia: Holt–Sounders (1976).

[AM78]   R. Abraham and J.E. Marsden, *Foundations of mechanics*. 2nd edn. Amsterdam: Benjamin–Cummings Publication Company, London (1978).

[AM90]   J. Audretsch and K. Mainzer, *Wieviele Leben hat Schrödingers Katze?*. Mannheim: BI Wissenschaftsverlag (1990).

[Ama91a]   A. Amann, Chirality: a superselection rule generated by the molecular environment? *J. Math. Chem.* **6** (1991) 1–15.

[Ama91b] A. Amann, Molecules coupled to their environment, In *Large scale molecular systems: quantum and stochastic aspects* (Maratea, Italy, 1990). W. Gans, A. Blumen and A. Amann (Eds.), NATO–ASI. New York, London: Plenum Press (1991).

[Amr81]   W.O. Amrein, *Non–relativistic quantum dynamics*. Dordrecht, Holland: D. Reidel Publication Company (1981).

[AMR88]   R. Abraham, J.E. Marsden and T. Ratiu, *Manifolds, tensor analysis, and applications*. Berlin, Heidelberg; New York: Springer (1988).

[And58]   P.W. Anderson, Random–phase approximation in the theory of superconductivity, *Phys. Rev.* **112** (1958) 1900–1916.

[And64]   P.W. Anderson, Special effects in superconductivity, *The many–body problem* (Ravello). E.R. Caianiello (Ed.), New York: Academic Press (1964), pp. 113–136.

[AR63]   P.W. Anderson and J.M. Rowell, Probable observation of the Josephson superconducting tunneling effect, *Phys. Rev. Lett.* **10** (1963) 230–232.

[AR82]   H. Araki and G.A. Raggio, A remark on transition probability, *Lett. Math. Phys.* **6** (1982) 237–240.

[Ara68]   H. Araki, On the diagonalization of a bilinear Hamiltonian by a Bogoliubov transformation, *Publications of RIMS, Kyoto University Series A* (1968) 387–412.

[Arn85]   V.I. Arnold, *Mathematical methods of classical mechanics*. Berlin, Heidelberg; New York: Springer (1985).

[Arv74]   W. Arveson, On groups of automorphisms of operator algebras, *J. Funct. Anal.* **15** (1974) 217–243.

[AS76]   E.M. Alfsen and F.W. Shultz, Non–commutative spectral theory for affine functions on convex sets, *Mem. Am. Math. Soc.* **172** (1976).

[AS78]   E.M. Alfsen and F.W. Shultz, State spaces of Jordan algebras, *Acta Mathematica* **140** (1978) 155–190.

[AS79]   E.M. Alfsen and F.W. Shultz, On non–commutative spectral theory and Jordan algebras, *Proc. L. Math. Soc.* **38** (1979) 497–516.

[AS95]   G. Alli and G.L. Sewell, New methods and structures in the theory of the multi–mode Dicke laser model, *J. Math. Phys.* **36** (1995) 5598–5626.

[AS98a]   E.M. Alfsen and F.W. Shultz, On orientation and dynamics in operator algebras, *Commun. Math. Phys.* **194** (1998) 87–108.

[AS98b]   E.M. Alfsen and F.W. Shultz, Orientation in operator algebras, *Proc. Natl. Acad. Sci. USA* **95** (1998) 6596–6601.

[ASH80]   E.M. Alfsen, F.W. Shultz and H. Hanche-Olsen, State spaces of C*-algebras, *Acta Mathematica* **144** (1980) 267–305.

[AU83]   P.M. Alberti and A. Uhlmann, Stochastic linear maps and transition probability, *Lett. Math. Phys.* **7** (1983) 107–112.

[AW63]   H. Araki and E.J. Woods, Representations of the canonical commutation relations describing a nonrelativistic infinite free Bose gas, *J. Math. Phys.* **5** (1963) 637–662.

[AZ96]   J.R. Anglin and W.H. Zurek, A precision test for decoherence, arXiv:quant-ph **1308.5290** (1996).

[Bae87]   J. Baez, Bell's inequality for C*-algebras, *Lett. Math. Phys.* **13** (1987) 135–136.

[Bak97]   H.F. Baker, Alternants and continuous groups, *Proc. L. Math. Soc.* **28** (1897) 381–390.

[Bar54]   V. Bargmann, On unitary ray representations of continuous groups, *Ann. Math.* **59** (1954) 1–46.

[BB94]   I. Bialynicki–Birula, On the wave function of the photon, *Acta Phys. Pol. A*
            86 (1994) 97.

[BB06]   I. Bialynicki–Birula, Photon as a quantum particle, *Acta Phys. Pol. B* **37** (2006)
            935–946.

[BC81]   E.G. Beltrametti and G. Cassinelli, *The logics of quantum mechanics*. Reading:
            Addison–Wesley (1981).

[BCS57]   J. Bardeen, L.N. Cooper and J.R. Schrieffer, Theory of superconductivity, *Phys.
            Rev.* **108** (1957) 1175–1204.

[BE91]   J. Bergou and B.–G. Englert, Operators of the phase. Fundamentals, *Ann.
            Phys.* **209** (1991) 479–505.

[Bel64]   J.S. Bell, On the Einstein Podolsky Rosen paradox, *Physics* (Long Island City,
            N.Y.) **1** (1964) 195–200.

[Bel71]   J.S. Bell, Introduction to the hidden–variable question, *Proceedings of the inter-
            national school of physics 'Enrico Fermi': foundation of quantum mechanics*
            (Varenna, Lago di Como, Italy, 1970). B. d'Espagnat (Ed.). New York: Aca-
            demic Press (1971), pp. 171–181.

[Ben76]   F. Bentosela, Scattering from impurities in a crystal, *Commun. Math. Phys.*
            46 (1976) 153–166.

[Ben10]   M. Benner, Quantization of collective variables in many–body systems. *Tech-
            nical Report*, University Tübingen, *Inst. Theor. Phys.* (2010).

[Ber66]   F.A. Berezin, *The method of second quantization*. New York: Academic Press
            (1966).

[Ber74]   F.A. Berezin, Quantization, *Math. USSR Izv.* **8** (1974) 1109–1163.

[Bes32]   A.S. Besicovitch, *Almost periodic functions*. Dover: Dover Publications (1932).

[BF⁺78]   F. Bayen, M. Flato, C. Fronsdal, A. Lichnerovicz and D. Sternheimer, Defor-
            mation theory and quantization, *Ann. Phys.* **111** (1978) 61–151.

[BH76]   H.P. Baltes and E.R. Hilf, *Spectra of finite systems*. Mannheim, Wien, Zürich:
            BI Wissenschaftsverlag (1976).

[BHJ26]   M. Born, W. Heisenberg and P. Jordan, Zur Quantenmechanik II, *Z. Physik*
            36 (1926) 557–615.

[BHR91]   C. Bendjaballah, O. Hirota and S. Reynaud, *Quantum Aspects of optical com-
            munication*. Berlin, Heidelberg, New York: Springer (1991).

[BHR04a]   E. Binz, R. Honegger and A. Rieckers, Construction and uniqueness of the
            C*-Weyl algebra over a general pre-symplectic form, *J. Math. Phys.* **45** (2004)
            2885–2907.

[BHR04b]   E. Binz, R. Honegger and A. Rieckers, Field–theoretic Weyl quantization as a
            strict and continuous deformation quantization, *Ann. Henri Poincaré* **5** (2004)
            327–346.

[BHR07]   E. Binz, R. Honegger and A. Rieckers, Infinite–dimensional Heisenberg group
            algebra and field–theoretic strict deformation quantization, *Int. J. Pure and
            Appl. Math.* **38** (2007) 43–78.

[BI79]   J. Bellisard and B. Iochum, Spectral theory for facially homogeneous symmetric
            selfdual cones, *Math. Scand.* **45** (1979) 118–126.

[Bin93]   E. Binz, On the irredundant part of the first Piola–Kirchhoff stress tensor, *Rep.
            Math. Phys.* **32**(2) (1993).

[BJ25]   M. Born and P. Jordan, Zur Quantenmechanik, *Z. Physik* **34** (1925) 858–888.

[Ble81]   D. Bleecker, *Gauge theory and variational principles*. New York: Addison–
            Wesley (1981).

[Blo28]   F. Bloch, Über die Qantenmechanik der Elektronen in Kristallgittern, *Z. Phys.*
            52 (1928) 555–600.

[Bog58]   N.N. Bogoliubov, On a new method in the theory of superconductivity, *Nuovo Cim.* **7** (1958) 794.

[Bog90]   N.N. Bogoliubov, *Collected works II: quantum and classical statistical mechanics.* New York: Gordon and Breach (1990).

[Boh13]   N. Bohr, On the constitution of atoms and molecules, *Phil. Mag.* **26** (1913) 1–25.

[Boh28]   N. Bohr, The quantum postulate and the recent development of atomic theory, *Nature* **121** (1928) 580–590.

[Bol77]   L. Boltzmann, Über die Beziehung zwischen dem zweiten Hauptsatz der Wärmetheorie und der Wahrscheinlichkeitsrechnung respektive der Sätze über das Wärmegleichgewicht, *Sitz.ber. Akad. Wiss.* (Wien) **76** (1877) 373–435.

[Bon88]   P. Bona, The dynamics of a class of quantum mean–field theories, *J. Math. Phys.* **29** (1988) 2223–2235.

[Bon00]   P. Bona, Extended quantum mechanics, *Acta Physica Slovaca* **50** (2000) 1–198.

[Bor24]   M. Born, Über Quantenmechanik, *Z. Physik* **26** (1924) 379–395.

[Bor26]   M. Born, Zur Wellenmechanik der Stoßvorgänge, *Nachr. Ges. Wiss. Göttingen* (1926) 146–160.

[Bor66]   H.J. Borchers, Energy and momentum as observables in quantum field theory, *Commun. Math. Phys.* **2** (1966) 49–54.

[Bor99]   H.J. Borchers, On revolutionizing of quantum field theory with Tomita's modular theory, *Vienna Preprint ESI no 773* (1999) 1–162.

[Bös76]   W. Bös, Direct integrals for selfdual cones and standard forms of von Neumann algebras, *Inv. Math.* **37** (1976) 241–251.

[BP82]   A. Barone and G. Paternò, *Physics and applications of the Josephson effect.* New York: John Wiley & Sons (1982).

[BP08]   E. Binz and S. Pods, The geometry of the Heisenberg groups, *Amer. Math. Soc.*, Providence (2008).

[BPS03a] E. Binz, S. Pods and W. Schempp, Heisenberg groups — a unifying structure of signal theory, holography and quantum information theory, *J. Appl. Math. Comput.* **11** (2003) 1–57.

[BPS03b] E. Binz, S. Pods and W. Schempp, Heisenberg groups — the fundamental ingredient to describe information, its transmission and quantization, *J. Phys. A: Math. Gen.* **36** (2003) 6401–6421.

[BR80]   A.O. Barut and R. Raczka, *Theory of group representations and applications.* Warszawa: PWN-Polish Scientific Publishers (1980).

[BR87]   O. Bratteli and D.W. Robinson, *Operator algebras and quantum statistical mechanics 1*, 2nd edn. Berlin, Heidelberg; New York: Springer (1987).

[BR97]   O. Bratteli and D.W. Robinson, *Operator algebras and quantum statistical mechanics 2*, 2nd edn. Berlin, Heidelberg; New York: Springer (1997).

[BR05]   M. Benner and A. Rieckers, Spectral properties of weakly inhomogeneous BCS–models in different representations, *Z. Naturforsch.* **60a** (2005) 343–365.

[Bre85]   R. Brendle, Einstein condensation in a macroscopic field, *Z. Naturforsch.* **40a** (1985) 1189–1198.

[BRW99]   M. Bordemann, H. Römer and S. Waldmann, KMS-states and star product quantization, *Rep. Math. Phys.* **44** (1999).

[BS59]   N.N. Bogoliubov and D.V. Shirkov, *Introduction to the theory of quantized fields.* New York: Addison–Wesley (1959).

[BS67]   G. Bethe and A. Sommerfeld, *Elektronentheorie der Metalle.* Berlin: Springer–Verlag (1967).

[BS70] R.C. Busby and H.A. Smith, Representations of twisted group algebras, *Trans. Amer. Math. Soc.* **149** (1970) 503–537.

[BSF88] E. Binz, J. Sniatycki and H. Fischer, Geometry of classical fields, *Mathematics Studies* 154. Amsterdam: North–Holland (1988).

[Buc90] W. Buckel, *Supraleitung*. Weinheim: Wiley–VCH (1990).

[Bur69] D. Bures, An extension of Kakutani's theorem on infinite product measures to the tensor product of semifinite W*–algebras, *Trans. Amer. Math. Soc.* **135** (1969) 199–212.

[BW97] S. Bates and A. Weinstein, Lectures on the geometry of quantization, *Amer. Math. Soc.*, Berkeley (1997).

[Byr10] P. Byrne, *The many worlds of hugh Everett III: multiple universes, mutual assured destruction and the meltdown of a nuclear family*. Oxford: Oxford University Press (2010).

[Cam05] J.E. Campbell, On a law of combination of operators bearing on the theory of continuous transformation groups, *Proc. L. Math. Soc.* **3** (1905) 24–47.

[Can73] J.T. Cannon, Infinite volume limits of the canonical free Bose gas states on the Weyl algebra, *Commun. Math. Phys.* **29** (1973) 89–104.

[Can75] V. Cantoni, Generalized "transition probability", *Commun. Math. Phys.* **44** (1975) 125–128.

[Cav81] C.M. Caves, Quantum limits on noise in linear amplifiers, *Phys. Rev. D* **23** (1981) 1693.

[Cav82] C.M. Caves, Quantum limits on noise in linear amplifiers, *Phys. Rev. D* **26** (1982) 1817–1839.

[CC87] C.M. Caves and D.D. Crouch, Quantum wideband traveling-wave analysis of a degenerate parametric amplifier, *J. Opt. Soc. Am. B* **4** (1987) 1535–1545.

[CDG89] C. Cohen–Tannoudji, J. Dupont–Roc and G. Grynberg, *Photons & atoms, introduction to QED*. New York; Toronto; Singapore: John Wiley & Sons (1989).

[CH62] R. Courant and D. Hilbert, *Methods of mathematical physics I, II*. Interscience Publications (1953, 1962).

[CH87] A.L. Carey and K.C. Hannabuss, Temperature states on loop groups, theta functions and the Luttinger model, *J. Func. Anal.* **75** (1987) 128–160.

[Cha68] J.M. Chaiken, Number operators for representations of the canonical commutation relations, *Commun. Math. Phys.* **8** (1968) 164–184.

[Cha84] I. Chavel, *Eigenvalues in Riemannian geometry*. New York: Academic Press (1984).

[Cha12] N. Chandrasekar, Quantum mechanics of photons, *Adv. Studies Theor. Phys.* **6** (2012) 391–397.

[CK99] W. Chow and S. Koch, *Semiconductor–laser fundamentals*. Berlin, Heidelberg; New York: Springer–Verlag (1999).

[CL83] A.O. Caldeira and A.J. Leggett, Macroscopic quantum coherence, *Ann. Phys.* **149** (1983) 374.

[CN68] P. Carruthers and M.M. Nieto, Phase and angle variables in quantum mechanics, *Rev. Mod. Phys.* **40** (1968) 411.

[Coh80] D.L. Cohn, *Measure theory*. Boston: Birkhäuser (1980).

[Com23] A.H. Compton, A quantum theory of scattering of X–rays by light elements, *Phys. Rev.* **21**(2) (1923) 483–502.

[Con73] A. Connes, Une classification des facteurs de type III, *Ann. Scient. Ecole Norm. Sup.* **6** (1973) 133–252.

[Con74] A. Connes, Orientation, *Ann. Inst. Fourier* **24** (1974) 121–133.

[Con85]   J.B. Conway, *A course in functional analysis.* Berlin, Heidelberg; New York: Springer (1985).

[CS78]   J.F. Clauser and A. Shimony, Bell's theorem: experimental tests and implications, *Rep. Prog. Phys.* **41** (1978) 1881–1927.

[CS86]   C.M. Caves and B.L. Schumaker, Broadband squeezing, *Springer Proceedings in Physics* 12. Berlin, Heidelberg; New York: Springer (1986,) pp. 20–30.

[Da89]   P. Delsing *et al.*, Time–correlated single–electron tunneling in one–dimensional arrays of ultrasmall tunnel junctions, *Phys. Rev. Lett.* **63** (1989) 1861.

[Dav73a] E.B. Davies, Exact dynamics of an infinite-atom Dicke maser model I, *Commun. Math. Phys.* **33** (1973) 187–205.

[Dav73b] E.B. Davies, The infinite atom Dicke maser model II, *Commun. Math. Phys.* **34** (1973) 237–249.

[Dav76]   E.B. Davies, *Quantum theory of open systems.* New York; London; Sydney: Academic Press (1976).

[Dav80]   E.B. Davies, *One-parameter semigroups.* New York; London; Sydney: Academic Press (1980).

[Dav81]   E.B. Davies, Symmetrie breaking for molecular open systems, *Ann. Inst. Henri Poincaré* **XXXV** (1981) 149–171.

[Deb23]   P. Debye, Zerstreuung von Röntgenstrahlen nach der Quantentheorie, *Phys. Zs.* **24** (1923) 161–166.

[DFN90]   B.A. Dubrovin, A.T. Fomenko and S.P. Novikov, *Modern geometry — methods and applications I, II, III.* Berlin, Heidelberg, New York: Springer–Verlag (1984, 1985, 1990).

[DG73]   B.S. DeWitt and N. Graham, *The many–worlds interpretation of quantum mechanics.* Princeton: Princeton University Press (1973).

[Dic54]   R.H. Dicke, Coherence in spontaneous radiation processes, *Phys. Rev.* **93** (1954) 99–110.

[Die60]   J. Dieudonné, *Foundations of modern analysis.* New York: Academic Press (1960).

[Dir26a] P.A.M. Dirac, On quantum algebra, *Proc. Camb. Phil. Soc.* **23** (1926) 412–418.

[Dir26b] P.A.M. Dirac, Quantum mechanics, *Proc. Roy. Soc.* A **110** (1926) 561–579.

[Dir30]   P.A.M. Dirac, *The principles of quantum mechanics.* Oxford: Oxford University Press (1930).

[Dit90]   J. Dito, Star–product approach to quantum field theory: the free scalar field, *Lett. Math. Phys.* **20** (1990) 125–134.

[Dit92]   J. Dito, Star–products and nonstandard quantization for the Klein–Gordon equation, *J. Math. Phys.* **33** (1992) 791–801.

[Dix56]   J. Dixmier, Sur la relation $i(PQ - QP) = I$, *Comp. Math.* **13** (1956) 263–269.

[Dix69]   J. Dixmier, *Les Algèbres d'Opérateur dans l'Espace Hilbertien.* Berlin, Heidelberg, New York: Springer (1969).

[Dix77]   J. Dixmier, *C*–algebras.* Amsterdam: North–Holland (1977).

[DKS69]   S. Doplicher, D. Kastler and E. Størmer, Invariant states and asymptotic Abelianess, *J. Func. Anal.* **3** (1969) 419–434.

[DL83]   M. DeWilde and P.B.A. Lecompte, Existence of star-products and of formal deformations of a Poisson Lie algebra of arbitrary symplectic manifolds, *Lett. Math. Phys.* **7** (1983) 487–496.

[DL88]   M. DeWilde and P.B.A. Lecompte, Formal deformations of a Poisson Lie algebra of a symplectic manifold and star products. Existence, equivalence, derivations, In *Deformation theory of algebras and structures and applications*, M. Hazewinkel and M. Gerstenhaber (Eds.). Dordrecht: Kluwer (1988).

[DL93]   R. Dautray and J.L. Lions, *Mathematical analysis and numerical methods for science and technology 1–6*. New York, Berlin: Springer (1990–1993).

[DMC85]   M.H. Devoret, J.M. Martinis and J. Clarke, Measurement of macroscopic quantum tunneling out of the zero–voltage state at a current biased Josephson junction, *Phys. Rev. Lett.* **55** (1985) 1908–1911.

[DM⁺88]   M.H. Devoret, J.M. Martinis, D. Esteve and J. Clarke, Macroscopic quantum mechanics experiments, *Helv. Phys. Acta* **61** (1988) 622–635.

[DMP98]   S. Dragan, M. Megan and A. Pogan, On a class of semigroups of linear operators in locally convex spaces, University of West Timisoara, Romania, Preprint Series in Mathematics, Prof. Mihail Megan, (Ed.) mmegan@info.uvt.ro, **88** (1998).

[Dov68]   C.B. Dover, Properties of the Luttinger model, *Ann. Phys.* **50** (1968) 500–533.

[DR88]   E. Duffner and A. Rieckers, On the global quantum dynamics of multi-lattice systems with nonlinear classical effects, *Z. Naturforsch.* **43a** (1988) 521–532.

[DS66]   N. Dunford and J.T. Schwartz, *Linear operators I, II*. New York; London: John Wiley & Sons (1963, 1966).

[Dub74]   D.A. Dubin, *Solvable models in algebraic statistical mechanics*. Oxford: Claredon Press (1974).

[DW92]   N.G. Duffield and R.F. Werner, Local dynamics of mean–field quantum systems, *Helv. Phys. Acta* **65** (1992) 1016–1054.

[Eas71]   M.S.P. Eastham, The Schrödinger equation with a periodic potential, *Proc. Roy. Soc.* **69a** (1971) 125–131.

[Eas73]   M.S.P. Eastham, *The spectral theory of periodic differential equations*. Edinburg: Scottish Academic Press (1973).

[Ebe92]   K.J. Ebeling, *Integrierte Optoelektronik*, 2nd edn. Berlin; Heidelberg; New York: Springer (1992).

[Eff77]   E.G. Effros, Nuclear C*–algebras and injectivity: the general case, *Indiana University Mat. J.* **33** (1977) 443–446.

[EG66]   G. Emch and M. Guenin, Gauge invariant formulation of the BCS model, *J. Math. Phys.* **7** (1966) 915–921.

[Ehr27]   P. Ehrenfest, Bemerkung über die angenäherte Gültigkeit der klassischen Mechanik innerhalb der Qantenmechanik, *Z. Phys.* **48** (1927) 455–457.

[Ein05]   A. Einstein, Über einen die Erzeugung und Verwandlung des Lichtes betreffenden heuristischen Gesichtspunkt, *Ann. d. Phys.* **17**(4) (1905) 132–148.

[Ein09a]   A. Einstein, Über die Entwicklung unserer Anschauung über das Wesen und die Konstitution der Strahlung, *Phys. Zs.* **10** (1909) 817–826.

[Ein09b]   A. Einstein, Zum gegenwärtigen Stand des Strahlungsproblems, *Phys. Zs.* **10** (1909) 185–193.

[Ein17]   A. Einstein, Zur Quantentheorie der Strahlung, *Phys. Zs.* **18** (1917) 121–128.

[Ein25]   A. Einstein, Quantentheorie des einatomigen idealen Gases, 2. Abhandlung, *Sitz.ber. Preuss. Akad. Wiss.* **x** (1925) 3–14.

[EK91]   A.K. Ekert and P.L. Knight, Relationship between semiclassical and quantum-mechanical input–output theories of optical response, *Phys. Rev. A* **43** (1991) 3934–3938.

[EKV70]   G.G. Emch, J.F. Knops and E.J. Verboven, The breaking of Euclidean symmetry with an application to the theory of crystalization, *J. Math. Phys.* **11** (1970) 1655–1668.

[EL69]   C.M. Edwards and J.T. Lewis, Twisted group algebras I, II, *Commun. Math. Phys.* **13** (1969) 119–141.

[EL77]   D.E. Evans and J.T. Lewis, Dilations of irreversible evolutions in algebraic quantum theory, Communications of the Dublin Institute of Adv. Studies Series A (*Theor. Phys.*) 24, Dublin Institute for Advanced Studies, Dublin (1977).

[Eng96]   B.-G. Englert, Fringe visibility and which–way information: an inequality, *Phys. Rev. Lett.* **77** (1996) 2154–2175.

[Eng99]   B.-G. Englert, Remarks on some basic issues in quantum mechanics, *Z. Phys.* **54a** (1999) 11–32.

[Eng13]   B.-G. Englert, On quantum theory, arXiv:quant-ph **1308.5290** (2013).

[EPR35]   A. Einstein, B. Podolsky and N. Rosen, Can quantum–mechanical description of physical reality be considered complete? *Phys. Rev.* **47** (1935) 777–780.

[EvZM92] W.J. Elion, H.S.J. van der Zant and J.E. Mooij, Quantum phase transitions in Josephson junction arrays, *Helv. Phys. Acta* **65** (1992) 381–382.

[Fed94]   B. Fedosov, A simple geometric construction of deformation quantization, *J. Diff. Geom.* **40** (1994) 213–238.

[Fed96]   B. Fedosov, *Deformation quantization and index theory*. Berlin: Academie–Verlag (1996).

[Fel81]   B. Felsager, *Geometry, particles and fields*. Odense: Odense University Press (1981).

[FGN60]   C. Foiaş, L. Gehér and B. Sz.–Nagy, On the permutability condition of quantum mechanics, *Acta Sci. Math.* **21** (1960) 78–89.

[Fil65]   P.A. Fillmore, Perspectivity in projection lattices, *Proc. Amer. Math. Soc.* **16** (1965) 383–387.

[Fis76]   H.R. Fischer, Differentialrechnung in lokalkonvexen Räumen und Mannig-faltigkeiten von Abbildungen, Technical Report, University of Mannheim (1976).

[FK64]   H. Fujita and T. Kato, On the Navier–Stokes initial value problem I, *Arch. Rat. Mech. Anal.* **16** (1964) 269–315.

[FK08]   H. Fischer and H. Kaul, *Mathematik für Physiker 2*, 3rd edn. Wiesbaden: Teubner–Verlag (2008).

[Fle83]   W. Fleig, On the symmetry breaking mechanism of the strong–coupling BCS–model, *Acta Phys. Austr.* **55** (1983) 135–153.

[FLS66]   R.P. Feynman, R.B. Leighton and M. Sands, *Lectures on physics III*. Reading: Addison–Wesley (1966).

[FNV88]   M. Fannes, B. Nachtergaele and A. Verbeure, The equilibrium states of the spin–Boson model, *Commun. Math. Phys.* **114** (1988) 537–548.

[Fra97]   Th. Frankel, *The geometry of physics*. Cambridge: Cambridge University Press (1997).

[Fra08]   P. Frampton, *Gauge field theories*. Weinheim, New York: Wiley–VCH (2008).

[Fug67]   B. Fuglede, On the relation $PQ - QP = -iI$, *Math. Scand.* **20** (1967) 79–88.

[Gar47]   L. Garding, Note on continuous representations of Lie groups, *Proc. N.A.S.* **33** (1947) 331–332.

[Gar91]   C.W. Gardiner, *Quantum noise*. Berlin, Heidelberg; New York: Springer–Verlag (1991).

[Gel50]   I.M. Gelfand, Expansion in eigenfunctions of an equation with periodic coefficients, *Dokl. Akad. Nauk SSSR* **73** (1950) 1117–1120.

[Ger93]   T. Gerisch, Internal symmetries and limiting Gibbs states in quantum lattice mean field theories, *Physica A* **197** (1993) 284–300.

[Ger95]   T. Gerisch, Konvergente Störungsreihen für eine Klasse von Vielteilchenmod-ellen mit Quantenkondensat, Ph.D. thesis, University of Tübingen, Institute of Theoretical Physics (1995).

[GH88]   H. Grundling and C.A. Hurst, A note on regular states and supplementary conditions, *Lett. Math. Phys.* **15** (1988) 205–212.

[GHR93]   T. Gerisch, R. Honegger and A. Rieckers, Limiting dynamics of generalized BCS–models beyond the pair algebra, *J. Math. Phys.* **34** (1993) 943–968.

[GHR03]   T. Gerisch, Algebraic quantum theory of the Josephson microwave radiator, *Ann. Henri Poincaré* **4** (2003) 1051–1082.

[GHW09]   D. Greenberger, K. Hentschel and F. Weinert (Eds.), *Compendium of quantum physics: concepts, experiments, history and philosophy.* Heidelberg, Berlin; New York: Springer (2009).

[Gib02]   J.W. Gibbs, *Elementary principles in statistical mechanics.* New York: Charles Scribner's Sons (1902).

[GK60]   J. Glimm and R.V. Kadison, Unitary operators in C*–algebras, *Pacific J. Math.* **10** (1960) 547–548.

[GK04]   P.W. Gross and P.R. Kotiuga, *Electromagnetic theory and computation: a topological approach.* Cambridge: Cambridge University Press (2004).

[Gla63a]   R.J. Glauber, Coherent and incoherent states of the radiation field, *Phys. Rev.* **131** (1963) 2766–2788.

[Gla63b]   R.J. Glauber, The quantum theory of optical coherence, *Phys. Rev.* **130** (1963) 2529–2539.

[Gla64]   R.J. Glauber, Optical coherence and photon statistics, Quantum Optics and Electronics, C. de Witt, A. Blandin and C. Cohen-Tannoudji (Eds.). New York: Gordon and Breach (1964).

[Gli60]   J. Glimm, On a certain class of operator algebras, *Trans. Amer. Math. Soc.* **95** (1960) 216–244.

[GMR99]   T. Gerisch, R. Münzner and A. Rieckers, Global C*–dynamics and its KMS–states of weakly inhomogeneous bipolaronic superconductors, *J. Stat. Phys.* **97** (1999) 751–779.

[Gol59]   H. Goldstein, *Classical mechanics.* Reading MA: Addison–Wesley (1959).

[Gol85]   J.A. Goldstein, *Semigroups of linear operators and applications.* New York; Oxford: Oxford University Press; Clarendon Press (1985).

[GP91]   A. Galindo and P. Pascual, *Quantum mechanics I, II.* Berlin; Heidelberg; New York: Springer (1989, 1991).

[GR90]   T. Gerisch and A. Rieckers, The quantum statistical free energy minimum principle for multi–lattice mean field theories, *Z. Naturforsch.* **45a** (1990) 931–945.

[GR97]   T. Gerisch and A. Rieckers, Limiting dynamics, KMS–states, and macroscopic phase angle for inhomogeneous BCS–models, *Helv. Phys. Acta* **70** (1997) 727–750.

[GR98]   T. Gerisch and A. Rieckers, Limiting Gibbs states and phase transitions of a bipartite mean–field Hubbard–model, *J. Stat. Phys.* **91** (1998) 759–786.

[Gre69]   F.P. Greanleaf, *Invariant means of topological groups.* New York: Van Nostrand–Reinhold (1969).

[Gro92]   D.J. Gross, Gauge theory — past, present and future, *Chinese J. Phys.* **30** (1992) 955–972.

[Gru97]   H. Grundling, A group algebra for inductive limit groups. Continuity problems of the canonical commutation relations, *Acta Appl. Math.* **46** (1997) 107–145.

[GRV98]   T. Gerisch, A. Rieckers and H.-J. Volkert, Thermodynamic formalism and phase transitions of generalized mean–field quantum lattice models, *Z. Naturforsch.* **53a** (1998) 179–207.

[GR03]   T. Gerisch and A. Rieckers, Heisenberg generators and Arveson spectra of long range interacting quantum lattice systems, Preprint, University of Tübingen (2003).

[GRZ03]   T. Gerisch, A. Rieckers and S. Zanzinger, Operator algebraic transition probabilities in many–body physics I, II, Preprints, University of Tübingen (2003).

[GS64]   I.M. Gelfand and G.E. Shilov, *Generalized functions I.* New York: Academic Press (1964).

[GT83]   D. Gilbarg and N.S. Trudinger, *Elliptic differential equations of second order.* Berlin; Heidelberg; New York: Springer (1983).

[Gud78]   S. Gudder, Cantoni's generalized transition probability, *Commun. Math. Phys.* **63** (1978) 265–267.

[Gui74]   A. Guichardet, Systèmes dynamiques non commutatifs, *Soc. Math.* France, Paris (1974).

[Gut77]   J. Gutknecht, Die C_Γ^∞–Struktur auf der Diffeomorphismengruppe einer kompakten Mannigfaltigkeit, Ph.D. thesis, University of Zürich, 1977.

[GVV91]   D. Goderis, A. Verbeure and P. Vets, Fluctuations? *Commun. Math. Phys.* **128** (1991) 533.

[GW54]   L. Garding and A. Wightman, Representations of the anticommutation relations, *Proc. N.A.S.* **40** (1954) 617–621.

[GY56]   I.M. Gelfand and A.M. Yaglom, Integration in function spaces and its application to quantum physics, *Usp. Mat. Nauk.* **2** (1956) 77–114.

[Haa62]   R. Haag, The mathematical structure of the Bardeen–Cooper–Schrieffer model, *Nuovo Cim.* **25** (1962) 287–299.

[Haa92]   J. Haag, *Local quantum physics.* Berlin; Heidelberg; New York: Springer (1992).

[Had82]   N. Hadjisavvas, On Cantoni's generalized transition probability, *Commun. Math. Phys.* **83** (1982) 43–48.

[Hak73]   H. Haken, *Quantenfeldtheorie des Festkörpers.* Suttgart: Teubner (1973).

[Hak85]   H. Haken, *Light 1, 2.* Amsterdam, New York; Oxford: North–Holland (1981, 1985).

[Hal81]   F.D.M. Haldane, 'Luttinger liquid theory' of one–dimensional quantum fields: I Properties of the Luttinger model and their extension to the general 1D interacting spinless Fermi gas, *J. Phys. C: Solid State Phys.* **14** (1981) 2585–2609.

[Ham82]   R.S. Hamilton, The inverse function theorem of Nash and Moser, *Bulletin of AMS, New Ser.* **7** (1982) 65–222.

[Ham97]   J. Hamilton, *Aharonov–Bohm and other cyclic phenomena.* Berlin; Heidelberg; New York: Springer (1997).

[Has10]   F. Hasselbach, Progress in electron– and ion–interferometry, *Rep. Prog. Phys.* **73** (2010) 1–43.

[Hau06]   F. Hausdorff, Die symbolische Exponentialformel in der Gruppentheorie, *Leibzig Ber.* **58** (1906) 19–48.

[Hei25]   W. Heisenberg, Über quantentheoretische Umdeutung kinematischer und mechanischer Beziehungen, *Z. Phys.* **33** (1925) 879–893.

[Hei27]   W. Heisenberg, Über den anschaulichen Inhalt der quantenmechanischen Kinematik und Mechanik, *Z. Phys.* **43** (1927) 172–198.

[Hel58]   H. Helmholtz, Über Integrale der hydrodynamischen Gleichungen, welche den Wirbelbewegungen entsprechen, *J. Reine Angew. Math.* **55** (1858) 25–55.

[Hen81]   D. Henry, Geometric theory of semilinear parabolic equations, *Lecture Notes in Mathematics* 840. Berlin, Heidelberg; New York: Springer (1981).

[Hep75]   K. Hepp, Two models for Josephson oscillators, *Ann. Phys.* **90** (1975) 285–294.

[Her91]   J. Hertle, Macroscopically inhomogeneous Bose–Einstein condensation, In *Large scale molecular systems: quantum and stochastic aspects* (Maratea, Italy, 1990), W. Gans, A. Blumen and A. Amann (Eds.), NATO–ASI. New York, London: Plenum Press (1991).

[HH92a]   J. Hertle and R. Honegger, Limiting Gibbs states and dynamics for thermal photons, *J. Math. Phys.* **33** (1992) 143–151.

[HH92b]   J. Hertle and R. Honegger, Rigorous derivation of Planck's law in the thermodynamic limit, *J. Math. Phys.* **33** (1992) 343–348.

[HH⁺02]   J. Hellmich, R. Honegger, C. Köstler, B. Kümmerer and A. Rieckers, Couplings to classical and non–classical squeezed white noise as stationary Markov processes, *Publ. RIMS Kyoto Univ.* **38** (2002) 1–31.

[HHW67]   R. Haag, N. Hugenholtz and M. Winnink, On the equilibrium states of quantum statistical mechanics, *Commun. Math. Phys.* **5** (1967) 215–136.

[Hid80]   T. Hida, *Brownian motion.* Berlin, Heidelberg; New York: Springer (1980).

[Hil85]   M. Hillery, Classical pure states are coherent states, *Phys. Lett. A* **111** (1985) 409–411.

[Hin88]   J. Hinken, *Supraleiter–Elektronik.* Berlin, Heidelberg; New York: Springer–Verlag (1988).

[Hir04]   O. Hirota, *Quantum information, statistics, probability.* Berlin: Rinton Pr. Inc. (2004).

[HK64]   R. Haag and D. Kastler, An algebraic approach to quantum field theory, *J. Math. Phys.* **5** (1964) 848–861.

[HK89]   J. Huang and P. Kumar, Photon–counting statistics of multimode squeezed light, *Phys. Rev. A* **40** (1989) 1670–1673.

[HL73a]   K. Hepp and E.H. Lieb, On the superradiant phase transitions for molecules in a quantized radiation field: the Dicke maser model, *Ann. Phys.* **76** (1973) 360–404.

[HL73b]   K. Hepp and E.H. Lieb, Phase transitions in reservoir driven open systems with applications to lasers and superconductors, *Helv. Phys. Acta* **46** (1973) 573–603.

[Hol01]   A.S. Holevo, *Statistical structure of quantum theory.* Berlin: Springer (2001).

[Hon90a]   R. Honegger, Decomposition of positive sesquilinear forms and the central decomposition of gauge–invariant quasi–free states on the Weyl algebra, *Z. Naturforsch.* **45a** (1990) 17–28.

[Hon90b]   R. Honegger, On the temperature states of the spin-Boson model in the thermodynamic limit, *V. International Conference on selected topics in quantum field theory and mathematical physics* (Liblice, Tschechoslowakia, 1989), J. Niederle and J. Fischer (Eds.). Singapore: World Scientific (1990).

[Hon90c]   R. Honegger, Unbounded perturbations of Boson equilibrium states in their GNS–representation, *Helv. Phys. Acta* **63** (1990) 139–155.

[Hon91a]   R. Honegger, Globale Quantentheorie der Strahlung, Ph.D. thesis, University of Tübingen, Institute of Theoretical Physics (1991).

[Hon91b]   R. Honegger, On the dynamics and the temperature states of the spin-Boson model, *Lett. Math. Phys.* **21** (1991) 351–359.

[Hon91c]   R. Honegger, Unbounded perturbations of Boson equilibrium states in Fock space, *Z. Naturforsch.* **46a** (1991) 293–303.

[Hon93a]   R. Honegger, The extremal microscopic coherent Boson states, *Lett. Math. Phys.* **28** (1993) 155–164.

[Hon93b]   R. Honegger, The general form of the microscopic coherent Boson states, *Physica A* **198** (1993) 179–209.

[Hon93c]   R. Honegger, On Heisenberg's uncertainty principle and the CCR, *Z. Natur-forsch.* **48a** (1993) 447–451.

[Hon93d]   R. Honegger, Time–asymptotic Boson states from infinite mean field quantum systems coupled to the Boson gas, *Lett. Math. Phys.* **27** (1993) 191–203.

[Hon96]   R. Honegger, The weakly coupled infinite Dicke model, *Physica A* **225** (1996) 391–411.

[Hon98]   R. Honegger, Enlarged testfunction spaces for the global free folia dynamics on the CCR–algebra, *J. Math. Phys.* **39** (1998) 1153–1169.

[Hör97]   G. Hörmann, Regular Weyl–systems and smooth structures on Heisenberg groups, *Commun. Math. Phys.* **184** (1997) 51–63.

[HR70]   E. Hewitt and K.A. Ross, *Abstract harmonic analysis I, II.* Berlin, Heidelberg; New York: Springer (1963, 1970).

[HR90]   R. Honegger and A. Rieckers, The general form of non-Fock coherent Boson states, *Publications RIMS Kyoto University* **26** (1990) 397–417.

[HR96]   R. Honegger and A. Rieckers, Squeezing Bogoliubov transformations on the infinite mode CCR–algebra, *J. Math. Phys.* **37** (1996) 4292–4309.

[HR97a]   R. Honegger and A. Rieckers, Squeezed variances of smeared Boson fields, *Helv. Phys. Acta* **70** (1997) 507–541.

[HR97b]   R. Honegger and A. Rieckers, Squeezing of optical states on the CCR–algebra, Publications of RIMS Kyoto University **33** (1997) 869–892.

[HR97c]   R. Honegger and A. Rieckers, Squeezing operations in Fock space and beyond, *Physica A* **242** (1997) 423–438.

[HR98a]   F. Hofmann and A. Rieckers, Phase dynamics at the SQUID and macro–realism, *Int. J. Theor. Phys.* **37** (1998) 537–543.

[HR98b]   R. Honegger and A. Rieckers, Coherence properties of squeezed photon states, *Lett. Math. Phys.* **45** (1998) 147–159.

[HR98c]   R. Honegger and A. Rieckers, Unitary implementations of one–parameter squeezing groups, *J. Math. Phys.* **39** (1998) 777–801.

[HR01]   R. Honegger and A. Rieckers, Construction of classical and non–classical coherent photon states, *Ann. Phys.* **289** (2001) 213–231.

[HR03]   R. Honegger and A. Rieckers, Partially classical states of a Boson field, *Lett. Math. Phys.* **64** (2003) 31–44.

[HR04]   R. Honegger and A. Rieckers, Non–classicality and coherence of squeezed states, *Physica A* **335** (2004) 487–510.

[HR05]   R. Honegger and A. Rieckers, Some continuous field quantizations, equivalent to the C*–Weyl quantization, *Publications RIMS Kyoto University* **41** (2005) 113–138.

[HRS08]   R. Honegger, A. Rieckers and L. Schlafer, Field–theoretic Weyl deformation quantization of enlarged Poisson algebras, *SIGMA (Special Issue on Deformation Quantization)* **4** (2008) 047 (37 pages).

[HSU80]   R. Heidenreich, R. Seiler and D.A. Uhlenbrock, The Luttinger model, *J. Stat. Phys.* **22** (1980), 27–57.

[HT01]   O. Hirota and P. Tombesi, *Quantum communication, computing and measurement 3.* Berlin, Heidelberg; New York: Springer (2001).

[Hur86]   C.A. Hurst, Quantum theory of the free electromagnetic field, *Symmetries in Science II*, B. Gruber and R. Leuczewski (Eds.). New York; London: Plenum Press (1986).

[HW01]   A. Huckleberry and T. Wurzbacher, *Infinite dimensional Kähler manifolds.* Basel: Birkhäuser Verlag (2001).

[Ja99]   P. Joyez *et al.*, The Josephson effect in nano scale tunnel junctions, *J. Supercond.* **12** (1999) 757.

[Jac75]   J.D. Jackson, *Classical electrodynamics.* New York: John Wiley & Sons (1975).

[Jau68]   J.M. Jauch, *Foundation of quantum mechanics.* MA; London: Addison–Wesley (1968).

[Jea05]   J.H. Jeans, On the partition of energy between matter and aether, *Phil. Mag.* **10** (1905) 91–98.

[Jön61]   C. Jönsson, Elektroneninterferenzen an mehreren künstlich hergestellten Feinspalten, *Z. Phys.* **161** (1961) 454–474.

[Jor32]   P. Jordan, Über eine Klasse nichtassoziativer hyperkomplexer Algebren, *Nachr. Ges. Wiss. Göttingen, Math.–Phys. Klasse* (1932) 569–575.

[Jor36]   P. Jordan, *Anschauliche Quantentheorie.* Berlin: Springer–Verlag (1936).

[Jos62]   B.D. Josephson, Possible new effects in superconductive tunneling, *Phys. Lett.* **1** (1962) 251–253.

[JR93]   G. John and A. Rieckers, C*–algebraic mean–field systems and geometric quantization, classical and quantum systems — foundations and symmetries, *Proceedings of II. International Wigner Symposium* (Goslar, Germany, 1991), H.D. Doebner, W. Scherer and F. Schroeck (Eds.). Singapore: World Scientific (1993).

[Kak93]   M. Kaku, *Quantum field theory.* New York, Oxford: Oxford University Press (1993).

[Kal83]   G. Kalmbach, *Orthomodular lattices.* London: Academic Press (1983).

[Kar97]   Y.E. Karpeshina, *Perturbation theory for the Schrödinger operator with a periodic potential.* Berlin, Heidelberg; New York: Springer (1997).

[Kas65]   D. Kastler, The C*–algebras of a free Boson field, *Commun. Math. Phys.* **1** (1965) 14–48.

[Kas67]   D. Kastler, Broken symmetries and the Goldstone theorem in axiomatic field theory, *Proceedings of the 1967 international conference on particles and fields*, C.R. Hagen *et al.* (Ed.). New York: John Wiley (1967).

[Kat63]   T. Kato, On the commutation relation $AB - BA = C$, *Arch. for Rat. Mech. and Anal.* **10** (1963) 273–275.

[Kat78]   T. Kato, Trotter's product formula for an arbitrary pair of self–adjoint contraction semigroups, *Topics in functional analysis, advances in mathematics supplementary studies* 3. New York; London: Academic Press (1978).

[Kat84]   T. Kato, *Perturbation theory for linear operators*, 2nd edn. Berlin, Heidelberg; New York: Springer (1984).

[Kay79]   B.S. Kay, A uniqueness result in the Segal–Weinless approach to linear Bose fields, *J. Math. Phys.* **20** (1979) 1712–1714.

[KB12]   J. Kofler and C. Brukner, A condition for macroscopic realism beyond the Leggett–Garg inequalities, arXiv: quant-ph **1207.3666v2** (2012), 1–5.

[Kel74]   H.H. Keller, Differential calculus in locally convex spaces, *Lecture notes in mathematics* 417. Berlin: Springer (1974).

[KH25]   H.A. Kramers and W. Heisenberg, Über die Streuung von Strahlung durch Atome, *Z. Phys.* **9** (1925) 293–320.

[Kle65]   A. Kleppner, Multipliers on Abelian groups, *Math. Ann.* **158** (1965) 11–34.

[KL95]   J.-P. Kahane and P.-G. Lemarié–Rieusset, *Fourier series and wavelets.* London, New York: Gordon and Breach (1995).

[KN69]   S. Kobayashi and K. Nomizu, *Foundations of differential geometry I, II.* New York: John Wiley (1963, 1969).

[Kob72]   S. Kobayashi, *Transformation groups in differential geometry*. Berlin, Heidelberg; New York: Springer (1972).

[Kol41]   A.N. Kolmogorov, Stationary sequences in Hilbert's space, *Byull. Mosk. Gosud. Univ. Matematika* **2**(6) (1941) 40.

[Kos83]   H. Kosaki, On the Bures distance and Uhlmann's transition probability of states on a von Neumann algebra, *Proc. Amer. Math. Soc.* **89** (1983) 285.

[KR86]   R.V. Kadison and J.R. Ringrose, *Fundamentals of the theory of operator algebras I, II*. New York: Academic Press (1983, 1986).

[Kra24]   H.A. Kramers, The quantum theory of dispersion, *Nature* **114** (1924) 310–311.

[Kre78]   E. Kreyszig, *Introductory functional analysis with applications*. New York: John Wiley & Sons (1978).

[KS68]   J.R. Klauder and E.C.G. Sudarshan, *Fundamentals of quantum optics*. New York: Benjamin (1968).

[KS⁺10]   J. Klaers, J. Schmitt, F. Vewinger and M. Weitz, Bose–Einstein condensation of photons in an optical microcavity, *Nature* **468** (2010) 545.

[La12]   C.-M. Li *et al.*, Wittnessing quantum coherence: from solid–state to biological systems, *Sci. Rep.* **2** (2012) 885.

[Lad21]   R. Ladenburg, Die quantentheoretische Deutung der Zahl der Dispersionselektronen, *Z. Phys.* **4** (1921) 451–468.

[Lad63]   O.A. Ladyzhenskaia, *The mathematical theory of viscous incompressible flow*. New York: Gordon and Breach (1963).

[Lan87]   L.J. Landau, Experimental tests of general quantum theories, *Lett. Math. Phys.* **14** (1987) 33–40.

[Lan98a]   N.P. Landsman, *Mathematical topics between classical and quantum mechanics*. Berlin, Heidelberg; New York: Springer (1998).

[Lan98b]   N.P. Landsman, Strict quantization of coadjoint orbits, *J. Math. Phys.* **39** (1998) 5372–5383.

[LB05]   A. Lyakhov and C. Bruder, Quantum state transfer in arrays of flux qubits, arXiv:cond-mat **0509478** (2005).

[Leg80]   A.J. Leggett, Macroscopic quantum systems and the quantum theory of measurement, *Progr. Theor. Phys.* **69** (1980) 80.

[Leg87]   A.J. Leggett, Quantum mechanics on the macroscopic level, *Chance and matter*, J. Souletie, J. Vannimenus and R. Stora (Eds.). Amsterdam: North–Holland (1987).

[Leg00]   A.J. Leggett, New life for Schrödinger's cat, *Physics World* **67** (2000) 23–24.

[Leh90]   G. Lehner, *Elektromagnetische Feldtheorie*. Berlin, Heidelberg: Springer (1990).

[Lei86]   R. Leis, *Initial boundary value problems in mathematical physics*. Stuttgart, New York: Teubner, J. Wiley & Sons (1986).

[Lep65]   H. Leptin, Verallgemeinerte L^1-Algebren, *Math. Ann.* **159** (1965) 51–76.

[Lep67a]   H. Leptin, Verallgemeinerte L^1-Algebren und projektive Darstellungen lokal kompakter Gruppen I, *Inv. Math.* **3** (1967) 257–281.

[Lep67b]   H. Leptin, Verallgemeinerte L^1-Algebren und projektive Darstellungen lokal kompakter Gruppen II, *Inv. Math.* **4** (1967) 68–86.

[Lew26]   G. Lewis, The conservation of photons, *Nature* **118** (1926) 874.

[LG85]   A.J. Leggett and A. Garg, Quantum mechanics versus macroscopic realism: is the flux there if nobody looks, *Phys. Rev. Lett.* **54** (1985) 857–860.

[Lig58]   M.J. Lighthill, *Fourier analysis and generalized functions*. Cambridge: Cambridge University Press (1958).

[LK87]   R. Loudon and P.L. Knight, Squeezed light, *J. Mod. Opt.* **34** (1987) 709–759.

[LL63]   J.M. Lévy-Leblond, Galilei group and non–relativistic quantum mechanics, *J. Math. Phys.* **4** (1963) 776–788.

[LM66]   E.H. Lieb and D.C. Mattis, *Mathematical physics in one dimension.* New York; London: Academic Press (1966).

[LM87]   P. Libermann and C.-M. Marle, *Symplectic geometry and analytical mechanics.* Dordrecht, Holland: D. Reidel Publ. Company (1987).

[Lob92]   C.J. Lobb, Josephson junction arrays and superconducting wire networks, *Helv. Phys. Acta* **65** (1992) 219–227.

[Lon50]   F. London, *Superfluids I, II.* New York: John Wiley (1950).

[Lor12]   H.A. Lorentz, *Théorie du Rayonnement.* Paris: Paris Pub. Gauthier (1912).

[Lou79]   R. Loudon, *The quantum theory of light.* Oxford: Clarendon Press (1979).

[LP74]   J.T. Lewis and J.V. Pulè, The equilibrium states of the free Boson gas, *Commun. Math. Phys.* **36** (1974) 1–18.

[LR69]   O.E. Lanford and D. Ruelle, Observables at infinity and states with short range correlations in statistical mechanics, *Commun. Math. Phys.* **13** (1969) 194–215.

[LS09]   E.H. Lieb and R. Seiringer, *The stability of matter in quantum mechanics.* Cambridge: Cambridge University Press (2009).

[Lud74]   G. Ludwig, *Einführung in die theoretische Physik, Band II.* Düsseldorf: Bertelsmann Universitätsverlag (1974).

[Ma99]   J.E. Mooij *et al.*, Josephson persistent–current qubit, *Science* **285** (1999) 1036–1039.

[Mac52]   G.W. Mackey, Induced representations of locally compact groups I, *Ann. Math.* **55** (1952) 101–139.

[Mac58]   G.W. Mackey, Unitary representations of group extensions I, *Acta Math.* **99** (1958) 265–311.

[Mac63]   G.W. Mackey, *Mathematical foundations of quantum mechanics.* New York: Benjamin (1963).

[Mad70]   O. Madelung, *Gundlagen der Halbleiterphysik.* Berlin: Springer (1970).

[Mad73]   O. Madelung, *Festkörpertheorie I–III.* Berlin, Heidelberg; New York: Springer (1972, 1973).

[Man59]   L. Mandel, *Proc. Phys. Soc. London* **74** (1959) 233.

[Man68]   J. Manuceau, C*–algèbre de relations de commutation, *Ann. Inst. Henri Poincaré* **VIII**(2) (1968) 139–161.

[Mar79]   Ph.A. Martin, *Modèles en Mécanique statistique de processus irréversible.* Berlin, Heidelberg; New York: Springer (1979).

[Mar92]   J.E. Marsden, *Lectures on mechanics.* Cambridge, New York: Cambridge University Press (1992).

[Mau68]   K. Maurin, *Generalized eigenfunction expansions and unitary group representations of topological groups.* Warsaw: PWN–Polish Scientific Publishers (1968).

[Max65]   J.C. Maxwell, A dynamical theory of the electromagnetic field, *Phil. Trans. Roy. Soc.* **155** (1865) 459–512.

[Max73]   J.C. Maxwell, *A treatise on electricity and magnetism I, II.* Oxford: Clarendon Press (1873).

[MB62]   G. Möllenstedt and W. Bayh, Messung der kontinuierlichen Phasenschiebung von Elektronenwellen im kraftfeldfreien Raum durch das magnetische Vektorpotential einer Luftspule, *Naturw.* **49** (1962) 61–62.

[Mie68]   B. Mielnik, Geometry of quantum states, *Commun. Math. Phys.* **9** (1968) 55–80.

[Mil83]   J. Milnor, Remarks on infinite–dimensional lie groups, *Proceedings of the Summer School on Quantum Gravity* (Les Houches), B. DeWitt (Ed.). Plenum Press (1983).

[MM99]   M.G. Moore and P. Meystre, Theory of superradiant scattering of laser light from Bose–Einstein condensates, *Phys. Rev. Lett.* **83** (1999) 5202.

[Moy49]   J.E. Moyal, Quantum mechanics as a statistical theory, *Proc. Cambridge Philos. Soc.* **45** (1949) 99–124.

[MR82]   J. Mehra and H. Rechenberg, *The historical development of quantum theory I–III.* Berlin, Heidelberg; New York: Springer (1982).

[MR90]   X. Ma and W. Rhodes, Multimode squeeze operators and squeezed states, *Phys. Rev. A* **41** (1990) 4625–4631.

[MR94]   J.E. Marsden and T. Ratiu, *Introduction to mechanics and symmetry.* Berlin, Heidelberg; New York: Springer (1994).

[MR00a]   R. Münzner and A. Rieckers, Green's functions at finite and zero temperature in different ensembles for a bipolaronic superconductor, Preprint, University of Tübingen (2000).

[MR00b]   R. Münzner and A. Rieckers, Spectral properties and Green's functions for perturbed mean field models, Preprint, University of Tübingen (2000).

[MS67]   S. Miracle–Sole, Traitment de la convolution gauche pour les systèmes infinis, *Ann. Inst. Henri Poincaré* **VI**(1) (1967) 59–71.

[MS90]   P. Meystre and M. Sargent III, *Elements of quantum optics.* Berlin, Heidelberg; New York: Springer (1990).

[MS⁺73]   J. Manuceau, M. Sirugue, D. Testard and A. Verbeure, The smallest C*–algebra for canonical commutation relations, *Commun. Math. Phys.* **32** (1973) 231–243.

[MTW73]   Ch.W. Misner, K.S. Thorne and J.A. Wheeler, *Gravitation.* San Francisco: Freeman (1973).

[Mur90]   G. Murphy, *C*–Algebras and operator theory.* Boston, New York: Academic Press (1990).

[MV68]   J. Manuceau and A. Verbeure, Quasi-free states of the C.C.R.-algebra and Bogoliubov transformations, *Commun. Math. Phys.* **9** (1968) 293–302.

[MW95]   L. Mandel and E. Wolf, *Optical coherence and quantum optics.* Cambridge: Cambridge University Press (1995).

[MYI87]   S. Machida, Y. Yamamoto and V. Itaya, Observation of amplitude squeezing in a constant–current–driven semiconductor laser, *Phys. Rev. Lett.* **58** (1987) 1000–1003.

[MYR92]   S. Machida, Y. Yamamoto and W.H. Richardson, Photon number squeezed states in semiconductor lasers, *Sci. Mag.* **256** (1992) 1219–1224.

[Na05]   A.O. Niskanen *et al.*, Evidence of Cooper-pair pumping with combined flux and voltage control, *Phys. Rev. B* **71** (2005) 012513.

[Nar05]   H. Narnhofer, Josephson junction revisited, *Sitz. Ber. Öst. Akad. Wiss. Abt. II* **214** (2005) 161–180.

[NC00]   M.A. Nielsen and I.L. Chuang, *Quantum computation and quantum information.* Cambridge: Cambridge University Press (2000).

[Nee01]   K.-H. Neeb, Infinite–dimensional groups and their representations, *Infinite dimensional Kähler manifolds*, A. Huckleberry and T. Wurzbacher (Eds.). Basel: Birkhäuser (2001), pp. 131–178.

[Nel59]   E. Nelson, Analytic vectors, *Ann. Math.* **70** (1959) 572–615.

[Nie68]   M.M. Nieto, Quantized phase effect and Josephson tunneling, *Phys. Rev.* **167** (1968) 416.

[NO98]   J.W. Negele and H. Orland, *Quantum many particle systems.* Reading MA: Perseus Books (1998).

[NPT99]   Y. Nakamura, Y. Pashkin and J. Tsai, Coherent control of macroscopic quantum states in a single-Cooper-pair box, *Nature* **398** (1999) 786.

[Nus73]   H.M. Nussenzveig, *Introduction to quantum optics*. London; New York; Paris: Gordon and Breach (1973).

[Odz92]   A. Odzijewicz, Coherent states and geometric quantization, *Commun. Math. Phys.* (1992) 385–413.

[Oji81]   I. Ojima, Thermo field dynamics and the KMS condition and their extension to gauge theories, *Ann. Phys.* **137** (1981) 1–32.

[OK64]   F. Odeh and J.B. Keller, Partial differential equations with periodic coefficients and Bloch waves in crystals, *J. Math. Phys.* **5** (1964) 1499–1504.

[Omo74]   H. Omori, *Infinite-dimensional lie transformation groups*. Berlin, Heidelberg; New York: Springer–Verlag (1974).

[Omo97]   H. Omori, *Infinite–dimensional lie groups*, Translations of mathematical monographs 158, American Mathematical Society, Providence, Rhode Island (1997).

[OMY92]   H. Omori, Y. Maeda and A. Yoshioka, Existence of a closed star product, *Lett. Math. Phys.* **26** (1992) 285–294.

[OR03]   A. Odzijewicz and S. Ratiu, Banach Lie–Poisson spaces and reduction, *Commun. Math. Phys.* **243** (2003) 1–54.

[OR04]   A. Odzijewicz and T.S. Ratiu, Extensions of Banach Lie–Poisson spaces, *J. Funct. Anal.* **217** (2004) 103–125.

[Ouc73]   S. Ouchi, Semigroups of operators in locally convex spaces, *J. Math. Soc. Japan* **25** (1973) 265–276.

[Oza97]   M. Ozawa, Phase operator problem and macroscopic extension of quantum mechanics, arXiv:quant-ph **9705034v1** (1997) 1–26.

[Pac96]   J.A. Packer, Moore cohomology and central twisted crossed product C*-algebras, *Canad. J. Math.* **48** (1996) 159–174.

[Pai82]   A. Pais, *Subtle is the lord*. Oxford: Oxford University Press (1982).

[Par69]   R.D. Parks, *Superconductivity 1*. New York: Marcel Dekker Inc. (1969).

[Par96]   G. Parisi, A mean field theory for arrays of Josephson junctions, *J. Math. Phys.* **37** (1996) 5158–5170.

[Pat13]   A. Pathak (Ed.), *Elements of quantum computation and quantum communication*. New York: Taylor–Francis (2013).

[Pau33]   W. Pauli, Die allgemeinen Prinzipien der Wellenmechanik, *Handbuch der Physik* **24/1** (1933).

[PB89]   D.T. Pegg and S.M. Barnett, Phase properties of the quantized single–mode electromagnetic field, *Phys. Rev. A* **39** (1989) 1665.

[Ped79]   G.K. Pedersen, *C*–Algebras and their automorphism groups*. London: Academic Press (1979).

[Pen51]   O. Penrose, On the quantum mechanics of He II, *Philos. Mag.* **42** (1951) 1373–1377.

[Pet90]   D. Petz, An invitation to the algebra of canonical commutation relations, *Leuven notes in Mathematics and Theoretical Physics* 2, Leuven, Belgium: Leuven University Press (1990).

[Pit89]   I. Pitowsky, *Quantum probability — quantum logic*. Berlin, Heidelberg; New York: Springer Verlag (1989).

[Pfe80]   P. Pfeifer, Chiral molecules — a superselection rule induced by the radiation field, Ph.D. thesis, ETH Zürich, No. 6551 (1980).

[Pla99]   M. Planck, Über irreversible Strahlungsvorgänge, *Sitz.ber. Preuss. Akad. Wiss.* **5** (1899) 440–480.

[Pla00a]   M. Planck, Über eine Verbesserung der Wienschen Spektralgleichung, *Verh. Deutsch. Phys. Ges.* **2** (1900) 202–204.

[Pla00b]   M. Planck, Zur Theorie des Gesetzes der Energieverteilung im Normalspek-
           trum, *Verh. Deutsch. Phys. Ges.* **2** (1900) 237–245.
[Pla21]   M. Planck, *Wärmestrahlung*. Leipzig: Ambrosius Barth (1921).
[Poi99]   H. Poincaré, Les Méthodes Nouvelles de la Méchaniques Céleste 3. Paris:
           Gauthier–Villars (1899).
[Pow70]   R. Powers, Fermi field algebra. In *Cargese lectures in physics*, D. Kastler (Ed.).
           New York: Gordon and Breach (1970).
[PR89]   J.A. Packer and I. Raeburn, Twisted crossed products of C*-algebras, *Math.
           Proc. Camb. Phil. Soc.* **106** (1989) 293–311.
[Pri83]   H. Primas, *Chemistry, quantum mechanics and reductionism*. Berlin, Heidel-
           berg; New York: Springer (1983).
[Pru71]   E. Prugovečki, *Quantum mechanics in Hilbert spaces*. New York: Academic
           Press (1971).
[PR$^+$74] J.P. Provost, F. Rocca, G. Vallee and M. Sirugue, Phase properties of some
           photon states with nonzero energy density, *J. Math. Phys.* **15** (1974) 2079–
           2085.
[PRV75]   J.P. Provost, F. Rocca and G. Vallee, Coherent states, phase states and con-
           densed states, *Ann. Phys.* **49** (1975) 307.
[PS00]   L. Parnovski and A.V. Sobolev, On the Bethe–Sommerfeld conjecture, *J. équ.
           dér. part.* (2000) 1–13. Available at: http://eudml.org/doc/93394.
[Put67]   C.R. Putnam, *Commutation properties of Hilbert space operators and related
           topics*. Berlin, Heidelberg; New York: Springer (1967).
[Rag82]   G.A. Raggio, Generalized transition probability and applications, *Quantum
           probability and applications to the quantum theory of irreversible processes*,
           L. Accardi, A. Frigerio and V. Gorini (Eds.). *Lecture notes in mathematics*
           1055. Berlin, Heidelberg; New York; Tokyo: Springer (1982), pp. 327–335.
[Rag88]   G.A. Raggio, A remark on Bell's inequality and decomposable normal states,
           Lett. Math. Phys. **15** (1988) 27–29.
[Rau91]   J. Rauch, *Partial differential equations*. Berlin; New York: Springer (1991).
[Ray00]   J. Rayleigh, Remarks upon the law of complete radiation. *Phil. Mag.* **49** (1900)
           539–540.
[RB02]   A. Rieckers and K. Bräuer, *Einladung zur Mathematik*. Berlin: Logos Verlag
           (2002).
[Rel46]   F. Rellich, Der Eindeutigkeitssatz für die Lösungen der quantenmechanischen
           Vertauschungsrelationen, *Nachr. Akad. Wiss. Göttingen, Math.–Phys. Klasse*
           (1946) 107–115.
[Ric65]   G. Rickayzen, *Theory of superconductivity*. New York: John Wiley (1965).
[Ric66]   H. Richter, *Wahrscheinlichkeitstheorie*, 2nd edn. Berlin, Heidelberg; New York:
           Springer (1966).
[Rie78]   A. Rieckers, Equivalence of Kadison and Wigner symmetries in traditional
           quantum mechanics, *Group theoretical methods in physics* (Tübingen, 1977),
           P. Kramer and A. Rieckers (Eds.). Berlin: Springer (1978).
[Rie80]   A. Rieckers, Fundamentals of algebraic quantum theory, *Groups, systems and
           many body physics* (Tübingen), P. Kramer and M. Dal Cin (Eds.). Braun-
           schweig: Vieweg (1980).
[Rie84]   A. Rieckers, On the classical part of the mean field dynamics for quantum
           lattice systems in grand canonical representations, *J. Math. Phys.* **25** (1984)
           2593–2601.

[Rie86] A. Rieckers, Macroscopic quantum phenomena as weakly coupled spontaneous symmetry breaking, *XXI Winter School of Theoretical Physics* (Karpacz, 1985). Singapore: World Scientific (1986).

[Rie87] A. Rieckers, On the covariance representation of global quantum dynamics and its symmetries, *XV international colloquium on group theoretical methods in physics*, R. Gilmore (Ed.). Singapore: World Scientific (1987).

[Rie90] A. Rieckers, Macroscopic coherent states of the quantized electromagnetic field. In *New frontiers in qed and quantum optics* (Istanbul, 1989), A.O. Barut, M.O. Scully and H. Walther (Eds.), NATO–ASI. New York; London: Plenum Press (1990).

[Rie91] A. Rieckers, Condensed cooper pairs and macroscopic quantum phenomena. In *Large scale molecular systems: quantum and stochastic aspects* (Maratea, Italy, 1990), W. Gans, A. Blumen and A. Amann (Eds.), NATO–ASI. New York; London: Plenum Press (1991).

[Rie93] M.A. Rieffel, Deformation quantization for actions of $\mathbb{R}^d$, *Mem. Amer. Math. Soc.* **106** (1993) 1–93.

[Rie94] M.A. Rieffel, Quantization and C*-algebras, C*-Algebras: 1943–1993, R.S. Doran (Ed.), Contemporary Mathematics 167, Providence, RI, American Mathematical Society (1994), pp. 67–97.

[Rie98a] M.A. Rieffel, *Quantization and operator algebras*, Proceedings of the XII International Congress of Mathematical Physics (Brisbane, 1997), A.J. Bracken, D. De Witt, M. Gould and P. Pearce (Eds.). Singapore: International Press (1998).

[Rie98b] M.A. Rieffel, Questions on quantization, *Contemp. Math.* **228** (1998).

[Rie99] A. Rieckers, Macroscopic quantum phenomena at the SQUID. In *On quanta, mind and matter: Hans Primas in context* (*Fundamental Theories of Physics*, vol. **102**) H. Atmanspacher, A. Amann and U. Müller-Herold (Eds.). Dordrecht: Kluwer Academic Publishers (1999).

[Rig77] C. Rigotti, Algèbres d'opérateur et leur application en physique mathematique. Marseille: Colloques Internationaux du C.N.R.S. **274** (1977) 307–320.

[RJ96] C. Rojas and J.V. José, Critical properties of two-dimensional Josephson junction arrays with zero-point quantum fluctuations, Preprint, cond-mat/9610051, 1996.

[Rob29] H.P. Robertson, The uncertainty principle, *Phys. Rev.* **34** (1929) 163–164.

[Rob65a] D.W. Robinson, The ground state of the Bose gas, *Commun. Math. Phys.* **1** (1965) 159–174.

[Rob65b] D.W. Robinson, A theorem concerning the positive metric, *Commun. Math. Phys.* **1** (1965) 89–94.

[Rob93] P.L. Robinson, Symplectic pathology, *Quart. J. Math. Oxford* **44** (1993) 101–107.

[Röc96] A. Röck, Pulsed laser radiation — a rigorous model for the collective spontaneous emission, *Helv. Phys. Acta* **69** (1996) 26–45.

[RN82] F. Riesz and B. Sz.-Nagy, *Vorlesungen über Funktionalanalysis*. Berlin: VEB Deutscher Verlag der Wissenschaften (1982).

[RPB05] G. Robb, N. Piovella and R. Bonifacio, The semiclassical and quantum regimes of superradiant light scattering from a Bose–Einstein condensate, arXiv:cond-mat **0410077** (2005) v1.

[RR83] G. Raggio and A. Rieckes, Coherence and incompatibility in W*-algebras, *Int. J. Theor. Phys.* **22** (1983) 267–291.

[RR89]   A. Rieckers and H. Roos, Implementations of Jordan-isomorphisms for general von Neumann algebras, *Ann. Inst. Henri Poincaré* **50** (1989) 95–113.

[RS73a]   F. Rocca and M. Sirugue, Phase operator and condensed systems, *Commun. Math. Phys.* **34** (1973) 111–121.

[RS73b]   M. Reed and B. Simon, *Functional analysis*, Vol. I. New York: Academic Press (1973).

[RS75]   M. Reed and B. Simon, *Fourier analysis, self-adjointness*, Vol. II. New York: Academic Press (1975).

[RS78]   M. Reed and B. Simon, *Analysis of operators*, Vol. IV. New York: Academic Press (1978).

[RS79]   M. Reed and B. Simon, *Scattering theory*, Vol. III. New York: Academic Press (1979).

[RST70]   F. Rocca, M. Sirugue and D. Testard, On a class of equilibrium states under the Kubo–Martin–Schwinger condition, *Commun. Math. Phys.* **19** (1970) 119–141.

[RU85a]   A. Rieckers and M. Ullrich, Condensed Cooper pairs and quasi particles in a gauge invariant finite temperature BCS–model, *Acta Phys. Austriaca* **56** (1985) 259–274.

[RU85b]   A. Rieckers and M. Ullrich, Extended gauge transformations and the physical dynamics in a finite temperature BCS–model, *Acta Phys. Austriaca.* **56** (1985) 131–152.

[RU86]   A. Rieckers and M. Ullrich, On the microscopic derivation of the finite–temperature Josephson relation in operator form, *J. Math. Phys.* **27** (1986) 1082–1092.

[Rüt83]   G.T. Rüttimann, Dedectable properties and spectral quantum logics. Interpretation and foundation of quantum theory (Mannheim), H. Neumann (Ed.), Bibliography, Institute Mannheim (1983), pp. 35–47.

[RW86]   M.D. Reid and D.F. Walls, Violations of classical inequalities in quantum optics, *Phys. Rev. A* **34** (1986) 1260–1276.

[RW89]   G.A. Raggio and R.F. Werner, Quantum statistical mechanics of general mean field systems, *Helv. Phys. Acta* **62** (1989) 980–1003.

[Sak71]   S. Sakai, *C*-Algebras and W*-Algebras.* Berlin, New York: Springer (1971).

[SB33]   A. Sommerfeld and H. Bethe, Elektronentheorie der Metalle, *Handbuch d. Physik 24* **II** (1933) 332–622.

[SBK13]   S. Schmidt, G. Blatter and J. Keeling, From the Jaynes–Cummings–Hubbard to the Dicke model, *J. Phys. B* **46** (2013) 151–160.

[Sch25]   E. Schrödinger, Zur Einsteinschen Gastheorie, *Phys. Z.* **27** (1925) 95–101.

[Sch26a] E. Schrödinger, Quantisierung als Eigenwertproblem (1. Mitteilung), *Ann. d. Phys.* **79** (1926) 361–376.

[Sch26b] E. Schrödinger, Quantisierung als Eigenwertproblem (2. Mitteilung), *Ann. d. Phys.* **79** (1926) 489–527.

[Sch26c] E. Schrödinger, Über das Verhältnis der Heisenberg–Born–Jordanschen Quantenmechanik zu der meinen, *Ann. d. Phys.* **79** (1926) 734–756.

[Sch27]   E. Schrödinger, Quantisierung als Eigenwertproblem (3. Mitteilung), *Ann. d. Phys.* **80** (1927) 437–490.

[Sch60]   J.T. Schwartz, On Nash's implicit functional theorem, *Comm. Pure and Appl. Math.* **13** (1960) 509–530.

[Sch62]   S.S. Schweber, *An introduction to relativistic quantum field theory.* New York: Harper & Row (1962).

[Sch63]   B. Schroer, Infrateilchen in der Quantenfeldtheorie, *Fortschr. Phys.* **173** (1963) 1527.

[Sch66]   H.H. Schaefer, *Topological vector spaces*. New York: Macmillan Company (1966).

[Sch78a]   R. Schmid, Die Symplektomorphismen–Gruppe als Fréchet–Lie Gruppe, Ph.D. thesis, University of Zürich (1978).

[Sch78b]   L.S. Schulman, Note on the quantum recurrence theorem, *Phys. Rev. A* **18** (1978) 2379–2380.

[Sch79]   R. Schmid, Convergence structures and applications I, *Abh. Akad. Wiss. DDR* **4 N** (1979) 201–206.

[Sch83]   R. Schmid, Convergence structures and applications II, *Abh. Akad. Wiss. DDR* **2 N** (1983) 201–206.

[Sch88a]   M. Schneider, *Satellitengeodäsie–Grundlagen*. Mannheim: BI Wissenschaftsverlag (1988).

[Sch88b]   F. Schwabl, *Quantenmechanik*. Berlin; New York; Tokyo: Springer (1988).

[Sch90]   A. Schenzle, An introduction to quantum noise. In *New frontiers in QED and quantum optics* (Istanbul, 1989), A.O. Barut, M.O. Scully and H. Walther (Eds.), NATO–ASI. New York, London: Plenum Press (1990).

[Sch95a]   G. Scharf, *Finite quantum electrodynamics*. Berlin; New York: Springer (1995).

[Sch95b]   G. Schwarz, Hodge decompositions — a method for solving boundary value problems, *Lecture Notes in mathematics* 1607. Berlin; New York: Springer (1995).

[Sch96]   M. Schneider, *Himmelsmechanik III, Gravitationstheorie*. Heidelberg: Spektrum Akad. Verlag (1996).

[Sch09]   B. Schroer, A note on infraparticles and unparticles, arXiv [hep-th] **0804.3563v5** (2009) 1–24.

[Sch51]   L. Schwartz, *Théorie des distributions*. Paris: Dunod (1950/1951).

[Seg51]   I.E. Segal, A class of operator algebras, *Duke. Math. J.* **18** (1951) 221–265.

[Seg59]   I.E. Segal, Foundations of the theory of dynamical systems of infinitely many degress of freedom I, *Kgl. Danske Vidensk. Selsk., Mat.-fys. Medd.* **31** (1959) 39.

[Seg61]   I.E. Segal, Foundations of the theory of dynamical systems of infinitely many degress of freedom II, *Canad. J. Math.* **13** (1961) 1–18.

[Seg62]   I.E. Segal, Mathematical characterization of the physical vacuum for a linear Bose–Einstein field (Foundations of the dynamics of infinite systems III), *Jllinois J. Math.* **6** (1962) 500–523.

[Sew73]   G.L. Sewell, States and dynamics of infinitely extended physical systems, *Commun. Math. Phys.* **33** (1973) 43–51.

[Sew86]   G.L. Sewell, *Quantum theory of collective phenomena*. Oxford: Clarendon Press (1986).

[Sew02]   G.L. Sewell, *Quantum mechanics and its emergent macrophysics*. Princeton, Oxford: Princeton University Press (2002).

[SG64]   L. Susskind and J. Glogower, Quantum mechanical phase and time operator, *Physics* **1** (1964) 49.

[Sha62]   D. Shale, Linear symmetries of free Boson fields, *Trans. A.M.S.* **103** (1962) 149–167.

[She78]   Z. Shen, On absolute continuity of the periodic Schrödinger operator, *J. d'Anal. Math.* **33** (1978) 146–167.

[SHV89]   W. Schleich, R.J. Horowicz and S. Varro, Bifurcation in the phase probability of a highly squeezed state, *Phys. Rev. A* **40** (1989) 7405.

[Sil07]   L. Silberstein, Elektromagnetische Grundgleichungen in bivektorieller Behandlung, *Ann. d. Phys.* **74** (1907) 783.

[Sko74]   A.V. Skorohod, *Integration in Hilbert space*. Berlin; New York: Springer (1974).

[Skr85]   M. Skriganov, The spectrum band structure of the three-dimensional Schrödinger operator with periodic potential, *Inv. Math.* **80** (1985) 107–121.

[Sla71]   J. Slawny, On factor representations and the C*–algebra of the canonical commutation relations, *Commun. Math. Phys.* **24** (1971) 151–170.

[SM11]   P.L. Saldanha and C.H. Monken, Interaction between light and matter: a photon wave function approach, *New J. Phys.* **13** (2011) 073015.

[Son06]   P. Sonnentag, Ein Experiment zur kontrollierten Dekohärenz in einem Elektronen–Biprisma–Interferometer, Ph.D. thesis, University Tübingen, (2006).

[Spo89]   H. Spohn, Ground state(s) of the spin–Boson Hamiltonian, *Commun. Math. Phys.* **123** (1989) 277–304.

[SR76]   H. Stumpf and A. Rieckers, *Thermodynamik I*. Braunschweig: Vieweg–Verlag (1976).

[SR07]   B.J. Smith and M.G. Raymer, Photon wave functions, wave–packet quantization of light and coherence theory, *New J. Phys.* **9** (2007) 414–451.

[SS64]   D. Shale and W.F. Stinespring, States on the Clifford algebra, *Ann. Math.* **80** (1964) 365–381.

[Sta01]   J. Stachel, *Einsteins Annus Mirabilis*. Reinbeck: Rowohlt Taschenbuch Verlag (2001).

[Ste51]   N. Steenrod, *Topology of fiber bundles*. Princeton: Princeton University Press (1951).

[Ste03]   D. Sternheimer, Presentation of deformation quantization and of deformation theory as powerful tool in physics modeling, Contribution to *Poisson geometry, deformation quantization and group representations* **4** (2003) 1–17.

[Sto67]   E. Stormer, Large groups of automorphisms of C*–algebras, *Commun. Math. Phys.* **3** (1967) 133.

[Sto69]   E. Stormer, Symmetric states of infinite tensor products of C*-algebras, *J. Funct. Anal.* **3** (1969) 48–68.

[SW64]   R.F. Streater and A.S. Wightman, *PCT, spin and statistics, and all that*. New York: Benjamin (1964).

[Swi69]   J.A. Swieca, Goldstone's theorem and related topics, *Cargese Lectures IV*, D. Kastler (Ed.). New York: Gordon and Breach (1969).

[SZ79]   S. Stràtilà and L. Zsidó, *Lectures on von Neumann Algebras*. Turnbridge Wells, Kent England: Abacus Press (1979).

[SZ97]   M.O. Scully and M.S. Zubairy, *Quantum optics*. Cambridge: Cambridge University Press (1997).

[Sze39]   G. Szegö, *Orthonormal polynomials*. American Mathematical Society, Reading (1939).

[Ta04]   A. Trifonov *et al.*, Singlephoton counting at telecom wavelength and quantum key distribution, *J. Mod. Optics* **51** (2004) 1399–1415.

[Tak79]   M. Takesaki, *Theory of operator algebras 1*. New York: Springer (1979).

[Tak02]   M. Takesaki, *Theory of operator algebras 2*. New York: Springer (2002).

[Tay96]   M.E. Taylor, *Partial differential equations I–III*. Berlin, Heidelberg, New York: Springer (1996).

[TG65]   U.M. Titulaer and R.J. Glauber, Correlation functions and coherent fields, *Phys. Rev.* **140** (1965) B676–B682.

[TG66]   U.M. Titulaer and R.J. Glauber, Density operators for coherent fields, *Phys. Rev.* **145** (1966) 1041–1050.

[Thi68]   W. Thirring, On the mathematical structure of the B.C.S. model II, *Commun. Math. Phys.* **7** (1968) 181–189.

[Thi77]   W. Thirring, *Lehrbuch der mathematischen Physik I–IV*. Berlin, New York: Springer (1977).

[Tho61]   D.J. Thouless, *The quantum mechanics of many body systems*. New York, London: Academic Press (1961).

[Tho73]   L.E. Thomas, Time dependent approach to scattering from impurities in a crystal, *Commun. Math. Phys.* **33** (1973) 335–343.

[Til63]   H.G. Tillmann, Zur Eindeutigkeit der Lösungen der quantenmechanischen Vertauschungsrelationen, *Acta Sci. Math.* **24** (1963) 258–270.

[Tin75]   M. Tinkham, *Introduction to superconductivity*. Tokyo: Mc Graw–Hill (1975).

[TN77]   S. Takeno and M. Nagashima, A^2–term, renormalization of matter-photon interaction and coherent states in matter-photon systems, *Prog. Theor. Phys.* **57** (1977) 1507–1522.

[Ton93]   A. Tonomura, *Electron holography*. Berlin, Heidelberg; New York: Springer (1993).

[Uhl67]   D.A. Uhlenbrock, Fermions and associated Bosons of one-dimensional model, *Commun. Math. Phys.* **4** (1967) 64–76.

[Uhl76]   A. Uhlmann, The "transition probability" in the state space of a *-algebra, *Rep. Math. Phys.* **9** (1976) 273–279.

[Uhl85]   A. Uhlmann, The transition probability for states of *-algebras, *Ann. Phys.* **42** (1985) 524–532.

[UIO90]   M. Ueda, N. Imoto and T. Ogawa, Quantum theory for continuous photodetection processes, *Phys. Rev. A* **41** (1990) 3891–3904.

[Ull86]   M. Ullrich, Calculation of the limiting Gibbs states for weakly coupled macroscopic quantum systems with application to the Josephson oscillator, *Rep. Math. Phys.* **23** (1986) 67–81.

[Ume65]   Y. Umemura, Measures on infinite–dimensional vector spaces. *Publications of the RIMS Kyoto University* **A1** (1965), 1–47.

[Ume95]   H. Umezawa, *Advanced field theory*, American Institute of Physics, New York (1995).

[Unn89]   Th. Unnerstall, Dynamics of the current-driven Josephson junction, *J. Stat. Phys.* **54** (1989) 379–403.

[UR89]   Th. Unnerstall and A. Rieckers, Quasispin-operator description of the Josephson tunnel junction and the Josephson plasma frequency, *Phys. Rev. B* **39** (1989) 2173–2179.

[UR92]   Th. Unnerstall and A. Rieckers, Frequency pulling in Josephson radiation, *Phys. Rev. B* **45** (1992) 10115–10118.

[Va13]   B. Vlastakis *et al.*, Deterministically encoding quantum information using 100–photon Schrödinger cat states, *Science* **342** (2013) 607–610.

[Vai94]   I. Vaisman, *Lectures on the geometry of Poisson manifolds*. Basel: Birkhäuser (1994).

[Val58]   J.G. Valatin, Comments on the theory of superconductivity, *Nuovo Cim.* **7** (1958) 843.

[vDT84]   T. van Duzer and C.W. Turner, *Principles of superconducting devices and circuits*. New York: Elsevier (1984).

[vDV71]   A. van Daele and A. Verbeure, Unitary equivalence of Fock representations on the Weyl algebra, *Commun. Math. Phys.* **20** (1971) 268–278.

[vW67]   B.L. van der Waerden, *Sources of quantum mechanics*. Amsterdam: North–Holland (1967).

[Vel06]   O.A. Veliev, Perturbation theory for the periodic multidimensional Schrödinger operator and the Bethe–Sommerfeld conjecture, ArXiv:math-ph **061005** (2006) 335–343.

[vH80]   J.L. van Hemmen, A note on the diagonalization of quadratic Boson and Fermion Hamiltonians, *Z. Physik B-Condens. Matt.* **38** (1980) 271–277.

[vHvW80]   J.L. van Hemmen and W. von Waldenfels, On the dynamical structure of the Dicke maser model, *Physica A* **100** (1980) 85–99.

[vN31]   J. von Neumann, Die Eindeutigkeit der Schrödingerschen Operatoren, *Math. Ann.* **104** (1931) 570–578.

[vN32]   J. von Neumann, *Mathematische Grundlagen der Quantenmechanik*. Berlin: Springer (1932).

[vN36]   J. von Neumann, On an algebraic generalization of the quantum mechanical formalism (part I), *Mat. Sornik* **1** (1936) 415–484.

[vN38]   J. von Neumann, On infinite direct products, *Compos. Math.* **6** (1938) 1–77.

[vN40]   J. von Neumann, On rings of operators, reduction theory, *Ann. Math.* **41** (1940) 370–427.

[vN61]   J. von Neumann, *John von Neumann collected works I–VI*. Oxford: Pergamon Press (1961).

[vOFS94]   A. van Otterlo, R. Fazio and G. Schön, Quantum vortices near the super-conductor–insulator transition in Josephson junction arrays, *Proceedings of 20 international conference on low temperature physics* (Eugene, 1993), *Physica B*, 194–196 (1994), pp. 1153–1154.

[VS91]   K. Vogel and W. Schleich, Phase distribution of a quantum state without using phase states, *Phys. Rev. A* **44** (1991) 7642.

[VWW01]   W. Vogel, D.-G. Welsch and S. Wallentowitz, *Quantum optics, an introduction*. Berlin: Wiley–VCH (2001).

[Wal75]   P. Walters, *Ergodic theory — introductory lectures*. Berlin; New York: Springer–Verlag (1975).

[Wal83]   D.F. Walls, Squeezed states of light, *Nature* **306** (1983) 141–146.

[War82]   H.A. Warchall, Implementation of automorphism groups in certain representations of the canonical commutation relations, *J. Math. Phys.* **23** (1982) 2221–2228.

[Wat58]   G.N. Watson, *A treatise on the theory of Bessel functions*. Cambridge: Cambridge University Press (1958).

[WDY06]   E. Waks, E. Diamanti and Y. Yamamoto, Generation of photon number states, *New J. Phys.* **8**(4) (2006) 1–8.

[Wea97]   N. Weaver, Deformation quantization for Hilbert space actions, *Commun. Math. Phys.* **188** (1997) 217–232.

[Web01]   H. Weber, *Die partiellen Differential-Gleichungen der mathematischen Physik nach Riemanns Vorlesungen*. Braunschweig: Friedrich Vieweg und Sohn (1901).

[Wei63]   J. Wei, Note on the global validity of the Baker–Hausdorff and Magnus theorems, *J. Math. Phys.* **4** (1963) 1337–1341.

[Wei69]   M. Weinless, Existence and uniqueness of the vacuum for linear quantized fields, *J. Funct. Anal.* **4** (1969) 350–379.

[Wei80]   J. Weidmann, *Linear operators in Hilbert spaces*. Berlin, Heidelberg; New York: Springer (1980).

[Wei94]   A. Weinstein, Deformation quantization, *Séminaire Bourbaki 46ème annee* **789** (1994).

[Wey18]   H. Weyl, Gravitation und Elektrizität, *Sitz.ber. Preuss. Akad. Wiss.* (1918) 465–480.

[Wey28]   H. Weyl, Quantenmeachnik und Gruppentheorie, *Z. Phys.* **46** (1928), 1–46.

[Wey31]   H. Weyl, *The theory of groups and quantum mechanics.* Reprinted by Dover Publication, New York (1950), Methuen, London (1931).

[Wey53]   H. Weyl, *Mathematische Analyse des Raumproblems und Was ist Materie?* Darmstadt: Wiss. Buchgesellschaft (1953).

[WH03]   M. Watanabe and D.B. Haviland, Quantum effects in small-capacitance Josephson junctions, *Phys. Rev.* B **67** (2003) 094505.

[Wie96]   W. Wien, Über die Energieverteilung im Emissionsspektrum eines schwarzen Körpers, *Ann. d. Phys.* **58** (1896) 662–669.

[Wie65]   N. Wiener, *Mathematik mein Leben.* Frankfurt am Main: Fischer Bücherei (1965).

[Wie49]   H. Wielandt, Über die Unbeschränktheit der Schrödingerschen Operatoren der Quantenmechanik, *Math. Ann.* **121** (1949) 21.

[Win47]   A. Wintner, The unboundedness of quantum–mechanical matrices, *Phys. Rev.* **71** (1947) 738–739.

[Wlo82]   J. Wloka, *Partielle Differentialgleichungen.* Stuttgart: Teubner–Verlag (1982).

[WM94]   D.F. Walls and G.J. Milburn, *Quantum optics.* Berlin, Heidelberg; New York: Springer (1994).

[WTF58]   Y. Wada, F. Takano and N. Fukuda, Exact treatment of Bardeen's theory of superconductivity in the strong coupling limit, *Progr. Theor. Phys.* (Kyoto) **19** (1958) 597–598.

[WWW52] G.C. Wick, A.S. Wightman and E.P. Wigner, The intrinsic parity of elementary particles, *Phys. Rev.* **88** (1952) 101–105.

[Yan62]   C.N. Yang, Concept of off–diagonal long–range order and the quantum phases of liquid He and of superconducters, *Rev. Mod. Phys.* **34** (1962) 694.

[YM54]   C.N. Yang and R.L. Mills, Conservation of isotopic spin and isotopic gauge invariance, *Phys. Rev.* **96** (1954) 191–195.

[YS78]   H.P. Yuen and J.H. Shapiro, Optical communication with two–photon coherent states, part I, *IEEE Trans. Inf. Th.* **IT–24** (1978) 657–668.

[YS79]   H.P. Yuen and J.H. Shapiro, Optical communication with two–photon coherent states, part II, *Opt. Lett.* **4** (1979) 334.

[YS80]   H.P. Yuen and J.H. Shapiro, Optical communication with two–photon coherent states, part III, *IEEE Trans. Inf. Th.* **IT–26** (1980) 78–93.

[YTK05]   Y. Yoshikawa, Y. Torii and T. Kuga, Superradiant light scattering from thermal atomic vapors, *Phys. Rev. Lett.* **94** (2005) 083602.

[Yue75]   H.P. Yuen, Generalized coherent states and the statistics of two–photon–lasers, *Phys. Lett.* A **51** (1975) 1–2.

[Yue76]   H.P. Yuen, Two–photon coherent states of the radiation field, *Phys. Rev.* A **13** (1976) 2226–2243.

[Zan90]   S. Zanzinger, Kohärente Zustandsüberlagerung im Rahmen der verbandstheoretischen Grundstruktur statistischer Theorien, Master's thesis, University of Tübingen, Institute of Theoretical Physics (1990).

[Zan95]   S. Zanzinger, Verallgemeinerte Übergangswahrscheinlichkeiten und Quasientropien in der Vielteilchenphysik, Ph.D. thesis, University of Tübingen, Institute of Theoretical Physics (1995).

[Zbi04]   H. Zbinden, Photon counting at telecom wavelengths with commercial InGaAs/InP avalanche photodiodes: current performance, *J. Mod. Optics* **51** (2004) 1381–1398.

[Zie89]   W.P. Ziemer, *Weakly differentiable functions*. Berlin, New York: Springer
           (1989).
[ZN05]   O. Zobay and G.M. Nikolopoulos, Dynamics of matter-wave and optical fields
           in superradiant scattering from Bose–Einstein condensates, *Phys. Rev. A* **72**
           (2005) 410.
[Zor06]   A.B. Zorin, Bloch inductance in small–capacitance Josephson junctions, *Phys.
           Rev. Lett.* **96** (2006) 167001.

Index